PURE MATHEMATICS

Alan Sherlock MA FIMA
Director of Mathematics, Millfield School

Elizabeth Roebuck BA
Millfield School

Timothy Heneage BA
Formerly of Millfield School

Shirley Beck MA
Millfield School

John Murray Albemarle Street London

Printed and bound in Great Britain by
J. W. Arrowsmith Ltd, Bristol

0 7195 3379 1

Preface

This comprehensive text was written to meet the needs of students of all abilities who are studying for A level, or for equivalent examinations, in mathematics.

Today, because of the increasingly complex technology of our age, more and more pupils are continuing their study of mathematics into the sixth form. This means that many of the present pupils do not have the knowledge, experience or enthusiasm for mathematics which characterized some of their predecessors. Weak candidates predominate on many of the courses and it is for them, with their problems in mind, that the text has been made so detailed.

Great attention has been paid to the problems of both teaching and learning at this level, with the result that the ideas are presented simply and logically, supported by careful organization of worked examples, exercises and selected examination questions.

All the material has been tried and tested over a period of a number of years and its effectiveness is attested by the success of the students who have used it.

'Modern' and 'Traditional' ideas have been integrated to present a coherent picture of mathematics at this level. The availability of electronic calculators has made it possible to introduce work on numerical methods which was previously very tedious. A wide variety of syllabuses is catered for, and so some of the topics are not necessarily applicable to them all. A chapter on algebraic structure has been included for the sake of completeness.

Acknowledgements

We are very grateful to the teachers at Millfield who have used the material and provided helpful criticism. Thanks are also due to our retired colleague, Mr. John Carr, for his assistance with the answers. Thanks are also due to those Examination Boards who have allowed us to use their questions in the Miscellaneous Examination Questions sections.

Contents

Chapter 1

Series 1

1 A first look at series

1.1 Introduction

A collection of numbers in a particular order is called a *sequence*. For example, 31, −5, 20, −8, 42 is a sequence of numbers with 31 being the first term, −5 the second and so on.

We shall call a sequence a *series* if

1 the terms are to be summed, and
2 there is a definite pattern (or formula) which enables us to find the next term. (This is always possible unless the terms are random.)

For example, consider the series

$$3+6+12+24+\dots$$

The first term is 3, the second 6, and so on. We can write this information in a table and then look for a pattern or formula which will give us a *general term* in the series. This general term is usually taken as the rth.

Number of term in the series:	1*st*	2*nd*	3*rd*	4*th*
Term:	3	6	12	24

We notice that the terms have a common factor of 3, so we rewrite them

$$3\times 1 \quad 3\times 2 \quad 3\times 4 \quad 3\times 8$$

We can now see that the other factor is a power of 2, so again the terms are

$$3\times 2^0 \quad 3\times 2^1 \quad 3\times 2^2 \quad 3\times 2^3$$

From this pattern we can suggest the rth term as $3\times 2^{r-1}$. Check that this is correct for $r=1$ and $r=2$.

Here are some more examples of series with a general term. In each case check that the general term is correct for $r=1$ and $r=4$.

1 $1+2+3+4+\dots+r+\dots+2401$

2 $\dfrac{1\times 3}{4\times 6}+\dfrac{3\times 5}{6\times 8}+\dfrac{5\times 7}{8\times 10}+\dots+\dfrac{(2r-1)(2r+1)}{(2r+2)(2r+4)}+\dots+\dfrac{207\times 209}{210\times 212}$

3 $1^2+2^2+3^2+4^2+\ldots+r^2+\ldots+25^2$

4 $x^1+x^2+x^3+x^4+\ldots+x^r+\ldots+x^{75}$

5 $1+2x+3x^2+4x^3+\ldots+rx^{r-1}+\ldots+15x^{14}$

For a method of finding the general term in less obvious cases, see page 33.

Exercise 1.1

Find the next two terms, and the rth term in the following

1 1, 2, 3, 4 . . .

2 1, 3, 5, 7 . . .

3 1, 2, 4, 8, 16 . . .

4 1, 4, 9, 16 . . .

5 3, 7, 11, 15 . . .

6 2, 7, 14, 23 . . .

7 7, 21, 63, 189 . . .

1.2 Σ (sigma) notation

Frequently we have to find the sum of a large number of results (numbers) or quantities (in terms of unknown numbers). This occurs particularly when we are calculating means, standard deviations and so on, in statistics or perhaps when we are doing numerical work—in calculus, for instance. It would be very tiresome to write out all the terms in, for example,

$$1+2+3+4+\ldots+r+\ldots+2401$$

so a shorthand notation is used for the word 'sum'; it is Σ (sigma), the Greek capital letter S. When we require the complete sum of a series we use the *general term* and write the five examples above as

1 Σr **2** $\Sigma \frac{(2r-1)(2r+1)}{(2r+2)(2r+4)}$ **3** Σr^2 **4** Σx^r **5** Σrx^{r-1}

The Σ represents the word *sum* but we need to know also where to start the summing and where to stop it. We do this by writing, at the bottom of the Σ, where to start and, at the top, where to stop. Hence the five series are

1 $\sum_{r=1}^{r=2401} r$ **2** $\sum_{r=1}^{r=104} \frac{(2r-1)(2r+1)}{(2r+2)(2r+4)}$

3 $\sum_{r=1}^{r=25} r^2$ **4** $\sum_{r=1}^{r=75} x^r$ **5** $\sum_{r=1}^{r=15} rx^{r-1}$

If you wish, check each of these limits by substituting the lower value of r to give the first term and the top value of r to give the last term. When we write, for example,

$$\sum_{r=1}^{r=75} x^r$$

we mean the sum of $x^1+x^2+\ldots+x^{75}$, where r takes all the whole number values (integral values) from 1 to 75 inclusive.

Exercise 1.2a

Write out the following sums in full.

1 $\sum_{r=1}^{r=4} r^3$ **2** $\sum_{r=1}^{r=6} (2r+1)$ **3** $\sum_{r=1}^{r=6} (9+r)$

4 $\sum_{r=10}^{r=15} r$ **5** $\sum_{r=1}^{r=5} 3^{2r}$ **6** $\sum_{r=1}^{r=5} \frac{3r-1}{5r+2}$

Use $\sum$ notation to write more briefly the following sums.

7 $1^2+2^2+3^2+\ldots+7^2$ **8** $2+4+6+\ldots+30$

9 $\frac{1}{1}+\frac{1}{2}+\frac{1}{3}+\ldots+\frac{1}{77}$ **10** $1+8+27+64+\ldots$ for 10 terms.

11 $\frac{1\times3}{2\times4}+\frac{2\times4}{3\times5}+\frac{3\times5}{4\times6}+\ldots+\frac{19\times21}{20\times22}$

12 $(1\times5)+(3\times7)+(5\times9)+\ldots$ for 12 terms.

13 $3^2+7^2+11^2+15^2+\ldots$ for 20 terms.

14 $a+(a+5)+(a+10)+(a+15)+\ldots+(a+100)$

15 $a+(a+d)+(a+2d)+(a+3d)+\ldots+(a+50d)$

16 $2+6+18+54+\ldots$ for 21 terms.

17 $a+3a+9a+27a+\ldots$ for 21 terms.

18 $a+ak+ak^2+ak^3+\ldots$ for 21 terms.

In the following exercise we shall investigate certain properties of the sigma notation.

Exercise 1.2b

1(a) Write out in full $\sum_{r=1}^{r=6} x_r$

(b) Evaluate the sum in (a) if $x_1 = x_2 = x_3 = x_4 = x_5 = x_6 = 1$.

(c) Evaluate $\sum_{r=1}^{r=6} 1$ **(d)** Evaluate $\sum_{r=1}^{r=6} 6$

(e) Evaluate $\sum_{r=4}^{r=6} 6$ **(f)** Evaluate $\sum_{r=1}^{r=n} 1$

2 Evaluate the following sums

(a) $\sum_{r=1}^{r=2} r$ **(b)** $\left(\sum_{r=1}^{r=2} r\right)^2$ **(c)** $\sum_{r=1}^{r=2} r^2$

3 Evaluate

(a) $\left[\sum_{r=3}^{r=5} (r+1)\right]^2$ **(b)** $\sum_{r=3}^{r=5} (r+1)^2$

4 By considering $n = 2$, or otherwise, explain the difference between

$$\left[\sum_{r=1}^{r=n} x_r\right]^2 \quad \text{and} \quad \sum_{r=1}^{r=n} x_r^2$$

5 Evaluate the sums

(a) $\sum_{r=1}^{r=6} r$ **(b)** $\sum_{r=1}^{r=6} 3r$ **(c)** $3 \times \sum_{r=1}^{r=6} r$

6 Explain with reasons whether or not

(a) $\sum_{r=1}^{r=n} kx_r = k\left(\sum_{r=1}^{r=n} x_r\right)$ **(b)** $\sum_{r=1}^{r=n} rx_r = r\left(\sum_{r=1}^{r=n} x_r\right)$

7 Evaluate the following sums

(a) $\sum_{r=1}^{r=5} r + \sum_{r=1}^{r=5} 2r^2$ **(b)** $\sum_{r=1}^{r=5} r(2r+1)$

Can you explain your results?

8 Is it true that $\sum_{r=1}^{r=n} x_r + \sum_{r=1}^{r=n} y_r = \sum_{r=1}^{r=n} (x_r + y_r)$?

Explain your answer.

9(a) Find the value of $(-1)^r$ if (i) $r=1$ (ii) $r=2$ (iii) $r=3$ (iv) $r=4$

(b) Write out in full the sum $\sum_{r=1}^{r=n} (-1)^r x$ where $n=4$

(c) Hence evaluate it in the cases (i) $n=5$ (ii) $n=6$ (iii) $n=7$

10 Write out in full the sums

(a) $\sum_{r=1}^{r=5} (-1)^{r+1} r^2$ **(b)** $\sum_{r=1}^{r=5} (-1)^r (2r+1)$

(c) $\sum_{r=1}^{r=5} (-1)^{2r+1} (r+3)$

11 If $\sum_{r=1}^{r=7} x_r^2 = 100$ and $\sum_{r=1}^{r=7} x_r = 10$

find the value of $\sum_{r=1}^{r=7} (x_r - 2)^2$

12 Prove that

$$\sum_{r=1}^{r=n} (y_r + d)^3 = \sum_{r=1}^{r=n} y_r^3 + 3d \sum_{r=1}^{r=n} y_r^2 + 3d^2 \sum_{r=1}^{r=n} y_r + d^3 n$$

where d is a constant.

13 If

$$s = \sqrt{\frac{\sum_{r=1}^{r=n} (x_r - \bar{x})^2}{n}} \qquad \text{and} \qquad \bar{x} = \frac{\sum_{r=1}^{r=n} x_r}{n}$$

prove that

$$s = \sqrt{\frac{\sum_{r=1}^{r=n} x_r^2}{n} - \left(\frac{\sum_{r=1}^{r=n} x_r}{n}\right)^2}$$

NOTE. $\bar{x}$ is the *mean* value of a set of readings $x_1, x_2, \ldots x_n$ and s is the *standard deviation.*

Summary of results

1 $\sum_{r=1}^{r=n} a = na \qquad \left[\text{also } \sum_{r=m}^{r=n} a = (n-m+1)a\right]$

2 $\sum_{r=1}^{r=n} kr = k \sum_{r=1}^{r=n} r$

3 $\sum_{r=1}^{r=n} (x_r + y_r) = \sum_{r=1}^{r=n} x_r + \sum_{r=1}^{r=n} y_r$

Any combination of these results also holds; in particular,

$$\sum_{r=1}^{r=n} (kr + a) = k \sum_{r=1}^{r=n} r + na$$

NOTE $\qquad \left(\sum_{r=1}^{r=n} r\right)^2$ does *not* equal $\sum_{r=1}^{r=n} r^2$.

$(-1)^r$ is a useful device for alternating the sign of the terms.

1.3 Recurrence relations

We have shown how to illustrate a series by giving the rth term. Another method of defining a series is to give the relationship between one general term in the series and other terms in the same series. Since this relationship recurs throughout the series it is known as a *recurrence relation* (or sometimes *difference equation*). To specify the series completely we then have to know the first term or possibly the first few terms. Note that in a recurrence relation the suffix k is frequently used for the general term.

Example

Write down the first five terms in the series defined by

$$u_1 = 2, \qquad u_k = 4u_{k-1}$$

Now putting $k = 2$, $u_2 = 4u_1 = 8$

$u_3 = 4u_2 = 32$

$u_4 = 4u_3 = 128$

$u_5 = 4u_4 = 512$

Hence, the first five terms are 2, 8, 32, 128 and 512.

Exercise 1.3

Write down the first five terms in the series specified by the following:

1 $u_1 = 2, \quad u_k = 2 + 3u_{k-1}$

2 $u_1 = 5, \quad u_k = 5 + \dfrac{u_{k-1}}{10}$

3 $u_1 = 0, \quad u_k = \dfrac{1}{3 - u_{k-1}}$

4 $u_1 = 1, \quad u_2 = 3, \quad u_k = 2u_{k-1} + u_{k-2}$

5 $u_1 = 0, \quad u_2 = 1, \quad u_k = 3u_{k-1} - u_{k-2}$

Write down a *recurrence relation* between the terms in the following series.

6 1, 3, 5, 7, . . .

7 4, 12, 36, 108, . . .

8 1, 5, 17, 53, . . .

9 1, 2, 4, 7, 11, 16, . . .

10 1, 1, 2, 3, 5, 8, . . .

1.4 Summing some useful series by pattern

There are several different ways of finding the sum of a series. We shall first add the terms and see if there is any pattern in the sums.

Example 1

Consider $\sum_{r=1}^{r=n} r = 1+2+3+4+\ldots+r+\ldots+n$

r	*Terms*	*Sum*	*Rewritten*
1	1	1	$1\times 2/2$
2	$1+2$	3	$2\times 3/2$
3	$1+2+3$	6	$3\times 4/2$
4	$1+2+3+4$	10	$4\times 5/2$
5	$1+2+3+4+5$	15	$5\times 6/2$
⋮	⋮	⋮	⋮
n	$\sum_{r=1}^{r=n} r$		$n\times\dfrac{(n+1)}{2}$

When the sums have been rewritten the pattern becomes clearer, and it appears that

$$\sum_{r=1}^{r=n} r = \frac{n(n+1)}{2}$$

—which is in fact true.

NOTE that the sum is n times the average of the first and last terms.

Example 2

Similarly consider $\sum_{r=1}^{r=n} r^2 = 1^2+2^2+3^2+\ldots+r^2+\ldots+n^2$

As before, we start by adding the terms then looking for a pattern.

r	*Terms*	*Sum*	*Rewritten*	*Rearranged*
1	1	1	1	$3\times1/3$
2	$1+4$	5	1×5	$5\times3/3$
3	$1+4+9$	14	2×7	$7\times6/3$
4	$1+4+9+16$	30	3×10	$9\times10/3$
5	$1+4+9+16+25$	55	5×11	$11\times15/3$
6	$1+4+9+16+25+36$	91	7×13	$13\times21/3$
⋮	⋮	⋮	⋮	⋮
n	$\sum_{r=1}^{r=n} r^2$			$(2n+1)\times\left[\frac{n(n+1)}{2}\right]\times\frac{1}{3}$ (since the part arrowed is the same as the sum in Example 1)

The pattern seems to show that

$$\sum_{r=1}^{r=n} r^2 = \tfrac{1}{6}n(n+1)(2n+1)$$

—which is again true.

Example 3

Finally, consider

$$\sum_{r=1}^{r=n} r^3 = 1^3+2^3+3^3+\ldots+r^3+\ldots+n^3$$

r	*Terms*	*Sum*	*Rewritten*
1	1	1	1^2
2	1+8	9	3^2
3	1+8+27	36	6^2
4	1+8+27+64	100	10^2
5	1+8+27+64+125	225	15^2
⋮	⋮	⋮	⋮
n	$\sum_{r=1}^{r=n} r^3$		$\left[\frac{n(n+1)}{2}\right]^2$ (since the numbers are the same as in Example 1)

This time the pattern seems to show that

$$\sum_{r=1}^{r=n} r^3 = \left[\frac{n(n+1)}{2}\right]^2$$

and once again this is true.

In each of these three examples we have worked out a pattern and said that it *seems* or *appears* to be the answer, and you may be wondering why this element of uncertainty has crept in: the patterns look certain to continue beyond the values that we have worked out. But can we be absolutely sure that they will? The answer is that we cannot, unless we have some more powerful method of proving it.

1.5 Pattern is not proof

Another example may enable you to realize the problem.

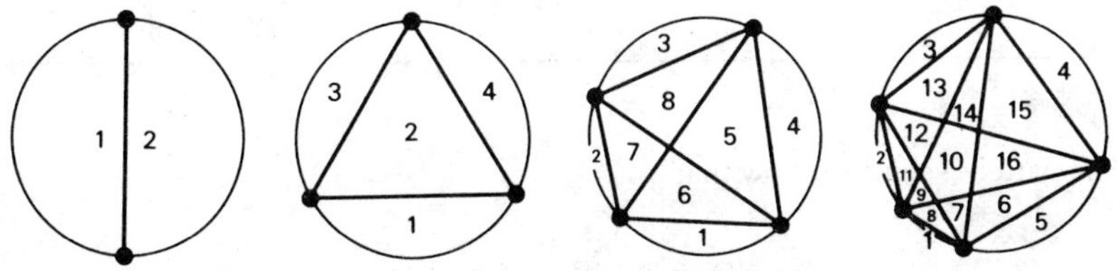

(a) (b) (c) (d)

The idea is to mark points on the circumference of a circle. In (a) there are two points, in (b) three points, in (c) four points and in (d) five points. Each marked point is then joined up to every other one in the diagram. This divides the circle into various areas as shown. The results are given below:

Number of points:	2	3	4	5
Number of areas:	2	4	8	16

The pattern appears to be clearly established, but is it?

Draw the next two diagrams, with six and seven points on the circumference. Join up the points and count the areas carefully. (Try not to space points evenly in case this causes problems.) You will find that your expected results simply do not occur. We can often guess a pattern but to show that it is *always* true is not quite so easy.

Exercise 1.5

1 A pupil uses the formula n^2+n+11 and puts $n = 1, 2, 3, 4$, respectively, and obtains a prime number each time. He therefore predicts that any number of the form n^2+n+11, where n is a positive integer is prime.

Can you find a value for which this argument is *not* true?

2 Notice that

$$2^0 = 1$$

$$2^1 = 1+1$$

$$2^2 = 1+2+\frac{2\times 1}{2!} \quad *$$

$$2^3 = 1+3+\frac{3\times 2}{2!}+\frac{3\times 2\times 1}{3!}$$

$$2^4 = 1+4+\frac{4\times 3}{2!}+\frac{4\times 3\times 2}{3!}+\frac{4\times 3\times 2\times 1}{4!}$$

Find a series whose sum is 2^n.

3 Notice that $10-1$, $20-2$, $30-3$, $40-4$ are all divisible by 9. Can you find a formula which is true in the general case?

4 For $n \geqslant r$, ${}^nC_r$ is defined by $\quad {}^nC_r = \dfrac{n!}{r!(n-r)!}$

Find the value of $1+{}^nC_2+{}^nC_4$ when $n = 1, 2, 3, 4, 5$. Can you predict the value when $n = 6$ and $n = 7$? Try to do so before calculating it.

5 For $n = 2, 3, 4$ and 5 find the value of

$$M = 2^{n-1} - \frac{(n-1)(n-2)(n-3)(n-4)(n-5)}{(n-1)}$$

Can you predict the value of M when $n = 6$? Calculate this value as a check.

2 The principle of mathematical induction

2.1 An Analogy

Consider a set of dominoes standing in a line (which represent the *terms* in our series). For our model we place them so the distance between the dominoes is less than the height of the domino. Seen sideways-on we have:

* Where $n!$ is, as usual, $n(n-1)(n-2)\ldots 3\times 2\times 1$. (If $n<r$, then ${}^nC_r = 0$. $0!$ is defined to be 1.)

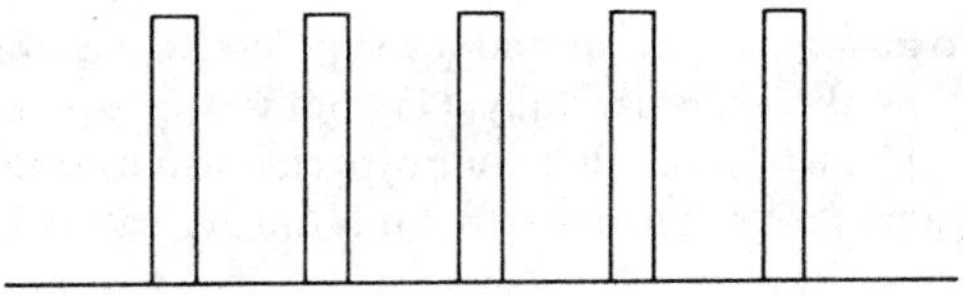

We now push over the first domino (*towards* the others).

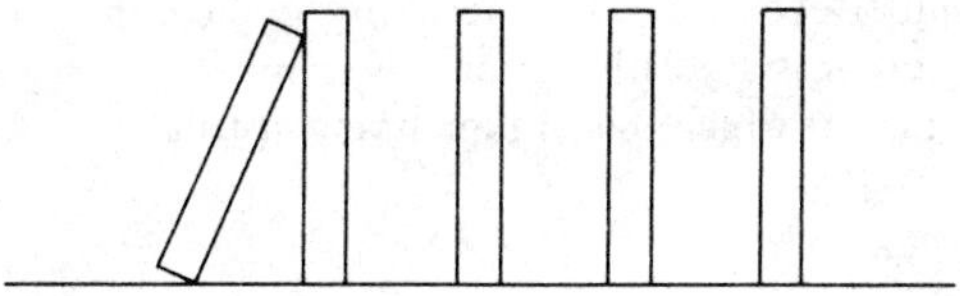

Of course, this causes a chain reaction:

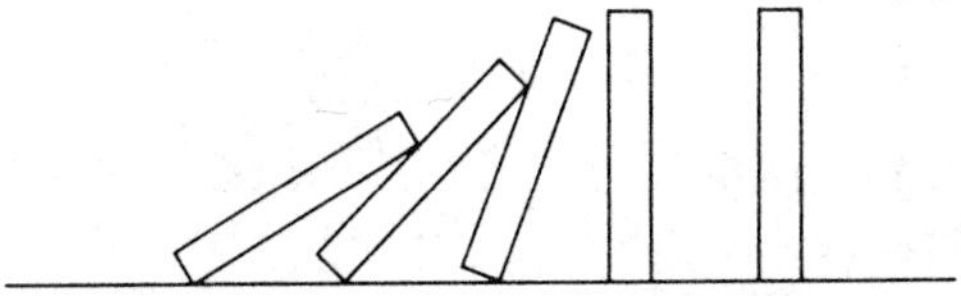

Each domino falls onto the next one and, if everything is arranged carefully, they all fall down!

The requirement for *all* the dominoes to fall can be expressed by two statements:

1 We push over the first domino, and

2 Each domino knocks down the next one.

The *principle of mathematical induction* is applied as follows.

1 We prove that a formula is true for $n = 1$.

(This corresponds to knocking down the first domino.)

2 We prove that if the formula is true for a particular value of n ($n = k$, say), then it is true for the next value of n (i.e. $n = k+1$).

(This corresponds to one domino knocking down the next one.)

We deduce that the formula is true for *all* integral values of n $(n \geqslant 1)$. (All the dominoes fall down!)

2.2 Worked example

We have considered the series $1+2+3+ \ldots +n$ and arrived at the formula

$$\sum_{r=1}^{r=n} r = \frac{n(n+1)}{2}$$

We now prove that this is correct.

1 When $n = 1$, then $1 = \frac{1(1+1)}{2}$, so the formula is true for $n = 1$.

2 We now use the idea that the sum of $k+1$ terms in the series is given by the sum of k terms plus the $(k+1)$th term, i.e. $S_{k+1} = S_k + u_{k+1}$.

Assuming that the formula *is* true for $n = k$,

$$1+2+\ldots+k = \frac{k(k+1)}{2}$$

If we then add the next term,

$$\begin{aligned} 1+2+\ldots+k+(k+1) &= \frac{k(k+1)}{2}+(k+1) \\ &= (k+1)\left(\frac{k}{2}+1\right) \\ &= \frac{(k+1)(k+2)}{2} \end{aligned}$$

This is the formula for the sum of the series with $n = k+1$ and shows that *if* the formula was true for $n = k$ then it is *also* true for $n = k+1$. Hence the formula is true for all integral values of $n(\geqslant 1)$.

2.3 Summary of method

1 We try to find a pattern in the series and from this guess a formula (giving the sum correctly in the cases we have considered).

2 We show that the formula is true for $n = 1$.

3 We prove that, *if* the formula is true for $n = k$, *then* it is true for the next value $n = k+1$.

4 We deduce by the *principle of mathematical induction* that the formula is true for all positive integers n.

Exercise 2.3

Use the principle of mathematical induction in questions 1 to 7 to prove that

1 $1^2+2^2+3^2+\ldots+n^2 = \frac{1}{6}n(n+1)(2n+1)$

2 $1^3+2^3+3^3+\ldots+n^3 = \frac{1}{4}n^2(n+1)^2$

3 $\sum_{r=1}^{r=n} r(r+1)(r+2) = \frac{1}{4}n(n+1)(n+2)(n+3)$

4 $(1\times 2)+(2\times 3)+(3\times 4)+\ldots+n(n+1) = \frac{1}{3}n(n+1)(n+2)$

5 $a+(a+d)+(a+2d)+(a+3d)+\ldots+[a+(n-1)d] = \frac{1}{2}n[2a+(n-1)d]$

6 $a+ar+ar^2+ar^3+\ldots+ar^{n-1}=\dfrac{a(1-r^n)}{1-r}$

7 $\displaystyle\sum_{r=1}^{r=n}\frac{1}{r(r+1)}=\frac{n}{n+1}$

8 A careless pupil copied down his homework as

'Prove by induction that $\displaystyle\sum_{r=2}^{r=n}\frac{1}{r^2-1}=\frac{3}{5}-\frac{2n+1}{2n(n+1)}$,'

His answer was as follows:
'Assume the formula is true for $n = k$. Hence

$$\sum_{r=2}^{r=n}\frac{1}{r^2-1}=\frac{1}{3}+\frac{1}{8}+\frac{1}{15}+\ldots+\frac{1}{k^2-1}$$
$$=\frac{3}{5}-\frac{2k+1}{2k(k+1)},$$

Now

$$\frac{1}{3}+\frac{1}{8}+\frac{1}{15}+\ldots+\frac{1}{k^2-1}+\frac{1}{(k+1)^2-1}=\frac{3}{5}-\frac{2k+1}{2k(k+1)}+\frac{1}{(k+1)^2-1}$$

so
$$\sum_{r=2}^{r=k+1}\frac{1}{r^2-1}=\frac{3}{5}-\frac{2k+1}{2k(k+1)}+\frac{1}{(k^2+2k+1)-1}$$
$$=\frac{3}{5}-\frac{2k+1}{2k(k+1)}+\frac{1}{k(k+2)}$$
$$=\frac{3}{5}-\frac{(2k+1)(k+2)-2(k+1)}{2k(k+1)(k+2)}$$
$$=\frac{3}{5}-\frac{2k^2+5k+2-2k-2}{2k(k+1)(k+2)}$$
$$=\frac{3}{5}-\frac{2k^2+3k}{2k(k+1)(k+2)}$$
$$=\frac{3}{5}-\frac{2(k+1)+1}{2(k+1)(k+2)}$$

'Hence the formula is true for $n = k+1$ and so by the principle of mathematical induction it is true for all positive integers.'

He was upset when the answer was marked wrong. Can you explain this mistake?

9 Try to prove by induction that

(a) $\displaystyle\sum_{r=1}^{r=n} r(r+2)=1+\tfrac{1}{6}n(n+1)(2n+7)$

(b) $\displaystyle\sum_{r=1}^{r=n} r(r+2)=\tfrac{1}{6}n(n+1)(2n+7)$

3 Various methods of summing series

3.1 Arithmetic series

Example 1

Consider again the series

$$\sum_{r=1}^{r=n} r = 1+2+3+\dots+n$$

Call the sum S. Then

$$S = 1+2+3+\dots+n$$

Reverse the terms: $S = n+(n-1)+(n-2)+\dots+2+1$

Add these two equations: $2S = (n+1)+(n+1)+\dots+(n+1)+(n+1)$

$$= n(n+1)$$

so $S = \frac{n}{2}(n+1)$

This method of summing a series (by reversing the terms) works whenever the difference between one term and the previous one is constant. Series like this are called *arithmetic series*.

Example 2

Suppose that you drop a stone down a disused mineshaft. It travels 1 foot in the first quarter-second, 3 feet in the next quarter-second, 5 feet in the third .... Six seconds after dropping the stone, you hear it splash into the water at the bottom of the shaft. How deep is the shaft?

Suppose the depth is D feet. Then

$$D = 1+3+5+\dots \text{ to 24 terms}$$

so $D = 1+3+5+\dots+(2r-1)+\dots+47$

Reverse the terms:

$$D = 47+45+43+\dots+1.$$

Add the last two equations

$$2D = 48+48+48+\dots+48$$

$$2D = 24\times 48$$

$$D = 576 \text{ ft (96 fathoms in mining terms).}$$

(The formula for a stone which has dropped a distance of S ft in t seconds is $S=16t^2$.)

Example 3

In general, if the first term of an arithmetic series is a, if the constant difference between one term and the previous one is d, and if there are n terms,

$$S = a+(a+d)+(a+2d)+\ \ldots\ +[a+(n-1)d]$$

Reverse the terms:

$$S = [a+(n-1)d]+[a+(n-2)d]+[a+(n-3)d]+\ \ldots\ +a$$

Add: $$2S = [2a+(n-1)d]+[2a+(n-1)d]+\ \ldots\ +[2a+(n-1)d]$$

so $$2S = n[2a+(n-1)d]$$

$$\mathbf{S = \frac{n}{2}[2a+(n-1)d]}$$ ◀

Notice that the last (or nth term) in the series is

$$\mathbf{l = a+(n-1)d}$$ ◀

So the sum of the series may be written

$$\mathbf{S = \frac{n}{2}(a+l)}$$ ◀

This last result is particularly useful.

Exercise 3.1

1 Which of the following sequences are arithmetic?

(a) 6, 9, 12, 15...
(b) 6, 4, 2, 0 ...
(c) 3, 6, 12, 24 ...
(d) 4/3, 1/3, −2/3, −5/3 ...
(e) 1/2, 1/3, 1/4, 1/5 ...

2 For the arithmetic sequences in question 1 find (i) the common difference, (ii) the 6th term, and (iii) the nth term.

3 Fill in the missing terms in the arithmetic sequences

(a) 8, —, 14
(b) 3, —, —, −9
(c) 1/5, —, —, —, 9/5

4 Find the sum of the series

(a) 1+4+7+10+... for 8 terms
(b) 8+5+2+ ... for 10 terms
(c) 2+4+6+...+24
(d) 3/2+6/2+9/2+...+27/2

5 Find the sum of
 (a) the first fifty integers, i.e. 1–50
 (b) the positive even numbers up to 50
 (c) the positive odd numbers up to 50.

6 Write out the following series in full and find their sum

(a) $\sum_{r=1}^{r=5} (3r+1)$ **(b)** $\sum_{r=1}^{r=4} (3-2r)$ **(c)** $\sum_{r=1}^{r=6} (r/2+3/2)$

3.2 Method of differences

Example 4

Consider again the sum of the series (used in 3.1)

$$S = 1+2+3+\ldots+r+\ldots+n$$

A common method of summing the series is to find *two* carefully chosen terms whose *difference* will lead to the rth term. These terms need to be of a higher degree in r than our general term, and must also be chosen so that when the series is written in this new form nearly all the terms will cancel. So, for our example with general term r, we shall use terms involving r^2.

Consider

$$(r+1)^2 - r^2 = r^2 + 2r + 1 - r^2$$
$$= 2r+1$$

Now substitute:

$r = 1$	$2^2 - 1^2$	$= 2\times 1+1$
$r = 2$	$3^2 - 2^2$	$= 2\times 2+1$
$r = 3$	$4^2 - 3^2$	$= 2\times 3+1$
$r = 4$	$5^2 - 4^2$	$= 2\times 4+1$
...	...	...
$r = n$	$(n+1)^2 - n^2$	$= 2\times n+1$

Now add $\quad (n+1)^2 - 1^2 = 2(1+2+3+\ldots+n) + n\times 1$

so $\quad (n+1)^2 - 1^2 = 2\sum_{r=1}^{r=n} r + n$

$$n^2+2n+1-1-n = 2\sum_{r=1}^{r=n} r$$

$$n^2+n = 2\sum_{r=1}^{r=n} r$$

hence, again, $\quad \dfrac{n(n+1)}{2} = \sum_{r=1}^{r=n} r$

Since this method depends upon the difference between two chosen terms being connected with the general term of the series we are interested in, it is called the *method of differences.* The main difficulty is in the choice of the two terms whose differences will lead to a general term of lower degree. However, for summing the three useful series mentioned in 1.4 we can use this same idea. The difference of squares, cubes and fourth powers give general terms of lower degree:

$$(r+1)^2-r^2 = 2r+1$$

$$(r+1)^3-r^3 = 3r^2+3r+1$$

$$(r+1)^4-r^4 = 4r^3+6r^2+4r+1$$

In many problems you will be helped by being asked to calculate the difference between two terms before being told to find the sum of the series. Here is such a case.

Example 5

Show that

$$\frac{1}{r(r+2)} = \frac{1}{2}\left(\frac{1}{r}-\frac{1}{r+2}\right)$$

and hence find the sum of the series

$$\frac{1}{1\times 3}+\frac{1}{2\times 4}+\frac{1}{3\times 5}+\ldots+\frac{1}{n(n+2)}$$

Now

$$\frac{1}{2}\left(\frac{1}{r}-\frac{1}{r+2}\right) = \frac{1}{2}\left(\frac{r+2-r}{r(r+2)}\right)$$

$$= \frac{1}{2}\left(\frac{2}{r(r+2)}\right)$$

$$= \frac{1}{r(r+2)}$$

hence

$$\frac{1}{r(r+2)} = \frac{1}{2}\left(\frac{1}{r}-\frac{1}{(r+2)}\right)$$

Now we substitute:

$r=1$ $$\frac{1}{1\times 3} = \frac{1}{2}\left(\frac{1}{1}-\frac{1}{3}\right)$$

$r=2$ $$\frac{1}{2\times 4} = \frac{1}{2}\left(\frac{1}{2}-\frac{1}{4}\right)$$

$r=3$ $$\frac{1}{3\times 5} = \frac{1}{2}\left(\frac{1}{3}-\frac{1}{5}\right)$$

$r=4$ $$\frac{1}{4\times 3} = \frac{1}{2}\left(\frac{1}{4}-\frac{1}{6}\right)$$

... ...

(The next two lines are included because the pattern of cancelling is not as obvious as it was in the earlier example.)

$r = n-2 \qquad \dfrac{1}{(n-2)n} = \dfrac{1}{2}\left(\dfrac{1}{n-2} - \dfrac{1}{n}\right)$

$r = n-1 \qquad \dfrac{1}{(n-1)(n+1)} = \dfrac{1}{2}\left(\dfrac{1}{n-1} - \dfrac{1}{n+1}\right)$

$r = n \qquad \dfrac{1}{n(n+2)} = \dfrac{1}{2}\left(\dfrac{1}{n} - \dfrac{1}{n+2}\right)$

By adding $\quad \dfrac{1}{1\times 3} + \dfrac{1}{2\times 4} + \ldots \dfrac{1}{n(n+2)} = \dfrac{1}{2}\left(\dfrac{1}{1} + \dfrac{1}{2} - \dfrac{1}{n+1} - \dfrac{1}{n+2}\right)$

so, $\quad \displaystyle\sum_{r=1}^{r=n} \frac{1}{r(r+2)} = \frac{1}{2}\left(\frac{3}{2} - \frac{1}{n+1} - \frac{1}{n+2}\right)$

Exercise 3.2

1 Show that $(r+1)^2 - (r-1)^2 = 4r$ and hence find $\sum_1^n r$.

2 Show that $r(r+1)(r+2) - (r-1)r(r+1) = 3r(r+1)$ and hence sum the series $\sum_1^n r(r+1)$.

3 Show that $\quad \dfrac{1}{(n+1)(n+2)} = \dfrac{1}{n+1} - \dfrac{1}{n+2}$

and hence find, to n terms, the sum of the series

$$\frac{1}{2\times 3} + \frac{1}{3\times 4} + \ldots$$

4 Show that $\quad \dfrac{1}{(n+2)(n+4)} = \dfrac{1}{2}\left(\dfrac{1}{n+2} - \dfrac{1}{n+4}\right)$

and hence find, to n terms, the sum of the series

$$\frac{1}{3\times 5} + \frac{1}{4\times 6} + \ldots$$

3.3 Using standard sums

It is often easy to sum series using the 'standard' sums,

$$\sum_1^n 1 = n, \qquad \sum_1^n r = \tfrac{1}{2}n(n+1), \qquad \sum_1^n r^2 = \tfrac{1}{6}n(n+1)(2n+1),$$

$$\sum_1^n r^3 = [\tfrac{1}{2}n(n+1)]^2$$

Example 6

Find the sum of n terms of the series

(a) $(1\times 3)+(2\times 4)+(3\times 5)+\ldots+r(r+2)\ldots+n(n+2)$

(b) $(3\times 4)+(4\times 5)+(5\times 6)+\ldots+(r+2)(r+3)+\ldots+(n+2)(n+3)$

(a) The first series can be written as

$$\sum_1^n r(r+2) = \sum_1^n (r^2+2r)$$

$$= \sum_1^n r^2 + 2\sum_1^n r$$

$$= \tfrac{1}{6}n(n+1)(2n+1) + 2\times\tfrac{1}{2}n(n+1)$$

$$= \tfrac{1}{6}n(n+1)(2n+7)$$

(b) The second series can be written as

$$\sum_1^n (r+2)(r+3) = \sum_1^n (r^2+5r+6)$$

$$= \sum_1^n r^2 + 5\sum_1^n r + 6\sum_1^n 1$$

$$= \tfrac{1}{6}n(n+1)(2n+1) + 5\times\tfrac{1}{2}n(n+1) + 6n$$

$$= \tfrac{1}{3}n(n^2+9n+26)$$

The method of standard sums *cannot* be used for 'fraction' series—for instance, a series like that in Example 5—but it can be put to work as follows.

Example 7

To find the area under the curve $y = x^2$.

The problem is to find the area 'under' the curve between $x = 0$, and $x = 2$ and the x axis. As a first idea, the range has been divided into four parts at $x = 0.5$, $x = 1.0$, $x = 1.5$ and $x = 2.0$, with corresponding y values of $(0.5)^2$, $(1.0)^2$, $(1.5)^2$, and $(2.0)^2$. Clearly the dark grey area (A_D) is less than the area required (A) which is in turn less than the light grey area (A_L). So,

$$A_D < A < A_L.$$

We can easily calculate the area of the rectangles making up A_D and A_L to give us

$$0.5(0.5)^2+0.5(1.0)^2+0.5(1.5)^2 < A < 0.5(0.5)^2+0.5(1.0)^2+0.5(1.5)^2+0.5(2.0)^2$$

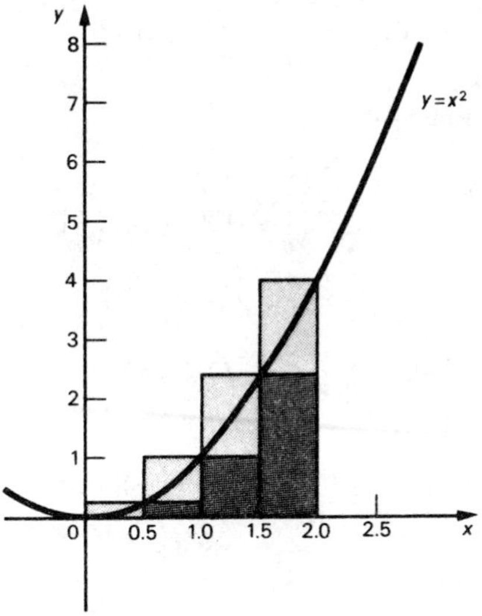

or $$0.5\{(0.5)^2+(1.0)^2+(1.5)^2\}<A<0.5\{(0.5)^2+(1.0)^2+(1.5)^2+(2.0)^2\}$$

$$0.5(0.25+1.0+2.25)<A<0.5(0.25+1.0+2.25+4)$$

$$1.75<A<3.75$$

Hence we might take an estimate for A, the average of the two values and say that $A \approx 2.75$.

Now this is not very accurate as we only divided the range into four strips — however, it does show the principle. Let us now be a little more ambitious and divide the range into n strips. If we do this each strip will be $2/n$ units wide. An enlarged portion of the diagram will show

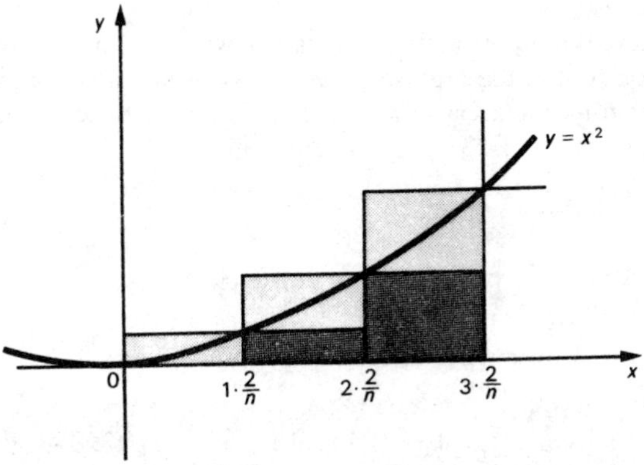

The x values will be $1\times\frac{2}{n}, 2\times\frac{2}{n}, 3\times\frac{2}{n}, 4\times\frac{2}{n}$, etc.,

with corresponding y values $\left(\frac{2}{n}\right)^2, \left(\frac{4}{n}\right)^2, \left(\frac{6}{n}\right)^2, \left(\frac{8}{n}\right)^2$

rearranged as $1^2\left(\frac{2}{n}\right)^2, 2^2\left(\frac{2}{n}\right)^2, 3^2\left(\frac{2}{n}\right)^2, 4^2\left(\frac{2}{n}\right)^2$

As before, $A_D < A < A_L$

$$\frac{2}{n}\times 1^2\left(\frac{2}{n}\right)^2+\frac{2}{n}\times 2^2\left(\frac{2}{n}\right)^2+\frac{2}{n}\times 3^2\left(\frac{2}{n}\right)^2\ldots+\frac{2}{n}\times(n-1)^2\left(\frac{2}{n}\right)^2 < A$$

and $$A < \frac{2}{n}\times 1^2\left(\frac{2}{n}\right)^2+\frac{2}{n}\times 2^2\left(\frac{2}{n}\right)^2+\frac{2}{n}\times 3^2\left(\frac{2}{n}\right)^2+\ldots+\frac{2}{n}\times n^2\left(\frac{2}{n}\right)^2$$

so $$\frac{8}{n^3}[1^2+2^2+3^2+\ldots+(n-1)^2] < A < \frac{8}{n^3}[1^2+2^2+3^2+\ldots+n^2]$$

At last we have a series that we have seen before! Now we can use the standard sum

$$\sum_1^n r^2 = \tfrac{1}{6}n(n+1)(2n+1)$$

for the first series of $n-1$ terms and the second series of n terms,

$$\frac{8}{n^3}\frac{(n-1)n(2n-1)}{6} < A < \frac{8}{n^3}\frac{n(n+1)(2n+1)}{6}$$

$$\frac{4}{3n^2}(2n^2-3n+1) < A < \frac{4}{3n^2}(2n^2+3n+1)$$

$$\frac{8}{3}-\frac{4}{n}+\frac{4}{3n^2} < A < \frac{8}{3}+\frac{4}{n}+\frac{4}{3n^2}$$

If n is very large $4/n$ and $4/3n^2$ are both very small and A is sandwiched between two numbers each of which is approximately 8/3; we say that, in the limit as $n\to\infty$, the area is 8/3 units.

Fortunately there is a simple method which you will meet in calculus (integration) which enables you to find the area very easily; essentially it is the same process—that of adding together the areas of a 'very large' number of 'very thin' strips.

Exercise 3.3a

1 Prove that $$\sum_1^n r^2 = \tfrac{1}{6}n(n+1)(2n+1)$$

The x axis from $x = 1$ to $x = 2$ is divided into n equal intervals by the points

$$(1, 0), \left(1+\frac{1}{n}, 0\right), \left(1+\frac{2}{n}, 0\right)\ldots\left(1+\frac{n-1}{n}, 0\right), (2, 0)$$

Rectangles with sides parallel to the axes are drawn on these intervals with one vertex on the curve $y = x^2$ and the rest of each rectangle between the curve and the x axis. Show that the sum of the areas of these rectangles is

$$1+\left(1-\frac{1}{n}\right)\left(\frac{4}{3}-\frac{1}{6n}\right)$$

Show further that, as n increases, this sum increases but remains less than $7/3$.

2 Explain briefly how the area under a curve can be found by dividing the area into thin strips. Using this method show that the area under the line $y = 1$, for $x = 0$ to $x = a$, is a and that the area under the line $y = x$ between $x = 0$ and $x = a$ is $\frac{1}{2}a^2$.

3 Use the ideas suggested in the figure to find the volume V of a cone of height h and base radius a. First divide the cone into four slices and 'box' it as shown.

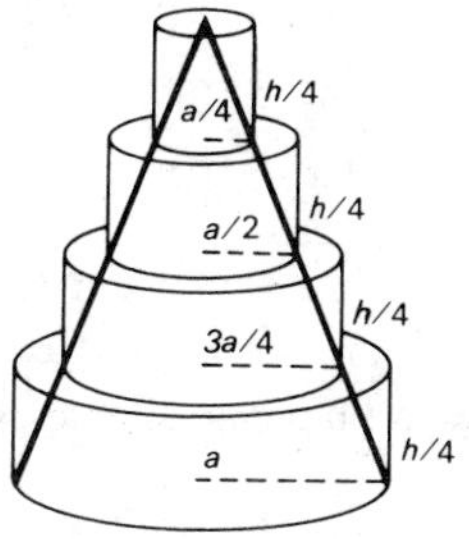

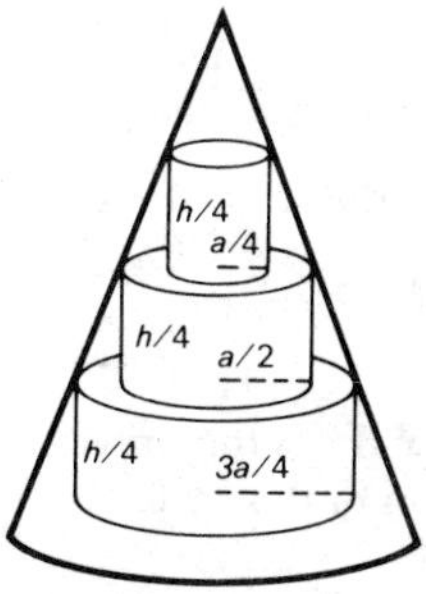

Hence show that
$$\frac{7\pi a^2 h}{32} < V < \frac{15\pi a^2 h}{32}$$

Now divide the cone into n slices, and obtain a pile of n cylinders, each of height h/n. Sandwich the cone between two piles of cylinders and show that

$$\tfrac{1}{6}\pi a^2 h\left(2-\frac{3}{n}+\frac{1}{n^2}\right) < V < \tfrac{1}{6}\pi a^2 h\left(2+\frac{3}{n}+\frac{1}{n^2}\right)$$

Deduce that if n is very large, $V = \frac{1}{3}\pi a^2 h$.

Exercise 3.3b

Find the sum of each of the following series.

1 $(3\times1)+(6\times2)+(9\times3)+\ldots$ to n terms.

2 $(1\times5)+(2\times7)+(3\times9)+\ldots$ (a) to 5 terms, and (b) to n terms.

3 $(1\times3)+(3\times5)+(5\times7)+\ldots$ to n terms.

4 $(1\times11)+(2\times12)+(3\times13)+\ldots$ to n terms.

5 $(1^2\times3)+(2^2\times4)+(3^2\times5)+\ldots$ to n terms.

6 $(1\times2\times4)+(2\times3\times5)+(3\times4\times6)+\ldots$ (a) to 5 terms, and (b) to n terms.

3.4 Geometric series

There is a story which tells of a wily old courtier who was promised by the King that one wish would be fulfilled. The courtier asked for a chess board and his request was for one grain of wheat on the first square, two on the second, four on the third, eight on the fourth and so on, doubling the number each time.

Could the King make good his promise?

The total number of grains required is

$$S = 1+2+4+8+\ldots+2^{63}$$

To sum this series we multiply it by 2:

$$2S = 2+4+8+\ldots+2^{63}+2^{64}$$

Subtracting gives $$S = 2^{64}-1$$

This is greater than 10^{19} grains of wheat—a vast quantity!

Example 8

(i) Consider the series $1+x+x^2+\ldots+x^{r-1}+\ldots+x^{n-1}$, i.e.

$$S = \sum_1^n x^{r-1}$$

Each term is x times the previous term and so far we have no simple procedure to give us the sum of this series.

Now

$$S = 1+x+x^2+\ldots+x^{r-1}+\ldots+x^{n-1}$$

Multiply each term by x

$$Sx = x+x^2+\ldots+x^r+\ldots+x^n$$

Subtract

$$S-Sx = 1-x^n$$

$$S(1-x) = 1-x^n$$

$$S = \frac{1-x^n}{1-x}$$

(ii) Now consider the series

$$S = 3+3x+3x^2+\ldots+3x^{r-1}+\ldots+3x^{n-1}$$

where each term is three times the corresponding term in (i).

Multiply each term by x

$$Sx = 3x+3x^2+3x^r+\ldots+3x^n$$

Subtract

$$S-Sx = 3-3x^n$$

$$S = \frac{3(1-x^n)}{1-x}$$

As we would expect, this sum is three times the previous sum.

Example 9

Each year I invest £50 in an insurance policy. Compound interest at eight per cent is added at the end of each year. Ignoring inflation, company profits and so on, what amount should be paid after twenty years?

Compound interest works as follows: £50 invested for one year at eight per cent means that the interest will be

$$\frac{50 \times 8 \times 1}{100}$$

(The traditional formula is $I = PRT/100$). So the interest is £4. For the next year £4 is added to the capital (£50), so that £54 is invested. The interest on this is

$$\frac{£54 \times 8 \times 1}{100}$$

which is added at the end of the year and so on.

At the end of my first year my £50 becomes

$$£50(1+\tfrac{8}{100})$$

at the end of the second year it has grown to

$$£50(1+\tfrac{8}{100})^2$$

and, eventually, at the end of the twentieth year it has reached

$$£50(1+\tfrac{8}{100})^{20}$$

To make the problem simpler, substitute $(1+\frac{8}{100}) = x$. Then after 20 years, my first £50 has become $£50x^{20}$.

The £50 invested at the start of the second year becomes $£50x^{19}$.

The £50 invested at the start of the third year becomes $£50x^{18}$.

Finally, the £50 invested at the start of the 20th year becomes $£50x$.

The total amount due in pounds is

$$50x + 50x^2 + 50x^3 + \ldots + 50x^{20}$$

$$= 50x(1 + x + x^2 + \ldots + x^{19})$$

$$= 50x\left(\frac{1-x^{20}}{1-x}\right)$$

Now $x = 1 + \frac{8}{100} = 1.08$. Hence the total amount due is £2468.

Series like those shown in Examples 8 and 9 are called *geometric series*—each term is a constant ratio times the previous term. These series can always be summed quickly and easily by multiplying through by the constant ratio and subtracting as shown in Example 8.

Exercise 3.4

1 Which of the following sequences are geometric?

(a) $2x, 4x, 8x \ldots$

(b) 1/3, 2/3, 4/3 . . .
(c) 1, −3/4, +9/16 . . .
(d) 27, 18, 12, 8 . . .
(e) $2x, 3x^2, 4x^3 \ldots$

2 For the geometric sequences in question 1 find (i) the common ratio, (ii) the 6th term, and (iii) the *n*th term.

3 Fill in the missing terms in the geometric sequences
(a) 50, —, 2
(b) x, —, —, $27x^4$
(c) $\frac{a}{2}$, —, $\frac{a^3}{32}$

4 How many terms are there in the series?
(a) $3+6+12+\ldots+384$
(b) $ap+ap^2+ap^3+\ldots+ap^{2n-1}$
(c) $1-\frac{3}{2}+\frac{9}{4}+\ldots+\frac{6561}{256}$.

5 Find the sum of the series
(a) $3-6+12-\ldots$ for 6 terms, 7 terms and 8 terms
(b) $1+\frac{a}{3}+\frac{a^2}{9}+\ldots+\frac{a^6}{3^6}$
(c) $1+1.06+1.06^2+\ldots+1.06^8$

6 Each year I invest £100 in an insurance policy with compound interest at nine per cent. What will I be paid after 25 years?

4 Series with and without sums

4.1 Convergent and divergent series

When we consider a series with an infinite number of terms the series may or may not have a sum. If the series has a sum it is said to *converge*; if not, we say that the series *diverges*.

To illustrate these ideas we can plot a graph of the sums against the number of terms.

Example 1

Consider the series $2+4+6+8+\ldots+2n+\ldots$ (arithmetic).

Then S_1 (the sum of one term) is 2, S_2 (the sum of two terms) is 6 and so on.

$$S_3 = 12, \quad S_4 = 20, \quad S_5 = 30.$$

It is clear that the larger the number of terms, the greater is the sum, so the series has *no* sum 'to infinity'. The series is a *divergent* one.

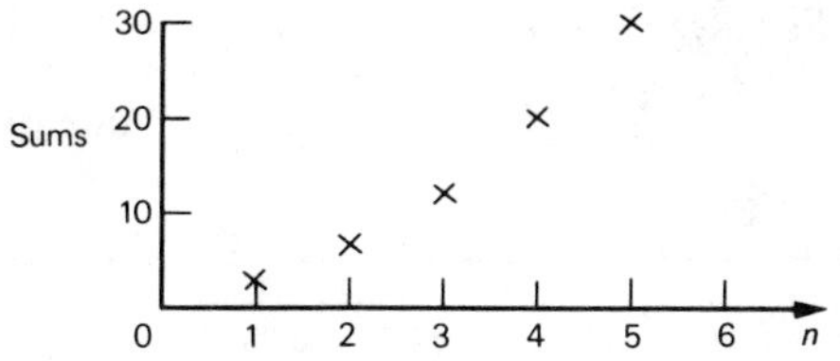

Example 2

Consider the series $6+2+2/3+2/9+2/27+\ldots+6(1/3)^{r-1}+\ldots$ (geometric).

$$S_1 = 6, \quad S_2 = 8, \quad S_3 = 8.\dot{6}, \quad S_4 = 8.\dot{8}, \quad S_5 = 8.96.$$

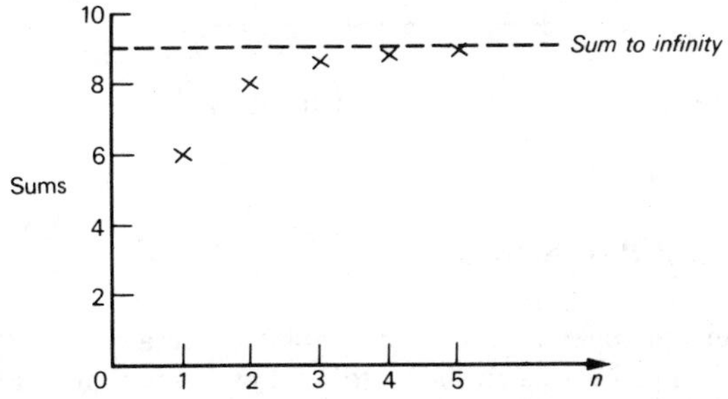

The sum approaches a particular value as we consider the sum of more and more terms in the series. This sum is called the *sum to infinity* and in this case the value to which the series *converges* is 9.

Example 3

So far we have considered series in which all the terms are positive. Similar cases can be imagined when all the terms are negative. However, if the terms alternate in sign, we have what is called an *oscillating* series. These too may have a sum or may not.

Consider the series $2-4+6-8+10-\ldots+(-1)^{n-1}2n+\ldots.$

$$S_1 = 2, \quad S_2 = -2, \quad S_3 = +4, \quad S_4 = -4, \quad S_5 = +6.$$

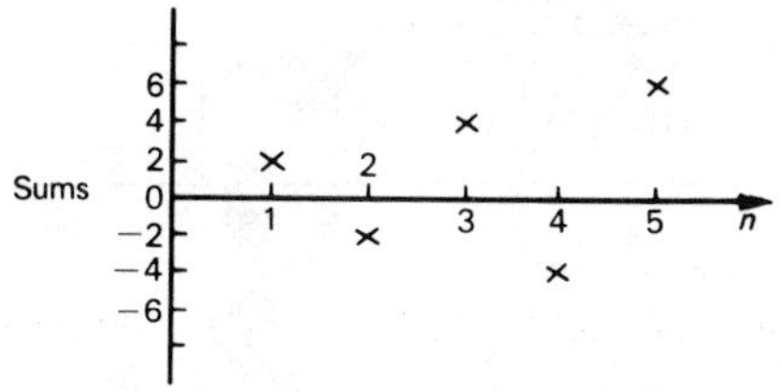

This series again has *no* sum 'to infinity' and *diverges*.

Example 4

Consider the series $6-2+2/3-2/9+2/27-\ldots+(-1)^{n-1}6(1/3)^{n-1}$.

$$S_1 = 6, \quad S_2 = 4, \quad S_3 = 4.\dot{6}, \quad S_4 = 4.\dot{4}, \quad S_5 = 4.518.$$

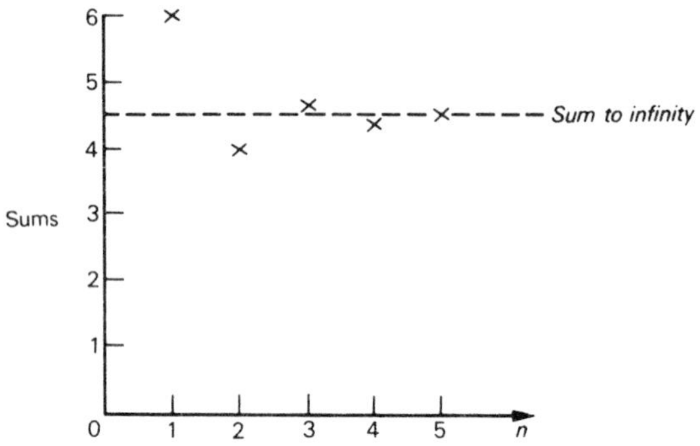

The sum oscillates and *converges* to the particular value 4.5, which is the sum 'to infinity' in this case.

4.2 Achilles and the tortoise

Achilles can run ten times as fast as a tortoise can crawl. If Achilles gives the tortoise a start, can he ever catch the tortoise? Let us say that Achilles runs at ten metres per second whilst the tortoise moves at one metre per second, and the tortoise has a hundred metre start.

Whilst Achilles travels the first hundred metres in ten seconds, the tortoise travels ten metres. It takes Achilles one second to cover the ten metres, but the tortoise has then completed another metre which Achilles covers in one tenth of a second, but by then the tortoise . . .

The tortoise travels a distance, in metres, of $10+1+1/10+1/100+1/1000+\ldots$ before being caught. The series carries on forever—it is an *infinite* geometric series with common ratio 1/10. Has the series got a sum? Is the tortoise caught? Obviously—common sense tells us that!

Consider

$$S = 10+1+\frac{1}{10}+\frac{1}{10^2}+\frac{1}{10^3}+\ldots+\frac{1}{10^{r-2}}+\frac{1}{10^{r-1}}+\ldots$$

Multiply by ratio 1/10:

$$\frac{1}{10}S = \quad 1+\frac{1}{10}+\frac{1}{10^2}+\frac{1}{10^3}+\ldots \quad +\frac{1}{10^{r-1}}+\frac{1}{10^r}+\ldots$$

Subtract $\frac{9}{10}S = 10$

so $\quad S = 11\frac{1}{9}$ metres.

We can obtain this *convergent* result because the last term is negligible, although strictly speaking there is no 'last' term since the series goes on indefinitely. However, if we considered the sum to 100 terms we should subtract $1/10^{99}$, which is very small compared with the other numbers.

General geometric series

If the series is written as $a + ax + ax^2 + \ldots + ax^{n-1}$ we have

$$S = a + ax + ax^2 + \ldots + ax^{n-1}$$

Multiply through by x: $$Sx = ax + ax^2 + \ldots + ax^{n-1} + ax^n$$

and subtract $$S - Sx = a - ax^n$$

$$S(1-x) = a(1-x^n)$$

$$\mathbf{S = \frac{a(1-x^n)}{(1-x)}}$$ ◀

$$= \frac{a}{1-x} - \frac{ax^n}{1-x}$$

Now if x is a fraction between -1 and $+1$ (i.e. $-1 < x < 1$), then x^n becomes smaller and smaller as n becomes larger. We say that *as n tends to infinity, x^n tends to zero* ($n \to \infty$, $x^n \to 0$). So that $(ax^n/1-x)$ term tends to zero.

The sum of an infinite number of terms in the general geometric series is

$$\mathbf{S = \frac{a}{1-x}}$$ ◀

where $-1 < x < 1$.

4.3 The snowflake curve

Suppose we start with an equilateral triangle (a) and trisect each side. We then construct equilateral triangles on the middle section of each side as shown in (b). This process can be continued for as many steps as we like.

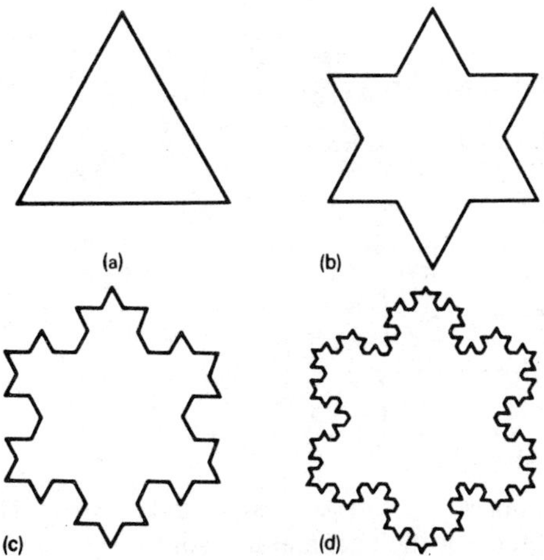

The area enclosed by the figure is always less than the area of the circumscribing circle of the original triangle; but the perimeter . . .

Suppose the original perimeter is 3 units.

The second perimeter is $3+1=4$ units.

The third is $3+1+4/3$ units, whilst that of the fourth is $3+1+(4/3)+(4/3)^2$. The perimeter is always increasing so the sum of this infinite series, $3+1+4/3+(4/3)^2+\ldots$, is infinitely large. It is a *divergent* series.

4.4 A famous divergent series

One of the most well-known series, which looks as if it has a sum (but hasn't!) is the series $S=1+\frac{1}{2}+\frac{1}{3}+\frac{1}{4}+\frac{1}{5}+\frac{1}{6}+\ldots$ By grouping the terms 2 together, 4 together, 8 together etc.,

$$S=1+\tfrac{1}{2}+(\tfrac{1}{3}+\tfrac{1}{4})+(\tfrac{1}{5}+\tfrac{1}{6}+\tfrac{1}{7}+\tfrac{1}{8})+\ldots$$

$$S>1+\tfrac{1}{2}+\quad\tfrac{1}{2}\quad+\qquad\tfrac{1}{2}\qquad+\ldots$$

So S increases and increases, although as the series continues we need to increase the number of terms grouped together so that they give a sum $>\frac{1}{2}$. This is another divergent series.

Use this method of grouping for a convergent series, e.g. $1+\frac{1}{2}+\frac{1}{4}+\frac{1}{8}+\ldots$, and investigate the process.

Exercise 4.4

Consider the following series. Discuss whether or not they have a sum to an infinite number of terms, and find the sum if it exists.

1 $1+2+3+4+\ldots$

2 $1+\frac{1}{3}+\frac{1}{9}+\frac{1}{27}+\ldots$

3 $1-\frac{1}{3}+\frac{1}{9}-\frac{1}{27}+\ldots$

4 $2-2+2-2+\ldots$

5 $(1-\frac{1}{2})+(\frac{1}{2}-\frac{1}{4})+(\frac{1}{4}-\frac{1}{8})+\ldots$

6 $2+4-6+2+4-6+2+4-6+\ldots$

7 $\dfrac{1}{1^2}+\dfrac{1}{2^2}+\dfrac{1}{3^2}+\dfrac{1}{4^2}+\ldots$

8 $1-\frac{1}{3}+\frac{1}{5}-\frac{1}{7}+\ldots$

9 $\dfrac{1}{6}+\dfrac{1}{6}\left(\dfrac{5}{6}\right)+\dfrac{1}{6}\left(\dfrac{5}{6}\right)^2+\dfrac{1}{6}\left(\dfrac{5}{6}\right)^3+\ldots$

10 $\dfrac{1}{10}+\dfrac{1}{10}\left(\dfrac{9}{10}\right)+\dfrac{1}{10}\left(\dfrac{9}{10}\right)^2+\dfrac{1}{10}\left(\dfrac{9}{10}\right)^3+\ldots$

11 Draw the first four stages in the 'antisnowflake' curve. This is similar to the snowflake curve except that the equilateral triangles are drawn *inside* the original equilateral triangle. Find the perimeter in each case and comment on the length of the perimeter as $n \to \infty$.

12 Consider the following arguments:

(a)
$$\begin{aligned} S &= 1-2+4-8+16-32+64- \dots \\ \Rightarrow S &= 1-2(1-2+4-8+16-32+\dots) \\ &= 1-2S \\ 3S &= 1 \\ S &= \tfrac{1}{3} \end{aligned}$$

(b)
$$\begin{aligned} S &= 1+(-2+4)+(-8+16)+(-32+64)+ \dots \\ \Rightarrow S &= 1+2+8+32+ \dots \end{aligned}$$

so S diverges towards $+\infty$.

(c)
$$\begin{aligned} S &= (1-2)+(4-8)+(16-32)+ \\ \Rightarrow S &= -1 \quad -4 \quad -8 \quad -16 \dots \end{aligned}$$

so S diverges towards $-\infty$.
What is the sum of the series?

5 Recurrence relations

[This section may be left to a second reading.]

There are many series in which one term is a combination of two previous terms. A well known and interesting example of this involves the *Fibonacci sequence.*

5.1 The Fibonacci sequence

A man bought a pair of white mice (one of each sex). This pair produced a pair of offspring after one month, and another pair the following month. They then stopped breeding. Each new pair of mice produced two more pairs in the same way, and then stopped breeding. How many new pairs of mice does the man gain each month and how many pairs of mice does he have after n months? In the diagram overleaf each cross represents a new pair of white mice.

The number of new pairs follows the sequence

$$1, 1, 2, 3, 5, 8, 13, 21, 34, 55, 89, 144 \dots$$

This is a series which is associated with several occurrences in nature, e.g. the way leaves spiral round the stem of certain plants. Let us try to find the *general term* and the *sum* of this series, $1+1+2+3+5+8+ \dots$

Clearly the series is not an arithmetic series since the difference between one term and the previous one is not constant. To see whether the numbers form a

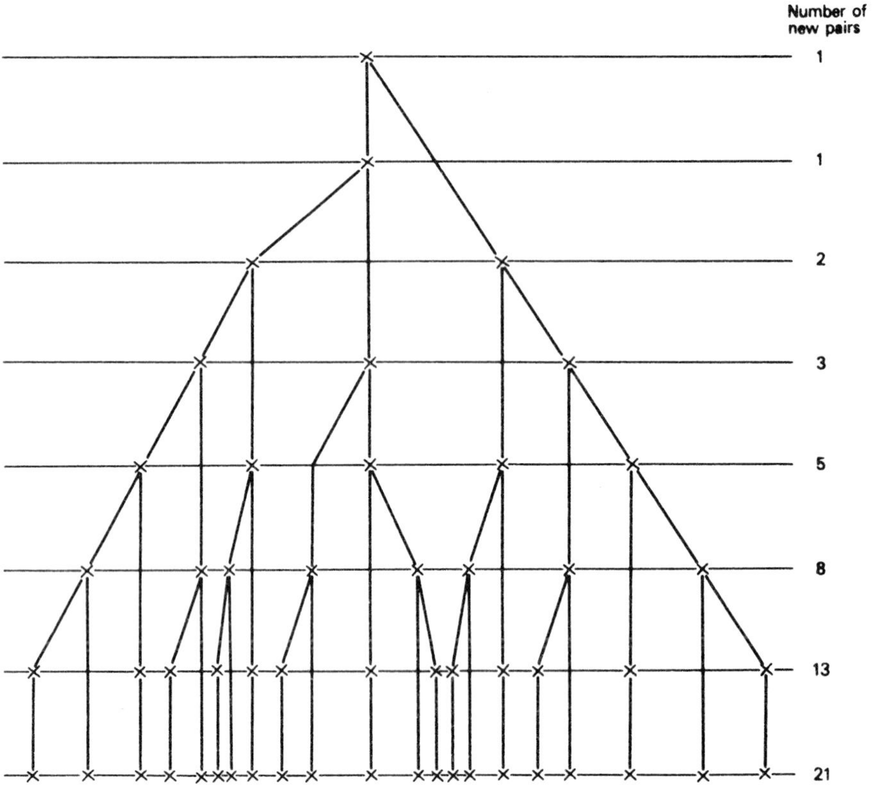

geometric series we divide one term by the previous one, to find out whether there is a constant ratio.

$$\frac{1}{1} = 1.0, \quad \frac{2}{1} = 2.0, \quad \frac{3}{2} = 1.5, \quad \frac{5}{3} = 1.\dot{6}, \quad \frac{8}{5} = 1.6, \quad \frac{13}{8} = 1.625,$$

$$\frac{21}{13} \approx 1.615, \quad \frac{34}{21} \approx 1.619, \quad \frac{55}{34} \approx 1.6176, \quad \frac{89}{55} \approx 1.6182.$$

The early terms do not give a constant ratio, but the later terms of the series give a ratio which is approaching a value of about 1.618. Thus we can suppose, for large values of n, that the terms are approximately geometric. We might write the kth term as $u_k \approx Ax^k$, where A is constant, but we do not know what x is. However, the connection between the terms is easy to see.

$$k\text{th term} = (k-1)\text{th term} + (k-2)\text{th term}$$

or $$u_k = u_{k-1} + u_{k-2}$$

Suppose $$u_k = Ax^k$$

then $\quad u_{k-1} = Ax^{k-1} \quad$ and $\quad u_{k-2} = Ax^{k-2}$

so
$$Ax^k = Ax^{k-1} + Ax^{k-2}$$

Divide through by Ax^{k-2}

$$x^2 = x+1$$

$$x^2 - x - 1 = 0$$

$$x = \frac{1 \pm \sqrt{5}}{2}$$

This is a surprise for we have *two* answers:

$$x = \frac{1+\sqrt{5}}{2} \quad \text{or} \quad x = \frac{1-\sqrt{5}}{2}$$

If $u_k = Ax^k$ where $x = (1+\sqrt{5})/2$ then u_k becomes larger as k becomes larger, whilst if $x = (1-\sqrt{5})/2 = (1-2.236)/2 = -0.618$, u_k becomes smaller and smaller as k becomes larger and larger. We might make an intelligent guess that the answer could be a combination of these two values of x.

Let

$$t = \frac{1+\sqrt{5}}{2}, \qquad s = \frac{1-\sqrt{5}}{2}$$

and suppose $\quad u_k = Ct^k + Ds^k$

Now $\quad u_1 = 1 = Ct + Ds$

and $\quad u_2 = 1 = Ct^2 + Ds^2$

Solving this pair simultaneously gives

$$C = \frac{1}{\sqrt{5}}, \qquad D = \frac{-1}{\sqrt{5}}$$

So the general term is

$$u_k = \frac{1}{\sqrt{5}}\left(\frac{1+\sqrt{5}}{2}\right)^k - \frac{1}{\sqrt{5}}\left(\frac{1-\sqrt{5}}{2}\right)^k$$

The *sum* of the series is finally revealed as the difference of two geometric series.

$$S = \left(\frac{1}{\sqrt{5}}t - \frac{1}{\sqrt{5}}s\right) + \left(\frac{1}{\sqrt{5}}t^2 - \frac{1}{\sqrt{5}}s^2\right) + \ldots + \left(\frac{1}{\sqrt{5}}t^k - \frac{1}{\sqrt{5}}s^k\right) + \ldots + \left(\frac{1}{\sqrt{5}}t^n - \frac{1}{\sqrt{5}}s^n\right)$$

$$= \frac{1}{\sqrt{5}}(t + t^2 + \ldots + t^n) - \frac{1}{\sqrt{5}}(s + s^2 + \ldots + s^n)$$

$$= \frac{1}{\sqrt{5}}t\left(\frac{1-t^n}{1-t}\right) - \frac{1}{\sqrt{5}}s\left(\frac{1-s^n}{1-s}\right)$$

t is called the *golden section*. It occurs in Greek architecture, in the pentagon, and even the humble postcard has its sides approximately in the ratio of $t:1$.

5.2 The solution of difference equations

An equation like $u_k = u_{k-1} + u_{k-2}$ is a *recurrence relation* or *difference equation.*

Difference equations occur frequently in economics, for example, the size of next year's gross national product depends on the size of both this year's and last year's products. The 'solution' to the equation enables us to estimate the level of the product for any given year in the future, assuming that the relationship remains the same.

When we solve the equation we are finding an expression for the general term of the series which satisfies the relation.

We assume that the kth term is of the form Ax^k, i.e. $u_k = Ax^k$.

Example

Solve $u_k - 5u_{k-1} + 6u_{k-2} = 0;\quad u_1 = 0,\quad u_2 = 1.$

Suppose that u_k can be written as $u_k = Ax^k$. Then

$$u_{k-1} = Ax^{k-1}, \qquad u_{k-2} = Ax^{k-2}$$

so $$Ax^k - 5Ax^{k-1} + 6Ax^{k-2} = 0$$

Divide through by Ax^{k-2} $$x^2 - 5x + 6 = 0$$

$$(x-2)(x-3) = 0$$

$$x = 2 \text{ or } 3$$

We now consider the general term as $u_k = B(2)^k + C(3)^k$ where B and C are constants.

Now $u_1 = 0$, so $0 = 2B + 3C$

and $u_2 = 1$, so $1 = 4B + 9C$

This pair solved simultaneously give $C = \frac{1}{3}$ and $B = -\frac{1}{2}$

Our final solution is $$u_k = -\tfrac{1}{2}(2)^k + \tfrac{1}{3}(3)^k$$
$$= 3^{k-1} - 2^{k-1}$$

and the series is $0 + 1 + 5 + 19 + \ldots$

Exercise 5.2

Solve the following difference equations.

1 $u_k - 4u_{k-1} + 3u_{k-2} = 0$

2 $u_k + 2u_{k-1} - 3u_{k-2} = 0$

3 $u_k - 4u_{k-1} - 12u_{k-2} = 0$

4 $u_k - 3u_{k-1} + 2u_{k-2} = 0 \quad u_1 = 0, \quad u_2 = 1$

5 $u_k + 3u_{k-1} - 10u_{k-2} = 0 \quad u_1 = 0, \quad u_2 = 5$

6 $u_k - 4u_{k-1} + 4u_{k-2} = 0 \qquad u_1 = 0, \quad u_2 = 2$

(The quadratic equation $x^2 - 4x + 4 = 0$ has equal roots and the solution to the recurrence relation is of the form $(A + Bk)2^k$.)

7 $u_k - 6u_{k-1} + 9u_{k-2} = 0 \qquad u_1 = 1, \quad u_2 = 3$

8 What do you think might be the solution of the following recurrence relation:

$$u_k - 3u_{k-1} + 3u_{k-2} - u_{k-3} = 0$$

5.3 To find the formula for the *n*th term in a series

Suppose we know the value of various terms in a series and we wish to know the formula for the nth term. We shall tackle this problem by using series with a known formula for the nth term.

Linear *n*th term

Consider for example the series whose nth term is $f(n) = 2n + 1$.

			*1st difference**	*2nd difference*
If $n = 0$	then	$f(0) = 1$		
			2	
$n = 1$		$f(1) = 3$		0
			2	
$n = 2$		$f(2) = 5$		0
			2	
$n = 3$		$f(3) = 7$		0
			2	
$n = 4$		$f(4) = 9$		0
			2	
$n = 5$		$f(5) = 11$		

* NOTE. The difference column is found by subtracting the top number from the next down in the table.

We can see that

1 If $f(n)$ is linear, then the first differences are constant (=2).

2 The second differences are 0.

3 The formula is given by n times the (constant 1st difference)+$f(0)$. This is $2n + 1$.

Quadratic *n*th term

Consider a series whose nth term is given by $f(n) = 3n^2 + 2n - 1$.

			1st differences	2nd differences	3rd differences
If $n=0$	then	$f(0)=-1$			
			5		
$n=1$		$f(1)=\ 4$		6	
			11		0
$n=2$		$f(2)=15$		6	
			17		0
$n=3$		$f(3)=32$		6	
			23		0
$n=4$		$f(4)=55$		6	
			29		
$n=5$		$f(5)=84$			

Here we can see that

1. If $f(n)$ is quadratic, then the second differences are constant (=6).
2. The third differences are 0.
3. The formula is given by

$$\frac{n(n-1)}{2\times 1}\times(\text{2nd difference underlined}) + n\ (\text{1st difference underlined}) + f(0)$$

$$= \frac{n(n-1)}{2\times 1}\times 6 + 5n - 1$$

$$= 3n^2 + 2n - 1$$

The slanting line in the table indicates from where the coefficients are derived.

Cubic *n*th term

Consider a series whose nth term is a cubic given by $f(n) = n^3 - 2n^2 + 3n + 3$.

			1st differences	2nd differences	3rd differences	4th differences
If $n=0$	then	$f(0)=3$				
			2			
$n=1$		$f(1)=5$		2		
			4		6	
$n=2$		$f(2)=9$		8		0
			12		6	
$n=3$		$f(3)=21$		14		0
			26		6	
$n=4$		$f(4)=47$		20		
			46			
$n=5$		$f(5)=93$				

Again we see that

1 If $f(n)$ is cubic, then the third differences are constant (=6).

2 The fourth differences are zero.

3 The formula is given by

$$\frac{n(n-1)(n-2)}{3\times2\times1}\times\begin{pmatrix}\text{3rd differences}\\\text{underlined}\end{pmatrix}+\frac{n(n-1)}{2\times1}\times\begin{pmatrix}\text{2nd differences}\\\text{underlined}\end{pmatrix}$$

$$+n\begin{pmatrix}\text{1st difference}\\\text{underlined}\end{pmatrix}+f(0)$$

$$=\frac{n(n-1)(n-2)}{6}\times6+\frac{n(n-1)}{2}\times2+2n+3$$

$$=n^3-3n^2+2n+n^2-n+2n+3$$

$$=n^3-2n^2+3n+3$$

We often write the 1st differences as Δf, the second differences $\Delta^2 f$ and so on. The terms are very like those from a binomial expansion (see page 174).

In general,

$$f\equiv f(0)+n\Delta f(0)+\frac{n(n-1)}{1\times2}\Delta^2 f(0)+\frac{n(n-1)(n-2)}{1\times2\times3}\Delta^3 f(0)+\ldots$$

This is called the *Gregory-Newton formula* and we shall discuss it later.

Exercise 5.3

Find the formula for the nth term in the following series with

1 $f(0)=-1, f(1)=2, f(2)=5, f(3)=8, f(4)=11, f(5)=14.$

2 $f(0)=1, f(1)=0, f(2)=3, f(3)=10, f(4)=21, f(5)=36.$

3 $f(0)=1, f(1)=3, f(2)=1, f(3)=-5, f(4)=-15, f(5)=-29.$

4 $f(0)=-1, f(1)=-1, f(2)=5, f(3)=29, f(4)=83, f(5)=179.$

5 $f(0)=1, f(1)=1, f(2)=2, f(3)=4, f(4)=8, f(5)=16, f(6)=31.$

Miscellaneous examination questions 1

(O. & C. unless stated otherwise)

1(a) In the series 1, 2, 3, 4, 5, etc., every third term is multiplied by 2 so that the series becomes 1, 2, 6, 4, 5, 12 etc. Find the sum of the first 60 terms of this series.

(b) The first term of a geometric series is 5 and its common ratio is 1.04. Using logarithms, find the 13th term to two places of decimals. Also write down an expression, without simplifying it, for the sum of the first n terms of this series.

2(a) The first term of an arithmetic series is 3. Find the common difference if the sum of the first eight terms is twice the sum of the first five terms.

(b) An arithmetic series and a geometric series have the same third term, and both have 4 for the first term. Given that the eleventh term of the arithmetic series is equal to the square of the second term of the geometric series, find the common difference of the arithmetic series.

3(a) The tenth term of an arithmetic series is 28 and the fourth term is 14; find the first term.

(b) Write down the second term of the series whose nth term is $3n$; also the second term of the series whose nth term is $(1.1)^n$. Find the sum of the first 20 terms of each of these series (in the second case to one place of decimals).

4(a) The sum to n terms of a certain arithmetic series is $5n^2-3n$. Find the first, second and nth terms.

(b) Jones invests £60 at three per cent per annum compound interest on the first day of January each year. He commenced on 1st January, 1960. What amount should be standing to his credit on 31st December, 1980?

5 A company, wishing to employ a young executive on a ten year contract, offers him a starting salary of £1500 per annum which is to be increased by 10 percent each year. Calculate how much (in all) the executive expects to receive in ten years. After considering the offer, the executive says that he would prefer a fixed annual rise in salary. If the company decides to give him the same starting salary, find the fixed annual rise which will give him the same total income over ten years. (O.)

6 A man invests £200 at the beginning of each year and receives compound interest at five percent per annum. By forming a series, show that the total amount of accumulated capital and interest at the end of n years is £4200 $\{(1.05^n-1\}$. Taking $\log 1.05 = 0.02119$ calculate, as accurately as your tables of logarithms allow, the total amount of accumulated capital and interest at the end of twenty years. Determine also the least number of years that the man would need to continue his investments in order to accumulate not less than £10 000. (O.)

7 Establish a formula for the sum of the first n positive integers $1+2+3+\ldots+n$. The positive integers are arranged in groups containing one, two, three, ... integers as follows:

$$1, (2+3), (4+5+6), (7+8+9+10), \ldots$$

By taking the last integer in each group, the series 1, 3, 6, 10 ... is formed. Find a formula for the nth term of this series. Also find

(a) the difference between the nth term and the $(n-1)$th term, and

(b) the value of n if the nth term $= 300$. (O.)

8 A child uses square tiles to lay out the shape shown. How many tiles are required?

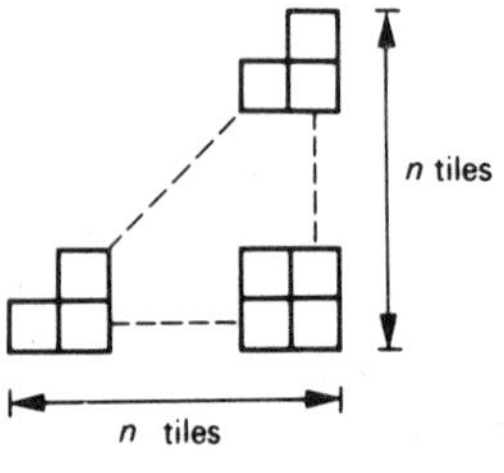

He now goes on to complete the shape shown below. How many tiles does he need now? If he were to change the measurement up the page from n tiles to $m+n$ tiles, while keeping the general shape the same, how many extra tiles would be required?

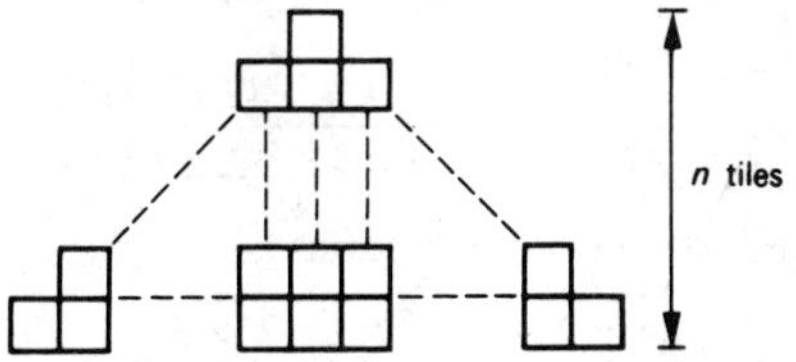

(O.)

9 Given that the first, third and fourth terms of a certain geometric series are in arithmetic series and that the sum to infinity is $\sqrt{5}-1$, find the first term. (M.E.I.)

10 Write down the sum to n terms (S_n), and the sum to infinity (S) of the geometric series $a+ar+ar^2+\ldots$ and state the range of values of r for which S exists.

Show that, if $a>0$, then $S>4ar$ except for one value of r and state this exceptional value.

Find all the real values of a and r for which $S_4 = 40$ and $S = 81/2$. (M.E.I.)

11 Prove that the sum of the first n terms of the series $x+x^2+x^3+\ldots$ (where the rth term is x^r) is $\dfrac{x(1-x^n)}{1-x}$.

Find the sum of the first $2m$ terms of the series

$$x+x^2+x^4+x^5+x^7+x^8+\ldots+x^{3r+1}+x^{3r+2}+\ldots$$

where m is a positive integer.

12 The sum of the first five terms of the geometric series a, ar, $ar^2\ldots$ is 5; the sum of the fifth to ninth terms (both inclusive) is 80. Prove that $r=\pm2$ and find the two possible values of a.

13(a)(i) The fourth term of an arithmetic series is 55, and the tenth term is 45. Calculate the sum of all the positive terms.

(ii) Find, correct to one decimal point, the sum of the first fifteen terms of the geometric series $1+1.02+(1.02)^2+(1.02)^3+\ldots$

(b) Show that $4r^3 = [r(r+1)]^2-[r(r-1)]^2$ and hence evaluate $\sum_{r=1}^{r=n} r^3$.

14 Prove that the sum of n terms of the series $2+3\times2+4\times2^2+5\times2^3+\ldots$is $n2^n$.

15 Given that

$$\frac{1}{x(x+3)} = \frac{1}{3}\left(\frac{1}{x}-\frac{1}{x+3}\right)$$

find the sum of n terms of the series

$$\frac{1}{1\times4}+\frac{1}{2\times5}+\frac{1}{3\times6}+\ldots$$

16 Write down the nth term of the series $1\times2+2\times5+3\times8+4\times11+\ldots$ and prove that the sum of the first n term is $n^2(n+1)$.

17 Prove that the sum of n terms of the series

$$\frac{2}{3}+\frac{2\times4}{3\times5}+\frac{2\times4\times6}{3\times5\times7}+\ldots$$

is equal to

$$-2+\frac{2\times4\ldots(2n+2)}{1\times3\ldots(2n+1)}$$

18 Write down the nth term of the series

$$\frac{2\times1}{2\times3}+\frac{2^2\times2}{3\times4}+\frac{2^3\times3}{4\times5}+\ldots$$

Prove that the sum of the first n terms of this series is

$$\frac{2^{n+1}}{n+2}-1$$

19 Prove that

$$\frac{(2n+1)(2n+3)}{(n+1)(n+2)}-\frac{(2n-1)(2n+1)}{n(n+1)}=\frac{2(2n+1)}{n(n+1)(n+2)}$$

Find the sum of the first n terms of the series

$$\frac{3}{1\times2\times3}+\frac{5}{2\times3\times4}+\frac{7}{3\times4\times5}+\ldots.$$

20 For all values of n, find A, B independent of n such that

$$\frac{1}{n(n+1)(n+2)}=\frac{A}{n(n+1)}+\frac{B}{(n+1)(n+2)}$$

Prove that the sums of the first n terms of the series whose rth terms are

$$\frac{1}{(r+1)(r+2)} \quad \text{and} \quad \frac{1}{r(r+1)(r+2)}$$

are, respectively,

$$\frac{1}{2}-\frac{1}{n+2} \quad \text{and} \quad \frac{1}{4}-\frac{1}{2(n+1)(n+2)}$$

21 Prove that $$1^3+2^3+3^3+\ldots+n^3=\tfrac{1}{4}n^2(n+1)^2$$

Find the sum of the cubes of the first n even numbers and the sum of the cubes of the first n odd numbers. Show that the difference between these two sums is $n^2(4n+3)$.

22 Prove that the sum of the first n natural numbers is $\frac{1}{2}n(n+1)$. Prove that

$$\tfrac{1}{2}\times1\times2+\tfrac{1}{2}\times2\times3+\ldots+\tfrac{1}{2}n(n+1)=\tfrac{1}{6}n(n+1)(n+2)$$

Show that every number of the form $n(n+1)(n+2)$ is divisible by 6.

23 Without quoting the formulae for $\sum r^2$ and $\sum r^3$ prove that

$$\sum_{r=1}^{r=n} r(r+1) = \tfrac{1}{3}n(n+1)(n+2)$$

and
$$\sum_{r=1}^{r=n} r(r+1)(r+2) = \tfrac{1}{4}n(n+1)(n+2)(n+3)$$

Hence obtain the formulae for

$$\sum_{r=1}^{r=n} r^2 \quad \text{and} \quad \sum_{r=1}^{r=n} r^3$$

24 Given that the sum of the cubes of the first n positive integers is

$$\{\tfrac{1}{2}n(n+1)\}^2$$

prove by induction that $S_7+S_5 = 2(S_3)^2$ where $S_r = 1^r+2^r+\ldots+n^r$. (M.E.I.)

25 Prove by induction that the sum of the squares of the first n positive integers is $\frac{1}{6}n(n+1)(2n+1)$.

Find the sum of the squares of the numbers $1, 4, 7, \ldots 3n-2$. (M.E.I.)

26 Prove by induction or otherwise that

$$\sum_{r=1}^{r=n} r(r+1)(\tfrac{1}{2})^{r-1} = 16-(n^2+5n+8)(\tfrac{1}{2})^{n-1}$$ (M.E.I.)

27 Prove by induction that the sum of the squares of the first n odd positive integers is $\frac{1}{3}n(4n^2-1)$. (M.E.I.)

28(a) Prove that the sum of the first n terms of the arithmetic series in which the first term is a and the common difference is d is

$$\tfrac{1}{2}n[2a+(n-1)d]$$

The sum of the squares of three consecutive terms of a diminishing arithmetic series is 35/9 times the square of the middle term, and the product of the three terms is 15. Find the three terms.

(b) Establish the identity $n^3-(n-1)^3 = 3n^2-3n+1$ and hence find the sum to n terms of the series $1^2+2^2+3^2+\ldots$

29(a) Express $4r^3-6r^2+2r$ in the form $Ar(r+1)(r+2)+Br(r+1)+Cr$ where A, B, C are independent of r.

Evaluate
$$\sum_{r=1}^{r=n} (4r^3-6r^2+2r)$$

(b) Evaluate
$$\sum_{r=2}^{r=n} \frac{1}{r^2-1}$$ (O.)

30 Prove that
$$\frac{1}{r(r+1)}-\frac{1}{(r+1)(r+2)} = \frac{2}{r(r+1)(r+2)}$$

Find the sum of the first n terms of the series whose rth term is

$$\frac{1}{r(r+1)(r+2)}$$

31 Prove that $$1+x+x^2+\ldots x^{n-1}=\frac{1-x^n}{1-x}$$

provided $x \neq 1$.

Deduce that the error in calculating $(1-x)^{-1}$ by means of the approximation $1+x+x^2+\ldots+x^{n-1}$ is

$$\frac{x^n}{1-x}$$

Find how many terms of the approximation must be used in order to calculate $(0.7)^{-1}$ with an error not exceeding 0.5×10^{-4}.

Chapter 2

Algebra 1

1 Introduction

1.1 Sets of numbers

During our excursions into pure mathematics we shall meet several sets of numbers. We are all familiar with the set of *counting numbers*:

$$\mathbb{N} = \{1, 2, 3, 4, \ldots\}$$

These numbers enable us to solve equations like $n+3 = 5$. Using only this set, however, we cannot solve the equation $z+5 = 3$, and so we extend our number system to the set of *integers*:

$$\mathbb{Z} = \{\ldots -3, -2, -1, 0, +1, +2, +3, \ldots\}$$

We are still unable to solve simple equations of the type $3q = 5$, so we further extend the number system to include all the fractions or '*ratio-nal*' *numbers*:

$$\mathbb{Q} = \{\ldots -3, -\tfrac{5}{2}, -2, -\tfrac{4}{3}, -1, 0, +\tfrac{1}{4}, +\tfrac{1}{3}, +\tfrac{1}{2}, +1, +1\tfrac{1}{2}, +2, +2\tfrac{1}{3}, \ldots\}$$

(—only a few of the rational numbers can be listed here, of course.) In decimal form a fraction either terminates or recurs, e.g. $\frac{1}{2} = 0.5$ but $\frac{1}{3} = 0.\dot{3}$.

Yet we still cannot solve equations like $r^2 = 2$ since if r is a rational number l/m with l, m having no common factors (i.e. r is a fraction in its lowest terms), then $(l/m)^2 = 2$, so $l^2 = 2m^2$. But even numbers square to give even numbers, and odd numbers square to give odd numbers, so l must be an even number.

If we put $l = 2n$, then $(2n)^2 = 2m^2$ and $4n^2 = 2m^2$, so $2n^2 = m^2$. Hence m^2 is an even number, which means that m is also even. Now if l is even and m is even, they must have a common factor 2 but this is a contradiction since we said that l and m had no common factors: it follows that r is not a rational number.

We must therefore extend the number system even further to include *irrational numbers* (such as $\sqrt{2}$, $\sqrt{3}$, $\sqrt{5}, \ldots$), which neither recur nor terminate when written in decimal form (e.g. $\sqrt{3} = 1.7321\ldots$).

Real numbers

The set of numbers containing *all* the counting numbers, the integers, the rational numbers and the irrational numbers is known as the set of *real numbers*, $\mathbb{R}$. There are irrational numbers which are *not* real roots of 'simple' equations like $r^2 = 2$. These numbers are known as *transcendental numbers*. The two most common ones are $\pi = 3.14159\ldots$ and $e = 2.71828\ldots$

Complex numbers

In order to solve equations like $c^2 = -2$ the number system must be extended still further by introducing the symbol j, where $j^2 = -1$. The number system containing *all* the numbers mentioned is called $\mathbb{C}$, the set of *complex numbers*, and our number system is now complete.

Summary

$\mathbb{N}$ is the set of *natural* numbers,
$\mathbb{R}$ is the set of all *real* numbers,
$\mathbb{Q}$ is the set of all *rational* numbers,
$\mathbb{C}$ is the set of all *complex* numbers,
$\mathbb{Z}$ is the set of all *integers* (NOTE $0 \in \mathbb{Z}$),
$\mathbb{Z}^+$ is the set of all *positive integers*, and
$\mathbb{Z}_0^+$ is the set of all *non-negative integers*.

1.2 Introduction to functions

In pure mathematics we often say that y is a *function of* x, and this is written as $y = f(x)$. The idea of a function is a very important one, which is explained simply as follows:

For each value of x, there corresponds one and only one value of y.

This value is found by substituting the value of x into the expression for y.

Example

If we write $y = f(x) = x^2 + 2x - 3$ we mean that y is a function of x and that the expression for y is $x^2 + 2x - 3$. To find the value of y corresponding to, say, $x = 1$, we substitute in $x^2 + 2x - 3$, to get $1^2 + 2 \times 1 - 3 = 0$, and so on.

Graphically, if $y = f(x)$ then if we draw in a vertical line for any value of x, it will cut the curve representing $y = f(x)$ in *one* place only. Here are some graphs to illustrate the idea.

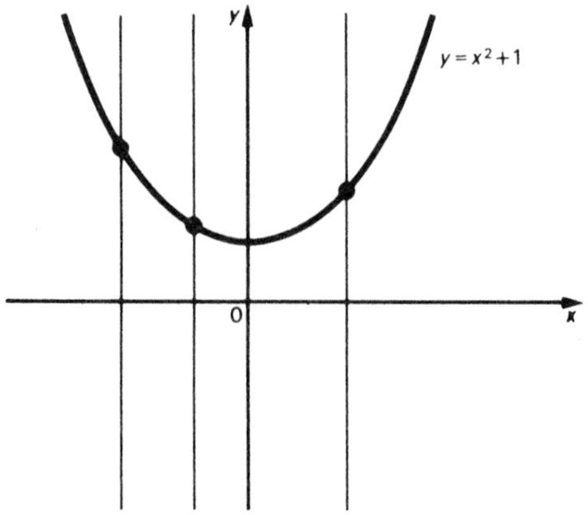

Any vertical line cuts the curve *once*

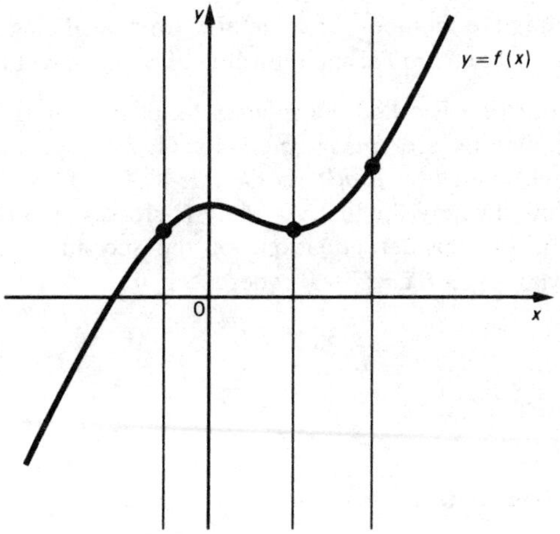

Any vertical line cuts the curve *once*

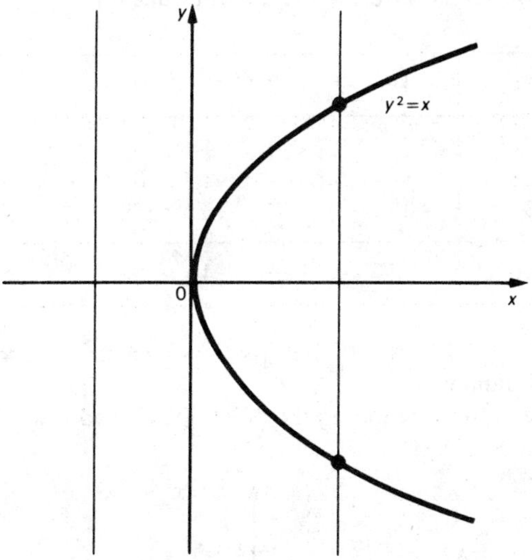

Here the vertical line can cut the curve *twice*, hence

$$y \neq f(x) \qquad [y = \pm\sqrt{x}]$$

In the case when $y \neq f(x)$ we have to introduce the idea of a *parameter* (see Chapter 4).

1.3 Solving equations

When we 'solve' the equation $3x - 12 = 0$ we are doing two things:

1 We are finding the 'number' or value of x which will make this true.
2 If $f(x) = 3x - 12$, we are finding the value of x which will make $f(x) = 0$.

This number or value of x is called the *solution* to, or the *root* of the equation.

The simplest equations are *linear equations* of the type $Ax + B = 0$, where $A \neq 0$. All linear equations have *one* root, since if $Ax + B = 0$, then $x = -B/A$. Graphically, it is found where the line $y = Ax + B$ crosses the line $y = 0$.

The next step is to consider equations of the second degree, or *quadratic equations* of the type $Ax^2 + Bx + C = 0$, where $A \neq 0$.

2 Quadratic equations

2.1 Graphical treatment

Example 1

To solve the equation $x^2 + 2x - 3 = 0$ we consider the associated *function* $y = f(x) = x^2 + 2x - 3$. First we draw up a table of values of y for different values of x.

x	-4	-3	-2	-1	0	1	2
x^2	16	9	4	1	0	1	4
$+2x$	-8	-6	-4	-2	0	2	4
-3	-3	-3	-3	-3	-3	-3	-3
y	5	0	-3	-4	-3	0	5

As the table shows, $x^2 + 2x - 3 = 0$ when $x = -3$ or when $x = 1$; so these values are the roots of the equation.

A graph can be drawn by plotting the points (x, y), and it will be found to be a parabolic curve.

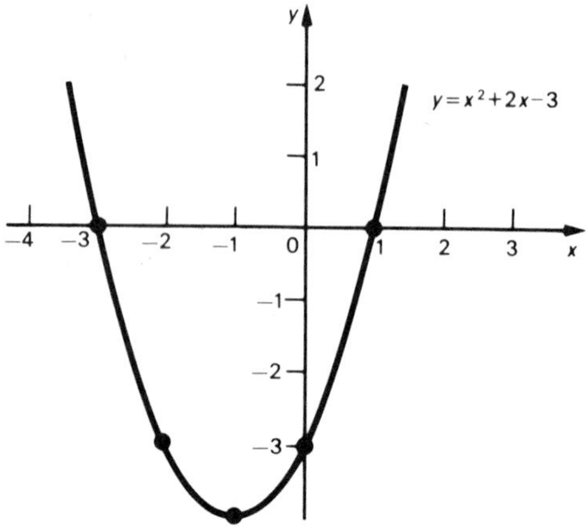

NOTE. The x coordinate of the points of intersection of the graphs, $y = x^2+2x-3$ and $y = 0$, are the roots of the equation, $x^2+2x-3 = 0$. Also, the line $x = -1$ is a line of symmetry for the curve.

Example 2

To solve $x^2+4x = 0$, we draw up a table of values for $y = x^2+4x$.

x	-5	-4	-3	-2	-1	0	1
x^2	25	16	9	4	1	0	1
$4x$	-20	-16	-12	-8	-4	0	4
y	5	0	-3	-4	-3	0	5

From the table we see that $y = 0$ when $x = -4$ and when $x = 0$. So $x = -4$ and $x = 0$ are the roots of the equation $x^2+4x = 0$.

If we plot the points, we find that the curve is identical with that in Example 1, but translated 1 unit to the left; so here $x = -2$ is the line of symmetry.

So far we have been lucky enough to find two roots in our table more or less by *trial and error.*

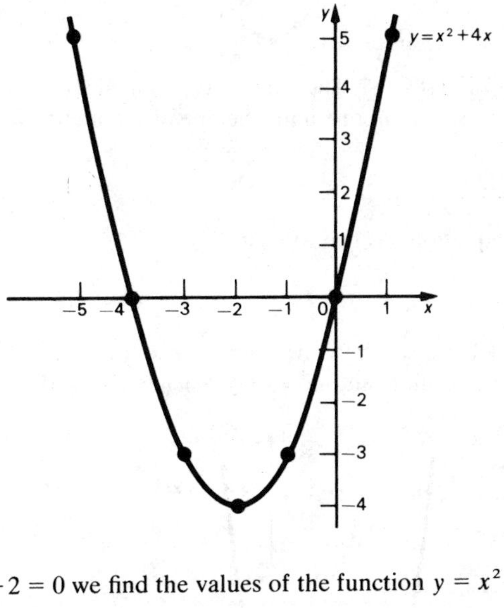

Example 3

To solve $x^2+2x-2 = 0$ we find the values of the function $y = x^2+2x-2$.

x	-4	-3	-2	-1	0	1	2
x^2	16	9	4	1	0	1	4
$2x$	-8	-6	-4	-2	0	2	4
-2	-2	-2	-2	-2	-2	-2	-2
y	6	1	-2	-3	-2	1	6

This time we see that $y = 0$ when x lies between -3 and -2 and again when x lies between 0 and 1, since y *changes sign* between these values. If we draw a graph carefully we can estimate the roots of the equation $x^2+2x-2 = 0$ from the x coordinates, α and β, of the points of intersection of the parabola and the x-axis.

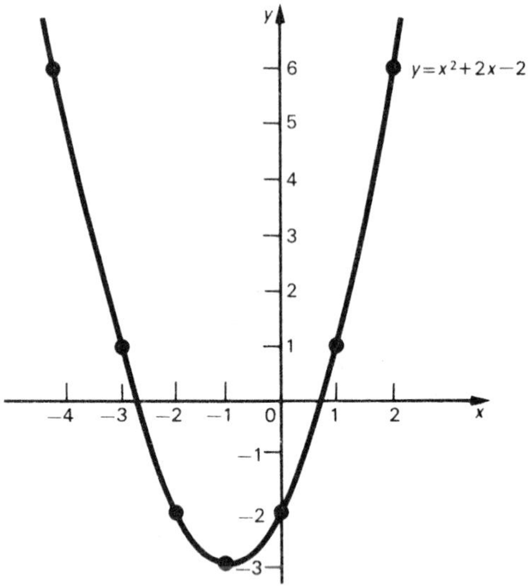

Here $\alpha \approx -2.67$ and $\beta \approx 0.7$. The parabola is again identical with that in Example 1, but this time translated *up* one unit; the line of symmetry is again $x = -1$.

Hypothesis

Every quadratic equation has two roots in $\mathbb{R}$.

Difficulty 1

To solve $x^2+2x+1 = 0$ we draw the graph $y = x^2+2x+1$ but we find that it has moved up three more units and now only *touches* the x-axis at one point, when $x = -1$.

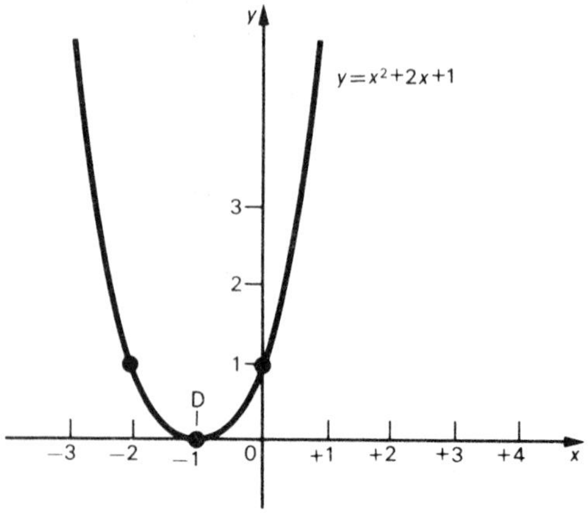

x	-4	-3	-2	-1	0	1	2
x^2	16	9	4	1	0	1	4
$+2x$	-8	-6	-4	-2	0	2	4
$+1$	1	1	1	1	1	1	1
y	9	4	1	0	1	4	9

The two points at which the parabola has cut the x-axis in each example so far have now coincided, and we must therefore modify our hypothesis so that it reads: 'Every quadratic equation has two roots in $\mathbb{R}$ (which may be equal or different)'.

Difficulty 2

What happens if the parabola moves up even further and we have to solve $x^2+2x+2=0$?

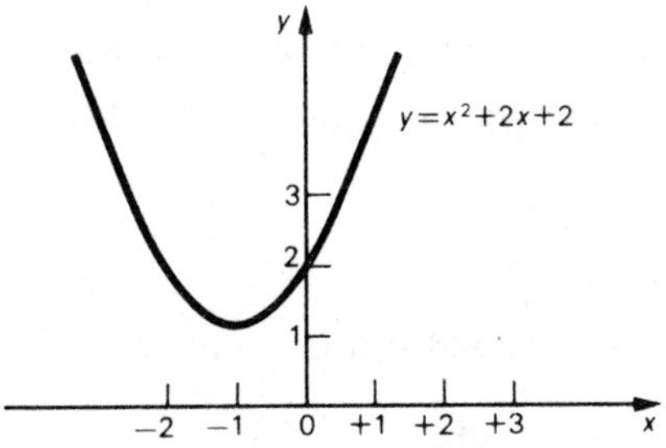

This time the curve $y = x^2+2x+2$ does not cut the x axis at all so there can be no *real* roots to the equation, and our hypothesis is false. But we are not defeated! The complex number system was invented to deal with precisely this problem and we can modify our hypothesis yet again: 'Every quadratic equation has two roots (which may be equal or different, real or complex)'.

So far we have solved our quadratic equations by trial and error or (approximately) graphically, but there are more systematic approaches.

2.2 Solution by factors (when the roots are rational)

Points on factors

1 $ab = 0 \Leftrightarrow a = 0$ or $b = 0$

2 If $\left.\begin{array}{r}(x-1)(x+3)=0\\ x^2+2x-3=0\end{array}\right\}$ either $x-1=0 \Leftrightarrow x=1$ or $x+3=0 \Leftrightarrow x=-3$

3 If $\left.\begin{array}{r}x(x+4)=0\\ x^2+4x=0\end{array}\right\}$ either $x=0$ or $x+4=0 \Leftrightarrow x=-4$

4 If $\left.\begin{array}{r}(5x+4)(x-3)=0\\ 5x^2-11x-12=0\end{array}\right\}$ either $5x+4=0 \Leftrightarrow x=-\frac{4}{5}$ or $x-3=0 \Leftrightarrow x=3$

In each case, clearly the two statements cannot be true at the same time.

5 But if $\left.\begin{array}{r}(x+2)(2x+4)=0\\ 2x^2+8x+8=0\end{array}\right\}$ either $x+2=0 \Leftrightarrow x=-2$ or $2x+4=0 \Leftrightarrow x=-2$

This time the two statements are the same and the equation is said to have a *repeated root*, $x = -2$.

We see that *if* we are able to factorize the equation *then* the roots can be quickly found; the problem is finding the factors. This is largely a matter of experience but there are one or two short cuts.

Sum and product of roots

Suppose the roots of an equation are $x = \alpha$ and $x = \beta$; then these answers must have come from the equation $(x-\alpha)(x-\beta) = 0$. If we expand the expression we have $x^2-(\alpha+\beta)x+\alpha\beta = 0$. In other words we have

$$\mathbf{x^2 - (sum\ of\ the\ roots)x + (product\ of\ the\ roots) = 0}$$ ◀

This is a great help in solving the equations.

Examples A

(i) Solve $x^2-8x+12 = 0$.

We require two numbers α and β with $\alpha+\beta = 8$ and $\alpha\beta = 12$. Clearly $\alpha = 6$, $\beta = 2$ or vice versa.

Factors are $(x-6)(x-2)$; roots are $x = 6$, $x = 2$.

(ii) Solve $x^2+11x+24 = 0$.

We require $\alpha+\beta = -11$, and $\alpha\beta = 24$. Clearly $\alpha = -8$, $\beta = -3$ or vice versa.

Factors are $(x+8)(x+3)$; roots are $x = -8$, $x = -3$.

(iii) Solve $x^2-x-30 = 0$.

We require $\alpha+\beta = +1$, and $\alpha\beta = -30$ so $\alpha = -6$, $\beta = 5$ or vice versa.

Factors are $(x+6)(x-5)$; roots are $x = -6$, $x = +5$.

You will have noticed that all the answers are integers. Our next step is to solve equations whose roots are not integers. The procedure is not quite the same as before and it is more complicated. The quickest method is by 'trial and error'.

Examples B

(i) To solve $3x^2+5x-2 = 0$ we try the following possible factors:

(a) $(3x+2)(x-1)$ **(c)** $(x+2)(3x-1)$
(b) $(3x+1)(x-2)$ **(d)** $(x+1)(3x-2)$

We must now try multiplying out these factors until we have the coefficient of x as 5. The only case where this occurs is in **(c)**.

We have $(x+2)(3x-1) = 0$, so either

$$x+2 = 0 \Leftrightarrow x = -2$$

or

$$3x-1 = 0 \Leftrightarrow x = \tfrac{1}{3}$$

(ii) For $6x^2+5x-6 = 0$ there are many possible factors of $6x^2$ and of -6. We must guess factors and multiply them out until we obtain a solution with the coefficient of x as 5. Then $(3x-2)(2x+3) = 0$ gives either

$$3x-2 = 0 \Leftrightarrow x = \tfrac{2}{3}$$

or

$$2x+3 = 0 \Leftrightarrow x = -\tfrac{3}{2}$$

NOTE. It is only by experience that it becomes easy to pick out the factors in questions of this kind. Fortunately, there is another method of solving this type of equation.

Exercise 2.2

Solve the following equations (where $x \in \mathbb{Q}$).

1 $x^2+5x+6 = 0$
2 $x^2+3x-4 = 0$
3 $x^2-7x+6 = 0$
4 $x^2-5x-6 = 0$
5 $2x^2-5x+3 = 0$
6 $12x^2-x-6 = 0$
7 $8x^2+5x-3 = 0$
8 $9x^2-12x+4 = 0$

2.3 Solution by completing the square (when the roots are irrational or complex)

So far we have dealt with equations having solutions which are rational numbers. We shall now investigate equations with irrational or complex solutions; this will lead us to a general method of solving quadratic equations *which is always applicable.* It can be used, for example, when the equation does have factors but they are not obvious.

Irrational roots

Example 1

Solving $3x^2 = 2$ gives $x^2 = \tfrac{2}{3}$ and so either $x = +\sqrt{\tfrac{2}{3}}$ or $x = -\sqrt{\tfrac{2}{3}}$.

If we can arrange our equation in the form $X^2 = A$ we shall be able to solve it. (In this case X is x and A is $\tfrac{2}{3}$.)

Suppose X is $x+1$. Then

$$(x+1)^2 = \tfrac{2}{3}$$

Taking the square root gives either

$$x+1 = +\sqrt{\tfrac{2}{3}} \Rightarrow x = \sqrt{\tfrac{2}{3}}-1$$

or

$$x+1 = -\sqrt{\tfrac{2}{3}} \Rightarrow x = -\sqrt{\tfrac{2}{3}}-1.$$

If we expand our original equation we have

$$(x+1)^2 = \tfrac{2}{3}$$

$$x^2+2x+1 = \tfrac{2}{3}$$

giving

$$x^2+2x+\tfrac{1}{3} = 0$$

The problem is to work in the reverse order, i.e. to start with the equation $x^2+2x+\frac{1}{3} = 0$, put it in the form $X^2 = A$ and then solve it. The difficulty is to write the equation in this form.

Example 2

What must be added to x^2-6x to make the result a perfect square?

Now x^2-6x is part of $(x-3)^2$, which is x^2-6x+9, so we must add 9 to the original expression to make it a perfect square.

Example 3

To solve $x^2-4x-2 = 0$, let us try to use the idea of Example 1 by rearranging the equation as $x^2-4x = 2$.

To make the left-hand side into a perfect square we must add $(-\frac{4}{2})^2$; we must also add this quantity to the right-hand side, and this gives

$$x^2-4x+(-\tfrac{4}{2})^2 = 2+(-2)^2$$

$$(x-2)^2 = 2+4$$

$$(x-2)^2 = 6$$

Taking the square root of both sides gives either

$$(x-2) = +\sqrt{6} \Leftrightarrow x = 2+\sqrt{6}$$

or

$$(x-2) = -\sqrt{6} \Leftrightarrow x = 2-\sqrt{6}$$

Example 4

Solve $3x^2+4x+1 = 0$.

Dividing through by 3 to get the equation in the same form as for Example 3 gives

$$x^2+\tfrac{4}{3}x+\tfrac{1}{3} = 0$$

which is

$$x^2+\tfrac{4}{3}x = -\tfrac{1}{3}$$

To make the left-hand side into a square we add

$$\left(\frac{+4/3}{2}\right)^2$$

so we must also add this quantity to the right-hand side.

$$(x+\tfrac{2}{3})^2 = -\tfrac{1}{3}+\tfrac{4}{9}$$

$$(x+\tfrac{2}{3})^2 = \tfrac{1}{9}$$

Either $(x+\frac{2}{3}) = +\frac{1}{3}, \Rightarrow x = -\frac{1}{3}$

or $(x+\frac{2}{3}) = -\frac{1}{3}, \Rightarrow x = -1$

The equation did, in this case, factorize to give us

$$(3x+1)(x+1) = 0$$

NOTE that in general we have

$$\left[x+\frac{1}{2}\left(\begin{matrix}\text{the coefficient of } x\\ \text{in the equation}\end{matrix}\right)\right]^2$$

on one side of the equation and we add ($\frac{1}{2}$ the coefficient of x)^2 to the other side.

Exercise 2.3a

Solve the following equations ($x \in \mathbb{R}$):

1 $2x^2-3x-4=0$
2 $4x^2-2x-1=0$
3 $3x^2-2x-8=0$
4 $x^2+2x-2=0$
5 $2x^2-5x-6=0$
6 $3x^2-2x-1=0$
7 $3x^2-4x-5=0$
8 $x^2-5x+2=0$
9 $2x^2-7x+4=0$
10 $6x^2-13x-5=0$

Complex roots

Can we now solve every type of quadratic equation? What about this one?

$$x^2+2=0 \Leftrightarrow x^2=-2$$

This equation has no solutions in real numbers but *every quadratic equation has two roots* (which may be equal or different, real or *complex*). The complex number system copes with this difficulty. We shall not dig deeply into it yet. For the moment we shall be satisfied with introducing a symbol j and suppose that j^2 can be replaced by -1.

So in this example $x^2 = 2j^2$ gives either

$$x = +\sqrt{2}j$$

or $$x = -\sqrt{2}j$$

We can now solve *all quadratic equations.* In fact, it can be shown that *all algebraic equations* can now be solved without the further introduction of any new systems.

Example

Solve the equation $x^2+2x+4=0$ (where $x \in \mathbb{C}$).

$$x^2+2x = -4$$

$$(x+1)^2 = -4+1$$

$$(x+1)^2 = -3$$

$$(x+1)^2 = 3j^2$$

so either $x+1 = +\sqrt{3}\text{j}, \quad x = -1+\sqrt{3}\text{j}$

or $x+1 = -\sqrt{3}\text{j}, \quad x = -1-\sqrt{3}\text{j}$

Exercise 2.3b

Solve the following equations ($x \in \mathbb{C}$).

1 $x^2+4x+9 = 0$

2 $2x^2-3x+6 = 0$

3 $3x^2-x+3 = 0$

4 $3x^2+2x+8 = 0$

5 $x^2+9 = 0$

6 $4x^2+12 = 0$

7 $2x^2+x+3 = 0$

8 $5x^2-x+4 = 0$

9 $2x^2-x+5 = 0$

10 $x^2+6x-4 = 0$

2.4 Formula for the solution of a general quadratic equation

We are now in a position to solve a general quadratic equation $Ax^2+Bx+C=0$, where A, B and C are real numbers ($A \neq 0$). We proceed exactly as before using the method of *completing the square.*

$$Ax^2+Bx+C = 0$$

$$x^2+\frac{B}{A}x+\frac{C}{A} = 0$$

$$\left(x+\frac{B}{2A}\right)^2 = \frac{B^2}{4A^2}-\frac{C}{A}$$

$$\left(x+\frac{B}{2A}\right)^2 = \frac{B^2-4AC}{4A^2}$$

Either

$$x+\frac{B}{2A} = \frac{+\sqrt{(B^2-4AC)}}{2A} \quad \text{or} \quad x+\frac{B}{2A} = \frac{-\sqrt{(B^2-4AC)}}{2A}$$

$$\boldsymbol{x = -\frac{B}{2A}+\frac{\sqrt{(B^2-4AC)}}{2A}} \quad \textbf{or} \quad \boldsymbol{x = -\frac{B}{2A}-\frac{\sqrt{(B^2-4AC)}}{2A}} \quad ◄$$

The discriminant

The most important part of the solution is B^2-4AC since the *type* of solution will depend on its value. There are three possible cases, corresponding to the sketches drawn below.

Case 1

$B^2-4AC > 0$. The square root is that of a positive number and so it is real. This means that the equation has two different real roots. If the square root is an integer, the roots are rational.

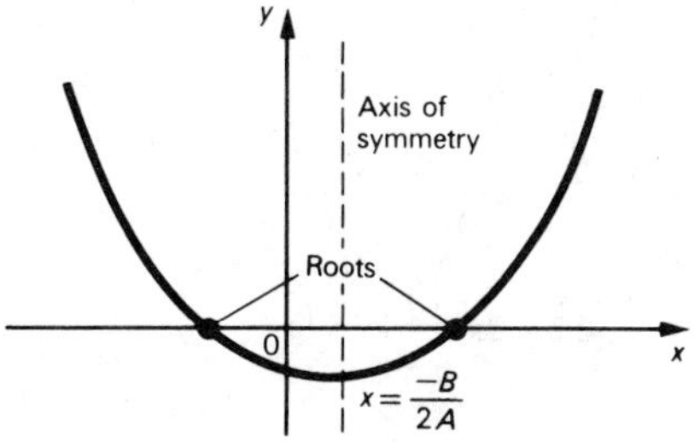

Case 2

$B^2-4AC=0$. The square root is zero and so we have two equal real answers, equal to $-B/2A$.

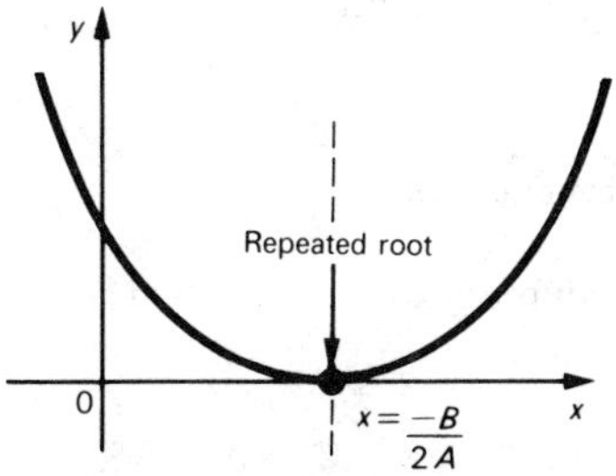

Case 3

$B^2-4AC<0$. The square root is that of a negative number and so is complex. This time the equation will have no real roots but two different complex roots. (They cannot be shown in the diagram.)

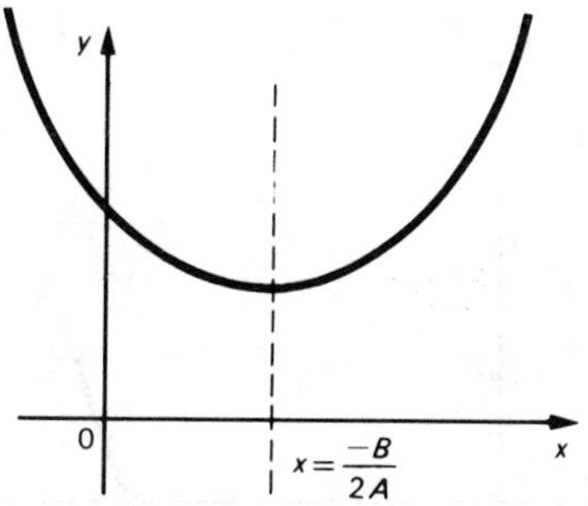

Exercise 2.4

Solve the following equations:

1 $3x^2-7x+4=0$

2 $3x^2-7x+5=0$

3 $3x^2-8x+4=0$

4 $3x^2-8x+5=0$

5 $2x^2+5x-20=0$

6 $2x^2-3x-3=0$

7 $x^2+11x-14=0$

8 $x^2+2x+3=0$

9 $\frac{1}{2}x^2+x-5=0$

10 $\dfrac{x}{6}+\dfrac{3}{2x}=1$

11 $\dfrac{x-2}{4}=\dfrac{x+2}{x}$

12 $2x+\dfrac{1}{x}=5-\dfrac{1}{x}$

2.5 Forming equations with roots related to those of other equations

We now illustrate some of the techniques used in forming equations with given roots, and with roots related to those of another equation.

Using known roots to form equations

(a) Form an equation with roots $x=-1$, $x=3$. Then $x+1=0$ or $x-3=0$, so

$$(x+1)(x-3)=0$$

and

$$x^2-2x-3=0$$

is the required equation.

We sketch the curve $y=x^2-2x-3$ showing the axis of symmetry, the minimum point, and the point $x=0$, $y=-3$.

NOTE that the curve $y=-x^2+2x+3$ also cuts the x-axis at the same points.

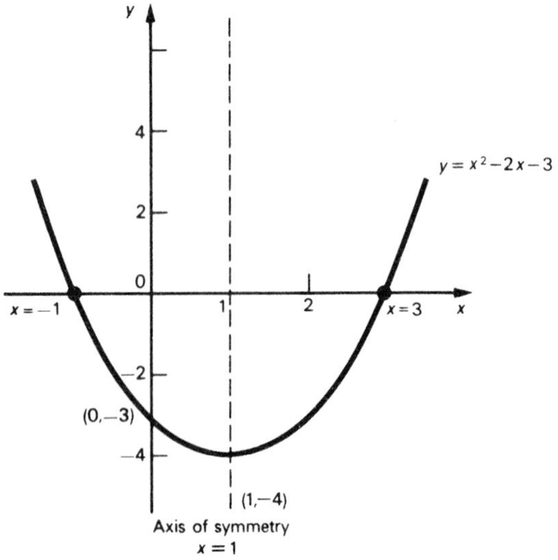

(b) Form an equation with roots each 3 more than the roots of $x^2-2x-3=0$. Here we require $x=2$, $x=6$, so

$$(x-2)(x-6)=0$$

$$x^2-8x+12=0$$

$y=x^2-8x+12$ is a similar curve to the previous one—having been translated 3 units to the right.

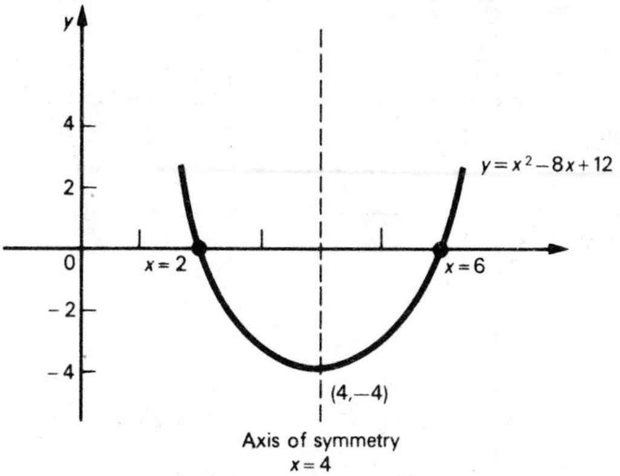

(c) Form an equation whose roots are twice the value of the roots of the equation $x^2-2x-3=0$. The roots this time will be $x=-2$, $x=6$, and the equation

$$(x+2)(x-6)=0$$

so
$$x^2-4x-12=0$$

The graph of $y=x^2-4x-12$ has been sketched (with $y=x^2-2x-3$) at half the previous scale.

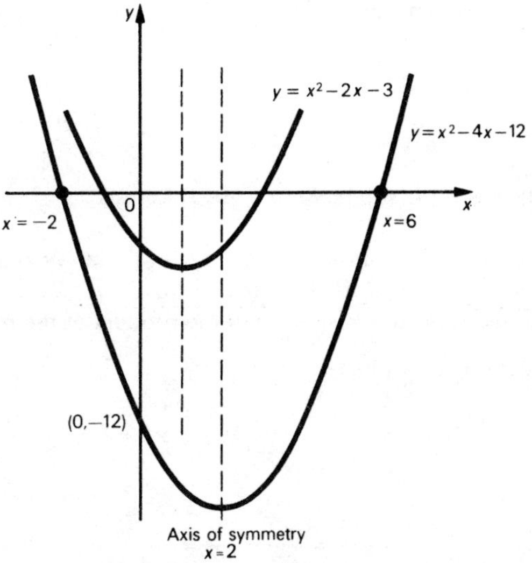

(d) Form an equation whose roots are the square of the roots of the equation $x^2-2x-3=0$. The roots will be $x=1$, $x=9$, and the equation

$$(x-1)(x-9)=0$$

so
$$x^2-10x+9=0$$

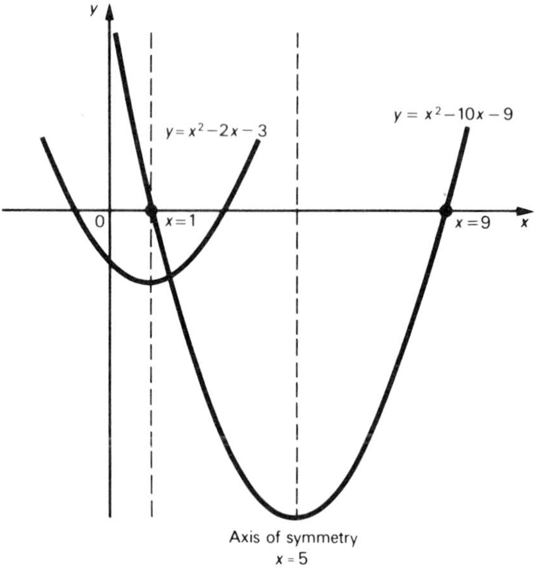

(e) Now form equations with roots

$$\left.\begin{array}{l}\text{the reciprocal of}\\ \text{three times}\\ \text{two less than}\\ \text{minus twice}\end{array}\right\}\ \text{the roots of } x^2-2x-3=0$$

sketching the curves in each case.

Forming equations when the original roots are unknown

If α, β are the roots of an equation $x^2+4x-2=0$, find the equation whose roots are (a) $1/\alpha, 1/\beta$ (b) $10\alpha, 10\beta$ (c) $5+\alpha, 5+\beta$.

Now the sum of the roots $\alpha+\beta=-4$, and the product of the roots $\alpha\beta=-2$.

(a) The new equation has a sum of roots

$$\frac{1}{\alpha}+\frac{1}{\beta}=\frac{\beta+\alpha}{\alpha\beta}=\frac{-4}{-2}=2$$

and a product of roots

$$\frac{1}{\alpha}\times\frac{1}{\beta}=\frac{1}{\alpha\beta}=\frac{1}{-2}=-\frac{1}{2}$$

Hence the new equation is

$$x^2-2x-\tfrac{1}{2}=0$$

or

$$2x^2-4x-1=0$$

(b) The sum of the roots is

$$10\alpha+10\beta = 10(\alpha+\beta) = -40$$

and the product of the roots is

$$\begin{aligned} &10\alpha\times 10\beta \\ &= 100\alpha\beta \\ &= -200 \end{aligned}$$

So the new equation is $x^2+40x-200=0$.

(c) The sum of the roots is

$$\begin{aligned} 5+\alpha+5+\beta &= 10+(\alpha+\beta) \\ &= 10+(-4)=6 \end{aligned}$$

and the product of the roots is

$$\begin{aligned} (5+\alpha)(5+\beta) &= 25+5(\alpha+\beta)+\alpha\beta \\ &= 25+5(-4)-2 \\ &= 3 \end{aligned}$$

Hence the new equation is $x^2-6x+3=0$.

NOTE. The roots of the equation $x^2+4x-2=0$, must satisfy this equation themselves so $\alpha^2+4\alpha-2=0$ and $\beta^2+4\beta-2=0$.

This procedure may often be of use if we have to find, for example, $\alpha^2+\beta^2$. Here, by adding the equations we have

$$\alpha^2+\beta^2+4(\alpha+\beta)-4=0$$

so

$$\begin{aligned} \alpha^2+\beta^2 &= -4(\alpha+\beta)+4 \\ &= 20 \end{aligned}$$

Roots of quadratic equations in general terms

Suppose we have to solve the equation $Ax^2+Bx+C=0$ where $A, B, C, \in \mathbb{R}$, $A \neq 0$, and the roots are $x=\alpha$ and $x=\beta$. Then

$$(x-\alpha)(x-\beta)=0$$

i.e.

$$x^2-(\alpha+\beta)x+\alpha\beta=0$$

or

$$x^2-(\text{sum of the roots})x+(\text{product of the roots})=0$$

which is identical with

$$x^2+\frac{B}{A}x+\frac{C}{A}=0$$

Hence $$\boldsymbol{\alpha+\beta=-\frac{B}{A}},\qquad \boldsymbol{\alpha\beta=\frac{C}{A}}$$ ◀

In the next three examples, α and β are the roots of the equation $Ax^2+Bx+C=0$.

Example 1

To find the equation whose roots are α^2, β^2.

The sum of the roots is $\alpha^2+\beta^2$, the product of the roots is $\alpha^2\beta^2$. Now

$$\alpha^2+\beta^2=(\alpha+\beta)^2-2\alpha\beta$$

$$=\frac{B^2}{A^2}-\frac{2C}{A}$$

$$\alpha^2\beta^2=\frac{C^2}{A^2}$$

Hence the new equation is

$$x^2-\left(\frac{B^2}{A^2}-\frac{2C}{A}\right)x+\frac{C^2}{A^2}=0$$

Alternatively we may find $\alpha^2+\beta^2$ using the fact that α, β are the roots of the equations. So

$$A\alpha^2+B\alpha+C=0$$

and $$A\beta^2+B\beta+C=0$$

Adding, $$A(\alpha^2+\beta^2)+B(\alpha+\beta)+2C=0$$

$$\alpha^2+\beta^2=\frac{-B(\alpha+\beta)-2C}{A}$$

$$=\frac{-B(-B/A)-2C}{A}$$

which, as before, $$=\frac{B^2}{A^2}-\frac{2C}{A}$$

Example 2

To find the equation whose roots are $\alpha+k$, $\beta+k$, where k is a constant.

Method 1

The sum of the roots is $\alpha+\beta+2k$, the product of the roots is

$$(\alpha+k)(\beta+k)=\alpha\beta+k(\alpha+\beta)+k^2$$

So the sum of the roots is $-B/A+2k$, and the product is $C/A-(B/A)k+k^2$. Hence the equation is

$$x^2-\left(-\frac{B}{A}+2k\right)x+\left(\frac{C}{A}-\frac{B}{A}k+k^2\right)=0$$

Method 2

If we substitute $y = x + k$ where x satisfies $Ax^2 + Bx + C = 0$, then y has one of the values $\alpha + k$, $\beta + k$. So $x = y - k$, and the required equation is

$$A(y-k)^2 + B(y-k) + C = 0$$

or
$$A(y^2 - 2ky + k^2) + By - Bk + C = 0$$

i.e.
$$y^2 - \left(-\frac{B}{A} + 2k\right)y + \left(\frac{C}{A} - \frac{B}{A}k + k^2\right) = 0$$

This method is an easy one to use when we are considering the 'transformation' of equations.

Example 3

To find the equation whose roots are $k\alpha$, $k\beta$, where k is a constant.

Method 1

The sum of the roots is $k\alpha + k\beta = k(\alpha + \beta)$, the product $k^2\,\alpha\beta$. Hence the equation is

$$x^2 - \left(-\frac{kB}{A}\right)x + k^2\frac{C}{A} = 0$$

Method 2

If we substitute $y = kx$ where x satisfies $Ax^2 + Bx + C = 0$, then y has one of the values $k\alpha$, $k\beta$. Put $x = y/k$. Hence

$$A\left(\frac{y}{k}\right)^2 + B\left(\frac{y}{k}\right) + C = 0$$

$$y^2 - \left(-\frac{kB}{A}\right)y + \frac{k^2C}{A} = 0$$

Example 4

Suppose we know that the equations

$$\left.\begin{aligned} x^2 + px + 1 &= 0 \\ \text{and} \qquad x^2 + x + q &= 0 \end{aligned}\right\}$$

have a common root, $x = \alpha$ say.

Find the condition connecting p and q.

Since $x = \alpha$ satisfies both equations

$$\left.\begin{aligned} \alpha^2 + p\alpha + 1 &= 0 \\ \text{and} \qquad \alpha^2 + \alpha + q &= 0 \end{aligned}\right\}$$

Subtracting,
$$\alpha(p-1) + (1-q) = 0$$

$$\alpha = \frac{q-1}{p-1}$$

Substitute into our first equation,

$$\left(\frac{q-1}{p-1}\right)^2+p\left(\frac{q-1}{p-1}\right)+1=0$$

$$(q-1)^2+p(q-1)(p-1)+(p-1)^2=0$$

Exercise 2.5

1 Express in the form $ax^2+bx-c=0$, where a, b, c, are positive integers, an equation whose roots are $1/3$ and $-5/6$.

2 The roots of the equation $4x^2-2x-7=0$ are α, β. Without solving the equation, find the values of $\alpha^2+\beta^2$ and $\alpha^3+\beta^3$.

3 The roots of the equation $x^2+gx+f=0$ are $x=\frac{2}{3}$ and $x=-3$. Find the values of g and f.

4 If α, β are the roots of $x^2-3x+1=0$, find **(a)** $\alpha^3+\beta^3$ **(b)** $\alpha^6+\beta^6$. [Hint: $\alpha^2-3\alpha+1=0$ so $\alpha^3-3\alpha^2+\alpha=0$ etc.]

5 If the roots of $2x^2+3x-1=0$ are α, β find the values of

(a) $\alpha^2+\beta^2$ **(b)** $(\alpha-\beta)^2$ **(c)** $\alpha^2-\beta^2$

(d) $\alpha^3+\beta^3$ **(e)** $\left(\alpha^2+\frac{1}{\beta^2}\right)\left(\beta^2+\frac{1}{\alpha^2}\right)$

6 If the roots of the equation $2x^2-3x+r=0$ are equal, find r.

7 If the roots of $3x^2-7x+1=0$ are α, β, find the equations whose roots are

(a) $3\alpha, 3\beta$ **(b)** α^2, β^2 **(c)** $\frac{1}{\alpha}, \frac{1}{\beta}$

(d) α^3, β^3 **(e)** $\alpha+\frac{1}{3\beta}, \beta+\frac{1}{3\alpha}$ **(f)** $\alpha-3\beta, \beta-3\alpha$

8 If the roots of $px^2+qx+r=0$ are α, β, find the equations with roots

(a) $2\alpha+\frac{1}{\beta}, 2\beta+\frac{1}{\alpha}$ **(b)** $3-\frac{\beta}{\alpha}, 3-\frac{\alpha}{\beta}$

9 Given that the equation $x^2-ax+b=0$ where $b \neq 0$ has roots α, β, find the equation which has roots $\alpha+\frac{1}{\beta}, \beta+\frac{1}{\alpha}$

10 Given that the roots of the equation $x^2+px+q=0$ are α, β, find the equation with roots

(a) $5\alpha, 5\beta$ **(b)** $\frac{1}{\alpha}, \frac{1}{\beta}$ **(c)** $\alpha-2, \beta-2$

(d) $\frac{1}{\alpha}+1, \frac{1}{\beta}+1$ **(e)** $-\frac{1}{2\alpha}, -\frac{1}{2\beta}$

3 Cubic equations

3.1 Graphical solutions

We have already shown (p. 44) how to sketch the curve $y = x^2+2x-3$ by drawing up a table of values. We have seen that we can solve the equation $x^2+2x-3 = 0$ by considering where the curve cuts the horizontal axis $y = 0$, i.e. we have found the intersection of $y = x^2+2x-3$ with $y = 0$. There are several other methods. Some of these methods are illustrated below, and they contain ideas which will be of considerable help when we are solving equations without integer solutions (see Chapter 15).

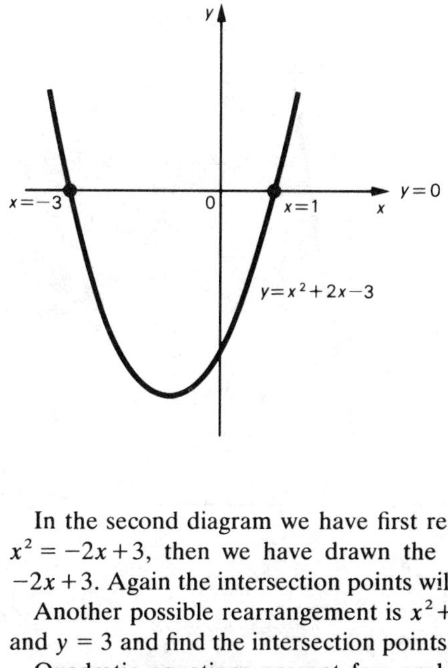

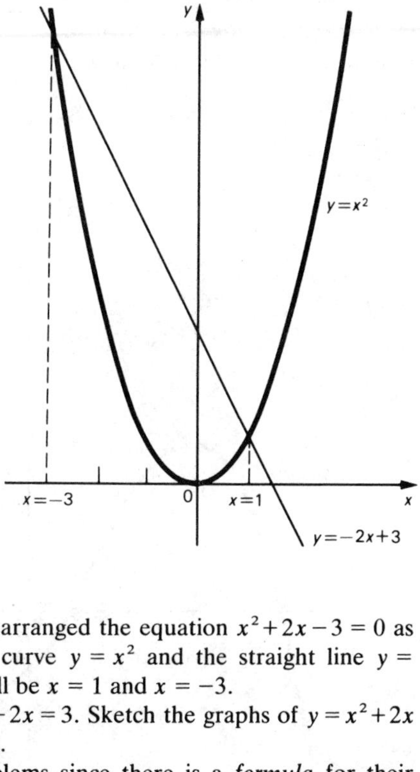

In the second diagram we have first rearranged the equation $x^2+2x-3 = 0$ as $x^2 = -2x+3$, then we have drawn the curve $y = x^2$ and the straight line $y = -2x+3$. Again the intersection points will be $x = 1$ and $x = -3$.

Another possible rearrangement is $x^2+2x = 3$. Sketch the graphs of $y = x^2+2x$ and $y = 3$ and find the intersection points.

Quadratic equations present few problems since there is a *formula* for their solution. Unfortunately there is no such easy method for solving cubic or quartic or higher degree equations. However, it *is* possible to solve the equations *approximately* by plotting the graph of $y = f(x)$ and finding where this cuts $y = 0$. Alternatively we have the possibility of rearranging the equation and finding other intersections as above.

Example

Solve $x^3+2x^2-2x-1 = 0$.

Consider $y = f(x) = x^3 + 2x^2 - 2x - 1$. We draw up a table of values for x between, say, -4 and $+4$.

x	-4	-3	-2	-1	0	1	2	3	4
x^3	-64	-27	-8	-1	0	1	8	27	64
$+2x^2$	32	18	8	2	0	2	8	18	32
$-2x$	$+8$	$+6$	$+4$	$+2$	0	-2	-4	-6	-8
-1	-1	-1	-1	-1	-1	-1	-1	-1	-1
y	-25	-4	3	2	-1	0	11	38	87

An approximate sketch shows

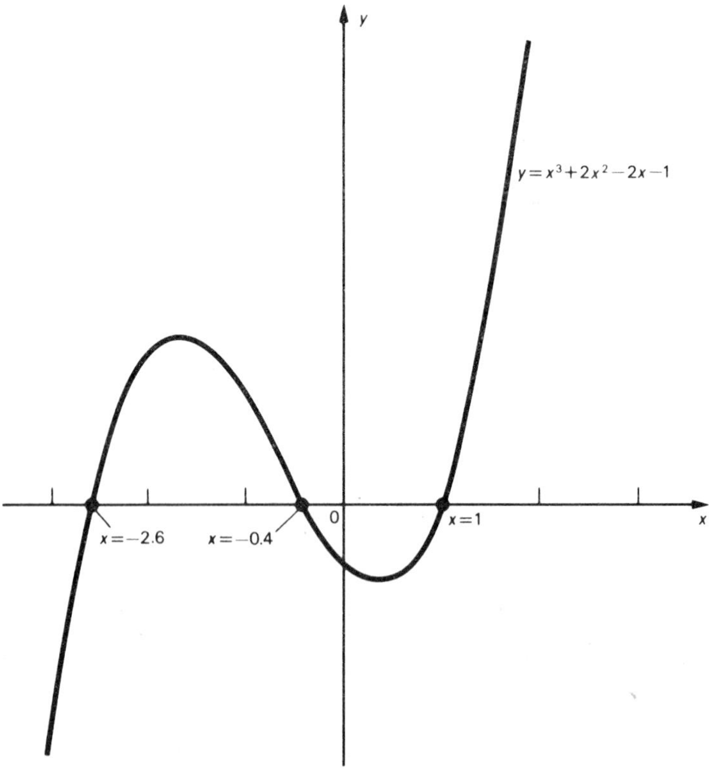

It is clear that to solve $y = x^3 + 2x^2 - 2x - 1$ and $y = 0$, we shall obtain $x \approx -0.4$, $x \approx -2.6$, $x = 1$.

An alternative method of solution is to rearrange the equation as $x^3 = -2x^2 + 2x + 1$ and to find where the two curves intersect. The table of values can easily be found from the first table.

x	-4	-3	-2	-1	0	1	2	3	4
x^3	-64	-27	-8	-1	0	1	8	27	64
$-2x^2+2x+1$	-39	-23	-11	-3	$+1$	$+1$	-3	-11	-23

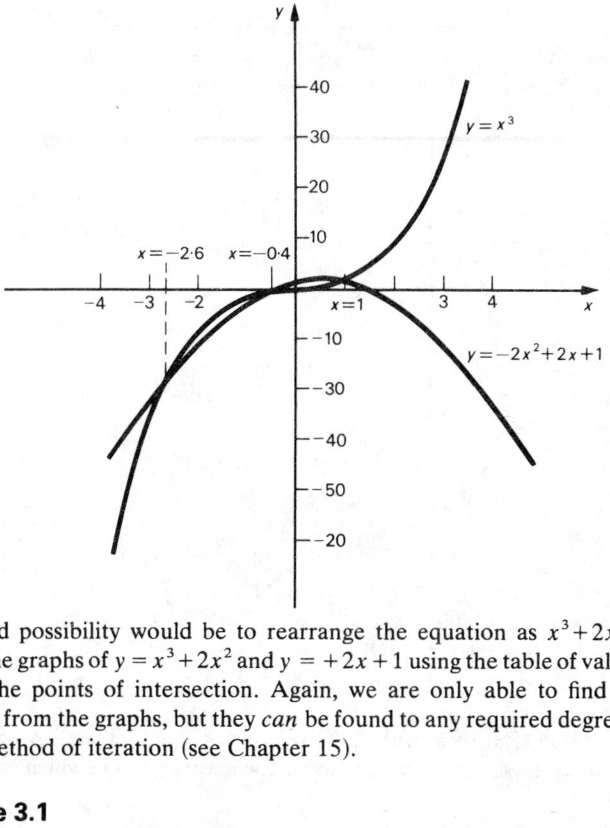

A third possibility would be to rearrange the equation as $x^3+2x^2 = +2x+1$. Sketch the graphs of $y = x^3+2x^2$ and $y = +2x+1$ using the table of values given and so find the points of intersection. Again, we are only able to find approximate solutions from the graphs, but they *can* be found to any required degree of accuracy by the method of iteration (see Chapter 15).

Exercise 3.1

Solve the following equations by graphical methods, using in each case two different rearrangements of the equation.

1 $x^3-5x+3=0$ **2** $x^3-x^2-x-2=0$ **3** $2x^3-3x=6$

3.2 The Remainder Theorem

Solving cubic and quartic equations, and so on, by sketching graphs can be tedious and in any case only gives approximate solutions. Hence other methods have to be found. So long as at least one of the roots is integral, help is at hand in the *Remainder Theorem*.

Consider the equation $x^3-4x^2+x+6=0$. First draw up a table of values for $y=x^3-4x^2+x+6$.

x	-2	-1	0	1	2	3	4
x^3	-8	-1	0	1	8	27	64
$-4x^2$	-16	-4	0	-4	-16	-36	-64
x	-2	-1	0	1	2	3	4
6	6	6	6	6	6	6	6
y	-20	0	6	4	0	0	10

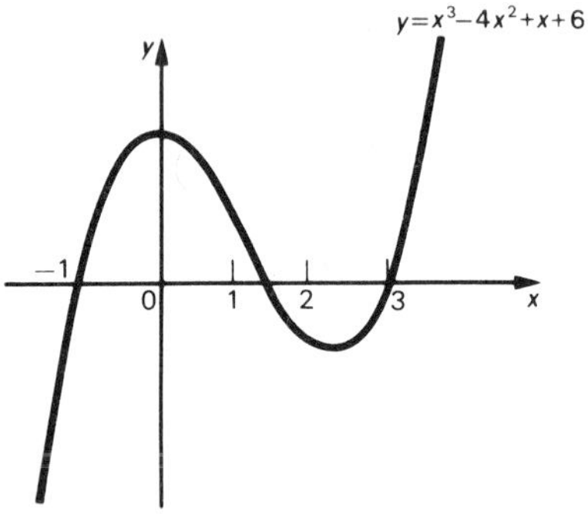

We see that $y=0$ when $x=-1$, $x=2$ and $x=3$. Suppose

$$f(x)=x^3-4x^2+x+6$$

then $$f(x)=(x+1)(x-2)(x-3)$$

So if $x=-1$, $f(-1)=0$; if $x=2$, $f(2)=0$; and if $x=3$, $f(3)=0$.

Now $f(x)$ is exactly divisible by $(x+1)$ and $(x-2)$ and $(x-3)$. So when dividing $f(x)$ by $(x+1)$ the remainder is 0 and

$$f(x)=(x+1)(x^2-5x+6)+0$$

Hence, given a function of x with unknown factors we can find the factors by substituting values for x, say $x=p$, and finding when $f(p)=0$ in which case $(x-p)$ is a factor.

General statement of the remainder theorem

Suppose that $f(x)$ is a function of x of degree n, i.e.

$$f(x)\equiv ax^n+bx^{n-1}+\ldots+h \qquad n>0$$

where $a, b, \ldots h$ are all real numbers.* Then

$$f(x)\equiv g(x)(x-p)+R$$

where $g(x)$ is another function of x of degree $n-1$ and R is the remainder.

* This should be read as $f(x)$ is *identically* equal to $ax^n+\ldots$ An identity is an equation which is true for all values of x.

Substituting $x = p$ gives

$$f(p) = g(p)(p-p)+R$$

i.e.

$$f(p) = R$$

The remainder R, when $f(x)$ is divided by $x-p$, is given by $R = f(p)$. If $f(p) = 0$, then $R = 0$ so that $x-p$ is a factor of $f(x)$.

Example 1

Find the remainder when x^3-7x+1 is divided by $x-2$

Write $$x^3-7x+1 \equiv (x-2)g(x)+R$$

Put $x = 2$, then $-5 = R$.

Example 2

Solve the equation $x^3-2x^2-x+2 = 0$

Write $$f(x) \equiv x^3-2x^2-x+2$$

Then
$$f(0) = +2$$
$$f(1) = 1-2-1+2 = 0$$
$$f(-1) = -1-2+1+2 = 0$$
$$f(2) = 8-8-2+2 = 0$$

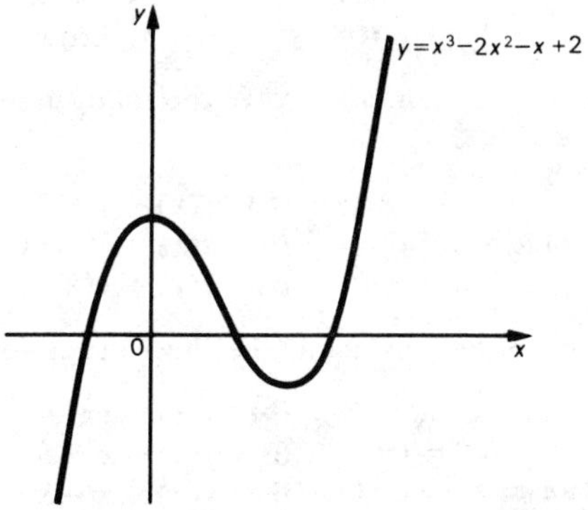

So by the Remainder Theorem, $x-1$, $x+1$, and $x-2$ are factors of $f(x)$ and the roots are $x = 1, -1, 2$.

Example 3

Solve the equation $x^3-2x-4 = 0$.

Write
$$f(x) \equiv x^3-2x-4$$
$$f(0) = -4$$
$$f(1) = -5$$
$$f(-1) = -3$$
$$f(2) = 0$$

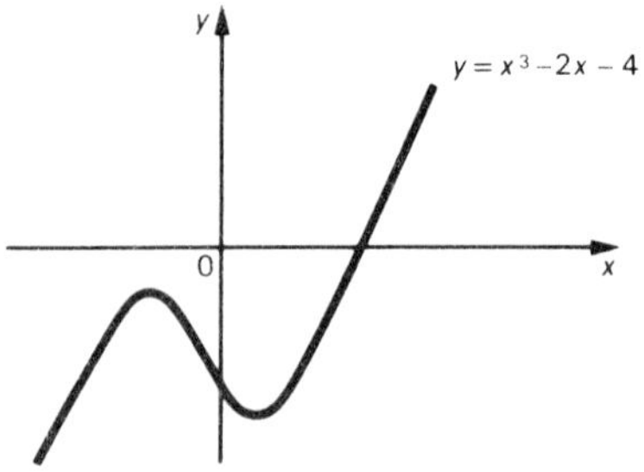

So we know that $x-2$ is a factor of x^3-2x-4. Our next step is to divide by this factor to get

$$x^3-2x-4 \equiv (x^2+2x+2)(x-2)$$

Now when $x^3-2x-4=0$, either $x-2=0 \Rightarrow x=2$ or $x^2+2x+2=0$. This latter equation cannot be solved in $\mathbb{R}$ because $B^2<4AC$. Hence the only real solution is $x=2$.

Exercise 3.2

1 Find the remainders when the first expression is divided by the second.

(a) $x^2-4x+4;\ x+1$ **(b)** $x^2+5x+6;\ x+2$
(c) $x^2-9x+8;\ x-1$ **(d)** $x^3-3x^2+3x-2;\ x-1$
(e) $x^3+4x^2-2x+3;\ x-2$ **(f)** $x^3-3x^2+5x+6;\ x-3$

2 Given that $f(x)$ has integer solutions, solve the following equations using the remainder theorem.

(a) $f(x)\equiv x^2-x-6=0$ **(b)** $f(x)\equiv x^2-7x+12=0$
(c) $f(x)\equiv x^3-6x^2+11x-6=0$ **(d)** $f(x)\equiv x^3+3x^2-x-3=0$
(e) $f(x)\equiv x^3-x^2-14x+24=0$ **(f)** $f(x)\equiv x^3+2x^2-8x=0$

3 Solve the following equations, given that they have at least one integer solution.

(a) $f(x)\equiv x^3-4x^2+6x-4=0$ **(b)** $f(x)\equiv x^3+4x^2+2x-1=0$
(c) $f(x)\equiv 2x^3-7x^2+5x+2=0$ **(d)** $f(x)\equiv x^3+6x^2-x-30=0$
(e) $f(x)\equiv x^3-3x^2-4x+12=0$ **(f)** $f(x)\equiv x^3-8=0$

4 Find the factors of **(a)** $12x^2+11x-56$, **(b)** x^3-1, and **(c)** x^3-x^2-x-2.
By using the factors, show that the expression x^3-x^2-x-2 is positive when x is a number greater than 2.

5 Given that 3 is one of the roots of the equation

$$2x^3-13x^2+6x+45=0,$$

find the other two roots.

6 Find the value of k if $x^3+3x^2+kx-12$ is divisible by $x+2$.

7 If the expressions $x^3-(a+2)x+2b$ and $2x^3+ax^2-4x-b$ have a common factor $x+3$, find the values of a and b and find a second common factor.

8 Find the remainder when x^6+66 is divided by x^2+4.

9 Find which of the expressions $(x-a)$ and $(x+a)$ is a factor of

$$6x^3+7ax^2-a^2x-2a^3$$

and factorize this expression completely.

4 Theory of logarithms

4.1 Revision of ideas

If $x=a^l$, then we say that l is the *logarithm* of x to the base a or $l=\log_a x$. The logarithm of a number, x, is the power l to which the base a must be raised in order to equal the number. So, a logarithm is a power or index.

For example $8=2^3$; the logarithm of 8 to the base 2 is 3, or $3=\log_2 8$. Again, $2=16^{1/4}$, $\frac{1}{4}=\log_{16} 2$, but $\frac{1}{4}=2^{-2}$ so $-2=\log_2 \frac{1}{4}$. (We usually write -2 as $\bar{2}$ when we are using logs to the base 10 for computation.)

NOTE. Since $a^0=1$ (for $a \neq 0$) we have $\log_a 1=0$, and $a^1=a$ so $\log_a a=1$.

We now revise our ideas of logarithms. First we sketch the graph $y=2^x$, for $x \in \mathbb{Z}$ and assume that we may join up the points on the graph.

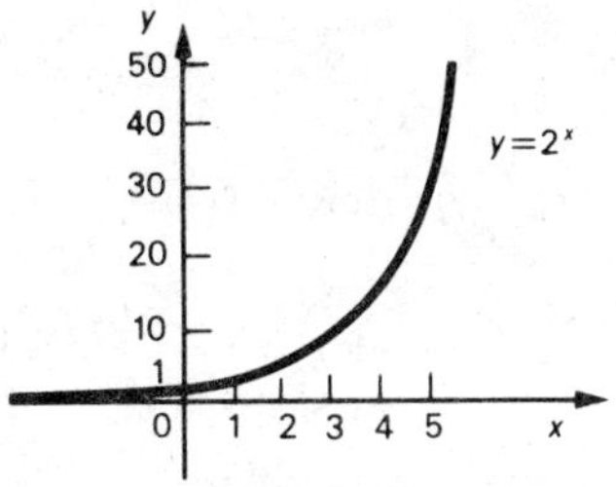

Now if $y=2^x$, then we say that $x=\log_2 y$.

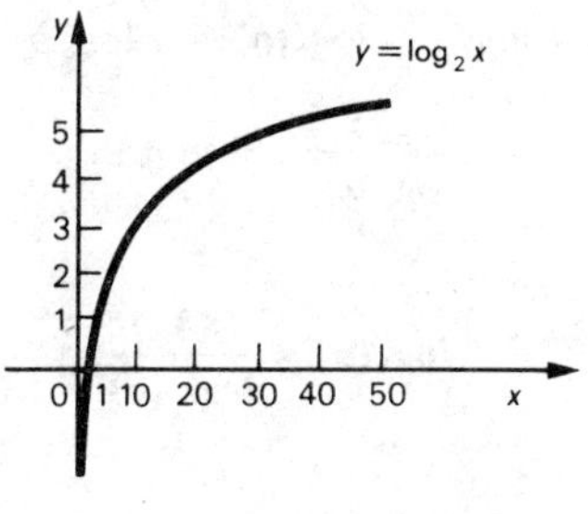

Above is the graph of $y=\log_2 x$. Notice that the curve is identical to the previous one but with the axes interchanged. The graphs of $y=10^x$ and $y=\log_{10} x$ will have similar shapes to the two graphs above.

4.2 Properties of logarithms

(1) $$\log_a xy = \log_a x + \log_a y$$ ◄

(i.e. when we multiply numbers, we *add* their logarithms.)

Suppose $\log_a x = l, \quad \log_a y = m$

then $x = a^l, \quad y = a^m$

and $xy = (a^l)(a^m) = a^{l+m}$

so $\log_a xy = l + m = \log_a x + \log_a y$

(2) $$\log_a \frac{x}{y} = \log_a x - \log_a y$$ ◄

Now as before

$$\frac{x}{y} = \frac{a^l}{a^m} = a^{l-m}$$

so $\log_a \frac{x}{y} = l - m = \log_a x - \log_a y.$

(3) $$\log_a(x^k) = k \log_a x$$ ◄

If $\log_a x = l$ then $x = a^l$, and

$$x^k = (a^l)^k = a^{lk}$$

so $\log_a(x^k) = lk = kl = k \log_a x$

It follows from this that

$$\log_a\left(\frac{1}{x^p}\right) = \log_a x^{-p} = -p \log_a x$$

and $\log_a(\sqrt[q]{x}) = \log_a x^{1/q} = \frac{1}{q}\log_a x$

(4) $$\log_b x = \frac{\log_a x}{\log_a b}$$ ◄

Suppose $\log_b x = r$ then $x = b^r$, and

$$\log_a x = \log_a(b^r) = r \log_a b$$

Hence $\frac{\log_a x}{\log_a b} = r = \log_b x$

NOTE that if $x = a$,

$$\log_b(a) = \frac{1}{\log_a(b)}$$ ◄

Exercise 4.2a

1 Write down the values of

(a) $8^{2/3}$ **(b)** 2^{-3} **(c)** $(\frac{1}{3})^{-2}$ **(d)** $16^{-3/2}$

2 Simplify $(4x^6 y^{-4})^{-1/2}$ expressing your answer with positive indices.

3 Express as powers of 2

(a) 32 **(b)** $\frac{1}{8}$ **(c)** 16^2 **(d)** $2^x \div 2^7$ **(e)** $4^{2t+1/2}$

4 Without using calculators or tables write down the values of $32^{3/5}$, $81^{-1/4}$, 7^0, $27^{2/3}$.

5 Find without using calculators or tables the value of $4^{1/3} \times 6^{1/2} \times 864^{1/6}$.

Exercise 4.2b

1 Plot the graph of $y = \log_{10} x$ for x between 0 and 10. Read off from your graph approximate values for

(a) $(0.6)^{1/3}$ **(b)** $(0.5)^{5/4}$ **(c)** $(1.2)^{3/2}$ **(d)** $(5.4)^{1/2}$

2 Prove that $\log_{10} a^3 = 3 \log_{10} a$.
With the help of tables, evaluate to four significant figures **(a)** $\sqrt[3]{437.1}$, and **(b)** $2\pi\sqrt{(l/g)}$ when $l = 32.7$, $g = 981$ and $\pi = 3.142$.

3 Calculate $(1.008)^9$ and also the cube root of 0.8, each to three significant figures.

4 **(a)** Explain how you would justify the convention that $x^{1/3} = \sqrt[3]{x}$. **(b)** Evaluate $\sqrt[5]{0.3872}$.

5 Evaluate $(0.34)^{-1.4}$ giving your answer correct to three significant figures.

6 Taking $\log_{10} 2$ as 0.301 030 and $\log_{10} 3$ as 0.477 121 find, without using tables, the values of $\log_{10} 1.2$ and $\log_{10} \frac{20}{27}$ expressing your answer correct to five decimal places.

7 Solve the equation $3^{\log_{10} x} = 9^{4/5}$ giving your answer correct to three significant figures.
Given that $3 \log_{10} x - \log_{10} y = 1$, express y in terms of x.

8 What is meant by the statement that the logarithm of p to the base q equals a, that is $\log_q p = a$? Prove that

(a) $\log_q p = \dfrac{1}{\log_p q}$ **(b)** $\log_q p \log_r q \log_p r = 1$

Find the value of $3 \log_3 10$ giving the answer to three significant figures.

9 Solve the equation $5^{11-3x} = 2^x$.

10(a) Given that $\log_b a = c$ and $\log_c b = a$, prove that $\log_c a = ac$.
(b) Solve the equation $(5^x)(2^{-2x}) = 4$ giving the answer to three significant figures.

4.3 Naperian or natural logarithms

The property

$$\log_b x = \frac{\log_a x}{\log_a b}$$

is particularly helpful when using common logarithms (i.e. to the base 10) and natural logarithms (to the base e). You will meet the latter when working on series, and with the calculus.

$$\mathbf{\log_{10} x = \frac{\log_e x}{\log_e 10} = \frac{\ln x}{\ln 10}}$$ ◄

e is a *transcendental* number (like π); its value is 2.718 . . . ln is the usual terminology for 'log natural', i.e. logarithms to the base e.

Use of tables (if no electronic calculator is available)

You will find a page in your book of four- or five-figure tables which lists natural logarithms. The table runs from 1.0000 to 9.9999; a subsidiary table at the bottom gives $\log_e 10^x$ for $x = 1$ to $x = 6$.

Example

To find	ln 3.85 we read in the table	ln 3.85	$= 1.3481$
For	ln 38.5, we write it as	$\ln (3.85 \times 10^1)$	$= \ln 3.85 + \ln 10^1$
			$= 1.3481 + 2.3026$
			$= 3.6507$
and	ln 385 becomes	$\ln (3.85 \times 10^2)$	$= \ln 3.85 + \ln 10^2$
			$= 1.3481 + 4.6052$
			$= 5.9533$
Similarly,	ln 0.385 is	$\ln (3.85 \div 10^1)$	$= \ln 3.85 - \ln 10^1$
			$= 1.3481 - 2.3026$
			$= \bar{1}.0455$

Exercise 4.3

Use your tables to find

1 ln 5.381 **2** ln 538.1 **3** ln 0.5381 **4** ln 0.005381

Find x in the following:

5 $\ln x = 2.9741$ **6** $\ln x = 5.342$ **7** $\ln x = 5.6847$ **8** $\ln x = 8.3947$

9 Use tables of Naperian logarithms to help you sketch the graph of $y = \ln x$. On the same graph sketch $y = e^x$.

5 Variation

5.1 Introduction

When we are experimenting in Physics or some other practical science, we frequently wonder whether two quantities are related and, if so, how. We may, for example, be attaching weights to a spring. It seems clear that the extension of the spring depends on the weight we attach. Our next step is to draw a graph of the extension against the weight. If the graph is approximately a straight line we can say that

(1) the extension varies with the weight
(2) x varies directly with W
(3) x is proportional to W
(4) $x \propto W$
(5) $x = kW$

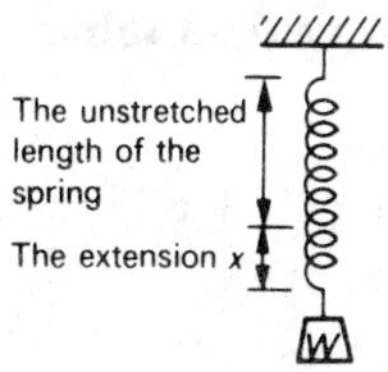

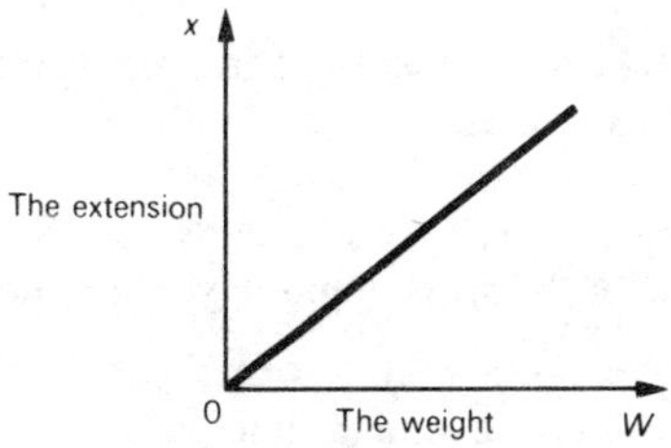

If the graph was not a straight line, we might try plotting the graph of x against W^2, or x against W^3, or x against $1/W$ and so on until we eventually found ourselves with a straight line graph. This process can be long and tiresome and so we usually draw the graph of $\log_{10} x$ against $\log_{10} W$. The slope of the graph then gives us the power of W we are looking for (see 5.3).

More types of variation

(1) If we were to drop a stone from the top of a cliff, we should find that the distance fallen is proportional to the time squared. I.e. $s \propto t^2$, hence $s = kt^2$ where k is a constant.

(2) Kepler's third law of planetary motion states that the time of orbit T of a planet and r, the length of the semi-major axis of the elliptical orbit, are related by $T^2 \propto r^3$. I.e. $T^2 = kr^3$ where k is a constant.

(3) Boyle's law for a given mass of gas at a constant temperature tells us that pressure times volume is constant. I.e. $pv = c$, or $p = c/v$. Hence $p \propto 1/v$, and we say that p varies inversely with v.

(4) The force exerted between two masses (e.g. the Moon and the Earth) is inversely proportional to r^2 (if the distance between the centres is r). I.e. $F \propto 1/r^2$, $F = k/r^2$.

Perhaps you have heard of this as Newton's Inverse Square Law.

Example

The time of swing of a simple pendulum varies with the square root of its length. If a pendulum 3 m long makes a complete oscillation in 3.45 s, what would be the time of swing of a pendulum 2 m long?

Now $t \propto \sqrt{l}$, hence $t = k\sqrt{l}$, or $t^2 = Kl$ (where $K = k^2$)

so when $l = 300$ cm, $t = 3.45$ s, $(3.45)^2 = K(300)$

and $K = \dfrac{(3.45)^2}{300}$

When $l = 200$ cm, $t^2 = \dfrac{(3.45)^2}{300}(200)$

$t = 2.82$ s

5.2 Graphs showing the relationship between two variable quantities

To represent a relationship between two quantities we usually draw a graph. Here are some of the sorts of graph you are most likely to meet.

(1) $y \propto x$, i.e. $y = kx$.

This will give a straight line passing through the origin. The value of k will give the slope of the line (i.e. it tells us how steep the line is).

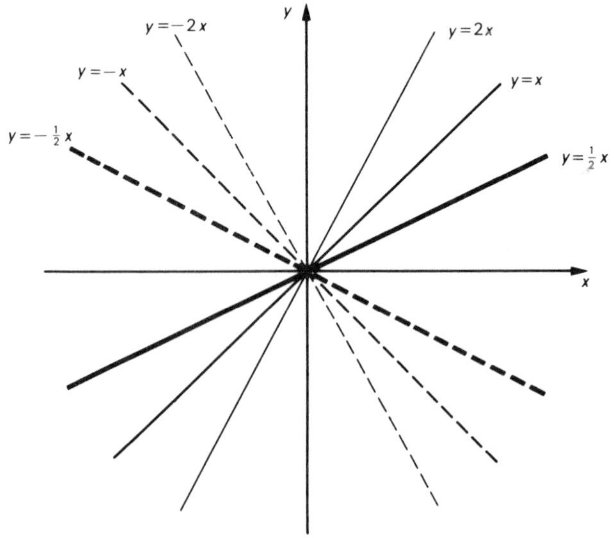

This is an illustration of $y = kx$ for different values of k.

(2) $y \propto x^2$, i.e. $y = kx^2$

This produces a parabola passing through the origin.

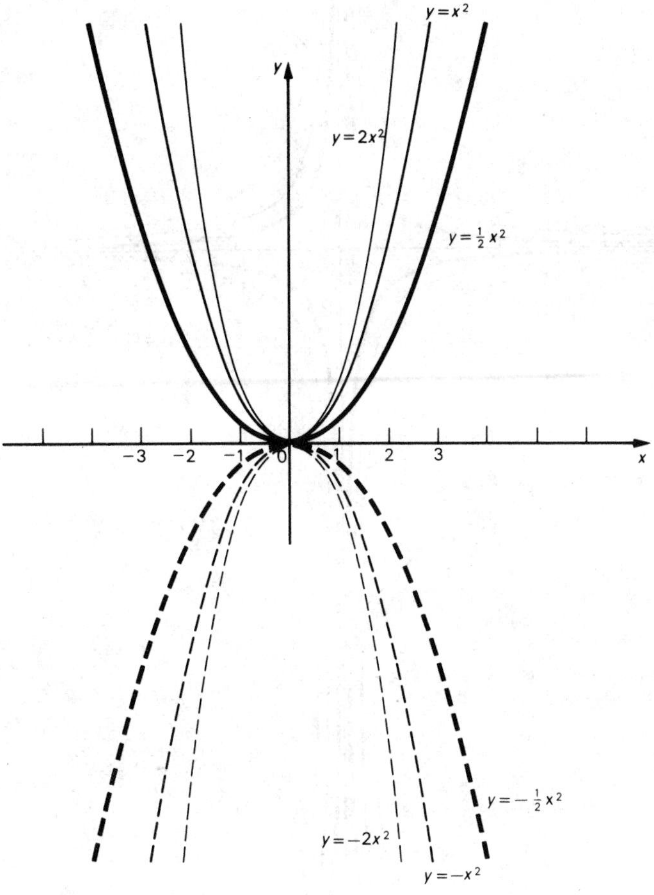

The diagram shows this relationship with different values of k.

(3) $y \propto \frac{1}{x}$, i.e. $y = \frac{k}{x}$

This time the curve is a rectangular hyperbola. (See illustration at top of the next page.)

The curves have been drawn again for $k = \pm\frac{1}{2}, \pm 1, \pm 2$

(4) $y \propto \frac{1}{x^2}$, i.e. $y = \frac{k}{x^2}$

(See illustration at bottom of the next page.)

This is a most important relationship as many quantities obey the 'inverse square' law.

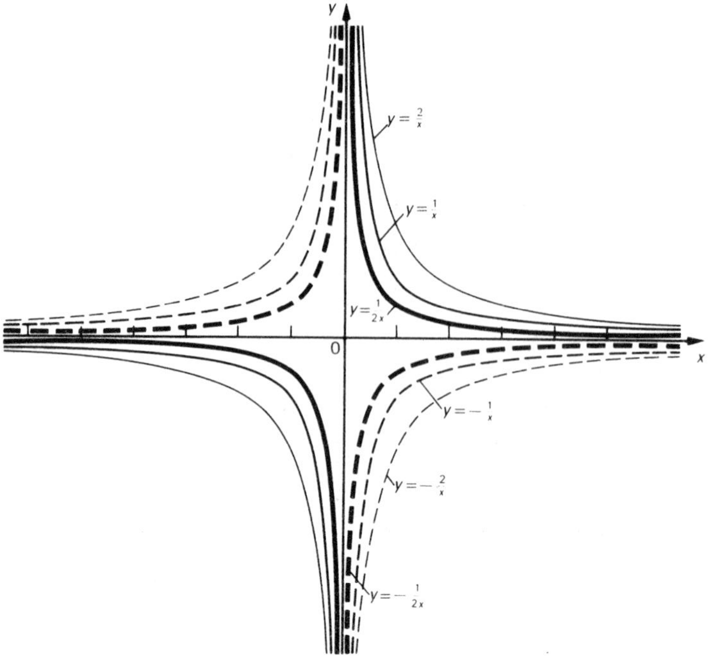

y
x
0
$y = \frac{2}{x}$
$y = \frac{1}{x}$
$y = \frac{1}{2x}$
$y = -\frac{1}{x}$
$y = -\frac{2}{x}$
$y = -\frac{1}{2x}$

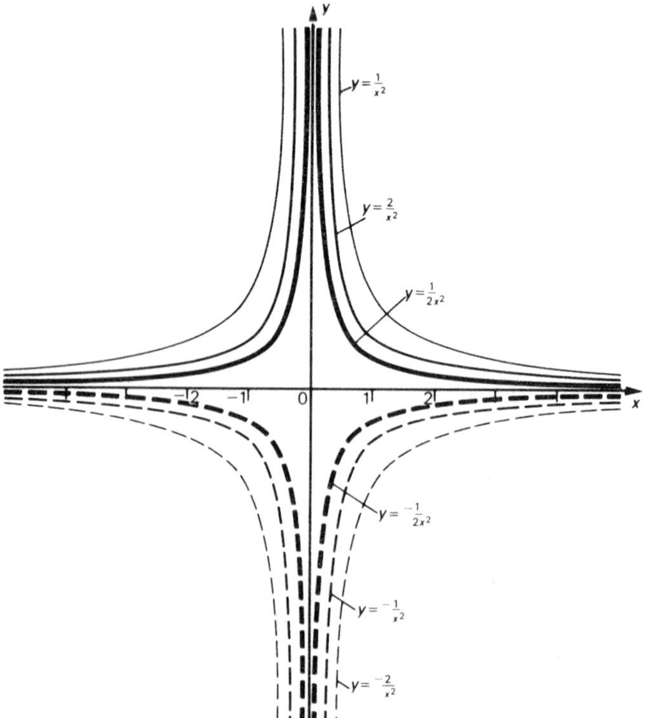

y
x
−2
−1
0
1
2
$y = \frac{1}{x^2}$
$y = \frac{2}{x^2}$
$y = \frac{1}{2x^2}$
$y = \frac{-1}{2x^2}$
$y = \frac{-1}{x^2}$
$y = \frac{-2}{x^2}$

5.3 An experiment to illustrate variation

A pendulum was made by hanging a small, heavy weight on the end of a length of cotton. The pendulum was suspended and allowed to swing through a small arc. The time for ten oscillations was measured.

Length in cm	100	95	90	85	80	75	70	65	60	
Time in s	20.1	19.5	19.0	18.5	18.0	17.4	16.8	16.2	15.6	
Length in cm	55	50	45	40	35	30	25	20	15	10
Time in s	15.0	14.3	13.5	12.8	12.0	11.2	10.3	9.3	7.9	6.4

It is reasonable to assume that the time of oscillation depends in some way on the length of the cotton. So our first idea is to draw the graph of T against L, where T is the time in seconds for one oscillation and L is the length in metres from the point of suspension to the centre of the bob.

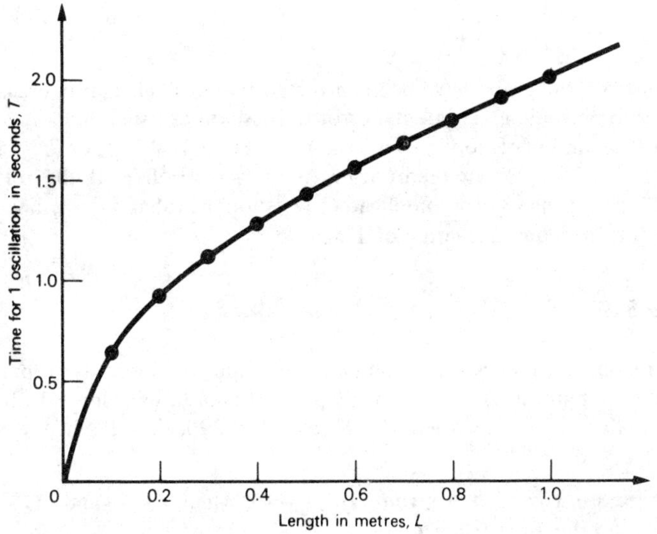

From our graph we can see that T is not proportional to L — since if it was the graph would be a straight line. From the appearance of the curve (which looks like a part of a parabola) we might guess that $T^2 \propto L$. However, if the graph of T^2 against L, was not a straight line, then we should have to try perhaps T^3 against L, and so on. What we need to know is the power of T which *is* proportional to L. We can find this by plotting the graph of $\log_{10} T$ against $\log_{10} L$, the slope of which will give us the reciprocal of the required power. I.e. if

$$\log_{10} T = k \log_{10} L + c$$

$$\frac{1}{k} \log_{10} T = \log_{10} L + c^1 \quad \text{and} \quad T^{1/k} = c''L$$

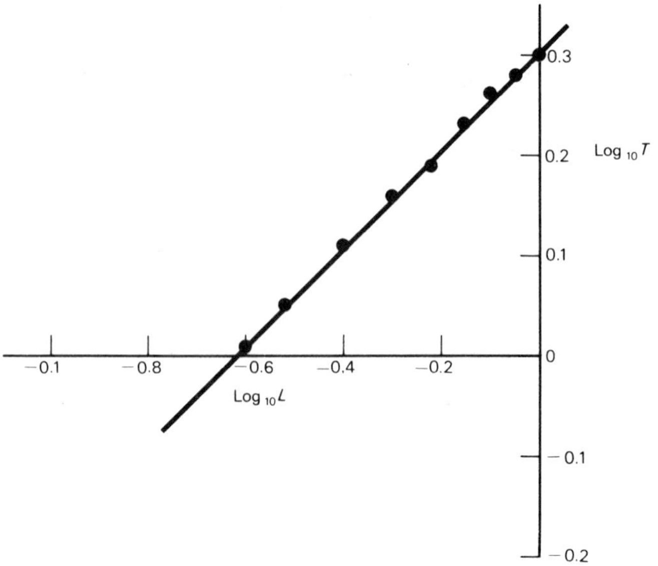

The values on the graph have been corrected to two significant figures. There is also bound to be some experimental error but, as you can see, the points are very close to a straight line of slope $\frac{1}{2}$ so we can reason that $T \propto L^{1/2}$, or $T^2 \propto L$.

In fact, it can be shown theoretically that $T^2 = 4\pi^2 L/g$. If the relationship between T and L had been complicated, we should probably have been able to recognize this from our first graph of T against L.

Exercise 5.3

1 The pressure P of a gas, expanding under certain conditions, is proportional to its absolute temperature T and inversely proportional to its volume V. It is found experimentally that $P = 17$ when $V = 87$ and $T = 290$. Find P when $V = 72$ and $T = 345$.

2 If $A = px + q/x^2$ and it is given that $A = 42$ when $x = 2$, and $A = 25$ when $x = 3$ find the value of A when $x = 4$.

3(a) If A varies inversely as r^2, and $A = 1.5$ when $r = 12$, find the value of A when $r = 1.5$.

(b) Given that $y = Kx^n$, where n is an integer, find the values of K and n from the following table of values of x and y.

x	2	4	6	
y	12.8	102.4		1600

Now find the values of x and y required to complete the table.

4 If A varies as $B^{2/3}$ and B varies as $C/\sqrt{A}$, find an expression for A in terms of C only, given that $A = 3$ when $C = 16$.

5 If A is inversely proportional to x and B is directly proportional to x^2, find the values of A, B, when $x = 2$, given that $A - B = 3\frac{2}{3}$ when $x = 1$, and that $A + B = 4\frac{1}{3}$ when $x = 3$.

6 Miscellaneous techniques for the solution of equations

You may come across various other types of equation to solve. This next section illustrates some of the techniques required.

6.1 Solution of equations by substitution

Example

Solve the equation

$$3 \times 2^{2x+1} - 5 \times 2^x - 4 = 0$$

by putting $2^x = y$. Give the value of x correct to three significant figures.

If $y = 2^x$, then $y^2 = (2^x)^2 = 2^{2x}$ and $2^{2x+1} = 2 \times 2^{2x} = 2y^2$. Hence the equation becomes

$$6y^2 - 5y - 4 = 0$$

$$(3y - 4)(2y + 1) = 0$$

Either $\quad 3y - 4 = 0 \Rightarrow y = \frac{4}{3}$

or $\quad 2y + 1 = 0 \Rightarrow y = -\frac{1}{2}$

But $y = 2^x$ (which is *always* positive), hence

$$2^x = \tfrac{4}{3} \Rightarrow x \quad \log_{10} 2 = \log_{10} 1.333$$

$$x(0.3010) = 0.1249$$

$$x = 0.415$$

6.2 Solution of equations involving powers

These can generally be solved by taking logarithms of both sides and solving the resulting equations.

Example

Solve the equation $(2^{3x})(3^{4x-1})(4^{x-3}) = 1$

Taking logarithms,

$$\log_{10} 2^{3x} + \log_{10} 3^{4x-1} + \log_{10} 4^{x-3} = \log_{10} 1$$

$$3x \log_{10} 2 + (4x - 1) \log_{10} 3 + (x - 3) \log_{10} 4 = \log_{10} 1$$

$$3x(0.3010)+(4x-1)(0.4771)+(x-3)(0.6021) = 0$$
$$0.9030x+1.9084x-0.4771+0.6021x-1.8063 = 0$$
$$3.4135x = 2.2834$$
$$x = 0.669$$

6.3 Equations involving square roots

A useful method is to square the equations and then square again. The only problem is that by doing so we may obtain an answer which does not satisfy the original equation, hence we should *always* check that our answers do indeed satisfy the equation.

Example

Solve the equation $\surd(6x+1)-\surd(2x-4) = 3$, where the positive values of the square root are to be taken.

Square the equation:

$$[\surd(6x+1)]^2-2[\surd(6x+1)][\surd(2x-4)]+[\surd(2x-4)]^2 = 9$$
$$6x+1-2[\surd(6x+1)][\surd(2x-4)]+2x-4 = 9$$
$$-2[\surd(6x+1)][\surd(2x-4)] = -8x+12$$
$$[\surd(6x+1)][\surd(2x-4)] = 4x-6$$

Square the equation again:

$$(6x+1)(2x-4) = (4x-6)^2$$
$$12x^2-22x-4 = 16x^2-48x+36$$
$$-4x^2+26x-40 = 0$$
$$2x^2-13x+20 = 0$$
$$(2x-5)(x-4) = 0$$

so either $x-4 = 0 \Rightarrow x = 4$

or $2x-5 = 0 \Rightarrow x = 2\frac{1}{2}$

Check

Put $x = 4$: $\surd 25-\surd 4 = 5-2 = 3$

Put $x = 2\frac{1}{2}$: $\surd 16-\surd 1 = 4-1 = 3$

Hence $x = 2\frac{1}{2}$ or $x = 4$

Why check? Consider $x = 2$. Squaring gives $x^2 = 4$, i.e.

$$x^2-4 = 0$$
$$(x-2)(x+2) = 0$$

so $x = 2$ or -2

but we know that $x = 2$. By squaring the equation, we have introduced a further solution $x = -2$ which does *not* satisfy the original equation. Hence, we *always* check.

Exercise 6.3

1 Solve the equation $\qquad 2^{2x} - 5(2^x) + 6 = 0$

2 Express $3^{2x+1} - 3^{x+1} - 3^x + 1$ in terms of y, where $y = 3^x$. Hence solve the equation $3^{2x+1} - 3^{x+1} - 3^x + 1 = 0$.

3 Find the only value of x which satisfies

$$\sqrt{(2x-3)} - \sqrt{(x+10)} = 1$$

4(a) Solve the equation $(\frac{4}{3})^x = 6$, giving your answer correct to two significant figures.

(b) From the relation $p_1 v_1^{\frac{x}{}} = p_2 v_2^{\frac{x}{}}$ find, to three significant figures, the value of x given that $p_1 = 16.7$, $p_2 = 36.8$, $v_1 = 57.3$, $v_2 = 32.6$.

5 Solve the equation $2\sqrt{(x+1)} - \sqrt{(3x-5)} = 2$ where the positive values of the square roots are taken.

6.4 Simultaneous equations

We often need to know when two lines, a line and a curve or two curves intersect. There are several different ways of finding the coordinates of the point of intersection. We have already seen in **5.2** a graphical method. Now we shall use the idea of substitution.

You have met the equation of a line in several different forms. For work in 2D and the calculus we usually write the equation as $y = mx + c$ where m gives the gradient (or steepness of the line) and c the value of y when $x = 0$ (i.e. the intercept on the y axis).

Example 1

Find the intersection of the lines $y = 2x + 3$ and $y = 3x - 4$.

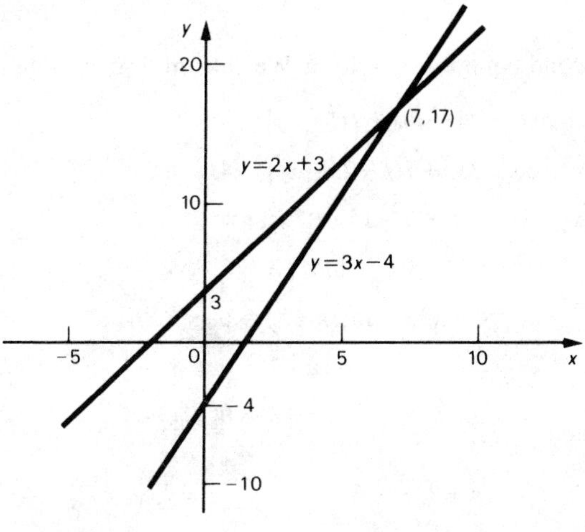

Solve the simultaneous equations

$$\left.\begin{aligned} y &= 2x+3 \\ y &= 3x-4 \end{aligned}\right\}$$

Since the values of x and y must be the same for both equations at the point of intersection, we substitute for y from the first equation into the second one; so

$$2x+3 = 3x-4$$

$$7 = x$$

When $x = 7$, $y = 17$, so the lines intersect at (7, 17).

Example 2

Find the intersection of the curve $y^2 = 9x$ (a parabola) and the line $y = x+2$.

To solve the simultaneous equations $\left.\begin{aligned} y^2 &= 9x \\ y &= x+2 \end{aligned}\right\}$

we square the second equation $y^2 = x^2+4x+4$

and substitute in the first $x^2+4x+4 = 9x$

$$x^2-5x+4 = 0$$

$$(x-4)(x-1) = 0$$

$$x = 4 \quad \text{or} \quad x = 1$$

When $x = 4$, $y = 6$ and when $x = 1$, $y = 3$. The curve and the line therefore intersect at two points, (4, 6) and (1, 3).

Example 3

Solve $\left.\begin{aligned} 2x^2+3xy+7y^2 &= 4 \\ x+y &= 1 \end{aligned}\right\}$

You will meet expressions of this form in Chapter 19. The first equation represents a tilted ellipse.

From the second equation $y = 1-x$. We substitute this value in the first equation. Then

$$2x^2+3(1-x)x+7(1-x)^2 = 4$$

$$2x^2+3x-3x^2+7(1-2x+x^2) = 4$$

$$2x^2+3x-3x^2+7-14x+7x^2 = 4$$

$$6x^2-11x+3 = 0$$

$$(3x-1)(2x-3) = 0$$

Either $3x-1 = 0 \Rightarrow x = \frac{1}{3}$

or $2x-3 = 0 \Rightarrow x = \frac{3}{2}$

The solutions are

$$x = \tfrac{1}{3},\ y = \tfrac{2}{3} \qquad \text{or} \qquad x = \tfrac{3}{2},\ y = -\tfrac{1}{2}$$

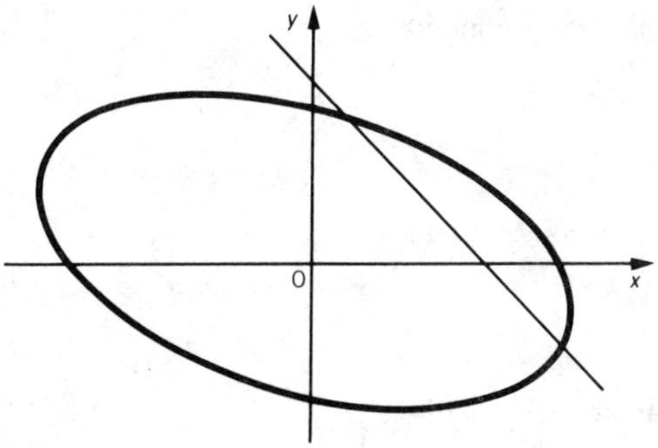

Simultaneous equations involving *x*, *y*, *z* in 'ratio' form

When dealing with lines and planes in 3D the following type of problem is often encountered.

Example 4

Solve the simultaneous equations

$$\left.\begin{aligned} 2x = 3y &= -4z \\ x^2-9y^2-4z+8 &= 0 \end{aligned}\right\}$$

The idea is to put $2x = 3y = -4z = k$, say, and then substitute in the second equation. Now $x = k/2$, $y = k/3$ and $z = -k/4$, so

so $$\left(\frac{k}{2}\right)^2-9\left(\frac{k}{3}\right)^2-4\left(-\frac{k}{4}\right)+8=0$$

$$\frac{k^2}{4}-9\frac{k^2}{9}+k+8=0$$

$$k^2-4k^2+4k+32=0$$

$$3k^2-4k-32=0$$

$$(3k+8)(k-4)=0$$

Either $3k+8=0 \Rightarrow k=-\frac{8}{3}$

or $k-4=0 \Rightarrow k=4$

Hence the solutions are

$x=-\frac{4}{3},\quad y=-\frac{8}{9},\quad z=\frac{2}{3}$

or $x=2,\quad y=\frac{4}{3},\quad z=-1$

Exercise 6.4

1 Solve the simultaneous equations

$$3x+2y=1$$

$$x^2-xy+2y^2=4$$

2 Solve the simultaneous equations

$$\frac{x+3y+2}{x+6y+4} = \frac{2}{3}$$

$$x^2-2xy+2y^2-7x+18y = 20$$

3 Solve the simultaneous equations

$$x^2+y^2+6x+4y = 37$$

$$2x+y = 7$$

4 Solve the simultaneous equations

$$3x+y = 6$$

$$\frac{5}{x}-\frac{3}{y} = 4$$

5 Verify that $x^3+y^3 \equiv (x+y)(x^2-xy+y^2)$. Hence solve the simultaneous equations

$$x^3+y^3 = 117, \qquad x+y = 3$$

6 Find the real roots of the following simultaneous equations:

$$\frac{2x-y}{5} = \frac{3y+2z}{3} = \frac{5z+x}{-4}$$

$$2yz^2 = 9$$

7 Solve the simultaneous equations

$$x+y+z = 2$$

$$\frac{x+2y}{-3} = \frac{y+2z}{4} = \frac{z+2x}{5}$$

8 Solve the simultaneous equations

$$2x = 3y = 4z$$

$$x^2-y^2+2xy-2xz = 128$$

Miscellaneous examination questions 2

(O. & C. unless stated otherwise.)

1 Without solving the equation $ax^2+bx+c = 0$, prove that the sum and product of the roots are $-b/a$ and c/a respectively. Find the equation whose roots are the squares of the roots of the equation $3x^2-2x+p = 0$, and prove that if the roots of this second equation are real and distinct then $p < \frac{1}{3}$.

2(a) Find the values of a and b such that x^2+4x+3 is a factor of x^7-9x^5+ax+b.

(b) Find the values of k if the equation $x^2+6x+13 = k(x^2-5)$ has equal roots.

(c) The equations $kx^2+2x+1 = 0$ and $x^2+2x+k = 0$, in which k is a constant not equal to 1, are known to have a common root. Find the value of k.

3 The roots of the equation $ax^2+bx+c = 0$, where a, b, c, are non-zero constants, are α, β and the roots of $ax^2+2bx+c = 0$ are γ, δ. Without solving either equation, show that the equation whose roots are $\alpha\gamma+\beta\delta$ and $\alpha\delta+\beta\gamma$ is

$$a^3x^2-2ab^2x+c(5b^2-4ac) = 0$$

Show also that if this last equation has equal roots, then one and only one of the original equations has equal roots. (M.E.I.)

4 The equation $x^2+kx+1 = 0$, where k is a real constant, has roots α and β. Find the quadratic equation whose roots are γ and δ where

$$\gamma = \alpha(2+\alpha^2+\beta^2)$$

and

$$\delta = \beta(2+\alpha^2+\beta^2)$$

Find the values of k for which the roots γ, δ are real and distinct. (M.E.I.)

5 If α, β are the roots of

$$x^2-2ax+ab+c = 0$$

and γ, δ are the roots of

$$x^2-2bx+ab-c = 0$$

prove that

$$\tfrac{1}{2}(\alpha-\beta)(\gamma-\delta) = (\alpha-\delta)(\gamma-\beta) = (\alpha-\gamma)(\beta-\delta)$$

Hence, or otherwise, prove that, if the quadratic equations have a common root, it is a repeated root of one of them.

6(a) Find the two values of a for which $x^3+ax^2+a^2x+38$ has a factor $(x+2)$.
(b) Find all the factors of $2x^3-x^2-13x-6$ given that one factor is $(x-k)$ where k is a positive integer.

7 If x^3-3x^2+ax-7 is exactly divisible by $x+1$, find the remainder when the same expression is divided by $x-2$.

8(a) Use the identity $(x^4+x^2+1)+x^2 = (x^2+1)^2$ to find two quadratic factors of x^4+x^2+1.
(b) Find the values of a and b if $x-2$ and $3x+1$ are both factors of $3x^2-2x^2+ax+b$ and find the third factor of the expression.

9(a) The value of k is such that one factor of x^3-2x^2-x+k is $x+1$. Find the other two factors.
(b) The expression x^7-ax^3+b is divisible by $x-1$ without a remainder, but has a remainder 8 when divided by $x-2$. Find a and b, and find the remainder when the expression is divided by $x+2$.

10(a) Divide $x^3+2x^2y-5xy^2-6y^3$ by $x-2y$.

(b) Calculate the remainders when $2x^3+5x^2-4x-3$ is divided by (i) $x-1$ (ii) $x+2$.

Find all the factors of $2x^3+5x^2-4x-3$.

11 Calculate the values of the function $6x^3+19x^2+x-6$ **(a)** when $x=\frac{2}{3}$, and **(b)** $x=-\frac{2}{3}$.

Find all the factors of the expression $6x^3+19x^2+x-6$.

12 Simplify $(k^{2/3})^{4/3}$ and use logarithms to find its numerical value, correct to three significant figures, when $k=0.35$.

13 Simplify $2\log_{10}\frac{3}{2}-\log_{10}(0.075)+\log_{10}(3\frac{1}{3})$.

14(a) When $x=16$, without using tables evaluate $x^{3/4}$, $x^{-1/2}$ and x^0.

(b) Multiply $x^2+2x^{1/2}-3x^{-1}$ by $x-x^{-1/2}$.

(c) Solve the simultaneous equations $x^{-3/2}y=1$ and $x^2y^{-2/3}=4$.

15 Solve the simultaneous equations $x^3y^2=10$ and $\log_{10}x-\log_{10}y=3$.

16 Solve the equation $\sqrt{(6x+1)}-\sqrt{(2x-4)}=3$ where the positive values of the square roots are to be taken.

17 Solve the equation $2\sqrt{x}+\sqrt{(2x+1)}=7$ where the positive values of the square roots are taken.

18(a) Solve the equations $\dfrac{x}{3}+\dfrac{3}{y}=\dfrac{x}{4}-\dfrac{4}{y}=1$

(b) Solve the equations $x-y=1$, $x^2+xy=6$

(c) Prove that

$$\frac{(2a-b)^3+(a-2b)^3}{a^4+a^2b^2+b^4}=\frac{9(a-b)}{a^2+ab+b^2}$$

19 Solve the equations

(a) $9x^{2/3}+4x^{-2/3}=37$

(b) $x+2y=3,\quad 3x^2+4y^2+12x=7$

20 Solve the equations

(a) $3^{2(x+1)}-10(3^x)+1=0$

(b) $x^2+4y^2=25,\quad xy+6=0$

21 Solve the simultaneous equations

$$(x-3y)^2=1 \quad\text{and}\quad x^2-4y^2+3x=24$$

22(a) Solve the equation $\sqrt{(6+x)}-\sqrt{(4-x)}=2$ where the positive values of the square roots are to be taken.

(b) Solve the simultaneous equations

$$(x+3)(y+3)=10 \quad\text{and}\quad (x+3)(x+y)=2$$

23 Solve the equations

(a) $3x=-4y=2z$ and $x^2-2y^2-z+8=0$

(b) $(x^2-4x)^2+2x^2-8x-3=0$

24 Solve the simultaneous equations

$$2y - \frac{1}{x} = \frac{3y}{x} \quad \text{and} \quad x + \frac{4}{y} = \frac{3x}{y}$$

25 Solve the simultaneous equations

$$2x + 3y + 1 = 0 \quad \text{and} \quad 4x^2 - 2xy + y^2 + 4x = 11$$

Chapter 3

Trigonometry 1

1 Circular functions

1.1 Sine θ and cosine θ

You will have met the idea of the sine, cosine and tangent of an angle as the ratio of sides in a right-angled triangle. We now consider the sine, cosine and tangent as *circular functions*.

A function of θ, written $f(\theta)$ is such that it has one and only one value for each value of θ. (See p. 42.)

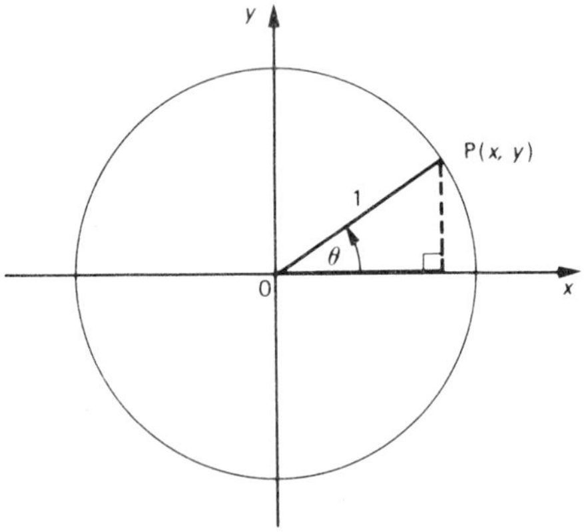

Definition

► **If any point P on a circle with centre the origin and radius one unit has co-ordinates (x, y), and if OP makes an angle θ with the positive x-axis, then**

$$\sin\theta = y$$

$$\cos\theta = x$$ ◄

Clearly these give $-1 \leq \sin\theta \leq 1$ and $-1 \leq \cos\theta \leq 1$

Draw a circle on the left-hand side of a sheet of paper with centre O, radius 5 cm and diameter BOA. Then using a protractor construct angles of 10°, 20°, . . . , 90° from OA, as shown in the diagram.

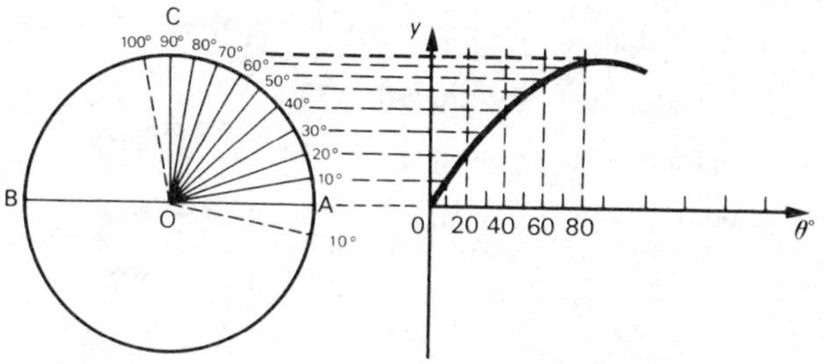

Plot points on a graph as illustrated. What does this curve represent?

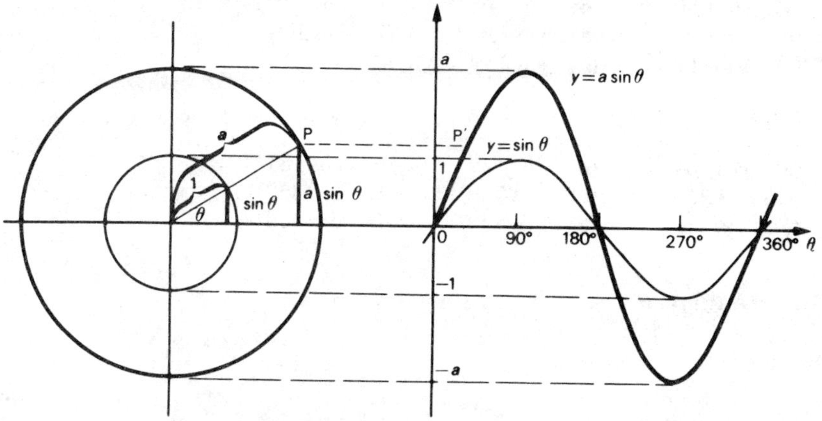

As P traces out a circle of radius a (which in this case is 5 cm), P′ describes the curve $y = a \sin \theta$. If we let a be one unit, then the curve is $y = \sin \theta$. We can continue this curve beyond 90°, or backwards for negative angles, by plotting more points on the circumference of the circle.

Draw another circle, this time measuring angles from OC in the anticlockwise direction. Plot points on an adjacent graph as before, and show that the new curve is $y = 5 \cos \theta$.

How often is the pattern in each of these curves repeated?

Oscillating functions of this kind often occur in the physical world—for instance, sound waves, alternating electric currents, stretched springs and tides all display oscillations similar to the sine and cosine curves.

We can make use of the properties of these curves to express the sine or cosine of *any* angle in terms of the sine or cosine of an angle between 0° and 90°.

Example

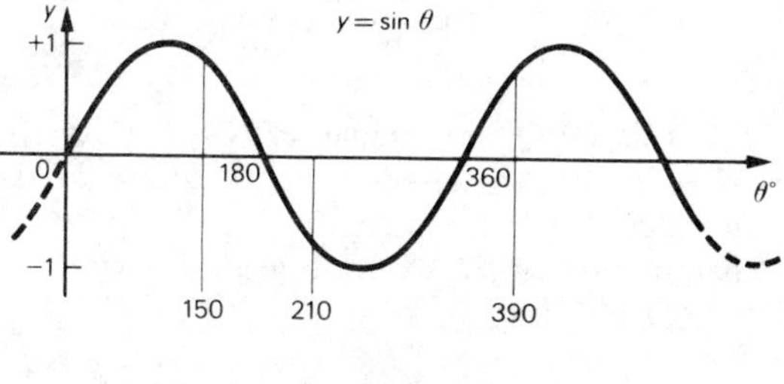

The curve is symmetrical about $\theta = 90°, 270° \ldots$. Thus

$$\sin 120° = \sin(90°+30°) = \sin(90°-30°) = \sin 60°$$

$$\sin 210° = \sin(180°+30°) = -\sin(180°-30°) = -\sin 150° = -\sin 30°$$

$$\sin 390° = \sin(360°+30°) = \sin 30°$$

Exercise 1.1

1 Express each of the following as the sine of an angle between 0° and 90°:

(a) sin 125° **(b)** sin 170° **(c)** sin 195°
(d) sin 230° **(e)** sin 280° **(f)** sin 305°
(g) sin 320° **(h)** sin 385° **(i)** sin 400°

2 Express each of the following as the cosine of an angle between 0° and 90°:

(a) cos 104° **(b)** cos 179° **(c)** cos 181°
(d) cos 255° **(e)** cos 300° **(f)** cos 358°
(g) cos 450° **(h)** cos 540° **(i)** cos 550°

1.2 Tangent θ

We define

$$\mathbf{tan}\,\boldsymbol{\theta} = \frac{\mathbf{sin}\,\boldsymbol{\theta}}{\mathbf{cos}\,\boldsymbol{\theta}} = \frac{y}{x}$$ ◀

(except when $x = 0$, when $\tan\theta$ is not defined.)

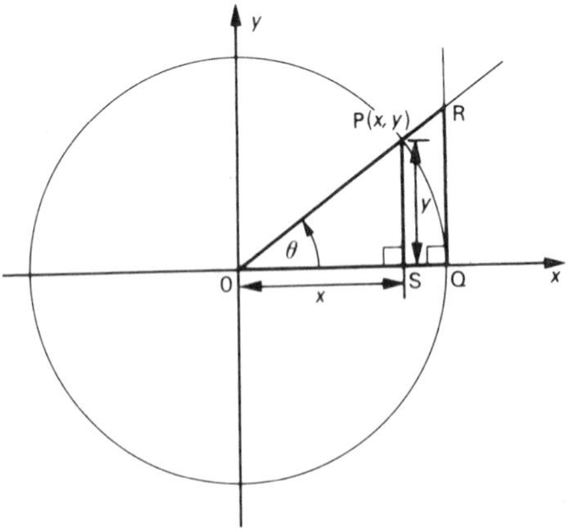

Since triangles OPS and ORQ are similar PS/OS = y/x = RQ/OQ = RQ/1. Hence RQ represents $\tan\theta$. Use this diagram as before to sketch the graph $y = \tan\theta$ for $0° \leqslant \theta < 90°$.

Remembering that, if $90° < \theta < 270°$, x is negative, sketch the curve from $0° \leqslant \theta \leqslant 360°$ ($\theta \neq 90°, \theta \neq 270°$).

Exercise 1.2

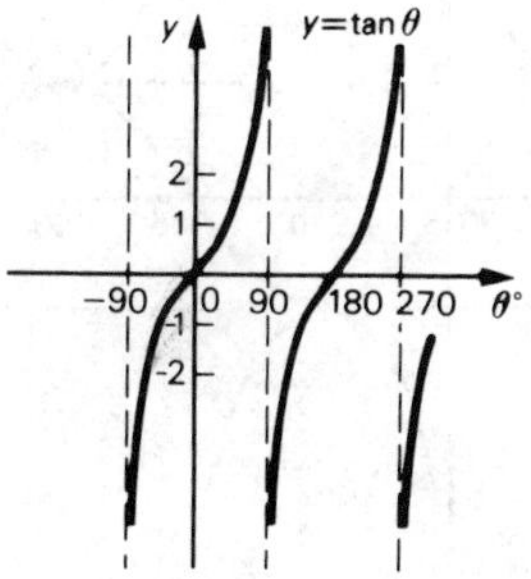

1 Use the diagram showing $y = \tan\theta$ to help you to express each of the following as the tangent of an angle between 0° and 90°.

(a) tan 91°	**(b)** tan (−40°)	**(c)** tan 430°
(d) tan 189°	**(e)** tan 262°	**(f)** tan 301°
(g) tan 490°	**(h)** tan (−89°)	**(i)** tan (−1°)

2 The diagram below shows angles between 0° and 360° for which sine, cosine and tangent are positive. Draw a similar diagram to show when they are negative.

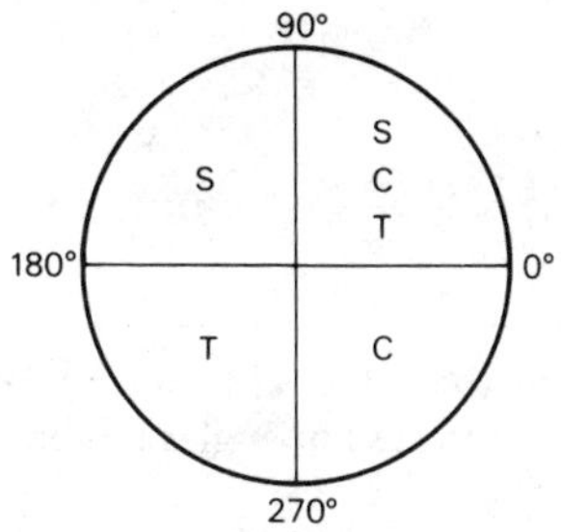

1.3 Cosecant θ, secant θ and cotangent θ

These may be defined as the reciprocal of sin θ, cos θ and tan θ respectively.

$$\mathbf{cosec}\,\boldsymbol{\theta} = \frac{\mathbf{1}}{\mathbf{sin}\,\boldsymbol{\theta}} = \frac{\mathbf{1}}{\boldsymbol{y}}, \qquad \boldsymbol{y \neq 0}$$ ◀

$$\mathbf{sec}\,\boldsymbol{\theta} = \frac{\mathbf{1}}{\mathbf{cos}\,\boldsymbol{\theta}} = \frac{\mathbf{1}}{\boldsymbol{x}}, \qquad \boldsymbol{x \neq 0}$$ ◀

$$\mathbf{cot}\,\boldsymbol{\theta} = \frac{\mathbf{1}}{\mathbf{tan}\,\boldsymbol{\theta}} = \frac{\boldsymbol{x}}{\boldsymbol{y}}, \qquad \boldsymbol{y \neq 0}$$ ◀

Here is the graph of $y = \text{cosec}\,\theta$, drawn on the same axes as $y = \sin\theta$.

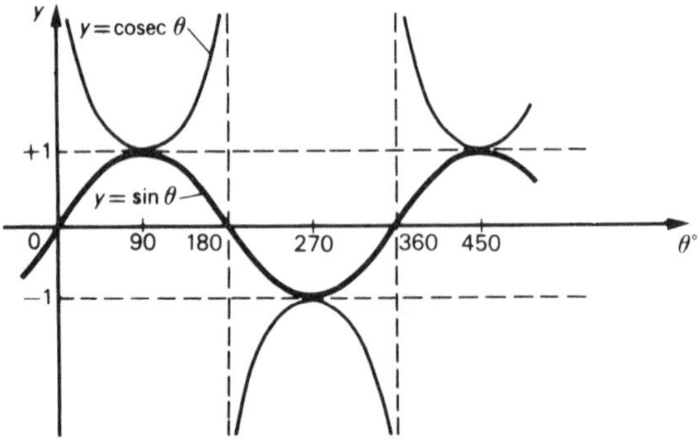

Sketch the graphs of $y = \sec\theta$ and $y = \cot\theta$ for $0° \leqslant \theta \leqslant 360°$. NOTE that $\theta \neq 90°, 270°$ for $\sec\theta$ and that $\theta \neq 0°, 180°, 360°$ for $\cot\theta$. The results may be summarized in a table except for the points where the functions are not defined which have been given above.

Angle	$0° \leqslant \theta < 90°$	$90° \leqslant \theta < 180°$	$180° \leqslant \theta < 270°$	$270° \leqslant \theta < 360°$
Angle to use for tables	θ	$180-\theta$	$\theta-180$	$360-\theta$
$\sin\theta$ $\operatorname{cosec}\theta$	+	+	−	−
$\cos\theta$ $\sec\theta$	+	−	−	+
$\tan\theta$ $\cot\theta$	+	−	+	−

NOTE. The *only* numbers in the table with our angles are 180° and 360° (and multiples of these, if we are interested in angles larger than 360°).

Positive angles

Positive angles are measured in an anticlockwise direction. The diagram shows the regions where the trigonometrical functions are positive:

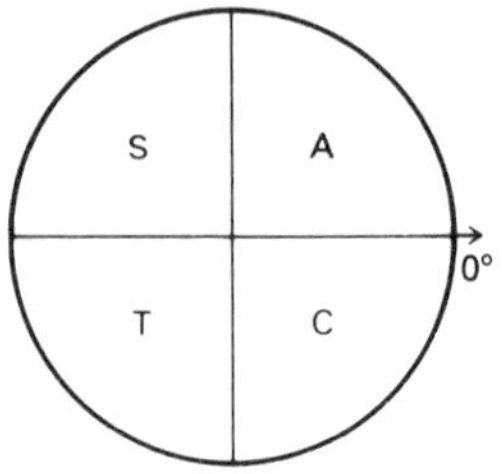

Remember CAST—cos, all, sin, tan.

Negative angles

Negative angles are measured clockwise, and the values of their sine, cosine, or tangent functions are worked out accordingly. For example:

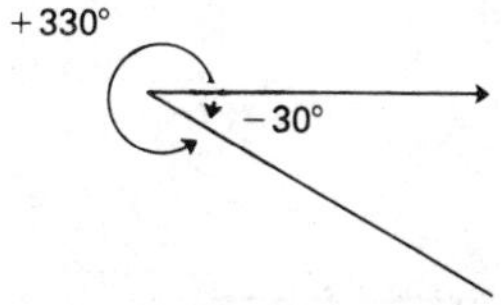

sin (−30°) is the same as
sin (360° − 30°) = sin 330°
or −sin 30°

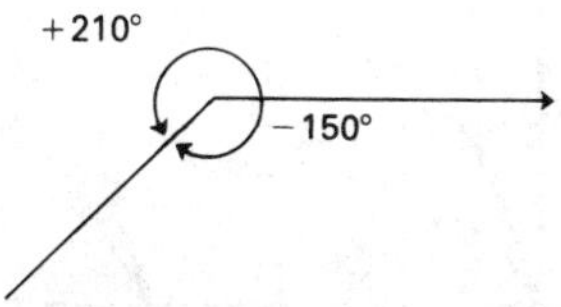

cos (−150°) is the same as
cos (360° − 150°) = cos 210°
or −cos 30°

Notice that −30° and +330° are in the same position on the circle, and so are −150° and +210°.

Exercise 1.3a

Write down the following in terms of angles between 0° and 90°:

1	cos 150°	**7**	cos −220°	**13**	cos 340°
2	sin 110°	**8**	sin −215°	**14**	sin 290°
3	tan 240°	**9**	tan −120°	**15**	tan 310°
4	cosec 320°	**10**	cosec −160°	**16**	cosec 280°
5	sec 315°	**11**	sec −260°	**17**	sec 112°
6	cot 135°	**12**	cot −270°	**18**	cot 320°

Exercise 1.3b

Solve the following equations for $0° \leqslant \theta \leqslant 360°$:

1	$\sin\theta = 0.8931$	**2**	$\cos\theta = 0.4387$	**3**	$\tan\theta = -0.7381$
4	$\text{cosec}\,\theta = 2.3472$	**5**	$\sec\theta = -1.0372$	**6**	$\cot\theta = 0.4519$

1.4 Curve sketching and simple trigonometric equations

It is often a great help when solving trigonometric equations to *sketch* the functions concerned. We can then see how many solutions there are, and their approximate values. It is very important to be able to make these sketches quickly and easily, and to know how the curves are related to the 'basic' curves—i.e. in our examples, those of $y = \sin\theta$ and $y = \cos\theta$.

Example 1

$$y = \sin\theta \qquad y = \cos\theta$$

$$y = 2\sin\theta \qquad y = 2\cos\theta$$

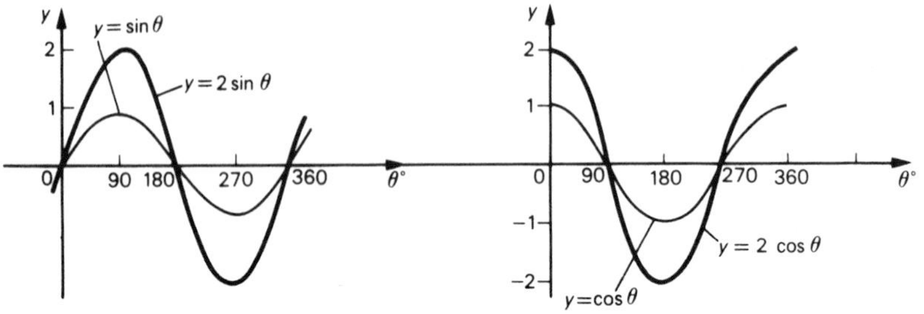

Notice that

1. the amplitude (height of 'wave') is *doubled*,
2. the period (or 'wave-length') is the same, and
3. the 'gradient' (slope of curve as it crosses the axis) is greater.

Example 2

$$y = \sin\theta \qquad y = \cos\theta$$

$$y = \sin 2\theta \qquad y = \cos 2\theta$$

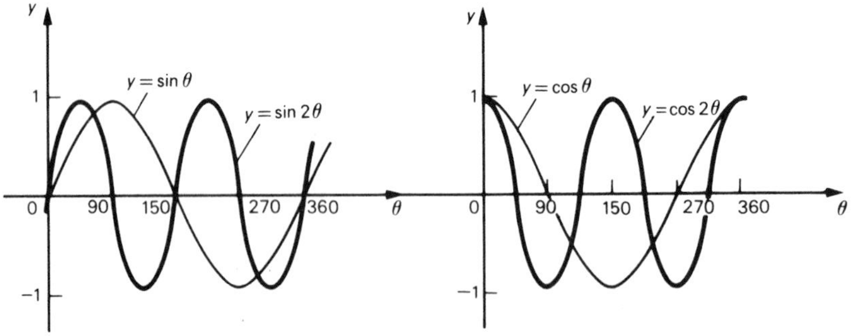

Here we notice that

1. the amplitude is the same,
2. the period is *halved*, and
3. the 'gradient' is *greater*.

Example 3

$$y = \sin\theta \qquad y = \cos\theta$$

$$y = \sin\tfrac{1}{2}\theta \qquad y = \cos\tfrac{1}{2}\theta$$

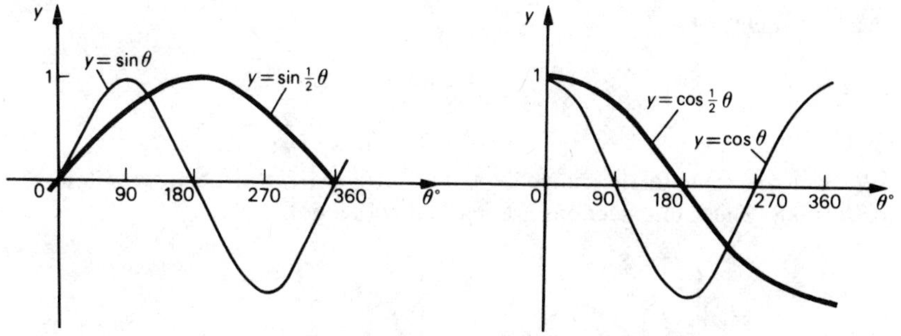

In this case

1 the amplitude is the same,
2 the period is doubled, but
3 the 'gradient' is less.

Example 4

$$y = \sin\theta \qquad y = \cos\theta$$

$$y = \sin(\theta + 45°) \qquad y = \cos(\theta - 45°)$$

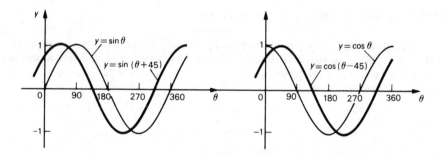

1 The amplitude,
2 the period, and
3 the 'gradient'

are *all* unchanged

BUT the curves have been translated (so suffering a phase change) through 45° in the direction of $-\theta$ in $y = \sin(\theta + 45°)$ or 45° in the direction of $+\theta$ in $y = \cos(\theta - 45°)$.

We shall now use similar curves to illustrate the solutions to simple trigonometric equations.

(a) Equations involving one trigonometric ratio

Suppose we have to solve $\sin 3\theta = 0.8$.

Make a sketch of $y = \sin\theta$

then one of $y = \sin 3\theta$

Draw in $y = 0.8$

We can see that, in the range $0° \leqslant \theta \leqslant 360°$, we can expect *six* solutions to $\sin 3\theta = 0.8$. These intersections are marked with a dot.

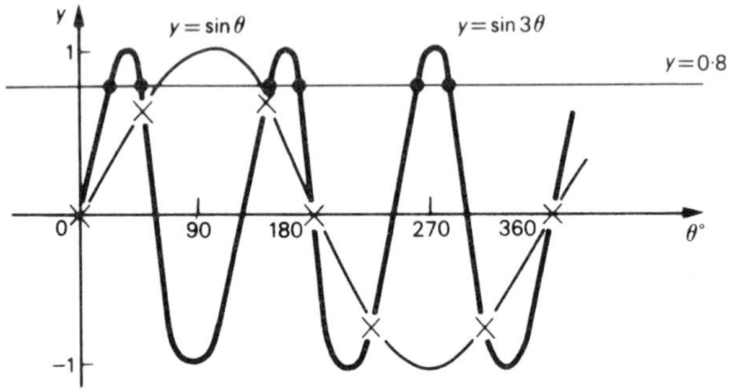

We find the first intersection using tables or a calculator and derive the others by symmetry.

(b) Equations involving multiples of an angle

From our sketch in **(a)** we could also find approximate solutions to $\sin 3\theta = \sin\theta$ for $0° \leqslant \theta \leqslant 360°$. The two curves intersect in *seven* positions, which are marked with a cross. We can read off the solutions 0°, 180°, 360° directly. We find the one between 0° and 90° where

$$\sin\theta = \sin(180° - 3\theta) \quad \text{since } \sin(180 - 3\theta) = \sin 3\theta$$

$$\theta = 180° - 3\theta$$

$$4\theta = 180°$$

so $$\theta = 45°$$

(c) Equations involving a known 'added' angle (or phase change)

To solve $\cos(\theta + 20°) = \cos 2\theta$, we sketch $y = \cos\theta$; then

$$y = \cos(\theta + 20°)$$

and $$y = \cos 2\theta$$

We can see that there are *four* solutions where the curves $y = \cos(\theta + 20°)$ and $y = \cos 2\theta$ intersect. For the first solution

$$\theta + 20° = 2\theta$$

$$\theta = 20°$$

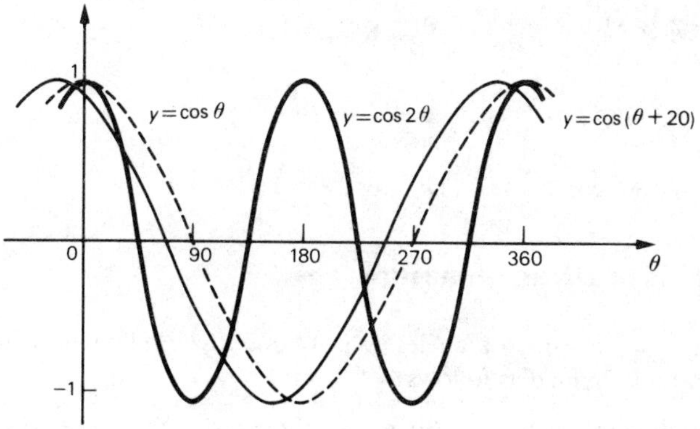

Later, we shall see how to find all the solutions analytically.

(d) Equations involving two trigonometric ratios

To solve $\cos\theta = 2-\sin 2\theta$, first sketch $y = \cos\theta$ and $y = 2-\sin 2\theta$.

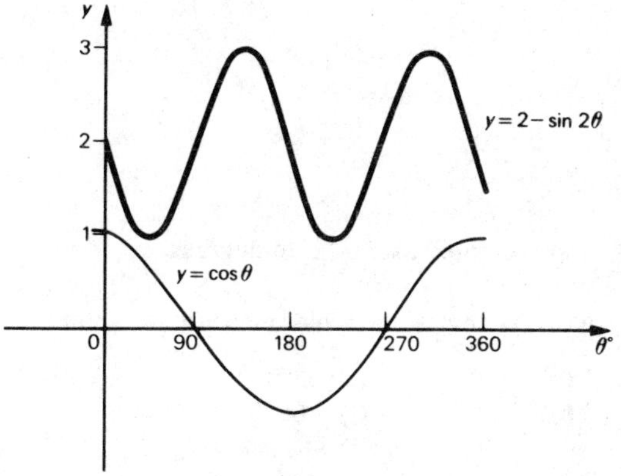

Since $2-\sin 2\theta$ has its *minimum* value of 1 when $\theta = 45$ and $\theta = 225°$ and since $\cos\theta$ is always less than 1, it is clear that the curves cannot meet and so the equation has *no* solution.

Exercise 1.4

Illustrate graphically the solutions to the following equations for $0° \leqslant \theta \leqslant 360°$.

1 $\sin 2\theta = -0.2341$

2 $\cos 3\theta = -0.6990$

3 $\tan\dfrac{3\theta}{2} = 1.5042$

4 $\operatorname{cosec}\dfrac{\theta}{2} = -1.6984$

5 $\sec\frac{3\theta}{4} = 2.3842$

6 $\cot\frac{\theta}{2} = 0.8990$

7 $\cos 2\theta = 4+3\cos\theta$

8 $\sin\frac{\theta}{2} = 1-2\sin\theta$

9 $2\sin(\theta+60) = \frac{1}{2}$

10 $\cos 2\theta = 1-2\sin\theta$

1.5 Radians or circular measure

The radian is a measure of angle; it is frequently used in both calculus and mechanics, and is defined as follows:

► **One radian (1^c or 1 rad) is the angle subtended at the centre of a circle by an arc equal in length to the radius of the circle.** ◄

$2\pi^c$ represents one complete revolution since the circumference of a circle is $2\pi r$.

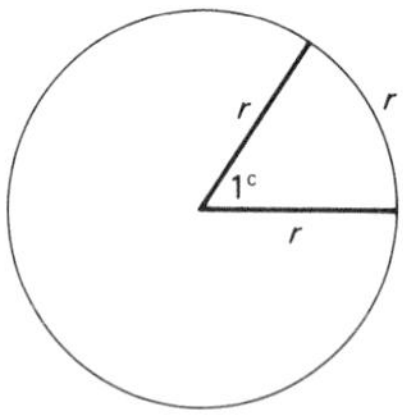

Exercise 1.5

1 Calculate the approximate value of 1^c in degrees.

2 Express the following angles in circular measure (as a multiple of π):

(a) 360° **(b)** 90° **(c)** 30°
(d) 45° **(e)** 135° **(f)** 60°

3 Express the following angles in degrees:

(a) $\frac{3\pi}{2}$ **(b)** $\frac{\pi}{8}$ **(c)** $\frac{4\pi}{3}$
(d) 4π **(e)** 3π **(f)** $\frac{11\pi}{6}$

4 The six trigonometrical ratios are periodic: we noticed when drawing the sketches that the patterns are repeated. Write down in circular measure the change in angle which represents one complete period of

(a) $\sin\theta$ **(b)** $\cos\theta$ **(c)** $\tan\theta$
(d) $\operatorname{cosec}\theta$ **(e)** $\sec\theta$ **(f)** $\cot\theta$

5 Sketch the graphs of $y = \sin x$, $y = \cos x$, $y = \tan x$, for $0 \leqslant x \leqslant 2\pi$ (in radians).

6 Convert the following angles into radians

(a) 75°	**(b)** 80°	**(c)** 120°	**(d)** 240°	**(e)** 63° 8′
(f) 312°	**(g)** 190°	**(h)** 390°	**(i)** 36° 52′	**(j)** 217° 42′

7 The area of a circle is πr^2 which subtends an angle of $2\pi^c$ at the centre.

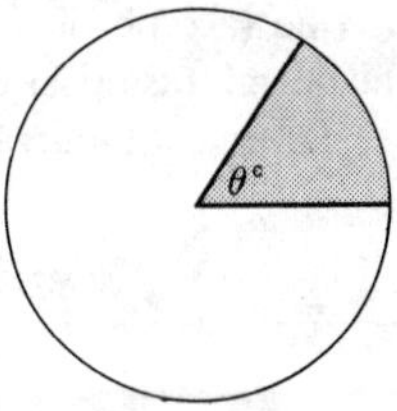

What is the area of the sector of a circle subtending θ^c at the centre?

8 The area of triangle OPT < area of sector OPT < area of triangle OTQ.

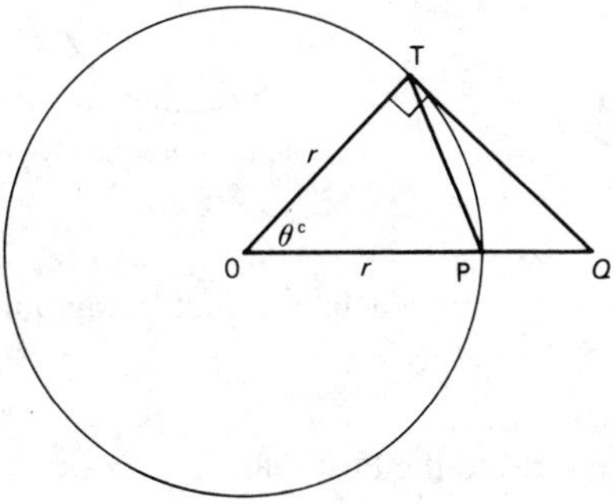

Write down the areas of these three and hence show that $\sin\theta^c < \theta^c < \tan\theta^c$.

Deduce that if θ^c is a very small angle $\sin\theta^c \approx \theta^c$. (Check by reference to your book of tables.)

9 Solve the following equations, where $0^c \leqslant \theta \leqslant 2\pi^c$,

(a) $\sin\theta = 0.4578$ **(b)** $\cos\theta = -0.6872$ **(c)** $\tan\theta = 0.3752$

(d) $\operatorname{cosec} 2\theta = -1.8010$ **(e)** $\sin 3\theta = 1.0502$ **(f)** $\cot\dfrac{\theta}{3} = -0.8920$

10 Draw on the same axes, the curves $y = 2\sin\theta$ and $y = \sin 2\theta$ for $0^c \leqslant \theta \leqslant 2\pi^c$ at intervals of 0.2^c.

What values of θ satisfy the equation $2\sin\theta = \sin 2\theta$?

1.6 Polar coordinates and curves

If you were asked where the waste-paper basket was, you would probably point to it and say 'It's over there'. If someone asked you where the Post Office was, you might point and say 'It's down there, about 400 metres'.

One of the most important inventions during the second world war was that of RADAR—Radio Aids to Detection And Ranging. A transmitter sends out 'bursts' or 'pulses' of very high frequency oscillations, each pulse being of very short duration and of very large amplitude. These pulses, transmitted from the aerials at the speed of light, travel on until they 'hit' something (an aircraft, a hill, a tower). The minute portion of the pulse reflected back to the aerial is then amplified (made larger) and shown on an oscilloscope (a type of television screen). From the time taken for the echo to return to the aerial it is possible to calculate the distance away of the object struck by the pulse. To find the elevation requires another measurement.

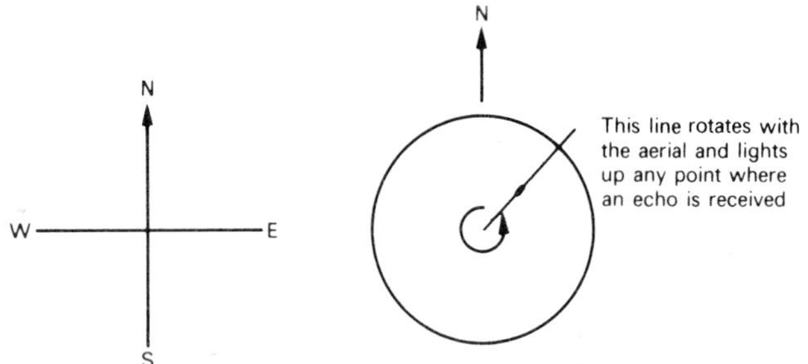

Cathode ray tube display showing bearing of an aircraft

To locate the objects mentioned in the first paragraph, we need to use two measurements:

1 a direction (over there)
2 a distance (400 metres to the Post Office)

Polar coordinates use these two basic ideas, but before we can give a direction as an angle, we must have a fixed base line and an origin. This fixed line is taken as a horizontal line to the east.

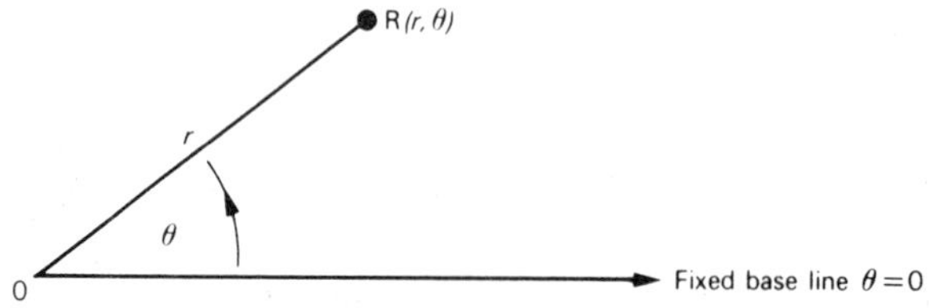

Having marked an origin O on this fixed line, we can give the position of any point on the plane in the form

$$(r, \theta)$$

where the distance from point O is given first, and the anticlockwise angle from the fixed base line is given second.

Although it may at first appear odd, *negative* values of r can be used. These may be plotted by going 'backwards' along the ray from the origin; for example,

$(-1, \pi/2)$ would be the same point as $(1, 3\pi/2)$, and $(2, \pi/6)$ is the same as $(-2, -5\pi/6)$. On the other hand $(2, 30°)$ and $(-2, 30°)$ are not the same.

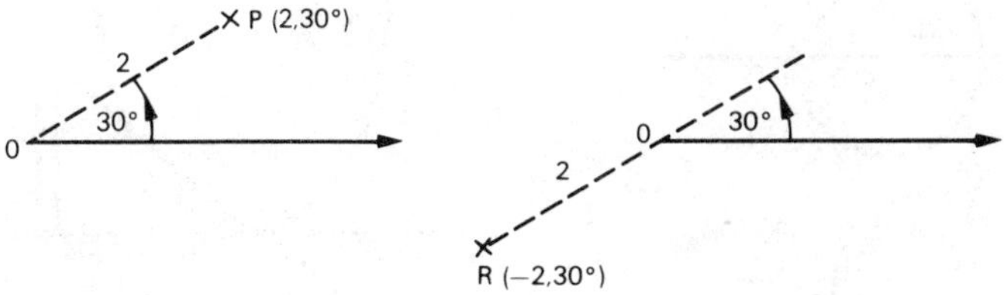

Exercise 1.6a

Plot the following points:

1 $(3, 0)$ **2** $(1, \pi/6)$ **3** $(-2, \pi/3)$ **4** $(2, 5\pi/6)$
5 $(-3, 3\pi/4)$ **6** $(4, 5\pi/3)$ **7** $(1, 45°)$ **8** $(-1, 135°)$

Trigonometric functions and their polar curves

To plot curves in polar form it is advisable to use special polar graph paper of concentric circles already marked with angles. If none is available it is possible to make some using a compass and protractor:

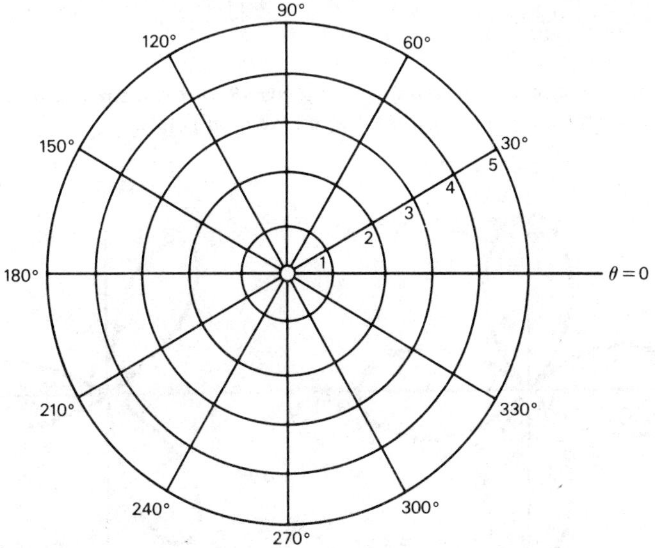

Simplified polar graph paper, of concentric circles of 1 cm ,....... 5 cm, and $\theta = 0$,.....360° in 30° intervals

Below are the polar curves of three trigonometrical functions.

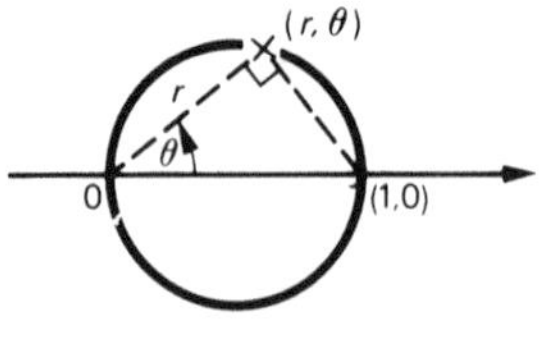

(i) $r = \cos\theta$

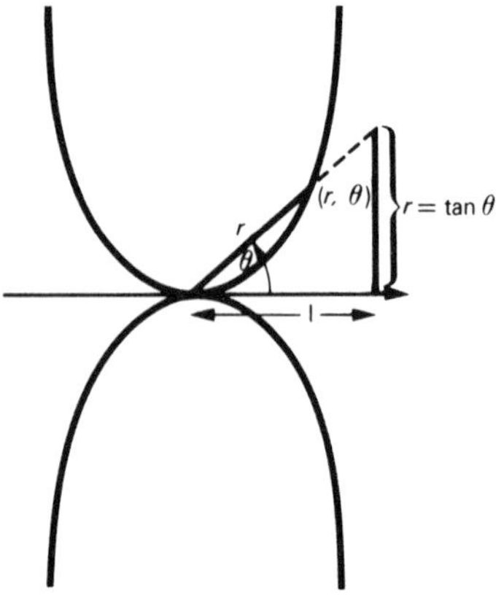

(ii) $r = \tan\theta$

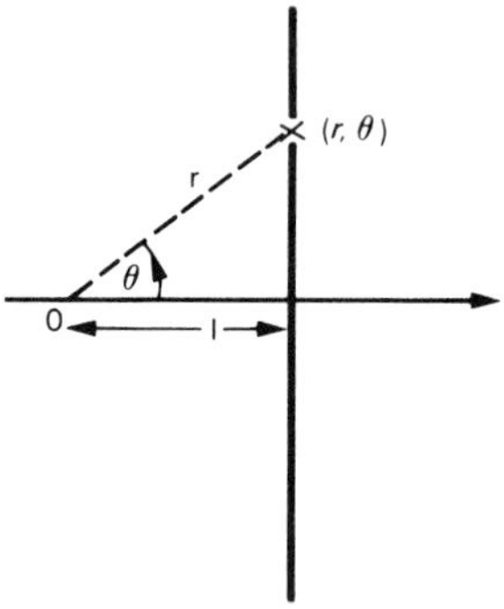

(iii) $r = \sec\theta$

Plot the next three curves yourself:

(iv) $r = \sin\theta$ **(v)** $r = \cot\theta$ **(vi)** $r = \operatorname{cosec}\theta$

The 'rose petal' family

The general equation for this family is $r = a\cos n\theta$ (or $r = a\sin n\theta$), where $n \in \mathbb{Z}^+$. If n is odd we have n petals; if n is even, we have $2n$ petals.

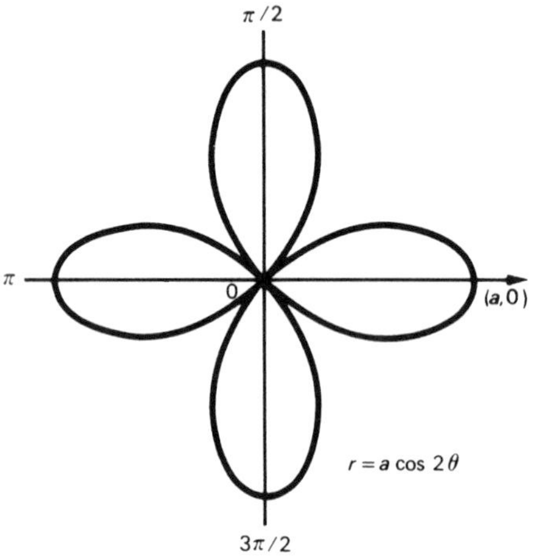

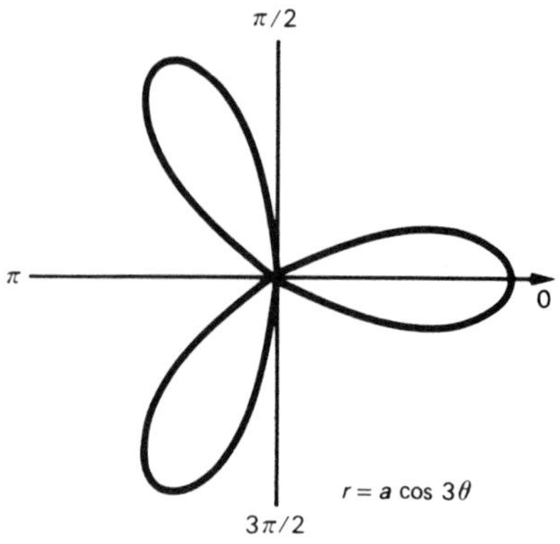

Exercise 1.6b

You can now draw curves yourself with the help of the table of values for cos θ given in Exercise 1.6c (or from your calculator).

1 $r = \cos 2\theta$ **2** $r = \cos 3\theta$

Now sketch

3 $r = \sin 2\theta$ **4** $r = \sin 3\theta$ **5** $r = \cos 4\theta$ **6** $r = \sin 4\theta$

The limaçon family

One of the basic polar curves is the *limaçon*. The limaçon family has the general equation

$$r = a + b\cos\theta$$

for different values of a and b.

(i) When

$$a = 0$$

$$r = b\cos\theta$$

which gives a circle.

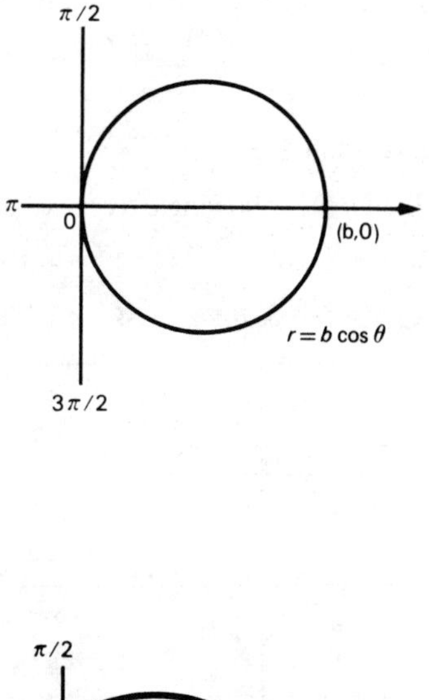

(ii) When

$$a = b$$

$$r = a(1+\cos\theta)$$

This is called a *cardioid* since it is heart-shaped.

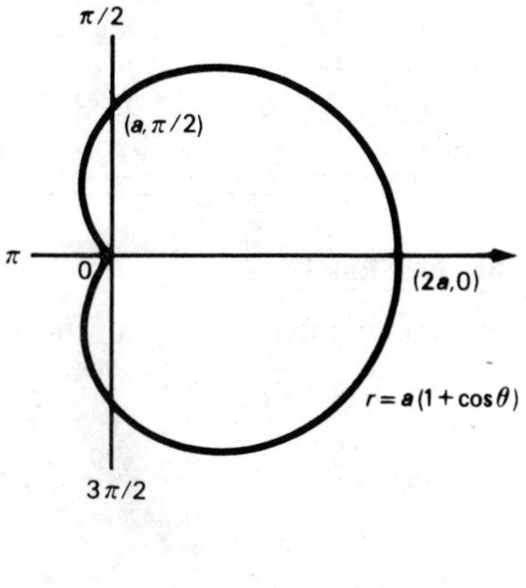

(iii) When

$$b > a$$

$$r = 1+2\cos\theta$$

This is a limaçon with a loop

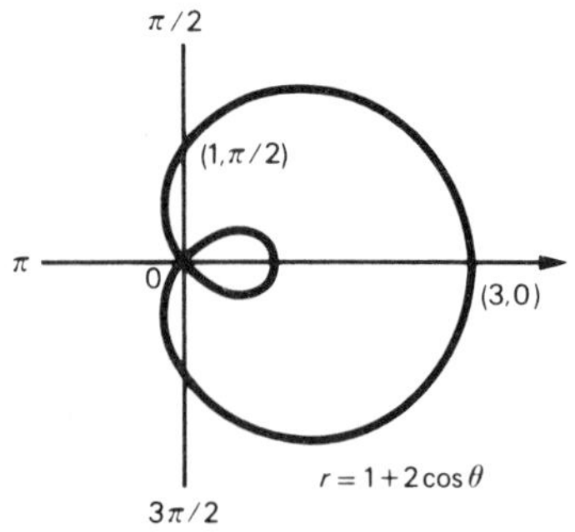

(iv) When

$$a > b$$

$$r = 1+\tfrac{1}{2}\cos\theta$$

This is a limaçon without a loop.

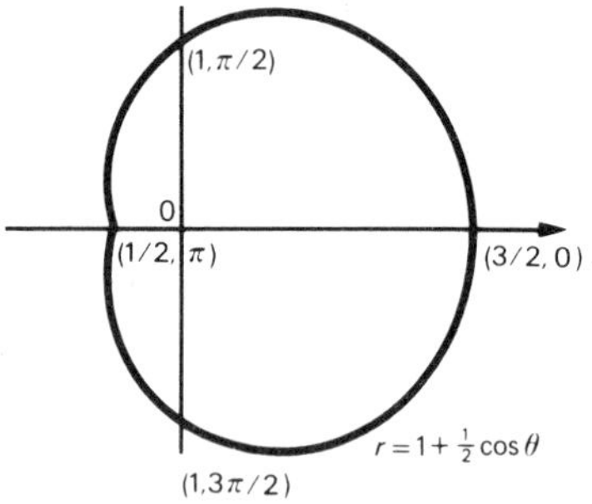

Exercise 1.6c

Sketch the following curves, using the table of approximate values for cos θ below.

1 $r = \frac{1}{2}\cos\theta$ **2** $r = 1+\frac{1}{4}\cos\theta$

3 $r = \frac{1}{2}+\cos\theta$ **4** $r = 2+2\cos\theta$

θ	0	15°	30°	45°	60°	75°	90°
cos θ	1.00	0.97	0.87	0.71	0.50	0.26	0
θ		105°	120°	135°	150°	165°	180°
cos θ		−0.26	−0.50	−0.71	−0.87	−0.97	−1.00
θ		195°	210°	225°	240°	255°	270°
cos θ		−0.97	−0.87	−0.71	−0.50	−0.26	0
θ		285°	300°	315°	330°	345°	360°
cos θ		0.26	0.50	0.71	0.87	0.97	1.00

The conic family

The general polar equation of the conic form is

$$\frac{l}{r} = 1+e\cos\theta$$

for different l, e.

Exercise 1.6d

Draw the curves

1 $\dfrac{1}{r} = 1+\cos\theta$ **2** $\dfrac{1}{r} = 1+2\cos\theta$ **3** $\dfrac{1}{r} = 1+\frac{1}{2}\cos\theta$

The first of these is a parabola, the second a hyperbola and the third an ellipse. We shall meet these again later, in Chapter 19.

Exercise 1.6e

Sketch the following:

1 $\theta = \pi/4$ **2** $r = 5$ **3** $r = \theta/2$ **4** $r = \sqrt{(\sin\theta)}$

5 $r = \sqrt{(\sin 2\theta)}$ **6** $4 = 1/\theta$ **7** $r^2 = \cos 4\theta$ **8** $r = \tan 3\theta$

2 Triangle relationships

2.1 Right-angled triangles

We now consider the circular functions as *ratios of sides* in a right-angled triangle. The sides are usually labelled a (opposite angle A), b (opposite B) and c (opposite C).

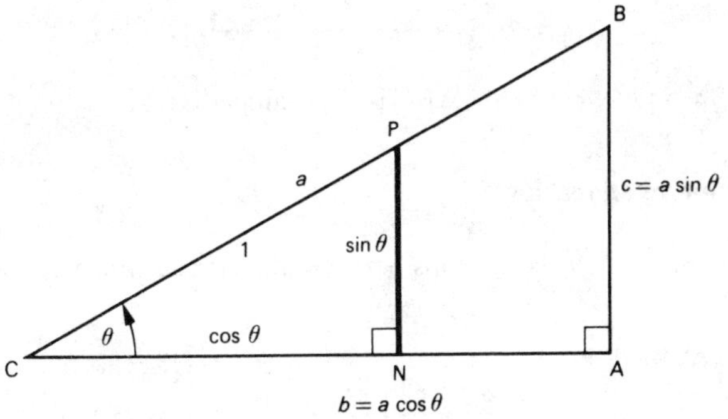

Enlarging triangle CPN by the scale factor a, we find

$$c = a\sin\theta$$

$$b = a\cos\theta$$

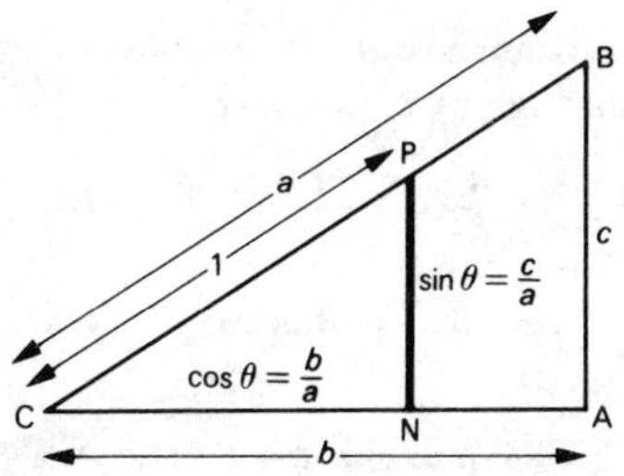

Reducing triangle ABC by the scale factor $1/a$, we find

$$\sin\theta = \frac{c}{a} = \cos(90° - \theta)$$

$$\cos\theta = \frac{b}{a} = \sin(90° - \theta)$$

and $$\tan\theta = \frac{c}{b} = \cot(90° - \theta)$$

Pythagoras' theorem

We are familiar with the use of Pythagoras' theorem in a right-angled triangle and with its converse to establish whether or not a triangle is right-angled.

If $\triangle$ABC is right-angled at A, then

$$\boldsymbol{a^2 = b^2 + c^2}$$ ◄

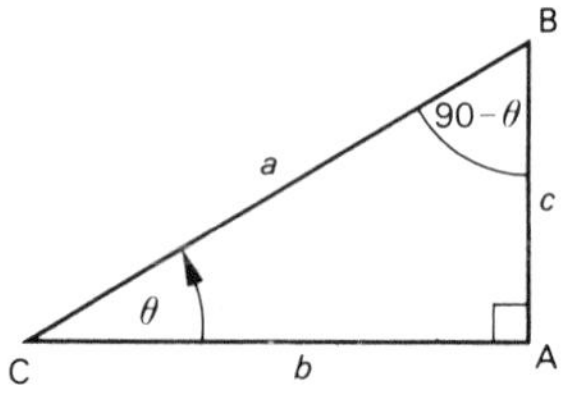

Conversely, if $a^2 = b^2 + c^2$ then $\triangle$ABC is right-angled at A.

Circular function relationships

To establish some of the relationships between the circular functions we use

$$a^2 = b^2 + c^2$$

Dividing through by a^2

$$\frac{a^2}{a^2} = \frac{b^2}{a^2} + \frac{c^2}{a^2}$$

gives $$1 = \left(\frac{b}{a}\right)^2 + \left(\frac{c}{a}\right)^2$$

$$\boldsymbol{1 = \cos^2\theta + \sin^2\theta}$$ ◄

NOTE. $(\cos\theta)^2$ is usually written $\cos^2\theta$.

Similarly, by dividing through by b^2 we have

$$\frac{a^2}{b^2} = 1 + \frac{c^2}{b^2}$$

$$\boldsymbol{\sec^2\theta = 1 + \tan^2\theta}$$ ◄

and likewise, by division by c^2,

$$\boldsymbol{\mathrm{cosec}^2\theta = \cot^2\theta + 1}$$ ◄

Exercise 2.1a

(No tables or calculators.)

1 If $\cos\theta = \frac{4}{5}$ find **(a)** $\sin\theta$ **(b)** $\tan\theta$ **(c)** $\operatorname{cosec}\theta$ **(d)** θ

2 If $\sin\theta = \frac{5}{13}$ find **(a)** $\cos\theta$ **(b)** $\tan\theta$ **(c)** $\sec\theta$

3 If $\tan\theta = \frac{1}{7}$ find **(a)** $\sin\theta$ **(b)** $\cos\theta$ **(c)** $\operatorname{cosec}\theta$

4 If $\cos\theta = -\frac{3}{5}$ find **(a)** $\sin\theta$ **(b)** $\tan\theta$

5 If $\sin\theta = -\frac{12}{13}$ find **(a)** $\cos\theta$ **(b)** $\tan\theta$

Exercise 2.1b

Write the following in terms of θ:

1 $\sec(90° - \theta)$ **2** $\operatorname{cosec}(90° - \theta)$ **3** $\sin(90° + \theta)$

4 $\cos(90° + \theta)$ **5** $\sin(270° + \theta)$ **6** $\tan(270° + \theta)$

7 $\operatorname{cosec}(90° + \theta)$ **8** $\cot(90° + \theta)$ **9** $\cos(180° - \theta)$

10 $\sin(180° - \theta)$

2.2 'Special' triangles

(a) The isosceles, right-angled triangle

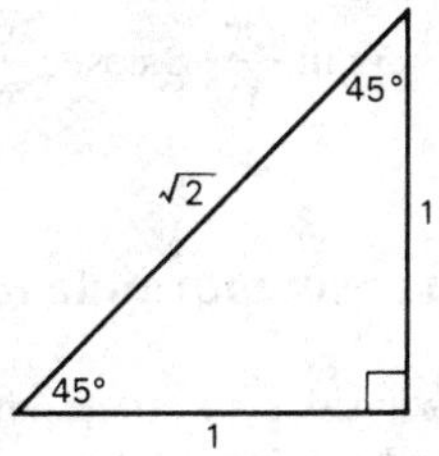

The sides are in the ratio $1:1:\sqrt{2}$. Hence

$$\sin 45° = \frac{1}{\sqrt{2}}, \qquad \cos 45° = \frac{1}{\sqrt{2}}, \qquad \tan 45° = 1, \text{ etc.}$$

(b) The equilateral triangle

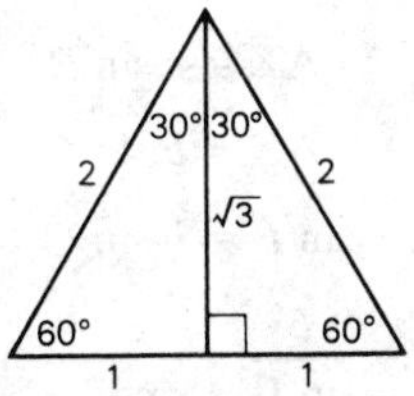

The sides are in the ratio 1:1:1 or 2:2:2. Divide the triangle as shown into two right-angled triangles with angles 60°, 30°, and 90°; Then

$$\sin 30° = \frac{1}{2}, \qquad \cos 30° = \frac{\sqrt{3}}{2}, \qquad \tan 30° = \frac{1}{\sqrt{3}}$$

$$\sin 60° = \frac{\sqrt{3}}{2}, \qquad \cos 60° = \frac{1}{2}, \qquad \tan 60° = \sqrt{3}$$

and so on. We shall meet these again later (p. 230).

Exercise 2.2

Evaluate the following, where the angles are in radians. Leave your answers in square root form, simplifying them when you can.

1 $7\cos\frac{\pi}{3} - \cos^2\frac{\pi}{6}$

2 $5\cos\frac{\pi}{6} + \sin\frac{2\pi}{3}$

3 $\cos^2\frac{3\pi}{2} + \sin^2\frac{\pi}{2}$

4 $2\cos\frac{5\pi}{6} + 3\sin\frac{\pi}{6}$

5 $\cos\frac{3\pi}{4} - 2\sin\frac{3\pi}{2}$

6 $\tan\frac{\pi}{4} + \cot\frac{3\pi}{4}$

7 $\operatorname{cosec}\frac{\pi}{6} + 3\sin\frac{2\pi}{3}$

8 $\sec\frac{7\pi}{4} - 2\operatorname{cosec}\frac{\pi}{4}$

9 $3\sin\frac{\pi}{4} - 5\cot\frac{5\pi}{4}$

10 $5\tan\frac{7\pi}{6} + 3\operatorname{cosec}\frac{5\pi}{6}$

2.3 The sine formula and cosine formula for *any* triangle

We may need to find unknown sides or angles in any triangle, whether it is right-angled or not. This is called *solving* a triangle. If we know *any side* and the *opposite angle*, together with *one other* angle or side, we may use the following relationship.

The sine formula (or rule)

Case 1: △ABC acute

In △ABX $\qquad \text{AX} = c \sin B$

For △ACX $\qquad \text{AX} = b \sin C$

Hence $\qquad c \sin B = b \sin C$

or
$$\frac{b}{\sin B} = \frac{c}{\sin C}$$

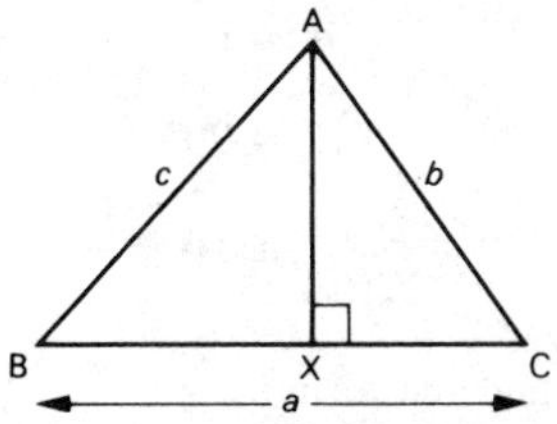

Similarly, by drawing in the perpendicular from B to AC, we should have $c \sin A = a \sin C$, or

$$\frac{c}{\sin C} = \frac{a}{\sin A}$$

Hence
$$\frac{a}{\sin A} = \frac{b}{\sin B} = \frac{c}{\sin C}$$

This is known as the *sine formula.*

Case 2: $\triangle$ABC obtuse

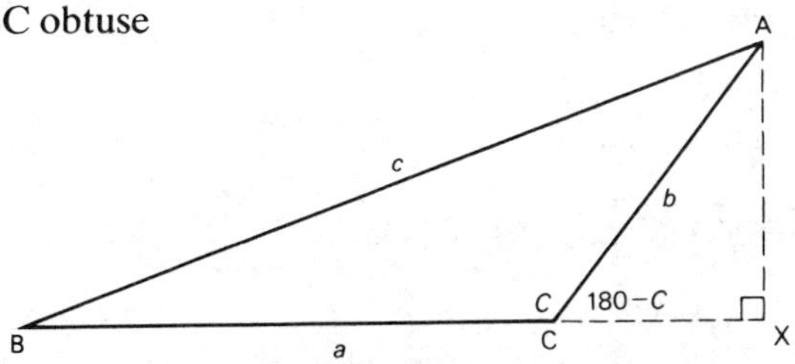

As before, in $\triangle$ABX $\quad$ $AX = c \sin B$

in $\triangle$ACX $\quad$ $AX = b \sin (180 - C) = b \sin C$

Hence $\quad$ $b \sin C = c \sin B$

and
$$\frac{b}{\sin B} = \frac{c}{\sin C}$$

Again we have
$$\frac{a}{\sin A} = \frac{b}{\sin B} = \frac{c}{\sin C}$$

Consider $\triangle$ABC, its circumcircle (radius R) and $\triangle$DBC, where DC is a diameter.

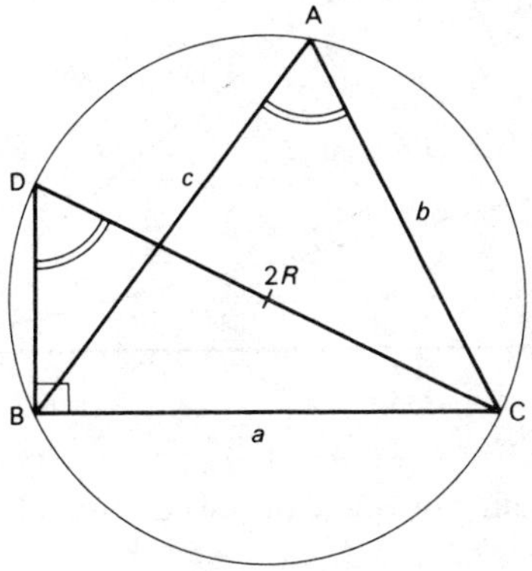

Then $\hat{A} = \hat{D}$ (same segment)

$D\hat{B}C = 90°$ (angle in semicircle)

Hence, in △DBC, $\dfrac{a}{\sin A} = 2R$

The complete statement for the sine formula is

$$\boldsymbol{\frac{a}{\sin A} = \frac{b}{\sin B} = \frac{c}{\sin C} = 2R}$$ ◀

Worked example

In △ABC, $a = 13.3$ cm, $c = 12.4$ cm and $C = 64°$. Find A, B and b.

Using $\dfrac{a}{\sin A} = \dfrac{c}{\sin C}$

gives $\dfrac{13.3}{\sin A} = \dfrac{12.4}{\sin 64°}$

so $\sin A = \dfrac{\sin 64°}{12.4} \times 13.3$

$A = 74.59°$

OR $A = 105.41°$

Hence $B = 180° - (64° + 74.59°) = 180° - 138.59°$

$= 41.41°$

OR $B = 180° - (64° + 105.41°) = 180° - 169.41°$

$= 10.59°$

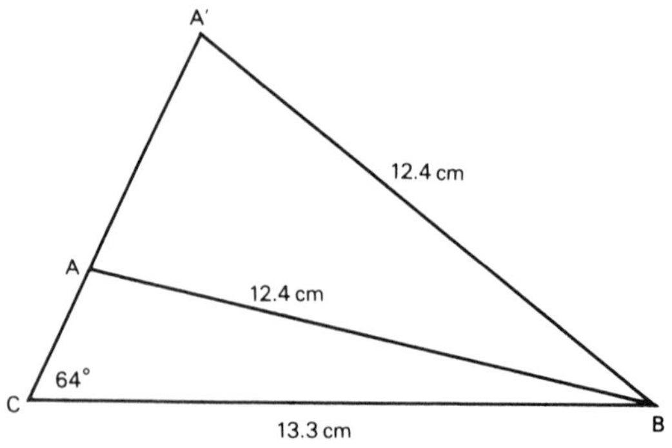

There are two possible values of A and of B, and hence of b, giving *two triangles*.

When $B = 41.41°$

$$\frac{b}{\sin 41.41°} = \frac{12.4}{\sin 64°}$$

$$b = 9.13 \text{ cm}$$

When $B = 10.59°$

$$\frac{b}{\sin 10.64°} = \frac{12.4}{\sin 64°}$$

$$b = 2.54 \text{ cm}$$

The cosine formula

This can be used if we know *two sides* of a triangle and the *angle between them,* and if we require the side opposite to the known angle OR if we know *all three* sides and require an angle.

Case 1: △ABC acute

Suppose AX = h, BX = x, then XC = $a - x$.

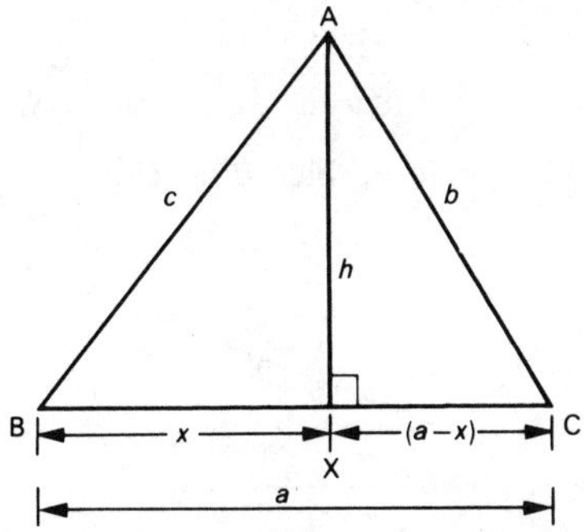

In △ABC $\quad h^2 + x^2 = c^2$

and in △ACX $\quad h^2 + (a-x)^2 = b^2$

Subtract $\quad x^2 - (a-x)^2 = c^2 - b^2$

$$x^2 - (a^2 - 2ax + x^2) = c^2 - b^2$$

$$x^2 - a^2 + 2ax - x^2 = c^2 - b^2$$

Now $\quad x = c \cos B$

so $\quad 2ac \cos B = a^2 + c^2 - b^2$

or $\quad b^2 = a^2 + c^2 - 2ac \cos B$

Similarly, by drawing in the other perpendiculars from B to AC and from C to AB, we have

$$\boldsymbol{a^2 = b^2 + c^2 - 2cb \cos A}$$ ◀

$$\boldsymbol{b^2 = c^2 + a^2 - 2ac \cos B}$$ ◀

$$\boldsymbol{c^2 = a^2 + b^2 - 2ba \cos C}$$ ◀

These results are known as the *cosine formula.*

Case 2: △ABC obtuse

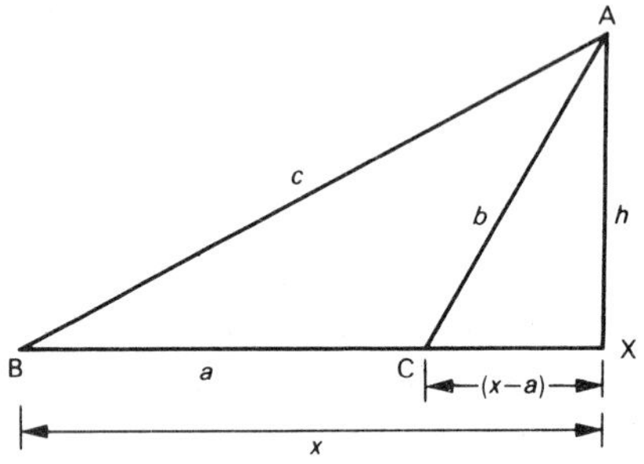

In △ABX $h^2 + x^2 = c^2$

and in △ACX $h^2 + (x-a)^2 = b^2$

Subtract $-a^2 + 2ax = c^2 - b^2$

As before $x = c \cos B$

and $b^2 = a^2 + c^2 - 2ac \cos B$

This gives the same result as before, since B is acute.

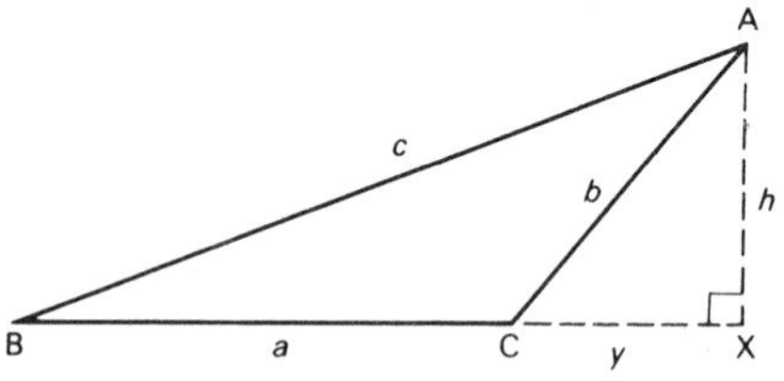

When, as here, C is obtuse, in △ABX

$$h^2 + (a+y)^2 = c^2$$

and in △ACX $h^2 + y^2 = b^2$

Subtract $a^2 + 2ay = c^2 - b^2$

$$c^2 = b^2 + a^2 + 2ay$$

Now $y = b \cos (180 - C)$

$$= -b \cos C$$

so $c^2 = b^2 + a^2 - 2ab \cos C$

—which is the result as before.

Thus, the cosine formula is true for acute *and* obtuse angled triangles. We must remember that if θ is obtuse, $\cos(180° - \theta) = -\cos\theta$.

Worked example

In $\triangle$ABC, $a = 12$ cm, $b = 4$ cm, and $C = 36°$. Find c, A and B.

$$\begin{aligned} c^2 &= a^2 + b^2 - 2ab\cos C \\ &= 144 + 16 - 96\cos 36° \\ &= 160 - 96 \times 0.8090 \\ &= 160 - 77.66 \\ &= 82.34 \end{aligned}$$

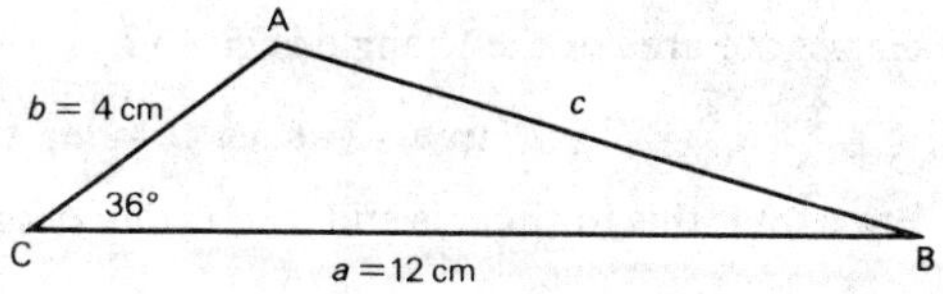

$$c = 9.07 \text{ cm}$$

To find A either the sine formula or the cosine formula could now be used. We illustrate the use of the cosine formula.

$$\begin{aligned} a^2 = b^2 + c^2 - 2bc\cos A \Rightarrow \cos A &= \frac{b^2 + c^2 - a^2}{2bc} \\ &= \frac{16 + 82.34 - 144}{8 \times 9.074} \\ &= -\frac{45.66}{72.59} = -0.629 \end{aligned}$$

Since $\cos A$ is negative, A is obtuse and

$$180° - A = 51° \Rightarrow A = 129°$$

Hence $$B = 180° - (36° + 129°) = 15°$$

2.4 The area of a triangle

We know that the area of a triangle (in suitable units) is given by $\frac{1}{2}$ base $\times$ perpendicular height. Depending on which base and which perpendicular height we consider, the area is $\frac{1}{2}ad$, or $\frac{1}{2}be$.

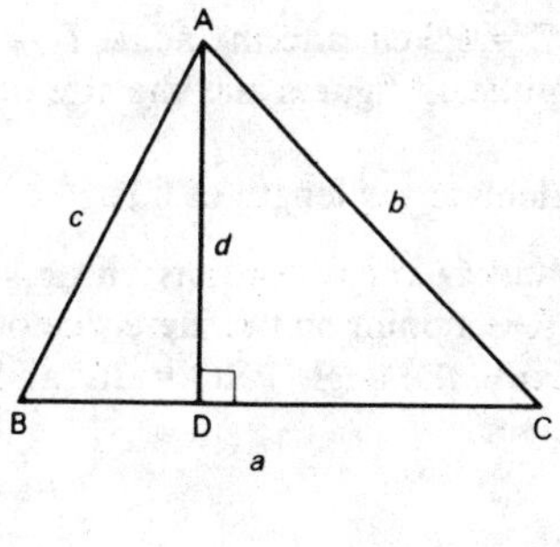

Now $\quad d = c\sin B \quad$ (from $\triangle$ABD)

$\quad\quad\;\; = b\sin C \quad$ (from $\triangle$ADC)

so the area is $\frac{1}{2}ac\sin B$

or $\quad \frac{1}{2}ab\sin C$

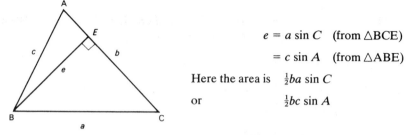

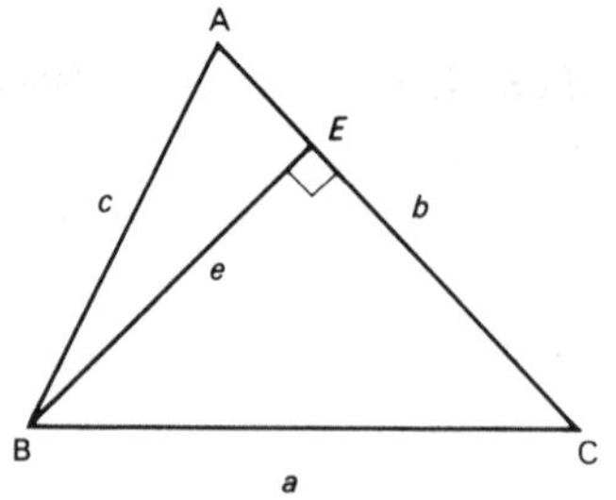

$$e = a \sin C \quad \text{(from } \triangle\text{BCE)}$$
$$= c \sin A \quad \text{(from } \triangle\text{ABE)}$$

Here the area is $\frac{1}{2}ba \sin C$

or $\frac{1}{2}bc \sin A$

Hence the area of the triangle is given by

$$\textbf{area} = \tfrac{1}{2}ab \sin C = \tfrac{1}{2}ac \sin B = \tfrac{1}{2}bc \sin A$$ ◄

Prove that this formula is still true for an obtuse angled triangle.

Exercise 2.4

Solve the following triangles; find all unknown angles and sides, and the area of each triangle.

1 $A = 108°, B = 21°, a = 12$ cm **2** $a = 58$ m, $b = 48$ m, $B = 48°$

3 $a = 10$ cm, $b = 12$ cm, $C = 130°$ **4** $a = 2$ m, $b = 3$ m, $c = 4$ m

5 Calculate the largest angle in a triangle with sides 7, 5 and 3 metres. Check your answer by drawing the figure accurately to a suitable scale, which should be stated.
Calculate also the area of the triangle.

6 A triangle ABC has AB = 5 cm, BC = 8 cm and angle $B = 40°$. Calculate the length of AC.
If AN is drawn perpendicular to BC and produced to a point R such that BR = 6 cm, calculate the angle R.

7 ABC is a triangle in which AB = 4 cm, BC = 7 cm and the angle B is 115°. Calculate AC.
AB is produced to D so that $\hat{D} = 50°$. Calculate BD. Calculate also the area of the triangle ACD.

8(a) A triangle ABC has BC = 26 cm, CA = 14 cm, AB = 30 cm. Calculate the angle A.
(b) A triangle ABC has BC = 30 cm, AC = 14 cm and angle $A = 60°$. BX and CY are perpendiculars drawn to CA and AB respectively. Calculate the length of XY.

9 ABC is a triangle in which AB = 8.4 cm, BC = 6.3 cm and the angle $B = 40°$. Calculate the length of the side CA to three significant figures and the size of the angle A to one decimal place.
If the bisector of the angle B cuts CA at P, calculate the length of CP.

10 A river has straight parallel banks and P and Q are two points on opposite banks so that PQ is perpendicular to the banks. R is a point on the same side of the river as P. PR makes an angle of 20° with the bank, the angle PRQ = 20° and the length PR = 250 m. Calculate the width of the river.

11 A shore station observes a ship to be due East (bearing 090°) and 10.0 nautical miles away at time 14.00, and 9.0 nautical miles distant on a bearing of 135° at time 14.45. Assuming the ship to be steaming steadily in a straight line, calculate its speed in nautical miles per hour and its direction of motion to the nearest degree.

12 A and B are two points on a horizontal straight line passing through the foot of a tower and on the same side of the tower. AB = 75 m. The elevations of the top of the tower from A and B are 19.5° and 31° respectively. Calculate the height of the tower.

3 Formulae

There are many very useful and hence important formulae involving relationships between circular functions. Many of these formulae are used so frequently that they *must* be learnt. These are printed in bold type, with the triangle symbol (◄) alongside. We shall meet all these formulae in Chapter 7 and derive them in a number of ways. In this chapter we introduce only the formulae concerning the sine or cosine of the sum or difference of two angles, and the formulae immediately derived from them, as you will need them for your work in coordinate geometry and in calculus.

3.1 The sine and cosine of the sum and difference of two angles

We demonstrate these geometrically, taking only the simple case where A, B and $(A+B)$ are all between 0° and 90° and $A > B$.

The sum of two angles

$$\sin(A+B) = \sin A \cos B + \cos A \sin B \qquad \text{I} ◄$$

$$\cos(A+B) = \cos A \cos B - \sin A \sin B \qquad \text{II} ◄$$

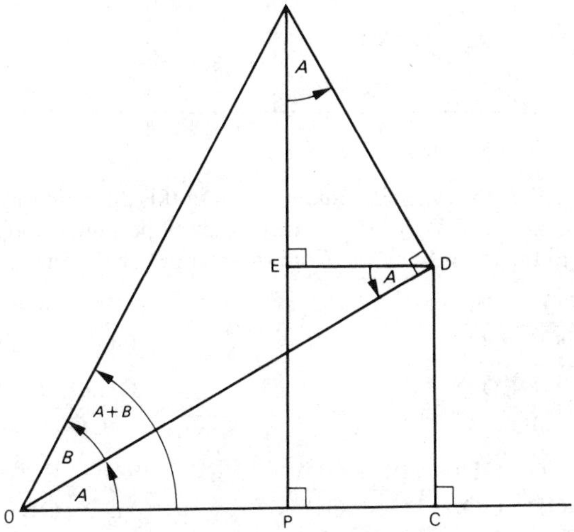

$$\sin(A+B) = \frac{PQ}{OQ} = \frac{PE+EQ}{OQ} = \frac{CD+EQ}{OQ} = \left(\frac{CD}{OD}\times\frac{OD}{OQ}\right)+\left(\frac{EQ}{QD}\times\frac{QD}{OQ}\right)$$

$$\cos(A+B) = \frac{OP}{OQ} = \frac{OC-PC}{OQ} = \frac{OC-ED}{OQ} = \left(\frac{OC}{OD}\times\frac{OD}{OQ}\right)-\left(\frac{ED}{QD}\times\frac{QD}{OQ}\right)$$

Hence

$\sin(A+B) = \sin A \cos B + \cos A \sin B$ and

$\cos(A+B) = \cos A \cos B - \sin A \sin B$

(OD is a 'link' between CD and OQ being the side common to triangles CDO and ODQ; similarly QD is the side common to triangles EQD and OQD.)

The difference of two angles

$$\mathbf{\sin(A-B) = \sin A \cos B - \cos A \sin B} \qquad \textbf{III}$$

$$\mathbf{\cos(A-B) = \cos A \cos B + \sin A \sin B} \qquad \textbf{IV}$$

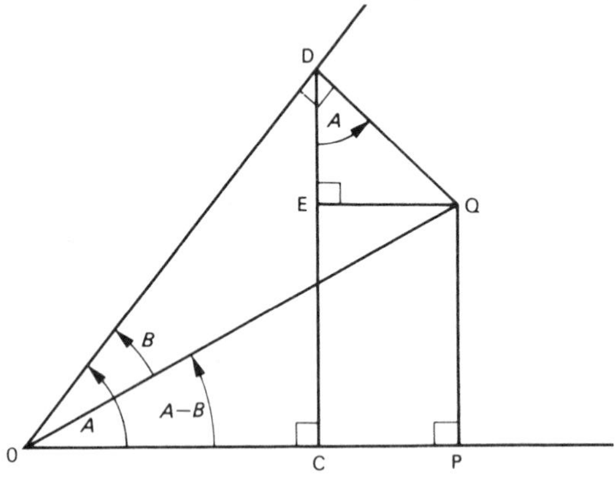

We derive these in a very similar manner, but in this diagram the perpendiculars are not in the same place as before. In fact we draw perpendiculars from 'the line we finish with' to the other lines, i.e. from the point Q on the line OQ in each case.

$$\sin(A-B) = \frac{PQ}{OQ} = \frac{CE}{OQ} = \frac{CD-ED}{OQ} = \left(\frac{CD}{OD}\times\frac{OD}{OQ}\right)-\left(\frac{ED}{QD}\times\frac{QD}{OQ}\right)$$

$$\cos(A-B) = \frac{OP}{OQ} = \frac{OC+CP}{OQ} = \frac{OC+EQ}{OQ} = \left(\frac{OC}{OD}\times\frac{OD}{OQ}\right)+\left(\frac{EQ}{QD}\times\frac{QD}{OQ}\right)$$

Hence

$\sin(A-B) = \sin A \cos B - \cos A \sin B$ and

$$\cos(A-B) = \cos A \cos B + \sin A \sin B$$

We assume that these formulae are true for all angles A, B. This may be easily verified, but of course the diagrams depend entirely on A, B, and $(A+B)$ being less than 90°.

3.2 The tangent of the sum and difference of two angles

Since

$$\tan A = \frac{\sin A}{\cos A}$$

$$\tan(A+B) = \frac{\sin(A+B)}{\cos(A+B)}$$

$$= \frac{\sin A \cos B + \cos A \sin B}{\cos A \cos B - \sin A \sin B}$$

It would be more useful if the formula for $\tan(A+B)$ contained $\tan A$ and $\tan B$ separately. So we divide each term in the numerator and the denominator by $\cos A \cos B$.

$$\tan(A+B) = \frac{\dfrac{\sin A \cos B}{\cos A \cos B} + \dfrac{\cos A \sin B}{\cos A \cos B}}{\dfrac{\cos A \cos B}{\cos A \cos B} - \dfrac{\sin A \sin B}{\cos A \cos B}}$$

$$\boldsymbol{\tan(A+B) = \frac{\tan A + \tan B}{1 - \tan A \tan B}} \qquad \text{V} \quad ◀$$

Similarly $$\tan(A-B) = \frac{\sin(A-B)}{\cos(A-B)}$$

$$= \frac{\sin A \cos B - \cos A \sin B}{\cos A \cos B + \sin A \sin B}$$

$$= \frac{\dfrac{\sin A \cos B}{\cos A \cos B} - \dfrac{\cos A \sin B}{\cos A \cos B}}{\dfrac{\cos A \cos B}{\cos A \cos B} + \dfrac{\sin A \sin B}{\cos A \cos B}}$$

$$\boldsymbol{\tan(A-B) = \frac{\tan A - \tan B}{1 + \tan A \tan B}} \qquad \text{VI} \quad ◀$$

This formula is very important because of its application to *perpendicular lines* and to the angle between lines in the plane.

Exercise 3.2a

Give alternative forms of

1 $\cos(\alpha+\beta)$
2 $\sin(\theta-\phi)$
3 $\cos(A-2B)$
4 $\sin(2A+B)$
5 $\cos(2x-y)$
6 $\sin(3x+y)$
7 $\sin(A+A)$
8 $\cos(A+A)$
9 $\tan(y-2x)$
10 $\tan(2\theta+\phi)$
11 $\cos(A+B)$
12 $\sec(\theta-\phi)$
13 $\tan(2A+A)$
14 $\operatorname{cosec}(\alpha+\beta)$
15 $\cos^2 A$

16 $\sin 3\theta \cos\phi - \cos 3\theta \sin\phi$
17 $\cos x \cos y + \sin x \sin y$
18 $\sin A \cos 2B - \cos A \sin 2B$
19 $\sin C \sin D - \cos C \cos D$
20 $\sin 30° \cos\theta + \cos 30° \sin\theta$
21 $\cos 60° \cos\phi - \sin 60° \sin\phi$
22 $\sin\phi \cos 20° + \cos\phi \sin 20°$
23 $\sin 2\theta \cos 30° - \cos 2\theta \cos 60°$
24 $\cos\theta \cos 4\theta - \sin 4\theta \sin\theta$
25 $\cos^2 \frac{1}{6}\pi^c + \sin^2 \frac{1}{6}\pi^c$
26 $\cos(\theta+\phi)\cos\phi + \sin(\theta+\phi)\sin\phi$
27 $\cos 4\theta \cos\theta + \sin 4\theta \sin\theta$

28 $\sin(\theta+\phi)\cos(\theta-\phi) + \cos(\theta+\phi)\sin(\theta-\phi)$

29 $\sin 75° \cos 15° - \cos 75° \sin 15°$

30 $\dfrac{\tan 75° + \tan 15°}{1 - \tan 75° \tan 15°}$

Exercise 3.2b

Simplify

1 $\sin(C+D) - \sin(C-D)$
2 $\cos(C+D) + \cos(C-D)$
3 $\sin(\theta+\phi) + \sin(\theta-\phi)$
4 $\cos(\theta+\phi) - \cos(\theta-\phi)$

Prove the following identities:

5 $\sin(\theta+\phi)\sin(\theta-\phi) = \sin^2\theta - \sin^2\phi$

6 $\dfrac{\sin\theta \sin\phi}{\cos(\theta+\phi)} = \dfrac{\tan\theta \tan\phi}{1-\tan\theta \tan\phi}$

7 $\tan A + \cot B = \dfrac{\cos(B-A)}{\sin B \cos A}$

8 $\cos(\theta-\phi) + \sin(\theta+\phi) = (\sin\theta + \cos\theta)(\sin\phi + \cos\phi)$

9 $\cos(A+B)\cos(A-B) = \cos^2 B - \sin^2 A$

10 $\cos^4\theta - \sin^4\theta = 2\cos^2\theta - 1$

11 $\cot(A-B)=\dfrac{\cot A\cot B+1}{\cot B-\cot A}$

12 $\cos A+\cos(A+120°)+\cos(A+240°)=0$

3.3 Double and half angles

Double angles

Suppose that $A = B = \theta$. Then

$$\sin(A+B)=\sin A\cos B+\cos A\sin B$$

$$\sin(\theta+\theta)=\sin\theta\cos\theta+\cos\theta\sin\theta$$

so

$$\mathbf{\sin 2\theta = 2\sin\theta\cos\theta} \qquad \textbf{VII} \blacktriangleleft$$

Similarly

$$\cos(A+B)=\cos A\cos B-\sin A\sin B$$

$$\cos(\theta+\theta)=\cos\theta\cos\theta-\sin\theta\sin\theta$$

$$\cos 2\theta=\cos^2\theta-\sin^2\theta$$

Now $\cos^2\theta+\sin^2\theta=1$ (see page 104) or $\cos^2\theta=1-\sin^2\theta$ and $\sin^2\theta=1-\cos^2\theta$, so

$$\mathbf{\cos 2\theta=\cos^2\theta-\sin^2\theta} \qquad \textbf{VIIIa} \blacktriangleleft$$

$$\mathbf{\cos 2\theta=2\cos^2\theta-1} \qquad \textbf{VIIIb} \blacktriangleleft$$

$$\mathbf{\cos 2\theta=1-2\sin^2\theta} \qquad \textbf{VIIIc} \blacktriangleleft$$

These three formulae are extremely useful alternative forms, especially when integrating, but you must select the appropriate form for the particular problem.

Similarly,

$$\tan(A+B)=\frac{\tan A+\tan B}{1-\tan A\tan B}$$

so

$$\tan(\theta+\theta)=\frac{\tan\theta+\tan\theta}{1-\tan\theta\tan\theta}$$

and

$$\mathbf{\tan 2\theta=\frac{2\tan\theta}{1-\tan^2\theta}} \qquad \textbf{IX} \blacktriangleleft$$

Half angles

Half angle formulae can be found from the double angle formulae. Since $\sin 2\theta = 2\sin\theta\cos\theta$, by replacing 2θ by ϕ or θ by $\phi/2$ we get

$$\mathbf{\sin\phi=2\sin\frac{\phi}{2}\cos\frac{\phi}{2}} \qquad \textbf{X} \blacktriangleleft$$

Similarly, substituting $\theta=\phi/2$ in the alternative forms,

$$\cos 2\theta=2\cos^2\theta-1$$

$$=\cos^2\theta-\sin^2\theta=1-2\sin^2\theta$$

which leads to

$$\mathbf{\cos\phi = 2\cos^2\frac{\phi}{2} - 1} \qquad \textbf{XIa} \blacktriangleleft$$

$$\mathbf{= \cos^2\frac{\phi}{2} - \sin^2\frac{\phi}{2}} \qquad \textbf{XIb} \blacktriangleleft$$

$$\mathbf{= 1 - 2\sin^2\frac{\phi}{2}} \qquad \textbf{XIc} \blacktriangleleft$$

and as

$$\tan 2\theta = \frac{2\tan\theta}{1-\tan^2\theta}$$

using $\theta = \phi/2$ gives

$$\mathbf{\tan\phi = \frac{2\tan\phi/2}{1-\tan^2\phi/2}} \qquad \textbf{XII} \blacktriangleleft$$

NOTE. If ϕ is small and measured in radians then $\sin\phi^c \approx \phi^c$ and $\sin(\phi/2)^c \approx (\phi/2)^c$. Now

$$\cos\phi = 1 - 2\sin^2\frac{\phi}{2}$$

so

$$\cos\phi \approx 1 - 2\left(\frac{\phi}{2}\right)^2$$

$$= 1 - \frac{\phi^2}{2}$$

Exercise 3.3

This exercise will familiarize you with formulae involving half-angles or multiple angles. Give the following in terms of the angles shown:

1 $\sin 2\theta$ (θ)

2 $\cos 4\theta$ (2θ)

3 $\tan 6\theta$ (3θ)

4 $1-\cos 2A$ (A)

5 $1+\cos 2B$ (B)

6 $\sin\theta$ $\left(\frac{\theta}{2}\right)$

7 $\sin^2\theta - \cos^2\theta$ (2θ)

8 $\cos 6\theta$ (3θ)

9 $\sin\frac{\phi}{4}\cos\frac{\phi}{4}$ $\left(\frac{\phi}{2}\right)$

10 $(\sin A + \cos A)^2$ $(2A)$

11 $(\cos\theta - \sin\theta)^2$ (2θ)

12 $\sin\frac{3\theta}{2}\cos\frac{3\theta}{2}$ (3θ)

13 $\cos 2\phi$ $(\tan\phi)$

14 $\sin 2\phi$ $(\tan\phi)$

15 $1-\cos A$ $\left(\frac{A}{2}\right)$

16 $1+\cos A$ $\left(\frac{A}{2}\right)$

17 $\dfrac{2\tan 22\frac{1}{2}^\circ}{1-\tan^2 22\frac{1}{2}^\circ}$ (45°)

18 $\dfrac{1-\tan^2 15^\circ}{1+\tan^2 15^\circ}$ (30°)

19 $\cos^2 15^\circ - \sin^2 15^\circ$ (30°)

20 $\operatorname{cosec} x \sec x$ $(2x)$

4 Polar equations

4.1 Polar and cartesian coordinates

There is a simple relationship between polar coordinates and cartesian co-ordinates. It can easily be seen from the diagram below:

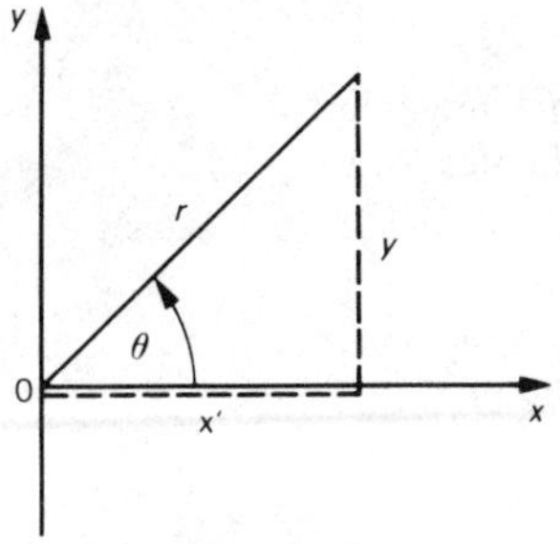

Here $x = r\cos\theta$, $y = r\sin\theta$, $x^2 + y^2 = r^2$ and $y/x = \tan\theta$

Next, we shall look at some of the simplest cartesian equations and find their equivalent polar representations. Further examples are in Chapter 19.

A straight line through 0

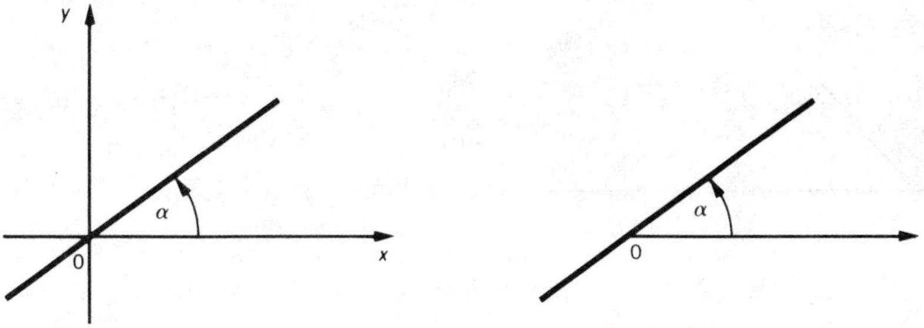

(a) In cartesians $y = x\tan\alpha$ **(b)** In polars $\theta = \alpha$

A straight line cutting the cartesian axes at a, b

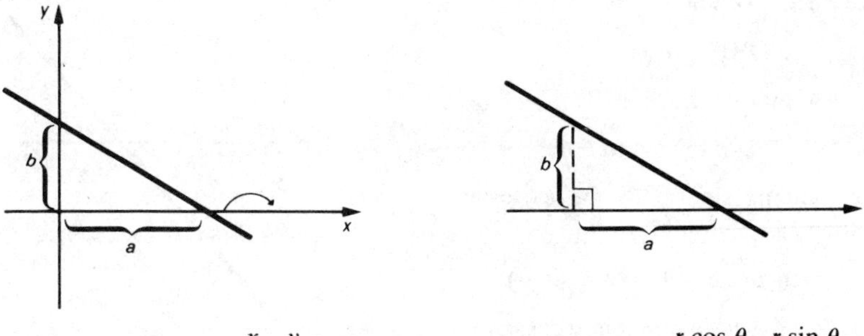

(a) In cartesians $\dfrac{x}{a} + \dfrac{y}{b} = 1$ **(b)** In polars $\dfrac{r\cos\theta}{a} + \dfrac{r\sin\theta}{b} = 1$

Here are some more polar equations of lines. In general, the equation is found using the basic property that for a straight line the perpendicular distance from the origin to the line is fixed.

Example 1

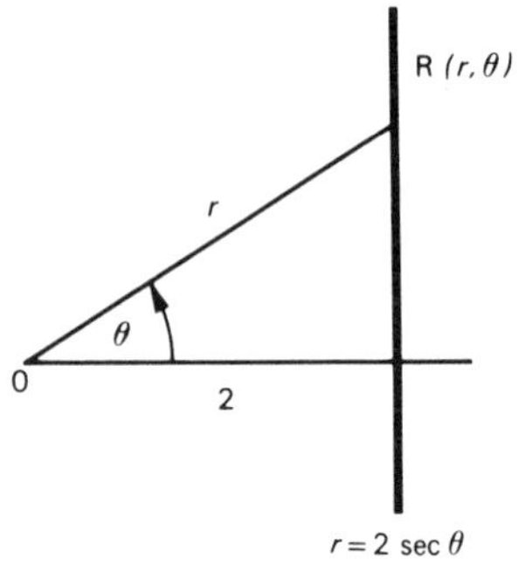

Consider the line shown. Pick any point R on it with polar coordinates (r, θ). Then the equation of the line is

$$r \cos \theta = 2$$

The equivalent cartesian equation is

$$x = 2$$

Example 2

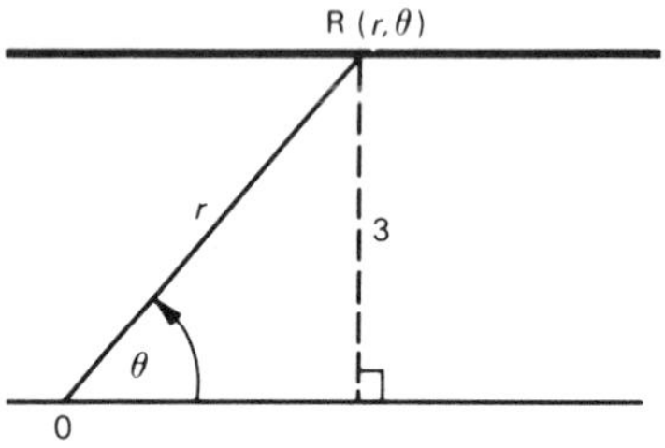

Here the line is given by

$$r \sin \theta = 3$$

The cartesian equation is

$$y = 3$$

Example 3

Consider a line making an angle α with the line $\theta = 0$ and perpendicular distance p from 0. Then

$$\angle \text{ORP} = \alpha - \theta$$

and the equation is

$$p = r \sin(\alpha - \theta)$$

By expanding $\sin(\alpha - \theta)$ the cartesian equation can be found:

$$p = r(\sin \alpha \cos \theta - \cos \alpha \sin \theta)$$

$$= r \cos \theta \sin \alpha - r \sin \theta \cos \alpha$$

so $\quad p = x \sin \alpha - y \cos \alpha$

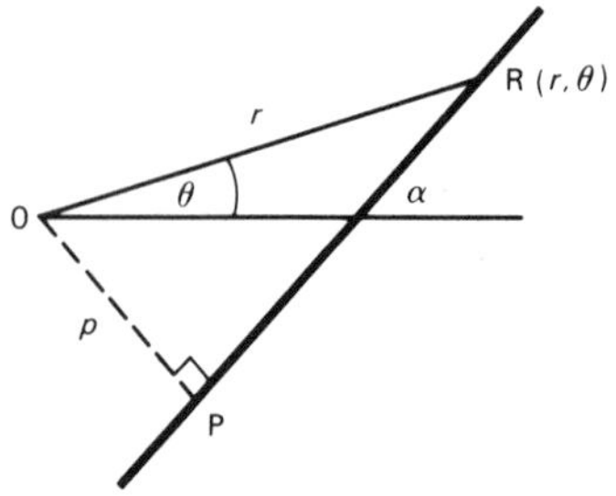

Example 4

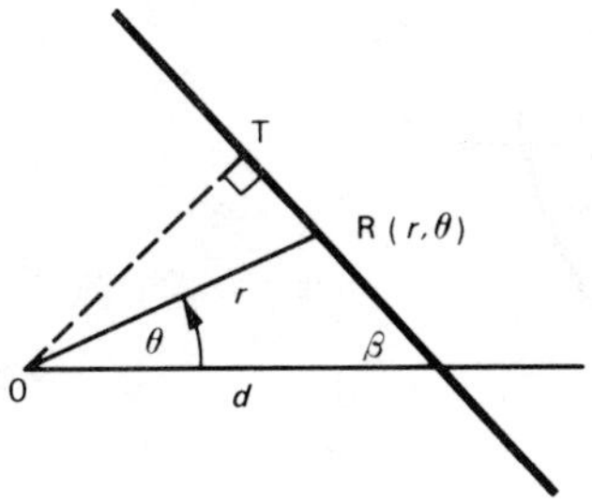

Consider a line as shown, cutting $\theta = 0$ when $r = d$ and at an angle $(180° - \beta)$ to $\theta = 0$. Then

$$OT = d \sin \beta$$

$$= r \sin(\theta + \beta) \quad \ldots \text{since } O\hat{R}T = \theta + \beta$$

and the equation is

$$r \sin(\theta + \beta) = d \sin \beta$$

By expansion,

$$r \sin \theta \cos \beta + r \cos \theta \sin \beta = d \sin \beta$$

Hence

$$y \cos \beta + x \sin \beta = d \sin \beta$$

Exercise 4.1

In each question, find the polar and cartesian equations for the straight lines.

1 (a) Parallel to the base line and 4 units from it (two possibilities)
(b) Perpendicular to the base line and 3 units from O (two possibilities)
(c) Through O at $\pm 135°$ to the base line (two possibilities)

2 Through the points with polar coordinates
(a) $(2, 0)$; $(4, \pi/2)$ **(b)** $(2, 0)$; $(4, -\pi/2)$ **(c)** $(-2, 0)$; $(1, \pi/2)$
(d) $(-2, 0)$; $(1, -\pi/2)$

3 Through $(2, 0)$ making an angle of
(a) 45° with the base line **(b)** 135° with the base line

4 At a perpendicular distance 4 units from O and making an angle with the base line of
(a) 30° **(b)** 60° **(c)** 120°

4.2 Intersections

The intersection between polar curves is easily found by substitution *if* the polar equations are simple.

Example 1

Find the intersection of the line $r \cos \theta = \frac{1}{2}$ and the circle $r = 2 \cos \theta$.

Substituting for r gives $\quad 2 \cos \theta \cos \theta = \frac{1}{2}$

$$\cos \theta = \pm\tfrac{1}{2}$$

$$\theta = 60°, 300° \text{ or } 120°, 240°$$

The points of intersection are $(1, 60°)$ and $(1, 300°)$, or alternatively $(-1, 120°)$ and $(-1, 240°)$.

Example 2

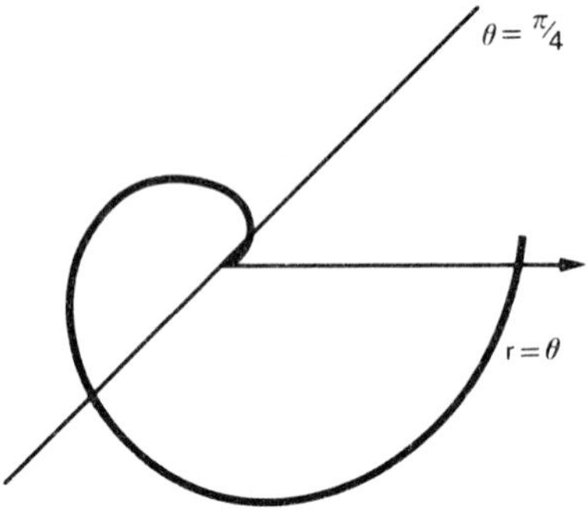

Find the intersection of $r = \theta$ and $\theta = \pi/4$ $(r \geqslant 0)$.

We see that the line cuts the spiral in an infinite number of points when $r = 0$ or $n\pi + \pi/4$ where $n \in \mathbb{Z}_0^+$.

Example 3

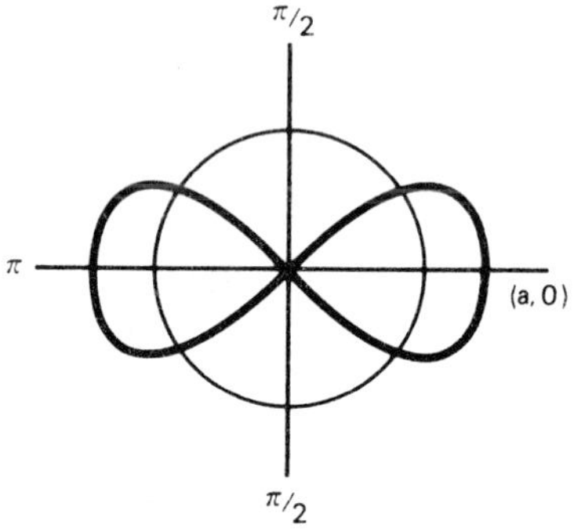

The diagram shows the lemniscate $r^2 = a^2 \cos 2\theta$. Find the intersection of this with the circle $r = a/\sqrt{2}$.

Substituting for r gives $$\frac{a^2}{2} = a^2 \cos 2\theta$$

$$\cos 2\theta = \tfrac{1}{2}$$

$$\theta = 30°, 330° \text{ or } 150°, 210°$$

Hence the points of intersection are $(a/\sqrt{2}, 30°)$, $(a/\sqrt{2}, 330°)$ or $(a/\sqrt{2}, 150°)$, $(a/\sqrt{2}, 210°)$.

It is always advisable to sketch the curves first, and then to find the values of θ. r can then be found, usually by substitution.

Exercise 4.2

1 Show that the polar equation $r \cos(\theta + 60°) + 1 = 0$ represents a straight line. Calling this line l, find

(a) the coordinates of the point P in which l meets the line $r\cos\theta - 1 = 0$
(b) the polar equation of the line through the point $(\sqrt{3}, 90°)$ parallel to l.
Show that the equation of the circle with its centre at point P and radius 2 units is $r = 4\cos(\theta - 60°)$.

2 Sketch on the same diagram the curves with polar equations $r = 2a\cos\theta$ and $2r(1+\cos\theta) = 3a$. Find the polar coordinates of their points of intersection. What is the polar equation of the common chord?

Miscellaneous examination questions 3

(O. unless stated otherwise)

1(a) If $\tan\alpha = \frac{1}{4}$, $\tan\beta = \frac{2}{3}$ and $\tan\gamma = \frac{1}{8}$, find, without using tables, the value of $\tan(\alpha+\beta)$. Hence, or otherwise, show that $\tan(\alpha+\beta-\gamma) = \frac{6}{7}$.
(b) Using the formula for $\cos(A+B)$, prove that

$$\cos 2\theta = 2\cos^2\theta - 1$$

Find the cosines of the largest and smallest angles of the triangle with sides 4, 5 and 6 units, and, **without using tables**, prove that one of these angles is exactly twice the other.

2(a) Write down the formula for the expansion of $\cos(A+B)$. Given that A, B and C are the angles of a triangle and that $\cos A\cos B = \frac{1}{4}$, $\sin A\sin B = \frac{1}{5}$, calculate the angles A, B and C.
(b) Solve the equation $\cos 2A + \cos A + 1 = 0$ giving values of A lying between $-180°$ and $180°$.

3(a) Solve for a and x the simultaneous equations

$$a\cos x = 2$$

$$a\sin x = 3$$

giving the solution which satisfies the conditions

$$a \geqslant 0, \qquad 0° \leqslant x < 360°$$

(b) Prove that

$$2\cos(A-45°)\cos(A+45°) = \cos 2A$$

4(a) Solve the equations

$$\text{(i)}\quad \cos x = 0.4 \qquad \text{(ii)}\quad \sin(90°+y) = 0.9$$

giving to the nearest 0.1 degree, all solutions between 0° and 360°.

(b) Prove the identity

$$\sin(A+B)\sin(A-B) = \sin^2 A - \sin^2 B$$

(c) Write down, in square root form where necessary, exact values for sin 30°, cos 30°, sin 45°, cos 45°. Derive in this form the values of sin 15° and cos 15° and prove that

$$\tan 15° = 2-\sqrt{3}$$

5 In the convex quadrilateral ABCD, AB = 24, BC = 7, CD = 15, DA = 20 units and the angle ABC is a right angle. Show that one of the other angles of the quadrilateral is a right angle, and that the quadrilateral is cyclic.

Without using tables, prove that the tangent of angle DAB is $\frac{4}{3}$ and calculate the length of DB.

6 In the diagram below, ABCD represents a square of side 50 centimetres. Arcs of circles with centres at A, B, C and D and with radii 50 cm intersect as shown at P, Q, R and S to form a church window PQRS.

Calculate, in radians, the sizes of **(a)** the angle PAB; **(b)** the angle PAS. Hence calculate the length of the perimeter of the window in metres and the area of the window in square metres, rounded to two significant figures.

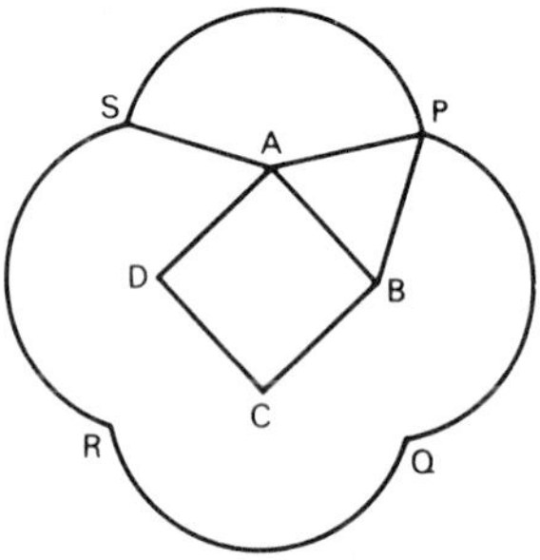

7 The figure represents a vertical section through the centre of a model of a new opera house. O is a point on the front edge of the stage, distant 48 cm horizontally from A. The back wall, AB, is 36 cm high and the sloping portion, BC, of the roof measures 25 cm. Angles OAB and OBC are right angles.

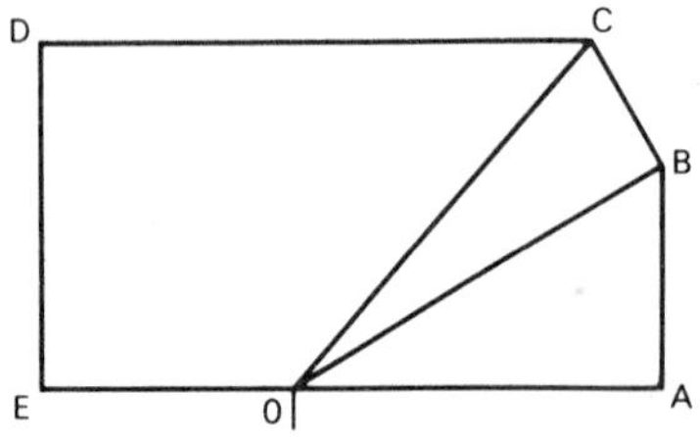

Calculate the distance OC and without further use of tables find the sine, cosine, and tangent of angle COA, leaving your answers as fractions. Hence, or otherwise, calculate the height of the horizontal portion CD of the roof above the level of O, and if DE, the back wall of the stage, is 29 cm behind O, find the length of CD.

It is desired to mount a spotlight at a point S on the wall AB so that the angles SOB and BOC are equal. Without using tables, calculate the height of S above A to the nearest millimetre.

8 W_1, W_2 and W_3 are three gear wheels which engage as indicated in the diagram. The radius of W_1 is 5 cm and the radius of W_2 is 3 cm. In ten seconds the wheel W_1

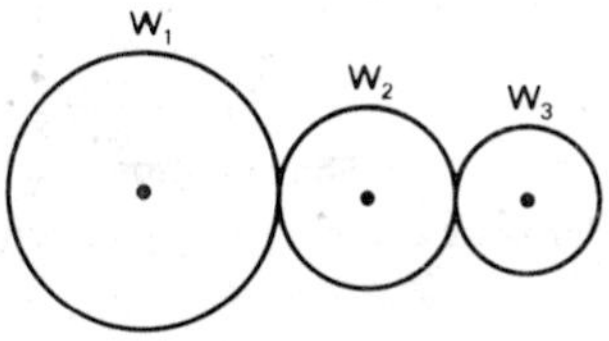

has turned through 2 radians. What is the length of arc described by a point on the circumference of W_1 in ten seconds? Write down the speed of a point on the circumference of W_1. Find also the angle turned through by the wheel W_2 in one second.

What should be the radius of W_3 in order that W_3 should turn at the rate of 1 radian in each second? (O. & C.)

9 Prove that in any triangle ABC

(a) $$\frac{a+b-c}{a+b+c} = \tan\frac{A}{2}\tan\frac{B}{2}$$

(b) If $A = 63.67°$, $B = 40.37°$ and the perimeter of a triangle is 15.32 cm, find the lengths of AB and BC to two places of decimals.

10 In the triangle ABC, $B = 30°$ and $c > b$. D is a point in BC such that AD $= b$. If BD $= \frac{1}{3}a$, prove that $b = (c\sqrt{7}/4)$ and that $\sin A = (3\sqrt{21}/14)$. (O. & C.)

11 The sides BC, CA, AB of a triangle ABC are of length $x+y$, x, $x-y$ respectively. Show that

$$\cos A = \frac{x-4y}{2(x-y)}$$

Show also that $\sin A - 2\sin B + \sin C = 0$.

12 A triangle ABC is right angled at A, AB = 3 cm, AC = 4 cm. M is the midpoint of BC and the bisector of ∠BAC meets BC in P. Without using tables, prove, in any order, that

$$\text{AP} = \frac{12\sqrt{2}}{7}\text{ cm} \qquad \sin\angle\text{APM} = \frac{7}{5\sqrt{2}} \qquad \sin\angle\text{AMP} = \frac{24}{25} \qquad \sin\angle\text{PAM} = \frac{1}{5\sqrt{2}}$$

(W.)

13 Three towns A, B, and C are all at sea level. The bearings of towns B and C from A are 36° and 247° respectively. If B is 120 km from A and C is 234 km from A, calculate the distance and bearing of town B from C. (A.E.B.)

14 A man observes a church spire in a direction due north and a tower in a direction 38° east of north. After walking 500 m due east along a road, he finds that the spire is in a direction 29° west of north and that the tower is due north. Calculate to the nearest metre the distances of the tower and the spire from the road and also the distance between them. (O. & C.)

Chapter 4

Coordinate Geometry 1

Coordinate geometry is the name given to that part of mathematics which describes *algebraically* the positions of points, straight lines, curves, planes and surfaces in space. We begin by investigating points and lines in a plane, and we shall do this in a systematic way which can later be developed for three-dimensional space.

1 Points, distances and loci

1.1 Points and distances

To describe a point in a plane

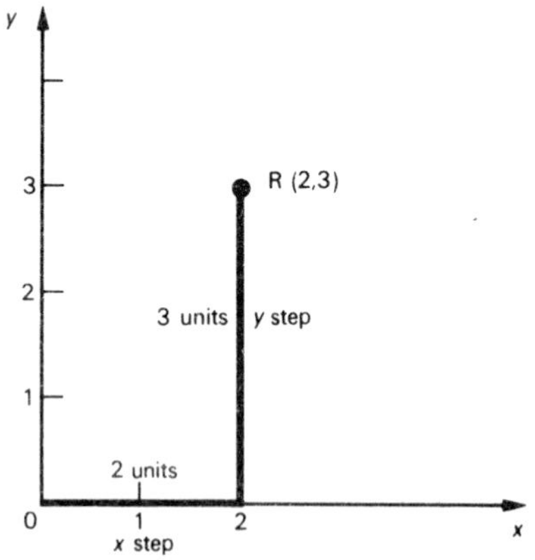

The most convenient axes to use are at right angles, and these are called *cartesian axes* after Descartes, who first used them.

In a plane, we fix the position of a point by giving it two coordinates x, y with respect to some original point, or origin O. For example, if R is the point (2, 3), we are showing

1 an 'x step' of two units, and
2 a 'y step' of three units.

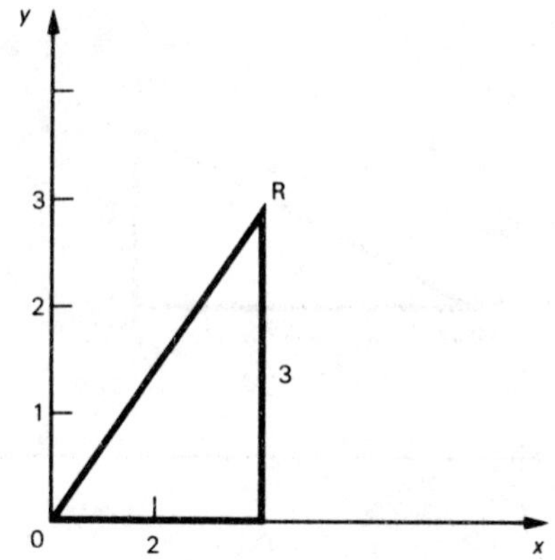

The distance of R from the origin is obtained by using Pythagoras' theorem:

$$(OR)^2 = 2^2 + 3^2 \Rightarrow OR = \sqrt{13}$$

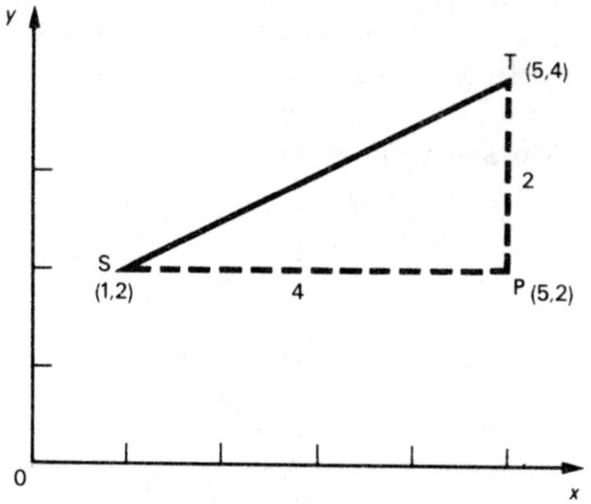

The distance between two points

Consider, for example, how to find the distance between S (1, 2) and T (5, 4). Complete the right-angled triangle STP. Then P is (5, 2) and

$$SP = 5 - 1 = 4 \qquad PT = 4 - 2 = 2$$

Again using Pythagoras' theorem

$$(ST)^2 = 4^2 + 2^2 \Rightarrow ST = \sqrt{20}$$

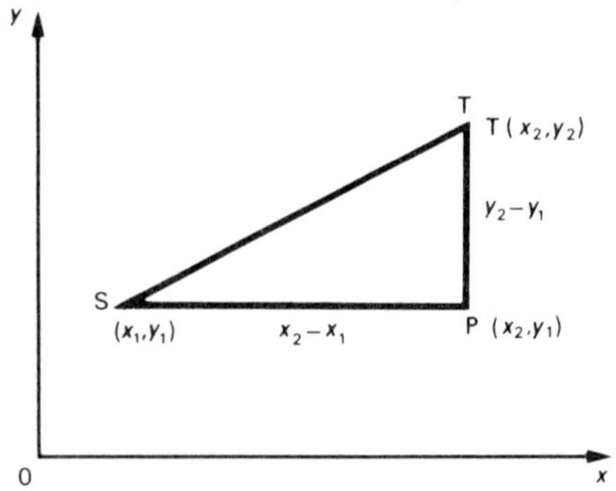

In general, if S is (x_1, y_1) and T is (x_2, y_2), then

$$SP = x_2 - x_1 \qquad PT = y_2 - y_1$$

$$(ST)^2 = (x_2 - x_1)^2 + (y_2 - y_1)^2$$

$$\mathbf{ST = [(x_2 - x_1)^2 + (y_2 - y_1)^2]^{\frac{1}{2}}}$$ ◀

1.2 The circle

A *locus* (plural *loci*) is a set of points satisfying a given condition and can be represented by an equation. For example, in the diagram above, the set of points equidistant from S and T is a line. The set of points which are a fixed distance from a fixed point lie on a circle, and this enables us to find the equation of a circle.

(a) Centre at the origin, and radius *r*

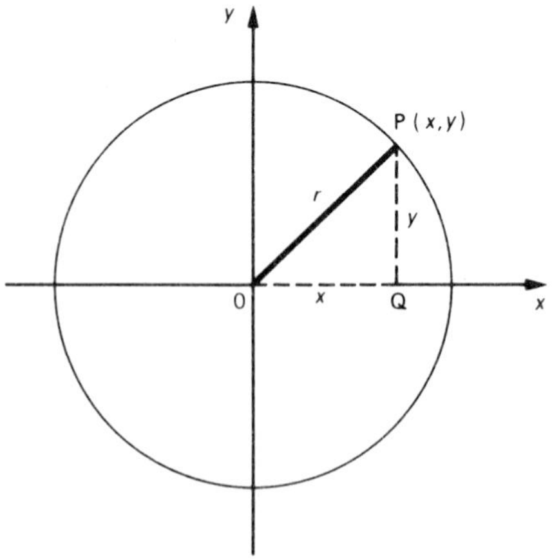

Suppose the radius is *r*. Any point P on the circle is such that OP is constant and equal to *r*. If P has coordinates (x, y) then by Pythagoras' theorem

$$\mathbf{x^2 + y^2 = r^2}$$ ◀

This is the required equation representing the locus.

(b) Centre at R (α, β), and radius r

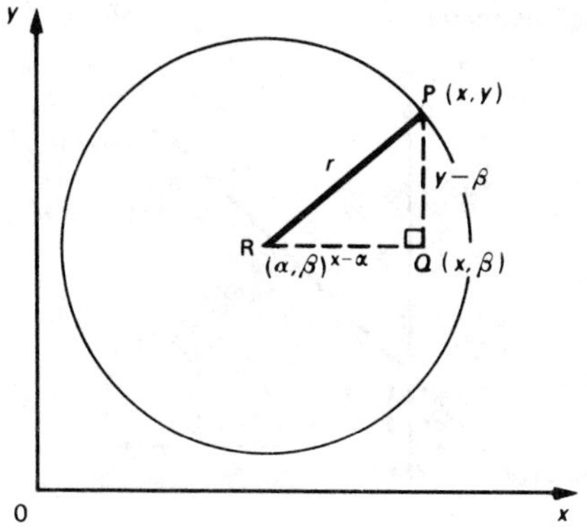

Suppose P is any point on the circle with coordinates (x, y). Then using Pythagoras' theorem once more,

$$(x-\alpha)^2+(y-\beta)^2 = r^2$$ ◀

Exercise 1.2

1 Find the distance between the points, leaving your answer in square root form.

(a) (5, 4) and (3, 1) **(b)** (6, 2) and (−1, −2)
(c) (−3, −4) and (2, 7) **(d)** (−2, −3) and (−6, −8)

2 Write down the equation of each of the following circles:

(a) centre O, radius 5 units **(b)** centre O, radius 7 units
(c) centre (1, 2) radius 6 units **(d)** centre (−2, 3), radius 4 units
(e) centre (−3, −4) radius 3 units

3 Find the centre and radius of each of the following circles:

(a) $x^2+y^2-12x-4y-9=0$ **(b)** $x^2+y^2-6x+2y-6=0$
(c) $x^2+y^2-25x+150=0$

4 ABCD is a quadrilateral in which A is the point (4, 4), B is (−2, 2), C is (−1, −1) and D is (1, −3). Calculate the lengths of the sides of this quadrilateral and the length of the diagonal AC, leaving your answers in square root form. Hence, using the converse of Pythagoras' theorem, show that the angle ABC is a right angle.

5 The vertices of a triangle are A (3, 4), B (−5, −4) and D (8, −1). Prove that the triangle ABD is right-angled.

6 A point P is such that its distance from the origin is five times its distance from (12, 0). Prove that the locus of P is the circle $(x-25/2)^2+y^2=(5/2)^2$. Write down the coordinates of the centre of this circle, and its radius.

1.3 The straight line

Preliminary knowledge expected

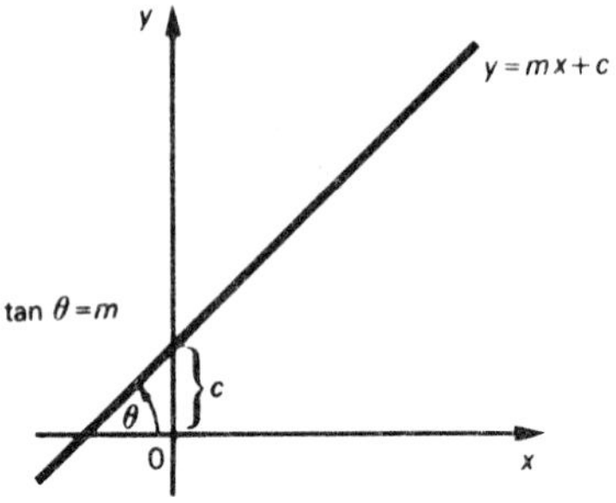

(1) The equation of a line may be written as

$$y = mx + c$$

where m is the gradient ($m = \tan\theta$) and c the intercept on the y axis.

(2) The gradient of the line joining (x_1, y_1) to (x_2, y_2) is given by

$$m = \frac{y \text{ step}}{x \text{ step}} = \frac{y_2 - y_1}{x_2 - x_1}$$

(3) The equation of the line through (h, k) with gradient m is

$$\frac{y-k}{x-h} = m$$

or $$y - k = m(x - h)$$

The line as a locus

Example

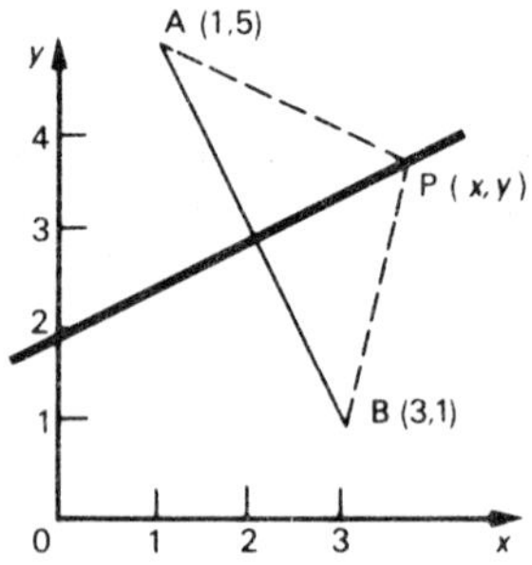

Find the equation of the set of points each of which is the same distance from A (1, 5) and B (3, 1).

Consider any point P (x, y) satisfying the condition. Then

$$AP = PB$$

so $$(AP)^2 = (PB)^2$$

hence $$(x-1)^2+(y-5)^2 = (x-3)^2+(y-1)^2$$

$$x^2-2x+1+y^2-10y+25 = x^2-6x+9+y^2-2y+1$$

$$4x-8y+16 = 0$$

or $$y = \tfrac{1}{2}x+2$$

which is the perpendicular bisector of AB.

NOTE. If P(x, y) is the midpoint of AB, then $x-1 = 3-x$. So

$$x = \frac{1+3}{2} = 2$$

and similarly $$y = \frac{5+1}{2} = 3$$

The midpoint (2, 3) lies on the line AB and on the locus since (2, 3) 'satisfies' the equation $y = \tfrac{1}{2}x+2$.

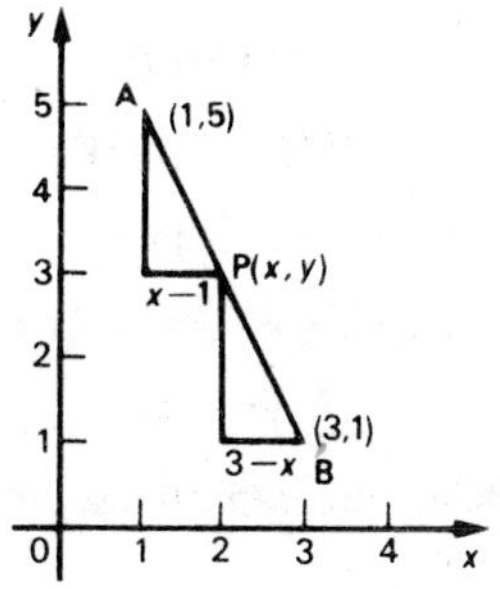

1.4 The parabola

This is the set of points equidistant from a point (called the *focus*) and a line (called the *directrix*).

Drawing the locus

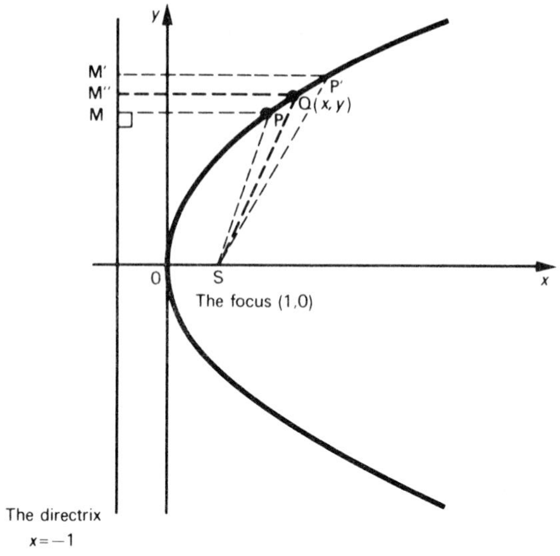

Suppose that we wish to find the set of points equidistant from $(1, 0)$ and $x = -1$. Draw in $x = -1$, and mark $(1, 0)$. Draw in the vertical lines one centimetre apart at $x = 0, 1, 2, \ldots$. With compass-point on S mark in the points—e.g. SP = PM = 3 cm, SP′ = P′M′ = 4 cm, etc. The points below the x axis can be marked symmetrically.

Equation of the locus

Consider a point Q (x, y) of the locus. Then

$$SQ = QM''$$

so

$$(SQ)^2 = (QM'')^2$$

Hence

$$(x-1)^2 + y^2 = (x+1)^2$$

$$x^2 - 2x + 1 + y^2 = x^2 + 2x + 1$$

$$y^2 = 4x$$

Sketch for yourself, on the same diagram, the set of points equidistant from
(a) $(1, 0)$ and $x = -1$ (as above)
(b) $(\frac{1}{2}, 0)$ and $x = -\frac{1}{2}$
(c) $(\frac{3}{2}, 0)$ and $x = -\frac{3}{2}$
Find the equations in cases (b) and (c).

These curves are 'similar' to each other and are of the same shape; they are *parabolas*. Parabolas occur naturally—as, for example, the path of a projectile in 'idealized' conditions. They are discussed in Chapter 19.

Two problems may occur to you; supposing that you have a particular parabola, how would you find its focus and its directrix?

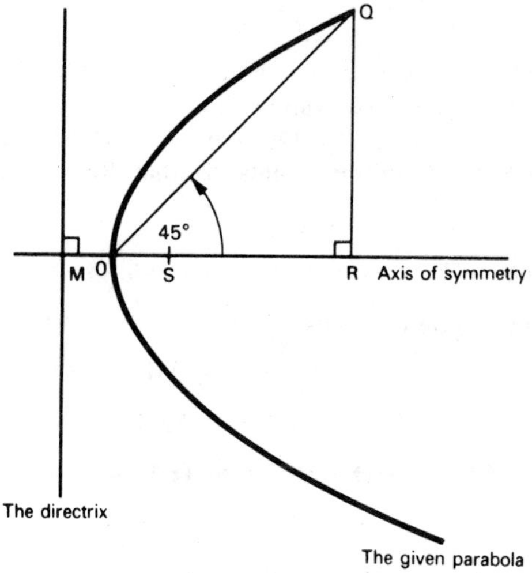

(1) From symmetry, mark the x axis. This gives O.
(2) Draw OQ at 45° to the axis, cutting the curve at Q.
(3) Draw QR perpendicular to the axis of symmetry.
(4) Then OS = $\frac{1}{4}$OR.
(5) Mark OM = OS as shown and the directrix will be perpendicular to the axis of symmetry. Check this procedure with the parabolas you have just drawn.

1.5 The ellipse

This is the set of points which are such that their distance from a fixed point is a multiple (called e—the *eccentricity*) of their distance from a fixed line. For an ellipse, $e < 1$.

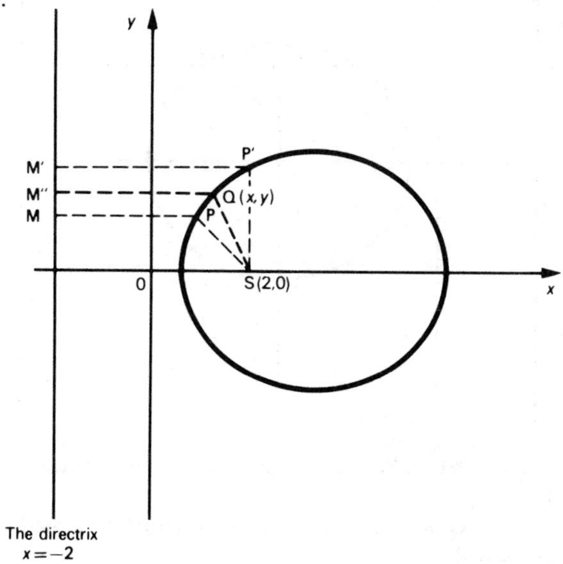

Drawing the locus

Suppose, for example, that we wish to find the set of points such that the distance of each from (2, 0) is half its distance from the line $x = -2$.

Draw in $x = -2$ and mark (2, 0). Draw in the vertical lines as before. With compass-point on S mark in the points so that SP = $\frac{1}{2}$PM, e.g. SP′ = 2 cm, P′M′ = 4 cm.

Equation of the locus

Consider a point Q (x, y) on the locus. Then

$$SQ = \tfrac{1}{2}QM''$$

so

$$(SQ)^2 = \tfrac{1}{4}(QM'')^2$$

$$(x-2)^2 + y^2 = \tfrac{1}{4}(x+2)^2$$

$$x^2 - 4x + 4 + y^2 = \tfrac{1}{4}(x^2 + 4x + 4)$$

$$4x^2 - 16x + 16 + 4y^2 = x^2 + 4x + 4$$

$$3x^2 - 20x + 4y^2 + 12 = 0$$

Use of symmetry

It is clear that the ellipse is a symmetrical curve. To make use of this, it is customary to arrange the axes as shown in the diagram:

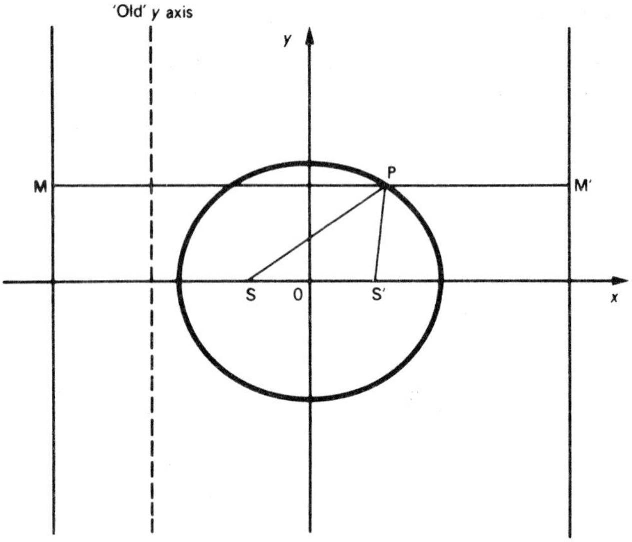

Because of the symmetry there are *two* foci and *two* directrices. Here SP = $\frac{1}{2}$PM and S′P = $\frac{1}{2}$PM′.

When the axes are chosen in this way, the equation representing the locus is much easier to deal with.

Example

Find the equation of the locus such that the distance of each point from (2, 0) is half its distance from the line $x = 8$. (The numbers have been carefully chosen to give an ellipse with its centre at O.)

$$SQ = \tfrac{1}{2}QM''$$

so

$$(SQ)^2 = \tfrac{1}{4}(QM'')^2$$

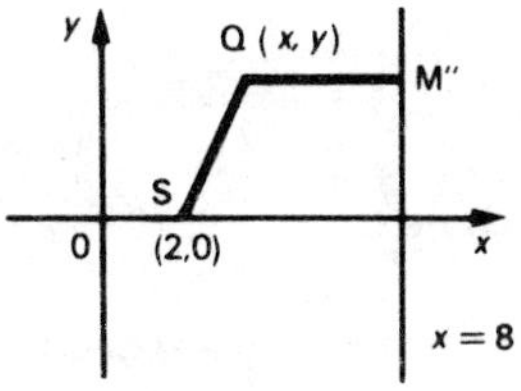

$$(x-2)^2 + y^2 = \tfrac{1}{4}(8-x)^2$$
$$x^2 - 4x + 4 + y^2 = \tfrac{1}{4}(64 - 16x + x^2)$$
$$4x^2 - 16x + 16 + 4y^2 = 64 - 16x + x^2$$
$$3x^2 + 4y^2 = 48$$

This can be written as

$$\frac{x^2}{(4)^2} + \frac{y^2}{(2\sqrt{3})^2} = 1$$

—which enables us to sketch the ellipse immediately, since

(1) its centre is O
(2) when $x = 0$, $y = \pm 2\sqrt{3}$, and
(3) when $y = 0$, $x = \pm 4$

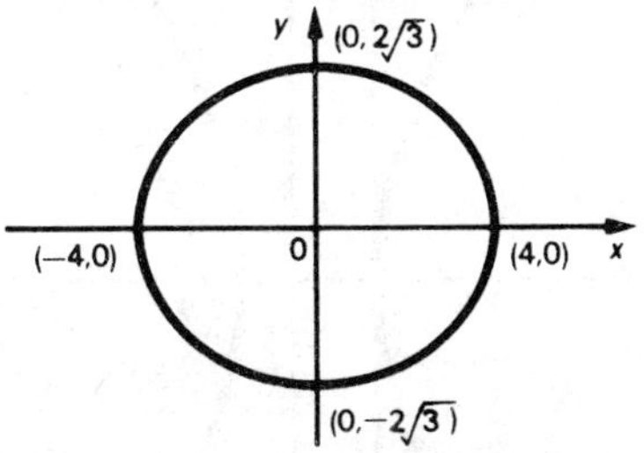

If we are given an ellipse and have to find the foci and directrices, this may be done easily by using some simple algebra (see Chapter 18). From symmetry, the axes can be inserted, then a, b can be read off and S found since $b^2 = a^2 - s^2$.

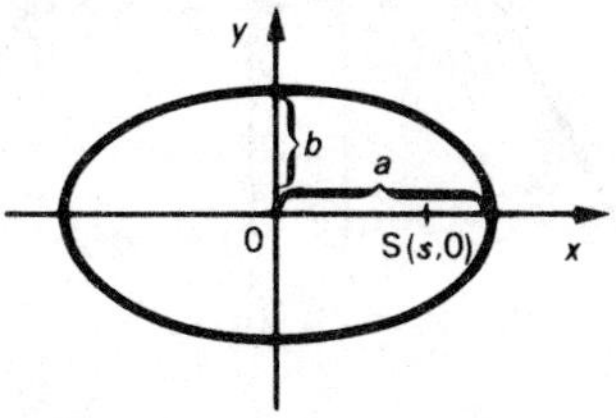

Exercise 1.5

1 Sketch the set of points such that the distance of each from (3, 0) is one-third its distance from $x = 15$. Find the equation of the ellipse.

2 Sketch the set of points such that the distance of each from $(-2, 0)$ is one-quarter its distance from $x = 5$. Find the equation of the ellipse.

3 Sketch the locus (x, y) such that

$$\frac{x^2}{16}+\frac{y^2}{9}=1$$

4 Sketch the locus (x, y) such that

$$\frac{x^2}{8}+\frac{y^2}{4}=1$$

1.6 The hyperbola

The definition is the same as that for the ellipse except that in this case $e > 1$.

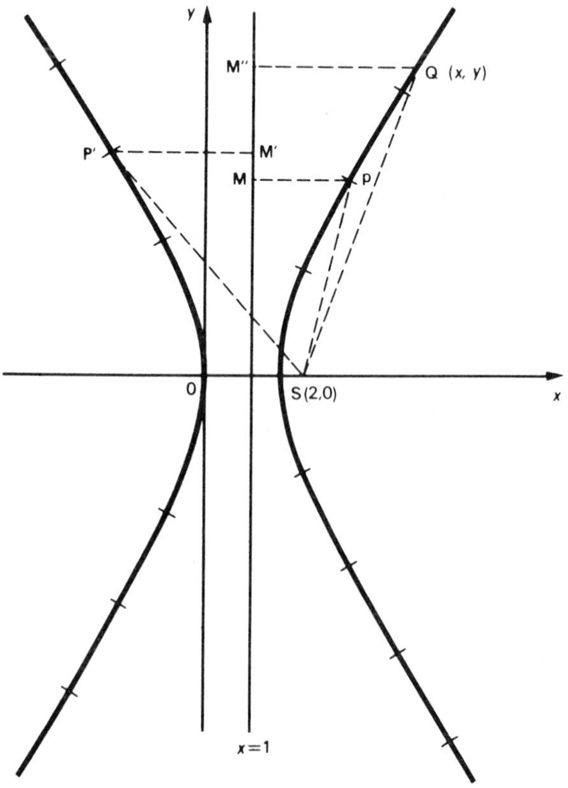

The diagram shows the set of points whose distance from (2, 0) is twice their distance from the line $x = 1$, drawn in a similar way to the ellipse. The right-hand arm of the curve is quickly drawn, but a minute's thought will reveal a left-hand arm as well.

Equation of the locus

Any point Q (x, y) of the locus is such that

$$SQ = 2QM''$$

and so

$$(SQ)^2 = 4(QM'')^2$$

$$(x-2)^2 + y^2 = 4(x-1)^2$$

$$x^2 - 4x + 4 + y^2 = 4(x^2 - 2x + 1)$$

$$x^2 - 4x + 4 + y^2 = 4x^2 - 8x + 4$$

$$3x^2 - y^2 - 4x = 0$$

Use of symmetry

Again, the hyperbola is a symmetrical curve. To make use of this we introduce axes as in the diagram below. As with the ellipse there are *two* foci and *two* directrices.

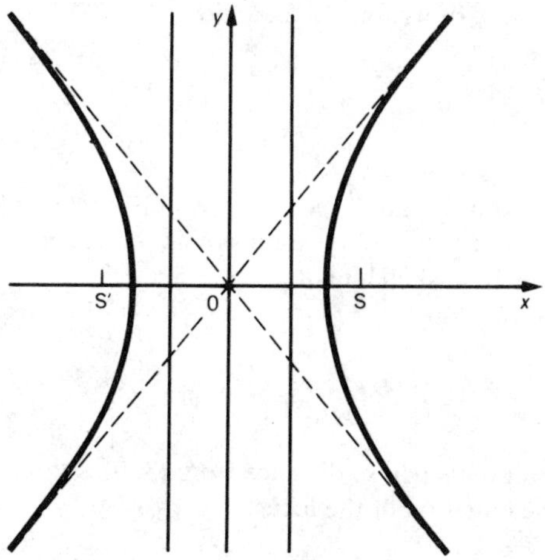

Example

Find the equation of the locus such that the distance of each of its points from (2, 0) is twice its distance from the line $x = \frac{1}{2}$. (The numbers have been carefully chosen to give a hyperbola with its centre at O.)

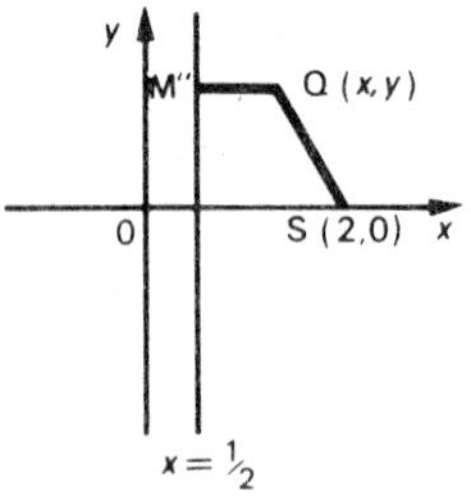

$$SQ = 2QM''$$

$$(SQ)^2 = 4(QM'')^2$$

$$(x-2)^2 + y^2 = 4(x-\tfrac{1}{2})^2$$

$$x^2 - 4x + 4 + y^2 = 4(x^2 - x + \tfrac{1}{4})$$

$$x^2 - 4x + 4 + y^2 = 4x^2 - 4x + 1$$

$$3x^2 - y^2 = 3$$

or

$$\frac{x^2}{1} - \frac{y^2}{3} = 1$$

—which is the usual way of writing the equation.

Asymptotes

It is clear that when x and y are large, then $(x^2/1) - (y^2/3) \approx 0$ or $y \approx \pm\sqrt{3}x$. The two lines $y = +\sqrt{3}x$ and $y = -\sqrt{3}x$ are known as the *asymptotes* to the curve and are of considerable help in sketching it.

Exercise 1.6a

1 Sketch the set of points whose distance from (3, 0) is three times their distance from $x = \frac{1}{3}$. Find the equation of the locus.

2 Sketch the set of points whose distance from (2, 0) is four times their distance from $x = \frac{1}{2}$. Find the equation of the locus.

3 Sketch the locus (x, y) such that

$$\frac{x^2}{9} - \frac{y^2}{16} = 1$$

4 Sketch the locus (x, y) such that

$$\frac{x^2}{4}-\frac{y^2}{8}=1$$

NOTE. The parabola, ellipse and hyperbola are considered in much more detail in Chapter 19.

Exercise 1.6b

In each question, *sketch* the locus or loci.

1 Show that a point equidistant from A $(-4, 2)$ and B $(2, -6)$ satisfies the equation $3x+5=4y+10$. Show that this equation can be written as

$$\frac{x+1}{4}=\frac{y+2}{3}$$

2 A point is such that its distance from the x-axis is equal to its distance from the point $(3, 2)$; find the equation of its locus.

3 Find the equations of
(a) the set of points which are equidistant from $(-1, 1)$ and $(7, 5)$
(b) the set of points which are 5 units from the point $(-1, 1)$

4 A point is such that its distance from the fixed point $(-3, 0)$ is twice its distance from the fixed point $(3, 0)$. Show that the locus is a circle with its centre at $(5, 0)$ and radius of 4 units.

5 Find the set of points whose distance from the point $(-2, 1)$ is **(a)** twice, **(b)** half and **(c)** equal to their distance from the origin. Give the equation in each case.

6 A is the point $(1, 0)$ and B the point $(-1, 0)$. Find the set of points P, such that
(a) $PA+PB=4$ **(b)** $PA-PB=2$ **(c)** $PA-PB=1$
(d) $PA-PB=0$

7 Find the set of points which are such that their distance from the point $(-2, 0)$ is **(a)** equal to, **(b)** twice and **(c)** half their distance from the y axis.

2 The equation of a line

We have met the straight line as the set of points equidistant from two fixed points and have assumed some familiarity with the equation of a line in the form $y = mx+c$. We now think of a straight line as having constant *direction* and develop its equation in ratio form and in parametric form.

2.1 The equation of a line in parametric form and in ratio form

A line through the origin

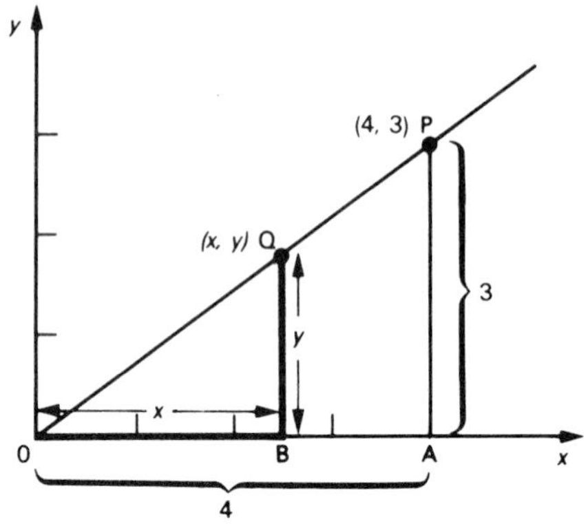

First we consider a line passing through the origin O and a point P (4, 3), say. Consider any point Q on the line with coordinates (x, y). Then the triangles OPA and OQB are similar and so, in *ratio form*,

$$\frac{x}{4} = \frac{y}{3}$$

We may call this ratio k and then $x/4 = y/3 = k$ gives us the *parametric form* of the equation as $x = 4k$, $y = 3k$. Different values of k, the parameter, will give us all the points on this line. Thus $k = 1$ gives (4, 3), $k = 2$ gives (8, 6), $k = 3$ gives (12, 9), $k = \frac{1}{2}$ gives $(2, \frac{3}{2})$ and so on. The *direction ratio* of the line is given by the 'x step':'y step', which here is 4:3.

A line through two points

We now consider the equation of a line joining two points and not passing through the origin.

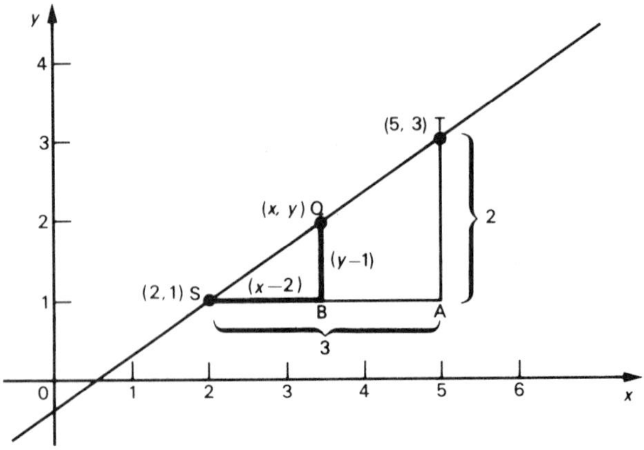

Consider Q (x, y) on the line joining S (2, 1) to T (5, 3). Again the triangles SQB and STA are similar so

$$\frac{x-2}{3} = \frac{y-1}{2}.$$

Note that the direction ratio is 3:2. This is the equation of the line in ratio form. If this ratio is k, then

$$\frac{x-2}{3} = \frac{y-1}{2} = k$$

and so parametrically $x = 3k+2$, $y = 2k+1$. This is the equation in its parametric form. Again, the different values of k give all the points on the line. $k = 0$ gives (2, 1)—the point S. $k = 1$ gives (5, 3)—the point T.

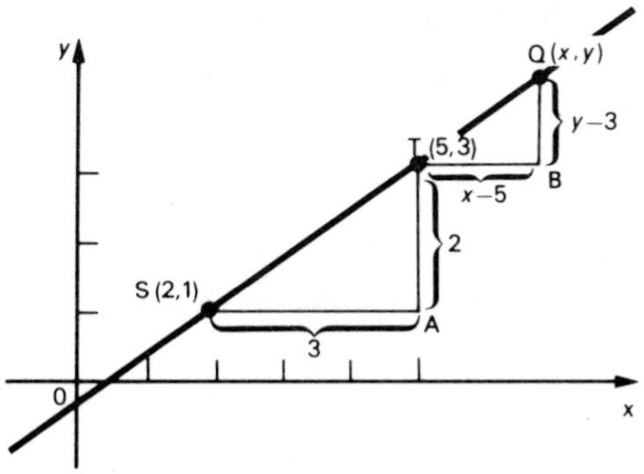

If Q is outside ST, we might use the triangle TQB, which is similar to triangle STA. Here

$$\frac{x-5}{3} = \frac{y-3}{2} = k' \quad \text{(say)}$$

and $$x = 3k'+5 \qquad y = 2k'+3$$

Note again the direction ratios 3:2. If $k' = 0$, we have (5, 3) which is T, $k' = -1$ gives S (2, 1).

We can see that

(1) A line through S (2, 1) with direction ratio 3:2 has equation

$$\frac{x-2}{3} = \frac{y-1}{2}$$

(2) A line through T (5, 3) with direction ratio 3:2 has equation

$$\frac{x-5}{3} = \frac{y-3}{2}$$

and so forth.

We may generalize this for a line through (α, β) with direction ratio $l:m$ has equation

$$\frac{x-\alpha}{l}=\frac{y-\beta}{m}$$ ◀

or parametrically

$$x = lk+\alpha$$
$$y = mk+\beta$$ ◀

NOTE that we may write our equations

$$\left.\begin{aligned} x &= 3k'+5 \\ y &= 2k'+3 \end{aligned}\right\} \quad \text{as} \quad \begin{pmatrix} x \\ y \end{pmatrix} = k'\begin{pmatrix} 3 \\ 2 \end{pmatrix} + \begin{pmatrix} 5 \\ 3 \end{pmatrix}$$

$$\left.\begin{aligned} x &= 3k+2 \\ y &= 2k+1 \end{aligned}\right\} \quad \text{as} \quad \begin{pmatrix} x \\ y \end{pmatrix} = k\begin{pmatrix} 3 \\ 2 \end{pmatrix} + \begin{pmatrix} 2 \\ 1 \end{pmatrix}$$

These equations *look* different but represent the same line.

The general form is $\begin{pmatrix} x \\ y \end{pmatrix} = k\begin{pmatrix} l \\ m \end{pmatrix} + \begin{pmatrix} \alpha \\ \beta \end{pmatrix}$

which can be written in the form

$$\mathbf{r} = k\mathbf{b} + \mathbf{c}$$ ◀

This last is the *vector* equation of a line and we shall meet it frequently later on.

Exercise 2.1

1 We have not illustrated this method in the cases when the line slopes 'backwards'. Show on a diagram that the idea may be extended to these cases.

Write down the equations in both parametric and ratio form of

(a) a line through O and $(-2, 1)$

(b) a line through $(-3, -2)$ and $(-4, 3)$

2 Write down the equations of the following lines, first in ratio form and then parametrically. (DR is an abbreviation for 'direction ratio'.)

(a) through O and $(3, -1)$

(b) through O and with DR $2:3$

(c) through $(-5, 1)$ and with DR $5:-1$

(d) through $(2, 3)$ and with DR $5:-1$

(e) through $(-5, 1)$ and $(2, 3)$

(f) through $(-2, 1)$ and with DR $3:0$

(g) through $(-3, 5)$ and with DR $0:-5$

3 Draw sketches of the following lines, and for lines **(f)** to **(k)** find the values of k at the given points.

(a) $\frac{x-3}{2}=\frac{y+4}{-1}$

(b) $\frac{x}{3}=\frac{y-2}{4}$

(c) $\frac{x-2}{0}=\frac{y+3}{2}$

(d) $\frac{x+4}{-1}=\frac{y+5}{-2}$

(e) $\frac{x+1}{3}=\frac{y}{0}$

(f) $x = 2k+3,\ y = -3k-1$ (3, −1), (5, −4)

(g) $x = -2k+2,\ y = k+1$ (0, 2), (−2, 3)

(h) $x = 3,\ y = 2k+4$ (3, 0), (3, 2)

(i) $x = -\frac{1}{2}k+1,\ y = \frac{1}{3}k-1$ (4, −3), (1, −1)

(j) $\begin{pmatrix} x \\ y \end{pmatrix} = k\begin{pmatrix} 3 \\ -1 \end{pmatrix} + \begin{pmatrix} -2 \\ -1 \end{pmatrix}$ (7, −4), (−11, 2)

(k) $\begin{pmatrix} x \\ y \end{pmatrix} = k\begin{pmatrix} -1 \\ 2 \end{pmatrix} + \begin{pmatrix} 2 \\ -1 \end{pmatrix}$ (4, −5), ($\frac{1}{2}$, 2)

4 Sketch the following lines:

(a) through (2, 3) with DR −1 : 2
(b) through (4, −1) with DR −1 : 2
(c) through (−2, −2), parallel to the line through (2, 3) and (4, −1)
(d) through (2, 3) with DR 2 : −1
(e) through (4, −1) with DR 2 : −1
(f) through (a, b) with DR −1 : 2
(g) through (a, b) with DR 2 : −1

NOTE
It is not always obvious whether or not two equations in ratio form represent the same line. Consider the equations

$$\frac{x-2}{1} = \frac{y-3}{1} \qquad (1)$$

and

$$\frac{x-5}{1} = \frac{y-6}{1} \qquad (2)$$

The direction ratios of both are 1 : 1 so the lines are parallel, at least. If they have one point in common they are identical, and have in fact *all* points in common.

Line 1 passes through (2, 3). Does line 2 pass through (2, 3)? It does, since

$$\frac{2-5}{1} = \frac{3-6}{1}$$

so the lines *are* identical.

2.2 Two lines in a plane

The lines may be (i) identical (ii) parallel or (iii) intersecting.

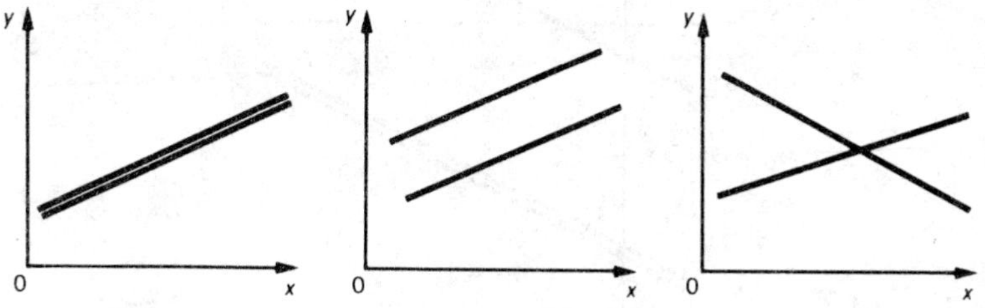

Cases (i) and (ii)

Suppose we have the equations of two lines given:

$$\frac{x}{2} = \frac{y-4}{1} \quad (1) \qquad \text{and} \qquad \frac{x}{2} = \frac{y-1}{1} \quad (2)$$

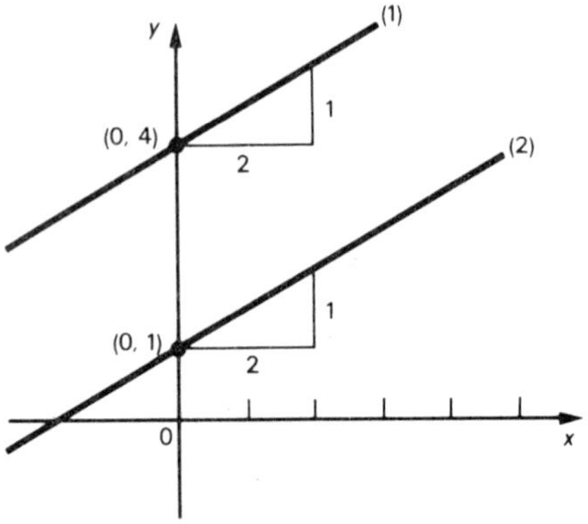

The two lines are parallel since the DR is 2 : 1 for each line. They are not identical since the first line passes through (0, 4) and the second through (0, 1). Consider two different lines:

$$\frac{x-3}{2} = \frac{y-1}{1} = p \quad (3) \qquad \text{and} \qquad \frac{x+1}{2} = \frac{y+4}{1} = q \quad (4)$$

then $x = 2p+3,\ y = p+1$ then $x = 2q-1,\ y = q-4$

When $p = 0$, $x = 3$ and $y = 1$ When $x = 3$, $q = 2$ and $y = -2$

We can see immediately that these two lines are parallel and not identical. Suppose we have another line:

$$\frac{x-1}{2} = \frac{y+3}{1} = r \quad (5)$$

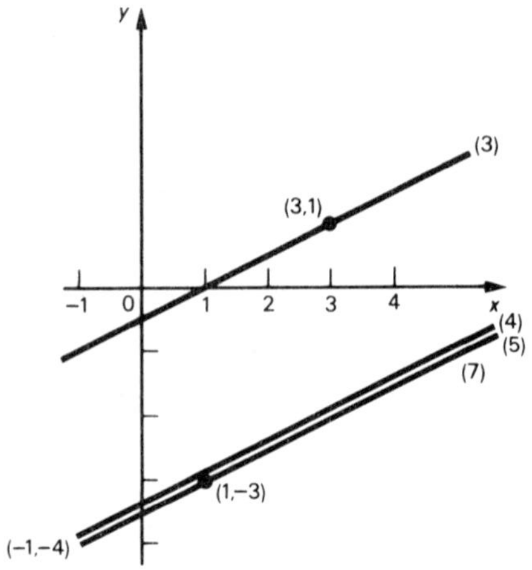

then

$$x = 2r+1, \qquad y = r-3$$

When $x = 3$, $\qquad r = 1$ and $y = -2$

So line (3) is parallel to lines (4) and (5), which are identical.

We have seen that lines with the same DR are parallel; the line with DR $2:-1$ is parallel to the line with DR $-6:3$. In general, suppose the DRs of two lines are $l_1 : m_1$, and $l_2 : m_2$ and we are told that the lines are parallel. Then

$$\frac{l_1}{m_1} = \frac{l_2}{m_2}$$

or

$$l_1 m_2 = l_2 m_1$$

$$\mathbf{l_1 m_2 - l_2 m_1 = 0}$$ ◀

This is the condition that two lines in a plane should be parallel.

Case (iii): intersecting lines

Consider, for example, the lines

$$\frac{x-2}{2} = \frac{y-1}{3} \quad (6) \qquad \text{and} \qquad \frac{x+1}{-3} = \frac{y+1}{-4} \quad (7)$$

Since the DRs are not the same, the lines must intersect. We can solve the equations by two methods.

Method 1

Multiply equation (6) by 6, and equation (7) by -12.

$$3x-6 = 2y-2 \Rightarrow 3x-2y = 4 \qquad (6')$$

$$4x+4 = +3y+3 \Rightarrow 4x-3y = -1 \qquad (7')$$

These can be solved by multiplying equation (6′) by 3 and equation (7′) by 2.

$$9x-6y = 12$$

$$8x-6y = -2$$

Subtracting gives $\qquad x = 14$

and by substitution $\qquad y = 19$

Hence the point of intersection is (14, 19).

Method 2

Parametrically, any point on the line

$$\frac{x-2}{2} = \frac{y-1}{3}$$

has coordinates $\qquad x = 2k+2, \qquad y = 3k+1$

If this point also lies on the line

$$\frac{x+1}{-3} = \frac{y+1}{-4}$$

then

$$\frac{2k+2+1}{-3} = \frac{3k+1+1}{-4}$$

$$-8k-12 = -9k-6$$

$$k = 6$$

So the point of intersection is (14, 19).

Exercise 2.2

1 Do the following equations represent parallel lines or the same line?

$$\frac{x-1}{2} = \frac{y-1}{1} \quad \text{and} \quad \frac{x-3}{2} = \frac{y-2}{1}$$

2 Find the point of intersection of the lines

$$\frac{x+4}{6} = \frac{y+4}{1} \quad \text{and} \quad \frac{x+6}{-8} = \frac{y}{3}$$

3 Find the point of intersection of the lines

$$\frac{x-3}{1} = \frac{y}{3} \quad \text{and} \quad \frac{x-1}{-3} = \frac{y-1}{5}$$

4 Find the vertices of the triangle whose sides have equations

$$\frac{x-2}{2} = \frac{y-1}{1} \qquad \frac{x-1}{1} = \frac{y+3}{4} \qquad \frac{x}{-3} = \frac{y-7}{2}$$

5 Show that the quadrilateral with vertices $(1, 2)$, $(3, 3)$, $(5, 7)$ and $(3, 6)$ is a parallelogram.

6 Find the equation of the set of points which are equidistant from the two fixed points $(1, 2)$ and $(7, 0)$. Verify that $(2, -5)$ lies on this locus and find the values of α and β if the points $(1, 2)$, $(2, -5)$, $(7, 0)$ and (α, β) are, in this order, the vertices of a rhombus.

2.3 Perpendicular lines and distances

In the diagram there are several examples of *perpendicular lines* in a plane with some of their DRs shown.

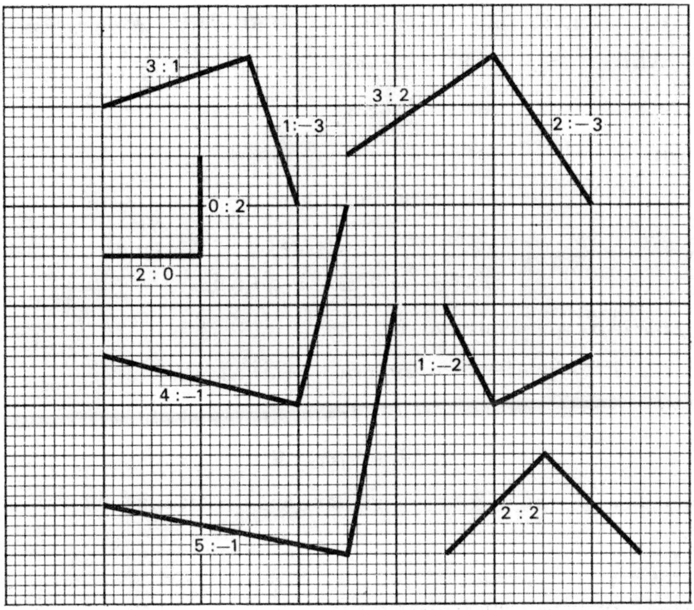

Complete the table below:

DR of line:	3:1	3:2	2:0	4:−1	1:−2	5:−1	2:2
DR of perpendicular line:	1:−3	2:−3	0:2				

What is the connection between the DR of a line and the DR of the perpendicular line?

Suppose that the line has DR $l_1 : m_1$ and the perpendicular line has DR $l_2 : m_2$. In each case we find

$$\frac{l_1}{m_1} = \frac{-m_2}{l_2}$$

hence $$l_1 l_2 + m_1 m_2 = 0$$

Condition that two lines should be perpendicular

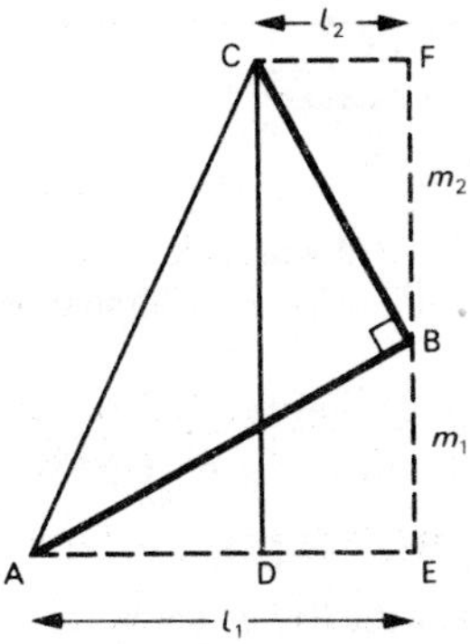

Suppose that AB (DR $l_1 : m_1$) is perpendicular to BC (DR $l_2 : m_2$).

Then in $\triangle$ABE, $AB^2 = l_1^2 + m_1^2$

and in $\triangle$BCF, $BC^2 = l_2^2 + m_2^2$

so in $\triangle$ABC $AC^2 = l_1^2 + m_1^2 + l_2^2 + m_2^2$

But $CD = m_1 + m_2$

and $AD = l_1 - (-l_2) = l_1 + l_2$

so $AC^2 = (m_1 + m_2)^2 + (l_1 + l_2)^2$

Equating the two expressions for AC^2,

$$l_1^2 + m_1^2 + l_2^2 + m_2^2 = (m_1 + m_2)^2 + (l_1 + l_2)^2$$
$$= m_1^2 + 2m_1m_2 + m_2^2 + l_1^2 + 2l_1l_2 + l_2^2$$

Hence $\boldsymbol{l_1l_2 + m_1m_2 = 0}$ ◀

The quantity $l_1l_2 + m_1m_2$ is very important and is called the *dot product* of the DR.

Equation of a circle on a given diameter

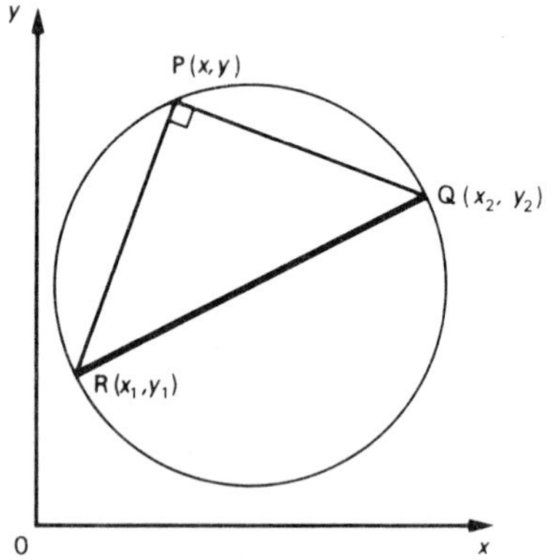

Consider a circle with diameter RQ where R is (x_1, y_1) and Q is (x_2, y_2). P (x, y) is any point on the circle. Since the angle in a semicircle is 90°, RPQ = 90° or PQ is perpendicular to PR.

The DR of PQ is $x_2 - x : y_2 - y$ and the DR of PR is $x_1 - x : y_1 - y$. Since PQ is perpendicular to PR, the dot product of their DRs is zero.

$$\boldsymbol{(x_2 - x)(x_1 - x) + (y_2 - y)(y_1 - y) = 0}$$ ◀

This is the equation of a circle with RQ as diameter.

Perpendicular distances

Distance of the origin from a line

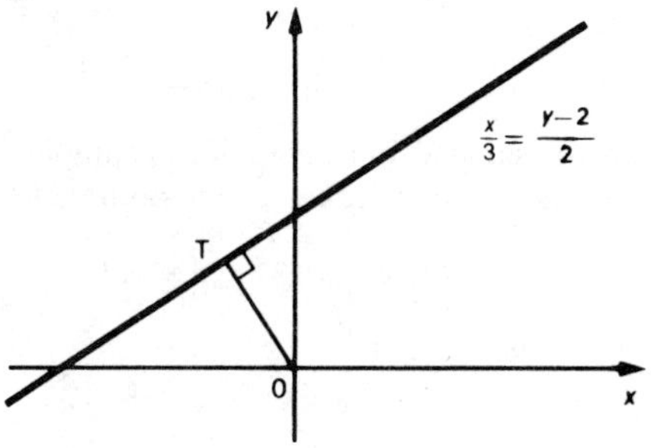

Suppose the line is $$\frac{x}{3}=\frac{y-2}{2}$$

The DR of OT will be $2:-3$ so T can be given the coordinates $(2k, -3k)$, and

$$OT = \sqrt{[(2k)^2+(-3k)^2]} = k\sqrt{(4+9)} = k\sqrt{13}$$

Since T $(2k, -3k)$ lies on the line

$$\frac{x}{3}=\frac{y-2}{2}$$

$$\frac{2k}{3}=\frac{-3k-2}{2}$$

$$13k = -6 \Rightarrow k = -\tfrac{6}{13}$$

Hence $$OT = -\tfrac{6}{13}\sqrt{13}$$

The distance of a point from a line

(a) Suppose the line passes through the origin and we have to find the distance from P (1, 5) to the line

$$\frac{x}{3}=\frac{y}{2}$$

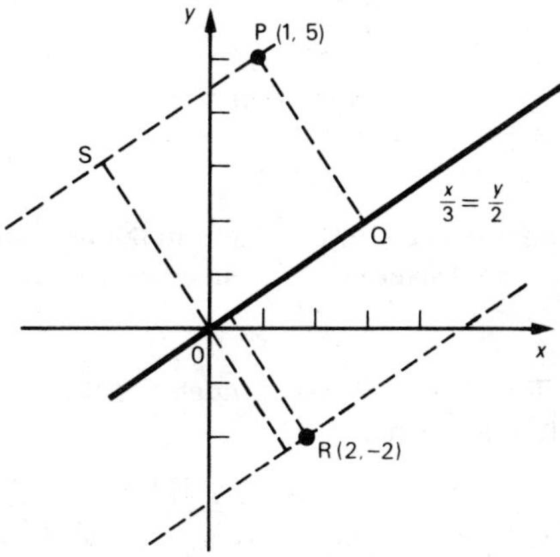

Clearly this distance is equal to the distance from the *origin* to a *parallel* line through P. The equation of this line is

$$\frac{x-1}{3}=\frac{y-5}{2}$$

and the problem is now the same as in the previous example.

The DR of OS is 2:−3, so S can be taken as the point $(2k, -3k)$, and again

$$OS = k\sqrt{13}$$

The point S $(2k, -3k)$ lies on

$$\frac{x-1}{3}=\frac{y-5}{2}$$

so

$$\frac{2k-1}{3}=\frac{3k-5}{2}$$

$$4k-2=-9k-15$$

$$13k=-13 \Rightarrow k=-1$$

and

$$OS = PQ = -\sqrt{13}$$

By a similar calculation, the distance from R (2, −2) to the line

$$\frac{x}{3}=\frac{y}{2}$$

is equal to the distance from the origin to the parallel line

$$\frac{x-2}{3}=\frac{y+2}{2}$$

and is given by $k\sqrt{13}$, where

$$\frac{2k-2}{3}=\frac{-3k+2}{2}$$

$$13k=10$$

$$k=\tfrac{10}{13}$$

R therefore lies at a distance $(10/13)\sqrt{13}$ from the line, and on the other side of it from P. The sign of the distance is determined by the side of the line on which the point lies.

(b) Suppose the line does not pass through the origin and we want to find the distance from P (1, 5) to the line

$$\frac{x}{3}=\frac{y-2}{2}$$

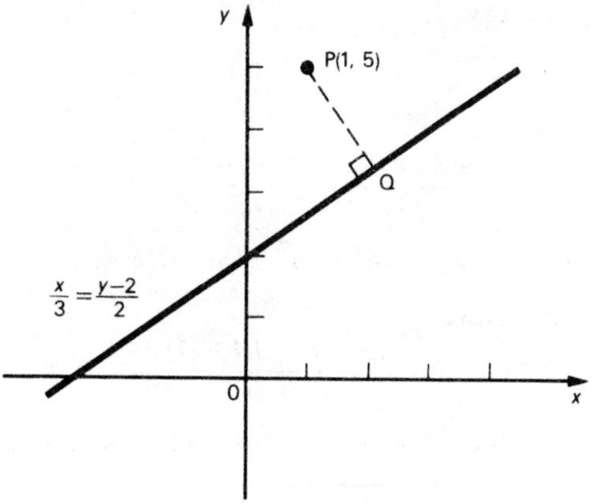

The DR of PQ is $2:-3$ and the equation of PQ is

$$\frac{x-1}{2}=\frac{y-5}{-3}=k$$

So Q is the point $(2k+1, -3k+5)$ and the distance PQ is

$$\sqrt{[(2k+1-1)^2+(-3k+5-5)^2]} = k\sqrt{13} \quad \text{(again!)}$$

Since Q $(2k+1, -3k+5)$ lies on

$$\frac{x}{3}=\frac{y-2}{2}$$

$$\frac{2k+1}{3}=\frac{-3k+5-2}{2}$$

$$13k = 7$$

$$k = \tfrac{7}{13}$$

and

$$PQ = \tfrac{7}{13}\sqrt{13}$$

To find the distance from P (a, b) to the line $\dfrac{x-\alpha}{l}=\dfrac{y-\beta}{m}$

If Q is the foot of the perpendicular from P to the line, PQ has DR $-m:l$ and equation

$$\frac{x-a}{-m}=\frac{y-b}{l}=k$$

Q has coordinates $(-mk+a, lk+b)$, and the distance PQ is given by

$$\sqrt{[(-mk+a-a)^2+(lk+b-b)^2]} = k\sqrt{(l^2+m^2)}$$

Since Q $(-mk+a, lk+b)$ lies on

$$\frac{x+\alpha}{l}=\frac{y-\beta}{m}$$

$$\frac{-mk+a-\alpha}{l}=\frac{lk+b-\beta}{m}$$

hence $$k(l^2+m^2)=m(a-\alpha)-l(b-\beta)$$

The distance PQ is therefore

$$\frac{m(a-\alpha)-l(b-\beta)}{\sqrt{(l^2+m^2)}}$$

Check the answers in the examples above by substitution in this formula.

The distance between parallel lines

This can be found in a similar manner by finding the distance of the 'obvious' point on one line from the other line.

Exercise 2.3

1 Find the distance of the origin from the line

$$\frac{x-2}{4}=\frac{y+3}{-3}$$

2 Find the distance of the point $(-2, 3)$ from the line

$$\frac{x-1}{3}=\frac{y-2}{2}$$

3 Find the distance between the parallel lines

(a) $$\frac{x-3}{2}=\frac{y+4}{1} \quad \text{and} \quad \frac{x-1}{2}=\frac{y-2}{1}$$

(b) $$\frac{x+1}{1}=\frac{y+4}{-2} \quad \text{and} \quad \frac{x}{1}=\frac{y-5}{-2}$$

4 O is the origin and A is the point $(7, 1)$. If P is any point on the line

$$\frac{x+9}{7}=\frac{y-3}{1}$$

show that the area of the triangle OAP is 15 square units. Find the coordinates of P when OA = OP.

5 The lines $$\frac{x+1}{-1}=\frac{y+1}{2} \quad \text{and} \quad \frac{x-7}{2}=\frac{y-3}{1}$$

are the sides of a rectangle whose other two sides intersect at the point (3, 4). Find the equations of these other sides and the area of the rectangle.

6 Prove that the points A (−2, −1), B (4, 3), C (6, 0) and D (0, −4) form the vertices of a rectangle. The straight line $x = 3$ meets the sides AB and DC in P and Q respectively. Calculate the area of the trapezium PBCQ.

7 A circle passes through the points (1, 1) and (1, 9), and touches the x axis. The coordinates of its centre are both positive. Find the length of its intercept on the y axis.

8 A circle has its centre at (5, 2) and passes through (8, 6). Find its equation. Show that the line joining (8, 6) and (2, −2) is a diameter.

9 Any straight line is drawn through the point (3, −2), and K is the foot of the perpendicular to this line from the point (−2, 1). Find the equation of the locus of K and state what curve it represents.

2.4 The angle between two intersecting lines

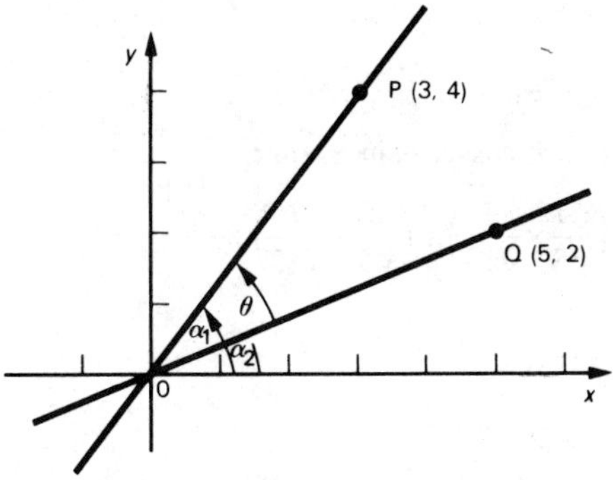

Suppose that the lines pass through the origin. Consider the lines $x/3 = y/4$ with DR 3:4 passing through P (3, 4) at angle α_1 to the x axis, and $x/5 = y/2$ with DR 5:2 passing through Q (5, 2) at angle α_2 to the x axis. We have to find θ, where $\theta = \alpha_1 - \alpha_2$. Now

$$\begin{aligned}\cos\theta &= \cos(\alpha_1 - \alpha_2)\\ &= \cos\alpha_1\cos\alpha_2 + \sin\alpha_1\sin\alpha_2\\ &= \left(\frac{3}{\sqrt{(3^2+4^2)}} \times \frac{5}{\sqrt{(5^2+2^2)}}\right) + \left(\frac{4}{\sqrt{(3^2+4^2)}} \times \frac{2}{\sqrt{(5^2+2^2)}}\right)\\ &= \frac{23}{5\sqrt{29}}\end{aligned}$$

For our second example we consider two lines which do not pass through the origin:

$$\frac{x-2}{3}=\frac{y-1}{2} \quad \text{through } (2, 1) \text{ with DR } 3:2$$

and

$$\frac{x-2}{-1}=\frac{y-1}{2} \quad \text{through } (2, 1) \text{ with DR } -1:2$$

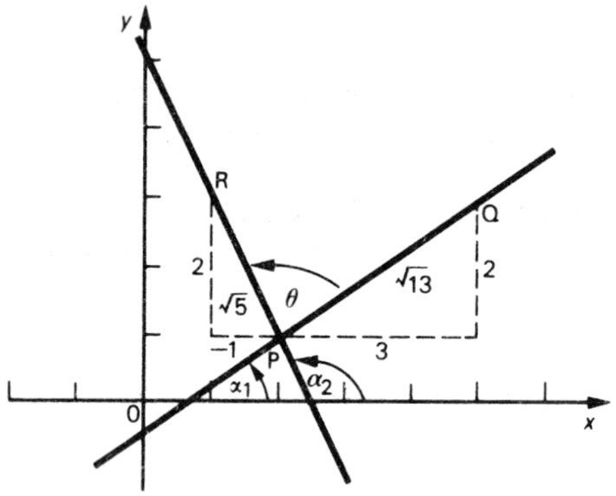

Again

$$\theta = \alpha_2 - \alpha_1$$

$$\cos\theta = \cos\alpha_2\cos\alpha_1 + \sin\alpha_2\sin\alpha_1$$

$$= \left(\frac{-1}{\sqrt{5}}\times\frac{3}{\sqrt{13}}\right)+\left(\frac{2}{\sqrt{5}}\times\frac{2}{\sqrt{13}}\right)$$

$$= \frac{1}{\sqrt{65}}$$

The method is easily generalized.

$$\cos\theta = \left(\frac{l_1}{\sqrt{(l_1^2+m_1^2)}}\times\frac{l_2}{\sqrt{(l_2^2+m_2^2)}}\right)+\left(\frac{m_1}{\sqrt{(l_1^2+m_1^2)}}\times\frac{m_2}{\sqrt{(l_2^2+m_2^2)}}\right)$$

$$= \frac{\boldsymbol{l_1 l_2 + m_1 m_2}}{\boldsymbol{\sqrt{(l_1^2+m_1^2)}\sqrt{(l_2^2+m_2^2)}}} \quad ◀$$

NOTE that this is the *dot product* of DR divided by PR × PQ.

Note on direction ratios and angles

The direction of any line—1 : −3, for instance—might equally well have been written −1 : 3, these two ratios being equal. Which of them is used will determine the sign of the expression for the cosine of the angle between two lines. There are, of course, two angles between the two lines, each the supplement of the other. Their cosines are equal in magnitude but opposite in sign.

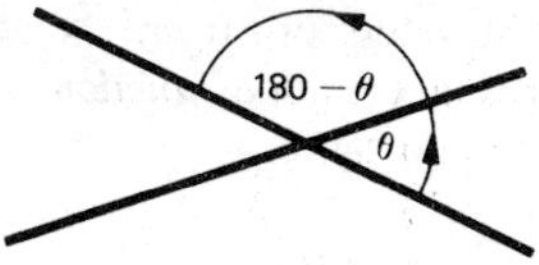

If *one* of the two angles is required rather than the other (for example, the internal angle of a triangle), a sketch may be necessary to determine whether the required angle is acute or obtuse.

Exercise 2.4

1 Find the cosine of the angle between the following pairs of lines:

(a) $\dfrac{x-2}{3}=\dfrac{y+4}{2}$ and $\dfrac{x-2}{-1}=\dfrac{y+4}{-2}$

(b) $\dfrac{x+1}{3}=\dfrac{y-2}{-1}$ and $\dfrac{x+1}{5}=\dfrac{y-2}{4}$

(c) $\dfrac{x+2}{4}=\dfrac{y-2}{3}$ and $\dfrac{x+1}{-4}=\dfrac{y+2}{-3}$

(d) $\dfrac{x-1}{3}=\dfrac{y-1}{-1}$ and $\dfrac{x+2}{-1}=\dfrac{y+1}{-3}$

2 Find the angles of the triangle enclosed by the x axis, and the lines

$$\frac{x}{3}=\frac{y}{4} \quad \text{and} \quad \frac{x-1}{-2}=\frac{y+1}{-1}$$

3 ABC are the vertices of a triangle where A is (−4, 2), B is (3, −1) and C is (2, 5). Find the angle ABC and the area of the triangle.

4 Find the area of the trapezium with vertices (2, 1), (4, 1), (7, 4) and (4, 3).

5 Find the equation of the line joining the origin to the point of intersection of

$$\frac{x-5}{3}=\frac{y-1}{-4} \quad \text{and} \quad \frac{x+3}{5}=\frac{y-2}{3}$$

Find the equation of the line which is parallel to $x/2 = y/-3$ and passes through this point of intersection. What is the angle between the two lines?

3 Parameters and curves

3.1 The use and choice of parameters

We have already seen (page 140), how the equation of a line may be written in parametric form. For example, the line $x/4 = y/3$ can be expressed as $x = 4t$,

$y = 3t$ where, by taking all the values of t from $-\infty$ to $+\infty$ we obtain all the points on the line. This idea of writing x as one *function* of the parameter (t) and y as another function of t is most important.

The need for parameters

The line is given by $y = \frac{3}{4}x$ and plotting different values of x will give us the line. But why do we need parameters at all?

There are two answers to this question. Parameters are needed for dealing with more complicated expressions where it is not possible to write the relationship either (i) as a function of x, or (ii) simply. For example:

(i) $y^2 = 4ax$ does not define a function since $y = \pm\sqrt{(4ax)}$ (see page 43), and

(ii) $x^3 + y^3 = 3axy$ cannot be solved simply by substituting values for x.

In each case, then, we hope to write $x = f(t)$, $y = g(t)$ so that one value of t will give us *one* point on the curve. Note that the functions chosen are not unique.

Choice of f(t), g(t)

The choice of f(t), g(t) depends on the form of the relationship. The shape of the curve, a knowledge of trigonometric identities and the manner of formation of the curve help us to decide on f(t) and g(t).

Example 1

The parabola $y^2 = 4ax$.

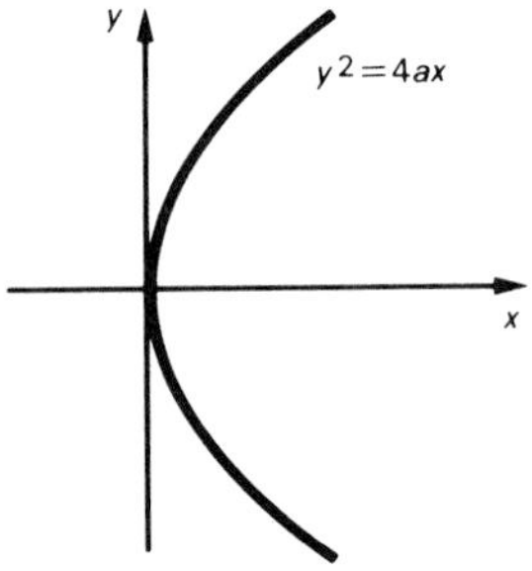

(1) All the x values are positive (suggesting that $x = kt^2$).

(2) y takes all values from $-\infty$ to $+\infty$ (suggesting that $y = ct$).

Try $x = t^2$, substituting $y = 2t\sqrt{a}$. Since y involves $\sqrt{a}$ we try $x = at^2$, then $y = 2at$. These are the usual parametric equations for the parabola.

Many parametric equations involve trigonometric identities as in examples 2 and 3. The parameter then is ϕ, and $x = f(\phi)$, $y = g(\phi)$.

Example 2

The circle $x^2 + y^2 = a^2$.

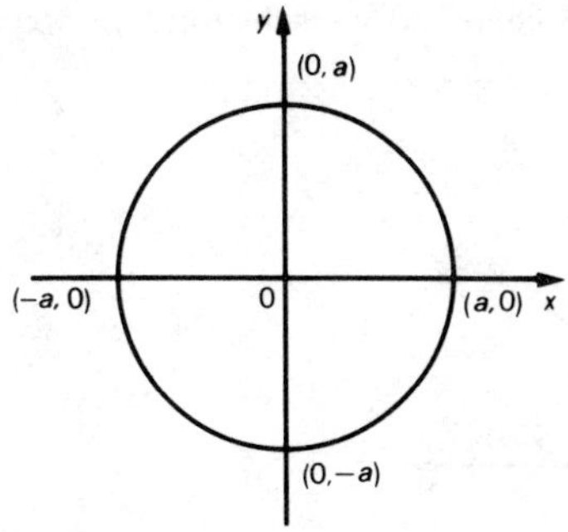

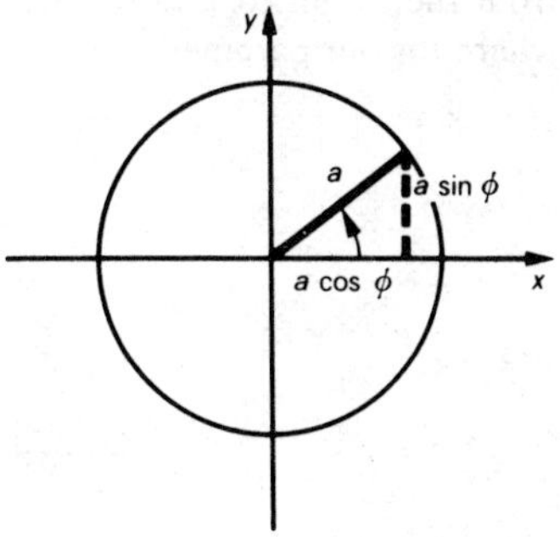

(1) $-a \leqslant x \leqslant a, -a \leqslant y \leqslant a$
(2) Remember that $\cos^2 \phi + \sin^2 \phi = 1$
(3) Try $\left.\begin{array}{l} x = a \cos \phi \\ y = a \sin \phi \end{array}\right\}$

Example 3

The ellipse $\dfrac{x^2}{a^2} + \dfrac{y^2}{b^2} = 1$

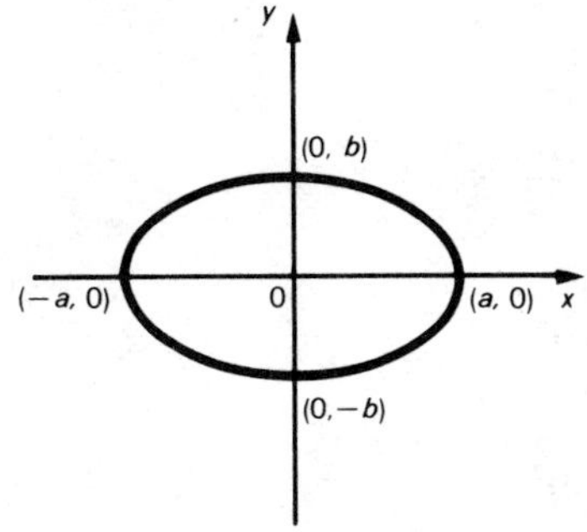

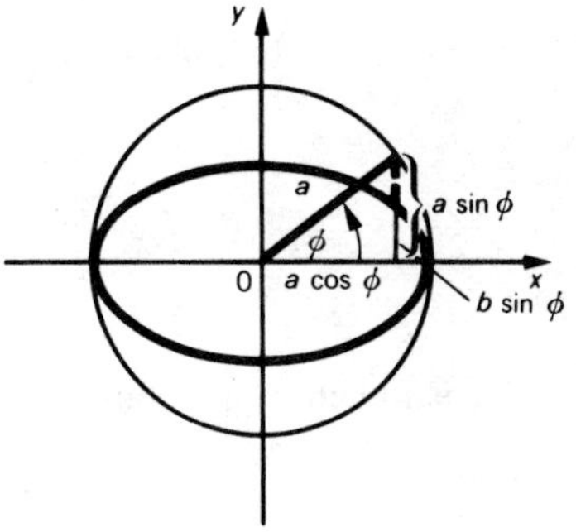

(1) $-a \leqslant x \leqslant a, -b \leqslant y \leqslant b$
(2) Remember $\cos^2 \phi + \sin^2 \phi = 1$
(3) Try $\left.\begin{array}{l} x = a \cos \phi \\ y = b \sin \phi \end{array}\right\}$

These may be linked with an actual angle ϕ in the 'director' circle shown. When $x = a \cos \phi$, by substitution $y = b \sin \phi$.

Complicated expressions

A relationship like $x^3 + y^3 = 3xy$ cannot readily be sketched by substituting values for x since the resulting cubic equation in y cannot be solved easily; when $x = 1$, $y^3 - 3y + 1 = 0$, which has no obvious solution. The idea is to send out 'search rays' from the origin to find out where they meet the curve, so we substitute $y = tx$, where t is our parameter.

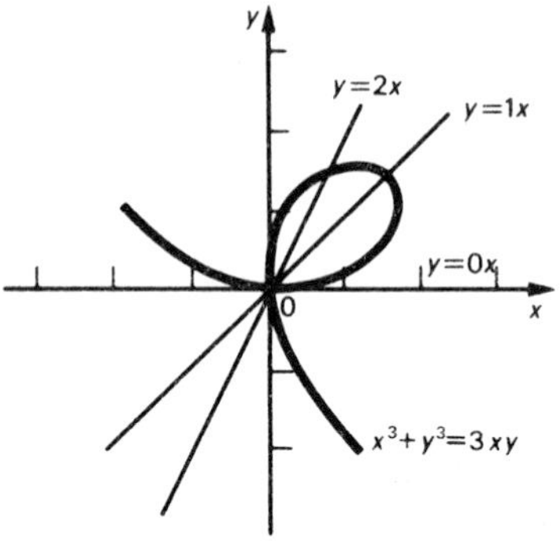

(i) $y = 0x$ gives $x = 0$
(ii) $y = 1x$ gives $x^3+x^3 = 3x^2$ or $2x^3 = 3x^2$, so $x = 0, \frac{3}{2}$
(iii) $y = 2x$ gives $x^3+8x^3 = 6x^2$. So $9x^3 = 6x^2$ and $x = 0, \frac{2}{3}$
. . . and so on.

The parametric equations are found by substituting $y = tx$, hence

$$x^3+t^3x^3 = 3x \times tx$$

$$x^3(1+t^3) = 3x^2t$$

$$x = 0 \quad \text{or} \quad x = \frac{3t}{1+t^3}$$

so

$$y = 0 \quad \text{or} \quad y = \frac{3t^2}{1+t^3}$$

The parametric equations are

$$x = \frac{3t}{1+t^3}, \qquad y = \frac{3t^2}{1+t^3}$$

and by taking different values for t we can plot all the points on the curve.

Exercise 3.1

Choose parametric equations to represent the following:

1 $y^2 = 12x$ **2** $\frac{x^2}{16}+\frac{y^2}{9} = 1$ **3** $\frac{x^3}{a^2}-\frac{y^2}{b^2} = 1$ **4** $y^2 = x^3$

By substituting $y = tx$, find parametric equations to represent the following:

5 $y^2 = x^3-x^2$ **6** $y^2 = x^2+3x$ **7** $y = 5x+1$

8 $xy = x-y$ **9** $y = x^2+4x$ **10** $3xy = y^2+9$

3.2 Curve sketching, given the parametric equations

Example 1

Sketch the curves given parametrically by $x = t^2$, $y = t^2 - 3t$ for $-6 \leqslant t \leqslant 6$.

t	−6	−5	−4	−3	−2	−1	0	1	2	3	4	5	6
$x = t^2$	36	25	16	9	4	1	0	1	4	9	16	25	36
$-3t$	18	15	12	9	6	3	0	−3	−6	−9	−12	−15	−18
$y = t^2 - 3t$	54	40	28	18	10	4	0	−2	−2	0	4	10	18

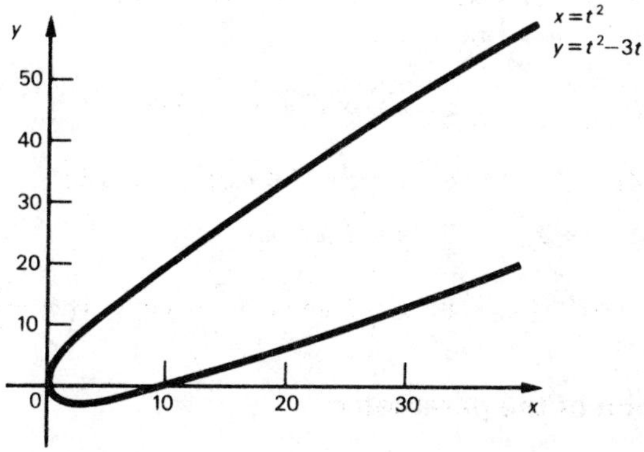

Example 2

Sketch the curve given parametrically by $x = \phi - \sin\phi$, $y = 1 - \cos\phi$ for $0 \leqslant \phi \leqslant 2\pi$.

ϕ	0	$\frac{\pi}{4}$	$\frac{\pi}{2}$	$\frac{3\pi}{4}$	π	$\frac{5\pi}{4}$	$\frac{3\pi}{2}$	$\frac{7\pi}{4}$	2π
ϕ^c	0	0.79	1.57	2.36	3.14	3.93	4.71	5.50	6.28
$\sin\phi$	0	0.71	1	0.71	0	−0.71	−1	−0.71	0
$\cos\phi$	1	0.71	0	−0.71	−1	−0.71	0	0.71	1
$x = \phi - \sin\phi$	0	0.08	0.57	1.65	3.14	4.64	5.71	6.21	6.28
$y = 1 - \cos\phi$	0	0.29	1	1.71	2	1.71	1	0.29	0

This is the *cycloid*, the path traced out by a point on the circumference of a circle as the circle rolls along a straight line.

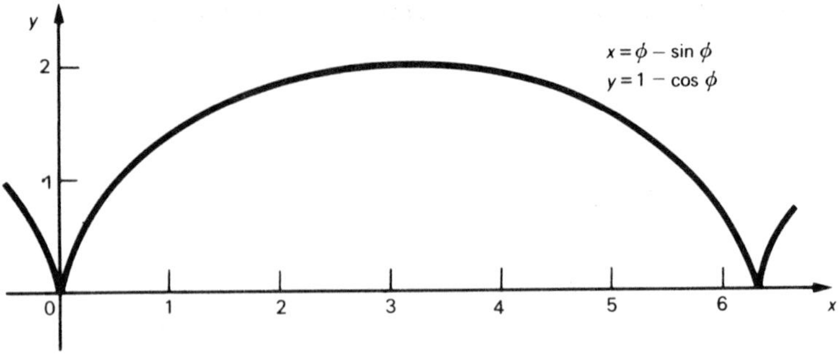

Exercise 3.2

Sketch the following curves whose equations have been given parametrically for $-6 \leqslant t \leqslant 6$ or for $0 \leqslant \phi \leqslant 2\pi$.

1 $x = \dfrac{12}{t}$, $y = t$

2 $x = 3t^2$, $y = 4t$

3 $x = 2t-1$, $y = 3t+2$

4 $x = 1+t$, $y = t+t^2$

5 $x = \cos 3\phi$, $y = \sin\phi$

6 $x = \cos(3\phi+\pi)$, $y = \cos 2\phi$

7 $x = 2\sec\phi$, $y = \tan\phi$

8 $x = 2\sin\left(\phi+\dfrac{\pi}{3}\right)$, $y = \cos\left(\phi-\dfrac{\pi}{4}\right)$

3.3 Elimination of the parameter

It is sometimes necessary to find the original cartesian equations from which the parametric equations have been derived.

Example 1

If $x = t+t^2$, $y = t^2+t^3$ find the cartesian equation of the locus.

Now $x = t(1+t)$, $y = t^2(1+t)$. Dividing, we get $y/x = t$. Now we substitute for t and find that

$$x = \frac{y}{x}\left(1+\frac{y}{x}\right)$$

$$x^3 = y(x+y)$$

$$x^3 = yx+y^2$$

NOTE that the curve can easily be sketched from its parametric form but not from its cartesian equation.

Example 2

Eliminate θ from the equations $x = \cos\theta+\sin\theta$, $y = \tan\theta$.

The second equation gives the trigonometric ratios for θ.

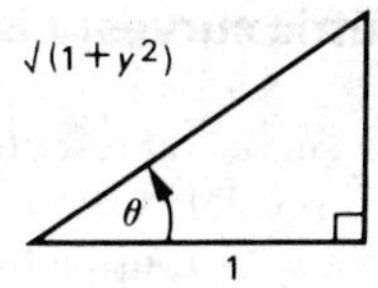

$$\tan\theta = y$$

hence
$$\cos\theta = \frac{1}{\surd(1+y^2)}$$

and
$$\sin\theta = \frac{y}{\surd(1+y^2)}$$

We substitute these values into the first equation:

$$x = \frac{1}{\surd(1+y^2)} + \frac{y}{\surd(1+y^2)}$$

$$x = \frac{1+y}{\surd(1+y^2)}$$

$$x^2 = \frac{(1+y)^2}{1+y^2}$$

$$x^2(1+y^2) = (1+y)^2$$

Exercise 3.3

Eliminate the parameter in the following, to give your solution as a cartesian equation in x and y.

1 $x = 4t-1, \quad y = 3t^2+2$

2 $x = 2t^2, \quad y = 3t^3$

3 $x = \dfrac{2t}{1+t^3}, \quad y = \dfrac{2t^2}{1+t^3}$

4 $x = \dfrac{t_1-t_2}{2}, \quad y = t_1^2+t_2^2, \quad t_1t_2 = -4$

5 $x = \dfrac{c(t_1+t_2)}{2}, \quad y = \dfrac{c}{2}\left(\dfrac{1}{t_1}+\dfrac{1}{t_2}\right), \quad t_1t_2 = -1$

6 $x = a\cos^3\theta, \quad y = a\sin^3\theta$

7 $x = \frac{1}{2}a\sin 2\theta\cos\theta, \quad y = \frac{1}{2}a\sin 2\theta\sin\theta$

8 $x = \sec\theta+\tan\theta, \quad y = \operatorname{cosec}\theta-1$

9 $x = \sin\theta+\cos\theta, \quad y = \sin 2\theta+\cos 2\theta$

10 Given that $x = \tan\theta-\sin\theta$, $y = \tan\theta+\sin\theta$, prove that $(x^2-y^2)^2 = 16xy$.

3.4 Combination of parametric curves; Lissajous' figures

We have not so far considered the curves represented by the parametric functions themselves. We now show how it is possible to combine the two functions, starting with the simple case of the parabola $y^2 = x$, using the parametric equations $x = t^2$, $y = t$.

Example 1

The table of values is as follows:

t	-3	-2	-1	0	1	2	3
$x = t^2$	9	4	1	0	1	4	9
$y = t$	-3	-2	-1	0	1	2	3

Here are rough sketches of $x = t^2$ and $y = t$:

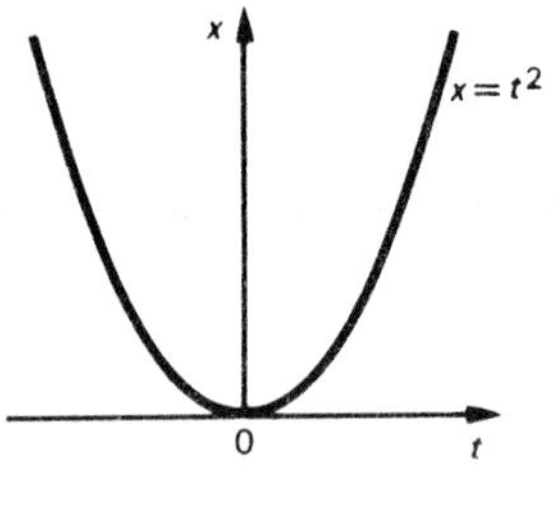

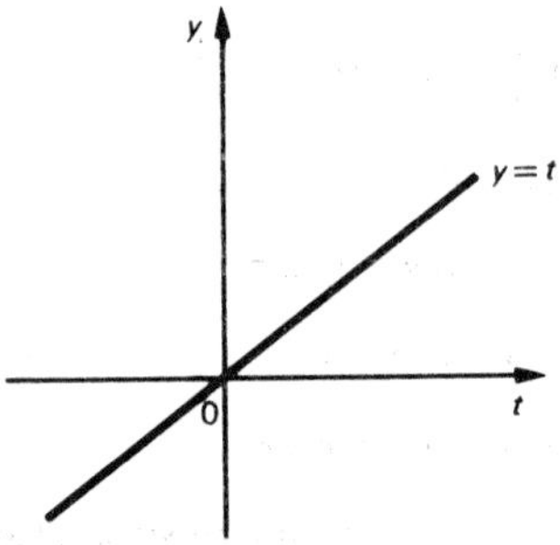

To combine these two, we arrange the two figures at right angles, using the same scales, so that the y values are on the usual y axis and the x values on the x axis. The values are then combined as shown:

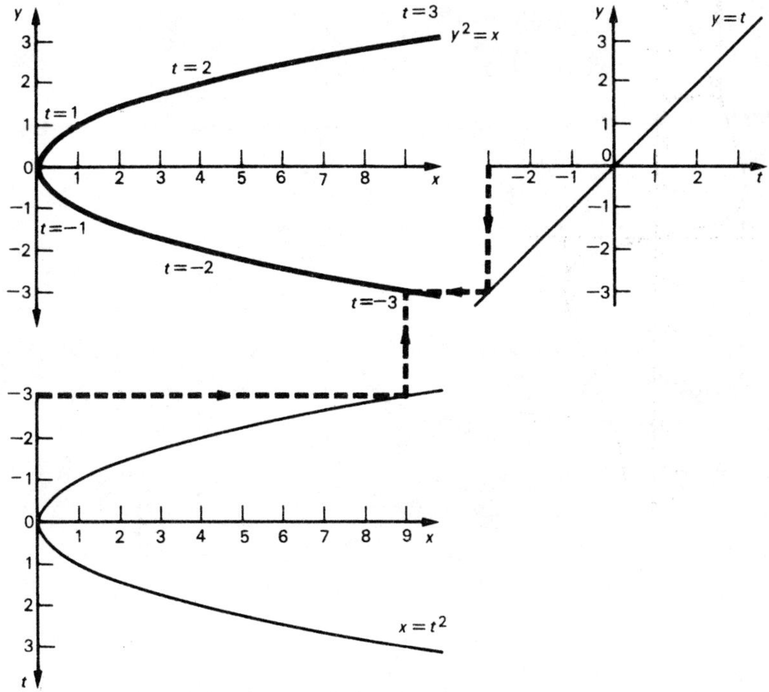

The bold dotted arrows illustrate the combination of x and y in the case when $t = -3$.

Here is a more complicated example.

Example 2

$$x = \frac{2t}{1+t^2}, \qquad y = \frac{1-t^2}{1+t^2}$$

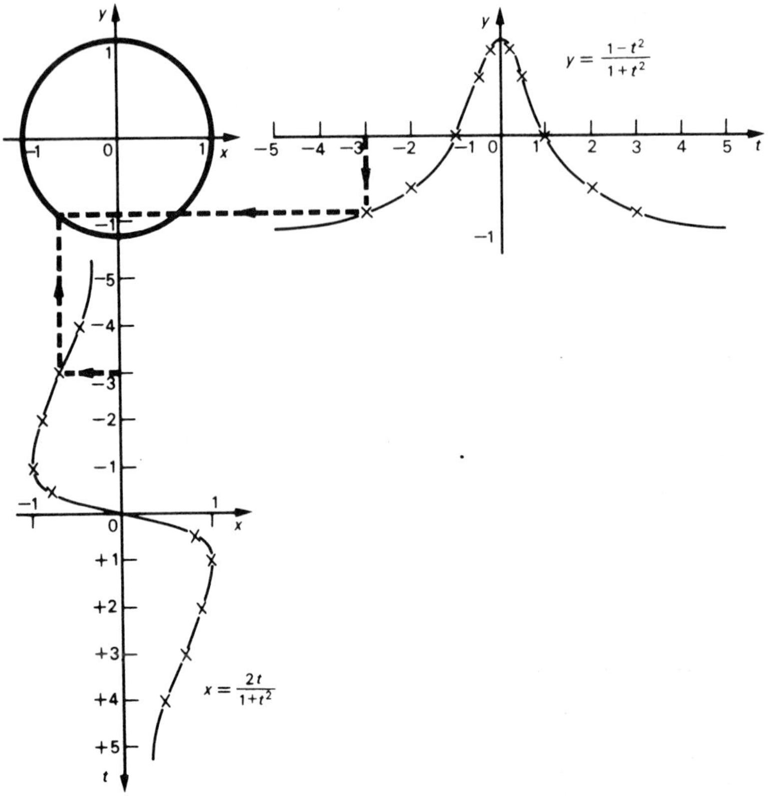

We have again shown how to find the point on the curve corresponding to $t = -3$. It seems, at first sight, surprising to find two such unlikely curves combining to give a circle. However, it becomes obvious why this is so if we substitute $t = \tan \theta/2$.

Lissajous' figures

Often, the parametric equations involve sine, cosine or other trigonometrical functions. In some cases it is easy to arrange a model of the situation by the use of two signal generators and a cathode-ray oscilloscope. The idea is that the parametric functions may be simulated by the generators and then applied to the appropriate X or Y plates of the oscilloscope, giving the picture of the 'combined' functions on the screen. See if you can persuade your physics teacher to give you a demonstration—he/she will know the resulting curves as Lissajous' figures.

Example 3

$x = \cos\phi$, $y = \sin\phi$

These combine to give the circle below, with equation $x^2 + y^2 = 1$.

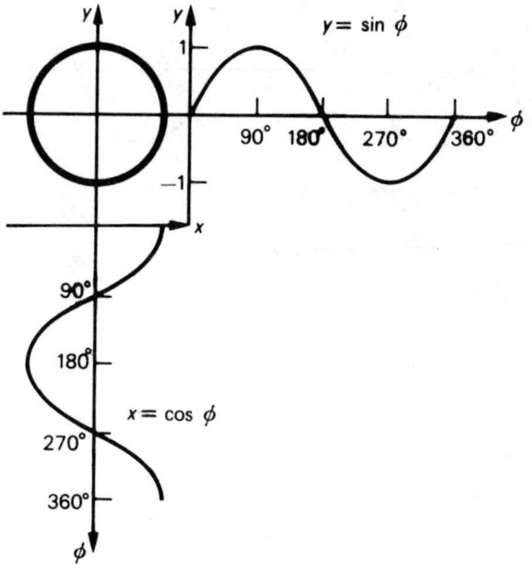

Example 4

$x = \sin\phi$, $y = \cos(\phi + \pi/4)$

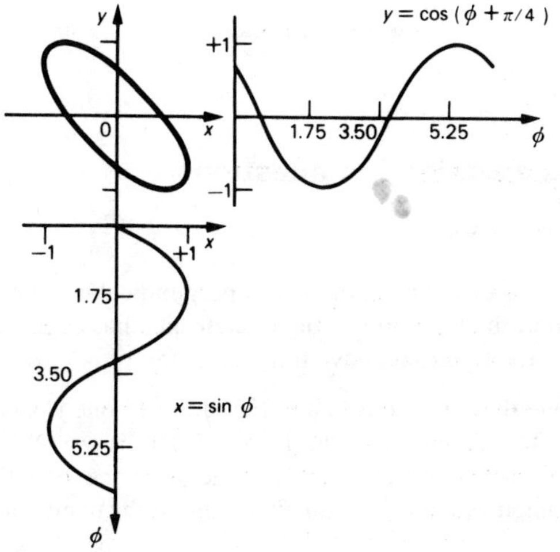

Example 5

$x = \sin 2\phi,\ y = \sin \phi$

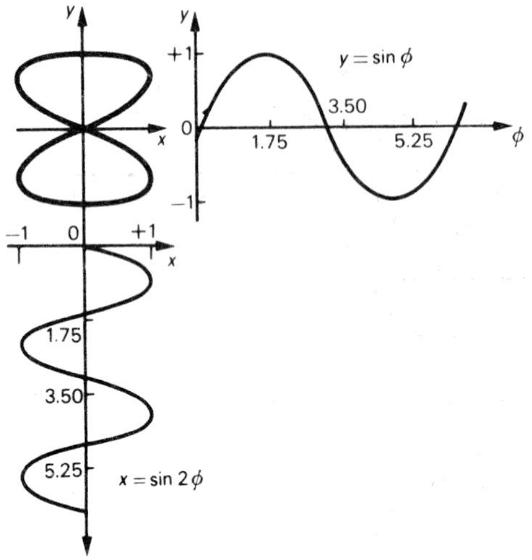

Exercise 3.4

Use the method shown above to sketch the curves represented by the following parametric equations.

1 $x = t^2,\ y = t^3$

2 $x = t + t^2,\ y = t^2 + t^3$

3 $x = \dfrac{6t}{1+t^3},\ y = \dfrac{t^2}{1+t^3}$

4 $x = \cos 2\phi,\ y = \sin \phi$

5 $x = \sin 3\phi,\ y = \sin 2\phi$

6 $x = \cos(3\phi + \pi/3),\ y = \sin(\phi - \pi/4)$

Miscellaneous examination questions 4

(O. unless otherwise stated)

1 Find the coordinates of the foot of the perpendicular from $(3, 2)$ to $x/-4 = (y - \frac{1}{2})/3$. Hence find the equation of the circle which has centre $(3, 2)$ and has the line as a tangent at the point you have found.

2 Two circles have the same centre, and the radius of one is five times as great as that of the other. The equation of the greater circle is $(x-24)^2 + (y-7)^2 = 625$. Find the equation of the smaller circle. Find also the equation of the circle which has for a diameter the line joining the origin to the common centre of the two circles. (O. & C.)

3 A is the point $(3, 2)$. Lines AB and AC are drawn with DR $4:3$ and $5:3$ respectively. Write down the equations of these lines.

Find the equation of the line through B and at right angles to AC, given that $AB = 15$ units. Find also the equation of the line through A which intersects the axes at equal positive distances from the origin. (O. & C.)

4 The triangle ABC has vertices A $(-5, 11)$, B $(-4, -2)$ and C $(5, 1)$. Find the coordinates of H, the point of intersection of the altitudes of the triangle. Without further working, write down the coordinates of the point of intersection of the altitudes of the triangle AHB. (O. & C.)

5 The vertices of a triangle are A $(-7, 9)$, B $(-9, -5)$ and C $(3, 4)$. Find the coordinates of the foot of the perpendicular from A to BC and prove that this point is a point of trisection of BC.

Calculate also the coordinates of the other point of trisection of BC. (O. & C.)

6 A circle passes through the points $(2, 0)$, $(12, 0)$ and $(0, 4)$. Calculate the distance from the origin to the other point in which the circle intersects the y axis. Hence calculate the centre and radius of the circle and give the equation of it in the form $(x-\alpha)^2+(y-\beta)^2 = r^2$ where (α, β) is its centre, r the radius. (O. & C.)

7 The equation $\lambda(x+2y-3)+\mu(8x+y+6) = 0$ represents a set of straight lines for different values of λ and μ. Write down the equations of the members of the set for which $\lambda = 0$, $\mu = 1$ and $\lambda = 1$, $\mu = 0$. Find the coordinates of A, their point of intersection, and show that every line of the set passes through A.

When $\lambda = 0$, $\mu = 1$ the line meets the y-axis in B and when $\lambda = 1$, $\mu = 0$ the line meets the x-axis in C. Find the coordinates of B and C.

Find values of λ and μ for the particular member of the set which passes through the mid-point of BC. Hence find the equation of this line and simplify it.

8 Calculate the coordinates of M, the foot of the perpendicular from B $(7, -4)$ to OA, where O is the origin and A is $(6, 3)$.

Hence calculate the coordinates of C and D, the other two vertices of the rhombus ABCD whose diagonals meet at M.

Find also the area of this rhombus.

9 The lines $x-3y+11 = 0$ and $3x-y+1 = 0$ form the two equal sides, AB and AC, of an isosceles triangle ABC. Find the coordinates of A and write down the gradients of AB and AC.

Prove that AB and AC make equal angles with the line $y = x$.

The third side, BC, of the triangle passes through the origin $(0, 0)$. Write down the equations of each of the possible lines BC which satisfy these conditions and find the coordinates of B in each case.

10 A $(3, 1)$ and C $(-3, 5)$ are opposite vertices of a rhombus. The vertex B of the rhombus lies on the line $7x-3y = 1$. Find the coordinates of B and also of D, the fourth vertex of the rhombus.

Verify that the length of one diagonal is twice the length of the other. Prove also that $\cos A\hat{B}C = \frac{3}{5}$.

Most of the rest of the examination questions involve a knowledge of calculus, and of tangents and normals to curves.

11 A is the point $(-1, 0)$ and B is $(1, 0)$. The two curves $y = x^2-1$ and $y = \cos \frac{1}{2}\pi x$ pass through A and B. Show the curves in a sketch.

The tangents at A and B to $y = x^2-1$ meet at C, while the tangents at A and B to $y = \cos \frac{1}{2}\pi x$ meet at D. Find the area of the quadrilateral ABCD.

Find in which quadrant the normal at A to $y = 1-x^2$ meets the normal at B to $y = \cos \frac{1}{2}\pi x$. Give clear reasons for your answer.

12 Find the equation of the tangent to $y = x^2/12$ at the point P $(18, 27)$ and the coordinates of the point R at which the tangent meets the y-axis. If S is the point $(0, 3)$ calculate the coordinates of Q, given that PQRS is a parallelogram with diagonal PR, and verify that QS is parallel to the normal at P. Hence or otherwise prove that PQRS is a rhombus and that PS and QP produced make equal angles with the normal at P.

13 Find the equation of the tangent to the curve $4y = x^2-6x+13$ at the point P on the curve where $x = 7$. Calculate the coordinates of the point A where this tangent meets the x axis.

Find the equation of the line through A parallel to the normal at P. Prove that this line is also a tangent to the curve and find the coordinates of the point of contact Q.

Prove that the length PQ is equal to the sum of the distances from P and Q to the x axis.

14 The chord AB of the parabola $y^2 = 16x$ passes through the point $(4, 0)$. If A is the point $(16, 16)$, find the coordinates of B.

Find the coordinates of the point P on the parabola at which the tangent is parallel to AB. Prove that the line joining P to the mid-point of AB is parallel to the axis of the parabola.

15 Find the equation of the tangent at the point A $(2, \frac{1}{4})$ to the curve which is given parametrically by the equations

$$x = \frac{1}{t}, \qquad y = t^2$$

Determine the coordinates of the point B where the tangent at A meets the curve again.

Prove that the normal at B does not meet the curve at any other point.

16 By giving values to the parameter t from -3 to 3, draw a sketch of the curve

$$x = t+2, \qquad y = t^2-1$$

Find the equation of the normal at the point A where $t = 1$, and find the parameter of the point B where this normal meets the curve again. Calculate the length of AB.

17 Find the equation of the chord joining the points whose parameters are 4 and 9 on the curve $x = 2t$, $y = 2/t$. Show that there are two points on the curve at which the tangent is parallel to this chord, and find the equations of the tangents at these points.

Find the equation of the tangent at the point where $t = u$, and hence the parameters of the points the tangents at which pass through $(-5, 1)$.

18 A curve is given parametrically by the equations

$$x = t - 1, \qquad y = \frac{1}{t+1}$$

By giving values to t, draw a rough sketch of the curve.

Find the equation of the chord joining the point $t = -2$ to the point $t = \frac{5}{4}$. Prove that there is no tangent to the curve parallel to this chord, but find the parameters of the points of the curve at which the normals are parallel to this chord.

19 Find the equations of the tangent and normal to the curve $x = t+2$, $y = t^2-1$ at the point P which has parameter $\frac{1}{2}$. Find the parameter of the point Q on the curve at which the tangent is parallel to the normal at P, and find the equation of this tangent.

These two tangents intersect on the line $y = k$. Prove that the length PQ is equal to the sum of the distances from P to $y = k$ and from Q to $y = k$.

20 A curve is given parametrically by the equations $x = t^2$, $y = t^3$. Find the equation of the tangent at the point where $t = u$ and calculate the coordinates of the point at which this tangent meets the curve again.

Find also the parametric equations of the set of midpoints of the line segment cut off on the tangent by the curve as u varies.

21 Sketch the curves whose parametric equations are

(a) $x = a\cos^3 t, \qquad y = a\sin^3 t$

(b) $x = 2t^2+1, \qquad y = t^2-2t$

22 A circle centre A and of radius a is rolled without slipping along the x axis. Originally a marked point P on the circumference of the circle is at the origin O. The circle rolls so that OB = PB and $\angle$PAB $= \theta$. Find the parametric equation of the locus and draw an accurate sketch of it.

23 Sketch the curves whose parametric equations are

(a) $x = 2\theta + \sin 2\theta, \qquad y = 4\sin\theta$

(b) $x = t^2, \qquad y = t - t^3$

Chapter 5

Series 2

1 Binomial theorem

1.1 Introduction

In a glass factory jars of all shapes and sizes, sherry decanters, glass egg-cups—and, of course, glasses—are made by taking the molten glass, moulding it, cooling it, removing any rough edges, and finally packing the products into attractive boxes. A number of processes are involved and as a result some of the glass may be misshapen, for a variety of reasons.

It is most important to test each product for shape, texture and cracks; the factory's reputation depends on the thoroughness with which this checking procedure is done. Any article with only a small defect is sold in the 'seconds' shop next door, while those with more serious flaws are melted down and remade.

After the 'seconds' have been removed the products are divided into two groups: those which are good (and saleable) are labelled G, and those with a defect are labelled D. So at the end of the inspection process any single article of glassware will have been labelled either G or D and the checking system can be tabulated as follows.

One article will be either

G or D

Two articles may be

GG	or	GD	or	DD
		DG		

Three articles may be

GGG	or	GGD	or	GDD	or	DDD
		GDG		DGD		
		DGG		DDG		

Four articles may be

GGGG	or	GGGD	or	GGDD	or	GDDD	or	DDDD
		GGDG		GDGD		DGDD		
		GDGG		GDDG		DDGD		
		DGGG		DDGG		DDDG		
				DGDG				
				DGGD				

. . . and so on.

From this table we can easily see the number of ways in which each outcome can occur:

1 article:	G	or	D						
Number of ways:	1		1						
2 articles:	GG	or	GD DG	or	DD				
Number of ways:	1		2		1				
3 articles:	GGG	or	GGD GDG DGG	or	GDD DGD DDG	or	DDD		
Number of ways:	1		3		3		1		
4 articles:	GGGG	or	GGGD GGDG GDGG DGGG	or	GGDD GDGD GDDG DDGG DGDG DGGD	or	GDDD DGDD DDGD DDDG	or	DDDD
Number of ways:	1		4		6		4		1

Suppose we consider GG as G^2, GD = DG, DD = D^2; GGD = GDG = DGG as G^2D and so on. We now have

1 article:	G	or	D						
Number of ways:	1		1						
2 articles:	G^2	or	GD	or	D^2				
Number of ways:	1		2		1				
3 articles:	G^3	or	G^2D	or	GD^2	or	D^3		
Number of ways:	1		3		3		1		
4 articles:	G^4	or	G^3D	or	G^2D^2	or	GD^3	or	D^4
Number of ways:	1		4		6		4		1

Is this a pattern that you have seen before?

$$G+D = 1G+1D$$

$$(G+D)^2 = 1G^2+2GD+1D^2$$

$$(G+D)^3 = 1G^3+3G^2D+3GD^2+1D^3$$

$$(G+D)^4 = 1G^4+4G^3D+6G^2D^2+4GD^3+1D^4$$

Pascal's triangle

The numbers in this pattern have been known for many, many years and are the numbers in the Chinese (or Pascal's) triangle.

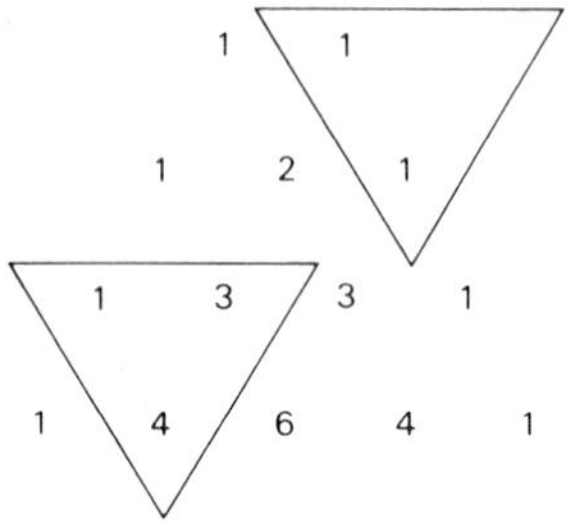

Written this way, each number is the sum of the two above it, as shown. (Where there is no number we count it as zero.)

Write down for yourself the next four rows of the pattern, until you reach

$$1 \quad 8 \quad 28 \quad 56 \quad 70 \quad 56 \quad 28 \quad 8 \quad 1$$

Now answer, in terms **(a)** of the glassware, and **(b)** of $(G+D)^8$, these questions: What is the meaning of the first 8? Of the 70? And of the 28?

We can extend the pattern indefinitely, but frequently we shall want to know particular numbers in the pattern without having to write out the complete sequence. Is there some formula which will give us one particular term? (See diagram at top of next page.)

The ratio of the numbers in the second diagonal to those in the first, of the numbers in the third diagonal to those in the second and so on, have been entered in the circles between the numbers. From the ratios we can easily find the nth row as

$$1 \qquad n \qquad \frac{n(n-1)}{2} \qquad \frac{n(n-1)(n-2)}{2\times 3} \qquad \frac{n(n-1)(n-2)(n-3)}{2\times 3\times 4} \ldots$$

This means that when n is a positive integer

$$(G+D)^n = 1G^n + nG^{n-1}D + \frac{n(n-1)}{2}G^{n-2}D^2$$

$$+\frac{n(n-1)(n-1)}{2\times 3}G^{n-3}D^3 + \ldots + nGD^{n-1} + D^n$$

NOTE

1 The total of the powers of G and D is always n in each term; for instance in

$$\frac{n(n-1)}{2}G^{n-2}D^2$$

The total of the powers is $n-2+2 = n$.

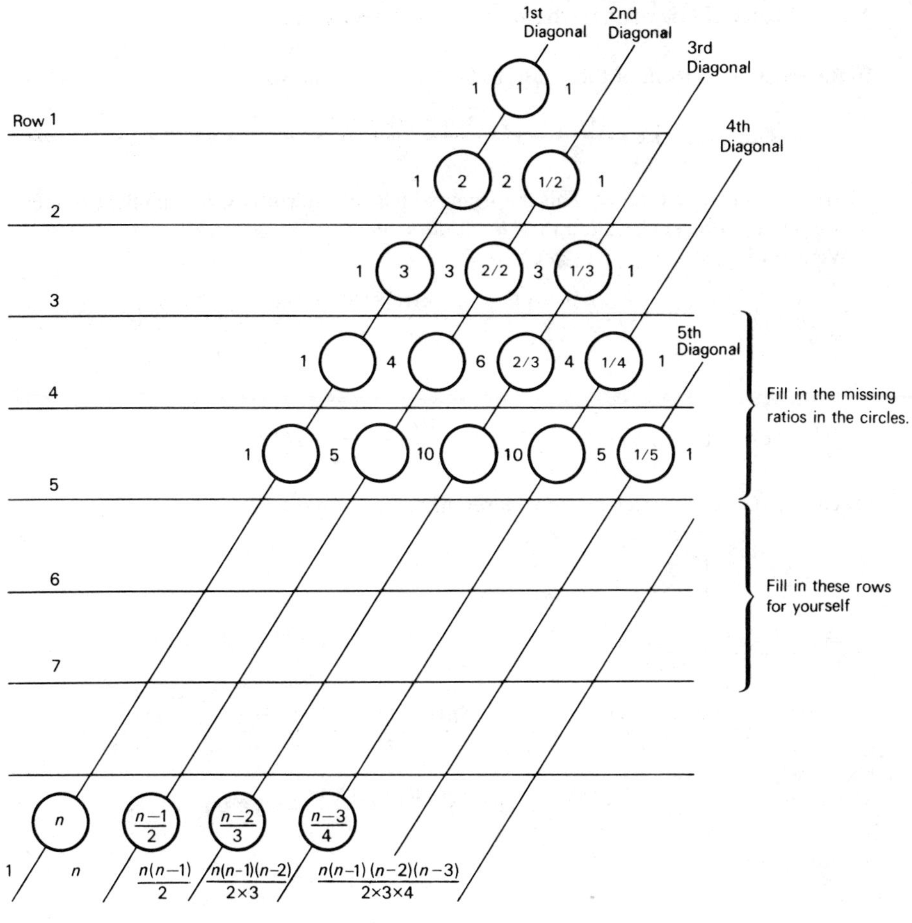

2 The pattern is symmetrical with two equal middle terms when n is odd, or one central term when n is even.

3 In the denominators of each term we have numbers like 1×2, $1\times2\times3$, $1\times2\times3\times4$, and so on (we have put in the 1 to clarify the idea). We have a shorthand way of writing these numbers, for example $1\times2\times3\times4 = 4!$ (read as 'four factorial'); $17!$ would mean $1\times2\times3\times4\times\ldots\times15\times16\times17$. $6! = 1\times2\times3\times4\times6 = 720$. We define $0!$ as 1 to fit in with our later work.

4 It is now possible to pick out a 'general' term (this time the $(r+1)^{\text{th}}$) which will be

$$\frac{n(n-1)(n-2)\ldots(n-r+1)}{r!}G^{n-r}D^{r}$$

5 This is *not* a proof of the expansion but rather a demonstration. If we wish to prove that it is true, we must use the method of induction. The proof is at the end of the chapter (page 191).

1.2 Binomial theorem when n is a positive integer

In the most usual form of the theorem G = 1, D = x and so

$$(1+x)^n = 1+nx+\frac{n(n-1)}{2!}x^2+\frac{n(n-1)(n-2)}{3!}x^3+\ldots+nx^{n-1}+1x^n \quad ◀$$

where n is a positive integer. This theorem (which is to do with expanding the sum of *two terms* to a power) is called the *binomial theorem.*

We can replace x by $-x$ to get

$$(1-x)^2 = 1+n(-x)+\frac{n(n-1)}{2!}(-x)^2+\frac{n(n-1)(n-2)}{3!}(-x)^3+\ldots+1(-x)^n$$

or x by $2x$ to get

$$(1+2x)^2 = 1+n(2x)+\frac{n(n-1)}{2!}(2x)^2+\frac{n(n-1)(n-2)}{3!}(2x)^3+\ldots+1(2x)^n$$

Of course $(\mathrm{G}+\mathrm{D})^n$, which we considered first, can be written

$$\left\{\mathrm{G}\left(1+\frac{\mathrm{D}}{\mathrm{G}}\right)\right\}^n$$

$$=\mathrm{G}^n\left(1+\frac{\mathrm{D}}{\mathrm{G}}\right)^n$$

$$=\mathrm{G}^n\left\{1+n\frac{\mathrm{D}}{\mathrm{G}}+\frac{n(n-1)}{2!}\left(\frac{\mathrm{D}}{\mathrm{G}}\right)^2+\frac{n(n-1)(n-2)}{3!}\left(\frac{\mathrm{D}}{\mathrm{G}}\right)^3+\ldots+\left(\frac{\mathrm{D}}{\mathrm{G}}\right)^n\right\}$$

$$=\mathrm{G}^n+n\mathrm{G}^{n-1}\mathrm{D}+\frac{n(n-1)}{2!}\mathrm{G}^{n-2}\mathrm{D}^2+\frac{n(n-1)(n-2)}{3!}\mathrm{G}^{n-3}\mathrm{D}^3+\ldots+\mathrm{D}^n$$

exactly as before.

Exercise 1.2

Use the binomial theorem to expand the following, giving the first four terms in the series and the last term.

1 $(1-2x)^7$ **2** $(1+2x)^5$ **3** $(1-\frac{1}{2}x)^6$

4 $(3+x)^8$ [Hint: $3+x=3\left(1+\frac{x}{3}\right)$] **5** $(2-3x)^6$

6 $(x+2y)^{10}$ **7** $(3y+2x)^5$ **8** $(2x-4y)^7$

9 $(x^2+y^2)^7$ **10** $(2-x(1-x))^3$ [Hint: Think of 2 as the first term, $-x(1-x)$ as the second]

Write down the coefficient of x^r in the expansion of

11 $(1+2x)^n$ **12** $(1-3x)^n$ **13** $(1+\frac{1}{2}x)^n$

14 $(1+x^2)^n$ **15** $(2x-3y)^n$

16 In a table of cubes, the value of 80^3 is 512,000. Use the binomial theorem to find an approximate value of 80.01^3.

17(a) Find the coefficient of x^3 in the expansion of $(2+3x)^5$.

(b) Using the binomial theorem to find the coefficient of x^4 in the product of $(1-2x)^5$ and $(1+2x)^5$.

18 The third and fifth terms in the expansion of $(1+x)^n$, where x and n are positive integers, are 112 and 1120 respectively. Find the values of x and n.

19(a) Write down the first four terms in the expansion of $(1-x)^{10}$ using the binomial theorem.

(b) Employ the binomial theorem to find 99^4.

1.3 Notation for binomial coefficients

The coefficients (the numbers in the Chinese triangle) are the number of ways in which it is possible to choose r out of n things, not taking into account the possible orders.

The nth row is

1	n	$\frac{n(n-1)}{2!}$	$\frac{n(n-1)(n-2)}{3!}$	...	$\frac{n(n-1)(n-2)\ldots(n-r+1)}{r!}$	...
↑	↑	↑	↑		↑	
Number of ways of choosing 0 from n	Number of ways of choosing 1 from n	Number of ways of choosing 2 from n	Number of ways of choosing 3 from n		Number of ways of choosing r from n	
$^nC_0$	$^nC_1$	$^nC_2$	$^nC_3$		^nC_r	
$\binom{n}{0}$	$\binom{n}{1}$	$\binom{n}{2}$	$\binom{n}{3}$		$\binom{n}{r}$	

You will often meet the shorthand notations shown in the bottom two rows, but we shall use the numbers from the nth row as given above—not the shorthand. The numerical values of the binomial coefficients are given in SMP Advanced Level Tables.

1.4 When *n* is a positive fraction

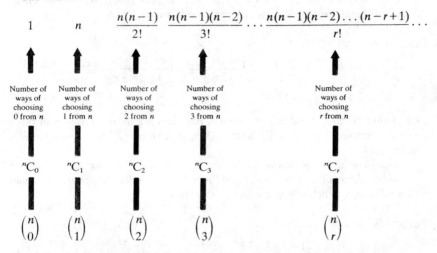

One of the most remarkable features of mathematics is that frequently we may prove a theorem for n being a positive integer, and find (sometimes to our surprise)

that the theorem is also true for n being a positive fraction. This is true of the binomial theorem. The proof is rather different and depends on Maclaurin's theorem (which you will meet in Calculus). Consider, for example, the expansion of $(1+x)^{1/2}$. Using the binomial theorem and supposing it works for $n=\frac{1}{2}$, we have

$$(1+x)^{1/2}=1+\tfrac{1}{2}x+\frac{\frac{1}{2}\times-\frac{1}{2}}{1\times 2}x^2+\frac{\frac{1}{2}\times-\frac{1}{2}\times-\frac{3}{2}}{1\times 2\times 3}x^3+\ldots$$

Previously the series ended after $n+1$ terms since the coefficient of x^{n+1} would be

$$\frac{n(n-1)(n-2)\ldots\{n-(n+1)-1\}}{(n+1)!}$$

which equals zero. (This is the general term with $r=n+1$.) Since r is a positive integer it is quite clear from the expansion that in the coefficients of $(1+x)^{1/2}$ we have numbers which can never be zero, so the terms continue as

$$\frac{\frac{1}{2}\times-\frac{1}{2}\times-\frac{3}{2}\times-\frac{5}{2}}{1\times 2\times 3\times 4}x^4+\frac{\frac{1}{2}\times-\frac{1}{2}\times-\frac{3}{2}\times-\frac{5}{2}\times-\frac{7}{2}}{1\times 2\times 3\times 4\times 5}x^5+\ldots$$

$$+\frac{\frac{1}{2}(\frac{1}{2}-1)(\frac{1}{2}-2)\ldots(\frac{1}{2}-r+1)}{r!}x^r+\ldots$$

Hence the series continues for ever and is an *infinite series.* We should check however, that the expansion does give reasonable answers!

Put $x=2$

$$3^{1/2}=1+\tfrac{1}{2}\times 2+\frac{\frac{1}{2}\times-\frac{1}{2}}{1\times 2}2^2+\frac{\frac{1}{2}\times-\frac{1}{2}\times-\frac{3}{2}}{1\times 2\times 3}2^3+\frac{\frac{1}{2}\times-\frac{1}{2}\times-\frac{3}{2}\times-\frac{5}{2}}{1\times 2\times 3\times 4}2^4+\ldots$$

$$=1+1-\tfrac{1}{2}+\tfrac{1}{2}-\tfrac{5}{8}+\tfrac{7}{8}-\ldots$$

Considering the right-hand side, the sum of one term is 1, of two terms 2, of three terms 1.5, of four terms 2, of five terms 1.375, of six terms 2.25, of seven terms is 0.9375 . . . .

This looks peculiar! We know that $3^{1/2}(=\sqrt{3})=1.732\ldots$ but our series does not seem to be adding up to this value. Could it be because $\sqrt{3}$ is irrational? Try again with a value of x which will give us an easier series.

Put $x=3$

$$4^{1/2}(=2)=1+\tfrac{1}{2}\times 3+\frac{\frac{1}{2}\times-\frac{1}{2}}{1\times 2}3^2+\frac{\frac{1}{2}\times-\frac{1}{2}\times-\frac{3}{2}}{1\times 2\times 3}3^3+\ldots$$

$$=1+\tfrac{3}{2}-\tfrac{9}{8}+\tfrac{27}{16}-\ldots$$

This time the sum of one term is 1, of two terms $2\frac{1}{2}$, of three terms $1\frac{3}{8}$, of four terms $3\frac{1}{16}$. This once again does not seem to be coming nearer to the value we want, which is 2.

What is happening?

If the series is to have a sum, the more terms we take, the nearer the value must be to that sum; as we get further along the series, the terms *must get smaller.* They may be positive or negative but they must get smaller. In the two series above, the terms are getting larger. It is clearly the *value of* x which is crucial—the value which is being substituted in the series.

Finally, hopefully, we substitute $x = \frac{1}{2}$.

Put $x = \frac{1}{2}$

$$(1\tfrac{1}{2})^{1/2}(\approx 1.225) = 1+\tfrac{1}{2}(\tfrac{1}{2})+\frac{\frac{1}{2}\times-\frac{1}{2}}{1.2}\times(\tfrac{1}{2})^2+\frac{\frac{1}{2}\times-\frac{1}{2}\times-\frac{3}{2}}{1\times2\times3}(\tfrac{1}{2})^3+\frac{\frac{1}{2}\times-\frac{1}{2}\times-\frac{3}{2}\times-\frac{5}{2}(\frac{1}{2})^4}{1\times2\times3\times4}+\ldots$$

$$= 1+\tfrac{1}{4}-\tfrac{1}{32}+\tfrac{1}{128}-\ldots$$

The sum of one term is 1, of two terms 1.25, of three terms 1.2197, of four terms 1.2275 and so on.

The three graphs illustrating the substitutions show what is happening. On the x axis is the number of terms and on the y axis their sum.

(1) Substituting $x = 2$

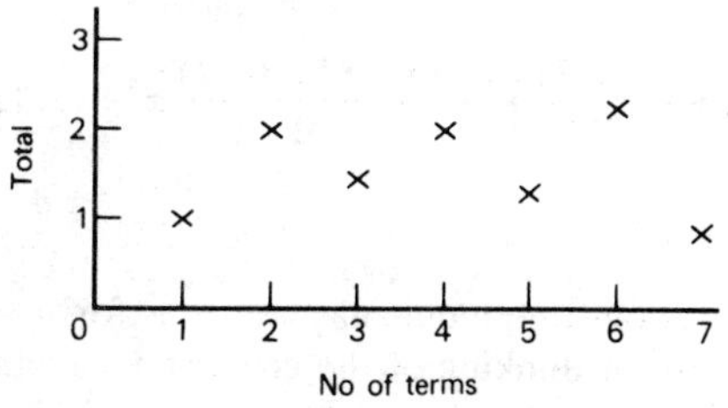

Diverging series

(2) Substituting $x = 3$

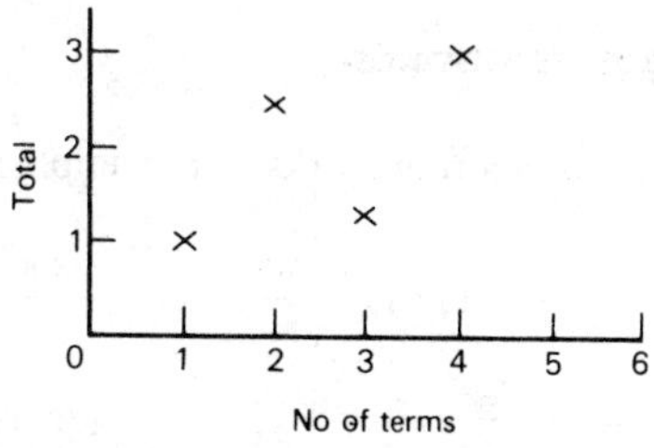

Diverging series

(3) Substituting $x = \frac{1}{2}$

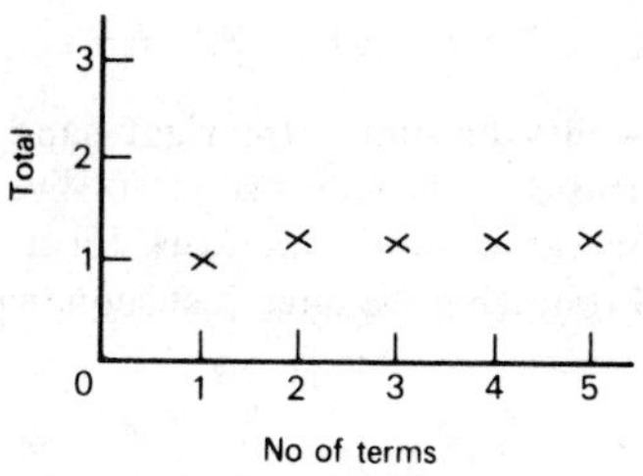

Converging series

The sum is alternately a little above and then a little below the true sum, getting closer to it each time.

We now know that the series will converge (or have a sum) if x is small, i.e. x lies between -1 and $+1$. The only question now is: does the series work if $x = 1$?

Put $x = 1$

$$2^{1/2}(\approx 1.414) = 1+\tfrac{1}{2}\times 1+\frac{\frac{1}{2}\times-\frac{1}{2}}{1\times 2}1^2+\frac{\frac{1}{2}\times-\frac{1}{2}\times-\frac{3}{2}}{1\times 2\times 3}1^3+\frac{\frac{1}{2}\times-\frac{1}{2}\times-\frac{3}{2}\times-\frac{5}{2}}{1\times 2\times 3\times 4}1^4+\ldots$$

$$= 1+\tfrac{1}{2}-\tfrac{1}{8}+\tfrac{1}{16}-\tfrac{5}{128}+\ldots$$

The sum of one term is 1, of two terms 1.5, of three terms 1.375, of four terms 1.4375, of five terms 1.3984 and so on. The series is slowly converging on $\sqrt{2}$, and the series *does* work when $x = 1$. However, this depends on the power n (in this case $n = \frac{1}{2}$). We usually play for safety in our series and say that x lies between -1 and $+1$.

The binomial theorem when n is a positive fraction is given as

$$\mathbf{(1+x)^n = 1+nx+\frac{n(n-1)}{2!}x^2+\frac{n(n-1)(n-2)}{3!}x^3+\ldots}\ \textbf{(an infinite series)} \blacktriangleleft$$

provided that $-1 < x < +1$.

NOTE that the series follows the identical pattern as for n a positive integer but there can be no question of thinking of the coefficients as the number of ways of choosing so many things (r) out of n (which might be the number of ways of choosing two things out of half a thing!).

1.5 When n is a negative number

Let us again suppose that the theorem works, for example with $n = -1$. Then

$$\frac{1}{1+x} = (1+x)^{-1} = 1+(-1)x+\frac{(-1)(-2)}{1\times 2}x^2+\frac{(-1)(-2)(-3)x^3}{1\times 2\times 3}+\ldots$$

$$= 1-x+x^2-x^3+x^4-\ldots \quad \text{(again an infinite series)}$$

Put $x = 2$, as previously

$$\tfrac{1}{3} = 3^{-1} = 1-2+4-8+16-\ldots$$

The left-hand side is $0.\dot{3}$, whilst the sum of the right-hand side is: of one term 1, of two terms -1, of three terms 3, of four terms -5, of five terms $+11$—going from bad to worse! The series certainly does not work for $x = 2$, since the terms are getting larger and larger. From what we have just seen, we ought to try $x = 1$.

Put $x = 1$

$$\tfrac{1}{2} = 2^{-1} = 1-1+1-1+1\ldots$$

The left-hand side is 0.5, whilst the sum of the right-hand side is: of one term 1, of two terms 0, of three terms 1, and so on alternating between 0 and 1. The sum cannot possibly be 0.5.

Put $x = \frac{1}{2}$

$$\frac{1}{1+\frac{1}{2}} = (1+\tfrac{1}{2})^{-1} = 1+-1(\tfrac{1}{2})+\frac{-1\times-2}{1\times2}(\tfrac{1}{2})^2+\frac{-1\times-2\times-3}{1\times2\times3}(\tfrac{1}{2})^3+\ldots$$

$$= 1-\tfrac{1}{2}+\tfrac{1}{4}-\tfrac{1}{8}+\ldots$$

i.e. $$0.6 = 1-\tfrac{1}{2}+\tfrac{1}{4}-\tfrac{1}{8}+\tfrac{1}{16}-\ldots$$

The sums of the right-hand side are 1, 0.5, 0.75, 0.625, 0.6875 which appear to be converging on 0.6.

The binomial theorem when n is a negative number is given as

$$\boldsymbol{(1+x)^n = 1+nx+\frac{n(n-1)}{2!}x^2+\frac{n(n-1)(n-2)}{3!}x^3+\ldots}$$ **(an infinite series)** ◀

provided that $-1 < x < +1$.

We have shown that the theorem works when $n = -1$, a negative integer, and could similarly show that it works when n is a negative fraction.

NOTE. The proviso that $-1 < x < 1$ can be expressed as $|x| < 1$, i.e. the *numerical* value of x is less than 1.

Validity of expansions

The validity of the series depends on the conditions. Some examples will clarify the idea.

Example 1

Expand $$\frac{1}{(1+2x)^2}$$

when **(a)** x is 'small' (i.e. $-\frac{1}{2} < x < \frac{1}{2}$) and **(b)** x is 'large' (i.e. $x > \frac{1}{2}$).

(a) $$(1+2x)^{-2} = 1+(-2)(2x)+\frac{-2\times-3}{1\times2}(2x)^2+\ldots$$

provided $-1 < 2x < 1, -\frac{1}{2} < x < \frac{1}{2}$.

(b) We rewrite the expansion $(1+2x)^{-2}$ so that instead of having a series with powers of $2x$ (which are now large) we have a series of powers of $\frac{1}{2}x$ (now small).

$$\frac{1}{(1+2x)^2} = \frac{1}{\left\{2x\left(\frac{1}{2x}+1\right)\right\}^2} = \frac{1}{\left\{2x\left(1+\frac{1}{2x}\right)\right\}^2} = \frac{1}{4x^2\left(1+\frac{1}{2x}\right)^2}$$

$$= \frac{1}{4x^2}\left(1+\frac{1}{2x}\right)^{-2}$$

$$= \frac{1}{4x^2}\left(1+(-2)\left(\frac{1}{2x}\right)+\frac{-2\times -3}{1\times 2}\left(\frac{1}{2x}\right)^2+\frac{-2\times -3\times -4}{1\times 2\times 3}\left(\frac{1}{2x}\right)^3\right)$$

provided $-1 < 1/2x < 1$ or $x > \frac{1}{2}$, $x < -\frac{1}{2}$.

Exercise 1.5

1 Expand the following, giving the first four terms and stating when the series is valid.

(a) $(1+x)^{-3}$

(b) $(1-2x)^{3/4}$

(c) $\dfrac{1}{\sqrt{(1+x^2)}}$

(d) $(1-x)^{-2}$

(e) $(1+3x)^{-1/2}$

(f) $(5x-1)^{-2}$

(g) $(1-2x)^{2/3}$

(h) $(1-x^2)^{-4/5}$

(i) $\sqrt{(9+x^2)}$

(j) $\dfrac{x}{\sqrt{(1-x^2)}}$

(k) $(1+nx)^{1/n}$

2 Write down the named terms in the series of the following

(a) 5th term in $(1-3x)^{-2}$ if $-\frac{1}{3}<x<\frac{1}{3}$

(b) 4th term in $(1+2x)^{3/2}$ if $-\frac{1}{2}<x<\frac{1}{2}$

(c) 6th term in $(1+3x^2)^{-5/2}$ if $-\dfrac{1}{\sqrt{3}}<x<\dfrac{1}{\sqrt{3}}$

(d) 7th term in $(1-5x)^{-n}$ if $-\frac{1}{5}<x<\frac{1}{5}$

3 Repeat question 2, expanding the expression in each case when x is large.

Example 2

Put $x=\frac{1}{3}$ in the expansion of $(1-x)^{-2}$ and hence find the approximate error in using the first four terms in the series.

$$\text{Now } (1-x)^{-2} = 1+(-2)(-x)+\frac{(-2)(-3)}{1\times 2}(-x)^2+\frac{(-2)(-3)(-4)}{1\times 2\times 3}(-x)^3+\ldots$$

$$= 1+2x+3x^2+4x^3 \qquad \text{(to four terms)}$$

$$(1-\tfrac{1}{3})^{-2} = 1+2(\tfrac{1}{3})+3(\tfrac{1}{3})^2+4(\tfrac{1}{3})^3$$

$$= 1+0.667+0.3333+0.1481$$

$$= 2.1481$$

But $$(1-\tfrac{1}{3})^{-2} = (\tfrac{2}{3})^{-2} = \frac{1}{(\frac{2}{3})^2} = \frac{1}{\frac{4}{9}} = 2.2500$$

Hence the error is $2.2500-2.1481 = 0.1019$.

Example 3

Use the expansion of $(1+\frac{2}{25})^{1/2}$ to find $\sqrt{3}$ correct to four decimal places.

Now $$(1+x)^{1/2} = 1+\tfrac{1}{2}x+\frac{\frac{1}{2}\times-\frac{1}{2}}{1\times 2}x^2+\frac{\frac{1}{2}\times-\frac{1}{2}\times-\frac{3}{2}}{1\times 2\times 3}x^3$$

$$= 1+\tfrac{1}{2}x-\tfrac{1}{8}x^2+\tfrac{1}{16}x^3+\dots$$

Put $$x = \tfrac{2}{25} = 0.08$$

Then $$(1+x)^{1/2} = 1+0.04-0.0008+0.000\,032$$

$$= 1.039\,238$$

But $$(1+\tfrac{2}{25})^{1/2} = (\tfrac{27}{25})^{1/2} = \tfrac{3}{5}\sqrt{3}$$

Hence $$\sqrt{3} = \frac{5\times 1.039\,238}{3}$$

$$= 1.732\,063$$

Correct to four decimal places $\sqrt{3} = 1.7321$.

Example 4

If x is small, find an approximation for

$$\sqrt[3]{\left(\frac{1-2x}{1+2x}\right)}$$

(neglect terms in x^4 and higher powers of x).

Now

$$\sqrt[3]{\left(\frac{1-2x}{1+2x}\right)} = (1-2x)^{1/3}(1+2x)^{-1/3}$$

$$= \left\{1+\tfrac{1}{3}(-2x)+\frac{\frac{1}{3}\times-\frac{2}{3}(-2x)^2}{1\times 2}+\frac{\frac{1}{3}\times-\frac{2}{3}\times-\frac{5}{3}}{1\times 2\times 3}(-2x)^3\right\}$$

$$\times\left\{1+-\tfrac{1}{3}(2x)+\frac{-\frac{1}{3}\times-\frac{4}{3}}{1\times 2}(2x)^2+\frac{-\frac{1}{3}\times-\frac{4}{3}\times-\frac{7}{3}}{1\times 2\times 3}(2x)^3\right\}$$

$$= \{1-\tfrac{2}{3}x-\tfrac{4}{9}x^2-\tfrac{40}{81}x^3\}\{1-\tfrac{2}{3}x+\tfrac{8}{9}x^2-\tfrac{112}{81}x^3\}$$

$$= 1-\tfrac{2}{3}x+\tfrac{8}{9}x^2-\tfrac{112}{81}x^3$$

$$-\tfrac{2}{3}x+\tfrac{4}{9}x^2-\tfrac{16}{27}x^3$$

$$-\tfrac{4}{9}x^2+\tfrac{8}{27}x^3$$

$$-\tfrac{40}{81}x^3$$

$$= 1-\tfrac{4}{3}x+\tfrac{8}{9}x^2-\tfrac{176}{81}x^3$$

Exercise 1.6

1 Find the percentage error in using the first four terms in the series for

(a) $(1+2x)^{-3}$ and putting $x=\frac{1}{4}$
(b) $(1-3x)^{-2}$ and putting $x=\frac{1}{9}$

2 Find from binomial expansions

(a) $\sqrt{1.04}$ to five decimal places
(b) $\sqrt[3]{888}$ to five decimal places
(c) $\sqrt{7}$ to five decimal places using the expansion of $(1-\frac{1}{64})^{1/2}$

3 Find approximations for the following (neglect terms in x^4 and higher powers of x).

(a) $(1+x)^{1/3}-(1-x)^{-1/3}$ **(b)** $\sqrt{\left(\frac{1+x}{1-x}\right)}$ **(c)** $\sqrt[3]{(1-2x+3x^2)}$

(d) $(1-2x)^{1/2}(1+3x)^{1/3}$ **(e)** $\sqrt{(1-\frac{1}{2}x)}-\sqrt[3]{(1+\frac{1}{3}x)}$ **(f)** $\dfrac{1+2x-3x^2}{(1+5x)^2}$

2 Partial fractions in binomial expansions

2.1 Identities and partial fractions

Undoubtedly one of the major uses of the binomial theorem is that it enables us to find a series of terms of powers of x which can represent a rational function. This is particularly useful when the terms rapidly become very small and we achieve a good approximation to the fraction in a few terms.

But before we can expand a rational function as a series of powers of x we often have to find the *partial fractions*. These are the simple rational functions which were combined to give the complicated fraction. For example

$$\frac{\frac{1}{3}}{x-1}-\frac{\frac{1}{3}}{x-2}\equiv\frac{1}{(x-1)(x-2)}$$

So to expand

$$\frac{1}{(x-1)(x+2)}$$

as a series we must first write the fraction as

$$\frac{\frac{1}{3}}{x-1}-\frac{\frac{1}{3}}{x+2}$$

This is an *identity*. We now discuss what this means. Consider the two functions

$$F(x)=x^2-1 \qquad \text{and} \qquad G(x)=(x-1)(x+1)$$

Then	$F(0) = -1$ (putting $x = 0$)	$G(0) = -1$ (putting $x = 0$)
	$F(1) = 0$	$G(1) = 0$
	$F(2) = 3$	$G(2) = 3$
	$F(3) = 8$	$G(3) = 8$

. . . and so on.

We soon realize that no matter what value we substitute for x then $F(x)$ and $G(x)$ will be the same—in fact $F(x)$ and $G(x)$ are identical. This should not surprise us in the least as

$$x^2-1 = (x-1)(x+1)$$

in fact we can write this as

$$x^2-1 \equiv (x-1)(x+1)$$

where . . . ≡ . . . means '. . . is identical with . . .' or '. . . is identically equal to . . .'.

Definition

We say that two functions of x are identically equal if they have the same numerical value *for all values of x.*

Example 1

What are the values of A and B if

$$2x+3 \equiv Ax+B?$$

Since this statement is true for all values of x we can

(a) put $x = 0$ $\quad 3 = B$ (note that we use the equals sign here)

(b) put $x = 1$ $\quad 5 = A+3$

$\quad 2 = A$

Note that the coefficients of x turn out to be the same on both sides of the equation and the constants also are the same.

Example 2

Find A, B and C if

$$(x+1)(x+2) \equiv Ax^2+Bx+C$$

As this is true for all values of x we

(a) put $x = 0$ $\quad 2 = C$

(b) put $x = 1$ $\quad 6 = A+B+2 \Rightarrow A+B = 4$

(c) put $x = -1$ $\quad 0 = A-B+2 \Rightarrow A-B = -2$

so $\quad A = 1, \quad B = +3 \quad$ and $\quad C = 2$

Note that $(x+1)(x+2) = x^2+3x+2$ so that once again the coefficients of x^2, x and the constants are the same on each side of the identity. This leads to what is known as *comparing coefficients.* In an identity the coefficients of the powers of x are the same, so if we are told

$$x^2+3x+2 \equiv Ax^2+Bx+C$$

Then, comparing coefficients of x^2 $\quad A = 1$

of x $\quad B = 3$

and also $\quad C = 2$

Example 3

Find A and B where

$$\frac{2}{(x+1)(x+2)} \equiv \frac{A}{(x+1)} + \frac{B}{(x+2)}$$

As usual with fraction equations, our first step is to multiply throughout by the L.C.M. of the denominators $(x+1)(x+2)$. Hence our problem changes to finding A and B where

$$2 \equiv A(x+2)+B(x+1)$$

Method 1 (substituting values for x)

This is an identity and so is true for all values of x.

Put $x = -1$ (this will eliminate B), so $2 = A$

Put $x = -2$ (to eliminate A) $\quad 2 = -B$

Method 2 (Comparing coefficients)

$$2 \equiv Ax+2A+Bx+B$$

Comparing x's $\quad 0 = A+B$

Comparing constants $\quad 2 = 2A+B$

Subtract $\quad A = 2$ and hence $B = -2$

Our solution is

$$\frac{2}{(x+1)(x+2)} \equiv \frac{2}{x+1} - \frac{2}{x+2}$$

NOTE. It often helps to use a combination of methods 1 and 2.

Exercise 2.1

Solve the following identities.

1 $(x-2)(x+1) \equiv x^2+Ax+B$. Find A and B.

2 $A(x-2)(x+1)+B(x-2)+C \equiv x^2$. Find A, B and C.

3 $A(x-2)(x-1)+B(x-1)+C \equiv x^2+x+1$. Find A, B and C.

4 $Ax(x-1)(x-2)+Bx(x-1)+Cx+D \equiv 2x^3+3x+1$. Find A, B, C and D.

5 $\dfrac{x+1}{(x-1)(x+2)} \equiv \dfrac{A}{(x-1)}+\dfrac{B}{(x+2)}$ Find A and B.

6 $\dfrac{3-x}{x(x+1)} \equiv \dfrac{A}{x}+\dfrac{B}{(x+1)}$ Find A and B.

7 $\dfrac{4x-2}{(x+1)^2} \equiv \dfrac{A}{(x+1)^2}+\dfrac{B}{(x+1)}$ Find A and B.

8 $\dfrac{3x+2}{(x-1)(x-2)(x+3)} \equiv \dfrac{A}{(x-1)}+\dfrac{B}{(x-2)}+\dfrac{C}{(x+3)}$ Find A, B and C.

9 $\dfrac{2x+1}{(x+2)^2(x-1)} \equiv \dfrac{A}{(x+2)^2}+\dfrac{B}{(x+2)}+\dfrac{C}{(x-1)}$ Find A, B and C.

2.2 Types of partial fraction

When a rational function is split into its partial fractions, there are certain points to be remembered.

(a) The rational function itself must be a fraction—in practical terms the *numerator* must be of a lower degree in x than the *denominator*; if not, the first task must be to divide out.

For example, find the partial fractions for

$$\frac{x^2+1}{x^2-1}$$

Suppose we assume (wrongly) that

$$\frac{x^2+1}{x^2-1} \equiv \frac{A}{x-1}+\frac{B}{x+1}$$

Hence $\qquad x^2+1 \equiv A(x+1)+B(x-1)$

Now this cannot possibly be an identity since the right-hand part contains no x^2 term. The fault is in our first supposition. The numerator is of the same degree as the denominator, hence we divide out first

$$\frac{x^2+1}{x^2-1} = 1+\frac{2}{x^2-1}$$

and now find partial fractions for

$$\frac{2}{x^2-1} \equiv \frac{A}{x-1}+\frac{B}{x+1}$$

(b) The partial fractions have numerators one degree less than their denominators. So the partial fractions for

$$\frac{1}{(x-1)(x^2+2)}$$

would be of the form

$$\frac{A}{x-1}+\frac{Bx+C}{x^2+2}$$

since $Bx+C$ is the 'general' function of first degree in x. Similarly

$$\frac{2}{(x+2)(x^3+3x^2-2x+1)}$$

would be

$$\frac{A}{x+2}+\frac{Bx^2+Cx+D}{x^3+3x^2-2x+1}$$

(c) If we have 'repeated' factors we can use either of two forms:

$$\frac{1}{(x-1)(x+2)^2} \equiv \frac{A}{x-1}+\frac{Bx+C}{(x+2)^2}$$

or

$$\equiv \frac{A}{(x-1)}+\frac{D}{(x+2)^2}+\frac{E}{(x+2)}$$

This is because

$$\frac{Bx+C}{(x+2)^2}$$

can be written

$$\frac{B(x+2)+(C-2B)}{(x+2)^2} = \frac{B}{(x+2)}+\frac{C-2B}{(x+2)^2}$$

Similarly

$$\frac{2}{(x-2)(x+1)^3} \equiv \frac{A}{x-2}+\frac{Bx^2+Cx+D}{(x+1)^3}$$

or

$$\equiv \frac{A}{x-2}+\frac{E}{(x+1)^3}+\frac{F}{(x+1)^2}+\frac{G}{(x+1)}$$

Exercise 2.2

Find the partial fractions in the following cases.

1 $\dfrac{2x+3}{(x+3)(x-1)}$ **2** $\dfrac{x-4}{(x+3)^2}$

3 $\dfrac{2x-9}{(x+4)(x-5)}$ **4** $\dfrac{3x-8}{(x-2)^2(x+1)}$

5 $\dfrac{4x+5}{(x-1)(x^2+2x+4)}$ **6** $\dfrac{2x+1}{(x+1)(x-2)}$

7 $\dfrac{x^2-3x+2}{(x^2-1)(x+3)}$ **8** $\dfrac{1}{(x+1)^3(x-1)}$

9 Determine possible values of K if the coefficient of x^2 is 63 in the product $(1-Kx+3Kx^2)(1-Kx-Kx^2)$.

10 Find P, Q, R, such that $3x^2-6x+5 \equiv P(x-Q)^2+R$. Hence find the greatest value of

$$\frac{6}{3x^2-6x+5}$$

2.3 Binomial expansion of fractions, using partial fractions

Example 1

Express

$$\frac{1}{(x-1)(x+2)}$$

as a sum of two partial fractions. Hence write the fraction as a series in the cases **(a)** when x is small and **(b)** when x is large, stating in each case the values of x for which the series is valid, and using the first three terms in each expansion.

Suppose

$$\frac{1}{(x-1)(x+2)} \equiv \frac{A}{x-1}+\frac{B}{x+2}$$

Multiply through by $(x-1)(x+2)$

$$1 \equiv A(x+2)+B(x-1)$$

Since this is an identity we can

(i) put $x = 1$, then $\quad 1 = A \times 3 \quad$ so $\quad A = \frac{1}{3}$

(ii) put $x = -2$ $\quad 1 = B \times -3 \quad$ so $\quad B = -\frac{1}{3}$

Hence

$$\frac{1}{(x-1)(x+2)} \equiv \frac{1}{3(x-1)}-\frac{1}{3(x+2)}$$

$$\equiv -\frac{1}{3(1-x)}-\frac{1}{6(1+x/2)} \qquad *$$

$$\equiv -\frac{1}{3}(1-x)^{-1}-\frac{1}{6}\left(1+\frac{x}{2}\right)^{-1}$$

Using the binomial theorem,

(a) $$-\frac{1}{3}(1-x)^{-1}-\frac{1}{6}\left(1+\frac{x}{2}\right)^{-1} = -\frac{1}{3}\left\{1+(-1)(-x)+\frac{(-1)(-2)}{1\times 2}(-x)^2+\ldots\right\}$$

(provided $-1 < x < 1$)

$$-\frac{1}{6}\left\{1+(-1)\left(\frac{x}{2}\right)+\frac{(-1)(-2)}{1\times 2}\left(\frac{x}{2}\right)^2+\ldots\right\}$$

(provided $-1 < x/2 < 1$ or $-2 < x < 2$)

$$= -\frac{1}{3}(1+x+x^2+\ldots)$$

$$-\frac{1}{6}\left(1-\frac{x}{2}+\frac{x^2}{4}-\ldots\right)$$

$$= -\tfrac{1}{2}-\tfrac{1}{4}x-\tfrac{3}{8}x^2-\ldots$$

Now the first part of the series is valid for $-1 < x < 1$ and the second part for $-2 < x < 2$

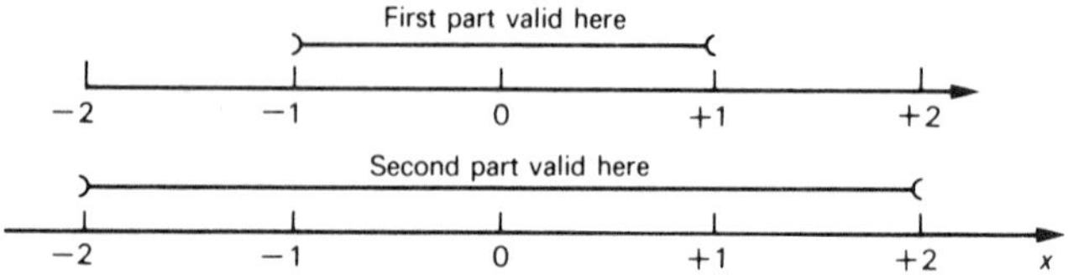

Both parts will be valid in the intersection (or overlapping region), i.e. $-1 < x < 1$.

(b) We have

$$\frac{1}{(x-1)(x+2)} \equiv \frac{1}{3(x-1)} - \frac{1}{3(x+2)}$$

$$\equiv \frac{1}{3x\left(1-\frac{1}{x}\right)} - \frac{1}{3x\left(1+\frac{2}{x}\right)} \qquad *$$

$$\equiv \frac{1}{3x}\left(1-\frac{1}{x}\right)^{-1} - \frac{1}{3x}\left(1+\frac{2}{x}\right)^{-1}$$

Using the binomial theorem

$$\frac{1}{3x}\left(1-\frac{1}{x}\right)^{-1} - \frac{1}{3x}\left(1+\frac{2}{x}\right)^{-1}$$

$$= \frac{1}{3x}\left\{1+(-1)\left(-\frac{1}{x}\right)+\frac{(-1)(-2)}{1\times 2}\left(-\frac{1}{x}\right)^2+\ldots\right\}$$

$$\left(\text{which is valid provided } -1 < \frac{1}{x} < 1\right)$$

$$-\frac{1}{3x}\left\{1+(-1)\left(\frac{2}{x}\right)+\frac{(-1)(-2)}{1\times 2}\left(\frac{2}{x}\right)^2+\ldots\right\}$$

$$\left(\text{provided } -1 < \frac{2}{x} < 1\right)$$

$$= \frac{1}{3x}\left(1+\frac{1}{x}+\frac{1}{x^2}+\ldots\right)$$

$$-\frac{1}{3x}\left(1-\frac{2}{x}+\frac{4}{x^2}-\ldots\right)$$

$$= \frac{1}{x^2} - \frac{1}{x^3} + \ldots$$

Now the first part of the series is valid for x greater than 1 or less than -1, the second part for x greater than 2 or less than -2. Both parts will be valid in the intersection of these two regions.

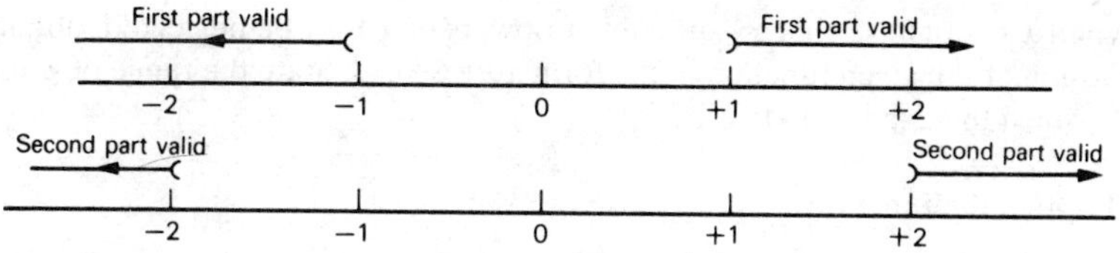

Hence both parts are valid for x greater than 2 or less than -2.

As you can see, we always arrange the series so that the terms in it become smaller and smaller. A 'decision point' is indicated by * above. Whenever we use the theorem, the decision point is the place where we must choose how to expand our fraction. Here are some more examples illustrating how we decide to expand.

Example 2

Expand

$$\frac{1}{(x+2)^2}$$

(a) when $-2 < x < 2$ and **(b)** when x is greater than 2 or less than -2.

(a) $$\frac{1}{(x+2)^2} = \frac{1}{\left\{2\left(1+\frac{x}{2}\right)\right\}^2} = \frac{1}{4}\left(1+\frac{x}{2}\right)^{-2} \quad \text{for } -2 < x < 2$$

(b) $$\frac{1}{(x+2)^2} = \frac{1}{\left\{x\left(1+\frac{2}{x}\right)\right\}^2} = \frac{1}{x^2}\left(1+\frac{2}{x}\right)^{-2} \quad \text{for } x > 2, \quad x < -2$$

Example 3

Expand

$$\frac{1}{(3x-2)^3}$$

(a) when $-\frac{2}{3} < x < \frac{2}{3}$ and **(b)** when x is greater than $\frac{2}{3}$ or less than $-\frac{2}{3}$

(a) $$\frac{1}{(3x-2)^3} = \frac{1}{\{-2(1-\frac{3}{2}x)\}^3} = -\tfrac{1}{8}(1-\tfrac{3}{2}x)^{-3} \quad \text{for } -\tfrac{2}{3} < x < \tfrac{2}{3}$$

(b) $$\frac{1}{(3x-2)^3} = \frac{1}{\left\{3x\left(1-\frac{2}{3x}\right)\right\}^3} = \frac{1}{27x^3}\left(1-\frac{2}{3x}\right)^{-3} \quad \text{for } x > \tfrac{2}{3} \text{ or } x < -\tfrac{2}{3}$$

Exercise 2.3

1 Express

$$\frac{2x+1}{(x-1)(x+2)^2}$$

as the sum of three partial fractions.

When x is small, so that x^3 and higher powers of x may be neglected, obtain the expansion of the given function in the form $a + bx + cx^2$. State the range of values of x for which the expansion is valid.

2 Express the function

$$\frac{7x-2x^2}{(x+1)(x-2)^2}$$

in terms of three partial fractions. If x is so large that $(1/x)^4$ and higher powers of $1/x$ can be neglected, prove that the function is approximately equal to

$$\frac{3+x-2x^2}{x^3}$$

3 Find the partial fractions of

$$\frac{2-4x}{x(x^2-x-2)}$$

and prove that if x is so large that x^{-4} can be neglected the expression is equal to $(-2/x^3)(2x+1)$.

4 Express

$$\frac{1}{1-x-2x^2}$$

in partial fractions and hence or otherwise find the coefficient a_n of x^n in the expansion of

$$\frac{1}{1-x-2x^2}$$

in ascending powers of x, stating the set of values of x for which the expansion is valid. Prove that $a_n + a_{n-1} = 2^n$.

5 Express

$$f(x) \equiv \frac{7x^2+12x+4}{(x+2)(x+1)^2}$$

in the form

$$\frac{A}{x+2}+\frac{B}{x+1}+\frac{C}{(x+1)^2}$$

where A, B, C are independent of x.

Hence, or otherwise, show that, when $x^2 < 1$, the first three terms in the expansion of $f(x)$ as a series of ascending powers of x are $2 + x - 3x^2$ and find the next two terms in the expansion.

6 Find the values of the constants a and b, if the term of lowest degree in the expansion of $(1-ax)(1+bx^2)^4-(1+2x)^{-3/2}$ in ascending powers of x is the term involving x^3.

2.4 Proof of the binomial theorem when n is a positive integer

The proof uses the ideas of *induction.*

Now $(1+x)^1 = 1+x$, so the theorem is true for $n = 1$. Suppose the theorem is true for a particular value of n, say $n = k$, then

$$(1+x)^k = 1+kx+\frac{k(k-1)}{2!}x^2+\ldots\frac{k(k-1)(k-2)\ldots(k-r+1)x^r}{r!}+\ldots+x^k$$

and

$$(1+x)^{k+1} = (1+x)^k(1+x)$$

$$= 1+kx+\frac{k(k-1)}{2!}x^2+\ldots\frac{k(k-1)(k-2)\ldots(k-r+1)}{r!}x^r+\ldots x^k$$

$$+x+kx^2+\ldots\frac{k(k-1)(k-2)\ldots(k-r+2)}{(r-1)!}x^r+\ldots kx^k+x^{k+1}$$

$$=1+(k+1)x+\left[\frac{k(k-1)}{2!}+k\right]x^2+\ldots+\left\{\frac{k(k-1)(k-2)\ldots(k-r+1)}{r!}\right.$$

$$\left.+\frac{k(k-1)(k-2)\ldots(k-r+2)}{(r-1)!}\right\}x^r+(1+k)x^k+x^{k+1}$$

Now

$$\left\{\frac{k(k-1)}{2!}+k\right\}=\frac{k^2-k+2k}{2!}=\frac{k^2+k}{2!}=\frac{(k+1)k}{2!}$$

and

$$\left\{\frac{k(k-1)(k-2)\ldots(k-r+1)}{r!}+\frac{k(k-1)(k-2)\ldots(k-r+2)}{(r-1)!}\right\}$$

$$=\frac{k(k-1)(k-2)\ldots(k-r+2)}{r!}[k-r+1+r]$$

$$=\frac{(k+1)k(k-1)(k-2)\ldots(k+1-r+1)}{r!}$$

This last expression is identical with the coefficient of x^r in our original formula, except that we have $k+1$ instead of k.

Hence

$$(1+x)^{k+1} = 1+(k+1)x+\frac{(k-1)k}{2!}x^2+\ldots$$

$$+\frac{(k+1)k(k-1)\ldots+\{(k+1)-r+1\}x^r}{r!}+\ldots+(k+1)x^k+x^{k+1}$$

So if the formula is true for $n = k$, it is also true for $n = k+1$. But it is true for $n = 1$, hence for $n = 2$ and so on. By the Principle of Mathematical Induction the formula is true for all positive integers n.

Miscellaneous examination questions 5

(O. & C. unless stated otherwise)

1 Given that $y = (1-2x)^{-1}(1-x)^{-2}$, express y in the form $A(1-2x)^{-1} + B(1-x)^{-1} + C(1-x)^{-2}$ where A, B, C are constants. Hence show that when $|x| < \frac{1}{2}$,

$$y = 1 + 4x + 11x^2 + 26x^3 + \ldots$$ (M.E.I.)

2 Write down the first three terms in the binomial expansion of $(1+x)^{1/2}$. Prove that the function

$$\frac{x(1+x)^{1/2}}{(x+2)^3}$$

is approximately equal to $\frac{1}{8}x(1-x)$ when x is small and approximately equal to $x^{-3/2}(1-\frac{11}{2}x^{-1})$ when x is large and positive.

3 Find the partial fractions of

$$\frac{1+3x^2}{x^3-x^2-x+1}$$

and prove that if x is so large that x^{-4} can be neglected, the expression is equal to

$$\frac{3x^2+3x+7}{x^3}$$

4 Find the first five terms in the expansion of $(1-2x)^{-1/2}$ in ascending powers of x. If the coefficient of x^r in this expansion is u_r find an explicit form for u_r and deduce that $u_r < 2u_{r-1}$.

By putting $x = 0.1$ in your expression, find $\sqrt{5}$ to three decimal places, showing that your answer has the required degree of accuracy.

5(a) Express

$$\frac{3x+4}{(x+1)(x+2)^2}$$

in partial fractions. Hence obtain the expansion of the given expression in ascending powers of x as far as the term in x^3, stating the necessary restrictions on the value of x.

(b) Prove (do not merely verify) that, if E denotes the function

$$\frac{x^2}{2-x+2\sqrt{(1-x)}}$$

then $E = 2-x-2\sqrt{(1-x)}$.

Deduce that if x is small, then E is approximately equal to $\frac{1}{4}x^2$.

6 Express

$$\frac{1}{(x+2)^2(2x+1)}$$

in partial fractions and hence expand this expression in ascending powers of x, giving the first four terms and the coefficient of x^n.

Show that, for values of x so small that x^4 may be neglected, the given expression can be represented by

$$\frac{1}{(3x+2)^2}+kx^3$$

for some number k, independent of x and find k.

7 Prove that if E denotes the function

$$\frac{1}{1+\sqrt{(1-x^2)}}$$

then

$$E=\frac{1}{x^2}(1-\sqrt{(1-x^2)})$$

Hence prove that, if x is small, then E is approximately equal to

$$\tfrac{1}{2}+\tfrac{1}{8}x^2+\tfrac{1}{16}x^4$$

8 Prove that the coefficients of x^n in the binomial expansions of $(1-x)^{-2}$ and $(1-x)^{-3}$ are $(n+1)$ and $\frac{1}{2}(n+1)(n+2)$. By putting $x=\frac{1}{2}$ in each of these two expansions, prove that

$$\frac{1^2}{2}+\frac{2^2}{2^2}+\frac{3^2}{2^3}+\ldots+\frac{n^2}{2^n}+\ldots=6$$

9 Express the function E given by

$$E=\frac{x+3}{(2x+1)(1+x^2)}$$

in partial fractions. Hence prove that, if x is so large that $1/x^4$ can be neglected, then

$$E=\frac{5+2x}{4x^3}$$

10 If x is small, so that x^3 and higher powers of x may be neglected, express the function

$$\frac{\sqrt{(4+x)}}{1-2x+(1+3x)^{2/3}}$$

in the form $a+bx+cx^2$.

Chapter 6

Algebra 2

1 Inequalities involving linear functions

1.1 Order

Perhaps the most important property of numbers is that they have *order*: one number is larger than, equal to, or less than another number. (On the number line, the larger number is to the *right* of the smaller one.)

Much of the work of mathematicians and scientists lies in trying to obtain the 'best' solution to a problem, given certain conditions. These conditions are usually expressed as inequalities. You will have met inequalities before in mathematics, probably in solving linear programming questions. We shall now look again at the algebra of inequalities.

Here are some examples of the rules governing inequalities.

	EXAMPLE	IN GENERAL
1	$3>2 \Rightarrow 3+4>2+4$ $-1<2 \Rightarrow -1-5<2-5$	$a>b \Rightarrow a+c>b+c$ $d<e \Rightarrow d-f<e-f$
2	$3>2 \Rightarrow 4\times 3>4\times 2$ $-1<0 \Rightarrow 4\times -1<4\times 0$	$\left.\begin{matrix} a>b \\ k>0 \end{matrix}\right\} \Rightarrow ak>bk$
but	$3>2 \Rightarrow -4\times 3<-4\times 2$ $-1<0 \Rightarrow -4\times -1>-4\times 0$	$\left.\begin{matrix} a>b \\ k<0 \end{matrix}\right\} \Rightarrow ak<bk$
3	$\left.\begin{matrix} 3>2 \\ 7>6 \end{matrix}\right\} \Rightarrow 3\times 7>2\times 6$	$\left.\begin{matrix} a>b>0 \\ c>d>0 \end{matrix}\right\} \Rightarrow ac>bd$
4	$3>2 \Rightarrow 3^5>2^5$	$\left.\begin{matrix} a>b>0 \\ n>0 \end{matrix}\right\} \Rightarrow a^n>b^n$
but	$3>2 \Rightarrow 3^{-2}<2^{-2}$	$\left.\begin{matrix} a>b>0 \\ n<0 \end{matrix}\right\} \Rightarrow a^n<b^n$

These rules show that inequalities can be treated as equations, except that multiplication by a negative number *reverses* the inequality and that great care has to be taken when considering negative powers as in **4** above. The algebraic solution may be quite complicated at times, and often the solution can be more easily found graphically by drawing a careful sketch of the curve. Sometimes it is possible to use calculus, particularly if you wish to show, for example, that some expression is greater than some particular value. This value is usually the minimum value of the expression, and can be found by differentiation and substitution. In the following examples the solutions will be given algebraically *and* graphically.

1.2 Linear inequalities

Example 1

Solve $$2x+3>5$$

Algebraically, this is very simple: $$2x>2$$
$$x>1$$

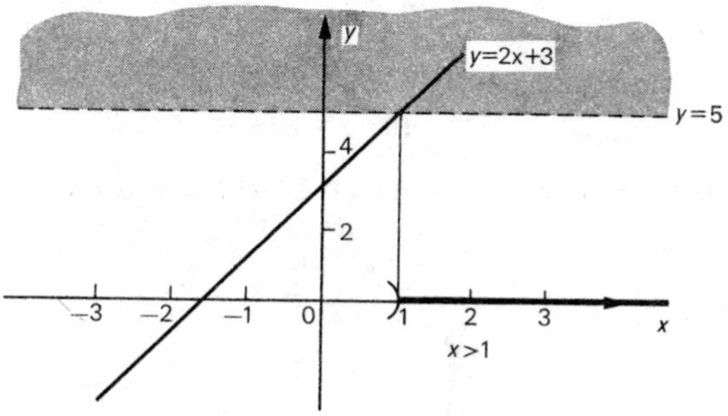

Graphically, we draw the line $y = 2x+3$ and see where this line is *above* the line $y = 5$. This is true where $x > 1$, as is indicated on the x axis.

NOTE that the symbols used are as shown in the figure below:

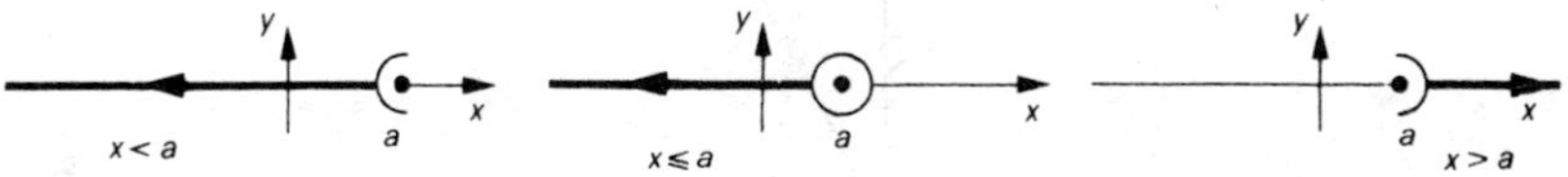

Example 2

Solve $$-2x+5>3$$
$$-2x>-2$$
$$-x>-1$$
$$x<1$$

The diagram on the next page shows the graphical solution to $-2x+5>3$.

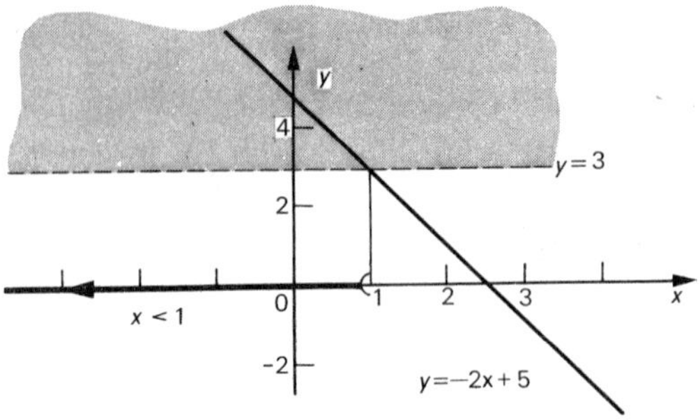

Example 3

Solve

$$3-5x < 2x-4$$
$$3+4 < 2x+5x$$
$$7 < 7x$$
$$1 < x$$

In the graph $3-5x$ is less than $2x-4$ when the first line is *beneath* the second.

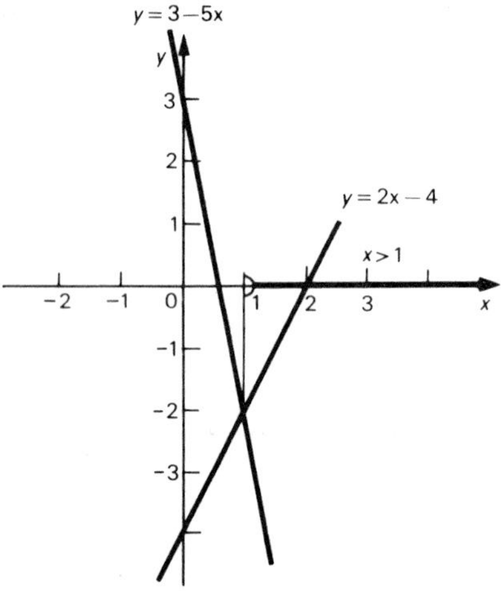

Exercise 1.2

Solve the following inequalities

1 $x+3 > -7$ **2** $5x+4 < 1$ **3** $3x-2 \geqslant 5$ **4** $2-3x < 1$

5 $\frac{1}{2}x+1 < x-2$ **6** $4-\frac{1}{3}x > 2$ **7** $6x-7 \geqslant 9x+4$

Curve sketching

To solve any inequality which is *not* linear by the graphical method we must, of course, draw or at least *sketch* the graph.

When we speak of sketching a curve we mean drawing it accurately enough to show any maximum or minimum points, any lines to which the curve tends, and the direction which the curve approaches for large positive and negative values of x. Where there is any doubt about the shape we can make up a table of values for the curve, and if necessary use calculus to find its slope, and any maxima or minima.

1.3 Rational functions with linear denominators

For our purposes a rational function is the quotient of linear or quadratic functions.

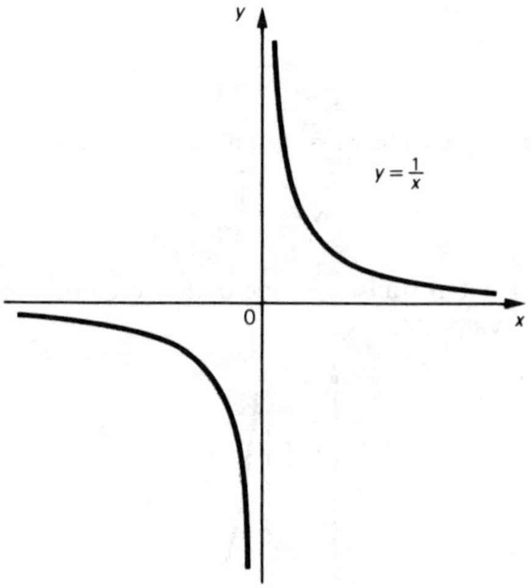

Sketching rational functions

We have met the graph of $y = 1/x$ in the section on variation in Chapter 2. It is called a *rectangular hyperbola* and has an *asymptote*, the line $x = 0$. *Here* y is not defined but 'jumps' from an infinitely large negative number to an infinitely large positive number as x increases from just below to just above zero. The x axis is also an asymptote, which the curve approaches from below, as x tends to $-\infty$ and from above as x tends to $+\infty$.

The graph of $y = -1/x$ is similar but occupies the other two quadrants.

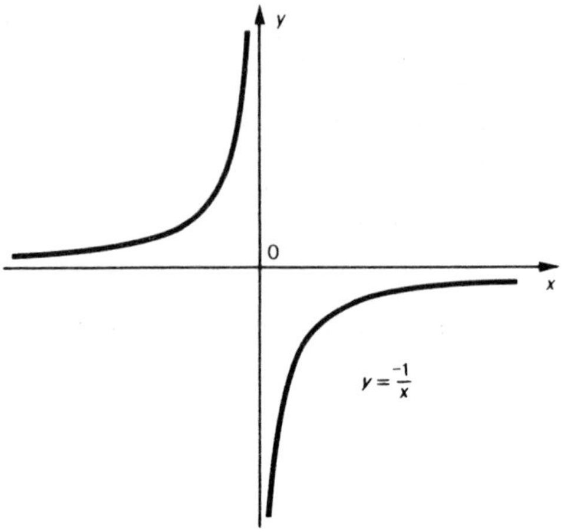

The function
$$y = \frac{1}{x-1}$$
has the same value at $x = 3$, as has $y = 1/x$ at $x = 2$, and so on. Hence the graph of
$$y = \frac{1}{x-1}$$
is identical with $y = 1/x$ but translated one unit in the positive x direction, so that the line $x = 1$ is the asymptote.

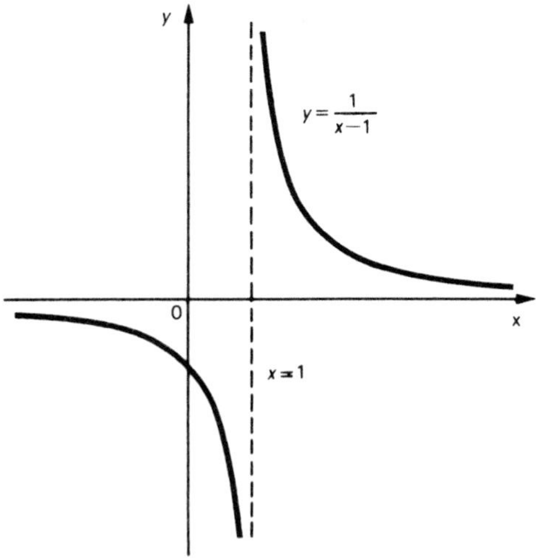

Again,
$$y = \frac{-1}{x-1} = \frac{1}{1-x}$$
occupies the other two quadrants.

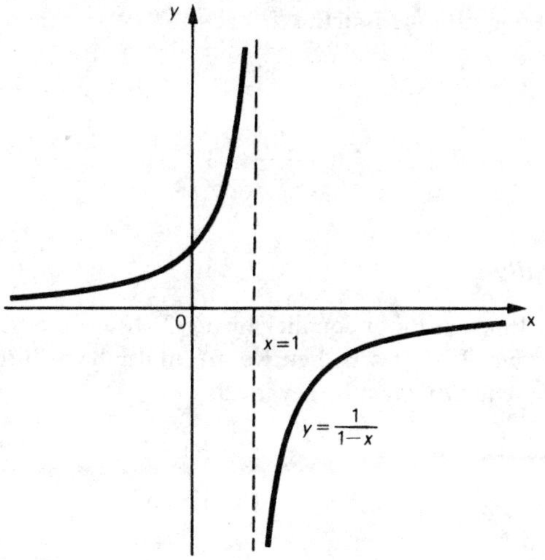

Consider now the function

$$y = \frac{x+3}{x-2}$$

and its graph.

(i) When $x = 0$, $y = -3/2$ and when $x = -3$, $y = 0$.
(ii) It has an asymptote, the line $x = 2$.
(iii) What happens when x is very large?

If $x = +100$, $y = 103/98 \approx 1$ (but greater than 1).
If $x = -100$, $y = -97/-10^2 \approx 1$ (but less than 1).

So as $x \to +\infty$, $y \to 1$ from above and as $x \to -\infty$, $y \to 1$ from below. We can arrive at the same conclusion directly, since if x is very large compared with 3

$$y = \frac{x+3}{x-2} \approx \frac{x}{x} = 1$$

We can now sketch the curve:

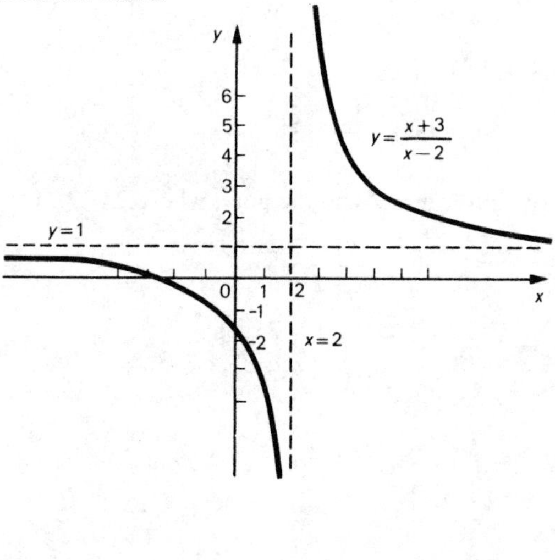

Inequalities involving rational functions

Example 4

Solve
$$\frac{1}{x-2} > 3$$

(a) Algebraically

We first multiply through the inequality by $x-2$. If $x-2>0$ then the inequality sign stays as it is *but* if $x-2<0$ then we are multiplying through by a negative quantity and the inequality must be reversed.

So if (1) $x>2$
$$1 > 3(x-2)$$
$$1 > 3x-6$$
$$7 > 3x$$
$$2\tfrac{1}{3} > x \qquad (2)$$

Combining (1) and (2) we have
$$2 < x < 2\tfrac{1}{3}$$

But if (3) $x<2$
$$1 < 3(x-2)$$
$$2\tfrac{1}{3} < x \qquad (4)$$

Here, if we combine (3) and (4), the inequalities ($x<2$ and $x>2\tfrac{1}{3}$) cannot *both* be true, hence there is *no* value of x satisfying the inequality if $x<2$. The final solution is
$$2 < x < 2\tfrac{1}{3}$$

(b) Graphically

A much easier and quicker method of solution is to sketch the graphs of
$$y = \frac{1}{x-2} \qquad \text{and} \qquad y = 3$$

We can then see at a glance that $\dfrac{1}{x-2} > 3$

only between the asymptote $x=2$ and the point where
$$\frac{1}{x-2} = 3$$

Then
$$1 = 3x-6$$
$$x = \frac{7}{3}$$

The solution is
$$2 < x < 2\tfrac{1}{3}$$

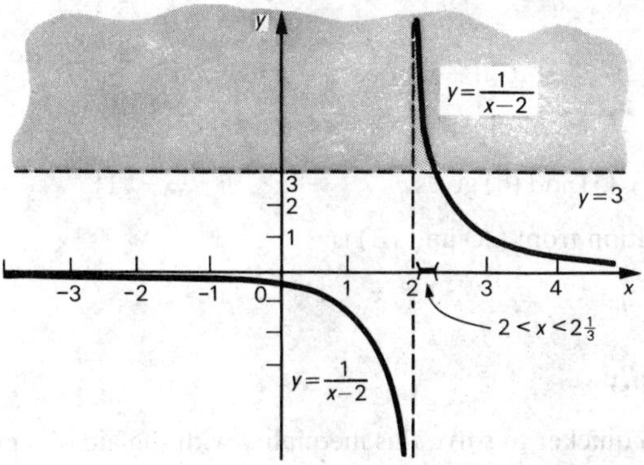

Example 5

Solve $$\frac{1}{x-2} > \frac{1}{1-x}$$

This is clearly more complicated than the previous example.

(*a*) *Algebraically*

(i) If $x-2>0$, then $\qquad x>2 \qquad$ (1)

Multiplying both sides by $x-2$,

$$1 > \frac{x-2}{1-x}$$

Either $1-x>0$, so $x<1$, which is incompatible with (1),

or $\quad 1-x<0$, so $\qquad x>1 \qquad$ (2)

Multiplying both sides by $1-x$,

$$1-x < x-2$$

$$3<2x \qquad \text{so} \quad x>\tfrac{3}{2} \qquad (3)$$

Combining (1), (2) and (3) gives $\qquad x>2 \qquad$ (A)

(ii) If $x-2<0$, then $\qquad x<2 \qquad$ (4)

and $$1 < \frac{x-2}{1-x}$$

Either $1-x>0$, so $x<1$

$$1-x<x-2$$

$$3<2x$$

$$x>\tfrac{3}{2}$$

—which is incompatible with $x<1$, so there is no solution when $x<1$;

or $1-x<0$, so $\quad x>1 \quad (5)$

$$1-x>x-2$$

$$2x<3 \quad \text{and} \quad x<1\tfrac{1}{2} \quad (6)$$

Combining (4), (5) and (6) gives $\quad 1<x<1\tfrac{1}{2} \quad$ (B)

So our final solution from (A) and (B) is

$$1<x<1\tfrac{1}{2}, \qquad x>2$$

(*b*) *Graphically*

Again it is much quicker to solve this inequality with the aid of a graph. The curves

$$y=\frac{1}{x-2} \qquad \text{and} \qquad y=\frac{1}{1-x}$$

intersect where

$$\frac{1}{x-2}=\frac{1}{1-x}$$

$$1-x=x-2$$

$$x=\tfrac{3}{2}$$

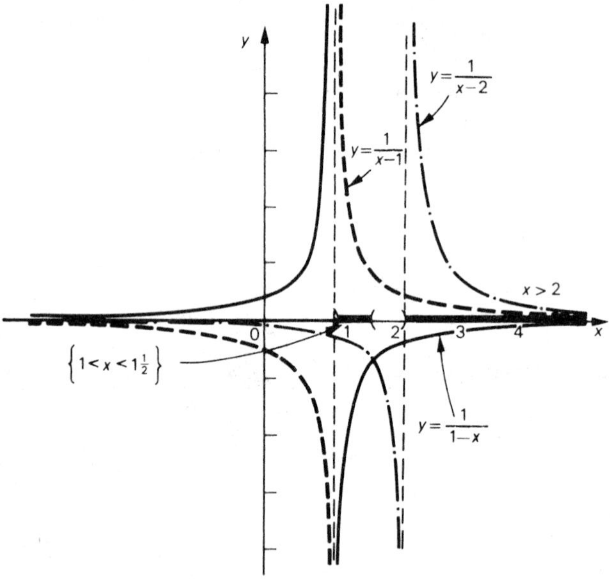

Now $\quad y=\dfrac{1}{x-2} \quad$ (dot-dash line)

is above $$y = \frac{1}{1-x}$$ (continuous line)

when $x > 2$ and when $1 < x < 1\frac{1}{2}$.

Exercise 1.3

Solve the following inequalities algebraically.

1 $\dfrac{1}{x+1} > 2$ 2 $\dfrac{1}{1-x} < 3$ 3 $\dfrac{2x-1}{x+2} < -1$

4 $\dfrac{3x+1}{1-2x} < 2$ 5 $\dfrac{2x-3}{3x-2} > 1$

Solve the following inequalities by the use of a sketch graph

6 $\dfrac{-2}{4x+3} > 5$ 7 $\dfrac{1}{x+\frac{1}{2}} \leqslant 2$ 8 $\dfrac{1}{x+3} > \dfrac{2}{1-x}$

9 $\dfrac{2}{x+2} < \dfrac{3}{x+1}$ 10 $\dfrac{5}{2x-3} < \dfrac{2}{3x+2}$ 11 $\dfrac{x+2}{x-4} \geqslant \dfrac{1}{x+3}$

2 Inequalities involving quadratic functions

2.1 Quadratic inequalities

We now look at quadratic inequalities. Again we can use either algebra or a graphical method.

Example 6

Solve $(x-2)(x-1) > 0$.

(*a*) *Algebraically*

$(x-2)(x-1) > 0$ so *either* $(x-2)$ and $(x-1)$ are both positive *or* $(x-2)$ and $(x-1)$ are both negative. (The reasoning is that we know that if we multiply two positive numbers we get a positive number, and similarly if we multiply two negative numbers we get a positive number.)

Either $x-2>0 \Rightarrow x>2$
and $x-1>0 \Rightarrow x>1$ } which is true for $x > 2$

or $x-2<0 \Rightarrow x<2$
and $x-1<0 \Rightarrow x<1$ } which is true for $x < 1$

Hence $x<1$ or $x>2$

This can be illustrated on a number line:

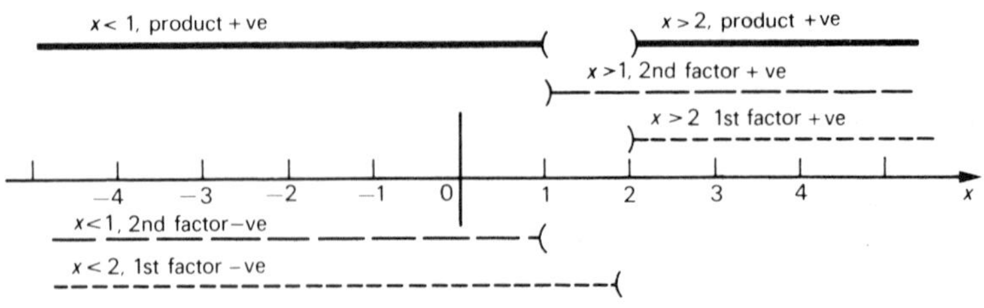

(*b*) *Graphically*

We can quickly sketch the curve $y = (x-2)(x-1)$ and read off the solution. Since we know that y is a quadratic expression in x, then the curve must be a parabola. Also it must be 'upright' and depending on whether the coefficient of x^2 is positive or negative, the sketch will look like

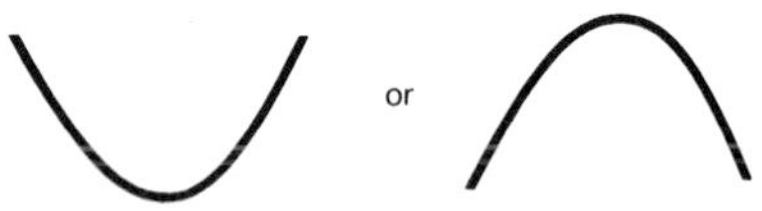

Since we do not need to know much about the curve except where it cuts the x axis, we proceed as follows:

If $y = 0$ $\qquad (x-2)(x-1) = 0 \Rightarrow x = 2 \quad$ or $\quad x = 1$

and if $x = 0$, $y = 2$.

We can now sketch the curve—inaccurately, but well enough for our purpose.

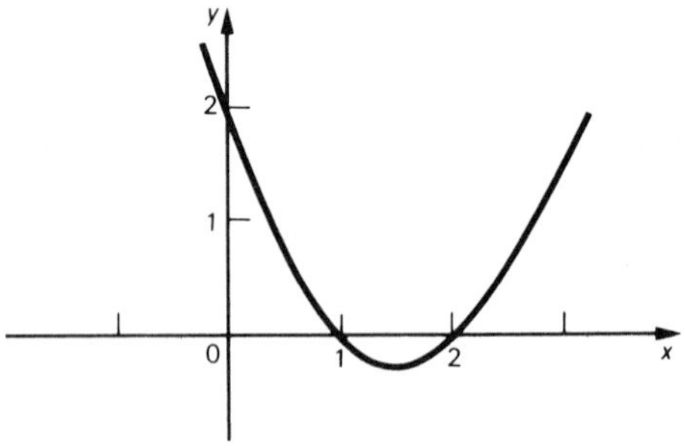

Clearly, $y > 0$ for $x < 1$, and $x > 2$.

Exercise 2.1

Solve the quadratic inequalities

1 $(2+x)(x-2) \geqslant 0$ **2** $(x+1)(x+2) < 0$ **3** $(3x-1)(2x+3) > 0$
4 $(1-x)(3-2x) \geqslant 0$ **5** $x^2-6x+9 > 0$

2.2   Rational functions with quadratic denominators

Example 2

Sketch the curve
$$y = \frac{x+2}{x(x-3)}$$

We first make up a table of values. It is not clear what values we should take for x, but it is usually sufficient to consider $-5 \leqslant x \leqslant 5$.

The *numerator* of the expression is zero when $x = -2$ whilst the *denominator* is zero and y is undefined, when $x = 0$ or $x = 3$. These lines are therefore asymptotes of the curve.

TABLE OF VALUES
$$y = \frac{x+2}{x(x-3)}$$

x	-5	-4	-3	-2	-1	0	1	2	3	4	5
$x+2$	-3	-2	-1	0	1	2	3	4	5	6	7
$x(x-3)$	-5×-8	-4×-7	-3×-6	-2×-5	-1×-4	0×-3	1×-2	2×-1	3×0	4×1	5×2
y	$-\frac{3}{40}$	$-\frac{2}{28}$	$-\frac{1}{18}$	0	$\frac{1}{4}$	*	$-\frac{3}{2}$	-2	*	$\frac{3}{2}$	$\frac{7}{10}$

(* in the table means that the value is undefined.)

If x is very large, we consider the highest power of x in the numerator and in the denominator, and ignore the other terms.

$$y \approx \frac{x}{x^2} = \frac{1}{x}$$

We also need one or two more values, e.g.

$$x = -\tfrac{1}{2} \qquad y = \tfrac{6}{7}$$
$$x = \tfrac{1}{2} \qquad y = -2$$

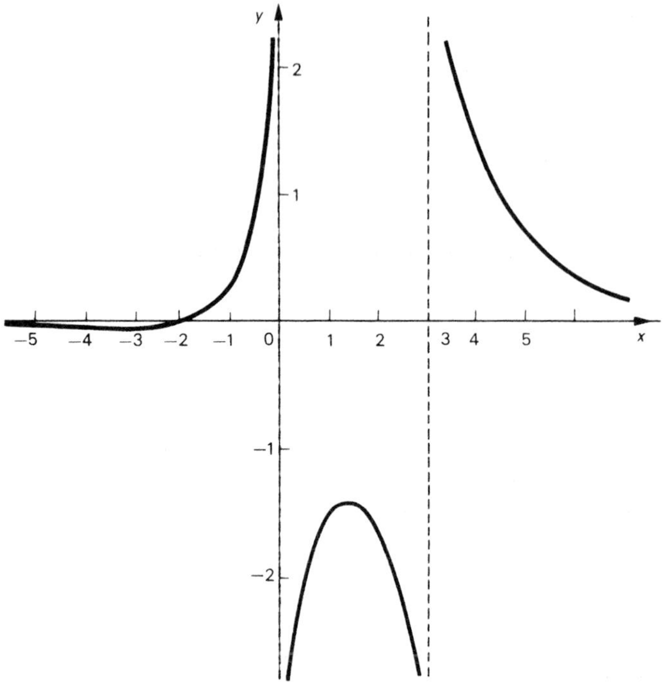

Example 3

Sketch the curve

$$y = \frac{x-2}{(x-1)(x-4)}$$

and state for what range of values the expression

$$\frac{x-2}{(x-1)(x-4)}$$

is positive.

Again we make up a table of values for $-5 \leqslant x \leqslant 5$. We note that when $x = 1$ and when $x = 4$, the denominator of the expression is zero and y is indeterminate.

TABLE OF VALUES $\qquad\qquad y = \dfrac{x-2}{(x-1)(x-4)}$

x	-5	-4	-3	-2	-1	0	1	2	3	4	5
$x-2$	-7	-6	-5	-4	-3	-2	-1	0	1	2	3
$(x-1)(x-4)$	-6×-9	-5×-8	-4×-7	-3×-6	-2×-5	-1×-4	0×-3	1×-2	2×-1	3×0	4×1
y	$-\frac{7}{54}$	$-\frac{6}{40}$	$-\frac{5}{28}$	$-\frac{4}{18}$	$-\frac{3}{10}$	$-\frac{2}{4}$	$*$	0	$-\frac{1}{2}$	$*$	$\frac{3}{4}$

From these values, we see that it would be useful to find y when $x = +\frac{1}{2}, +1\frac{1}{2}, +3\frac{1}{2}, +4\frac{1}{2}$, since, for example, between $x = 0$ and $x = 1$, y changes from $-\frac{1}{2}$ to an infinitely large negative value.

We find the further values

$$\left.\begin{matrix} x = +\frac{1}{2}, +1\frac{1}{2}, +3\frac{1}{2}, +4\frac{1}{2} \\ y = -\frac{6}{7}, +\frac{2}{5}, \ -\frac{6}{5}, \ \ +\frac{10}{7} \end{matrix}\right\}$$

and note that if x is large

$$y \approx \frac{x}{x^2} = \frac{1}{x}$$

We can now sketch the curve:

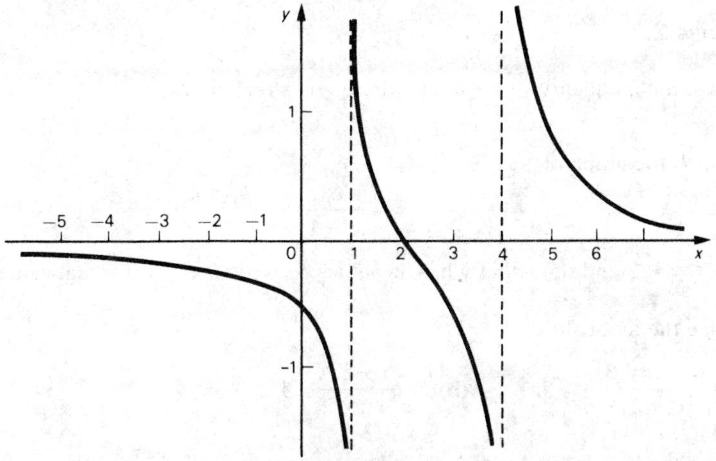

Our solution is the set of values of x for which y is positive. From the graph, $1 < x < 2$, $x > 4$.

NOTE

Suppose we were asked not to sketch the curve but merely to find for what value of x is

$$\frac{x-2}{(x-1)(x-4)} > 0$$

This can be solved easily using a number line as follows:

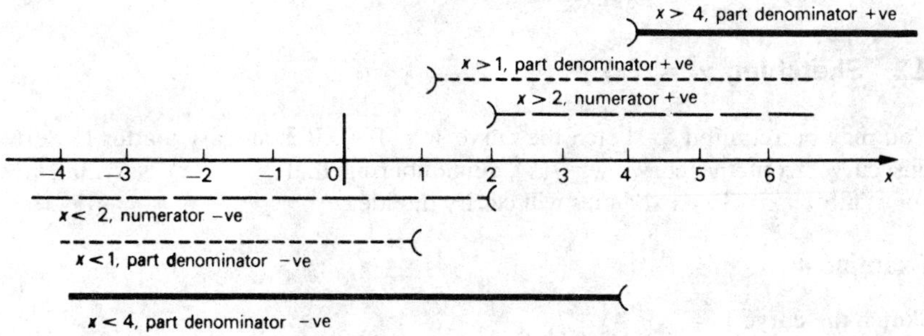

Our solution is the set of values of x where all three factors are positive, or where two factors are negative and one positive.

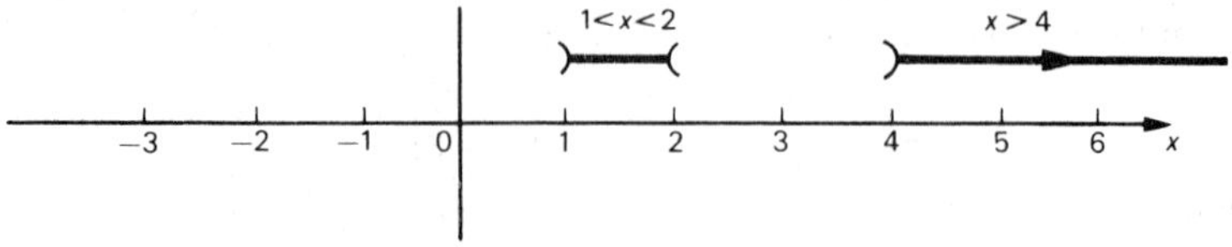

This method of solving inequalities has the great advantage that we do not have to draw the graph.

Exercise 2.2

1 Solve the inequality $\dfrac{x+5}{x-3} > x$ where x is a real number.

2 Sketch the graph of

$$y = \frac{x^2}{x^2-1}$$

for $-3 \leqslant x \leqslant 3$ and show that y has no values between 0 and 1, for real values of x.

3 Solve the inequalities

(a) $\dfrac{2x-3}{x^2+2x-4} > 1$ **(b)** $\dfrac{x-2}{x^2+x-2} < 1$

4 Solve the inequality

$$\frac{x}{x+1} \leqslant 3+x$$

Are the solutions the same as for

$$\frac{x}{(x+1)(3+x)} \leqslant 1$$

Sketch the graphs of

$$y = \frac{x}{x+1}, \qquad y = 3+x \qquad \text{and} \qquad y = \frac{x}{(x+1)(3+x)}$$

2.3 Sketching $y^2 = f(x)$

You may be required to sketch the curve $y^2 = f(x)$. It is an easy matter to derive this curve from the curve $y = f(x)$, remembering that $y^2 = f(x)$ is *symmetrical* about the x axis. Two examples will clarify the idea.

Example 4

Sketch the curve $y^2 = x^2 - 4x + 7$.

We first draw the parabola $y = x^2 - 4x + 7$.

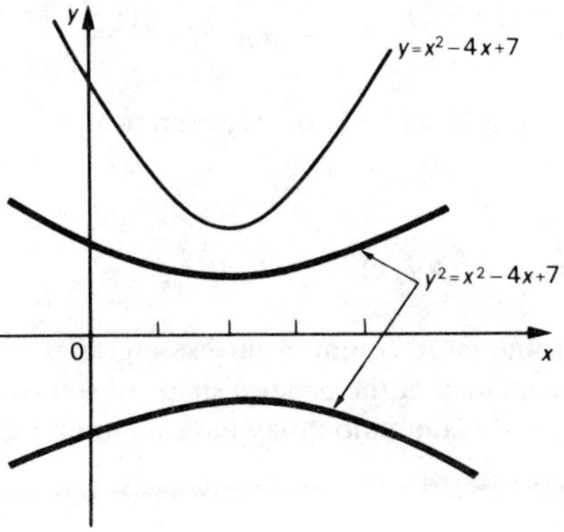

We now find points on the curve $y^2 = x^2 - 4x + 7$ by taking values for y on $x^2 - 4x + 7$ and finding their square roots. Thus when $x = 2$, $y = 3$, on $y = x^2 - 4x + 7$ hence when $x = 2$, $y = \pm\sqrt{3}$ for the curve $y^2 = x^2 - 4x + 7$ and so on.

Example 5

Sketch the curve

$$y^2 = \frac{(x+1)(x-2)}{(x+2)(x-3)}$$

As before, we first sketch

$$y = \frac{(x+1)(x-2)}{(x+2)(x-3)}$$

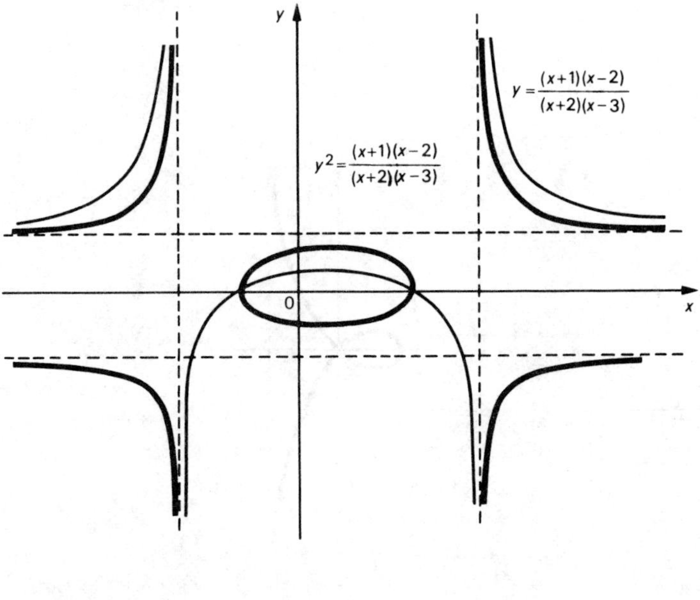

We shall only obtain values for

$$y^2 = \frac{(x+1)(x-2)}{(x+2)(x-3)} \qquad \text{when} \qquad \frac{(x+1)(x-2)}{(x+2)(x-3)} > 0$$

i.e. not between $x = -2$ and $x = -1$, or between $x = 2$ and $x = 3$. This curve is shown in bold lines

Some well-known curves: $y^2 = f(x)$

Here are sketches of some more common cartesian graphs which you may meet. It is most helpful to have an idea of the general shape of some of the curves and hope that any graph set in your examination may have a familiar look about it.

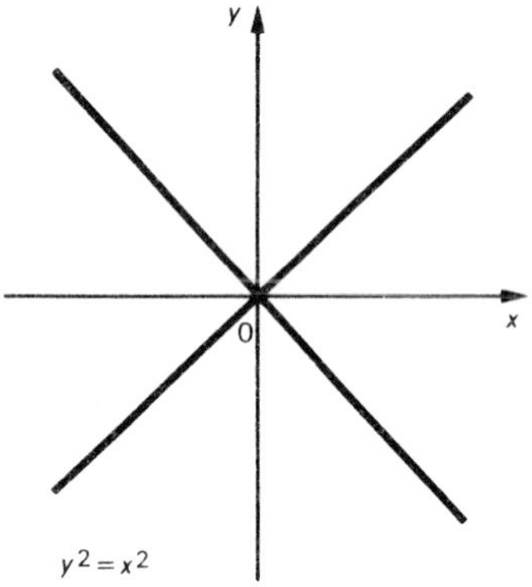

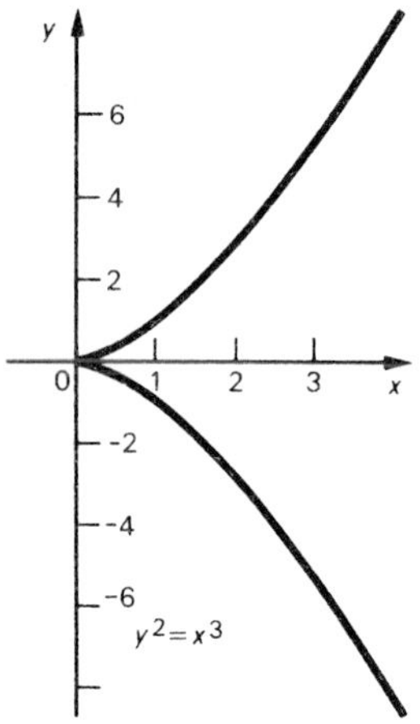

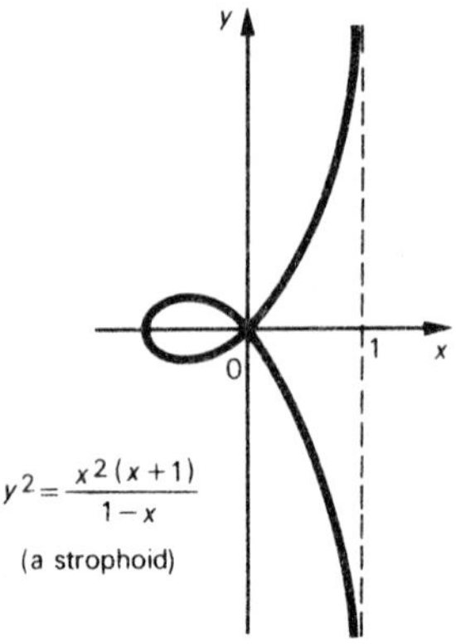

Below are the sketches of

(a) $y = x^2 - 4x$ and $y^2 = x^2 - 4x$
(b) $y = x^2 - 4x + 2$ and $y^2 = x^2 - 4x + 2$
(c) $y = x^2 - 4x + 4$ and $y^2 = x^2 - 4x + 4$
(d) $y = x^2 - 4x + 6$ and $y^2 = x^2 - 4x + 6$

Notice the change in shape of the hyperbolas and the special case (c) of a pair of straight lines ($y^2 = x^2 - 4x + 4$ gives $y = \pm(x-2)$).

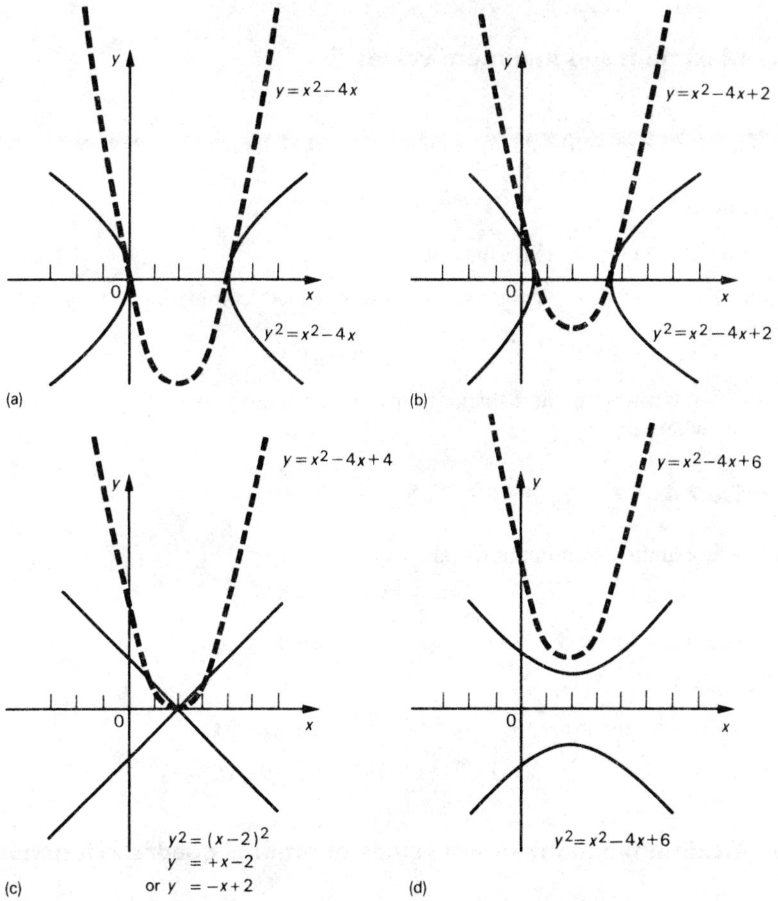

Exercise 2.3

Use your answers to Exercise 2.2 to help you to sketch the following curves.

1 $y^2 = \dfrac{x^2}{x^2-1}$ **2** $y^2 = \dfrac{2x-3}{x^2+2x-4}$ **3** $y^2 = \dfrac{x}{(x+1)(3+x)}$

Sketch the following.

4 $y^2 = 4x^2 - 12x + 9$ **5** $y^2 = (x-2)(x+1)(x+2)$ **6** $y^2 = x^2(4-x)$

7 $y^2 = x^2 - 6x$ **8** $y^2 = 9 - x$

Now try these. How do they differ from the above?

9 $y = \dfrac{1}{1+x^2}$ (a witch of Agnesi) **10** $xy = x^3 - 1$ (a trident)

2.4 Maximum and minimum values

A problem which you often meet involving quadratic inequalities is to find the minimum (or maximum) value of a quadratic expression.

Example 6

Show that $x^2 - 3x + 2 \geqslant -\frac{1}{4}$ for all values of x.

Consider $y = x^2 - 3x + 2$ and use the process called 'completing the square' (see page 49)

$$y = (x - \tfrac{3}{2})^2 - \tfrac{1}{4}$$

Now $(x - \frac{3}{2})^2$ is always greater than, or equal to, zero. So $y \geqslant -\frac{1}{4}$, the smallest value occurring when $x = \frac{3}{2}$.

Exercise 2.4

Find the maximum (or minimum) values of

1 $x^2 + 3x - 4$

2 $x^2 - 5x + 2$

3 $2x^2 - 3x + 5$

4 $3x^2 + 2$

5 $3 - 2x + x^2$

6 $2x + 3 - x^2$

7 $7x - 4 - 2x^2$

8 $3 - 2x^2$

9 $-4 - 5x - 3x^2$

10 $-6x - 9 - x^2$

2.5 Maximum and minimum values of rational quadratic functions

We are sometimes required to find both the maximum and the minimum values of a rational quadratic expression.

Example 7

Sketch the graph of
$$y = \frac{4x-6}{x^2+4}$$
and find the limiting values between which it lies.

Here we have a rational function with a quadratic denominator, but this time there are no asymptotes since the denominator has no real roots ($B^2 < 4AC$) so no real value of x will make it equal zero.

We can see that when $x = 0$, $y = -\frac{3}{2}$ and that $y = 0$ when $x = \frac{3}{2}$. Also that $y \approx 4/x$ when x is very large, and $y \to 0$ as $x \to \infty$. This gives us little guide to the shape of the curve, so we must draw up a table of values.

TABLE OF VALUES $\qquad y = \dfrac{4x-6}{x^2+4}$

x	-4	-3	-2	-1	0	1	2	3	4	5	6
$4x-6$	-22	-18	-14	-10	-6	-2	2	6	10	14	18
x^2+4	20	13	8	5	4	5	8	13	20	29	40
y	$-\frac{11}{10}$	$-\frac{18}{13}$	$-\frac{7}{4}$	-2	$-\frac{3}{2}$	$-\frac{2}{5}$	$\frac{1}{4}$	$\frac{6}{13}$	$\frac{1}{2}$	$\frac{14}{29}$	$\frac{9}{20}$

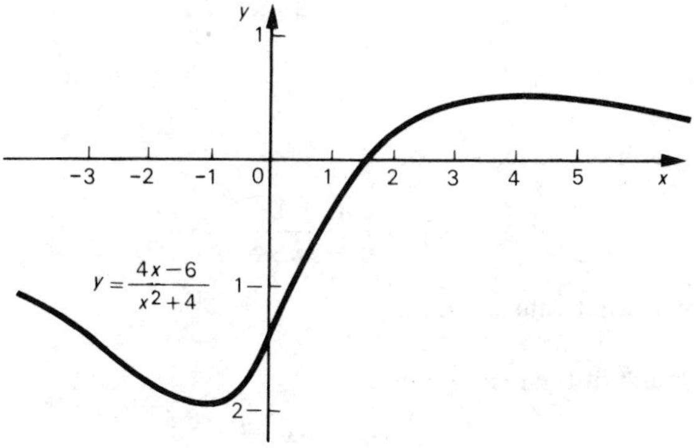

We can see that the graph lies wholly between two values of y which we have to find. We can do this by drawing a horizontal line which in general will cut the curve in two points (A and B).

This will be true for values of y between the maximum and the minimum, when this line becomes a tangent to the curve and meets it in one point only.

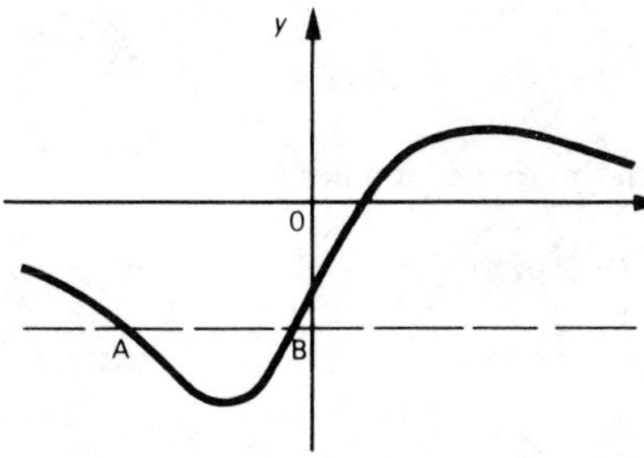

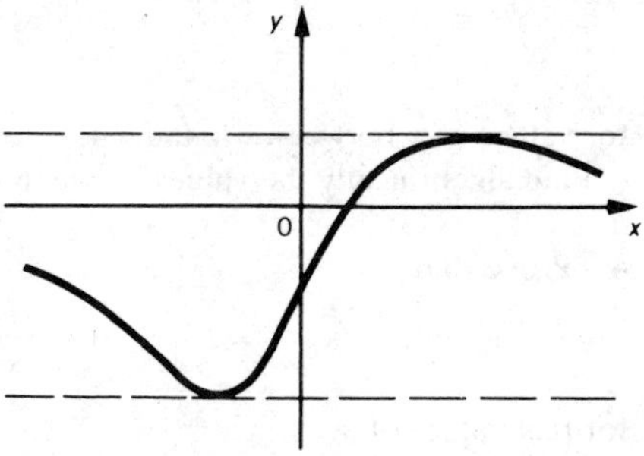

Suppose $y = (4x-6)/(x^2+4)$ is the curve and $y = k$ is the line which is a tangent to the curve. It will 'cut' the curve when $k = (4x-6)/(x^2+4)$ and this equation must have equal roots.

$$kx^2+4k = 4x-6$$

$$kx^2-4x+4k+6 = 0$$

This equation has equal roots if $B^2 = 4AC$, hence

$$(-4)^2 = 4k(4k+6)$$

$$16 = 16k^2+24k$$

$$2k^2+3k-2 = 0$$

$$(2k-1)(k+2) = 0$$

$$k = \tfrac{1}{2} \text{ or } -2$$

These values of k give the maximum and minimum values of the expression, so

$$-2 \leqslant \frac{4x-6}{x^2+4} \leqslant \tfrac{1}{2}$$

Exercise 2.5

1 Draw the graph of the expression

$$y = \frac{3(x-1)}{x^2+3x+5}$$

and find between what values y lies.

2 Draw the graph of the expression

$$y = \frac{9x^2+8x+3}{x^2+1}$$

Prove that when x is real

$$1 \leqslant \frac{9x^2+8x+3}{x^2+1} \leqslant 11$$

3 Draw the graph of

$$y = \frac{x^2-4x+3}{x^2+3}$$

for values of x between -4 and $+4$.

Find algebraically the values between which this expression lies.

4 Prove that

$$-1 \leqslant \frac{x(x+4)}{x^2+2} \leqslant 2$$

for real values of x.

Sketch the graph of

$$y = \frac{x(x+4)}{x^2+2}$$

3 Further inequalities

3.1 Inequalities and the modulus function

The modulus of x (abbreviated to 'mod x' and written $|x|$) is defined as follows:

$$|x| = x \quad \text{when} \quad x \geqslant 0$$

$$|x| = -x \quad \text{when} \quad x < 0$$

Thus

$$|2x+1| = 2x+1 \quad \text{when} \quad 2x+1 \geqslant 0,\ x \geqslant -\tfrac{1}{2}$$

$$|2x+1| = -2x-1 \quad \text{when} \quad 2x+1 < 0,\ x < -\tfrac{1}{2}$$

The graph of $y = |x|$ is:

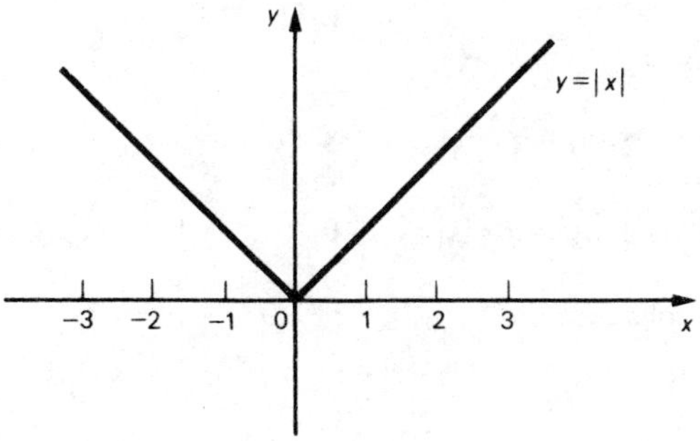

Here are some more examples of graphs involving $|x|$.

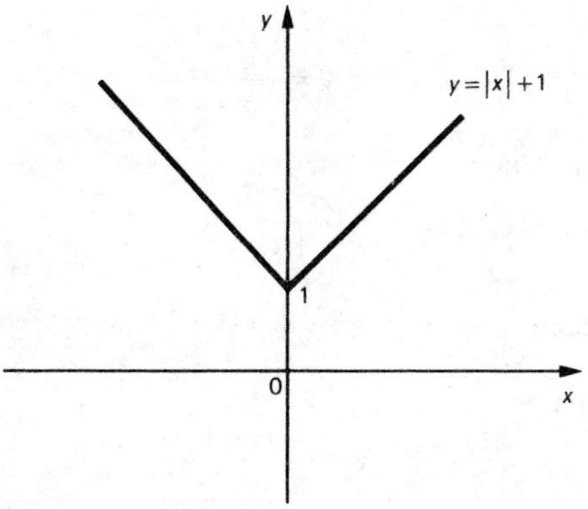

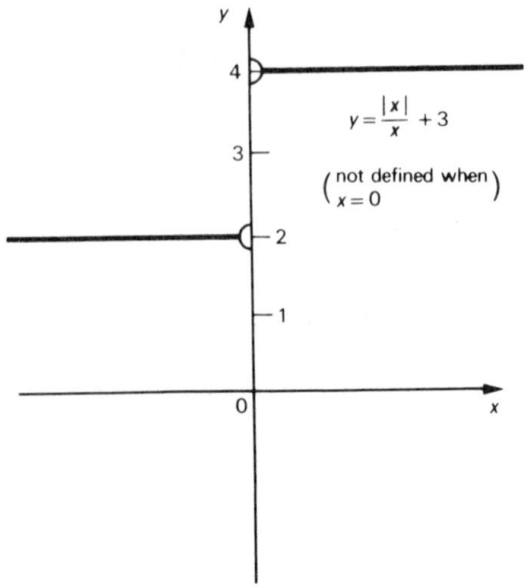

Exercise 3.1

Sketch the graphs of

1 $y = 2 + |x|$ **2** $y = 1 - |x|$ **3** $y = \frac{|x|}{x} - 2$

4 $y = x - |x|$ **5** $y = x \times |x|$ **6** $y = |x + 1|$

7 Sketch the graphs of

(a) $y = \frac{3x-1}{2x-3}$ **(b)** $y = \frac{3|x|-1}{2|x|-3}$

(c) $y = \frac{|3x-1|}{|2x-3|}$ **(d)** $|y| = \frac{3x-1}{2x-3}$

8 Sketch the graph of

$$y = \frac{x-2}{x+1}$$

Hence, or otherwise, solve

$$\left|\frac{x-2}{x+1}\right| < 2$$

9 Find the minimum value of $y = |x-1| + |x-2| + |x-3|$. Illustrate with a graph.

10 Draw the graph of

$$y = \frac{3x+1}{x^2 - 2x + 3}$$

and use it to solve

$$\left|\frac{3x+1}{x^2-2x+3}\right| > 1$$

3.2 Inequalities in the plane

So far the solution to the inequality has always been a set of values of x. We now investigate inequalities in a *plane*, where certain *regions* of the plane will satisfy the inequality, i.e. the solution is a set of values (x, y). For example, in a plane, $x > 2$ represents the region shown shaded in the diagram below, where $x = 2$ is *not* part of the region (hence dotted).

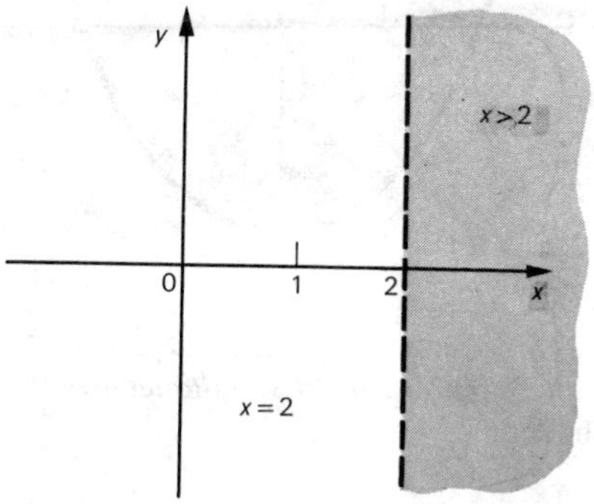

Similarly, $y \geqslant x+1$ is the region above the line $y = x+1$. Here $y = x+1$ belongs to the region and is shown as an *unbroken* line:

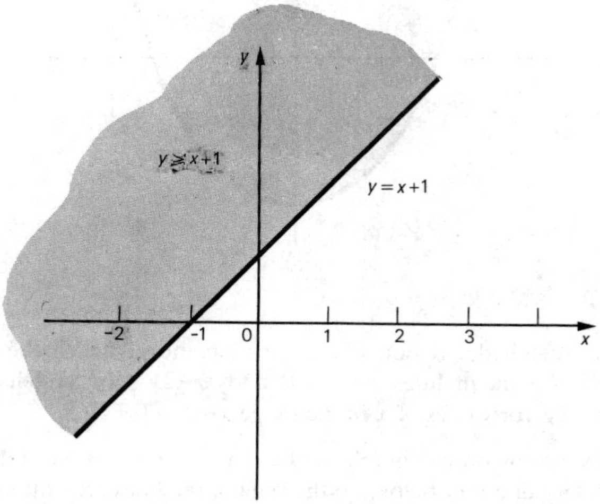

If there is any doubt as to which side of the line is the required region, check, using a known point. For example consider (0, 2). Since this point satisfies the inequality it lies in the required region.

The boundary between the regions need not be a straight line. For instance, $y \geqslant x^2 - 4$ is represented by the shaded region:

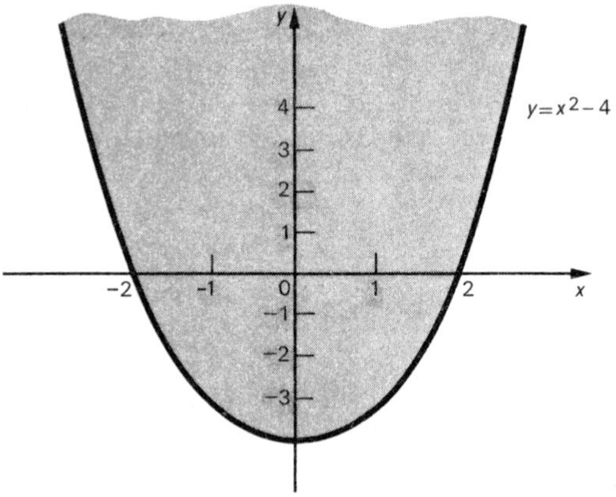

Again, the region in which points satisfy *simultaneously* the inequalities $y \geqslant x^2 - 4$ and $y \leqslant 2$ is shown shaded:

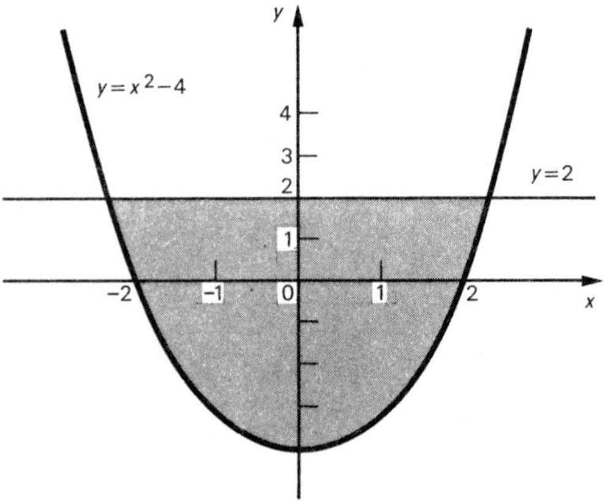

Example

Illustrate in a sketch the region of the (x, y) plane of which the points satisfy simultaneously the inequalities $x - 3 > 0$ and $x - 2y < 0$. Sketch the graph of $y = x - 3 + |x - 2y|$ for values of x in the range $x - 3 > 0$.

First of all we draw on our graph the lines $x = 3$ and $x = 2y$, but since in each case the boundary does not belong to the region, the lines are dotted.

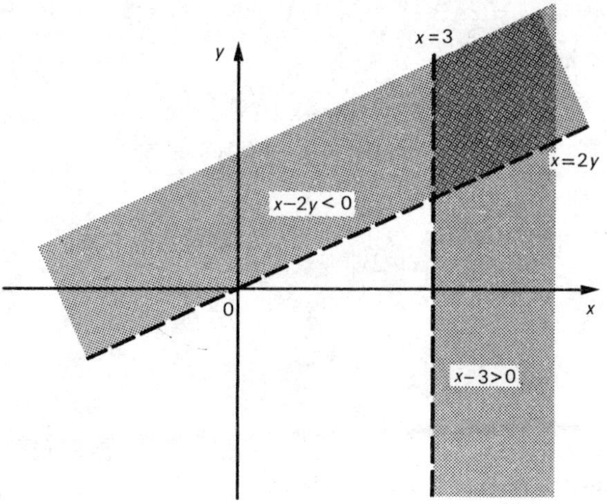

We shade the region where the inequality holds. To find which side of the boundary is permissible we check using the coordinates of a point which is clearly on one side of the boundary. Here we can consider the point (4, 0). This satisfies $x-3>0$ (since $4-3>0$) but does not satisfy $x-2y<0$ since $4-0 \nless 0$). The points satisfying both inequalities lie in the darkly-shaded area in the top right of the graph above.

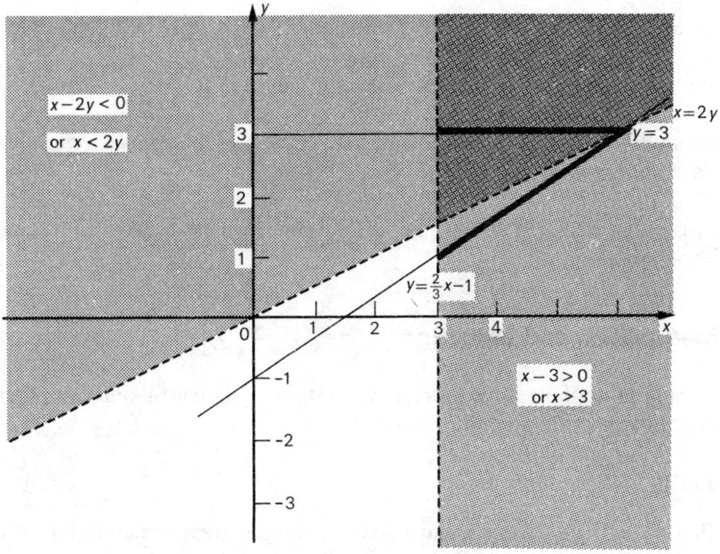

We now consider $y = x-3+|x-2y|$ in the two cases

(a) $x-2y < 0$ in which case

$$|x-2y| = 2y-x$$

Hence

$$y = x-3+2y-x$$

$$y = 3$$

(b) $x-2y > 0$, in which case

$$|x-2y| = x-2y$$

and

$$y = x-3+x-2y$$

$$3y = 2x-3$$

$$y = \tfrac{2}{3}x-1$$

Also, we know that $x > 3$. This enables us to draw in the two lines which make up the graph (shown in bold in the figure above).

Exercise 3.2

Sketch the graphs of

1 $|x|+|y| = 2$ **2** $|x-y| = x+1$ **3** $|2x+y| = y-1$

4 $y = x+2+|x-3y|$ **5** $y = |x+2y|-2x+1$ **6** $|y-2x| = x-3$

7 Sketch in the same diagram, the graphs of

(a) $y = x+|x|$ and **(b)** $y = 2+x-|x|$

Show that they enclose a parallelogram and find its area.

8 Illustrate in a sketch, the region of the plane of which the points simultaneously satisfy $y-2 < 0$ and $3x+4y < 0$.

Sketch the graph of $x = y-2+|3x+4y|$ for values of y where $y-2 < 0$.

9 Illustrate in a sketch the region of the plane which satisfies simultaneously $x^2+y^2 \leqslant 25$ and $x \leqslant y$.

10 Illustrate in a sketch the region of the plane which satisfies simultaneously $x^2+y^2 \leqslant 9$ and $x+y \geqslant 3$.

3.3 Inequalities and induction

The principle of mathematical induction is extremely powerful and can be used to prove certain types of inequality.

Example 2

Prove that $4^n \geqslant 3n^2+1$ for n being a positive integer greater than or equal to 1.

Check that the inequality is true for $n = 1$. L.H.S. 4, R.H.S. 4. Hence it is true for $n = 1$.

Suppose the inequality is true for $n = k$. Then

$$4^k \geqslant 3k^2+1$$

and $$4^{k+1} = 4^k \times 4 \geqslant (3k^2+1)4 = 12k^2+4$$

We must now show that $$4^{k+1} \geqslant 3(k+1)^2+1$$

$$4^{k+1} \geqslant 3(k^2+2k+1)+1$$

$$4^{k+1} \geqslant 3k^2+6k+4$$

Now if $$12k^2+4 \geqslant 3k^2+6k+4$$

the inequality will be true

$$9k^2-6k \geqslant 0$$

$$k(3k-2) \geqslant 0$$

so either $k \geqslant 0$ and $k \geqslant \frac{2}{3}$

or $k \leqslant 0$ and $k \leqslant \frac{2}{3}$

But k is a positive integer greater than or equal to 1. Hence the inequality is true for $n = k+1$, and so by PMI true for all positive integers $n \geqslant 1$.

Exercise 3.3

1 Prove by mathematical induction that $2^n \geqslant 1+n$, where n is a positive integer (i.e. $n \in \mathbb{Z}^+$).

2 Prove that, for all integers n greater than 3, $n! > 2^n$.

3 Prove that, for all integers n greater than or equal to 5, $2^n > n^2$. Where does the proof by induction break down for $n < 5$?

4 Prove by mathematical induction that $\binom{2n}{n} \leqslant \frac{4^n}{2}$, $n \in \mathbb{Z}^+$.

5 If $a \geqslant 0$, show that for all integers $n \geqslant 1$

$$(1+a)^n \geqslant 1+na+\frac{n(n-1)}{2}a^2$$

6 Prove that $\sum_{p=1}^{n-1} p^3 < \frac{n^4}{4} < \sum_{p=1}^{n} p^3$ for all integers $n \geqslant 2$.

7 Prove that $(2k+1)^2(3k+4) < (2k+2)^2(3k+1)$ where $k \in \mathbb{Z}^+$. Hence prove by mathematical induction that

$$\left(\frac{1}{2}\right)\left(\frac{3}{4}\right)\cdots\left(\frac{2n-1}{2n}\right) \leqslant \frac{1}{\sqrt{(3n+1)}} \qquad \text{for all } n \in \mathbb{Z}^+$$

8 Prove by mathematical induction, that the product

$$\prod_{p=2}^{n}\left(1-\frac{1}{p^2}\right)=\frac{n+1}{2n} \qquad \text{for } n\in\mathbb{Z}^+,\ n\geqslant 2$$

[The symbol stands for product: thus

$$\prod_{p=2}^{n}\left(1-\frac{1}{p^2}\right)=\left(1-\frac{1}{2^2}\right)\times\left(1-\frac{1}{3^2}\right)\times\left(1-\frac{1}{4^2}\right)\ldots\left(1-\frac{1}{n^2}\right)]$$

Miscellaneous examination questions 6

1 Find the solution set of the inequality

$$\frac{4-x}{x-2}>3$$ (C.)

2 Prove that

$$\frac{(1+x)^2}{9+x^2}$$ (C.)

lies between 0 and $\frac{10}{9}$.

3 Find the solution set of the inequality

$$\frac{x-5}{1-x}>1$$ (C.)

4 Calculate the range (or ranges) of values of x for which

$$3x^2-7x+4>0$$ (O.)

5 Find the values of x and y which are positive integers and which satisfy simultaneously the inequalities $2x+3y>12$, $x^2+y^2<6x+4y$. (C.)

6 Sketch the region satisfied by $0<y<x(2-x)$. Sketch the curve $y=|x(2-x)|$ and indicate the region where $y<|x(2-x)|$. (C.)

7 Solve the following inequalities by the use of a sketch

(a) $\left|\frac{3}{2+3x}\right|<1$ **(b)** $\left|\frac{2}{3-x}\right|>2$

(c) $\left|\frac{x^2+2x-1}{x^2+3x-1}\right|\geqslant 2$ **(d)** $\left|\frac{1}{(x-1)(x-2)}\right|<3$ (C.)

8 Use a sketch to solve $x^2=|x+2|$. (O. & C.)

9 Show by shading on a sketch of the x, y plane, the region for which $x^2+y^2\leqslant 1$, $y\geqslant x$ and $y\leqslant x+1$.

Hence find **(a)** the greatest value of y, and **(b)** the least value of $x+y$ for which these inequalities hold. (M.E.I.)

10 Sketch the curves

$$y^2 = 2x^3+3x^2-9x$$

and $$y = |2x^3+3x^2-9x|$$ (O. & C.)

11 Find constants p and q such that $x^2+6x+10 = (x+p)^2+q$ for all values of x. Deduce that if x is real

$$0 < \frac{1}{x^2+6x+10} \leqslant 1$$ (L.)

12 Given that x is real and that

$$y = \frac{x^2+2}{2x+1}$$

show that y cannot lie between -2 and 1. (L.)

13 Find the solution set of the inequality

$$\frac{(x-2)(x-3)}{(x+1)} < 0$$

where x takes real values. (A.E.B.)

14 Solve the inequality

$$\frac{(x+1)(x+2)}{(x+3)} < 0$$

where x takes real values. (A.E.B.)

15 Find the solution set, in the set of real numbers, of the inequality

$$\frac{(x-1)(x+2)}{x-3} < 0$$ (A.E.B.)

16 Show that the range of values taken by the function

$$\frac{x^2+x+7}{x^2-4x+5}$$

for real values of x is from $\frac{1}{2}$ to $13\frac{1}{2}$ inclusive. Sketch the graph of the function indicating its asymptote. (J.M.B.)

17 If x is real, find the set of possible values of

$$\frac{2x+1}{x^2+2}$$ (L.)

18 Determine constants a and b such that $x^2+4x+5 = (x+a)^2+b$ for all values of x. If x is any real number, prove that

$$0 < \frac{1}{x^2+4x+5} \leqslant 1$$

Sketch the curve

$$y = \frac{1}{x^2+4x+5}$$ (O. & C.)

19 Find the ranges of values of the real number x for which the following inequality holds

$$\frac{1}{x+6} < \frac{2}{2-3x}$$ (M.E.I.)

20 Draw the graph of the function

$$y = \frac{x(4x+3)}{x^2+1}$$

for values of x from -2 to $+4$ plotting points at unit intervals of x and also at $x = \pm\frac{1}{2}$. From your graph find the roots to two places of decimals, of the equation

$$2x(4x+3) = 3(x^2+1)$$

Find the range of values of y for which x is real. (O. & C.)

21 Sketch roughly the graph of

$$y = \frac{3x+2}{4x+1}$$

Using the graph, or by any other method, find the values of x for which

(a) $\left|\frac{3x+2}{4x+1}\right| < 1$ **(b)** $\left|\frac{3x^2+2}{4x^2-1}\right| < 1$ (M.E.I.)

Chapter 7

Trigonometry 2

1 Further formulae

1.1 Sum and difference formulae

For convenience we list here the formulae already met in Chapter 3.

$$\sin(A \pm B) = \sin A \cos B \pm \cos A \sin B \qquad \text{I, III}$$

$$\cos(A \pm B) = \cos A \cos B \mp \sin A \sin B \qquad \text{II, IV}$$

$$\tan(A \pm B) = \frac{\tan A \pm \tan B}{1 \mp \tan A \tan B} \qquad \text{V, VI}$$

$$\sin 2\theta = 2 \sin \theta \cos \theta \qquad \text{VII} \qquad \sin \phi = 2 \sin \frac{\phi}{2} \cos \frac{\phi}{2} \qquad \text{X}$$

$$\cos 2\theta = \cos^2 \theta - \sin^2 \theta \qquad \text{VIIIa} \qquad \cos \phi = \cos^2 \frac{\phi}{2} - \sin^2 \frac{\phi}{2} \qquad \text{XIa}$$

$$= 2\cos^2 \theta - 1 \qquad \text{VIIIb} \qquad = 2\cos^2 \frac{\phi}{2} - 1 \qquad \text{XIb}$$

$$= 1 - 2\sin^2 \theta \qquad \text{VIIIc} \qquad = 1 - 2\sin^2 \frac{\phi}{2} \qquad \text{XIc}$$

$$\tan 2\theta = \frac{2 \tan \theta}{1 - \tan^2 \theta} \qquad \text{IX} \qquad \tan \phi = \frac{2 \tan \frac{\phi}{2}}{1 - \tan^2 \frac{\phi}{2}} \qquad \text{XIIa}$$

$$\cos^2 \theta + \sin^2 \theta = 1 \qquad 1 + \tan^2 \theta = \sec^2 \theta \qquad \cot^2 \theta + 1 = \text{cosec}^2 \theta$$

Alternative derivation of the sum and difference formulae

This approach involves rotations about the origin. (If you are not familiar with transformations, leave this for a second reading.)

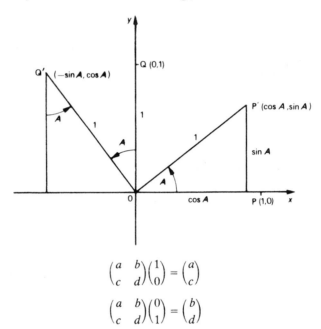

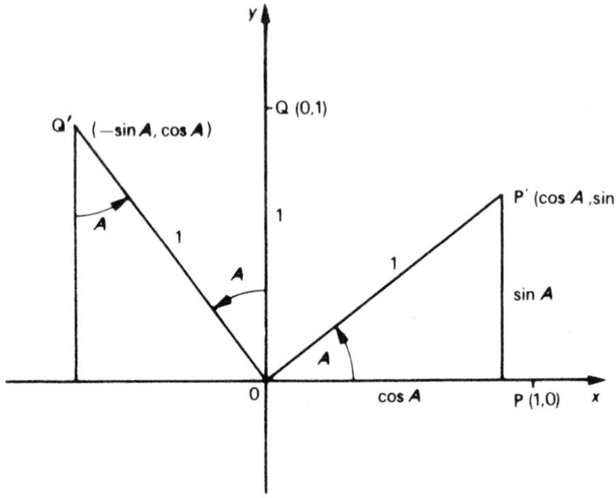

$$\begin{pmatrix} a & b \\ c & d \end{pmatrix}\begin{pmatrix} 1 \\ 0 \end{pmatrix} = \begin{pmatrix} a \\ c \end{pmatrix}$$

and

$$\begin{pmatrix} a & b \\ c & d \end{pmatrix}\begin{pmatrix} 0 \\ 1 \end{pmatrix} = \begin{pmatrix} b \\ d \end{pmatrix}$$

So if we can find the coordinates of P′ (the image of P(1, 0) under a rotation of OP through A about O) and of Q′ (the image of Q(0, 1) under a rotation of OQ through A about O) then we can write down the matrix representing a rotation through A. Since the coordinates of P′ are (cos A, sin A) and of Q′ are ($-$sin A, cos A), the rotation matrix $\boldsymbol{R}$ is given by

$$\boldsymbol{R}_A = \begin{pmatrix} \cos A & -\sin A \\ \sin A & \cos A \end{pmatrix}$$

Similarly $\boldsymbol{R}_B = \begin{pmatrix} \cos B & -\sin B \\ \sin B & \cos B \end{pmatrix}$

Now $\boldsymbol{R}_{A+B} = \boldsymbol{R}_B \times \boldsymbol{R}_A$ ($\boldsymbol{R}_A$ followed by $\boldsymbol{R}_B$)

$$= \begin{pmatrix} \cos B & -\sin B \\ \sin B & \cos B \end{pmatrix}\begin{pmatrix} \cos A & -\sin A \\ \sin A & \cos A \end{pmatrix}$$

$$= \begin{pmatrix} \cos A \cos B - \sin A \sin B & -(\sin A \cos B + \cos A \sin B) \\ \sin A \cos B + \cos A \sin B & \cos A \cos B - \sin A \sin B \end{pmatrix}$$

But $\mathbf{R}_{A+B} = \begin{pmatrix} \cos (A+B) & -\sin (A+B) \\ \sin (A+B) & \cos (A+B) \end{pmatrix}$

and since equal matrices have equal entries

$$\mathbf{\cos (A+B) = \cos A \cos B - \sin A \sin B}$$ ◀

and $$\mathbf{\sin (A+B)=\sin A \cos B+\cos A \sin B}$$ ◀

This demonstration uses the idea that a rotation through A followed by a rotation through B is equivalent to a rotation through $(A+B)$.

To obtain the formula for $(A-B)$ we can replace B by $-B$:

$$\cos (A-B) = \cos A \cos (-B)-\sin A \sin (-B)$$

But since $\cos (-B) = \cos B$ and $\sin (-B) = -\sin B$

$$\mathbf{\cos (A-B) = \cos A \cos B+\sin A \sin B}$$ ◀

Similarly $$\sin (A-B) = \sin A \cos (-B)+\cos A \sin (-B)$$

$$\mathbf{\sin (A-B) = \sin A \cos B-\cos A \sin B}$$ ◀

Further consequences of the sum and difference formulae

(*a*) *Multiple angles*

These formulae are often useful in integration, in complex numbers and in the solution of equations.

Suppose that $A = 2\theta$, $B = \theta$. Then

$$\begin{aligned}\sin (A+B) &= \sin A \cos B+\cos A \sin B\\ \sin (2\theta+\theta) &= \sin 2\theta \cos \theta+\cos 2\theta \sin \theta\\ &= 2 \sin \theta \cos \theta \cos \theta+(1-2 \sin^2 \theta) \sin \theta\\ &= 2 \sin \theta \cos^2 \theta+\sin \theta-2 \sin^3 \theta\\ &= 2 \sin \theta(1-\sin^2 \theta)+\sin \theta-2 \sin^3 \theta\end{aligned}$$

$$\boldsymbol{\sin 3\theta = 3 \sin \theta-4 \sin^3 \theta}$$ ◀

Similarly
$$\begin{aligned}\cos (A+B) &= \cos A \cos B-\sin A \sin B\\ \cos (2\theta+\theta) &= \cos 2\theta \cos \theta-\sin 2\theta \sin \theta\\ &= (2 \cos^2 \theta-1) \cos \theta-2 \sin \theta \cos \theta \sin \theta\\ &= 2 \cos^3 \theta-\cos \theta-2 \cos \theta(1-\cos^2 \theta)\end{aligned}$$

$$\boldsymbol{\cos 3\theta = 4 \cos^3 \theta-3 \cos \theta}$$ ◀

Again
$$\begin{aligned}\tan (A+B) &= \frac{\tan A+\tan B}{1-\tan A \tan B}\\ \tan (2\theta+\theta) &= \frac{\tan 2\theta+\tan \theta}{1-\tan 2\theta \tan \theta}\\ &= \frac{\dfrac{2 \tan \theta}{1-\tan^2 \theta}+\tan \theta}{1-\dfrac{2 \tan \theta \tan \theta}{1-\tan^2 \theta}}\end{aligned}$$

$$\boldsymbol{\tan 3\theta = \frac{3 \tan \theta-\tan^3 \theta}{1-3 \tan^2 \theta}}$$ ◀

(*b*) *Half angle formulae*

These formulae are particularly useful in certain types of integral, and involve the substitution $\tan \phi/2 = t$. Then

$$\tan \phi = \frac{2t}{1-t^2} \qquad \text{XIIb} \quad ◀$$

Now $\sin \phi = 2 \sin \frac{\phi}{2} \cos \frac{\phi}{2}$

$$= \frac{2 \sin \phi/2}{\cos \phi/2} \cos^2 \frac{\phi}{2}$$

$$= \frac{2(\sin \phi/2)/(\cos \phi/2)}{\sec^2 \phi/2}$$

But $\sec^2 \frac{\phi}{2} = 1 + \tan^2 \frac{\phi}{2}$

so $\sin \phi = \dfrac{2 \tan \phi/2}{1+\tan^2 \phi/2}$

$$\sin \phi = \frac{2t}{1+t^2} \qquad \text{XIV} \quad ◀$$

also $\cos \phi = \cos^2 \frac{\phi}{2} - \sin^2 \frac{\phi}{2}$

$$= \cos^2 \frac{\phi}{2}\left(1 - \frac{\sin^2 \phi/2}{\cos^2 \phi/2}\right)$$

$$= \frac{1-\tan^2 \phi/2}{\sec^2 \phi/2}$$

$$= \frac{1-\tan^2 \phi/2}{1+\tan^2 \phi/2}$$

$$\cos \phi = \frac{1-t^2}{1+t^2} \qquad \text{XIV} \quad ◀$$

Exercise 1.1: Derivation of formulae

1

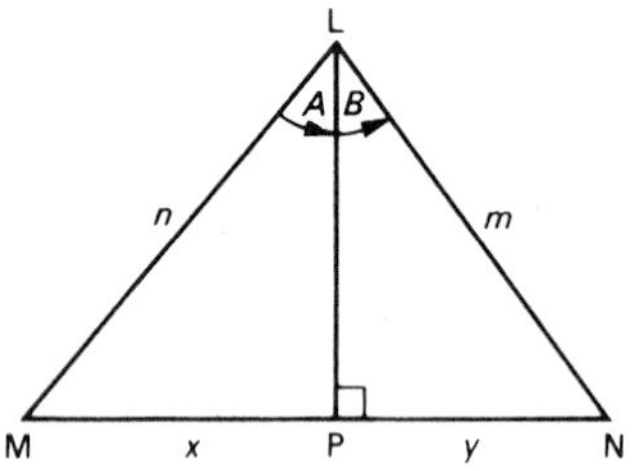

The area of $\triangle$LMN = area $\triangle$LPM + area $\triangle$LPN. Using this fact and the formula for the area of a triangle ($\frac{1}{2}ab \sin C$) show that

$$\sin (A+B) = \sin A \cos B + \cos A \sin B$$

What restrictions should be placed on $(A+B)$?

2

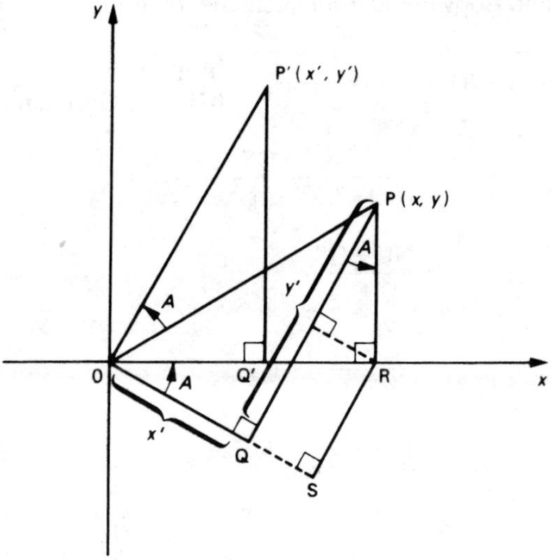

Suppose OP is rotated through A to OP′ where P is (x, y), P′ is (x', y'). Complete the figure as shown to illustrate that

$$x' = x \cos A - y \sin A$$

$$y' = x \sin A + y \cos A$$

Write down the matrix corresponding to a rotation through A. If P′(x', y') is now transformed by a further rotation through B to P″(x'', y''), use the corresponding matrices to show that

$$\sin (A+B) = \sin A \cos B + \cos A \sin B$$

and $$\cos (A+B) = \cos A \cos B - \sin A \sin B$$

3

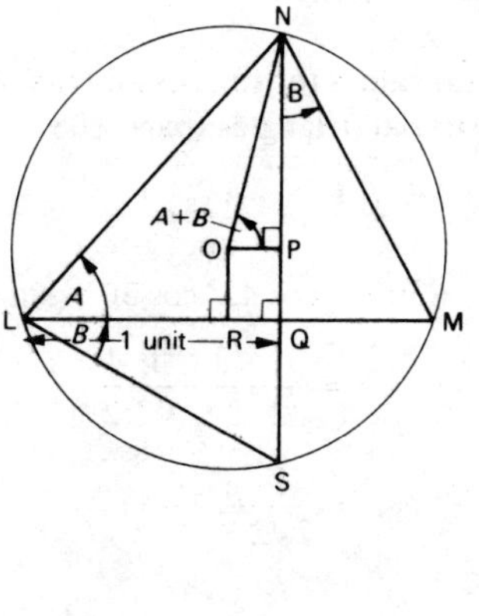

O is the centre of the circle. Show that P is the midpoint of NS and R the midpoint of LM. LQ is one unit. Copy out and complete the following:

In $\triangle$ONP, $\tan(A+B) = \dfrac{\dots}{\dots} = \dfrac{1}{2}\dfrac{\dots}{\dots}$ (proved)

(since OPQR is a rectangle)

$$= \frac{NQ+QS}{(LQ-LR)+(\dots-\dots)}$$

$$= \frac{NQ+QS}{1-\dots}$$

$$= \frac{\dots+\dots}{1-\dots}$$

4

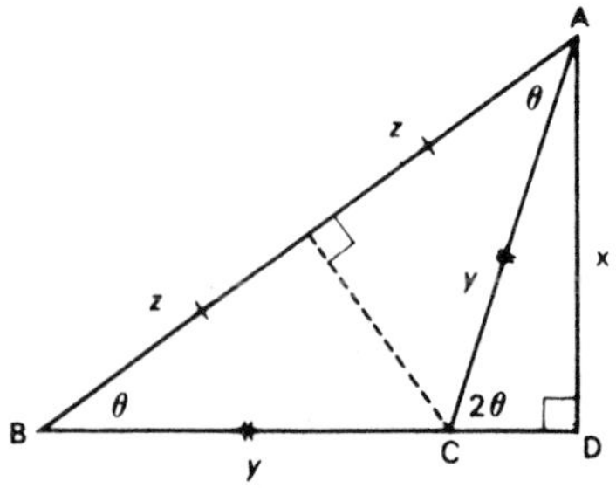

Use the diagram above to show that

$$\sin 2\theta = 2\sin\theta\cos\theta$$

What conditions should be imposed on θ?

1.2 Trigonometrical formulae in use

(a) Trigonometrical ratios in surd form

These formulae enable us to find values for sin, cos and tan of many angles in square root or surd form, using our 'special' triangles (page 105).

Example 1

$$\cos 75° = \cos(45°+30°) = \cos 45° \cos 30° - \sin 45° \sin 30°$$

$$= \frac{1}{\sqrt{2}}\frac{\sqrt{3}}{2} - \frac{1}{\sqrt{2}}\frac{1}{2}$$

$$= \frac{1}{2\sqrt{2}}(\sqrt{3}-1)$$

It is customary, however, to give the solutions with whole number denominators. To do this we multiply by $\sqrt{2}/\sqrt{2}$.

$$\cos 75° = \frac{1}{2\sqrt{2}}\frac{\sqrt{2}}{\sqrt{2}}(\sqrt{3}-1)$$

$$= \frac{\sqrt{2}}{4}(\sqrt{3}-1)$$

Example 2

$$\tan 15° = \tan (45°-30°) = \frac{\tan 45° - \tan 30°}{1+\tan 45° \tan 30°}$$

$$= \frac{1-1/\sqrt{3}}{1+1/\sqrt{3}}$$

$$= \frac{\sqrt{3}-1}{\sqrt{3}+1} \qquad \text{(multiplying by } \sqrt{3}/\sqrt{3}\text{)}$$

Again we need to convert the denominator into a whole number. To do this we remember that $a^2-b^2 = (a-b)(a+b)$. So here

$$(\sqrt{3}+1)(\sqrt{3}-1) = (\sqrt{3})^2-1 = 3-1 = 2$$

We multiply top and bottom by $\sqrt{3}-1$

$$\tan 15° = \frac{(\sqrt{3}-1)(\sqrt{3}-1)}{(\sqrt{3}+1)(\sqrt{3}-1)}$$

$$= \frac{(\sqrt{3})^2-2\sqrt{3}+1}{2}$$

$$= \frac{4-2\sqrt{3}}{2}$$

$$= 2-\sqrt{3}$$

Exercise 1.2a

Find in square root form:

1 sin 15°	**2** tan 75°	**3** cos 15°
4 sin 75°	**5** tan 105°	**6** cos 105°

7 Using $\cos 2\theta = 1-2\sin^2\theta$, find $\sin 7\frac{1}{2}°$

8 Using a formula for $\cos 2\theta$, find $\cos 22\frac{1}{2}°$

9 Find $\tan 52\frac{1}{2}°$

10 Find $\sin 67\frac{1}{2}°$

11 If $\sin\theta = 4/5$ find **(a)** $\sin 2\theta$ **(b)** $\cos 2\theta$ **(c)** $\tan 2\theta$ **(d)** $\cos(60°-\theta)$

12 If $\cos\theta = -5/13$ find **(a)** $\sin 2\theta$ **(b)** $\cos 2\theta$ **(c)** $\sin(45°+\theta)$ where θ is obtuse

(b) The angles between lines in the plane

Suppose we have two intersecting lines, with equations

$$y = m_1x + c_1 \qquad \text{and} \qquad y = m_2x + c_2$$

the angles between the line and the x axis being A and B respectively.

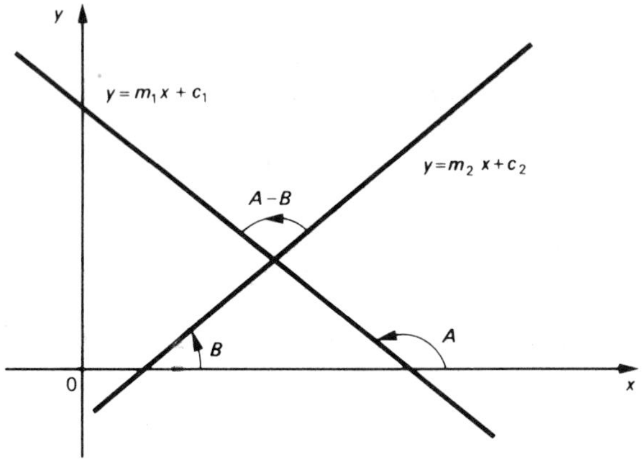

Then tan A = m_1, tan $B = m_2$ and the angle between the lines is $A - B$. Now

$$\tan(A-B) = \frac{\tan A - \tan B}{1 + \tan A \tan B} = \frac{m_1 - m_2}{1 + m_1m_2}$$

If the lines intersect at right angles, $A - B = 90°$. Since cot $90° = 0$

$$\frac{1 + m_1m_2}{m_1 - m_2} = \cot 90° = 0$$

$$\mathbf{1 + m_1m_2 = 0} \qquad \text{or} \qquad \mathbf{m_1m_2 = -1}$$ ◀

This is the condition for two lines to be perpendicular.

Exercise 1.2b

Find the acute angle between the following pairs of lines:

1 $y = 2x + 4$ and $y = 4x - 3$
2 $2x + y = 4$ and $2y - x = 6$
3 $y = x + 3$ and $y = -3x$
4 $y = 3x + 4$ and $2y - 6x = 7$

(c) Identities

Equations or relations which are true for all values of x (or θ) are called *identities*. To prove that an identity is true, it is usually advisable to begin with the more complicated expression and work towards the simpler one. Only as a very last resort should one attempt to use both sides of an identity at once.

Example 1

Prove that $$\sin 2x(\cot x - \cot 2x) \equiv 1$$

Now $$\sin 2x(\cot x - \cot 2x) = 2\sin x\cos x\left(\frac{\cos x}{\sin x} - \frac{\cos 2x}{\sin 2x}\right)$$

$$= 2\sin x\cos x\left(\frac{\cos x}{\sin x} - \frac{\cos 2x}{2\sin x\cos x}\right)$$

$$= 2\cos^2 x - \cos 2x$$

$$= 1$$

Example 2

Prove that $$\cos 4\theta \equiv 8\cos^4\theta - 8\cos^2\theta + 1$$

Now $$\cos 4\theta = \cos 2(2\theta)$$

$$= 2\cos^2 2\theta - 1$$

$$= 2(2\cos^2\theta - 1)^2 - 1$$

$$= 2(4\cos^4\theta - 4\cos^2\theta + 1) - 1$$

$$= 8\cos^4\theta - 8\cos^2\theta + 1$$

Example 3

Prove that $$\tan(x+45°) + \tan(x-45°) \equiv 2\tan 2x$$

Now $$\tan(x+45°) + \tan(x-45°) = \frac{\tan x + \tan 45°}{1 - \tan x\tan 45°} + \frac{\tan x - \tan 45°}{1 + \tan x\tan 45°}$$

$$= \frac{\tan x + 1}{1 - \tan x} + \frac{\tan x - 1}{1 + \tan x} \qquad \text{(since } \tan 45° = 1)$$

$$= \frac{(\tan x + 1)(1 + \tan x) + (\tan x - 1)(1 - \tan x)}{(1 - \tan x)(1 + \tan x)}$$

$$= \frac{\tan^2 x + 2\tan x + 1 - \tan^2 x + 2\tan x - 1}{1 - \tan^2 x}$$

$$= \frac{4\tan x}{1 - \tan^2 x}$$

$$= 2\tan 2x$$

Exercise 1.2c

Prove the following identities:

1 $(\sin\theta + \cos\theta)^2 \equiv 1 + \sin 2\theta$

2 $\dfrac{\sin\phi}{1 + \cos\phi} \equiv \tan\dfrac{\phi}{2}$

3 $\dfrac{\cos\theta}{\cos\theta/2+\sin\theta/2}\equiv\cos\dfrac{\theta}{2}-\sin\dfrac{\theta}{2}$

4 $\tan\phi+\cot\phi\equiv\dfrac{2}{\sin 2\phi}$

5 $\dfrac{\sin\theta}{1+\cos\theta}\equiv\dfrac{1-\cos\theta}{\sin\theta}\equiv\tan\dfrac{\theta}{2}$

6 $\dfrac{1}{1+\sec\theta}\times\dfrac{\sin 2\theta}{1+\cos 2\theta}\equiv\tan\dfrac{\theta}{2}$

7 $\sec A+\tan A\equiv\tan\left(45°+\dfrac{A}{2}\right)$

8 $\tan^2(45°+A)\equiv\dfrac{1+\sin 2A}{1-\sin 2A}$

9 $\cot\dfrac{\theta}{2}\equiv\cot\theta+\operatorname{cosec}\theta$

10 $\tan A+\sec A\equiv\dfrac{\cos A/2+\sin A/2}{\cos A/2-\sin A/2}$

11 $\tan(45°-\theta)+\tan 2\theta\equiv\sec 2\theta$

12 $\cos\left(\dfrac{\pi^c}{4}-\theta\right)\sin\left(\dfrac{\pi^c}{4}+\theta\right)\equiv\tfrac{1}{2}(1+\sin 2\theta)$

13 $\cot(A+B)\equiv\dfrac{\cot A\cot B-1}{\cot A+\cot B}$

14 $\cot 2x+\tan x\equiv\operatorname{cosec} 2x$

15 Using the formulae for $\sin 3\theta$ and $\cos 3\theta$ show that

$$\sin^3\theta\sin 3\theta+\cos^3\theta\cos 3\theta\equiv\cos^3 2\theta$$

16 Prove the identities:

(**a**) $\dfrac{\sec^2\theta+2\tan\theta}{(\cos\theta+\sin\theta)^2}\equiv\sec^2\theta$

(**b**) $4\cos\theta\cos(\theta+120°)\cos(\theta-120°)\equiv\cos 3\theta$

17 $\dfrac{\sin 3\theta}{\sin\theta}-\dfrac{\cos 3\theta}{\cos\theta}\equiv 2$

18 $(\sec\theta-\operatorname{cosec}\theta)^2\times\sin^2 2\theta+4\sin 2\theta\equiv 4$

19 $\dfrac{1+\sin\theta}{5+4\cos\theta}\equiv\dfrac{(1+\tan\theta/2)^2}{9+\tan^2\theta/2}$

20 $\cos^6 x+\sin^6 x\equiv 1-\tfrac{3}{4}\sin^2 2x$

1.3 Factor formulae

Remembering the formulae

$\sin(A+B)=\sin A\cos B+\cos A\sin B$, $\cos(A+B)=\cos A\cos B-\sin A\sin B$

$\sin(A-B)=\sin A\cos B-\cos A\sin B$, $\cos(A-B)=\cos A\cos B+\sin A\sin B$

we have, by addition and subtraction

$$\sin(A+B)+\sin(A-B) = 2\sin A\cos B$$

$$\sin(A+B)-\sin(A-B) = 2\cos A\sin B$$

$$\cos(A+B)+\cos(A-B) = 2\cos A\cos B$$

and

$$\cos(A+B)-\cos(A-B) = -2\sin A\sin B$$

We now substitute

$$\left.\begin{aligned} A+B &= C \\ A-B &= D \end{aligned}\right\} \Rightarrow \begin{aligned} A &= \tfrac{1}{2}(C+D) \\ B &= \tfrac{1}{2}(C-D) \end{aligned}$$

and obtain

$$\mathbf{\sin C+\sin D = 2\sin\tfrac{1}{2}(C+D)\cos\tfrac{1}{2}(C-D)} \qquad \textbf{XV} \quad \blacktriangleleft$$

$$\mathbf{\sin C-\sin D = 2\cos\tfrac{1}{2}(C+D)\sin\tfrac{1}{2}(C-D)} \qquad \textbf{XVI} \quad \blacktriangleleft$$

$$\mathbf{\cos C+\cos D = 2\cos\tfrac{1}{2}(C+D)\cos\tfrac{1}{2}(C-D)} \qquad \textbf{XVII} \quad \blacktriangleleft$$

$$\mathbf{\cos C-\cos D = -2\sin\tfrac{1}{2}(C+D)\sin\tfrac{1}{2}(C-D)} \qquad \textbf{XVIII} \quad \blacktriangleleft$$

The four factor formulae, again, are very important, not only for simplifying complicated expressions, but also in the solution of trigonometrical equations and in calculus (for integration).

Exercise 1.3a (oral)

(Answers given to a few odd numbers only)

Use these formulae to express the following in 'factor' form:

1 $\sin 60° + \sin 20°$

2 $\sin 60° - \sin 20°$

3 $\cos 60° - \cos 20°$

4 $\cos 60° + \cos 20°$

5 $\sin 150° - \sin 60°$

6 $\cos 30° + \cos 60°$

7 $\cos 30° - \cos 60°$

8 $\sin 90° + \sin 30°$

9 $\sin 120° - \sin 150°$

10 $\cos 10° - \cos 20°$

11 $\sin x + \sin 2x$

12 $\cos 3x - \cos 2x$

13 $\cos 3x + \cos 2x$

14 $\cos(A+B) - \cos A$

15 $\cos(A-B) + \cos(2A+B)$

16 $\cos x - \cos 4x$

17 $\cos(\phi - 2\theta) + \cos(\phi + 2\theta)$

18 $\cos(\pi^c/2 - x) + \cos x$

19 $\sin x + \cos x$

20 $\sin x + \cos 2x$

21 $\sin(\pi^c/2 - x) - \sin 3x$

22 $\cos(2A+2B) - \cos(2A-2B)$

23 $\cos 50° + \sin 40°$

24 $\sin x + \cos y$

25 $\cos y - \sin(2x - y)$

Exercise 1.3b

Express the following in terms of sums (or differences) of sines (or cosines):

1 $2 \sin 30° \cos 20°$

2 $2 \cos 60° \sin 80°$

3 $2 \sin 20° \cos 30°$

4 $2 \cos 60° \cos 80°$

5 $2 \sin 10° \cos 5°$

6 $2 \cos 20° \sin 30°$

7 $2 \sin 40° \sin 50°$

8 $2 \cos 45° \cos 15°$

9 $2 \sin 120° \cos 60°$

10 $2 \cos 60° \cos 120°$

11 $\sin 65° \cos 15°$

12 $\sin 25° \cos 55°$

13 $\sin 25° \sin 35°$

14 $\sin 120° \sin 60°$

15 $2 \sin 3A \cos A$

16 $2 \sin A \cos 3A$

17 $2 \sin x \sin 2x$

18 $2 \cos 4x \cos 2x$

19 $\sin (\theta - \phi) \sin (\theta + \phi)$

20 $\sin (\theta + \phi) \cos (\theta - \phi)$

21 $\sin (2A + B) \cos (2A + B)$

22 $\cos \frac{x}{2} \sin \frac{y}{2}$

23 $\cos \left(\frac{\theta + \phi}{2}\right) \cos \left(\frac{\theta - \phi}{2}\right)$

24 $\sin \frac{3\theta}{2} \cos \frac{5\theta}{2}$

25 $\sin \left(45° + \frac{\theta}{2}\right) \cos \left(45° - \frac{\theta}{2}\right)$

1.4 Worked examples of identities using factor formulae

Example 1

Establish the identity $\dfrac{\cos 5\theta - 2 \cos 3\theta + \cos \theta}{\sin \theta - \sin 5\theta} \equiv \tan \theta$

Now
$$\frac{\cos 5\theta - 2 \cos 3\theta + \cos \theta}{\sin \theta - \sin 5\theta}$$
$$= \frac{(\cos 5\theta + \cos \theta) - 2 \cos 3\theta}{\sin \theta - \sin 5\theta}$$

(It is common to have to 'regroup' terms like this)

$$= \frac{2 \cos 3\theta \cos 2\theta - 2 \cos 3\theta}{2 \cos 3\theta \sin (-2\theta)}$$

$$= \frac{2 \cos 3\theta(\cos 2\theta - 1)}{-2 \cos 3\theta \sin 2\theta} \qquad \text{since } \sin (-2\theta) = -\sin 2\theta$$

$$= \frac{-2 \sin^2 \theta}{-2 \sin \theta \cos \theta} \qquad \text{since } \cos 2\theta = 1 - 2 \sin^2 \theta$$

$$= \tan \theta$$

Example 3

Prove that $$\frac{\cos 4\theta - \cos 2\theta}{\sin 4\theta - \sin 2\theta} + \tan 3\theta = 0$$

$$\frac{\cos 4\theta - \cos 2\theta}{\sin 4\theta - \sin 2\theta} + \tan 3\theta = \frac{-2 \sin 3\theta \sin \theta}{2 \cos 3\theta \sin \theta} + \frac{\sin 3\theta}{\cos 3\theta}$$

$$= 0$$

Worked examples of identities using triangles

Example 3

Prove that if A, B and C are the angles in a triangle, then

$$\cos A + \cos B + \cos C = 1 + 4 \sin \frac{A}{2} \sin \frac{B}{2} \sin \frac{C}{2}$$

The important relationship here is that $A + B + C = 180°$.

$$\cos A + (\cos B + \cos C) = \cos A + 2 \cos \frac{B+C}{2} \cos \frac{B-C}{2}$$

$$= \cos (180° - (B+C)) + 2 \cos \frac{B+C}{2} \cos \frac{B-C}{2}$$

$$= 1 - 2 \sin^2 \left(90° - \frac{B+C}{2}\right) + 2 \cos \frac{B+C}{2} \cos \frac{B-C}{2} \quad (1)$$

$$= 1 - 2 \cos^2 \left(\frac{B+C}{2}\right) + 2 \cos \left(\frac{B+C}{2}\right) \cos \left(\frac{B-C}{2}\right) \quad (2)$$

$$= 1 + 2 \cos \left(\frac{B+C}{2}\right) \left\{\cos \left(\frac{B-C}{2}\right) - \cos \left(\frac{B+C}{2}\right)\right\}$$

$$= 1 + 2 \cos \left(90° - \frac{A}{2}\right) \left\{2 \sin \frac{B}{2} \sin \frac{C}{2}\right\} \quad (3)$$

$$= 1 + 4 \sin \frac{A}{2} \sin \frac{B}{2} \sin \frac{C}{2}$$

NOTES

(1) using $\cos 2\theta = 1 - 2 \sin^2 \theta$, so $\cos (180° - (B+C)) = 1 - 2 \sin^2 \left(90° - \frac{(B+C)}{2}\right)$

(2) $\cos (90° - \theta) = \sin \theta$, hence $\sin \left(90° - \frac{B+C}{2}\right) = \cos \left(\frac{B+C}{2}\right)$

(3) since $A + B + C = 180°$, $\frac{A}{2} + \frac{B+C}{2} = 90°$,

$$\cos \left(\frac{B+C}{2}\right) = \cos \left(90° - \frac{A}{2}\right) = \sin \frac{A}{2}$$

This is a difficult question as it is not easy to decide which formula to use for $\cos 2\theta$ and requires a knowledge not only of the formula for $\cos C - \cos D$, but also of $\sin (90° - \theta) = \cos \theta$ and $\cos (90° - \theta) = \sin \theta$.

Example 4

Using the sine rule $$\frac{a}{\sin A} = \frac{b}{\sin B} = \frac{c}{\sin C} = 2R$$

and the cosine rule $$a^2 = b^2 + c^2 - 2bc \cos A$$

prove that, in a triangle ABC,

$$\frac{\sin (A-B)}{\sin (A-C)} = \frac{b(a^2-b^2)}{c(a^2-c^2)}$$

$$\frac{\sin (A-B)}{\sin (A-C)} = \frac{\sin A \cos B - \cos A \sin B}{\sin A \cos C - \cos A \cos C}$$

$$= \frac{\frac{a}{2R}\left(\frac{c^2+a^2-b^2}{2ac}\right) - \left(\frac{b^2+c^2-a^2}{2bc}\right)\frac{b}{2R}}{\frac{a}{2R}\left(\frac{a^2+b^2-c^2}{2ab}\right) - \left(\frac{b^2+c^2-a^2}{2bc}\right)\frac{c}{2R}}$$

$$= \frac{b}{c}\left(\frac{c^2+a^2-b^2-b^2-c^2+a^2}{a^2+b^2-c^2-b^2-c^2+a^2}\right)$$

$$= \frac{b\ (a^2-b^2)}{c\ (a^2-c^2)}$$

Example 5

Prove that in a triangle ABC,

$$\frac{b-c}{b+c} = \frac{\tan \frac{B-C}{2}}{\tan \frac{B+C}{2}}$$

$$\frac{b-c}{b+c} = \frac{2R \sin B - 2R \sin C}{2R \sin B + 2R \sin C}$$

$$= \frac{\sin B - \sin C}{\sin B + \sin C}$$

$$= \frac{2 \sin \frac{B-C}{2} \cos \frac{B+C}{2}}{2 \sin \frac{B+C}{2} \cos \frac{B-C}{2}}$$

$$= \frac{\tan \frac{B-C}{2}}{\tan \frac{B+C}{2}}$$

Note also that since $A+B+C = 180°$, $B+C = 180°-A$,

$$\frac{B+C}{2} = 90° - \frac{A}{2}$$

so
$$\tan\frac{B+C}{2} = \tan\left(90° - \frac{A}{2}\right) = \cot\frac{A}{2}$$

Exercise 1.4

1(a) Assuming the formulae

$$\sin(A+B) = \sin A\cos B + \cos A\sin B$$
$$\cos(A+B) = \cos A\cos B - \sin A\sin B$$

prove that

$$\sin 3A = 3\sin A - 4\sin^3 A$$
$$\cos 3A = 4\cos^3 A - 3\cos A$$

and deduce, or prove otherwise that

$$\tan 3A = \frac{3\tan A - \tan^3 A}{1 - 3\tan^2 A}$$

Hence prove that $\tan 15° = 2 - \sqrt{3}$

explaining carefully why the solutions $2+\sqrt{3}$ and -1 are to be rejected. (*Hint*: $\tan 45° = \tan 3(15°) = 1$)

(b) Establish the identity

$$\frac{\tan 2\theta + \sec 2\theta - 1}{\tan 2\theta - \sec 2\theta + 1} \equiv \tan\left(\theta + \frac{\pi^c}{4}\right)$$

2(a) Prove that

$$\tan(A-B) = \frac{\tan A - \tan B}{1 + \tan A\tan B}$$

Hence without using tables, find the value of

$$\frac{1-\tan 15°}{1+\tan 15°}$$

(b) Given that $\cos\alpha = \frac{3}{5}$ and $\cos\beta = \frac{12}{13}$ where α and β are positive acute angles, calculate the values of $\operatorname{cosec}(\alpha+\beta)$ and $\tan(\alpha+\beta)$.

(c) Establish the identity

$$\sin^2(A+B) - \sin^2(A-B) \equiv \sin 2A\sin 2B$$

3(a) Write down the expansions of $\sin(A+B)$ and $\cos(A+B)$ and deduce that

$$\sin 2\theta = 2\sin\theta\cos\theta$$
$$\cos 2\theta = 2\cos^2\theta - 1$$

Express $2\cos\theta/2\cos 3\theta/2$ as the sum of two cosines and hence find the value of $\cos\theta/2\cos 3\theta/2$ when $\cos\theta = \frac{2}{3}$.

(b) Establish the identity

$$(\cos\theta+\sin\theta)(1-2\sin 2\theta) \equiv \cos 3\theta - \sin 3\theta$$

4(a) Establish the identity

$$\frac{\sec 2A + \sec 2B}{\tan 2A - \tan 2B} \equiv \frac{1-\tan A\tan B}{\tan A - \tan B}$$

(b) Prove that

$$\frac{\operatorname{cosec}^2\theta + \sec^2\theta}{\operatorname{cosec}^2\theta - \sec^2\theta} \equiv \sec 2\theta$$

2 Solution of trigonometrical equations

It is often necessary to solve equations involving sine, cosine, tangent or their inverses, cosecant, secant, cotangent. In some simple cases we have already found the number of solutions (within a given range) and some of their values by means of curve sketches (see p. 91). We now approach them algebraically. The equations fall into different types with different methods of solution.

2.1 General solutions

1 $\sin\theta = \sin\alpha$ (where α is a constant).
It is clear that this equation will have an infinite number of solutions.

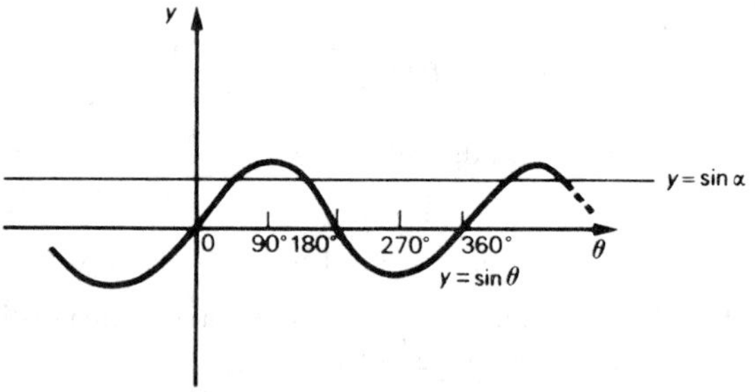

In radians,

$$\theta = \alpha, \quad \pi-\alpha, \quad 2\pi+\alpha, \quad 3\pi-\alpha\ldots$$

and the general solution is

$$\boldsymbol{\theta = n\pi + (-1)^n\alpha}$$ ◄

where n is an integer or zero.

2 If $\cos\theta = \cos\alpha$, similarly, the solutions are

$$\theta = \alpha, \quad 2\pi-\alpha, \quad 2\pi+\alpha, \quad 4\pi-\alpha\ldots$$

and the general solution is

$$\boldsymbol{\theta = 2n\pi\pm\alpha}$$ ◄

where n is an integer or zero.

3 If $\tan\theta = \tan\alpha$, then

$$\theta = \alpha, \quad \pi+\alpha, \quad 2\pi+\alpha, \quad 3\pi+\alpha\ldots$$

giving a general solution

$$\boldsymbol{\theta = n\pi+\alpha}$$ ◄

where n is an integer or zero.

Exercise 2.1

1 Write down the general solutions of the three equations 1, 2 and 3 (above) when θ and α are in degrees.

2 Solve the following equations, giving the general solutions (i) in radians, and (ii) in degrees. (Refer to the sketch graphs of $\sin\theta$, $\cos\theta$, $\tan\theta$.)

(a)	$\cos\theta = \frac{1}{2}$	**(e)**	$\sin\theta = 0.7071$	**(i)**	$\tan\theta = -0.7932$
(b)	$\sin\theta = 0.8660$	**(f)**	$\tan\theta = 2$	**(j)**	$\cos\theta = -0.6$
(c)	$\tan\theta = 1$	**(g)**	$\cos\theta = -\frac{2}{3}$	**(k)**	$\sin\theta = -0.3482$
(d)	$\cos\theta = \frac{3}{5}$	**(h)**	$\sin\theta = -0.8$	**(l)**	$\tan\theta = -0.1234$

2.2 Types of trigonometrical equations

This section is particularly important as a calculator only gives us *one* solution—called the 'principal' solution.

First type

Example 1

Find the value of x between 0° and 360° which satisfies the equation $\cos\frac{1}{2}x = -0.5230$.

From the calculator or tables $\cos 58.47° = 0.5230$ and as the angles whose cosines are -0.5230 are $180°-58.47°$, $180°+58.47°$, $540°-58.47°$ and so on, we have here

$$\tfrac{1}{2}x = 121.53°$$

(which can be obtained directly using arc cos -0.5230 on the calculator.)

$$x = 243.06°$$

which is the *only* solution for $0 \leqslant x \leqslant 360°$.

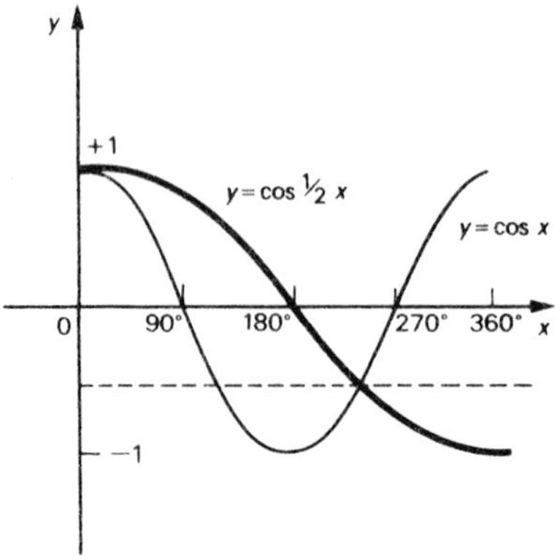

NOTE. In this type we have a trigonometrical function (cos) of a function ($\frac{1}{2}$) of x equal to a constant.

Second type

Example 2

Find the values of x between 0° and 360° which satisfy the equation

$$\cos(\theta + 20^\circ) = \cos 2\theta$$

We have met this equation before (page 94) where we sketched the curves and noted that there are four solutions. If

$$\cos(\theta + 20^\circ) = \cos 2\theta$$

then $$\theta + 20^\circ = 360n^0 \pm 2\theta$$

If $n = 0$ $$\theta + 20^\circ = 2\theta \Rightarrow \theta = 20^\circ \quad (1)$$

If $n = 1$ $$\theta + 20^\circ = 360^\circ - 2\theta \Rightarrow 3\theta = 340^\circ$$

$$\theta = 113.3^\circ \quad (2)$$

or $$\theta + 20^\circ = 360^\circ + 2\theta \Rightarrow \theta = -340^\circ$$

(This is equivalent to solution 1.)

If $n = 2$ $$\theta + 20^\circ = 720^\circ - 2\theta \Rightarrow \theta = \frac{700^\circ}{3} = 233.3^\circ \quad (3)$$

or $$\theta + 20^\circ = 720^\circ + 2\theta \Rightarrow \theta = -700^\circ$$

(—again equivalent to 1.)

If $n = 3$ $$\theta + 20^\circ = 1080^\circ - 2\theta \Rightarrow \theta = \frac{1060^\circ}{3} = 353.3^\circ \quad (4)$$

We have now found all four solutions in the given range.

NOTE. In this type we have a trigonometrical function (cos) of one function of θ ($\theta + 20^\circ$) equal to the same trigonometrical function of another function of θ (2θ).

Third type

Example 3

Find the values of x between 0 and 360° which satisfy the equation

$$4 \sin x + 3 \cos x - 2 = 0$$

The solution involves the use of the formula

$$\sin (x+\theta) = \sin x \cos \theta + \cos x \sin \theta$$

$$2 = \sin x \times 4 + \cos x \times 3$$

We cannot of course find an angle with $\cos \theta = 4$ and $\sin \theta = 3$, *but* if this were so

$$\frac{\sin \theta}{\cos \theta} = \tan \theta = \frac{3}{4}$$

From the triangle, $\sin \theta = \frac{3}{5}$, $\cos \theta = \frac{4}{5}$ and $\theta = 36.87°$.

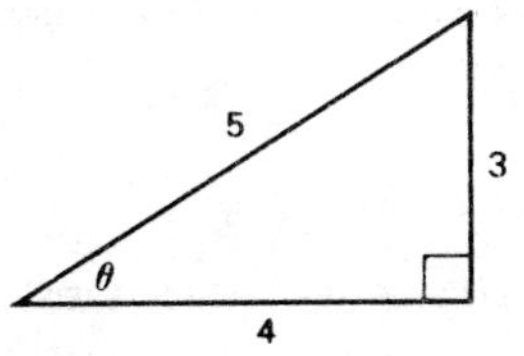

Hence we divide through our equation by 5 to give

$$\tfrac{4}{5} \sin x + \tfrac{3}{5} \cos x = \tfrac{2}{5}$$

$$\sin (x+\theta) = \sin 23.58°$$

$$x + 36.87° = 23.58°,\ 156.42°,\text{ or } 383.58°$$

$$x = 119.65° \quad\text{or}\quad 346.71°$$

NOTE. The choice of formula depends on the signs in the equation to be solved. We might have to use the formula for $\sin (x-\theta)$; $\cos (x+\theta)$ or $\cos (x-\theta)$ instead of $\sin (x+\theta)$.

Let us look again at the equation

$$4 \sin x + 3 \cos x - 2 = 0$$

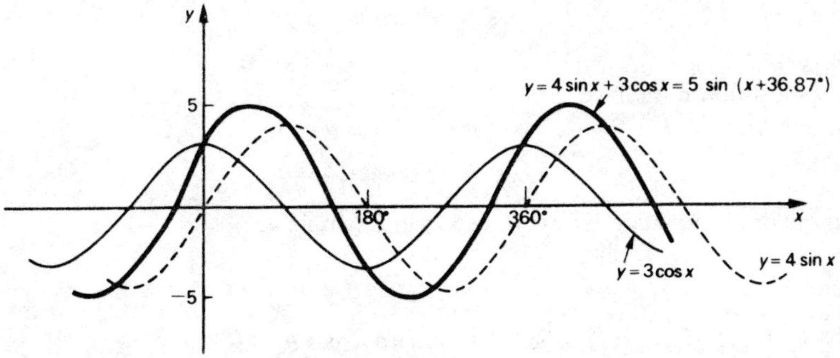

We have sketched in the curves (or waves) for $y = 4 \sin x$ and $y = 3 \cos x$. The sum of these two gives the bold curve

$$y = 4 \sin x + 3 \cos x = 5 \sin (x + 36.58°)$$

This is another wave of the type $y = k \sin (x + \theta)$, where k is the 'amplitude' and θ gives the 'phase shift' or change in the angle. It is clear that the maximum and minimum values of

$$y = 4 \sin x + 3 \cos x = 5 \sin (x + 36.87°)$$

are $+5$ and -5. The *maximum* occurs when $x + 36.87° = 90°$, $x = 53.13°$ and every 360° 'further on' or 'back', whilst the *minimum* occurs when $x + 36.87° = 270°$, $x = 233.13°$ and at intervals of 360° away from this.

Fourth type

These equations involve the use of various trigonometrical formulae in order to reduce the equation to one which we know is easily soluble. This usually means to a quadratic equation.

Example 4

Find the values of x between 0 and 360° which satisfy

$$3 \tan^2 x - 5 \sec x + 1 = 0$$

Now $$\tan^2 x = \sec^2 x - 1$$

Hence $$3(\sec^2 x - 1) - 5 \sec x + 1 = 0$$

$$3 \sec^2 x - 5 \sec x - 2 = 0$$

$$(3 \sec x + 1)(\sec x - 2) = 0$$

so either $$\sec x = 2 \quad \text{or} \quad \sec x = -\tfrac{1}{3}$$

$$x = 60°, 300°$$

These are the only solutions since $|\sec x| \not< 1$.

Example 5

Solve $$\cos 2\theta - 7 \cos \theta = 3$$

Now $$\cos 2\theta = 2 \cos^2 \theta - 1$$
so by substitution we have

$$2 \cos^2 \theta - 1 - 7 \cos \theta = 3$$

$$2 \cos^2 \theta - 7 \cos \theta - 4 = 0$$

This quadratic equation is now solved as in Example 4.

Example 6

Solve $$\cos 2\theta + \cos 4\theta = \cos \theta$$

Here we use the formula

$$\cos A + \cos B = 2\cos\frac{A+B}{2}\cos\frac{A-B}{2}$$

and proceed as follows

$$2\cos 3\theta\cos\theta = \cos\theta$$

$$2\cos 3\theta\cos\theta - \cos\theta = 0$$

$$\cos\theta(2\cos 3\theta - 1) = 0$$

Either $\cos\theta = 0$

or $2\cos 3\theta = 1$

This now becomes a problem to solve of the first type.

Other methods

It is often possible to solve equations of type 3 either (i) by squaring the equation, having substituted $\cos x = \sqrt{(1-\sin^2 x)}$, or (ii) by substituting

$$\tan\frac{x}{2} = t \qquad \sin x = \frac{2t}{1+t^2} \qquad \cos x = \frac{1-t^2}{1+t^2}$$

However, the solution of the quadratic equation obtained tends to be more complicated than the method given above. Moreover, the method of type 3 is often useful in differentiation and a similar method is employed in dealing with complex numbers (see page 392).

Exercise 2.2

1 Find the angles between 0 and 360° which satisfy the equations:

(a) $\operatorname{cosec} x = -2.568$
(b) $\cos 2\theta - 7\cos\theta - 3 = 0$
(c) $12\sin x - 5\cos x + 6 = 0$

2 Find the values of x between 0 and 360° which satisfy the equations

(a) $\tan\frac{1}{2}x = -0.4550$
(b) $\tan x + 4\cot x = 4\sec x$
(c) $4\cos x + \sin x = 1$

3 Find the values of x between 0 and 360° which satisfy the equations

(a) $\sin\frac{3}{2}x = -0.4266$
(b) $4\sin^2 x + 4\cos x - 1 = 0$
(c) $\cot 2x = 2 + \cot x$

4 Find the values of x between 0 and 360° which satisfy the equations

(a) $\cos \frac{1}{2}x = \tan 163°$
(b) $2 \sec^2 x = 1+3 \tan x$
(c) $4 \cos x - 3 \sin x + 1 = 0$

5(a) Find all the solutions between 0 and 180° inclusive of the equation

$$8 \sec \theta - 12 \tan \theta = 3$$

(b) Find all the solutions of the equation

$$\cos 2\theta + \cos 4\theta = \cos \theta$$

which lie between 0 and 2π leaving your answer in terms of π.

6(a) Find the solutions of the equation

$$\sin \tfrac{1}{2}x \sin \tfrac{3}{2}x + 2 \cos x + 1 = 0$$

which lie between 0 and 2π
(b) Find all the solutions of the equation

$$3 \sin \theta + 2 \sin (60° - \theta) = 2$$

between 0 and 360°

7(a) Express $\cos 2\theta$ and $\sin 2\theta$ in terms of $\tan \theta$. Hence or otherwise find the values of θ between 0 and 2π which satisfy

$$1 + \cos 2\theta + \sin 2\theta = \tan (\theta + \pi/4)$$

(b) Find the values of x between 0 and 360° which satisfy the equation

$$3 \cos x + 1 = 2 \sin x$$

8(a) Find the values of θ between 0 and 360° for which $\sec \theta \tan \theta = 2$
(b) Find in degrees and minutes, the angles between 0 and 360° which satisfy the equation

$$3 \cos \theta + \sin \theta = 2$$

3 Problems in three dimensions

We have 'solved' triangles in the plane as a simple exercise in calculation (see page 106). However, in surveying, in navigation and in most practical applications, we are concerned with triangles *in space*. It is not easy to draw a diagram to illustrate the correct perspective but it is worth taking some time to produce a clear sketch of the situation and mark in any right angles, given lengths and given angles. Once the diagram has been drawn, the problems are found to be similar to those we have solved before.

3.1 Worked examples

Example 1

A, B and C are three points on a river bank and X is the foot of a vertical pole on the other bank directly opposite the midpoint of AB; the angles of elevation of the top of the pole from A and C are α and β respectively and $\alpha = 2\beta$. Prove that if $\angle XAC = \theta$, $\angle XCA = \phi$, AB = $2a$ and BC = c, then

(a) $a \tan \theta = (a+c) \tan \phi$
(b) $\sin \theta = \sin \phi (1 + \sec \alpha)$

Suppose the top of the pole is Y, and the midpoint of AB is D

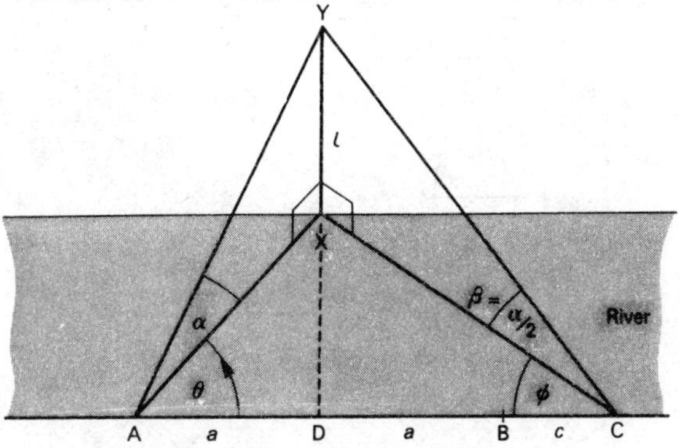

(a) in $\triangle$AXD, $\qquad$ $XD = a \tan \theta$

in $\triangle$CXD, $\qquad$ $XD = (a+c) \tan \phi$

Hence $\qquad$ $a \tan \theta = (a+c) \tan \phi$

(b) Suppose the pole is of length l. Then

$$AX = l \cot \alpha, \ CX = l \cot \frac{\alpha}{2} \quad \left(\text{since } \beta = \frac{\alpha}{2}\right)$$

Using the sine rule in $\triangle$AXC,

$$\frac{AX}{\sin \phi} = \frac{CX}{\sin \theta}$$

$$\frac{l \cot \alpha}{\sin \phi} = \frac{l \cot \frac{\alpha}{2}}{\sin \theta}$$

So

$$\sin \theta = \sin \phi \frac{\cot \frac{\alpha}{2}}{\cot \alpha}$$

Now

$$\frac{\cot\frac{\alpha}{2}}{\cot\alpha} = \frac{\cos\frac{\alpha}{2}}{\sin\frac{\alpha}{2}} \Big/ \frac{\cos\alpha}{\sin\alpha}$$

$$= \frac{\cos\frac{\alpha}{2}}{\sin\frac{\alpha}{2}} \times \frac{\sin\alpha}{\cos\alpha}$$

$$= \frac{\cos\frac{\alpha}{2}\, 2\cos\frac{\alpha}{2}\sin\frac{\alpha}{2}}{\sin\frac{\alpha}{2}\cos\alpha} \qquad \left(\text{since } \sin\alpha = 2\sin\frac{\alpha}{2}\cos\frac{\alpha}{2}\right)$$

$$= \frac{2\cos^2\frac{\alpha}{2}}{\cos\alpha}$$

$$= \frac{1+\cos\alpha}{\cos\alpha} \qquad \left(\text{since } \cos\alpha = 2\cos^2\frac{\alpha}{2} - 1\right)$$

$$= \frac{1}{\cos\alpha} + 1$$

$$= \sec\alpha + 1$$

Hence, finally,

$$\sin\theta = \sin\phi(1+\sec\alpha)$$

Example 2

A and B are two points on the top of a long, straight, vertical cliff of height 100 metres and the distance between them is 400 metres. A ship is moving parallel to the direction BA and at a certain time simultaneous observations of the ship are made from A and B. The angles of depression from A and B are found to be 4° and 5° respectively. Prove that the ship is approximately 885 metres from the nearest point of the cliff.

At the same time as the observations are made, a cutter sets out from the point P vertically below B on a straight course to intercept the ship. The cutter travels at the same speed as the ship, so that both craft cover equal distances before interception occurs. Calculate the distance travelled by the cutter and the direction of the course it must steer.

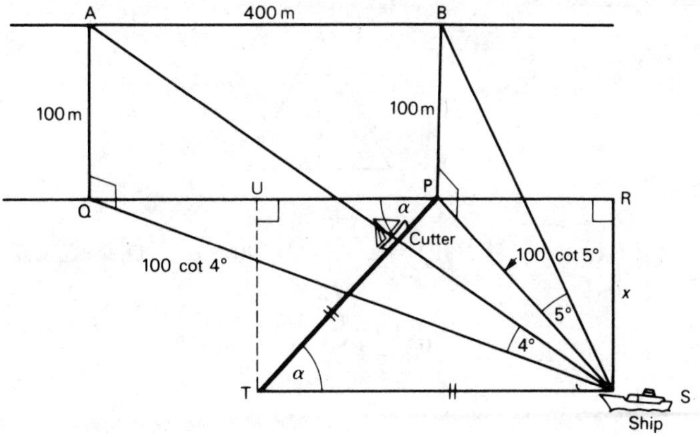

(i) To find x

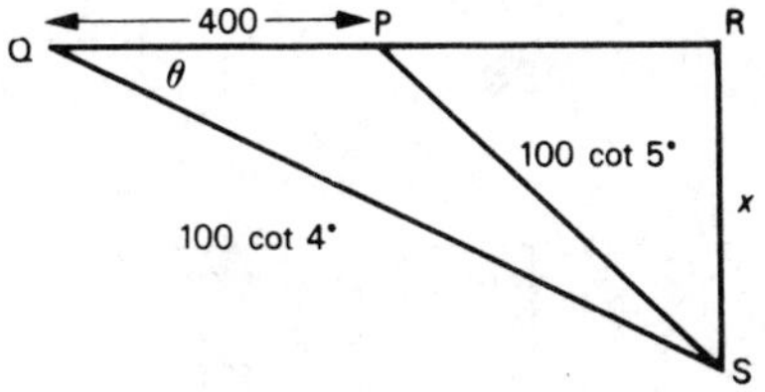

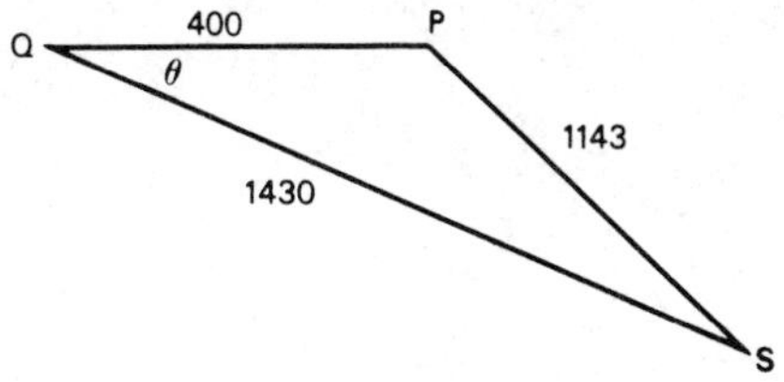

First of all we must find ∠PQS.

$$\cos\theta = \frac{(400)^2+(1430)^2-(1143)^2}{2\times400\times1430}$$

$$= 0.785\,36 \text{ (using a calculator)}$$

$$\theta = 38.25°$$

Now

$$x = 1430 \sin 38.25°$$

$$= 885.3 \text{ m}$$

(ii) If ∠RPS = ϕ then

$$\sin\phi = \frac{885.3}{1143}, \qquad \phi = 50.76°$$

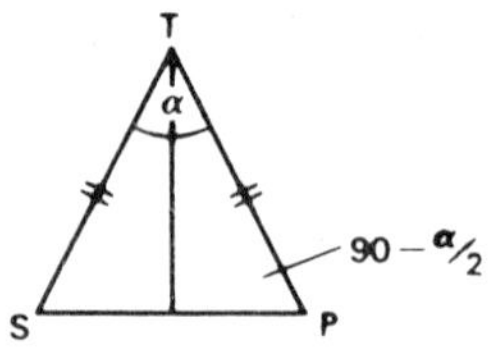

Since △PST is isosceles, if ∠QPT = α, ∠TPS = $90° - \alpha/2$. Therefore, since QPR is a straight line,

$$\alpha + 90° - \frac{\alpha}{2} + 50.76° = 180°$$

$$\frac{\alpha}{2} = 90° - 50.76°$$

$$\alpha = 78.48°$$

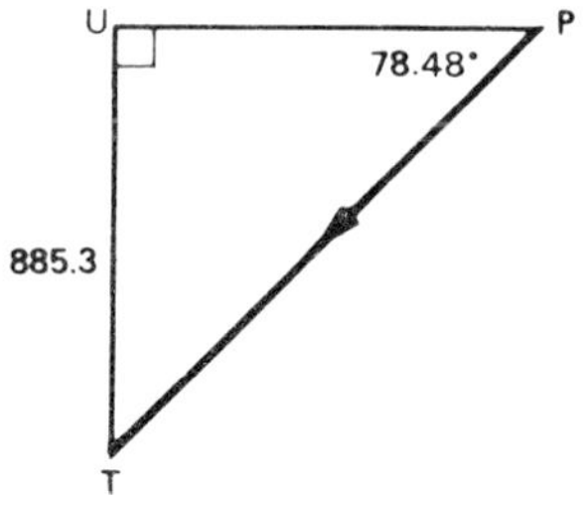

Finally $\quad$ PT = 885.3 cosec 78.48°

$= 904$ m

Example 3

An earth satellite is describing a circular orbit at height h in the plane of the equator. The equator may be regarded as a circle of radius R and centre O. The satellite moves from a point S, vertically above an observer at the point P, to a point S′ vertically above the point Q, where ∠POQ = ϕ and is then seen at an altitude θ by the observer at P. Show that

$$(R + h)\cos(\theta + \phi) = R\cos\theta$$

and that for θ to be positive, $\cos\phi$ must exceed $R/(R + h)$.

A further condition for the satellite to be visible from P when it is at S′ is that it must be in sunlight. If the Sun is in the plane of the equator and has set x minutes ago as seen by observer at Q, show that, for $R = 6400$ km and $h = 3600$ km, S′ will be visible if arc PQ < 5610 km and $x < 201$.

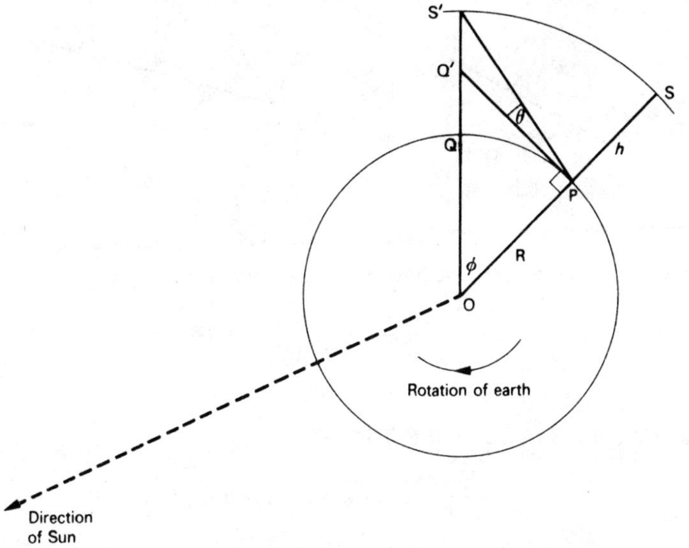

(i) Consider △OPS′:

We can fill in the angles shown. Using the sine rule

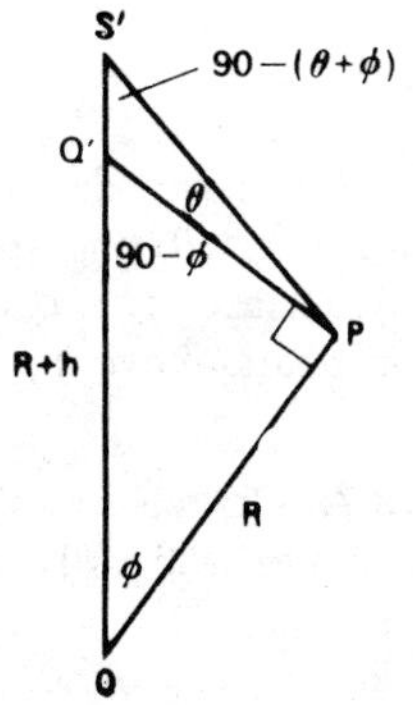

$$\frac{(R+h)}{\sin(90°+\theta)} = \frac{R}{\sin(90°-(\theta+\phi))}$$

$$(R+h)\cos(\theta+\phi) = R\cos\theta$$

(since $\sin(90°+\theta) = \sin(180°-(90°+\theta)) = \sin(90°-\theta) = \cos\theta$).

(ii)

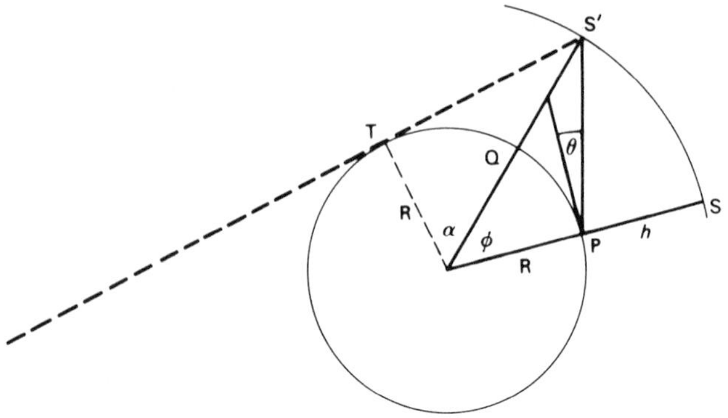

Sunlight will shine on S′ until we have the situation above, when

$$\cos\alpha = \frac{R}{R+h} = \frac{6400}{10\,000} = 0.64$$

$$\alpha = 50.2°$$

The time taken for Q to travel from T is

$$\frac{50.2}{360}\times 24\times 60 = 200.8 \text{ min}$$

The other limiting condition will be, at the same time, with S′P a tangent to the Earth, i.e. $\phi = 50.2°$.

The arc $$\text{PQ}(=R\phi^c) = 6400\times 0.8762$$

$$= 5607 \text{ km}$$

Exercise 3.1

1 A rectangular piece of cardboard whose sides are 6 cm and 4 cm in length rests in a horizontal position inside a fixed inverted cone whose axis is vertical, the corners of the cardboard touching the inside surface of the cone. The vertical angle of the cone is 40°. Find the height of the cardboard above the vertex of the cone to the nearest mm.

2 A square piece of cardboard ABCD has one side CD (of length 10 cm) on the horizontal ground and the plane of the cardboard is inclined at 35° to the ground. The midpoint of AD is M. Find

(a) the heights of M and B above the ground, and

(b) the inclination of the line BM to the ground.

3 The lid of a desk is 48 cm wide and the distance from the front edge to the hinges is 40 cm. The lid is inclined at an angle of 18° to the horizontal. A small insect crawls along the diagonal of the lid at $\frac{1}{2}$ cm per second. Find

(a) how long (to the nearest second) it will take to reach the top.

(b) the slope of its track.

4 A traffic post in a road is a framework consisting of a hollow pyramid 30 cm high, fitting exactly on a hollow column which is 72 cm high and on a base 24 cm square. It is strengthened by stays within the framework running from each bottom corner to the vertex. Find the lengths of the edges of the pyramid and of the stays, and find to the nearest degree the angle between any stay and the corresponding edge of the pyramid.

5 A and B are two stations at the same horizontal level 1600 m apart. M is the top of a mountain peak visible from A and B. From A the bearings of B and M are 41° and 111°. From B the bearing of M is 163° and the elevation of M is 10.5°. Calculate the height of M above the level AB and the elevation of M from A.

Miscellaneous examination questions 7

(O. & C. unless stated otherwise)

1(a) Express $\sin(A+B+C)$ in terms of sines or cosines of A, B, C, and deduce that if A, B, C are the angles of a triangle, then

$$\cot B \cot C + \cot C \cot A + \cot A \cot B = 1$$

(b) Prove that, when $\cos\phi = -\frac{1}{2}$ the value of the expression

$$\sin\theta + \sin(\theta+\phi) + \sin(\theta+2\phi) = 0$$

whatever the value of θ.

2(a) Prove that

$$\sin x \sin 2x + \sin x \sin 4x + \sin x \sin 6x = \sin 3x \sin 4x$$

(b) Prove that

$$\frac{\sin 5\theta + 2\sin 3\theta + \sin\theta}{\cos\theta - \cos 5\theta} = \cot\theta$$

3 Prove the formula

$$\sin(A+B) = \sin A \cos B + \cos A \sin B$$

where A, B, $A+B$ are acute angles.

The expression

$$(n+1)\sin n\theta - n\sin(n+1)\theta$$

is denoted by P_n. Prove that

$$P_n - P_{n-1} = 2n \sin n\theta(1-\cos\theta)$$

From this, by induction or otherwise prove that, when n is an integer, P_n has a factor $(1-\cos\theta)$.

4(a) Prove the identity

$$\sin(2x-y) + \sin(x-2y) \equiv (\sin x - \sin y)[1 + 2\cos(x-y)]$$

(b) Prove the identity

$$\tan x \equiv \cot x - 2\cot 2x$$

and hence show that

$$2\tan 20° + 4\tan 40° + 8\tan 80° = 9(\cot 10° - \tan 10°)$$

5(a) Find the values of x between 0 and 180° inclusive for which

$$\sin x + \sin 2x + \sin 3x = 0$$

(b) Find the values of x between 0 and 360° for which

$$2\cos x + 3\sin x = 3$$ (C.)

6(a) Express $3\cos\theta - \sin\theta$ in the form $r\cos(\theta+\alpha)$ and find in degrees the general solution of the equation

$$3\cos\theta - \sin\theta = 1.$$

(b) Find in radians the general solutions of the equations
(i) $\cos x = \cos 3x$
(ii) $\cos x + \cos 7x = \cos 4x$
(iii) $\sin x - \cos x = 1$

7(a) Find the general solution of the equation

$$5\sin x + 12\cos x = 11$$

(b) Find all solutions of the equation

$$\sin 2x = \cos 3x$$

which lie between 0 and 360° (W.)

8(a) Solve the equation

$$\cos x - \cos 2x = \sin 2x - \sin x$$

for values of x in the interval $0 \leqslant x \leqslant 2\pi$

(b) Solve the equation

$$\sin 4x = \cos x$$

for values of x between 0 and 180° (W.)

9(a) Find all solutions between 0 and 360° of the equations
(i) $2\tan^2 x = \sec x + 13$
(ii) $\sin x - \sin 2x + \sin 3x = 0$

(b) Express $y = 5\cos x - 2\sin x$ in the form $R\cos(x+\alpha)$ where R is a positive constant giving the value of R and the smallest positive value for the angle α. Hence, or otherwise,
(i) state the maximum and minimum values for y and the values of x between 0 and 360° for which they occur.
(ii) find all solutions between 0 and 360° of the equation

$$5\cos x - 2\sin x = 2$$ (S.)

10(a) Find all the solutions between 0 and 360° of the equations
(i) $\sin 2\theta = \sin \theta$ (ii) $\sec^2 \theta = 7 - \tan \theta$

(b) Express

$$y = \cos x - \sqrt{3} \sin x$$

in the form $y = \text{R} \cos (x + \alpha)$ where R is a positive constant, giving the value of R and the smallest positive value for α. Hence or otherwise

(i) Sketch the graph of y against x for values of x from 0 to 360°.

(ii) State the maximum value of y and the value of x (between 0 and 360°) for which it occurs.

(iii) Find all solutions between 0 and 360° of $\cos x - \sqrt{3} \sin x + 2 = 0$ (S.)

11(a) Find in radians the general solution of the equation

$$2 \sin \theta = \sqrt{3} \tan \theta$$

(b) Express $4 \sin \theta - 3 \cos \theta$ in the form $\text{R} \sin (\theta - \alpha)$ where α is an acute angle.

(i) Solve the equation $4 \sin \theta - 3 \cos \theta = 3$ giving all solutions between 0 and 360°.

(ii) Find the greatest and least value of

$$\frac{1}{4 \sin \theta - 3 \cos \theta + 6}$$

(L.)

12 Prove that for any plane triangle PQR

$$\cot P = \frac{q}{p} \operatorname{cosec} \text{R} - \cot \text{R}$$

To an observer standing at the top of a cliff, the bearings of two ships P and Q at sea are 5.65° and 127.23° respectively. If to the observer the angle of depression of ship P is 14.38° whilst that of ship Q is 10.12°, calculate the bearing of ship Q from ship P. (A.E.B.)

13 H is the top of a vertical tower of height h metres and K is the base. A is a point due south of K and at the same level. B is a point due east of the tower but at a level d metres higher than A and K. The angles of elevation of H from A and B are α and β respectively, and the length of AB is l metres. Show that h is given by a root of the equation

$$h^2(\cot^2 \alpha + \cot^2 \beta) - 2\text{R}d \cot^2 \beta + d^2 \operatorname{cosec}^2 \beta - l^2 = 0$$

If squares and higher powers of d may be neglected, show that one root of the equation is negative and h is given by the formula

$$h = \frac{l}{(\cot^2 \alpha + \cot^2 \beta)^{1/2}} + \frac{d \cot^2 \beta}{\cot^2 \alpha + \cot^2 \beta}$$

14 When a boat is at a horizontal distance x from the foot of a cliff on the edge of which is a light-house of height a, the angle subtended at the boat by the light-house is α; when the distance is $2x$ the corresponding angle is β. Prove that

$$3x = a(2 \cot \beta - \cot \alpha)$$

Find the value of a to the nearest metre, if $x = 80$ m, $\alpha = 15°$ and $\beta = 10°$.

15 A man walking along a straight, level road observes the elevation of a tower in the direction N 25° E to be α; later, the direction of the tower is N 35° W and the elevation of the tower is β. Prove that the direction in which the man is walking is N $(25°+\theta)$ E, where

$$\sqrt{3}\cot\theta = 2\tan\beta\cot\alpha - 1$$

Find the height of the tower to the nearest 0.1 m if $\alpha = 4.5°$, $\beta = 7°$ and the distance the man has walked between observations is 500 m.

16 A flagpole, which should be vertical, appears to be inclined at an angle α to the vertical when viewed from the east, and at an angle β to the vertical when viewed from the north. Find its true inclination to the vertical.

If the length of the pole is 12 m, $\alpha = 3°$ and $\beta = 5°$, find the distance through which the top of the pole has moved from its intended position. (W.)

17 VABC is a tetrahedron with VB = VC = AB = AC = $2a$. Angles VBA and VCA are both 30°, angles VBC and VCB are both 45°. Find, correct to the nearest degree, the angle between

(a) VA and the plane ABC

(b) planes VBC and ABC

(c) planes VAB and VAC

Find the volume of the tetrahedron, giving your answer in the form ka^3 where k is correct to two significant figures. (S.)

18 ABCD is a sloping plane surface of a ramp which is inclined at an angle α to the horizontal. EFCD is horizontal, with E and F vertically below A and B respectively. AB is also horizontal. If θ is the inclination of AD to the horizontal and angle ADC = angle BCD = β prove that $\sin\theta = \sin\alpha\sin\beta$. Find an expression in terms of α and β for the sine of angle EDC. Find in terms of α and β the angle which BD makes with the horizontal given that AB = AD. (S.)

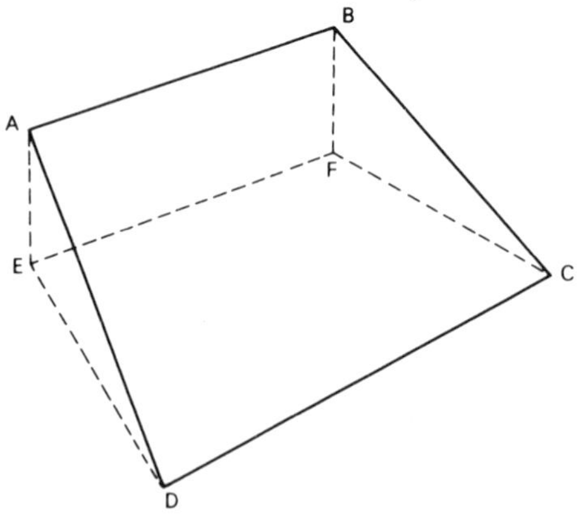

Chapter 8

Vectors 1

1 Vector addition in a plane

1.1 Informal introduction to vectors

Going places?

In our work in coordinate geometry we chose an origin and a pair of perpendicular axes to enable us to specify a point in a plane. We now look at a point rather differently by considering the routes by which we can arrive at that point from some starting-point. These routes, made up of straight 'legs', are called *vectors*. 'Vector' is the Latin word 'carrier' and is associated with the idea of movement from one place to another.

In cartesian coordinates we think of a line (or curve) as the set of points whose coordinates satisfy a certain condition. In our new system a straight line represents a route from one point to another. Each point on the line can be thought of as a point we pass through on our journey (or might pass through if our journey was continued in either direction). Hence each point on our line can be represented as a multiple of our journey, the multiple corresponding to each point being called a *parameter*. For example, going from A to B we shall pass a point C two-thirds of the way along.

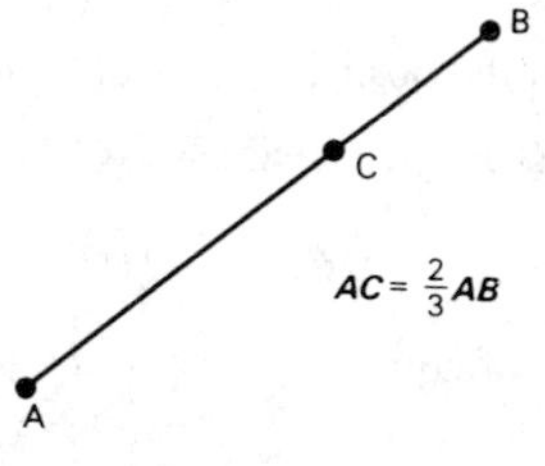

In fact, any point en route from A to B can be represented by $k\boldsymbol{AB}$ where $0 \leqslant k \leqslant 1$. If we allow k to have any value, then we shall have all the points on the line AB, continued in each direction.

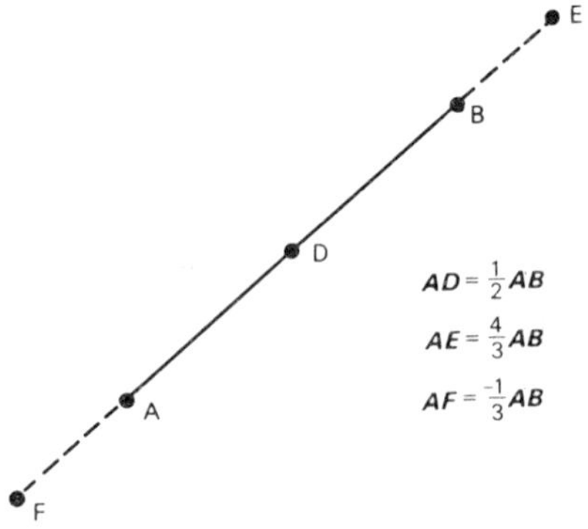

Vector routes from the origin

If we wish to go from O to P there are many different routes we can take:

(1) There is the direct route OP, making the journey in one leg.

(2) We might make the journey in two legs.

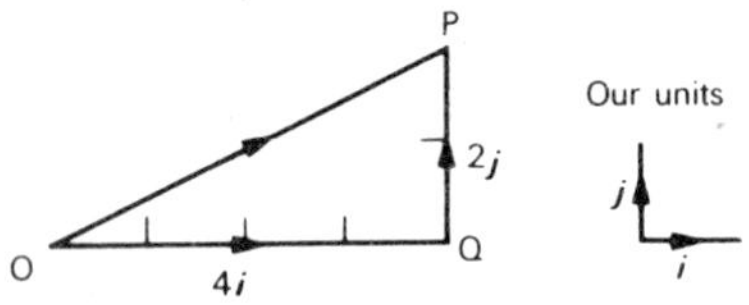

To enable us to describe this route, we need to define two units, with their lengths, directions and the sense in which they are traversed. We might say 'from O, travel 4 km east and then 2 km north'.

We have drawn in our units. $\boldsymbol{i}$ represents 1 unit (km) in the positive x axis direction (east). $\boldsymbol{j}$ represents 1 unit in the positive y axis direction (north). Then

$$\boldsymbol{OQ} = 4\boldsymbol{i} \qquad \text{and} \qquad \boldsymbol{QP} = 2\boldsymbol{j}$$

So we can say that
$$\boldsymbol{OP} = 4\boldsymbol{i} + 2\boldsymbol{j}$$

(3) We can introduce two different units, $\boldsymbol{c}$ and $\boldsymbol{d}$.

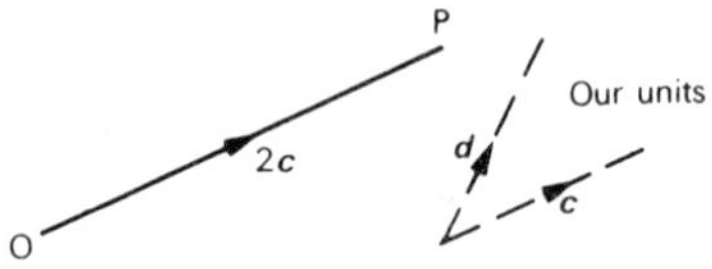

Here $$\boldsymbol{OP} = 2\boldsymbol{c} + 0\boldsymbol{d}$$

and this is the same as the direct route (1).

(4)

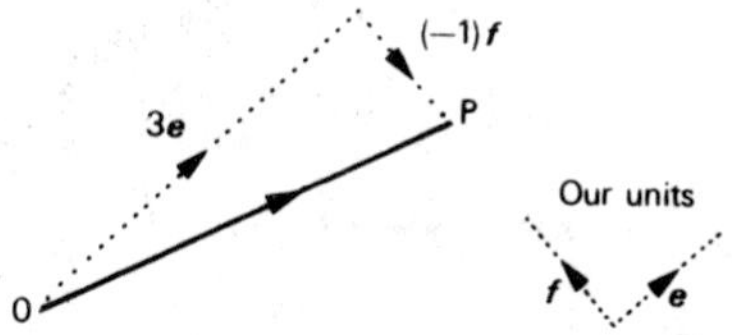

With $\boldsymbol{e}$ and f as defined in the figure

$$\boldsymbol{OP} = 3\boldsymbol{e} + (-1)f$$

(5)

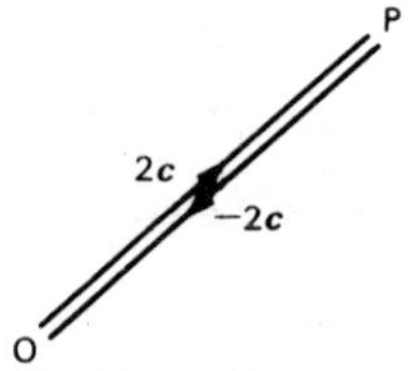

The next route returns us to our starting place

$$2\boldsymbol{c} + (-2)\boldsymbol{c} = \boldsymbol{O}$$

where $\boldsymbol{O}$ is the *zero vector.*

The diagrams show that when we 'add' vectors, represented by arrowed lines, the arrows must be arranged tip to tail, so that we can follow them on our journey. We could not travel from O to S following the arrows shown in a diagram like this:

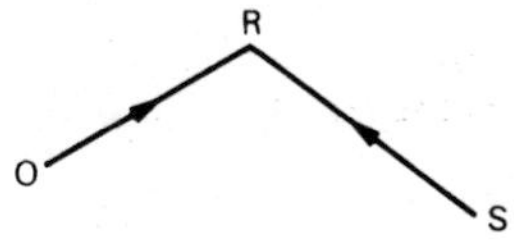

Base vectors

The units we have defined are called *base vectors.* In (2) the base vectors are $\boldsymbol{i}$ and $\boldsymbol{j}$; in (3) $\boldsymbol{c}$ and $\boldsymbol{d}$ and in (4) $\boldsymbol{e}$ and f. Any vector in the plane can be represented as a suitable combination of any two base vectors, but our base vectors must not both be in the same direction, since in that case no matter how they are combined, we can only achieve another vector in the same line.

Representation of a vector

The simplest way to represent a vector is as an ordered pair $\begin{pmatrix} x \\ y \end{pmatrix}$ where the upper number is the movement in the x direction, the lower being the y movement, these movements being referred to ordinary cartesian coordinates.

We can say that

$$\boldsymbol{i} = \begin{pmatrix} 1 \\ 0 \end{pmatrix} \quad \text{and} \quad \boldsymbol{j} = \begin{pmatrix} 0 \\ 1 \end{pmatrix}$$

and

$$\begin{aligned} \boldsymbol{OP} = \boldsymbol{p} &= 4\boldsymbol{i} + 2\boldsymbol{j} \\ &= 4\begin{pmatrix} 1 \\ 0 \end{pmatrix} + 2\begin{pmatrix} 0 \\ 1 \end{pmatrix} \\ &= \begin{pmatrix} 4 \\ 0 \end{pmatrix} + \begin{pmatrix} 0 \\ 2 \end{pmatrix} \\ &= \begin{pmatrix} 4 \\ 2 \end{pmatrix} \end{aligned}$$

Free and position vectors

When we represent a vector as, for example, $\begin{pmatrix} 1 \\ 0 \end{pmatrix}$ this means one of a whole set of vectors, each of unit length and in the x direction.

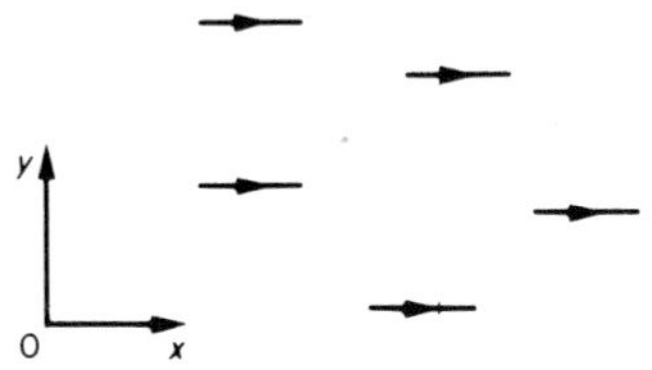

These are known as *free vectors.*

One of each set of free vectors will have its 'tail' at the origin. We call this particular vector a *position vector* since it effectively locates the position of the point at its tip relative to O.

Thus $\boldsymbol{OP} = \boldsymbol{p} = \begin{pmatrix} 4 \\ 2 \end{pmatrix}$ and P is the point (4, 2).

Exercise 1.1

The figure shows three superimposed grids, corresponding to the three pairs of base vectors:

(i) $\boldsymbol{i} = \begin{pmatrix} 1 \\ 0 \end{pmatrix}$, $\boldsymbol{j} = \begin{pmatrix} 0 \\ 1 \end{pmatrix}$ (continuous lines, 'black')

(ii) $\boldsymbol{c} = \begin{pmatrix} 2 \\ 1 \end{pmatrix}$, $\boldsymbol{d} = \begin{pmatrix} 1 \\ 2 \end{pmatrix}$ (shown dashed, 'red')

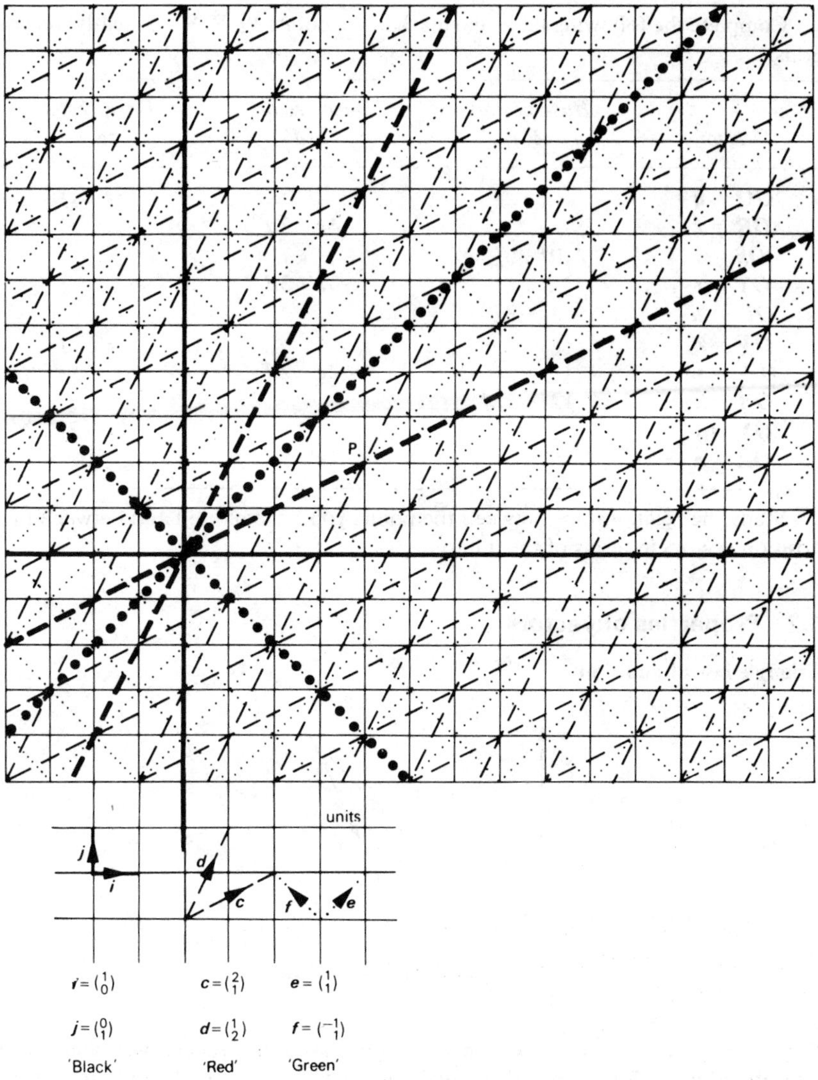

(iii) $e = \begin{pmatrix} 1 \\ 1 \end{pmatrix}$, $f = \begin{pmatrix} -1 \\ 1 \end{pmatrix}$ (shown dotted, 'green')

You are advised to copy the grids, on a larger scale, on to tracing paper, using a different sheet and colour for each grid. The sheets, overlaid, will then reproduce the figure above. (Keep the sheets carefully for use with Chapter 9.)

1 Check that $\boldsymbol{OP} = \boldsymbol{p} = 4\boldsymbol{i} + 2\boldsymbol{j}$ by the 'black' route

$\boldsymbol{p} = 2\boldsymbol{c} + 0\boldsymbol{d}$ by the 'red' route

and $\boldsymbol{p} = 3\boldsymbol{e} + (-1)\boldsymbol{f}$ by the 'green' route.

2 Complete the following table and mark in the points Q, R, S . . . (neatly) on your grids.

Vector	*Base vectors* $\boldsymbol{i}, \boldsymbol{j}$	*Base vectors* $\boldsymbol{c}, \boldsymbol{d}$	*Base vectors* $\boldsymbol{e}, \boldsymbol{f}$
$\boldsymbol{OQ} = \boldsymbol{q}$			$3\boldsymbol{e}+1\boldsymbol{f}$
$\boldsymbol{OR} = \boldsymbol{r}$		$4\boldsymbol{c}-2\boldsymbol{d}$	
$\boldsymbol{OS} = \boldsymbol{s}$	$0\boldsymbol{i}+6\boldsymbol{j}$		
$\boldsymbol{OT} = \boldsymbol{t}$		$-3\boldsymbol{c}+3\boldsymbol{d}$	
$\boldsymbol{OU} = \boldsymbol{u}$	$3\boldsymbol{i}+3\boldsymbol{j}$		
$\boldsymbol{OV} = \boldsymbol{v}$			$6\boldsymbol{e}-2\boldsymbol{f}$
$\boldsymbol{OW} = \boldsymbol{w}$		$2\boldsymbol{c}+2\boldsymbol{d}$	
$\boldsymbol{OX} = \boldsymbol{x}$	$12\boldsymbol{i}+12\boldsymbol{j}$		
$\boldsymbol{OY} = \boldsymbol{y}$			$0\boldsymbol{e}-2\boldsymbol{f}$
$\boldsymbol{OZ} = \boldsymbol{z}$		$-1\boldsymbol{c}+5\boldsymbol{d}$	

3 Study the relationships between the points you have plotted and between their position vectors in terms of the different base vectors.

1.2 Properties of vectors

Triangle law of addition

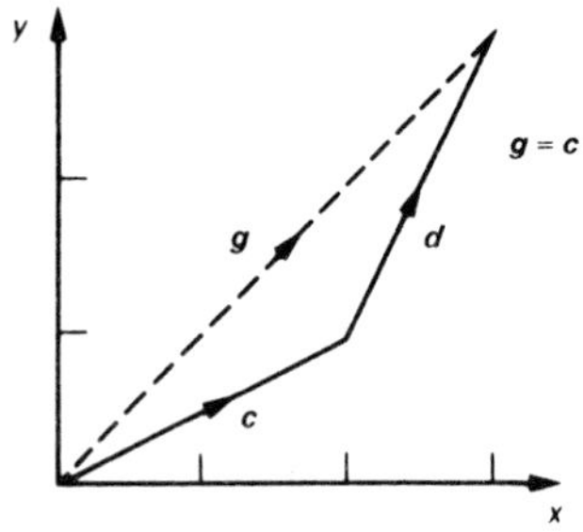

When we say $\boldsymbol{g} = \boldsymbol{c}+\boldsymbol{d}$ the + symbol is being used in a special way and can be interpreted as 'followed by'. The equals sign is also being used to tell us that the routes are equivalent, and if we start at the same point we shall also finish at the same point whether we traverse the direct route $\boldsymbol{g}$ or the two-leg route $\boldsymbol{c}$ followed by $\boldsymbol{d}$.

Now in the diagram we can see that $\boldsymbol{c} = \begin{pmatrix}2\\1\end{pmatrix}$ followed by $\boldsymbol{d} = \begin{pmatrix}1\\2\end{pmatrix}$ is equivalent to $\boldsymbol{g} = \begin{pmatrix}3\\3\end{pmatrix}$ and

$$\begin{pmatrix}2\\1\end{pmatrix}+\begin{pmatrix}1\\2\end{pmatrix}=\begin{pmatrix}3\\3\end{pmatrix}$$

so vector addition corresponds to ordinary addition of the numbers in the brackets.

This is usually called *the triangle law of addition*, since if two vectors are represented by two sides of a triangle, their vector sum is represented by the third side, directed as shown in the diagram above.

Properties of vectors under addition

We can now list some of the properties of vectors which we have used or discovered in our work so far, when they are combined under the triangle law of addition. Check the following by substituting $\boldsymbol{a} = \begin{pmatrix} -1 \\ 3 \end{pmatrix}$, $\boldsymbol{b} = \begin{pmatrix} 1 \\ 4 \end{pmatrix}$, $\boldsymbol{c} = \begin{pmatrix} 2 \\ 1 \end{pmatrix}$ and drawing diagrams.

Suppose that $\boldsymbol{a}, \boldsymbol{b}, \boldsymbol{c} \ldots$ are vectors, then under addition

1 $\boldsymbol{a}+\boldsymbol{b}$ is a vector.

2 $(\boldsymbol{a}+\boldsymbol{b})+\boldsymbol{c} = \boldsymbol{a}+(\boldsymbol{b}+\boldsymbol{c})$, the 'bracketing' law, or associative law.

3 There is a zero vector $\boldsymbol{0}$, such that for any vector $\boldsymbol{a}$

$$\boldsymbol{a}+\boldsymbol{0} = \boldsymbol{0}+\boldsymbol{a} = \boldsymbol{a}$$

4 To each vector $\boldsymbol{a}$, there corresponds a unique vector $(-\boldsymbol{a})$ so that

$$\boldsymbol{a}+(-\boldsymbol{a}) = (-\boldsymbol{a})+\boldsymbol{a} = \boldsymbol{0}$$

5 $\boldsymbol{a}+\boldsymbol{b} = \boldsymbol{b}+\boldsymbol{a}$, the commutative law.

When we multiply a vector by a number, i.e. a scalar, we have several more properties. Here, check using $l = 2$, $m = -3$ and by drawing diagrams.

6 $l\boldsymbol{a}$ is a vector.

7 $l(\boldsymbol{a}+\boldsymbol{b}) = l\boldsymbol{a} + l\boldsymbol{b}$.

8 $(l+m)\boldsymbol{a} = l\boldsymbol{a}+m\boldsymbol{a}$.

Solving vector equations

Example

Find λ and μ if

$$\boldsymbol{p} = \lambda\boldsymbol{q}+\mu\boldsymbol{r}$$

where $\boldsymbol{p} = \begin{pmatrix} 5 \\ -4 \end{pmatrix}$, $\boldsymbol{q} = \begin{pmatrix} 3 \\ 2 \end{pmatrix}$ and $\boldsymbol{r} = \begin{pmatrix} -1 \\ 3 \end{pmatrix}$

Method 1

We have solved similar problems in Exercise 1.1 with the aid of a grid, and here also we could draw part of the grid. We see that $\lambda = 1$, $\mu = -2$.

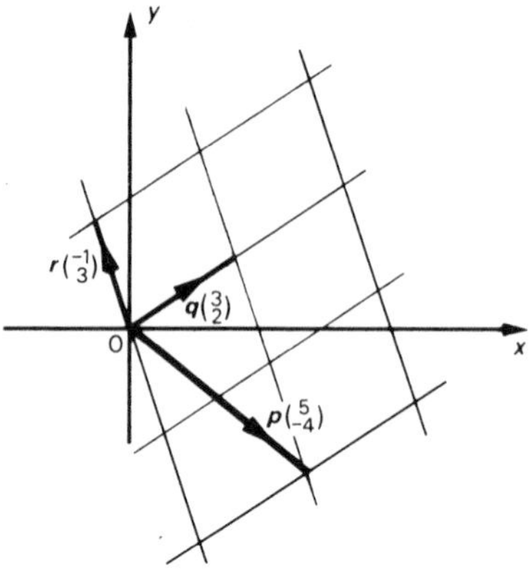

Method 2

We can use the properties of vectors to solve the equation algebraically.

$$\lambda\begin{pmatrix}3\\2\end{pmatrix}+\mu\begin{pmatrix}-1\\3\end{pmatrix}=\begin{pmatrix}5\\-4\end{pmatrix}$$

so $$3\lambda+(-1)\mu = 5 \qquad (1)$$

and $$2\lambda+3\mu = -4 \qquad (2)$$

Multiply (1) by 3 and add (2) and (3):

$$9\lambda+(-3)\mu = 15 \qquad (3)$$

$$11\lambda = 11$$

$$\lambda = 1, \quad \mu = -2$$

This is the *only* combination of $\boldsymbol{q}$ and $\boldsymbol{r}$ which will satisfy the equation, i.e. it is *unique*.

Parallel (or dependent) vectors

Is it possible to express *any* vector in terms of *any* other two? For example, can you find λ, μ if

$$\lambda\begin{pmatrix}1\\-2\end{pmatrix}+\mu\begin{pmatrix}-2\\4\end{pmatrix}=\begin{pmatrix}4\\5\end{pmatrix}$$

What do you find when you try to draw the grid or to solve the equations algebraically?

In a plane, *any* vector can be written as a sum of multiples of any other two vectors so long as these two are not parallel. I.e. given $\boldsymbol{a}$, $\boldsymbol{b}$, and $\boldsymbol{c}$, λ and μ can always be found so that $\boldsymbol{c} = \lambda\boldsymbol{a}+\mu\boldsymbol{b}$. If $\boldsymbol{a}$ and $\boldsymbol{b}$ are parallel, clearly there will only be a solution if $\boldsymbol{c}$ is also parallel to $\boldsymbol{a}$ and $\boldsymbol{b}$.

Exercise 1.2

Solve the following vector equations for λ and μ where possible. Illustrate your answers with a diagram.

1 $\lambda\begin{pmatrix}-2\\1\end{pmatrix}+\mu\begin{pmatrix}1\\1\end{pmatrix}=\begin{pmatrix}-5\\1\end{pmatrix}$

2 $\lambda\begin{pmatrix}0\\2\end{pmatrix}+\mu\begin{pmatrix}1\\-1\end{pmatrix}=\begin{pmatrix}3\\-1\end{pmatrix}$

3 $\lambda\begin{pmatrix}2\\3\end{pmatrix}+\mu\begin{pmatrix}1\\0\end{pmatrix}=\begin{pmatrix}-5\\-9\end{pmatrix}$

4 $\lambda\begin{pmatrix}1\\-3\end{pmatrix}+\mu\begin{pmatrix}-2\\1\end{pmatrix}=\begin{pmatrix}3\\1\end{pmatrix}$

5 $\lambda\begin{pmatrix}1\\-2\end{pmatrix}+\mu\begin{pmatrix}-2\\4\end{pmatrix}=\begin{pmatrix}3\\-6\end{pmatrix}$

6 $\lambda\begin{pmatrix}1\\-2\end{pmatrix}+\mu\begin{pmatrix}-2\\4\end{pmatrix}=\begin{pmatrix}3\\-5\end{pmatrix}$

1.3 Three vectors in a plane

We have found that any vector can be expressed as a combination of any two other vectors, provided these two are not parallel. We now prove this result.

► **I If a and b are any two non-parallel vectors, then any other vector c in the plane of a and b may be expressed as a unique combination of a and b, i.e. $c = \lambda a + \mu b$ where λ, μ are numbers.** ◄

(a) $\boldsymbol{a}$, $\boldsymbol{b}$, $\boldsymbol{c}$ can be represented by line segments with tail at O.

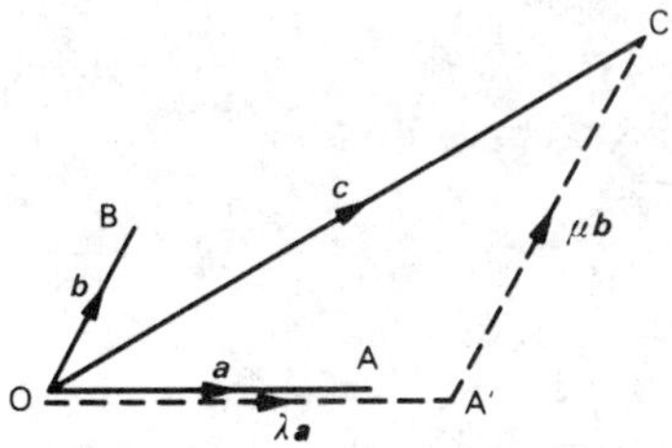

Through C draw a line parallel to $\boldsymbol{b}$, to cut OA at A′. This is always possible since $\boldsymbol{a}$, $\boldsymbol{b}$ are not parallel. Then if $\boldsymbol{OA'} = \lambda\boldsymbol{a}$, $\boldsymbol{A'C} = \mu\boldsymbol{b}$ from the triangle law

$$\boldsymbol{c} = \lambda\boldsymbol{a} + \mu\boldsymbol{b}$$

(b) To show that the values of λ, μ are unique. Suppose they are *not*, and that

$$\boldsymbol{c} = \lambda_1\boldsymbol{a} + \mu_1\boldsymbol{b} \quad \text{(say)}$$

and $\boldsymbol{c} = \lambda_2\boldsymbol{a} + \mu_2\boldsymbol{b}$ with $\lambda_1 \neq \lambda_2$, $\mu_1 \neq \mu_2$

Thus $\lambda_1\boldsymbol{a} + \mu_1\boldsymbol{b} = \lambda_2\boldsymbol{a} + \mu_2\boldsymbol{b}$

$$(\lambda_1 - \lambda_2)\boldsymbol{a} = (\mu_2 - \mu_1)\boldsymbol{b}$$

Now either $\lambda_1 - \lambda_2 = \mu_2 - \mu_1 = 0$ or $\boldsymbol{a}$ is parallel to $\boldsymbol{b}$, which is not true. Hence $\lambda_1 = \lambda_2$ and $\mu_1 = \mu_2$ and the solution is unique.

If $\quad c = \lambda a + \mu b$

then $\quad 0 = \lambda a + \mu b + (-c)$

since $\quad c + (-c) = 0 \quad$ (the zero vector)

This can be thought of as a three-stage journey with the third leg equal to the vector sum of the other two in length and direction, but opposite in sense, so returning us to our starting place. Such a route can be called a *closed vector route.*

If $\quad \lambda a + \mu b + (-c) = 0$

then $\quad 2\lambda a + 2\mu b + (-2c) = 0$

and in general $\quad la + mb + nc = 0$

where $l:m:n = \lambda:\mu:-1$. Statement **I** above can therefore be expressed in a slightly different form:

► **II If a, b, and c are three non-parallel vectors in a plane then they are related by an equation of the type $la + mb + nc = 0$, where l, m, n are real numbers. The *ratio* $l:m:n$ is unique.** ◄

This follows from **I** above, since c can be written as $\lambda_3 a + \mu_3 b$ (with λ_3, μ_3 unique). If $\lambda_3 = l/-n$, $\mu_3 = m/-n$ then

$$la + mb + nc = 0$$

Example

Given $\quad a = \begin{pmatrix} 1 \\ -3 \end{pmatrix}, \quad b = \begin{pmatrix} -2 \\ 1 \end{pmatrix}, \quad c = \begin{pmatrix} 3 \\ 1 \end{pmatrix}$

find l, m, n so that $\quad la + mb + nc = 0$

Method 1 (Graphical)

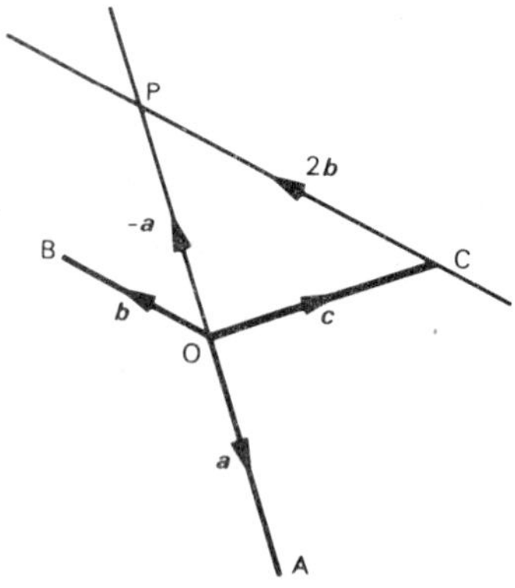

(a) Draw $c = \begin{pmatrix} 3 \\ 1 \end{pmatrix}$

(b) Through O draw a line parallel to $a = \begin{pmatrix} 1 \\ -3 \end{pmatrix}$

(c) Through C draw a line parallel to $\boldsymbol{b} = \begin{pmatrix} -2 \\ 1 \end{pmatrix}$

The two lines meet at P. Then $\boldsymbol{OP} = \lambda \boldsymbol{a}$, and $\boldsymbol{CP} = \mu \boldsymbol{b}$. By inspection $\boldsymbol{OP} = -1\boldsymbol{a}$, $\boldsymbol{PC} = -2\boldsymbol{b}$, i.e. $\lambda = -1$, $\mu = -2$. So one solution is

$$(-1)\boldsymbol{a} + (-2)\boldsymbol{b} + (-1)\boldsymbol{c} = \boldsymbol{0}$$

or, going round the other way

$$\boldsymbol{a} + 2\boldsymbol{b} + \boldsymbol{c} = \boldsymbol{0}$$

Are there any other solutions? Yes, of course. We can multiply through the equation by any number we like, e.g.

$$2\boldsymbol{a} + 4\boldsymbol{b} + 2\boldsymbol{c} = \boldsymbol{0} \quad \text{or} \quad -3\boldsymbol{a} - 6\boldsymbol{b} - 3\boldsymbol{c} = \boldsymbol{0}$$

and so on.

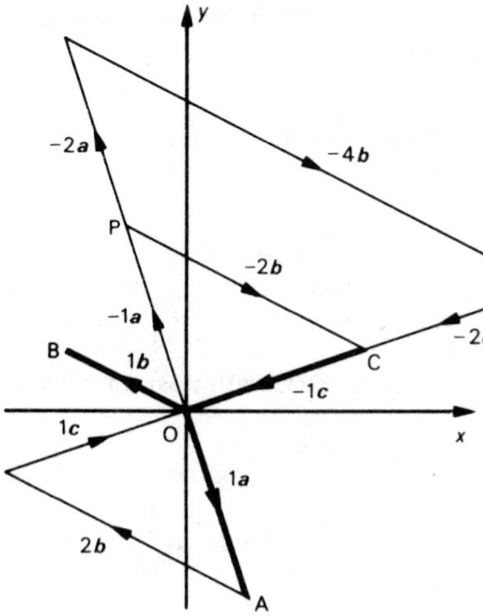

Method 2 (Algebraic)

$$l\begin{pmatrix} 1 \\ -3 \end{pmatrix} + m\begin{pmatrix} -2 \\ 1 \end{pmatrix} + n\begin{pmatrix} 3 \\ 1 \end{pmatrix} = \begin{pmatrix} 0 \\ 0 \end{pmatrix}$$

so
$$\left.\begin{aligned} l - 2m + 3n &= 0 \\ -3l + m + n &= 0 \end{aligned}\right\}$$
and

To solve these equations, divide both through by n and substitute

$$\lambda = \frac{l}{n}, \qquad \mu = \frac{m}{n}.$$

$$\left.\begin{aligned} \lambda - 2\mu + 3 &= 0 \\ -3\lambda + \mu + 1 &= 0 \end{aligned}\right\} \Rightarrow \lambda = 1, \mu = 2$$

$$\frac{l}{n} = 1, \qquad \frac{m}{n} = 2 \Rightarrow l : m : n = 1 : 2 : 1$$

Exercise 1.3

1 If $l\boldsymbol{a}+m\boldsymbol{b}+n\boldsymbol{c}=\boldsymbol{0}$, find by accurate drawing the ratio $l:m:n$ when

(a) $\boldsymbol{a}=\begin{pmatrix}-3\\-2\end{pmatrix}$, $\boldsymbol{b}=\begin{pmatrix}1\\8\end{pmatrix}$, $\boldsymbol{c}=\begin{pmatrix}4\\-1\end{pmatrix}$

(b) $\boldsymbol{a}=\begin{pmatrix}2\\1\end{pmatrix}$, $\boldsymbol{b}=\begin{pmatrix}1\\2\end{pmatrix}$, $\boldsymbol{c}=\begin{pmatrix}2\\-5\end{pmatrix}$

2 If $l\boldsymbol{p}+m\boldsymbol{q}+n\boldsymbol{r}=0$, find the ratio $l:m:n$ algebraically when

(a) $\boldsymbol{p}=\begin{pmatrix}-2\\0\end{pmatrix}$, $\boldsymbol{q}=\begin{pmatrix}2\\4\end{pmatrix}$, $\boldsymbol{r}=\begin{pmatrix}-1\\5\end{pmatrix}$

(b) $\boldsymbol{p}=\begin{pmatrix}4\\1\end{pmatrix}$, $\boldsymbol{q}=\begin{pmatrix}-3\\1\end{pmatrix}$, $\boldsymbol{r}=\begin{pmatrix}-5\\3\end{pmatrix}$

3 Find $l:m:n$ when $l\begin{pmatrix}-2\\3\end{pmatrix}+m\begin{pmatrix}0\\2\end{pmatrix}+n\begin{pmatrix}4\\0\end{pmatrix}=\begin{pmatrix}0\\0\end{pmatrix}$

What is the value of $l+m+n$?

Plot the points with position vectors $\begin{pmatrix}-2\\3\end{pmatrix}$, $\begin{pmatrix}0\\2\end{pmatrix}$, $\begin{pmatrix}4\\0\end{pmatrix}$. What do you notice?

4 Mark three collinear points A, B, C with position vectors $\boldsymbol{a}=\begin{pmatrix}-1\\1\end{pmatrix}$, $\boldsymbol{b}=\begin{pmatrix}5\\4\end{pmatrix}$, $\boldsymbol{c}=\begin{pmatrix}1\\2\end{pmatrix}$. Verify that

(a) $2\boldsymbol{a}+\boldsymbol{b}-3\boldsymbol{c}=\boldsymbol{0}$

(b) $-\boldsymbol{a}-\frac{1}{2}\boldsymbol{b}+\frac{3}{2}\boldsymbol{c}=\boldsymbol{0}$

(c) $3\boldsymbol{a}+\frac{3}{2}\boldsymbol{b}-\frac{9}{2}\boldsymbol{c}=\boldsymbol{0}$

Find λ and μ if

(d) $\lambda\boldsymbol{a}-(\lambda+\mu)\boldsymbol{b}+\boldsymbol{c}=\boldsymbol{0}$

(e) $\lambda\boldsymbol{a}-\boldsymbol{b}+(\lambda+\mu)\boldsymbol{c}=\boldsymbol{0}$

NOTE. We learn from questions 3 and 4 in this exercise that if A, B, and C lie in the same straight line, (are collinear) and their position vectors are related by

$$l\boldsymbol{a}+m\boldsymbol{b}+n\boldsymbol{c}=\boldsymbol{0} \qquad \text{or} \qquad \boldsymbol{c}=\lambda\boldsymbol{a}+\mu\boldsymbol{b}$$

then

$$l+m+n=0 \qquad \text{or} \qquad \lambda+\mu=1$$

This is a very important result and we shall return to it later (page 274).

1.4 Collinear points

Most of our routes so far have started at the origin, but consider the route *from* A *to* B (the order is very important).

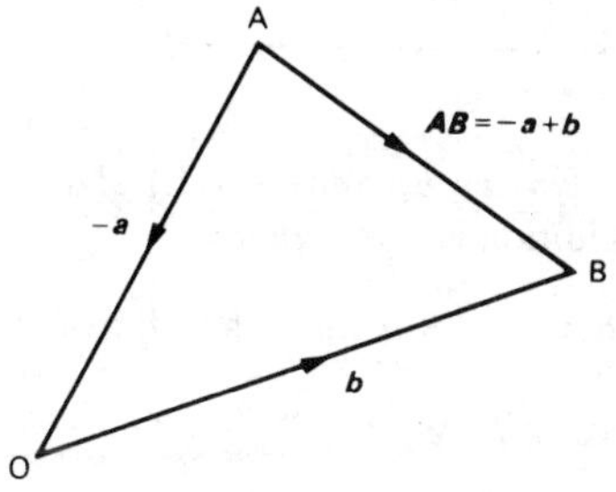

If $\boldsymbol{OA} = \boldsymbol{a}$ and $\boldsymbol{OB} = \boldsymbol{b}$, then

$$\boldsymbol{AB} = -\boldsymbol{a} + \boldsymbol{b}$$

and similarly $$\boldsymbol{BA} = -\boldsymbol{b} + \boldsymbol{a}$$

Remember that $\boldsymbol{a}$ can represent *either* the position vector $\boldsymbol{OA}$ of any point A, *or* any other member of the set of vectors equal to $\boldsymbol{OA}$, which are represented by lines equal and parallel to OA.

Vector routes in the parallelogram

Draw the triangle OAB, with $\boldsymbol{a} = \begin{pmatrix} 5 \\ 1 \end{pmatrix}$, $\boldsymbol{b} = \begin{pmatrix} 3 \\ 3 \end{pmatrix}$.

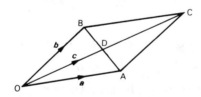

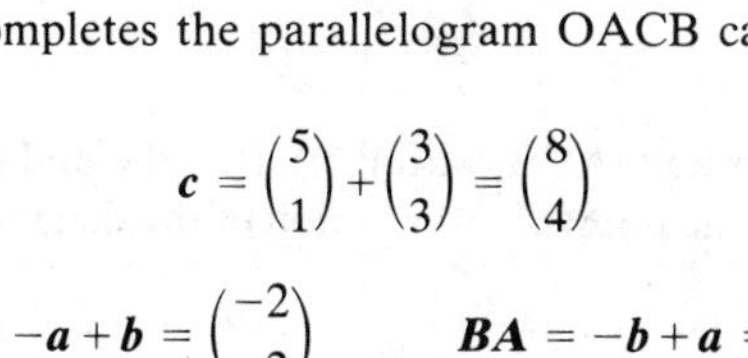

The point C which completes the parallelogram OACB can be found by making $\boldsymbol{BC} = \boldsymbol{OA}$. Then

$$\boldsymbol{c} = \begin{pmatrix} 5 \\ 1 \end{pmatrix} + \begin{pmatrix} 3 \\ 3 \end{pmatrix} = \begin{pmatrix} 8 \\ 4 \end{pmatrix}$$

Note that $\boldsymbol{AB} = -\boldsymbol{a} + \boldsymbol{b} = \begin{pmatrix} -2 \\ 2 \end{pmatrix}$ $\quad \boldsymbol{BA} = -\boldsymbol{b} + \boldsymbol{a} = \begin{pmatrix} 2 \\ -2 \end{pmatrix}$

Check that the position vector of D, the point of intersection of the diagonals is

$$\begin{pmatrix} 4 \\ 2 \end{pmatrix} = \tfrac{1}{2}\boldsymbol{c}$$

In general, in any parallelogram OACB

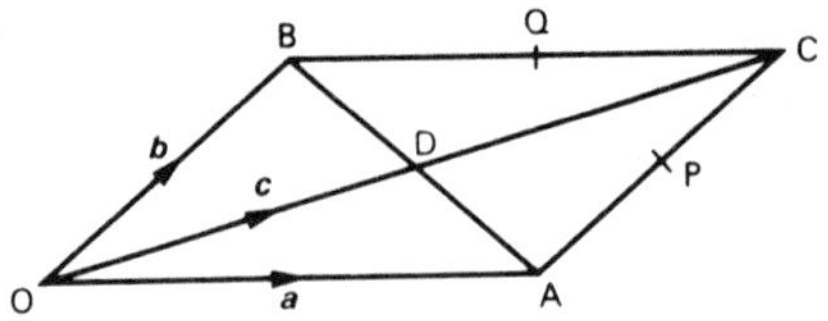

(i) The diagonal $\boldsymbol{OC} = \boldsymbol{c} = \boldsymbol{a} + \boldsymbol{b}$ (route via A) or $\boldsymbol{c} = \boldsymbol{b} + \boldsymbol{a}$ (route via B). This reminds us that vector addition is *commutative*.

(ii) $\boldsymbol{AB} = -\boldsymbol{a} + \boldsymbol{b}$ and $\boldsymbol{BA} = -\boldsymbol{b} + \boldsymbol{a}$ (the other diagonal).

(iii) To find the position vector of D consider first the direct route,

$$\boldsymbol{d} = \tfrac{1}{2}\boldsymbol{c} = \tfrac{1}{2}(\boldsymbol{a} + \boldsymbol{b})$$

Now, via A, $$\boldsymbol{d} = \boldsymbol{a} + \boldsymbol{AD}$$

but $$\boldsymbol{AD} = \tfrac{1}{2}\boldsymbol{AB} = \tfrac{1}{2}(-\boldsymbol{a} + \boldsymbol{b})$$

so $$\boldsymbol{d} = \boldsymbol{a} + \tfrac{1}{2}(-\boldsymbol{a} + \boldsymbol{b}) = \boldsymbol{a} - \tfrac{1}{2}\boldsymbol{a} + \tfrac{1}{2}\boldsymbol{b} = \tfrac{1}{2}(\boldsymbol{a} + \boldsymbol{b})$$

Similarly, via B, $$\boldsymbol{d} = \boldsymbol{b} + \boldsymbol{BD} = \boldsymbol{b} + \tfrac{1}{2}(-\boldsymbol{b} + \boldsymbol{a}) = \tfrac{1}{2}(\boldsymbol{a} + \boldsymbol{b})$$

Thus the mid-point of the line joining A to B has position vector $\tfrac{1}{2}(\boldsymbol{a} + \boldsymbol{b})$.

(iv) To find the position vector of P, the mid-point of AC, we see that

$$\boldsymbol{AC} = \boldsymbol{OB} = \boldsymbol{b} \quad \text{and} \quad \boldsymbol{AP} = \tfrac{1}{2}\boldsymbol{AC} = \tfrac{1}{2}\boldsymbol{b}$$

Then $$\boldsymbol{p} = \boldsymbol{OA} + \boldsymbol{AP} = \boldsymbol{a} + \tfrac{1}{2}\boldsymbol{b}$$

and similarly $$\boldsymbol{q} = \boldsymbol{b} + \tfrac{1}{2}\boldsymbol{a}$$

Note that $$\boldsymbol{PQ} = -\boldsymbol{p} + \boldsymbol{q} = -(\boldsymbol{a} + \tfrac{1}{2}\boldsymbol{b}) + (\boldsymbol{b} + \tfrac{1}{2}\boldsymbol{a})$$

$$= \tfrac{1}{2}(-\boldsymbol{a} + \boldsymbol{b}) = \tfrac{1}{2}\boldsymbol{AB}$$

This result may be familiar as the Mid-point Theorem.

Exercise 1.4a

1 Given the paralleogram OACB, with P, Q, R, S the mid-points of AC, CB, BO, OA respectively and D the point of intersection of the diagonals, express in terms of $\boldsymbol{a}$ and $\boldsymbol{b}$:

(**a**) $\boldsymbol{p}, \boldsymbol{q}, \boldsymbol{r}, \boldsymbol{s}, \boldsymbol{d}$

(**b**) $\boldsymbol{PS}, \boldsymbol{DP}, \boldsymbol{CR}, \boldsymbol{AD}, \boldsymbol{AQ}$

Verify your answers by means of a drawing, with

$$\boldsymbol{a} = \begin{pmatrix} -3 \\ 4 \end{pmatrix}, \qquad \boldsymbol{b} = \begin{pmatrix} 3 \\ 1 \end{pmatrix}$$

The vector equation of a line

We now return to an idea which we met at the beginning of the chapter, when we thought of the points in a straight line as points passed through on a journey, each one representing a multiple of the whole journey. From this we develop the vector equation of a line.

Consider again the parallelogram OACB.

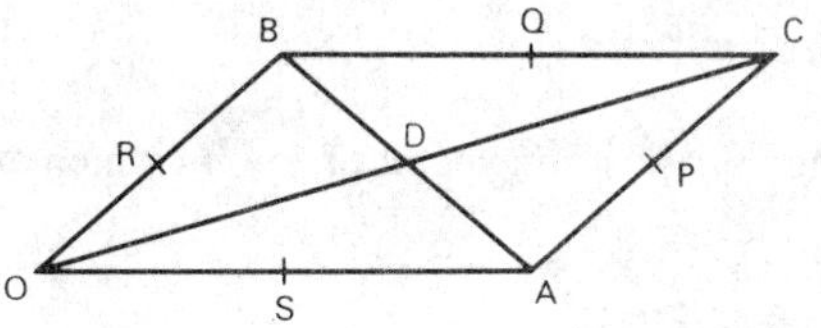

The position vector of S, the mid-point of OA is $\boldsymbol{s} = \frac{1}{2}\boldsymbol{a}$. The position vector of any point X on the line OA is $\boldsymbol{x} = \lambda \boldsymbol{a}$, where λ is a number or parameter. Different values of λ will give different points on the line. Similarly, the position vector of any point Y on OB is $\boldsymbol{y} = \lambda \boldsymbol{b}$. We have seen above that the position vector of P, the mid-point of AC is $\boldsymbol{p} = \boldsymbol{a} + \frac{1}{2}\boldsymbol{b}$, hence that of Z, any point on AC is $\boldsymbol{z} = \boldsymbol{a} + \lambda \boldsymbol{b}$ and similarly that of W, any point on BC is $\boldsymbol{w} = \boldsymbol{b} + \lambda \boldsymbol{a}$.

Again, the position vector of D, the mid-point of BA, is $\boldsymbol{d} = \boldsymbol{b} + \frac{1}{2}(-\boldsymbol{b} + \boldsymbol{a})$, so that of any point V on BA is $\boldsymbol{v} = \boldsymbol{b} + \lambda(-\boldsymbol{b} + \boldsymbol{a})$.

The position vector of a variable point on a line is a *vector equation* of that line. This equation is not unique.

Exercise 1.4b

1(a) Draw the line

$$\boldsymbol{x} = \begin{pmatrix} 2 \\ 2 \end{pmatrix} + t\begin{pmatrix} 3 \\ 1 \end{pmatrix}$$

Find the position vectors of A, B, C, D on the line, corresponding to $t = -1, 0, 2, 3$ and mark them on the diagram.

(b) On the same diagram draw the line

$$\boldsymbol{x} = \begin{pmatrix} 6 \\ 6 \end{pmatrix} + s\begin{pmatrix} 1 \\ 3 \end{pmatrix}$$

What are the values of s and t where the lines intersect at P? Find Q if it corresponds to $s = -2$.

(c) Draw in the line through Q, parallel to AD, and write down an equation for it in the form $\boldsymbol{x} = \boldsymbol{f} + s\boldsymbol{g}$.

2 Mark on a diagram the line joining points L and M with position vectors

$$\boldsymbol{l} = \begin{pmatrix} 3 \\ 2 \end{pmatrix} \quad \text{and} \quad \boldsymbol{m} = \begin{pmatrix} -3 \\ 4 \end{pmatrix}$$

Draw in the line PQ, where

$$\boldsymbol{p} = \begin{pmatrix} -1 \\ 8 \end{pmatrix} \qquad \text{and} \qquad \boldsymbol{q} = \begin{pmatrix} 1 \\ -2 \end{pmatrix}$$

What is MPLQ?

Write down an equation for the following lines in the form $\boldsymbol{x} = \boldsymbol{a} + t\boldsymbol{b}$: MP, QL, MQ, PL, ML and PQ.

1.5 The section formula

We might wish to find the position vector of a point which divides a line segment in a given *ratio*.

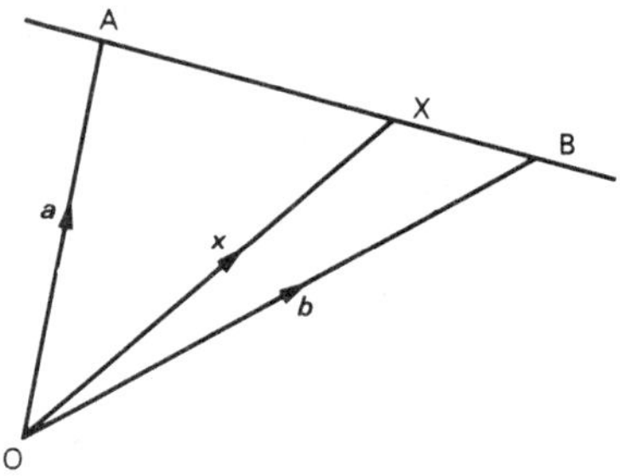

Suppose AX:XB = 3:1, then AX = $\frac{3}{4}$AB

$$\boldsymbol{x} = \boldsymbol{a} + \tfrac{3}{4}(-\boldsymbol{a} + \boldsymbol{b}) = \tfrac{1}{4}\boldsymbol{a} + \tfrac{3}{4}\boldsymbol{b}$$

or

$$\boldsymbol{x} = \frac{1\boldsymbol{a} + 3\boldsymbol{b}}{4}$$

Similarly if AX:XB = 3:5

$$\boldsymbol{x} = \boldsymbol{a} + \tfrac{3}{8}(-\boldsymbol{a} + \boldsymbol{b})$$

and

$$\boldsymbol{x} = \frac{5\boldsymbol{a} + 3\boldsymbol{b}}{8}$$

In general,

$$\textbf{if AX:XB} = l:m, \qquad \boldsymbol{x} = \frac{m\boldsymbol{a} + l\boldsymbol{b}}{l + m}$$ ◀

This formula is usually called the *Section Formula*.

We have considered the case when X is between A and B. Suppose X is outside AB, on the extension of AB and we have, for example AX:XB = 5:−2.

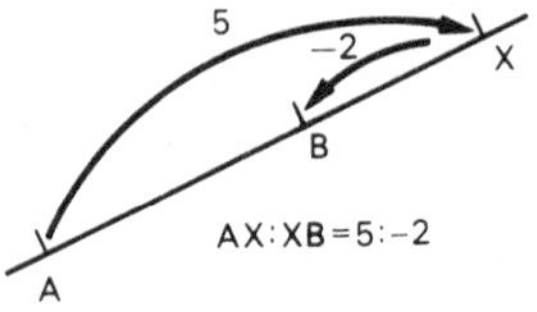

Then AX = $\frac{5}{3}$AB and

$$\boldsymbol{x} = \boldsymbol{a} + \tfrac{5}{3}(-\boldsymbol{a}+\boldsymbol{b})$$
$$= \frac{-2\boldsymbol{a}+5\boldsymbol{b}}{3}$$

Finally, if X lies on BA produced and we have, for example, AX : XB = −3 : 5, then

$$\boldsymbol{x} = \frac{5\boldsymbol{a}-3\boldsymbol{b}}{2}$$

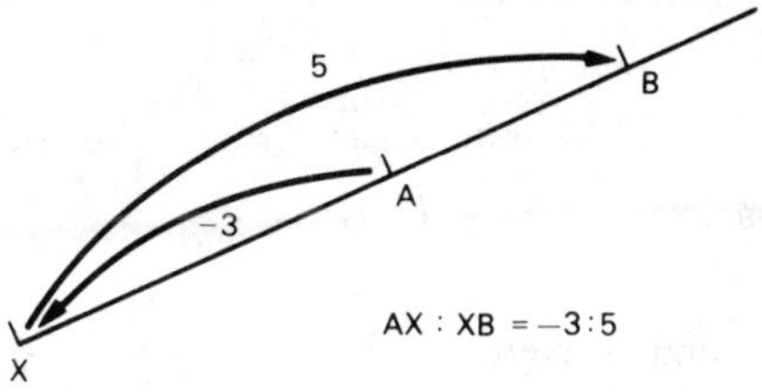

NOTE. We consider the direction from A to B as positive.

Example

Find $\boldsymbol{p}$, corresponding to P, with AP : PB = 5 : −2
and $\boldsymbol{q}$, corresponding to Q, with AQ : QB = −2 : 5,

when $\boldsymbol{a} = \begin{pmatrix}2\\3\end{pmatrix}$, $\boldsymbol{b} = \begin{pmatrix}8\\0\end{pmatrix}$

Applying the section formula:

$$\boldsymbol{p} = \frac{-2\boldsymbol{a}+5\boldsymbol{b}}{3} = \tfrac{1}{3}\left[-2\begin{pmatrix}2\\3\end{pmatrix}+5\begin{pmatrix}8\\0\end{pmatrix}\right] = \tfrac{1}{3}\begin{pmatrix}36\\-6\end{pmatrix} = \begin{pmatrix}12\\-2\end{pmatrix}$$

$$\boldsymbol{q} = \frac{5\boldsymbol{a}-2\boldsymbol{b}}{3} = \tfrac{1}{3}\left[5\begin{pmatrix}2\\3\end{pmatrix}-2\begin{pmatrix}8\\0\end{pmatrix}\right] = \tfrac{1}{3}\begin{pmatrix}-6\\15\end{pmatrix} = \begin{pmatrix}-2\\5\end{pmatrix}$$

Collinear points

If three points A, B and C with corresponding position vectors $\boldsymbol{a}$, $\boldsymbol{b}$ and $\boldsymbol{c}$ are collinear, then AC : CB must be in some ratio, say $l:m$.

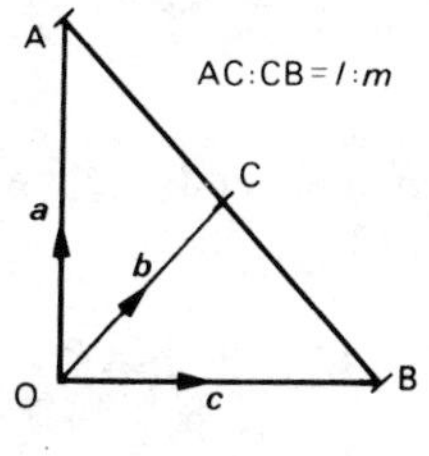

Hence $$\boldsymbol{c} = \frac{m\boldsymbol{a} + l\boldsymbol{b}}{l+m}$$

and, rearranged, $$(l+m)\boldsymbol{c} = m\boldsymbol{a} + l\boldsymbol{b}$$

so $$m\boldsymbol{a} + l\boldsymbol{b} - (l+m)\boldsymbol{c} = \boldsymbol{0}$$

If this is written $$\alpha\boldsymbol{a} + \beta\boldsymbol{b} + \gamma\boldsymbol{c} = \boldsymbol{0}$$

then $$\alpha + \beta + \gamma = 0$$

Conversely, if $\alpha\boldsymbol{a} + \beta\boldsymbol{b} + \gamma\boldsymbol{c} = \boldsymbol{0}$ and $\alpha + \beta + \gamma = 0$

then A, B and C are collinear. Also if

$$\boldsymbol{c} = \frac{m\boldsymbol{a} + l\boldsymbol{b}}{l+m} = \lambda\boldsymbol{a} + \mu\boldsymbol{b} \quad \text{(say)}$$

then $\lambda = \dfrac{m}{l+m}$, $\mu = \dfrac{l}{l+m}$ and $\lambda + \mu = 1$

This is the result we found in Exercise 1.3.

Alternatively, if C lies on AB, then

$$\boldsymbol{AC} = k\boldsymbol{AB}$$

$$-\boldsymbol{a} + \boldsymbol{c} = k(-\boldsymbol{a} + \boldsymbol{b})$$

$$(1-k)\boldsymbol{a} + k\boldsymbol{b} - 1\boldsymbol{c} = \boldsymbol{0}$$

and as before the coefficients of $\boldsymbol{a}$, $\boldsymbol{b}$ and $\boldsymbol{c}$ have zero sum.

Proof of the Section Formula

If P divides AB in the ratio AP : PB = $l : m$ then

$$\boldsymbol{p} = \frac{m\boldsymbol{a} + l\boldsymbol{b}}{l+m}$$

We consider the two cases: (1) when P is between A and B, and (2) when P is outside AB.

(1)

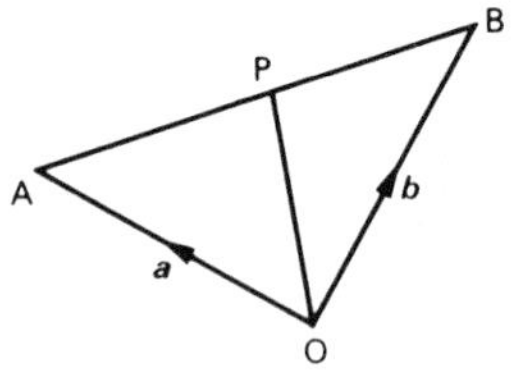

$$\boldsymbol{AB} = -\boldsymbol{a} + \boldsymbol{b} \qquad \text{and} \qquad \boldsymbol{AP} = -\boldsymbol{a} + \boldsymbol{p}$$

If AP : PB = $l : m$, then

$$\boldsymbol{AP} = \frac{l}{l+m}\boldsymbol{AB}$$

Hence
$$-\boldsymbol{a}+\boldsymbol{p} = \frac{l}{l+m}(-\boldsymbol{a}+\boldsymbol{b})$$
$$(l+m)(-\boldsymbol{a}+\boldsymbol{p}) = l(-\boldsymbol{a}+\boldsymbol{b})$$
$$(l+m)\boldsymbol{p} = m\boldsymbol{a}+l\boldsymbol{b}$$
$$\boldsymbol{p} = \frac{m\boldsymbol{a}+l\boldsymbol{b}}{l+m}$$

(2)

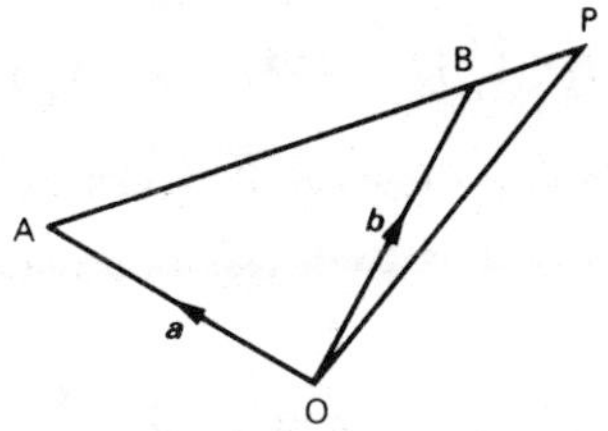

$$\text{AP}:\text{PB} = l:m$$

where l is numerically greater than m and m is negative. As before,

$$\boldsymbol{AP} = \frac{l}{l-(-m)}\boldsymbol{AB} = \frac{l}{l+m}\boldsymbol{AB}$$

and
$$\boldsymbol{p} = \frac{m\boldsymbol{a}+l\boldsymbol{b}}{l+m}$$

The same result applies if $l < m$ and l is negative.

Exercise 1.5

NOTE. Some vectors in this exercise are given in $\boldsymbol{i}$, $\boldsymbol{j}$ form, to remind you that $\boldsymbol{a} = \begin{pmatrix}4\\8\end{pmatrix}$ is a shorthand way of writing $\boldsymbol{a} = 4\boldsymbol{i}+8\boldsymbol{j}$, where $\boldsymbol{i} = \begin{pmatrix}1\\0\end{pmatrix}$, $\boldsymbol{j} = \begin{pmatrix}0\\1\end{pmatrix}$.

1 Use the Section Formula to find the following and verify your results on an accurate diagram.

(**a**) $\boldsymbol{t} = 4\boldsymbol{i}+8\boldsymbol{j}$, $\boldsymbol{n} = 12\boldsymbol{i}+4\boldsymbol{j}$ and TU : UN = 1 : 3. Find $\boldsymbol{u}$.

(**b**) $\boldsymbol{p} = 5\boldsymbol{i}+15\boldsymbol{j}$, $\boldsymbol{q} = 5\boldsymbol{i}+5\boldsymbol{j}$ and PR : RQ = 1 : 4. Find $\boldsymbol{r}$.

(**c**) $\boldsymbol{l} = 2\boldsymbol{i}-3\boldsymbol{j}$, $\boldsymbol{m} = 4\boldsymbol{i}+5\boldsymbol{j}$ and LW : WM = −2 : 3. (What does a negative ratio mean?) Find $\boldsymbol{w}$.

(**d**) $\boldsymbol{a} = -3\boldsymbol{i}+4\boldsymbol{j}$, $\boldsymbol{b} = 2\boldsymbol{i}+5\boldsymbol{j}$ and AC : CB = −1 : 2. Find $\boldsymbol{c}$.

2 Find the position vectors of the points P and Q which divide the line joining A to B, where

$$\boldsymbol{a} = \begin{pmatrix}2\\3\end{pmatrix} \quad \text{and} \quad \boldsymbol{b} = \begin{pmatrix}8\\9\end{pmatrix}$$

in the ratio 1 : 2 internally and externally respectively

3 Given

(**a**) $l\begin{pmatrix}-2\\3\end{pmatrix}+m\begin{pmatrix}2\\1\end{pmatrix}+n\begin{pmatrix}6\\-1\end{pmatrix}=\begin{pmatrix}0\\0\end{pmatrix}$ find the ratio $l:m:n$

(**b**) $p\begin{pmatrix}-6\\0\end{pmatrix}+q\begin{pmatrix}-2\\2\end{pmatrix}+r\begin{pmatrix}2\\4\end{pmatrix}=\begin{pmatrix}0\\0\end{pmatrix}$ find $p:q:r$.

What are the values of (*i*) $l+m+n$ (take $n = 1$) and (*ii*) $p+q+r$ (take $r = 3$). Draw a diagram in each case to illustrate your answers.

4 P and Q are given by

$$\boldsymbol{p}=\begin{pmatrix}3\\0\end{pmatrix} \quad \text{and} \quad \boldsymbol{q}=\begin{pmatrix}6\\6\end{pmatrix}$$

X has position vector $\boldsymbol{x}=\frac{2}{3}\boldsymbol{p}+\frac{1}{3}\boldsymbol{q}$. Show that P, X, Q are collinear and find the ratio of PX:XQ.

5 A has position vector

$$\boldsymbol{a}=\begin{pmatrix}-2\\0\end{pmatrix} \quad \text{and} \quad \text{B}, \boldsymbol{b}=\begin{pmatrix}0\\4\end{pmatrix}$$

Show on a diagram

$$\boldsymbol{p}=2\boldsymbol{a}-1\boldsymbol{b}, \qquad \boldsymbol{q}=-1\boldsymbol{a}+2\boldsymbol{b}, \qquad \boldsymbol{r}=-\tfrac{1}{2}\boldsymbol{a}+\tfrac{3}{2}\boldsymbol{b} \quad \text{and} \quad \boldsymbol{s}=\tfrac{3}{4}\boldsymbol{a}+\tfrac{1}{4}\boldsymbol{b}$$

If T, U also lie in the line, find λ, μ if

$$\boldsymbol{t}=\lambda\boldsymbol{a}-\tfrac{1}{2}\boldsymbol{b} \quad \text{and} \quad \boldsymbol{u}=-\tfrac{5}{2}\boldsymbol{a}+\mu\boldsymbol{b}$$

2 Scalar product of vectors

2.1 The length and direction of a vector

So far we have described a vector by two components in a column matrix, which corresponds to cartesian coordinates for the position of a point. But as polar coordinates specify a point by its distance from a fixed point and its direction relative to some fixed direction, so a vector can be described by its length (or magnitude) and the angle it makes with a fixed direction.

The *length* or *magnitude* of the vector $\boldsymbol{p}$ is written $|\boldsymbol{p}|$. If

$$\boldsymbol{a}=\begin{pmatrix}0\\-8\end{pmatrix} \qquad \boldsymbol{b}=\begin{pmatrix}-6\\0\end{pmatrix} \qquad \boldsymbol{c}=\begin{pmatrix}6\\8\end{pmatrix}$$

then $\quad |\boldsymbol{a}|=8 \qquad |\boldsymbol{b}|=6 \qquad |\boldsymbol{c}|=10$

and $\quad 2\boldsymbol{a}=\begin{pmatrix}0\\-16\end{pmatrix}$ so $|2\boldsymbol{a}|=16=2|\boldsymbol{a}|$

In general,

if $\boldsymbol{p}=\begin{pmatrix}r\\s\end{pmatrix}$ **then** $|\boldsymbol{p}|=\sqrt{(r^2+s^2)}$ **and** $|\lambda\boldsymbol{p}|=\lambda|\boldsymbol{p}|$

◀

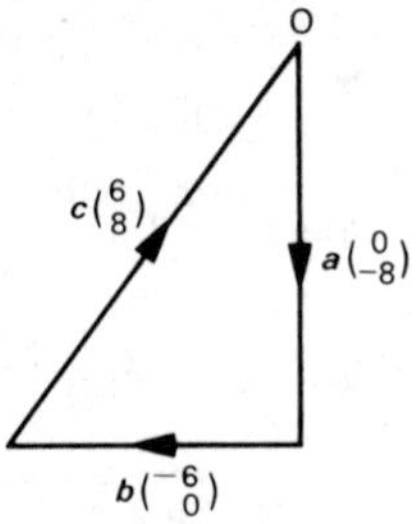

The length of a closed vector route

Consider the vector route $\boldsymbol{a}+\boldsymbol{b}+\boldsymbol{c}$. It is obvious that $\boldsymbol{a}+\boldsymbol{b}+\boldsymbol{c}=\boldsymbol{0}$ and so we have returned to O. But the distance travelled in completing the circuit is not zero. Here the length of the route is

$$|\boldsymbol{a}|+|\boldsymbol{b}|+|\boldsymbol{c}| = 8+6+10 = 24 \text{ units}$$

Note that $|(\boldsymbol{a}+\boldsymbol{b}+\boldsymbol{c})| = 0$.

The triangle inequality

The sum of two sides of a triangle must be greater than the third side (or else we should have no triangle).

$$|\boldsymbol{a}|+|\boldsymbol{b}| > |\boldsymbol{a}+\boldsymbol{b}|$$

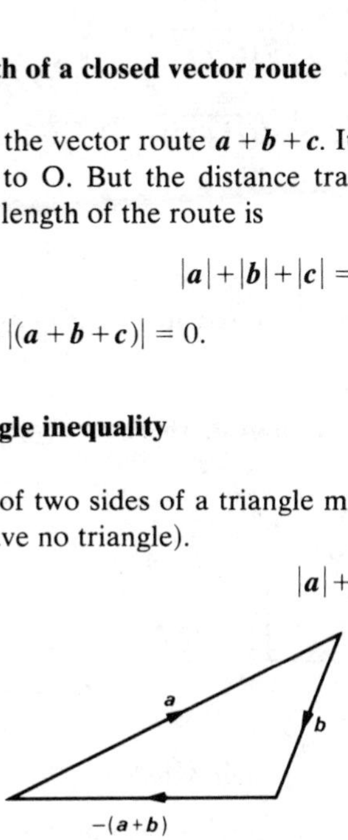

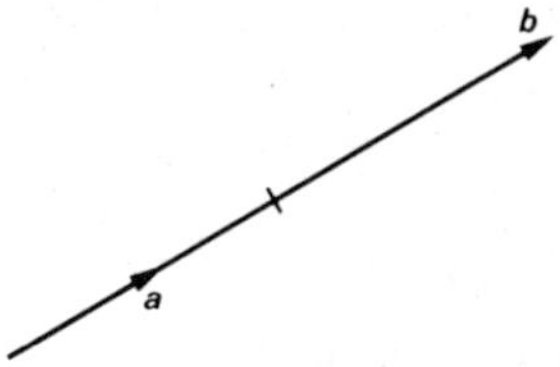

However, $$|\boldsymbol{a}|+|\boldsymbol{b}| = |\boldsymbol{a}+\boldsymbol{b}|$$

if $\boldsymbol{a}$ and $\boldsymbol{b}$ are in the same direction. Hence

$$|\boldsymbol{a}|+|\boldsymbol{b}| \geqslant |\boldsymbol{a}+\boldsymbol{b}|$$ ◀

which is *the triangle inequality*.

Vectors of unit length

It is often useful to know a vector of unit length in a given direction. We have met the unit vectors $\boldsymbol{i}$ and $\boldsymbol{j}$ in the directions of the x and y axes. A vector of unit length in the direction of $\boldsymbol{a}$ is given the symbol $\hat{\boldsymbol{a}}$, which is read as '$\boldsymbol{a}$ hat' where

$$\hat{\boldsymbol{a}} = \frac{1}{|\boldsymbol{a}|}\boldsymbol{a} \qquad \text{or} \qquad \boldsymbol{a} = |\boldsymbol{a}|\hat{\boldsymbol{a}}$$

If $\quad \boldsymbol{a} = \begin{pmatrix} 0 \\ -8 \end{pmatrix} \qquad \boldsymbol{b} = \begin{pmatrix} -6 \\ 0 \end{pmatrix} \qquad \boldsymbol{c} = \begin{pmatrix} 6 \\ 8 \end{pmatrix}$

$$\hat{\boldsymbol{a}} = \tfrac{1}{8}\begin{pmatrix} 0 \\ -8 \end{pmatrix} = \begin{pmatrix} 0 \\ -1 \end{pmatrix}, \qquad \hat{\boldsymbol{b}} = \tfrac{1}{6}\begin{pmatrix} -6 \\ 0 \end{pmatrix} = \begin{pmatrix} -1 \\ 0 \end{pmatrix}, \qquad \hat{\boldsymbol{c}} = \tfrac{1}{10}\begin{pmatrix} 6 \\ 8 \end{pmatrix} = \begin{pmatrix} \frac{3}{5} \\ \frac{4}{5} \end{pmatrix}$$

Of course, $\qquad |\hat{\boldsymbol{a}}| = |\hat{\boldsymbol{b}}| = |\hat{\boldsymbol{c}}| = 1$

In general,

$$\textbf{if } \boldsymbol{p} = \begin{pmatrix} r \\ s \end{pmatrix}, \qquad \textbf{then } \hat{\boldsymbol{p}} = \begin{pmatrix} \dfrac{r}{\sqrt{(r^2+s^2)}} \\ \dfrac{s}{\sqrt{(r^2+s^2)}} \end{pmatrix}$$ ◀

The direction of a vector

This is the angle between the vector and the positive x axis, measured between 0 and 180° anticlockwise, and 0 and −180° clockwise.

If $\boldsymbol{p} = \begin{pmatrix} r \\ s \end{pmatrix}$, then the direction of $\boldsymbol{p}$ is given by θ, where $\tan\theta = \dfrac{s}{r}$ ◀

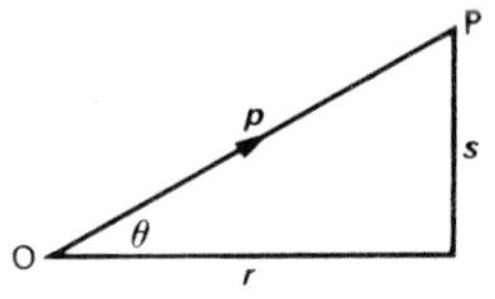

If $\boldsymbol{p} = \begin{pmatrix} -2 \\ 3 \end{pmatrix}$, then $\tan\theta = \dfrac{3}{-2}$ and if $\boldsymbol{q} = \begin{pmatrix} 2 \\ -3 \end{pmatrix}$, then $\tan\theta = \dfrac{-3}{2}$. The position vectors $\boldsymbol{p}$ and $\boldsymbol{q}$ lie in the same line, but are in opposite directions, P being in the second quadrant and Q in the fourth. Similarly R, with $\boldsymbol{r} = \begin{pmatrix} -2 \\ -3 \end{pmatrix}$, $\tan\theta = \dfrac{-3}{-2}$ is in the third quadrant.

Exercise 2.1

1 Find, and simplify, the length of the closed vector routes

(a) $|\boldsymbol{p}| + |\boldsymbol{q}| + |-(\boldsymbol{p}+\boldsymbol{q})|$ and **(b)** $|2\boldsymbol{p}| + |2\boldsymbol{q}| + |-(2\boldsymbol{p}+2\boldsymbol{q})|$ in the two cases

(i) $\boldsymbol{p} = \begin{pmatrix} 3 \\ 1 \end{pmatrix}, \boldsymbol{q} = \begin{pmatrix} -2 \\ 6 \end{pmatrix}$, and

(ii) $\boldsymbol{p} = \begin{pmatrix} 3 \\ 2 \end{pmatrix}, \boldsymbol{q} = \begin{pmatrix} -6 \\ -4 \end{pmatrix}$

Illustrate your answers on a diagram.

2 Mark A, B, C on a diagram, where the position vectors are

$$\boldsymbol{a} = \begin{pmatrix}-3\\-4\end{pmatrix}, \qquad \boldsymbol{b} = \begin{pmatrix}5\\12\end{pmatrix} \qquad \text{and} \qquad \boldsymbol{c} = \begin{pmatrix}1\\-7\end{pmatrix}$$

(a) Write down the vectors
(i) $\hat{\boldsymbol{a}}, \hat{\boldsymbol{b}}, \hat{\boldsymbol{c}}$ (ii) $(\boldsymbol{a}+\boldsymbol{b}+\boldsymbol{c})$ (iii) $(-\boldsymbol{a}+\boldsymbol{c})$

(b) Find the values of
(i) $|\boldsymbol{a}|+|\boldsymbol{b}|+|\boldsymbol{c}|$ (ii) $|\hat{\boldsymbol{a}}|+|\hat{\boldsymbol{b}}|+|\hat{\boldsymbol{c}}|$
(iii) $|(\boldsymbol{a}+\boldsymbol{b}+\boldsymbol{c})|$ (iv) $|(-\boldsymbol{a}+\boldsymbol{c})|$

3 If $\boldsymbol{a} = \begin{pmatrix}6\\3\end{pmatrix}$ and $\boldsymbol{b} = \begin{pmatrix}1\\-2\end{pmatrix}$ evaluate $|\boldsymbol{a}+\boldsymbol{b}|$ and $|\boldsymbol{a}-\boldsymbol{b}|$.

Explain the result geometrically.

4 If $\boldsymbol{a} = \begin{pmatrix}a_1\\a_2\end{pmatrix}$ and $\mathbf{b} = \begin{pmatrix}b_1\\b_2\end{pmatrix}$ show that $|\boldsymbol{a}+\boldsymbol{b}|^2 = |\boldsymbol{a}|^2+|\boldsymbol{b}|^2+2(a_1b_1+a_2b_2)$.

Write down a similar expression for $|\boldsymbol{a}-\boldsymbol{b}|^2$.
Interpret the results geometrically where $\boldsymbol{a}$ and $\boldsymbol{b}$ represent adjacent sides of a parallelogram.

2.2 The scalar (or dot) product of vectors

We now return to an idea we met before in Chapter 4 when we studied lines and their direction ratios. If we have two lines with DR $l:m$ and $\lambda:\mu$, then we can find the angle θ between them by

$$\cos\theta = \frac{l\lambda+m\mu}{\sqrt{(l^2+m^2)}\sqrt{(\lambda^2+\mu^2)}}$$

Suppose now that we have two vectors,

$$\boldsymbol{a} = \begin{pmatrix}a_1\\a_2\end{pmatrix}, \qquad \text{and} \qquad \boldsymbol{b} = \begin{pmatrix}b_1\\b_2\end{pmatrix}$$

with $\qquad |\boldsymbol{a}| = \sqrt{(a_1^2+a_2^2)} \qquad$ and $\qquad |\boldsymbol{b}| = \sqrt{(b_1^2+b_2^2)}$

Then in a similar way the angle between them is given by

$$\cos\theta = \frac{a_1b_1+a_2b_2}{|\boldsymbol{a}|\times|\boldsymbol{b}|}$$

If $\qquad \boldsymbol{a} = \begin{pmatrix}a_1\\a_2\end{pmatrix} \qquad$ and $\qquad \boldsymbol{b} = \begin{pmatrix}b_1\\b_2\end{pmatrix}$

then the product $\qquad a_1b_1+a_2b_2$

is called the *scalar product* (or *dot product*) of $\boldsymbol{a}$ and $\boldsymbol{b}$ and is written $\boldsymbol{a}\cdot\boldsymbol{b}$. If the angle between $\boldsymbol{a}$ and $\boldsymbol{b}$ is θ, then

$$\boldsymbol{a}\cdot\boldsymbol{b} = \boldsymbol{a_1b_1+a_2b_2} = |\boldsymbol{a}||\boldsymbol{b}|\cos\boldsymbol{\theta}$$ ◀

The angle between vectors

Example 1

Find the angle between

$$\boldsymbol{a} = \begin{pmatrix}1\\2\end{pmatrix} \quad \text{and} \quad \boldsymbol{b} = \begin{pmatrix}3\\1\end{pmatrix}$$

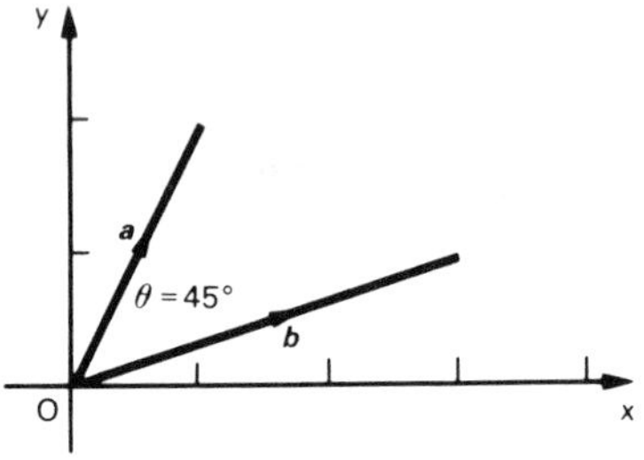

$$\cos\theta = \frac{\begin{pmatrix}1\\2\end{pmatrix}\cdot\begin{pmatrix}3\\1\end{pmatrix}}{\sqrt{(1^2+2^2)}\sqrt{(3^2+1^2)}} = \frac{1\times3+2\times1}{\sqrt{5}\sqrt{10}}$$

$$= \frac{5}{5\sqrt{2}} = \frac{1}{\sqrt{2}} \quad \text{and} \quad \theta = 45°$$

Example 2

Find the angle BAC where A, B, C are given by

$$\boldsymbol{a} = \begin{pmatrix}2\\1\end{pmatrix}, \quad \boldsymbol{b} = \begin{pmatrix}-1\\3\end{pmatrix}, \quad \boldsymbol{c} = \begin{pmatrix}0\\-2\end{pmatrix}$$

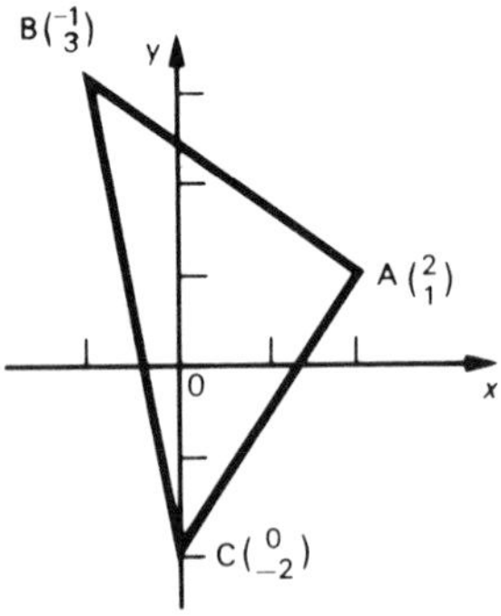

$$\boldsymbol{BA} = -\boldsymbol{b}+\boldsymbol{a} = -\begin{pmatrix}-1\\3\end{pmatrix}+\begin{pmatrix}2\\1\end{pmatrix} = \begin{pmatrix}3\\-2\end{pmatrix} \quad \text{so} \quad |\boldsymbol{BA}| = \sqrt{13}$$

$$\boldsymbol{CA} = -\boldsymbol{c} + \boldsymbol{a} = -\begin{pmatrix}0\\-2\end{pmatrix} + \begin{pmatrix}2\\1\end{pmatrix} = \begin{pmatrix}2\\3\end{pmatrix} \quad \text{so} \quad |\boldsymbol{CA}| = \sqrt{13}$$

$$\cos \angle BAC = \frac{\begin{pmatrix}3\\-2\end{pmatrix} \cdot \begin{pmatrix}2\\3\end{pmatrix}}{\sqrt{13}\sqrt{13}} = 0 \quad \text{so} \quad \angle BAC = 90°$$

Triangle ABC is thus a right-angled, isosceles triangle. Note that

$$|\boldsymbol{BC}| = |-\boldsymbol{b} + \boldsymbol{c}| = \left|\begin{pmatrix}1\\-5\end{pmatrix}\right| = \sqrt{26}$$

Projections

Since $|\hat{\boldsymbol{a}}| = |\hat{\boldsymbol{b}}| = 1$ and $\boldsymbol{a} \cdot \boldsymbol{b} = |\boldsymbol{a}||\boldsymbol{b}| \cos \theta = ab \cos \theta$

it follows that $\boldsymbol{a} \cdot \hat{\boldsymbol{b}} = |\boldsymbol{a}| \cos \theta = a \cos \theta$

$\hat{\boldsymbol{a}} \cdot \boldsymbol{b} = |\boldsymbol{b}| \cos \theta = b \cos \theta$

and $\hat{\boldsymbol{a}} \cdot \hat{\boldsymbol{b}} = \cos \theta$

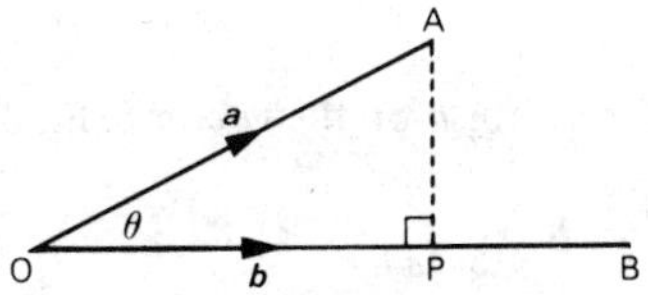

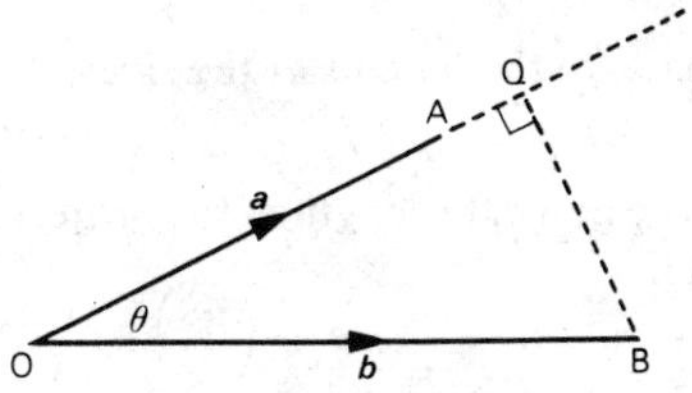

The length OP is called the *projection* of OA on OB and similarly, the length OQ is the projection of OB on OA (produced). The idea of projection is an important one in mechanics (e.g. in finding the components of a force) and vector notation gives us a simple way of expressing it.

$$OP = a \cos \theta = \boldsymbol{a} \cdot \hat{\boldsymbol{b}} = \frac{\boldsymbol{a} \cdot \boldsymbol{b}}{|\boldsymbol{b}|}$$

and similarly
$$OQ = b \cos \theta = \hat{\boldsymbol{a}} \cdot \boldsymbol{b} = \frac{\boldsymbol{a} \cdot \boldsymbol{b}}{|\boldsymbol{a}|}$$

Example 3

If $\boldsymbol{a} = \begin{pmatrix}2\\5\end{pmatrix}$ and $\boldsymbol{b} = \begin{pmatrix}4\\3\end{pmatrix}$

find the length of the projection of $\boldsymbol{a}$ on $\boldsymbol{b}$.

The length is $\dfrac{\boldsymbol{a} \cdot \boldsymbol{b}}{|\boldsymbol{b}|} = \dfrac{8+15}{5} = \dfrac{23}{5} = 4.6$

Exercise 2.2

1 (a) If $|\boldsymbol{a}| = |\boldsymbol{b}| = 3$ and $\boldsymbol{a} \cdot \boldsymbol{b} = -2$, find the angle between $\boldsymbol{a}$ and $\boldsymbol{b}$.
(b) If $|\boldsymbol{a}| = 5$ and $|\boldsymbol{b}| = 2$ and $\boldsymbol{a} \cdot \boldsymbol{b} = 12$, find $|\boldsymbol{a}-\boldsymbol{b}|$ and $|\boldsymbol{a}+\boldsymbol{b}|$.

2 If

$$\boldsymbol{a} = \begin{pmatrix}1\\2\end{pmatrix}, \quad \boldsymbol{b} = \begin{pmatrix}3\\1\end{pmatrix}, \quad \boldsymbol{c} = \begin{pmatrix}-1\\1\end{pmatrix}, \quad \boldsymbol{d} = \begin{pmatrix}2\\3\end{pmatrix}$$

(a) Find the cosine of the angles between $\boldsymbol{a}$ and $\boldsymbol{b}$ and between $(\boldsymbol{a}+\boldsymbol{b})$ and $(\boldsymbol{c}+\boldsymbol{d})$.

(b) Check your answers by measurement on a diagram where $\boldsymbol{a}$ is the position vector of A and so on.

3 Draw the triangle ABC with

$$\boldsymbol{a} = \boldsymbol{i}+4\boldsymbol{j}, \qquad \boldsymbol{b} = 5\boldsymbol{i}+2\boldsymbol{j}, \qquad \boldsymbol{c} = -3\boldsymbol{i}-4\boldsymbol{j}$$

Calculate the angles of the triangle using the scalar product, and check your answers by measurement.

4 The position vectors of the triangle PQR are

$$\boldsymbol{p} = \begin{pmatrix}-2\\2\end{pmatrix}, \qquad \boldsymbol{q} = \begin{pmatrix}1\\5\end{pmatrix} \qquad \text{and} \qquad \boldsymbol{r} = \begin{pmatrix}1\\-8\end{pmatrix}$$

Calculate **(a)** the lengths of the sides, **(b)** the interior angles, and **(c)** the area of the triangle.

5 Write down the length of the projection of the vector $\boldsymbol{a}$ on the vector $\boldsymbol{b}$. Find this length if

$$\boldsymbol{a} = \begin{pmatrix}-8\\4\end{pmatrix} \qquad \text{and} \qquad \boldsymbol{b} = \begin{pmatrix}-3\\-4\end{pmatrix}$$

Check your calculation with a diagram.

6 The position vectors of the triangle XYZ are

$$\boldsymbol{x} = \begin{pmatrix}0\\4\end{pmatrix} \qquad \boldsymbol{y} = \begin{pmatrix}4\\1\end{pmatrix} \qquad \boldsymbol{z} = \begin{pmatrix}1\\0\end{pmatrix}$$

Find the length of the projection of **(a)** YZ on XY, **(b)** XZ on XY.

2.3 Properties of the scalar product

Here are some important properties of the scalar product.

1 Although $\boldsymbol{a}$, $\boldsymbol{b}$ are vectors, $\boldsymbol{a} \cdot \boldsymbol{b}$ is a number i.e. a *scalar.*

2 $\boldsymbol{a} \cdot \boldsymbol{b} = \boldsymbol{b} \cdot \boldsymbol{a}$ (it is commutative).

3 $\boldsymbol{a} \cdot (\boldsymbol{b}+\boldsymbol{c}) = \boldsymbol{a} \cdot \boldsymbol{b} + \boldsymbol{a} \cdot \boldsymbol{c}$ (it is distributive over vector addition).

4 $(\lambda \boldsymbol{a}) \cdot \boldsymbol{b} = \boldsymbol{a} \cdot (\lambda \boldsymbol{b}) = \lambda(\boldsymbol{a} \cdot \boldsymbol{b})$ (multiplication by a scalar).

5 $\boldsymbol{a} \cdot \boldsymbol{a} = |\boldsymbol{a}|^2 = a^2$.

6 If $\boldsymbol{a} \cdot \boldsymbol{b} = 0$, then either $\boldsymbol{a} = \boldsymbol{0}$ or $\boldsymbol{b} = \boldsymbol{0}$ (or both) or $\boldsymbol{a}$ is perpendicular to $\boldsymbol{b}$.

7 If $\boldsymbol{a}\cdot\boldsymbol{b}=\boldsymbol{a}\cdot\boldsymbol{c}$ so that $\boldsymbol{a}\cdot(\boldsymbol{b}-\boldsymbol{c})=0$ then either $\boldsymbol{a}=\boldsymbol{0}$, or $\boldsymbol{b}-\boldsymbol{c}=\boldsymbol{0}\Rightarrow\boldsymbol{b}=\boldsymbol{c}$ or $\boldsymbol{a}$ is perpendicular to $(\boldsymbol{b}-\boldsymbol{c})$.

These properties may easily be verified, in a particular case, taking

$$\boldsymbol{a}=\begin{pmatrix}2\\1\end{pmatrix},\qquad \boldsymbol{b}=\begin{pmatrix}-1\\3\end{pmatrix},\qquad \boldsymbol{c}=\begin{pmatrix}0\\-2\end{pmatrix},\qquad \lambda=5$$

or established in general taking

$$\boldsymbol{a}=\begin{pmatrix}a_1\\a_2\end{pmatrix},\qquad \boldsymbol{b}=\begin{pmatrix}b_1\\b_2\end{pmatrix},\qquad \boldsymbol{c}=\begin{pmatrix}c_1\\c_2\end{pmatrix}$$

For example

$$\boldsymbol{a}\cdot\boldsymbol{b}=\begin{pmatrix}2\\1\end{pmatrix}\cdot\begin{pmatrix}-1\\3\end{pmatrix}=-2+3=1\qquad \boldsymbol{a}\cdot\boldsymbol{b}=\begin{pmatrix}a_1\\a_2\end{pmatrix}\cdot\begin{pmatrix}b_1\\b_2\end{pmatrix}=a_1b_1+a_2b_2$$

$$\boldsymbol{b}\cdot\boldsymbol{a}=\begin{pmatrix}-1\\3\end{pmatrix}\cdot\begin{pmatrix}2\\1\end{pmatrix}=-2+3=1\qquad \boldsymbol{b}\cdot\boldsymbol{a}=\begin{pmatrix}b_1\\b_2\end{pmatrix}\cdot\begin{pmatrix}a_1\\a_2\end{pmatrix}=b_1a_1+b_2a_2$$

$$\boldsymbol{a}\cdot\boldsymbol{b}=\boldsymbol{b}\cdot\boldsymbol{a}$$

$$\boldsymbol{a}\cdot(\boldsymbol{b}+\boldsymbol{c})=\begin{pmatrix}2\\1\end{pmatrix}\cdot\begin{pmatrix}-1+0\\3-2\end{pmatrix}=-2+1=-1\qquad \boldsymbol{a}\cdot(\boldsymbol{b}+\boldsymbol{c})=\begin{pmatrix}a_1\\a_2\end{pmatrix}\cdot\begin{pmatrix}b_1+c_1\\b_2+c_2\end{pmatrix}$$

$$\boldsymbol{a}\cdot\boldsymbol{b}+\boldsymbol{a}\cdot\boldsymbol{c}=\begin{pmatrix}2\\1\end{pmatrix}\cdot\begin{pmatrix}-1\\3\end{pmatrix}+\begin{pmatrix}2\\1\end{pmatrix}\cdot\begin{pmatrix}0\\-2\end{pmatrix}\qquad =a_1(b_1+c_1)+a_2(b_2+c_2)$$

$$=-2+3+0-2=-1\qquad =a_1b_1+a_1c_1+a_2b_2+a_2c_2$$

$$\boldsymbol{a}\cdot\boldsymbol{b}+\boldsymbol{a}\cdot\boldsymbol{c}=\begin{pmatrix}a_1\\a_2\end{pmatrix}\cdot\begin{pmatrix}b_1\\b_2\end{pmatrix}+\begin{pmatrix}a_1\\a_2\end{pmatrix}\cdot\begin{pmatrix}c_1\\c_2\end{pmatrix}$$

$$=a_1b_1+a_2b_2+a_1c_1+a_2c_2$$

$$\boldsymbol{a}\cdot(\boldsymbol{b}+\boldsymbol{c})=\boldsymbol{a}\cdot\boldsymbol{b}+\boldsymbol{a}\cdot\boldsymbol{c}$$

$$(\lambda\boldsymbol{a})\cdot\boldsymbol{b}=\begin{pmatrix}10\\5\end{pmatrix}\cdot\begin{pmatrix}-1\\3\end{pmatrix}\qquad (\lambda\boldsymbol{a})\cdot\boldsymbol{b}=\begin{pmatrix}\lambda a_1\\\lambda a_2\end{pmatrix}\cdot\begin{pmatrix}b_1\\b_2\end{pmatrix}$$

$$=-10+15=5\qquad =\lambda a_1b_1+\lambda a_2b_2$$

$$=\lambda(a_1b_1+a_2b_2)$$

$$\boldsymbol{a}\cdot(\lambda\boldsymbol{b})=\begin{pmatrix}2\\1\end{pmatrix}\cdot\begin{pmatrix}-5\\15\end{pmatrix}\qquad \boldsymbol{a}\cdot(\lambda\boldsymbol{b})=\begin{pmatrix}a_1\\a_2\end{pmatrix}\cdot\begin{pmatrix}\lambda b_1\\\lambda b_2\end{pmatrix}$$

$$=-10+15=5\qquad =a_1\lambda b_1+a_2\lambda b_2$$

$$=\lambda(a_1b_1+a_2b_2)$$

$$\lambda(\boldsymbol{a}\cdot\boldsymbol{b})=5\begin{pmatrix}2\\1\end{pmatrix}\cdot\begin{pmatrix}-1\\3\end{pmatrix}\qquad \lambda(\boldsymbol{a}\cdot\boldsymbol{b})=\lambda\begin{pmatrix}a_1\\a_2\end{pmatrix}\cdot\begin{pmatrix}b_1\\b_2\end{pmatrix}$$

$$=5(-2+3)=5\qquad =\lambda(a_1b_1+a_2b_2)$$

$$(\lambda\boldsymbol{a})\cdot\boldsymbol{b}=\boldsymbol{a}\cdot(\lambda\boldsymbol{b})=\lambda(\boldsymbol{a}\cdot\boldsymbol{b})$$

There are several more important results involving the scalar product:

8 $|\boldsymbol{a}+\boldsymbol{b}|^2 = |\boldsymbol{a}|^2+|\boldsymbol{b}|^2+2\boldsymbol{a}\cdot\boldsymbol{b}$

9 $|\boldsymbol{a}-\boldsymbol{b}|^2 = |\boldsymbol{a}|^2+|\boldsymbol{b}|^2-2\boldsymbol{a}\cdot\boldsymbol{b}$

10 $(\boldsymbol{a}+\boldsymbol{b})\cdot(\boldsymbol{a}-\boldsymbol{b}) = |\boldsymbol{a}|^2-|\boldsymbol{b}|^2 - a^2-b^2$.

11 The length of the projection of $\boldsymbol{a}$ on $\boldsymbol{b}$ is $\dfrac{\boldsymbol{a}\cdot\boldsymbol{b}}{|\boldsymbol{b}|}$.

Exercise 2.3

1 Verify the results **8** to **11** (above) taking

(a) $\boldsymbol{a} = \begin{pmatrix}3\\4\end{pmatrix}$, $\boldsymbol{b} = \begin{pmatrix}-2\\3\end{pmatrix}$ and **(b)** $\boldsymbol{a} = \begin{pmatrix}a_1\\a_2\end{pmatrix}$, $\boldsymbol{b} = \begin{pmatrix}b_1\\b_2\end{pmatrix}$.

2 Taking

$\boldsymbol{a} = \begin{pmatrix}1\\2\end{pmatrix}$, $\boldsymbol{b} = \begin{pmatrix}3\\1\end{pmatrix}$, $\boldsymbol{c} = \begin{pmatrix}-1\\1\end{pmatrix}$, $\boldsymbol{d} = \begin{pmatrix}2\\3\end{pmatrix}$

show that

(a) $(\boldsymbol{a}+\boldsymbol{b})\cdot(\boldsymbol{c}+\boldsymbol{d}) = \boldsymbol{a}\cdot\boldsymbol{c}+\boldsymbol{a}\cdot\boldsymbol{d}+\boldsymbol{b}\cdot\boldsymbol{c}+\boldsymbol{b}\cdot\boldsymbol{d}$.

(b) $(\boldsymbol{c}+\boldsymbol{d})\cdot(\boldsymbol{c}+\boldsymbol{d}) = |\boldsymbol{c}|^2+|\boldsymbol{d}|^2+2\boldsymbol{c}\cdot\boldsymbol{d}$.

3 The position vectors of the vertices OAB of a triangle are $\boldsymbol{0}$, $\boldsymbol{a}$, $\boldsymbol{b}$. Show that the area, Δ, of the triangle is given by

$$4\Delta^2 = |\boldsymbol{a}|^2\times|\boldsymbol{b}|^2-(\boldsymbol{a}\cdot\boldsymbol{b})^2$$

Hence find the area of the triangle whose vertices are (1, 1), (1, 3), (3, −1). Sketch the triangle and check your answer.

3 Vectors applied to geometry

3.1 Vector addition and geometry

Many geometrical facts can be stated in vector terms and vector addition can be used to prove several geometrical theorems. It is helpful sometimes to consider a special case first.

Parallelogram

We start again with the parallelogram PQRS, with position vectors $\boldsymbol{p}$, $\boldsymbol{q}$, $\boldsymbol{r}$, $\boldsymbol{s}$ and 0 outside the parallelogram.

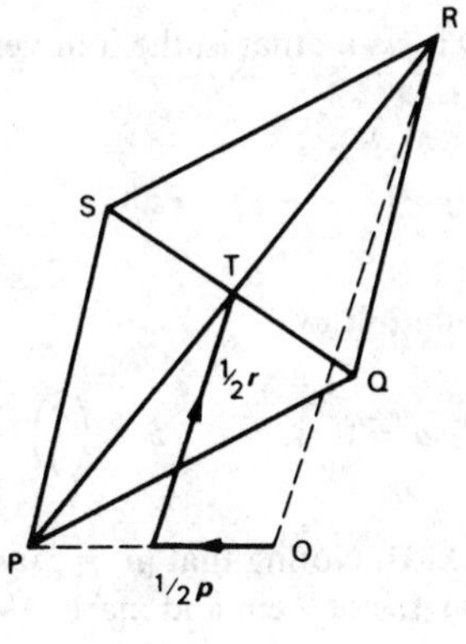

Since PS and QR are equal in length and are parallel, they represent equal free vectors. But $\boldsymbol{PS} = -\boldsymbol{p}+\boldsymbol{s}$ and $\boldsymbol{QR} = -\boldsymbol{q}+\boldsymbol{r}$, so

$$-\boldsymbol{p}+\boldsymbol{s} = -\boldsymbol{q}+\boldsymbol{r},$$

and, adding $\boldsymbol{p}+\boldsymbol{q}$ to both sides,

$$-\boldsymbol{p}+\boldsymbol{p}+\boldsymbol{q}+\boldsymbol{s} = -\boldsymbol{q}+\boldsymbol{q}+\boldsymbol{p}+\boldsymbol{r}$$

$$\boldsymbol{q}+\boldsymbol{s} = \boldsymbol{p}+\boldsymbol{r} = \boldsymbol{u} \text{ say}$$

This is the condition for PQRS to be a parallelogram. Notice that

$$\boldsymbol{OT} = \boldsymbol{t} = \tfrac{1}{2}\boldsymbol{u} = \tfrac{1}{2}(\boldsymbol{p}+\boldsymbol{r}) = \tfrac{1}{2}(\boldsymbol{q}+\boldsymbol{s})$$

Quadrilateral

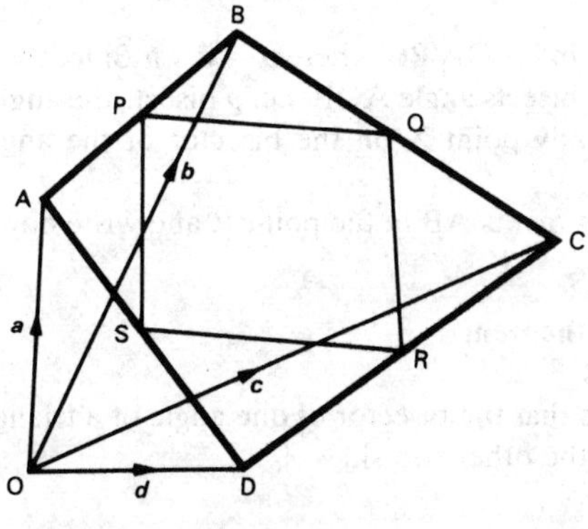

Consider the quadrilateral A, B, C, D given by position vectors $\boldsymbol{a}, \boldsymbol{b}, \boldsymbol{c}, \boldsymbol{d}$ with P, Q, R, S as the midpoints of its sides.

$$\boldsymbol{p} = \tfrac{1}{2}(\boldsymbol{a}+\boldsymbol{b}), \quad \boldsymbol{q} = \tfrac{1}{2}(\boldsymbol{b}+\boldsymbol{c}), \quad \boldsymbol{r} = \tfrac{1}{2}(\boldsymbol{c}+\boldsymbol{d}), \quad \boldsymbol{s} = \tfrac{1}{2}(\boldsymbol{d}+\boldsymbol{a}).$$

Thus $\qquad \boldsymbol{p}+\boldsymbol{r} = \boldsymbol{q}+\boldsymbol{s} \quad$ or $\quad -\boldsymbol{p}+\boldsymbol{s} = -\boldsymbol{q}+\boldsymbol{r}$

and PQRS is a parallelogram.

This is true even if ABCD is *skew*; that is, the four vertices of the quadrilateral do not lie in a plane.

Rhombus

Taking a scale of 2 cm to 1 unit, draw

$$\boldsymbol{a} = \begin{pmatrix} 3 \\ 4 \end{pmatrix}, \qquad \boldsymbol{b} = \begin{pmatrix} 3 \\ 0 \end{pmatrix}$$

and complete the triangle OAB. Noting that $|\boldsymbol{a}| = 5$ and $|\boldsymbol{b}| = 3$, mark each of the vectors $\boldsymbol{a}$ and $\boldsymbol{b}$ into unit lengths of 2 cm and mark A' where $\hat{\boldsymbol{a}} = \frac{1}{5}\boldsymbol{a}$ and B' where $\hat{\boldsymbol{b}} = \frac{1}{3}\boldsymbol{b}$.

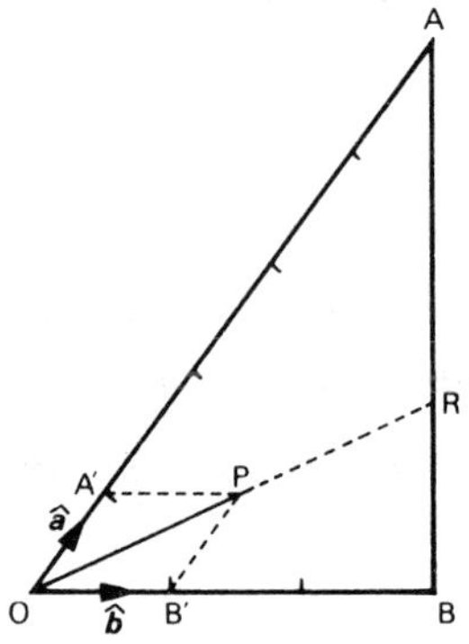

Complete the rhombus OA'PB' where $\boldsymbol{p} = \hat{\boldsymbol{a}} + \hat{\boldsymbol{b}}$. Since the diagonals of a rhombus bisect its angles OP bisects angle AOB, i.e. $\boldsymbol{p}$ bisects the angle between $\boldsymbol{a}$ and $\boldsymbol{b}$. The position vector of any point X on the bisector of the angle between $\boldsymbol{a}$ and $\boldsymbol{b}$ is $\boldsymbol{x} = \lambda(\hat{\boldsymbol{a}} + \hat{\boldsymbol{b}})$.

Produce OP till it meets AB in the point R and write down the ratio of AR : RB.

The angle bisector theorem

This theorem states that the bisector of one angle of a triangle divides the opposite side in the ratio of the other two sides.

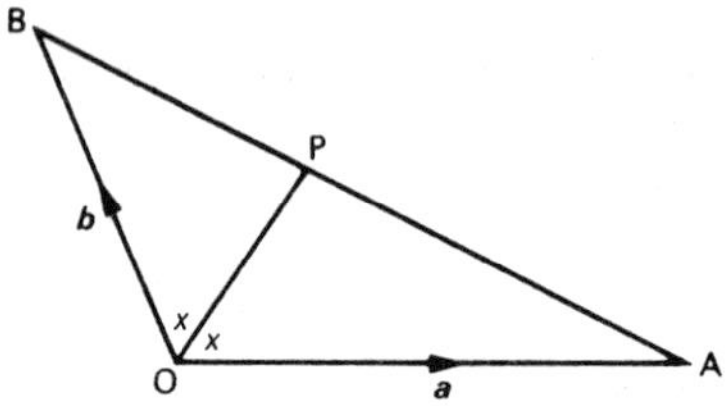

To prove this we have to show that

$$AP:PB = OA:OB = |\boldsymbol{a}|:|\boldsymbol{b}|$$

Now
$$\boldsymbol{p} = \lambda(\hat{\boldsymbol{a}} + \hat{\boldsymbol{b}}) = \lambda\left[\frac{\boldsymbol{a}}{|\boldsymbol{a}|} + \frac{\boldsymbol{b}}{|\boldsymbol{b}|}\right] \tag{1}$$

But if P divides AB in the ratio $l:m$, by the section formula

$$\boldsymbol{p} = \frac{m\boldsymbol{a} + l\boldsymbol{b}}{l+m} = \frac{m\boldsymbol{a}}{l+m} + \frac{l\boldsymbol{b}}{l+m} \tag{2}$$

Since $\boldsymbol{p}$ is a unique combination of $\boldsymbol{a}$ and $\boldsymbol{b}$, the coefficients of $\boldsymbol{a}$ in (1) and (2) must be equal and so must be those of $\boldsymbol{b}$.

Equating coefficients of $\boldsymbol{a}$,

$$\frac{\lambda}{|\boldsymbol{a}|} = \frac{m}{l+m}$$

and of $\boldsymbol{b}$
$$\frac{\lambda}{|\boldsymbol{b}|} = \frac{l}{l+m}$$

Hence
$$\lambda(l+m) = m|\boldsymbol{a}| = l|\boldsymbol{b}|$$

so
$$\frac{l}{m} = \frac{|\boldsymbol{a}|}{|\boldsymbol{b}|} \quad \text{or} \quad \frac{AP}{PB} = \frac{OA}{OB}$$

Exercise 3.1

1 Given the parallelogram PQRS with

$$\boldsymbol{p} = \begin{pmatrix}-4\\2\end{pmatrix} \quad \boldsymbol{q} = \begin{pmatrix}2\\4\end{pmatrix} \quad \boldsymbol{s} = \begin{pmatrix}-2\\6\end{pmatrix}$$

(a) Find $\boldsymbol{r}$.

(b) Write down the vector equations of ***PR*** and ***QS*** (i) in column vector form, and (ii) as a combination of $\boldsymbol{p}, \boldsymbol{q}, \boldsymbol{r}, \boldsymbol{s}$.

(c) Write down the position vector of the point of intersection of the diagonals.

(d) Write down the position vector of the point dividing SR in the ratio 2:1.

2 A quadrilateral ABCD has

$$\boldsymbol{a} = \begin{pmatrix}-5\\3\end{pmatrix} \quad \boldsymbol{b} = \begin{pmatrix}-1\\7\end{pmatrix} \quad \boldsymbol{c} = \begin{pmatrix}3\\5\end{pmatrix} \quad \boldsymbol{d} = \begin{pmatrix}3\\3\end{pmatrix}$$

The midpoints of AB, BC, CD, DA are L, M, N, P respectively.

(a) Show that LMNP is a parallelogram.

(b) Write down the position vector of T, the point of intersection of the diagonals (i) in column vector form, and (ii) as a combination of the vectors $\boldsymbol{a}, \boldsymbol{b}, \boldsymbol{c}, \boldsymbol{d}$.

(c) Find the vector equations of the lines LN and PM, in column vector form.

3 A, B have position vectors

$$\boldsymbol{a} = \begin{pmatrix}2\\-2\end{pmatrix} \quad \boldsymbol{b} = \begin{pmatrix}7\\1\end{pmatrix}$$

(a) Find unit vectors in the directions of the bisectors of the acute and obtuse angles between $\boldsymbol{a}$ and $\boldsymbol{b}$.

(b) The bisector of the acute angle intersects the line AB at K. Find AK:KB. Illustrate this with a diagram.

(c) Write down the vector equation of the line OK.

3.2 Centroid and orthocentre

The medians of a triangle

These are the lines joining each vertex to the mid-point of the opposite side. We take a special case first.

(1) On graph paper draw triangle ABC with

$$\boldsymbol{a} = \begin{pmatrix} 6 \\ -4 \end{pmatrix} \qquad \boldsymbol{b} = \begin{pmatrix} 8 \\ 10 \end{pmatrix} \qquad \boldsymbol{c} = \begin{pmatrix} -2 \\ 6 \end{pmatrix}$$

(2) If D, E are the midpoints of AB, BC, join CD, AE and let them intersect at G.

(3) From your drawing write down the position vector $\boldsymbol{g}$.

(4) Draw the vector route $\frac{1}{3}\boldsymbol{a} + \frac{1}{3}\boldsymbol{b} + \frac{1}{3}\boldsymbol{c}$ and hence write down $\boldsymbol{g}$ in terms of $\boldsymbol{a}$, $\boldsymbol{b}$ and $\boldsymbol{c}$.

(5) Verify that if BG produced cuts AC at F, then F is the mid-point of AC.

(6) Verify that AG:GE = BG:GF = CG:GD = 2:1.

In general

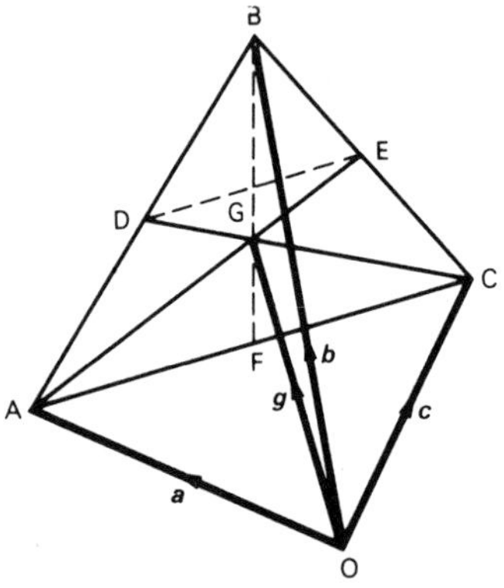

We have to find $\boldsymbol{g}$, where G is the point of intersection of the medians AE and CD.

Now
$$\boldsymbol{d} = \tfrac{1}{2}(\boldsymbol{a}+\boldsymbol{b}) \qquad \text{and} \qquad \boldsymbol{e} = \tfrac{1}{2}(\boldsymbol{b}+\boldsymbol{c})$$

So
$$\boldsymbol{DE} = -\boldsymbol{d}+\boldsymbol{e} = \tfrac{1}{2}(-\boldsymbol{a}+\boldsymbol{c})$$

But
$$\boldsymbol{AC} = -\boldsymbol{a}+\boldsymbol{c} \qquad \text{so} \qquad \boldsymbol{AC} = 2\boldsymbol{DE}$$

Since Δs ACG, EDG are similar
$$|\boldsymbol{AG}| = 2|\boldsymbol{GE}|$$

so
$$\boldsymbol{AG} = \tfrac{2}{3}(\boldsymbol{AE}) = \tfrac{2}{3}[-\boldsymbol{a}+\tfrac{1}{2}(\boldsymbol{b}+\boldsymbol{c})]$$

and
$$\boldsymbol{g} = \boldsymbol{a}+\boldsymbol{AG} = \boldsymbol{a}+\tfrac{2}{3}[-\boldsymbol{a}+\tfrac{1}{2}(\boldsymbol{b}+\boldsymbol{c})]$$

$$\boldsymbol{g} = \tfrac{1}{3}(\boldsymbol{a}+\boldsymbol{b}+\boldsymbol{c})$$

This expression is symmetrical in $\boldsymbol{a}$, $\boldsymbol{b}$ and $\boldsymbol{c}$ for if we interchange $\boldsymbol{a}$, $\boldsymbol{b}$, $\boldsymbol{c}$ the expression is unchanged. This means we could equally well have considered the third median BF, which will also pass through G with BG:GF = 2:1.

The point of intersection of the medians of a triangle is called the *centroid* of the triangle. The idea of symmetry in a vector expression is frequently used in this way.

The altitudes of a triangle

These are the lines drawn through each vertex, perpendicular to the opposite side. Again we take a special case first.

(1) Draw triangle ABC where

$$\boldsymbol{a} = \begin{pmatrix} -4 \\ -3 \end{pmatrix} \qquad \boldsymbol{b} = \begin{pmatrix} 3 \\ -4 \end{pmatrix} \qquad \boldsymbol{c} = \begin{pmatrix} 3 \\ 4 \end{pmatrix}$$

(2) With O as the centre, and radius 5 units, draw in the circle through A, B, and C. (Note that $|\boldsymbol{a}| = |\boldsymbol{b}| = |\boldsymbol{c}| = 5$).

(3) Complete the rhombus, OATB. (Note that OT is the perpendicular bisector of AB.)

(4) Complete the parallelogram, OTHC.

(5) Produce CH to meet AB in X, and note that CX∥OT, and OT ⊥ AB therefore CX is an altitude of the triangle.

(6) What is the position vector of H in terms of $\boldsymbol{a}$, $\boldsymbol{b}$ and $\boldsymbol{c}$?

(7) Similarly, complete rhombus OBSC and parallelogram OSJA and note that H and J coincide, and that AJ produced to meet BC in Y is also an altitude of the triangle.

(8) In a similar fashion, construct BZ, the third altitude.

In general

We can show that the altitudes of a triangle intersect at a point by taking as origin the centre of the circumcircle of the triangle.

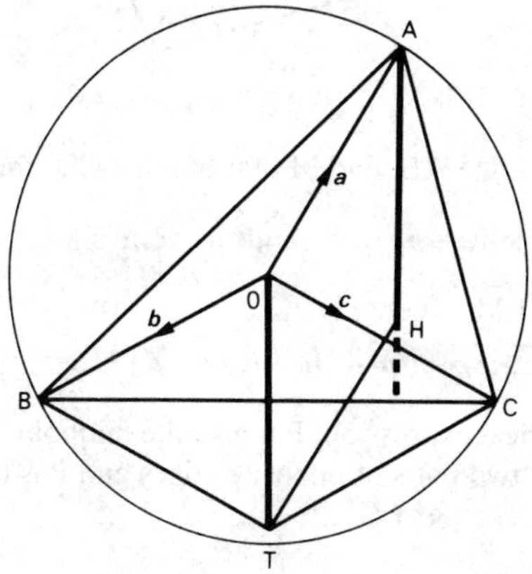

Since OA = OB = OC,

$$|\boldsymbol{a}| = |\boldsymbol{b}| = |\boldsymbol{c}|$$

Complete the rhombus OBTC so that $\boldsymbol{t} = \boldsymbol{b} + \boldsymbol{c}$ and OT ⊥ BC. Complete the parallelogram OTHA so that $\boldsymbol{h} = \boldsymbol{a} + \boldsymbol{t} = \boldsymbol{a} + \boldsymbol{b} + \boldsymbol{c}$. Now

$$\text{AH} \| \text{OT} \qquad \text{and} \qquad \text{OT} \perp \text{BC} \Rightarrow \text{AH} \perp \text{BC}$$

If AH is produced to meet BC in X, then AX is an altitude of the triangle.

But $\boldsymbol{h} = \boldsymbol{a} + \boldsymbol{b} + \boldsymbol{c}$ is symmetrical in $\boldsymbol{a}$, $\boldsymbol{b}$, $\boldsymbol{c}$ therefore H also lies on the other two altitudes BY and CZ, as similar constructions will show. The altitudes of a triangle therefore intersect in a point called the *orthocentre* of the triangle.

When the origin is the circumcentre, $\boldsymbol{h} = \boldsymbol{a} + \boldsymbol{b} + \boldsymbol{c}$, and the position vector of the centroid is $\boldsymbol{g} = \frac{1}{3}(\boldsymbol{a} + \boldsymbol{b} + \boldsymbol{c})$ (whatever the origin). This means that the circumcentre, the centroid and the orthocentre lie in the same straight line, with OG = $\frac{1}{3}$OH.

A more elegant proof of the intersection of the altitudes involves the dot product (page 296).

The centroid of a tetrahedron

The midpoint of the line AB has position vector $\boldsymbol{m} = \frac{1}{2}(\boldsymbol{a} + \boldsymbol{b})$. The centroid of the triangle ABC has position vector $\boldsymbol{g} = \frac{1}{3}(\boldsymbol{a} + \boldsymbol{b} + \boldsymbol{c})$. Can we go one step further into three-dimensional space?

Consider the tetrahedron ABCD:

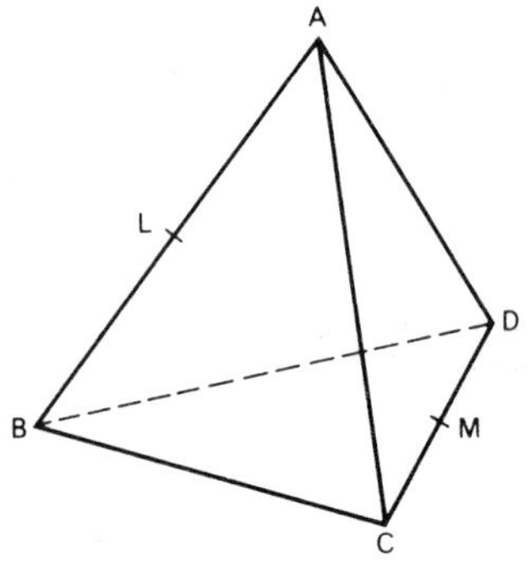

If L is the midpoint of edge AB, and M that of edge CD, then

$$\boldsymbol{l} = \tfrac{1}{2}(\boldsymbol{a} + \boldsymbol{b}) \qquad \text{and} \qquad \boldsymbol{m} = \tfrac{1}{2}(\boldsymbol{c} + \boldsymbol{d})$$

If P is the midpoint of LM,

$$\boldsymbol{p} = \tfrac{1}{4}(\boldsymbol{a} + \boldsymbol{b} + \boldsymbol{c} + \boldsymbol{d})$$

Since this is a symmetrical expression, P is also the midpoint of the lines joining the midpoints of the other two pairs of opposite edges and P is thus the centroid of the tetrahedron.

Exercise 3.2

1 In a triangle ABC, the midpoints of BC, CA, AB are O, P, Q, respectively. Express $\boldsymbol{OA}+\boldsymbol{OC}$ in terms of $\boldsymbol{OP}$ and show that $\boldsymbol{OA}-\boldsymbol{OC} = 2\boldsymbol{OQ}$.

2 The position vectors of P, Q, R, S are respectively $\boldsymbol{p}$, $\boldsymbol{q}$, $3\boldsymbol{p}+\boldsymbol{q}$, $-\boldsymbol{p}+2\boldsymbol{q}$.

(a) Express in terms of $\boldsymbol{p}$ and $\boldsymbol{q}$ the vectors $\boldsymbol{PQ}$, $\boldsymbol{PR}$, $\boldsymbol{PS}$, $\boldsymbol{QR}$, $\boldsymbol{QS}$ and $\boldsymbol{RS}$.

(b) Find also the position vectors of the midpoints of the segments PQ, QR, RS and SP.

(c) Find the position vectors of the centroids of the triangles PQR, PRS and QRS.

3 ABCD is a parallelogram, and $\boldsymbol{a}$, $\boldsymbol{b}$, $\boldsymbol{c}$ are the position vectors of A, B, C related to O inside the parallelogram.

(a) What is the position vector of D?

(b) Show that $\boldsymbol{OA}+\boldsymbol{OC} = \boldsymbol{OB}+\boldsymbol{OD}$.

4 If P, Q and R are the midpoints of BC, CA, AB respectively and O is any point, show that:

(a) $\boldsymbol{OA}+\boldsymbol{OB}+\boldsymbol{OC} = \boldsymbol{OP}+\boldsymbol{OQ}+\boldsymbol{OR}$

(b) $\boldsymbol{AP}+\boldsymbol{BQ}+\boldsymbol{CR} = \boldsymbol{0}$

5 LMN, L′M′N′ are two triangles and G, G′ their centroids. Prove that $\boldsymbol{LL}'+\boldsymbol{MM}'+\boldsymbol{NN}' = 3\boldsymbol{GG}'$.

6 Six points A, B, C, D, E, F are given (which may be in the plane or in space). P, Q, R, S are the centroids of triangles ABC, ABD, DEF, CEF. Show that P, Q, R, S are the vertices of a parallelogram.

7 If $\boldsymbol{a}$, $\boldsymbol{b}$, $\boldsymbol{c}$ are the position vectors of three vertices A, B, C of the regular hexagon ABCDEF, find the position vectors of the remaining three vertices in terms of $\boldsymbol{a}$, $\boldsymbol{b}$, $\boldsymbol{c}$. (Do *not* take O at the centre of the hexagon.)

3.3 The scalar product and geometry

The scalar product

$$\boldsymbol{a}\cdot\boldsymbol{b} = |\boldsymbol{a}||\boldsymbol{b}|\cos\theta = ab\cos\theta$$

is of great importance in geometric proofs since it enables some properties of the figures to be expressed very concisely. For example, if OA is perpendicular to OB, then $\boldsymbol{a}\cdot\boldsymbol{b} = 0$, or if OA = OB so that $|\boldsymbol{a}| = |\boldsymbol{b}| = a$, then $\boldsymbol{a}\cdot\boldsymbol{b} = a^2\cos\theta$.

NOTE ON VECTOR NOTATION

In most of our work so far, the symbol $\boldsymbol{a}$ has been used to represent the position vector $\boldsymbol{OA}$ or any other representative of the equivalence class of free vectors equal to $\boldsymbol{OA}$, and similarly $\boldsymbol{b}$ represents $\boldsymbol{OB}$. Any other vector in the plane (or in space) can be expressed in terms of two (or three) such vectors; for example, $\boldsymbol{AB} = -\boldsymbol{a}+\boldsymbol{b}$. It is often less cumbersome, however—particularly in the application of vector methods to geometry—to use a single letter for each line in the figure; for example, to let $\boldsymbol{c}$ represent $\boldsymbol{AB}$. It is also convenient, for reasons of symmetry, to let the vectors 'follow' each other around the figure, as in the diagram below.

It is important to realize that if a triangle is lettered according to the usual convention (as in the diagram on page 294), with the same letter for an angle and its *opposite* side, then $\boldsymbol{a}$, $\boldsymbol{b}$ and $\boldsymbol{c}$ do *not* represent the position vectors of A, B and C, and $\boldsymbol{b} = \boldsymbol{AC}$ is *not* equal to $-\boldsymbol{a}+\boldsymbol{c}$. We shall assume, however, that unless $\boldsymbol{a}, \boldsymbol{b}, \boldsymbol{c} \ldots$ are differently defined (as they are on page 294, where $\boldsymbol{a} = \boldsymbol{CB}$, $\boldsymbol{b} = \boldsymbol{AC}$ and $\boldsymbol{c} = \boldsymbol{AB}$) then $\boldsymbol{a}$, $\boldsymbol{b}$ and $\boldsymbol{c}$ *do* represent the position vectors of A, B and C relative to some origin, which if not marked in the diagram can be *anywhere.*

Properties of some common figures

Equilateral triangle

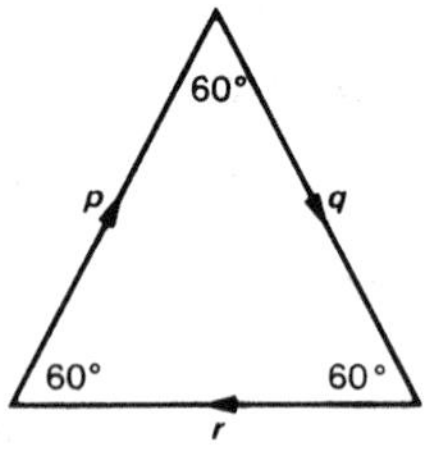

$$|\boldsymbol{p}\cdot\boldsymbol{q}| = |\boldsymbol{q}\cdot\boldsymbol{r}| = |\boldsymbol{r}\cdot\boldsymbol{p}| = \tfrac{1}{2}|\boldsymbol{p}|^2 \qquad (\text{since } \cos 60° = \tfrac{1}{2})$$

Isosceles triangle

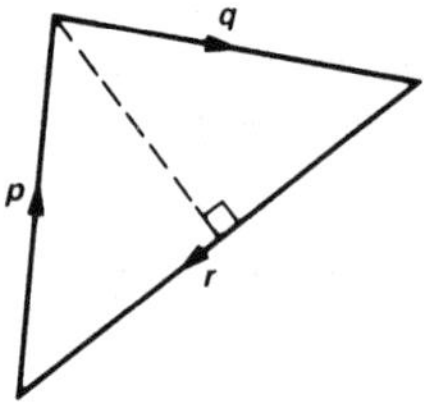

$$|\boldsymbol{p}\cdot\boldsymbol{r}| = |\boldsymbol{q}\cdot\boldsymbol{r}| \neq |\boldsymbol{p}\cdot\boldsymbol{q}|$$

Rhombus

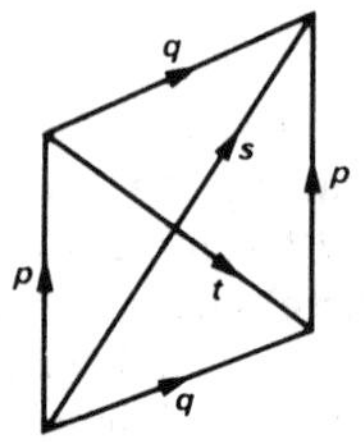

$$|\boldsymbol{p}| = |\boldsymbol{q}| \qquad \text{and} \qquad \boldsymbol{s}\cdot\boldsymbol{t} = 0$$

Orthocentre of a triangle

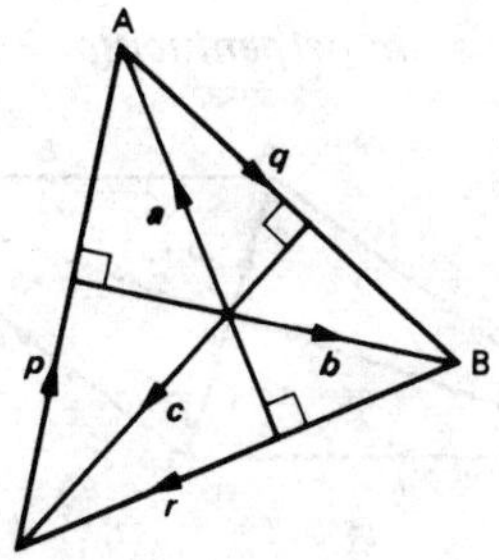

$$a \cdot r = b \cdot p = c \cdot q = 0$$

Right pyramid

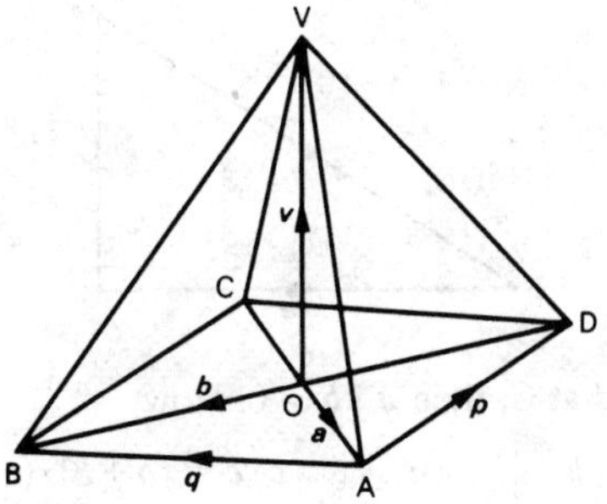

$$v \cdot a = v \cdot b = v \cdot c = v \cdot d = 0$$

'Corner' of a cube

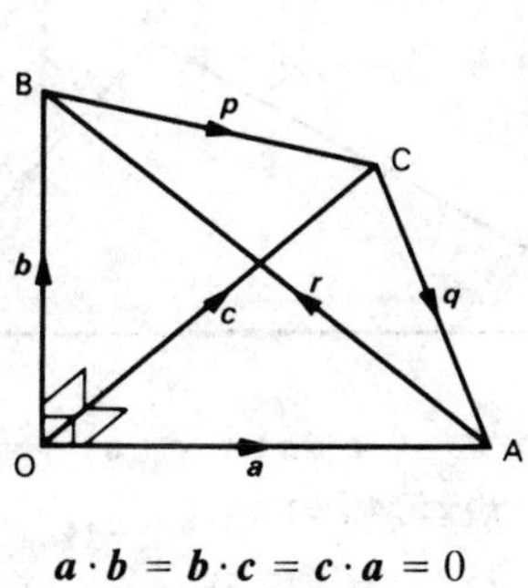

$$a \cdot b = b \cdot c = c \cdot a = 0$$

Vectors $\boldsymbol{a}$, $\boldsymbol{b}$ and $\boldsymbol{c}$ are described as being *mutually orthogonal.*

Standard geometric proofs

The diagonals of a rhombus are perpendicular

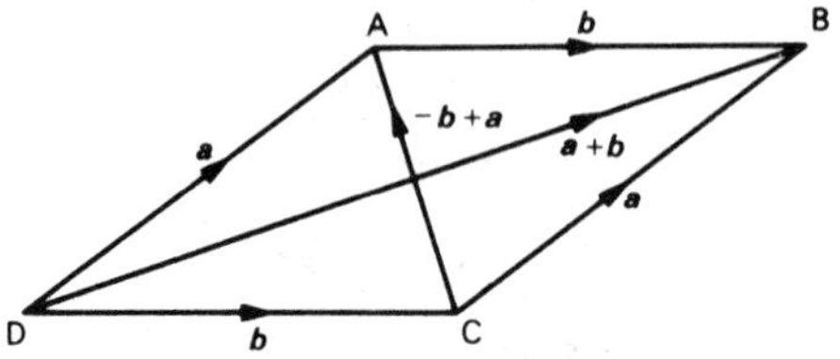

If ABCD is a rhombus, then $|\boldsymbol{a}| = |\boldsymbol{b}|$ or $a = b$. One diagonal is $\boldsymbol{a}+\boldsymbol{b}$, whilst the other is $-\boldsymbol{b}+\boldsymbol{a} = \boldsymbol{a}-\boldsymbol{b}$. Now

$$(\boldsymbol{a}+\boldsymbol{b}) \cdot (\boldsymbol{a}-\boldsymbol{b}) = a^2 - b^2 = 0$$

Hence the diagonals are perpendicular.

The theorem of Pythagoras

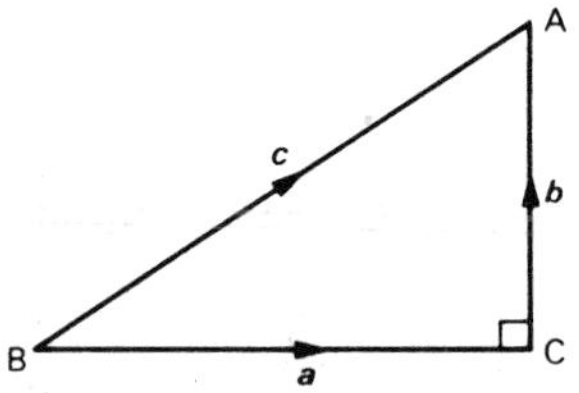

If $\triangle$ABC is right angled at C, then $\boldsymbol{a} \cdot \boldsymbol{b} = 0$. Now

$$\boldsymbol{c} = \boldsymbol{a}+\boldsymbol{b} \qquad \text{so} \qquad \boldsymbol{c}\cdot\boldsymbol{c} = (\boldsymbol{a}+\boldsymbol{b})\cdot(\boldsymbol{a}+\boldsymbol{b})$$

$$c^2 = a^2 + b^2 + 2\boldsymbol{a}\cdot\boldsymbol{b}$$

$$c^2 = a^2 + b^2$$

The cosine formula

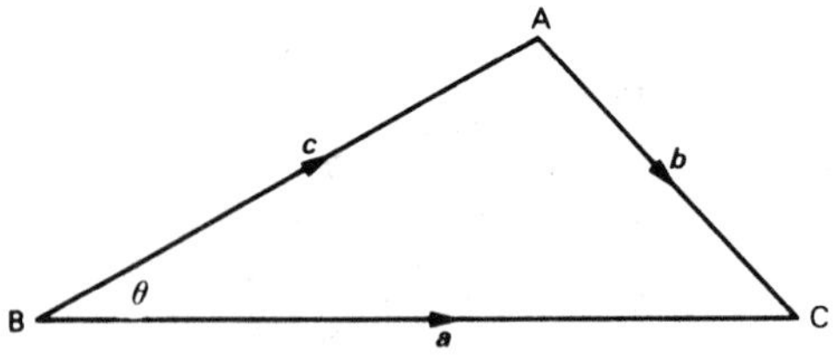

$$\boldsymbol{b} = -\boldsymbol{c}+\boldsymbol{a} \qquad \text{so} \qquad \boldsymbol{b}\cdot\boldsymbol{b} = (-\boldsymbol{c}+\boldsymbol{a})\cdot(-\boldsymbol{c}+\boldsymbol{a})$$

$$b^2 = a^2 + c^2 - \boldsymbol{c}\cdot\boldsymbol{a} - \boldsymbol{a}\cdot\boldsymbol{c}$$

$$b^2 = a^2 + c^2 - 2\boldsymbol{a}\cdot\boldsymbol{c} \quad \text{(scalar product is commutative)}$$

$$b^2 = a^2 + c^2 - 2ac \cos B$$

The sine formula

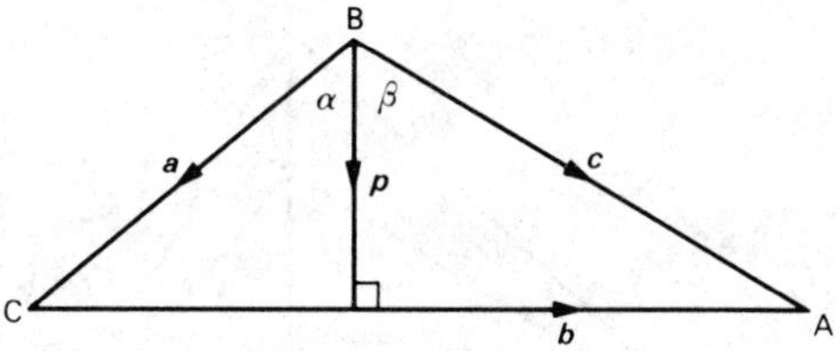

$\boldsymbol{p}$ is perpendicular to $\boldsymbol{b} = -\boldsymbol{a}+\boldsymbol{c}$, so

$$\boldsymbol{p}\cdot(-\boldsymbol{a}+\boldsymbol{c}) = 0$$

$$\boldsymbol{p}\cdot\boldsymbol{c}-\boldsymbol{p}\cdot\boldsymbol{a} = 0$$

$$pc\cos\beta - pa\cos\alpha = 0$$

Thus since $\boldsymbol{p} \neq \boldsymbol{0}$

$$c\sin A - a\sin C = 0$$

$$\frac{a}{\sin A} = \frac{c}{\sin C}$$

Similarly $$\frac{a}{\sin A} = \frac{b}{\sin B} = \frac{c}{\sin C}$$

Apollonius' theorem

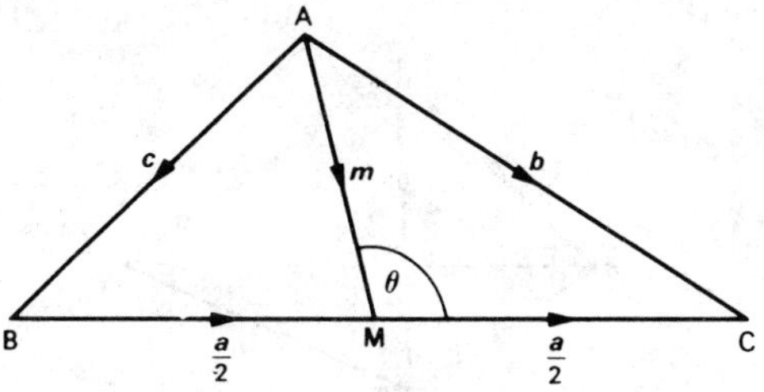

This states that $\quad AC^2+AB^2 = 2AM^2+2BM^2$

In ΔABM $\quad \boldsymbol{c} = \boldsymbol{m}-\tfrac{1}{2}\boldsymbol{a}$

$$\boldsymbol{c}\cdot\boldsymbol{c} = (\boldsymbol{m}-\tfrac{1}{2}\boldsymbol{a})\cdot(\boldsymbol{m}-\tfrac{1}{2}\boldsymbol{a})$$

$$c^2 = m^2+\tfrac{1}{4}a^2-2\times\tfrac{1}{2}\boldsymbol{a}\cdot\boldsymbol{m}$$

$$c^2 = m^2+\tfrac{1}{4}a^2-am\cos\theta \qquad (1)$$

In ΔACM $\quad \boldsymbol{b} = \boldsymbol{m}+\tfrac{1}{2}\boldsymbol{a}$

$$\boldsymbol{b}\cdot\boldsymbol{b} = (\boldsymbol{m}+\tfrac{1}{2}\boldsymbol{a})\cdot(\boldsymbol{m}+\tfrac{1}{2}\boldsymbol{a})$$

$$b^2 = m^2+\tfrac{1}{4}a^2+am\cos\theta \qquad (2)$$

Adding (1) and (2) $\quad b^2+c^2 = 2m^2+2(\tfrac{1}{2}a)^2$

The altitudes of a triangle intersect at one point

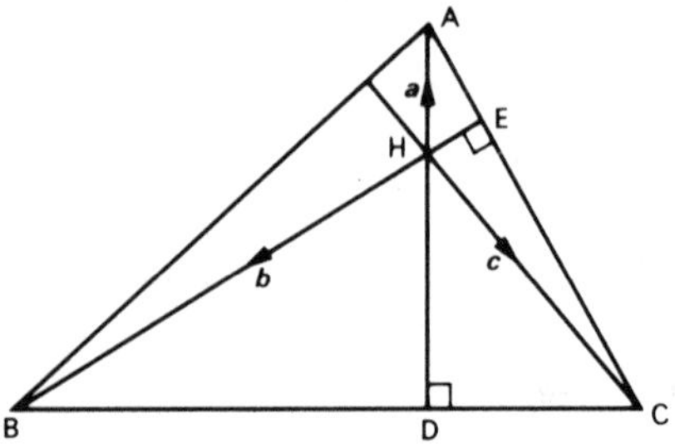

Since AH ⊥ BC $\quad a\cdot(-b+c)=0$

$(a\cdot c)-(a\cdot b)=0 \qquad (1)$

Since BH ⊥ AC $\quad b\cdot(-a+c)=0$

$(b\cdot c)-(b\cdot a)=0 \qquad (2)$

Subtracting (1) from (2), $\quad (b\cdot c)-(a\cdot c)=0$

Hence $\quad c\cdot(-a+b)=0 \quad$ and $\quad$ CH ⊥ AB

Tetrahedron with opposite edges perpendicular

If a tetrahedron has two pairs of mutually perpendicular opposite edges, then the third pair of opposite edges are also mutually perpendicular.

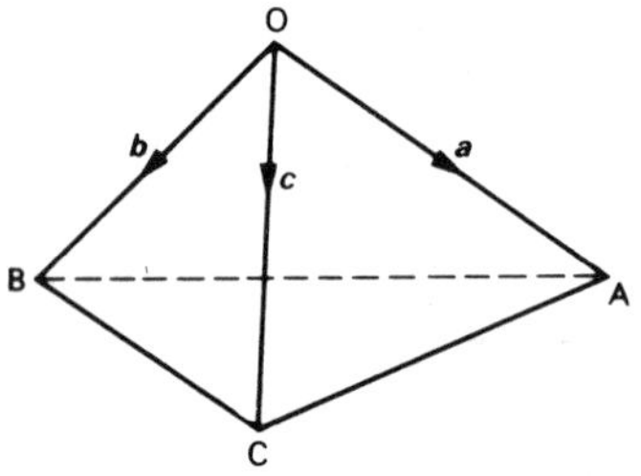

If OA ⊥ BC, then $\quad a\cdot(-b+c)=0 \qquad (1)$

If OB ⊥ AC, then $\quad b\cdot(-a+c)=0 \qquad (2)$

Subtracting (2) from (1), $\quad (a\cdot c)-(b\cdot c)=0$

Hence $\quad c\cdot(-b+a)=0 \quad$ and $\quad$ OC ⊥ AB

Exercise 3.3

1 Prove that, if the sum of the squares of two opposite edges of a tetrahedron is equal to the sum of the squares of another pair of opposite edges, then the remaining pair of opposite edges are perpendicular.

2 Prove that the sum of the squares on the six edges of any tetrahedron is equal to four times the sum of the squares on the three segments joining pairs of midpoints on opposite edges.

3 ABCD is a tetrehedron and G is the centroid of the base BCD. Prove that

$$AB^2 + AC^2 + AD^2 = GB^2 + GC^2 + GD^2 + 3GA^2$$

4 OXYZ is a rhombus of side a; P is any point of OY (or OY produced). Prove that $OP \times YP = XP^2 - a^2$.

5 Use the dot product to prove that the perpendicular bisectors of the sides of a triangle are concurrent.

6 In the quadrilateral ABCD

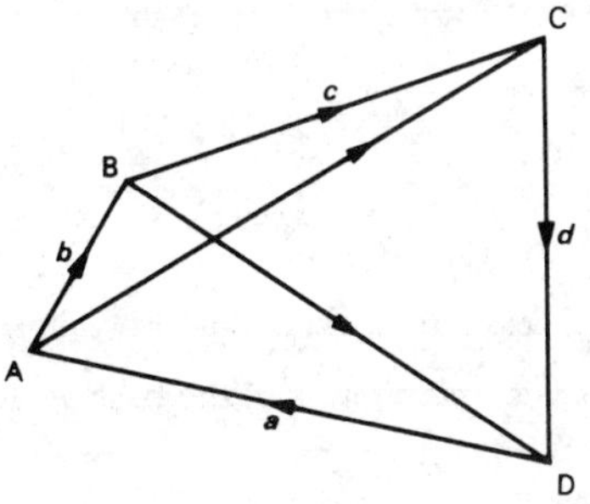

(a) Prove that $\quad \boldsymbol{AC} \cdot \boldsymbol{BD} = (\boldsymbol{AB} \cdot \boldsymbol{CD}) + (\boldsymbol{BC} \cdot \boldsymbol{AD})$

(b) If the quadrilateral is cyclic show that the result reduces to

$$AC \times BD = (AB \times CD) + (BC \times AD)$$

3.4 Solution of geometric problems by vector methods

Example 1

Given three vectors $\boldsymbol{a}$, $\boldsymbol{b}$, $\boldsymbol{c}$, where $|\boldsymbol{a}| = 3$, $|\boldsymbol{b}| = 4$ and $\boldsymbol{c} = 4\boldsymbol{a} + 3\boldsymbol{b}$, show that OC bisects angle AOB and find the position vector $\boldsymbol{r}$ of the point R where OC cuts AB.

(1) Make a reasonably accurate drawing, marking $|\boldsymbol{a}| = 3$, $|\boldsymbol{b}| = 4$ and $\boldsymbol{c} = 4\boldsymbol{a} + 3\boldsymbol{b}$

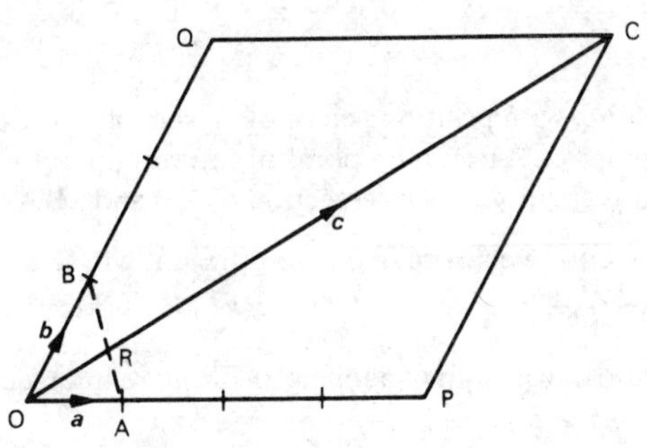

(2) Study the geometry of the figure.

(a) OPCQ is a rhombus, since

$$|\boldsymbol{OP}| = |4\boldsymbol{a}| = 12$$

and

$$|\boldsymbol{OQ}| = |3\boldsymbol{b}| = 12$$

The diagonals of a rhombus bisect its angles, hence OC bisects angle AOB.

(b) Applying the angle bisector theorem

$$\text{AR}:\text{RB} = |\boldsymbol{a}|:|\boldsymbol{b}| = 3:4$$

(3) By the section formula, $\boldsymbol{r} = \frac{4}{7}\boldsymbol{a} + \frac{3}{7}\boldsymbol{b}$.

This simple example suggests a method of attack for other, more difficult problems.

PLAN OF ACTION

Start

(1) Make a reasonably accurate drawing.

(2) Choose an origin (unless already given) and two base vectors (unless given).

(3) Express all obvious vectors in terms of the base vectors.

Geometry

(1) Do we know anything about lengths, ratios etc. from the geometry of the figure?

(2) Do we know anything about the direction of the vectors? Are any perpendicular, or parallel?

(3) Note any collinear points.

Study

(1) Are we trying to fina the ratio in which a line is divided? If so we might use either the section formula or the closed vector route ratio ($l:m:n$ being unique) etc.

(2) Are we trying to find the position vector of a point? If so we might find two vector routes to the point and equate them.

Example 2

Given a square OABC, with position vector of A = $\boldsymbol{a}$, of C = $\boldsymbol{c}$. P is the midpoint of OA, Q is the midpoint of AB; T, the point of intersection of CP and OQ. S is the midpoint of OC. U is the point of intersection of CP and SB.

(1) Express the position vector of T in two different ways.

(2) Hence find OT:OQ and CT:CP.

(3) Deduce the ratio in which the 'medians' of a square intersect. Does this hold for a rectangle?

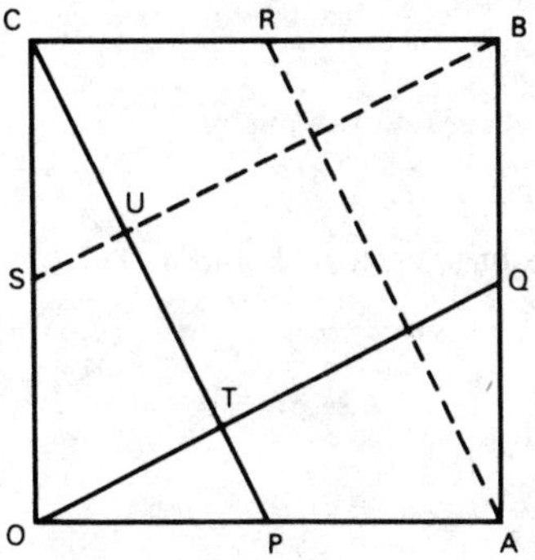

Start

(1) Make a reasonably accurate drawing.

(2) The origin O and $\boldsymbol{a}$, $\boldsymbol{c}$ are given.

Geometry

(1) Properties of a square—equal sides etc.

Study

(1) We have to find position vector of T in two different ways.

(2) Think! (a) Vector routes (b) T lies on OQ. Hence

(i) $\boldsymbol{OT} = \boldsymbol{OC} + \mu\boldsymbol{CP}$ $\quad \boldsymbol{t} = \boldsymbol{c} + \mu(-\boldsymbol{c} + \frac{1}{2}\boldsymbol{a})$.

(ii) $\boldsymbol{OT} = \lambda\boldsymbol{OQ}$, $\quad \boldsymbol{t} = \lambda(\boldsymbol{a} + \frac{1}{2}\boldsymbol{c})$.

Thus $\lambda(\boldsymbol{a} + \frac{1}{2}\boldsymbol{c}) = \boldsymbol{c} + \mu(-\boldsymbol{c} + \frac{1}{2}\boldsymbol{a})$.

Since A, T, C, are not collinear we may compare coefficients of $\boldsymbol{a}$, $\boldsymbol{b}$ and $\boldsymbol{c}$. So $\lambda = \mu/2$ and $\lambda/2 = 1 - \mu$, $\Rightarrow \mu = 4/5$, $\lambda = 2/5$.

$$\text{OT:OQ} = 2:5, \qquad \text{CT:CP} = 4:5$$

We deduce that PT:TU:UC = 1:2:2

(3) How would the proof change if OABC had been a rectangle?

Example 3

Points P, Q are on the sides of the parallelogram ABCD such that AP:PB = DQ:QA = 3:1. If PQ cuts AC at R, find AR:RC using vector methods.

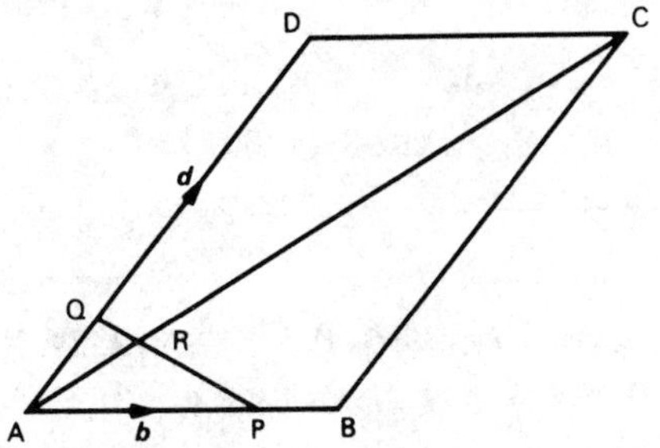

Start

(1) Make a reasonably accurate drawing.

(2) Choose a suitable origin—A.

(3) Choose two suitable base vectors, $\boldsymbol{b}$ and $\boldsymbol{d}$. Then

$$\boldsymbol{p} = \tfrac{3}{4}\boldsymbol{b}, \qquad \boldsymbol{q} = \tfrac{1}{4}\boldsymbol{d}$$

(4) $$\boldsymbol{c} = \lambda\boldsymbol{r} = \boldsymbol{d}+\boldsymbol{b}$$

(5) We require AR:RC.

Geometry

(1) P, Q, R are collinear so if we can find $l\boldsymbol{p}+m\boldsymbol{q}+n\boldsymbol{r} = \boldsymbol{0}$ then $l+m+n = 0$.

Study

(1) Look for a closed vector route in terms of $\boldsymbol{p}$, $\boldsymbol{q}$ and $\boldsymbol{r}$. Now

$$\boldsymbol{c} = \boldsymbol{b}+\boldsymbol{d} = \tfrac{4}{3}\boldsymbol{p}+4\boldsymbol{q} \qquad \text{and} \qquad \boldsymbol{c} = \lambda\boldsymbol{r}$$

Thus $$\lambda\boldsymbol{r} = \tfrac{4}{3}\boldsymbol{p}+4\boldsymbol{q} \qquad \text{or} \qquad \tfrac{4}{3}\boldsymbol{p}+4\boldsymbol{q}-\lambda\boldsymbol{r} = \boldsymbol{0}$$

Now as P, Q, R are collinear

$$\tfrac{4}{3}+4-\lambda = 0$$

$$\lambda = \tfrac{16}{3}$$

Thus $$\text{AR:RC} = 3:13$$

(2) Alternatively, think of the section formula. Suppose QR:RP $= 1:\alpha$ and let $\boldsymbol{c} = \lambda\boldsymbol{r}$. Then

$$\boldsymbol{r} = \frac{\alpha\boldsymbol{q}+1\boldsymbol{p}}{1+\alpha} \qquad \lambda\boldsymbol{r} = \boldsymbol{d}+\boldsymbol{b}$$

$$\boldsymbol{r} = \frac{\frac{\alpha}{4}\boldsymbol{d}+\frac{3}{4}\boldsymbol{b}}{1+\alpha} \qquad \boldsymbol{r} = \frac{\boldsymbol{d}+\boldsymbol{b}}{\lambda}$$

If we equate the coefficients of $\boldsymbol{b}$ and $\boldsymbol{d}$

$$\frac{\alpha}{4} = \frac{1+\alpha}{\lambda} \qquad \text{and} \qquad \frac{3}{4} = \frac{1+\alpha}{\lambda}$$

Hence $$\alpha = 3, \qquad \text{and} \qquad \lambda = \tfrac{16}{3}$$

Thus $$\text{AR:RC} = 3:13$$

Example 4

Given the position vectors $\hat{\boldsymbol{a}}$, $\hat{\boldsymbol{b}}$, $\hat{\boldsymbol{c}}$ of A, B, C (where $\hat{\boldsymbol{a}}$ etc. are unit vectors), and

$$l\hat{\boldsymbol{a}}+m\hat{\boldsymbol{b}}+n\hat{\boldsymbol{c}} = \boldsymbol{0}$$

The line AO meets BC at P. Find the length OP in terms of l, m, n using vector methods.

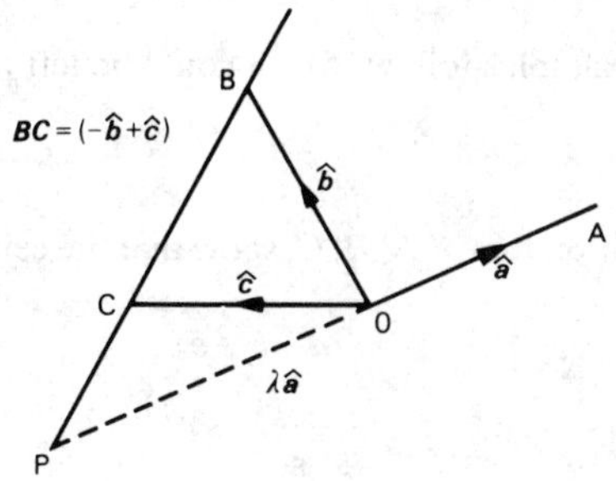

Start

(1) Make a reasonably accurate drawing, remembering that $\hat{\boldsymbol{a}}$, $\hat{\boldsymbol{b}}$, $\hat{\boldsymbol{c}}$ are unit vectors.

(2) Origin and base vectors given

(3)
$$\boldsymbol{PO} = \lambda\hat{\boldsymbol{a}}$$
$$\boldsymbol{BC} = -\hat{\boldsymbol{b}} + \hat{\boldsymbol{c}}$$
$$\boldsymbol{BP} = \mu(-\hat{\boldsymbol{b}} + \hat{\boldsymbol{c}})$$

Geometry

(1) ΔOBC is isosceles.

(2) POA, PCB are collinear.

Study

(1) Find two closed vector routes involving $\hat{\boldsymbol{a}}$, $\hat{\boldsymbol{b}}$, $\hat{\boldsymbol{c}}$.

(a) OBP
$$\hat{\boldsymbol{b}} + \mu(-\hat{\boldsymbol{b}} + \hat{\boldsymbol{c}}) + \lambda\hat{\boldsymbol{a}} = \boldsymbol{0}$$
or
$$\lambda\hat{\boldsymbol{a}} + (1-\mu)\hat{\boldsymbol{b}} + \mu\hat{\boldsymbol{c}} = \boldsymbol{0}$$

(b) Given
$$l\hat{\boldsymbol{a}} + m\hat{\boldsymbol{b}} + n\hat{\boldsymbol{c}} = \boldsymbol{0}$$

(2) We know that $l:m:n$ is constant, thus

$$\frac{\lambda}{l} = \frac{1-\mu}{m} = \frac{\mu}{n}$$

and
$$\mu = \frac{n}{n+m}, \quad \lambda = \frac{l}{n+m}$$

(3) The length of OP is

$$\frac{l}{n+m}|\hat{\boldsymbol{a}}|$$

and since $|\hat{\boldsymbol{a}}| = 1$,

$$\text{OP} = \frac{l}{n+m}$$

Two more difficult examples follow, which could be left to a second reading.

Example 5

If $\boldsymbol{a}$, $\boldsymbol{b}$, $\boldsymbol{c}$ are the position vectors of A, B, C, show that the centroid of the triangle has position vector

$$\boldsymbol{g} = \tfrac{1}{3}(\boldsymbol{a}+\boldsymbol{b}+\boldsymbol{c})$$

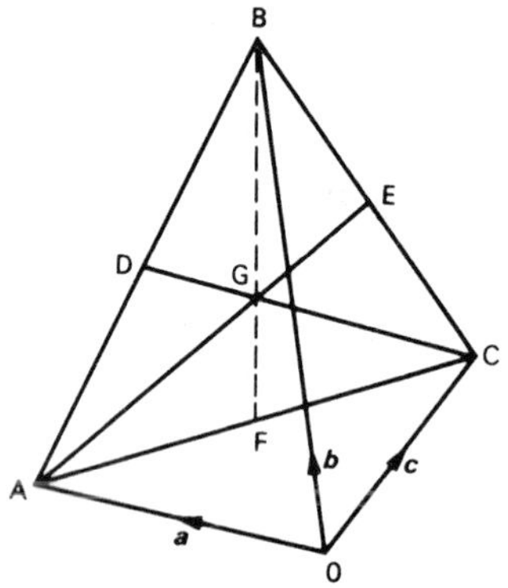

AE and CD are two medians of the triangle, intersecting at G.
G lies on CD, so

$$\begin{aligned}\boldsymbol{g} &= \boldsymbol{c}+\mu[-\boldsymbol{c}+\tfrac{1}{2}(\boldsymbol{a}+\boldsymbol{b})]\\ &= \tfrac{1}{2}\mu\boldsymbol{a}+\tfrac{1}{2}\mu\boldsymbol{b}+(1-\mu)\boldsymbol{c}\end{aligned}$$

G also lies on AE, so

$$\begin{aligned}\boldsymbol{g} &= \boldsymbol{a}+\lambda[-\boldsymbol{a}+\tfrac{1}{2}(\boldsymbol{b}+\boldsymbol{c})]\\ &= (1-\lambda)\boldsymbol{a}+\tfrac{1}{2}\lambda\boldsymbol{b}+\tfrac{1}{2}\lambda\boldsymbol{c}\end{aligned}$$

Hence $\quad \tfrac{1}{2}\mu\boldsymbol{a}+\tfrac{1}{2}\mu\boldsymbol{b}+(1-\mu)\boldsymbol{c} = (1-\lambda)\boldsymbol{a}+\tfrac{1}{2}\lambda\boldsymbol{b}+\tfrac{1}{2}\lambda\boldsymbol{c}$

and $\quad [\tfrac{1}{2}\mu-(1-\lambda)]\boldsymbol{a}+(\tfrac{1}{2}\mu-\tfrac{1}{2}\lambda)\boldsymbol{b}+(1-\mu-\tfrac{1}{2}\lambda)\boldsymbol{c} = \boldsymbol{0}$

Now $\quad (\tfrac{1}{2}\mu-1+\lambda)+(\tfrac{1}{2}\mu-\tfrac{1}{2}\lambda)+(1-\mu-\tfrac{1}{2}\lambda) = 0$

i.e. the coefficients of $\boldsymbol{a}$, $\boldsymbol{b}$ and **c** have zero sum. This means that *either* A, B, C are collinear—which is obviously not so—*or* the coefficients are separately equal to zero. So

$$\tfrac{1}{2}\mu-1+\lambda = \tfrac{1}{2}\mu-\tfrac{1}{2}\lambda = 1-\mu-\tfrac{1}{2}\lambda = 0$$

Thus $\quad \mu = \lambda \quad$ and $\quad 1-\lambda-\tfrac{1}{2}\lambda = 0$

$$1 = \tfrac{3}{2}\lambda$$

and $\quad \mu = \lambda = \tfrac{2}{3}$

So $$\boldsymbol{g} = \tfrac{1}{3}\boldsymbol{a} + \tfrac{1}{3}\boldsymbol{b} + \tfrac{1}{3}\boldsymbol{c} = \tfrac{1}{3}(\boldsymbol{a}+\boldsymbol{b}+\boldsymbol{c})$$

Since $\lambda = \mu = \tfrac{2}{3}$, $$\text{AG}:\text{AE} = \text{CG}:\text{CD} = 2:3$$

Moreover, since the expression is symmetrical in $\boldsymbol{a}$, $\boldsymbol{b}$, $\boldsymbol{c}$ we could equally well have considered the third median BF, which also passes through G, with BG:BF = 2:3.

Example 6

Given two sets of collinear points OAA′ and OBB′ with $\boldsymbol{OA} = \boldsymbol{a}$, $\boldsymbol{OA'} = \lambda\boldsymbol{a}$, $\boldsymbol{OB} = \boldsymbol{b}$ and $\boldsymbol{OB'} = \mu\boldsymbol{b}$ where the vectors $\boldsymbol{a}$ and $\boldsymbol{b}$ are not parallel, show that the vector $\boldsymbol{OX}$ where X is the point of intersection of AB′ and A′B is given by

$$\boldsymbol{OX} = \frac{\lambda(1-\mu)}{1-\lambda\mu}\boldsymbol{a} + \frac{\mu(1-\lambda)}{1-\lambda\mu}\boldsymbol{b}$$

provided that $$1-\lambda\mu \neq 0$$

Give a geometrical interpretation of the case

$$1-\lambda\mu = 0$$

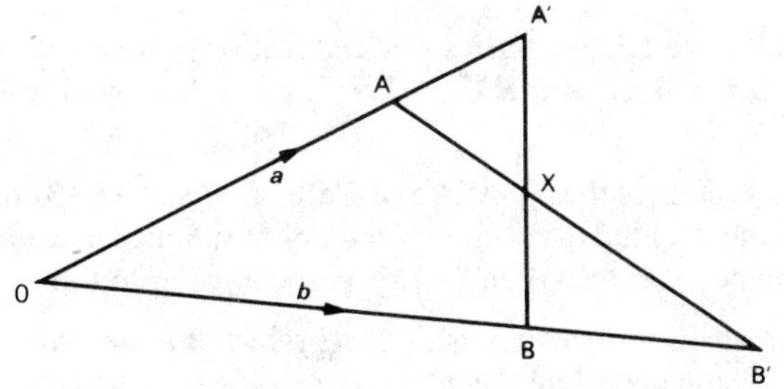

Suppose $\boldsymbol{AX} = p\boldsymbol{AB'}$, $\boldsymbol{BX} = q\boldsymbol{BA'}$

$= p(-\boldsymbol{a}+\mu\boldsymbol{b})$ $\quad= q(-\boldsymbol{b}+\lambda\boldsymbol{a})$

$$\boldsymbol{OX} = \boldsymbol{a}+\boldsymbol{AX} = \boldsymbol{a}+p(-\boldsymbol{a}+\mu\boldsymbol{b})$$
$$= (1-p)\boldsymbol{a}+p\mu\boldsymbol{b}$$

Also $$\boldsymbol{OX} = \boldsymbol{b}+\boldsymbol{BX} = \boldsymbol{b}+q(-\boldsymbol{b}+\lambda\boldsymbol{a})$$
$$= q\lambda\boldsymbol{a}+(1-q)\boldsymbol{b}$$

Hence $$(1-p)\boldsymbol{a}+p\mu\boldsymbol{b} = q\lambda\boldsymbol{a}+(1-q)\boldsymbol{b}$$

$\Rightarrow 1-p-q\lambda = p\mu-1+q = 0$ (since $\boldsymbol{a}$, $\boldsymbol{b}$ are not parallel)

$\Rightarrow$ $p = 1-q\lambda$

$$(1-q\lambda)\mu-1+q = 0$$

$$q = \frac{1-\mu}{1-\lambda\mu}$$

So
$$\boldsymbol{OX} = q\lambda\boldsymbol{a} + (1-q)\boldsymbol{b}$$
$$= \frac{(1-\mu)\lambda}{1-\lambda\mu}\boldsymbol{a} + \left(1 - \frac{1-\mu}{1-\lambda\mu}\right)\boldsymbol{b}$$
$$\boldsymbol{OX} = \frac{\lambda(1-\mu)}{1-\lambda\mu}\boldsymbol{a} + \frac{\mu(1-\lambda)}{1-\lambda\mu}\boldsymbol{b}$$

If $1-\lambda\mu = 0$,
$$\frac{\text{OA}'}{\text{OA}} = \frac{\text{OB}}{\text{OB}'}$$

Then AB′∥A′B and there is no point of intersection, X.

Miscellaneous examination questions 8

1 Two points P and Q have position vectors represented by $\boldsymbol{p}$ and $\boldsymbol{q}$ respectively. The point T divides PQ in the ratio m to n. Find a formula for $\boldsymbol{t}$ in terms of $\boldsymbol{p}$ and $\boldsymbol{q}$, where $\boldsymbol{t}$ represents the position vector of T. Show that this formula is independent of the choice of origin. (A.E.B.)

2 Points X and Y are taken on sides QR and RS, respectively, of a parallelogram PQRS, so that $\boldsymbol{QX} = 4\boldsymbol{XR}$ and $\boldsymbol{RY} = 4\boldsymbol{YS}$. The line XY cuts PR at Z. Prove that $\boldsymbol{PZ} = \frac{21}{25}\boldsymbol{PR}$. (J.M.B.)

3 The position vectors of the points A and B are $2\boldsymbol{i}-\boldsymbol{j}$ and $-\boldsymbol{i}+3\boldsymbol{j}$ respectively with respect to the origin O. Find the position vector of the point H in the plane OAB such that OH is perpendicular to AB and AH is perpendicular to OB. (L.)

4 The position vectors of the points A, B, C referred to an origin O in the plane ABC, are given by the unit vectors $\boldsymbol{a}$, $\boldsymbol{b}$, $\boldsymbol{c}$. Prove $\boldsymbol{a}$, $\boldsymbol{b}$, $\boldsymbol{c}$ are connected by a relation of the form $p\boldsymbol{a}+q\boldsymbol{b}+r\boldsymbol{c} = \boldsymbol{0}$ where $\boldsymbol{0}$ is the zero vector and p, q, r are scalar constants.

Describe the triangle ABC when the relation is

(a) $\boldsymbol{a}+\boldsymbol{b}+\boldsymbol{c} = \boldsymbol{0}$

(b) $\boldsymbol{b}+\boldsymbol{c} = \boldsymbol{0}$

In the general case, the line AO meets the line BC in U. Prove that OU is equal to the numerical value of
$$\frac{p}{(q+r)}$$
(C.)

5 (a) Show that the points A, B and C are collinear if $7\boldsymbol{OB} = \boldsymbol{OA}+6\boldsymbol{OC}$.

(b) Show that if O, A, B, C are four points and λ, μ, ν are three real numbers such that $\lambda+\mu+\nu = 0$ then if $\lambda\boldsymbol{OA}+\mu\boldsymbol{OB}+\nu\boldsymbol{OC} = \boldsymbol{0}$, the points A, B, and C are collinear. (O.)

6 The position vectors $\boldsymbol{OA}$, $\boldsymbol{OB}$ referred to the origin O of coordinates of two points A, B (not collinear with O) in the plane of the cartesian axes Oxy are $\boldsymbol{a}$, $\boldsymbol{b}$ respectively.

Show that the position vector $\boldsymbol{r} = \boldsymbol{OP}$ of an arbitrary point P on the line AB is given by $\boldsymbol{r} = \boldsymbol{a}+t(\boldsymbol{b}-\boldsymbol{a})$ where t is a scalar. Hence or otherwise, show that if K is the point of intersection of AB and A′B′ (produced if necessary) where $\boldsymbol{OA}' = 3\boldsymbol{a}$, $\boldsymbol{OB}' = 2\boldsymbol{b}$ then $\boldsymbol{OK} = -3\boldsymbol{a}+4\boldsymbol{b}$. (O. & C.)

7 The points A, B have position vectors $\boldsymbol{a}$, $\boldsymbol{b}$ respectively with respect to an origin O and $|\boldsymbol{a}| = 3$, $|\boldsymbol{b}| = 2$. By considering the cosines of the angles between the direction of the vector $\boldsymbol{c} = 2\boldsymbol{a}+3\boldsymbol{b}$ and OA, OB, show that the direction of $\boldsymbol{c}$ bisects the angle between OA, OB. Hence find the position vector of the point P in which the bisector of the angle AOB meets AB.

If the angle between OA and OB is $\cos^{-1}(-\frac{1}{4})$ find the number x if the bisector of the angle OBA is in the direction of the vector $\boldsymbol{a}+x\boldsymbol{b}$. (W.)

8 The position vectors of A, B with respect to an origin O are $\boldsymbol{a}$, $\boldsymbol{b}$ respectively where $|\boldsymbol{a}| = 1$, $|\boldsymbol{b}| = 3$ and the angle AOB is $\pi/3$. Show that $\frac{1}{9}\sqrt{3}(3\boldsymbol{a}-2\boldsymbol{b})$ is a unit vector perpendicular to OA.

Find (i) a unit vector perpendicular to AB, and (ii) the position vector of the orthocentre of the triangle OAB (the point of concurrence of the perpendiculars drawn from the vertices to the opposite sides). (C.)

9 Give a geometrical interpretation to the scalar product $(\boldsymbol{a}+\boldsymbol{b})\cdot(\boldsymbol{a}-\boldsymbol{b})$. Evaluate this scalar product when $|\boldsymbol{a}| = |\boldsymbol{b}|$, and explain its significance.

Two vectors $\boldsymbol{a}$ and $\boldsymbol{b}$ are such that $|\boldsymbol{a}| = 3$, $|\boldsymbol{b}| = 4$ and $\boldsymbol{a}\cdot\boldsymbol{b} = -5$. Find

(a) the angle between $\boldsymbol{a}$ and $\boldsymbol{b}$.

(b) the lengths of $\boldsymbol{a}+\boldsymbol{b}$ and $\boldsymbol{a}-\boldsymbol{b}$.

(c) the angle between $\boldsymbol{a}+\boldsymbol{b}$ and $\boldsymbol{a}-\boldsymbol{b}$. (M.M.E.)

10 Prove that if $\boldsymbol{a}$ and $\boldsymbol{b}$ are any two non-parallel vectors lying in a plane, then any other vector $\boldsymbol{p}$ lying in this plane can be expressed in the form $\boldsymbol{p} = l\boldsymbol{a}+m\boldsymbol{b}$ where l and m are scalars.

Find the scalars l, m when $\boldsymbol{a} = 2\boldsymbol{i}-3\boldsymbol{j}$, $\boldsymbol{b} = -\boldsymbol{i}+4\boldsymbol{j}$, $\boldsymbol{p} = 4\boldsymbol{i}-\boldsymbol{j}$ where $\boldsymbol{i}$, $\boldsymbol{j}$, are unit vectors directed along coordinate axes Ox, Oy respectively in the plane. (O. & C.)

11 OABC is a square of side $2a$. $\boldsymbol{i}$, $\boldsymbol{j}$ are unit vectors along OA, OC. The midpoint of AB is L; the midpoint of BC is M. OL, AM meet at P; BP meets OA at N. Show that the segment OP can be measured by the vector $\lambda(2a\boldsymbol{i}+a\boldsymbol{j})$ and also by the vector $2a\boldsymbol{i}+\mu(2a\boldsymbol{j}-a\boldsymbol{i})$. Hence determine λ and μ. Prove that ON $= \frac{2}{3}$OA. (O. & C.)

12 OACB is a parallelogram, and Y is a point on the side BC such that the line OY is perpendicular to the diagonal AB. $\boldsymbol{OA} = \boldsymbol{a}$, $\boldsymbol{OB} = \boldsymbol{b}$, and $\boldsymbol{BY} = h\boldsymbol{BC}$.

(a) Prove that $h(\boldsymbol{a}^2-\boldsymbol{a}\cdot\boldsymbol{b}) = \boldsymbol{b}^2-\boldsymbol{a}\cdot\boldsymbol{b}$.

(b) If OA = 5 m, OB = 4 m, and $\widehat{\text{AOB}} = 60°$, find the lengths of BY and OY. (M.M.E.)

13 Given that $\boldsymbol{a} = -\boldsymbol{i}+\boldsymbol{j}$ and $\boldsymbol{b} = \boldsymbol{i}+2\boldsymbol{j}$, find the vectors $\boldsymbol{a}+3\boldsymbol{b}$, and $5\boldsymbol{b}-16\boldsymbol{a}$, and calculate the numerical value of the three scalar products

$$(\boldsymbol{a}+3\boldsymbol{b})^2, \qquad (5\boldsymbol{b}-16\boldsymbol{a})^2 \qquad \text{and} \qquad (\boldsymbol{a}+3\boldsymbol{b})\cdot(5\boldsymbol{b}-16\boldsymbol{a})$$

In the triangle OPQ, $\boldsymbol{OP} = \boldsymbol{a}+3\boldsymbol{b}$, and $\boldsymbol{OQ} = 5\boldsymbol{b}-16\boldsymbol{a}$. Prove that the angle POQ is a right angle, and calculate the area of the triangle OPQ. (M.M.E.)

14 Define the scalar product $\boldsymbol{a}\cdot\boldsymbol{b}$ of the two vectors $\boldsymbol{a}$ and $\boldsymbol{b}$. If $\boldsymbol{a}$, $\boldsymbol{b}$, $\boldsymbol{c}$ are given vectors, in what circumstances is it true that $\boldsymbol{a}\cdot\boldsymbol{b} = \boldsymbol{a}\cdot\boldsymbol{c}$?

A straight line L is parallel to a vector $\boldsymbol{a}$ and passes through a point B whose position vector is $\boldsymbol{b}$. The point C has position vector $\boldsymbol{c}$ and $\boldsymbol{p}$ is the vector from C to L, perpendicular to L, with terminus on L. Prove that

$$\boldsymbol{p} = \boldsymbol{b} - \boldsymbol{c} - \frac{(\boldsymbol{b} - \boldsymbol{c}) \cdot \boldsymbol{a}}{|\boldsymbol{a}|^2}\boldsymbol{a}$$

(M.E.I.)

Chapter 9

Matrices and Transformations 1

1 Transformations of the plane

Most of you will have already met 2×2 matrices (those having two rows and two columns) and in what follows we assume that you know something about them.

1.1 Change of base vectors and axes

A *transformation* is a mapping of the points in a plane under which each point has a unique image point in the plane. In 2D we think of the plane as consisting of a cartesian grid with base vectors $\boldsymbol{i}$, $\boldsymbol{j}$ and with a point O as the origin. When we transform the plane into itself we choose two new base vectors $\boldsymbol{a}$ and $\boldsymbol{b}$ so that $\boldsymbol{i} \to \boldsymbol{a}$, and $\boldsymbol{j} \to \boldsymbol{b}$ whilst the origin O remains where it is.

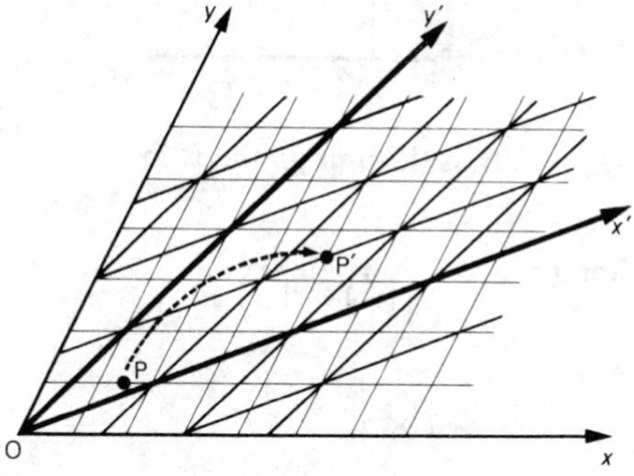

P is mapped into P′.

The new base vectors define new *axes* and hence a complete new grid. Thus $x \to x'$ and $y \to y'$ whilst any point P is mapped into a different point P′, but with the same coordinates referred to the *new* grid.

Consider the mapping

$$\underset{\begin{pmatrix}1\\0\end{pmatrix}}{\text{A}} \to \underset{\begin{pmatrix}2\\1\end{pmatrix}}{\text{A}'}$$

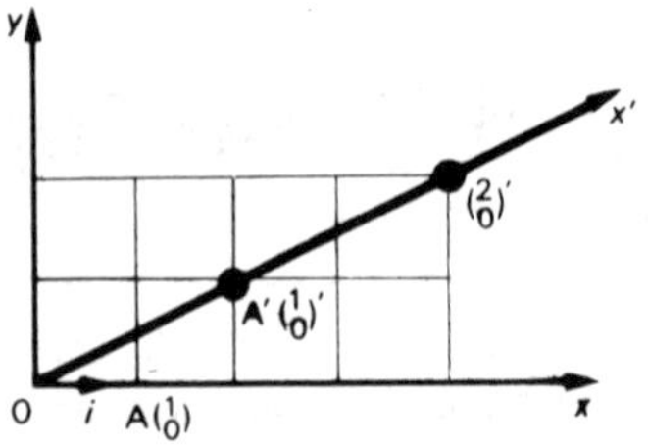

OA′ is the unit on the x' axis.

It follows that $$\begin{pmatrix}2\\0\end{pmatrix} \to \begin{pmatrix}4\\2\end{pmatrix}$$

and $$\begin{pmatrix}x\\0\end{pmatrix} \to \begin{pmatrix}2x\\x\end{pmatrix} \quad \text{or} \quad x\begin{pmatrix}1\\0\end{pmatrix} \to x\begin{pmatrix}2\\1\end{pmatrix}$$

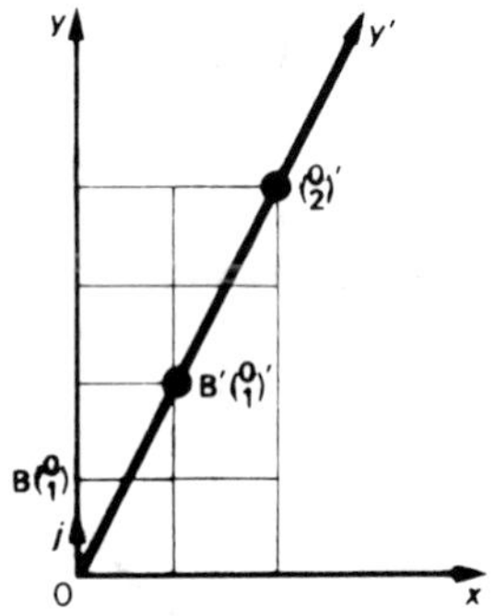

OB′ is the unit on the y' axis.

Now consider the mapping $$\overset{\text{B}}{\begin{pmatrix}0\\1\end{pmatrix}} \to \overset{\text{B}'}{\begin{pmatrix}1\\2\end{pmatrix}}$$

Similarly $$\begin{pmatrix}0\\3\end{pmatrix} \to \begin{pmatrix}3\\6\end{pmatrix}$$

and $$\begin{pmatrix}0\\y\end{pmatrix} \to \begin{pmatrix}y\\2y\end{pmatrix} \quad \text{or} \quad y\begin{pmatrix}0\\1\end{pmatrix} \to y\begin{pmatrix}1\\2\end{pmatrix}$$

The x axis ($y = 0$) has mapped into the x' axis ($y = \frac{1}{2}x$) and the y axis ($x = 0$) into the y' axis ($y = 2x$). In effect, each axis has 'swung round' (in opposite directions), and the lengths of OA and OB have been 'stretched' by a scale factor $\sqrt{5}$.

Suppose we combine the two mappings.

Then $$x\begin{pmatrix}1\\0\end{pmatrix} + y\begin{pmatrix}0\\1\end{pmatrix} \to x\begin{pmatrix}2\\1\end{pmatrix} + y\begin{pmatrix}1\\2\end{pmatrix}$$

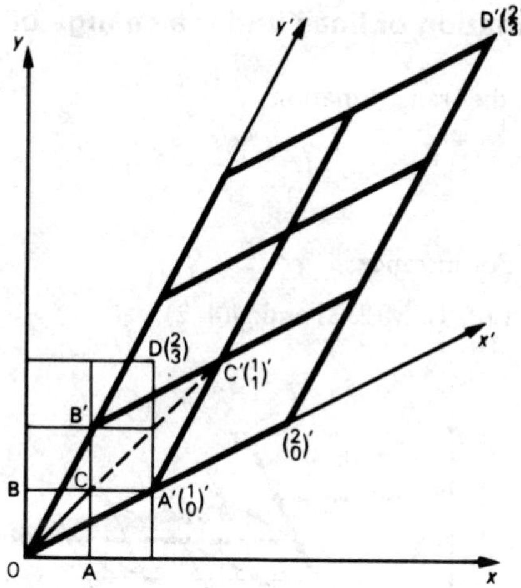

For example,

$$\begin{matrix} C & & C' \\ \begin{pmatrix}1\\1\end{pmatrix} & \to & \begin{pmatrix}3\\3\end{pmatrix} \end{matrix}$$

$$\begin{pmatrix}2\\3\end{pmatrix} \to \begin{pmatrix}4+3\\2+6\end{pmatrix} = \begin{pmatrix}7\\8\end{pmatrix}$$

So

$$\begin{pmatrix}x\\y\end{pmatrix} \to \begin{pmatrix}2x+y\\x+2y\end{pmatrix}$$

our new coordinates x' and y' can be written

$$\begin{pmatrix}x'\\y'\end{pmatrix} = \begin{pmatrix}2 & 1\\1 & 2\end{pmatrix}\begin{pmatrix}x\\y\end{pmatrix}$$

since, by matrix multiplication,

$$\begin{pmatrix}2 & 1\\1 & 2\end{pmatrix}\begin{pmatrix}x\\y\end{pmatrix} = \begin{pmatrix}2x+y\\x+2y\end{pmatrix}$$

A new, 'red' grid has been superimposed on the original, 'black' cartesian grid: the same 'black' (continuous lines) and 'red' (dashed lines) grids that we used in Chapter 8, Exercise 1.1. We can easily find the point to which any point on the original grid has been transformed by locating the same coordinates on the new grid. For example,

$$D\begin{pmatrix}2\\3\end{pmatrix}_{\text{black}} \to D'\begin{pmatrix}2\\3\end{pmatrix}_{\text{red}}$$

We can then read off the coordinates of D′ referred to on the old grid, as $D'\begin{pmatrix}7\\8\end{pmatrix}_{\text{black}}$. In the diagram, the coordinates referred to the *new* grid are marked with a prime as $D'\begin{pmatrix}2\\3\end{pmatrix}'$.

1.2 The transformation of lines under a change of axes

Consider the effect of the transformation

$$\begin{pmatrix} 2 & 1 \\ 1 & 2 \end{pmatrix}$$

on lines in the plane. For instance:

(1) The line joining L(0, 4), M(2, 3) and N(4, 2):

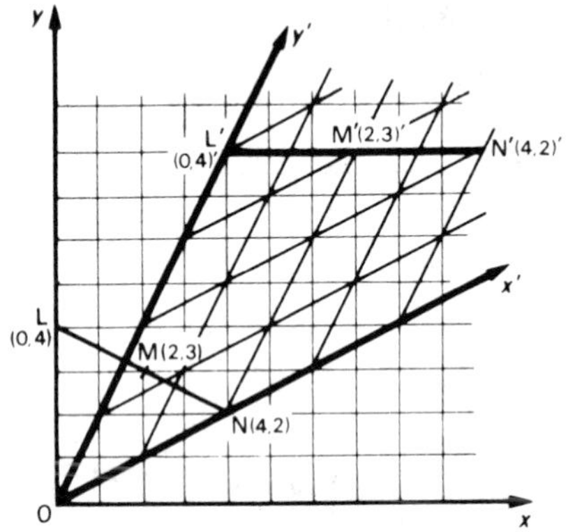

Note that the straight line LMN is mapped into another straight line L'M'N'.

(2) The line joining A(4, 0), B(2, 3), C(0, 6) and D(−2, 9):

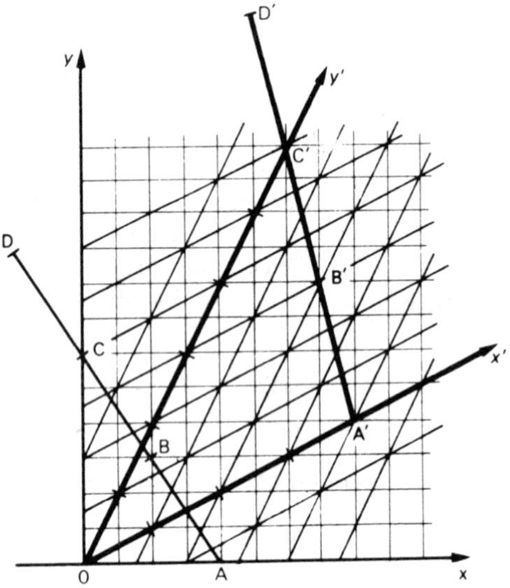

Note that the ratio AB : BC : CD = A′B′ : B′C′ : C′D′.

(3) The parallelogram P(1, 1), Q(3, 0), R(3, 4) and S(1, 5):

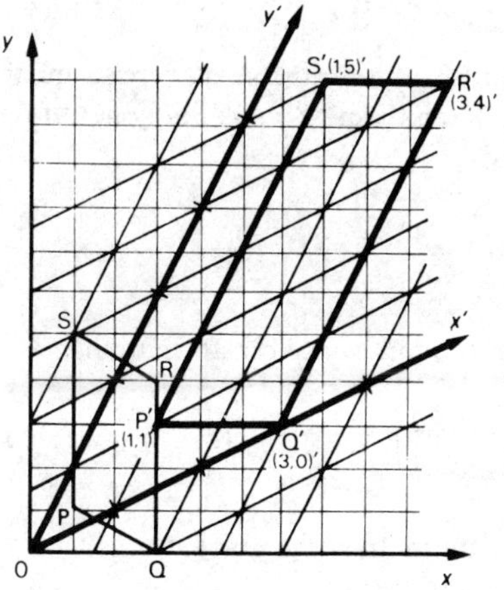

Note that
- (a) parallel lines have mapped into parallel lines, but
- (b) the angle between adjacent sides has changed.

(4) The lines joining E(1, 1) to F(4, 4) and G(1, 4) to H(3, 0) meet at J(2, 2):

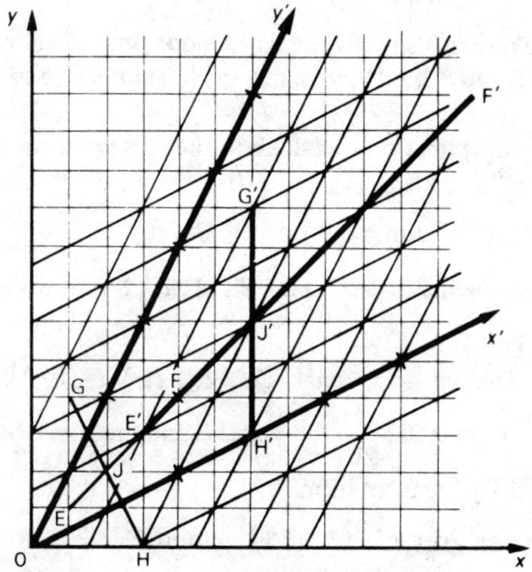

We notice that the point of intersection J maps into the point of intersection of the transformed lines, J′.

We have used the grid with base vectors

$$\boldsymbol{a} = \begin{pmatrix} 2 \\ 1 \end{pmatrix}, \qquad \boldsymbol{b} = \begin{pmatrix} 1 \\ 2 \end{pmatrix}$$

to illustrate the transformation of points and lines. We shall refer to this as the transformation of the plane using the matrix

$$\mathbf{A} = \begin{pmatrix} 2 & 1 \\ 1 & 2 \end{pmatrix}$$

You will need separate grids for the next exercise and for later work, so draw them on *tracing paper* and keep them! You will only get the 'feel' of transformations by using various grids.

Exercise 1.2

1 Draw the grids of the following transformations:

$$\mathbf{B} = \begin{pmatrix} 2 & 2 \\ 2 & -1 \end{pmatrix} \qquad \mathbf{C} = \begin{pmatrix} 1 & 3 \\ 1 & -1 \end{pmatrix} \qquad \mathbf{F} = \begin{pmatrix} 4 & -1 \\ 1 & 2 \end{pmatrix}$$

What happens if you try to draw the grid for

$$\mathbf{Z} = \begin{pmatrix} 3 & -6 \\ -1 & 2 \end{pmatrix}?$$

2(a) On the cartesian grid mark the quadrilateral P(2, 1), Q(4, 1), R(4, −3), S(2, −3). Then using the $\begin{pmatrix} 2 & 2 \\ 2 & -1 \end{pmatrix}$ grid **B**, mark P′(2, 1), Q′(4, 1), R′(4, −3) and S′(2, −3) on tracing paper (using the new grid coordinates). Now mark T and T′ with coordinates (3, −1) and (3, −1) on each grid. Join PR and QS, P′R′ and Q′S′. Comment.

(b) Use matrix multiplication to calculate the cartesian coordinates of P′, Q′, R′, S′, T′. Superimpose the tracing paper on the cartesian grid to check your results.

3(a) On the cartesian grid mark P(0, −1), Q(1, 0), R(2, 1) and S(3, 2). Using the $\begin{pmatrix} 1 & 3 \\ 1 & -1 \end{pmatrix}$ grid **C** and tracing paper, mark P′, Q′, R′, S′. Find the ratios PQ : QR : QS and P′Q′ : Q′R′ : R′S′.

(b) Using the cartesian grid, mark U′(−2, −2) V′(4, 0) W′(−7, −5) on tracing paper. Superimpose this on the $\begin{pmatrix} 1 & 3 \\ 1 & -1 \end{pmatrix}$ grid **C** and thus find the original coordinates of U, V, W before the transformation.

4(a) On the cartesian grid join O to P(2, 4) and Q(2, −1) to R(0, 5). Then on the $\begin{pmatrix} 4 & -1 \\ 1 & 2 \end{pmatrix}$ grid **F** join O′P′ and Q′R′. Find the point of intersection on each grid.

(b)(i) If two lines intersect at (−1, 2) what would be the coordinates of their point of intersection after they had been transformed using $\begin{pmatrix} 4 & -1 \\ 2 & 2 \end{pmatrix}$?

(ii) Two lines intersect at (−7, 5) *after* the transformation of (i). What were the coordinates of the point of intersection *before* the transformation?

5(a) On the cartesian grid mark the points L(2, 1), M(4, 2). Use the matrix $\mathbf{Z} = \begin{pmatrix} 3 & -6 \\ -1 & 2 \end{pmatrix}$ to transform them to L′ and M′. What line of points maps into the origin?

(b) Use the matrix **Z** to transform (6, −2) and (−3, 1). What can you deduce?

Summary of results

This exercise has illustrated the following facts. Under the transformations **A**, **B**, **C**, and **F**,

1 Straight lines have mapped into straight lines.

2 Parallel lines have mapped into parallel lines.

3 The ratios of segments of a line have remained constant.

4 The point of intersection of two lines has mapped into the point of intersection of the transformed lines.

5 Most lines have mapped on to a line in a different direction. However, under the transformation **Z**, the whole plane is mapped onto a line, and one line maps onto the origin (see page 334).

1.3 The transformation of points and lines by matrix multiplication

It is much quicker to calculate the coordinates of a particular point after a transformation than it is to draw the grid and see where the point has gone. We have already discovered how we could do this when we transformed the point (2, 3) using the matrix

$$\begin{pmatrix} 2 & 1 \\ 1 & 2 \end{pmatrix}$$

$$\begin{pmatrix} x' \\ y' \end{pmatrix} = 2\begin{pmatrix} 2 \\ 1 \end{pmatrix} + 3\begin{pmatrix} 1 \\ 2 \end{pmatrix} = \begin{pmatrix} 7 \\ 8 \end{pmatrix} \quad \text{or} \quad \begin{pmatrix} x' \\ y' \end{pmatrix} = \begin{pmatrix} 2 & 1 \\ 1 & 2 \end{pmatrix}\begin{pmatrix} 2 \\ 3 \end{pmatrix} = \begin{pmatrix} 7 \\ 8 \end{pmatrix}$$

In general, we can find the new position vector

$$\begin{pmatrix} x' \\ y' \end{pmatrix}$$

using matrix multiplication. If

$$\boldsymbol{a} = \begin{pmatrix} a_1 \\ a_2 \end{pmatrix} \quad \text{and} \quad \boldsymbol{b} = \begin{pmatrix} b_1 \\ b_2 \end{pmatrix}$$

are the new base vectors, then

$$\begin{pmatrix} x' \\ y' \end{pmatrix} = \begin{pmatrix} a_1 & b_1 \\ a_2 & b_2 \end{pmatrix}\begin{pmatrix} x \\ y \end{pmatrix} \quad \text{or} \quad \begin{aligned} x' &= a_1x + b_1y \\ y' &= a_2x + b_2y \end{aligned}$$

$$\text{or} \quad \begin{pmatrix} x' \\ y' \end{pmatrix} = x\begin{pmatrix} a_1 \\ a_2 \end{pmatrix} + y\begin{pmatrix} b_1 \\ b_2 \end{pmatrix}$$ ◀

So 2×2 matrices give us a concise method of writing down and describing transformations of a point. We now find the equation of a line in its new transformed position.

Example

Find the equation of the line $$\frac{x-5}{3}=\frac{y}{-1}$$

after it has been transformed by the matrix

$$\begin{pmatrix} 2 & 2 \\ 2 & -1 \end{pmatrix}$$

Method 1

(a) We find two points on the line, say (5, 0) and (0, 5/3).

(b) We transform them using matrix multiplication

$$\begin{pmatrix} 2 & 2 \\ 2 & -1 \end{pmatrix}\begin{pmatrix} 5 \\ 0 \end{pmatrix}=\begin{pmatrix} 10 \\ 10 \end{pmatrix} \quad \text{and} \quad \begin{pmatrix} 2 & 2 \\ 2 & -1 \end{pmatrix}\begin{pmatrix} 0 \\ \frac{5}{3} \end{pmatrix}=\begin{pmatrix} \frac{10}{3} \\ -\frac{5}{3} \end{pmatrix}$$

(c) We find the equation of the line joining these two points. It will have DR$(10-10/3):(10+5/3)=20/3:35/3=4:7$. Thus the equation of the transformed line is

$$\frac{x-10}{4}=\frac{y-10}{7}$$

Note that we could have used the grid B to find the coordinates of the transformed points and hence to deduce the equation of the line.

Method 2

Consider the line in its parametric form

$$x=3k+5,\ y=-k$$

Under the transformation, (x, y) is mapped into (x', y'), where

$$\begin{pmatrix} x' \\ y' \end{pmatrix}=\begin{pmatrix} 2 & 2 \\ 2 & -1 \end{pmatrix}\begin{pmatrix} 3k+5 \\ -k \end{pmatrix}=\begin{pmatrix} 4k+10 \\ 7k+10 \end{pmatrix}$$

so the new equation is

$$\frac{x-10}{4}=\frac{y-10}{7}$$

Exercise 1.3

Use squared paper and sketch your solutions.

1 Find the equations of the lines

(a) $\dfrac{x-3}{2}=\dfrac{y+1}{1}$ **(b)** $\dfrac{x}{-1}=\dfrac{y-2}{3}$

after the transformation by the matrix

$$\begin{pmatrix} 0 & -1 \\ 1 & 0 \end{pmatrix}$$

What was the angle between the lines (i) before, and (ii) after the transformation?

2 Find the equation of the line

$$\frac{x+3}{-2} = \frac{y-1}{4}$$

after it has been transformed, using

$$\begin{pmatrix} 3 & -1 \\ 0 & 2 \end{pmatrix}$$

Write down the equation of the line perpendicular to the given line and passing through the origin. Find the equation of the transform of this line.

3 Find the point of intersection of the lines

$$\frac{x-1}{2} = \frac{y+2}{5} \quad \text{and} \quad \frac{x}{3} = \frac{y-2}{1}$$

after they have been transformed by the matrix

$$\begin{pmatrix} -4 & 2 \\ -15 & 7 \end{pmatrix}$$

4 Find the coordinates of the centroid of the triangle A(1, 1), B(0, 2) and C(2, 3) after it has been transformed by the matrix

$$\begin{pmatrix} -1 & 0 \\ 2 & 3 \end{pmatrix}$$

5 The parallelogram OPQR is transformed by the matrix

$$\begin{pmatrix} 0 & -1 \\ 2 & 2 \end{pmatrix}$$

If P is (3, 1) and R is (1, 2), find the coordinates of **(a)** Q and **(b)** the intersection of the diagonals before and *after* the transformation. Find also the angle between the diagonals before and after the transformation.

6 Find the line of points which are mapped on to the origin by the matrix $\begin{pmatrix} 1 & 2 \\ 3 & 6 \end{pmatrix}$. If P is $\begin{pmatrix} -1 \\ -3 \end{pmatrix}$, find P′. Deduce the coordinates of Q′ if Q is $\begin{pmatrix} -20 \\ -60 \end{pmatrix}$. What line of points is mapped onto **(a)** P′, and **(b)** Q′?

1.4 Eigenvectors and eigenvalues

Consider the transformation of the plane by the matrix

$$\mathbf{H} = \begin{pmatrix} 4 & -1 \\ 2 & 1 \end{pmatrix}$$

Part of the transformed grid is shown, its axes marked x' and y', and column vectors referred to *these* axes are also marked with a prime.

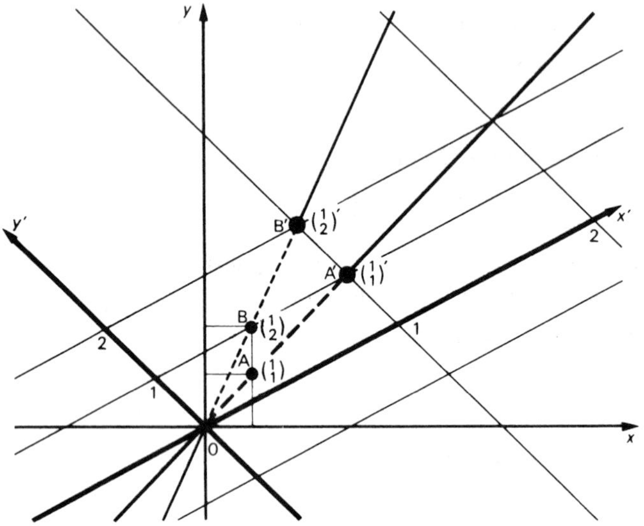

The axes have changed direction under the transformation and so have most vectors, e.g. $\begin{pmatrix}2\\1\end{pmatrix}$ and $\begin{pmatrix}2\\1\end{pmatrix}'$ do not lie in the same direction. Are there any vectors which *do* remain in the same direction under the transformation? In this case there are two such vectors, shown in the diagram.

$$\begin{pmatrix}1\\1\end{pmatrix}' \quad \text{is in line with} \quad \begin{pmatrix}1\\1\end{pmatrix}$$

and

$$\begin{pmatrix}1\\2\end{pmatrix}' \quad \text{is in line with} \quad \begin{pmatrix}1\\2\end{pmatrix}$$

Vectors which remain in the same direction under the transformation are called *eigenvectors*. Notice also that OA′ = 3OA and OB′ = 2OB. We say that the 'stretch' in the direction OAA′, is the *eigenvalue* corresponding to the eigenvector OA. Here

$$\begin{pmatrix}1\\1\end{pmatrix} \text{ is an eigenvector with eigenvalue 3}$$

and

$$\begin{pmatrix}1\\2\end{pmatrix} \text{ is an eigenvector with eigenvalue 2}$$

Any vector in the direction OA will remain in the same direction and similarly any vector in the direction OB will stay in that direction. For example,

$$\begin{pmatrix}1\\1\end{pmatrix}, \begin{pmatrix}2\\2\end{pmatrix}, \begin{pmatrix}3\\3\end{pmatrix} \ldots \begin{pmatrix}-1\\-1\end{pmatrix}, \begin{pmatrix}-2\\-2\end{pmatrix} \ldots$$

all have the same direction associated with eigenvalue +3, and similarly

$$\begin{pmatrix}1\\2\end{pmatrix}, \begin{pmatrix}2\\4\end{pmatrix}, \begin{pmatrix}3\\6\end{pmatrix} \cdots \begin{pmatrix}-1\\-2\end{pmatrix}, \begin{pmatrix}-2\\-4\end{pmatrix} \cdots$$

are associated with eigenvalue +2.

Another way of stating this is to say that under the transformation all points on the line $y = x$ remain on the line and similarly all points on $y = 2x$ stay on that line. The *directions* of these two lines are invariant, although the only invariant *point* is the origin.

In this case, we were lucky enough to spot the eigenvectors, but they are not always easy to pick out, so we now look at the algebra involved.

The algebra of eigenvectors

Consider the transformation using

$$\mathbf{A} = \begin{pmatrix}4 & -1\\2 & 1\end{pmatrix}$$

Suppose an eigenvector is

$$\begin{pmatrix}x\\y\end{pmatrix}$$

then under the transformation this becomes a vector in the same direction

$$\begin{pmatrix}kx\\ky\end{pmatrix}$$

where k is a real number. Then

$$\begin{pmatrix}4 & -1\\2 & 1\end{pmatrix}\begin{pmatrix}x\\y\end{pmatrix} = \begin{pmatrix}kx\\ky\end{pmatrix} = k\begin{pmatrix}x\\y\end{pmatrix}$$

so $$4x - y = kx \Leftrightarrow (4-k)x = y$$

$$2x + y = ky \Leftrightarrow 2x = y(k-1)$$

To solve these equations, we divide them to give

$$\frac{4-k}{2} = \frac{1}{k-1}$$

$$(4-k)(k-1) = 2$$

$$k^2 - 5k + 6 = 0$$

This is called the *characteristic equation* of the matrix **A**.

$$(k-3)(k-2) = 0$$

$$k = 2 \text{ or } 3$$

These values of k are the eigenvalues.

When $k = 2$ $\qquad 4x - y = 2x \Rightarrow y = 2x$

Any vector in the line $y = 2x$ stays in the same direction under the transformation.

We may choose $\begin{pmatrix}1\\2\end{pmatrix}$ as being a typical eigenvector; any multiple would also do, e.g.

$$\begin{pmatrix}2\\4\end{pmatrix}$$

This means that

eigenvector

$$\begin{pmatrix}4 & -1\\2 & 1\end{pmatrix}\begin{pmatrix}1\\2\end{pmatrix} = 2\begin{pmatrix}1\\2\end{pmatrix}$$

corresponding eigenvalue
(or stretch)

Similarly when $k = 3$

$$4x - y = 3x \Rightarrow y = x$$

A typical eigenvector in this line is

$$\begin{pmatrix}1\\1\end{pmatrix}$$

Hence

eigenvector

$$\begin{pmatrix}4 & -1\\2 & 1\end{pmatrix}\begin{pmatrix}1\\1\end{pmatrix} = 3\begin{pmatrix}1\\1\end{pmatrix}$$

eigenvalue

In general, if the transforming matrix is

$$\begin{pmatrix}a_1 & b_1\\a_2 & b_2\end{pmatrix}$$

we have, for the eigenvectors

$$\begin{pmatrix}a_1 & b_1\\a_2 & b_2\end{pmatrix}\begin{pmatrix}x\\y\end{pmatrix} = \begin{pmatrix}kx\\ky\end{pmatrix} = k\begin{pmatrix}x\\y\end{pmatrix}$$

$$a_1x + b_1y = kx \Rightarrow (a_1 - k)x = -b_1y \qquad (1)$$

$$a_1x + b_1y = ky \Rightarrow a_1x = (k - b_1)y \qquad (2)$$

Dividing equation (1) by equation (2)

$$\frac{a_1 - k}{a_2} = \frac{-b_2}{k - b_2}$$

which simplifies to give

$$k^2 - (a_1 + b_2)k + a_1b_2 - a_2b_1 = 0$$

which is the characteristic equation of the matrix.

The *sum* of the roots of this equation is $a_1 + b_2$ which is called the *trace* of the matrix. This is the sum of the elements on the leading diagonal (top left to bottom right) of the matrix. The *product* of the roots is $a_1b_2 - a_2b_1$ which is called the *determinant* of the matrix. The symbol $|\mathbf{A}|$ means the determinant of the matrix $\mathbf{A}$. The characteristic equation is therefore

$$\mathbf{k^2 - (trace)k + (determinant) = 0}$$ ◀

Exercise 1.4a

Find the eigenvectors and eigenvalues of the following matrices:

1 $\mathbf{A}=\begin{pmatrix}2 & 1\\ 1 & 2\end{pmatrix}$ **2** $\mathbf{B}=\begin{pmatrix}2 & 2\\ 2 & -1\end{pmatrix}$ **3** $\mathbf{C}=\begin{pmatrix}1 & 3\\ 1 & -1\end{pmatrix}$

4 $\mathbf{F}=\begin{pmatrix}4 & -1\\ 1 & 2\end{pmatrix}$ **5** $\mathbf{Z}=\begin{pmatrix}3 & -6\\ -1 & 2\end{pmatrix}$

Summary of results

Matrix	*Determinant*	*Eigenvalues*	*Sum of eigenvalues*	*Product of eigenvalues*	*Typical eigenvectors*
$\mathbf{H}=\begin{pmatrix}4 & -1\\ 2 & 1\end{pmatrix}$	$\lvert\mathbf{H}\rvert=6$	3, 2	5	6	$\begin{pmatrix}1\\1\end{pmatrix},\begin{pmatrix}1\\2\end{pmatrix}$
$\mathbf{A}=\begin{pmatrix}2 & 1\\ 1 & 2\end{pmatrix}$	$\lvert\mathbf{A}\rvert=3$	3, 1	4	3	$\begin{pmatrix}1\\1\end{pmatrix},\begin{pmatrix}-1\\1\end{pmatrix}$
$\mathbf{B}=\begin{pmatrix}2 & 2\\ 2 & -1\end{pmatrix}$	$\lvert\mathbf{B}\rvert=-6$	3, −2	1	−6	$\begin{pmatrix}2\\1\end{pmatrix},\begin{pmatrix}-1\\2\end{pmatrix}$
$\mathbf{C}=\begin{pmatrix}1 & 3\\ 1 & -1\end{pmatrix}$	$\lvert\mathbf{C}\rvert=-4$	2, −2	0	−4	$\begin{pmatrix}3\\1\end{pmatrix},\begin{pmatrix}1\\-1\end{pmatrix}$
$\mathbf{F}=\begin{pmatrix}4 & -1\\ 1 & 2\end{pmatrix}$	$\lvert\mathbf{F}\rvert=9$	3, 3	6	9	$\begin{pmatrix}1\\1\end{pmatrix}$, (twice)
$\mathbf{Z}=\begin{pmatrix}3 & -6\\ -1 & 2\end{pmatrix}$	$\lvert\mathbf{Z}\rvert=0$	0, 5	5	0	$\begin{pmatrix}3\\-1\end{pmatrix},\begin{pmatrix}2\\1\end{pmatrix}$

Exercise 1.4b

Find the eigenvalues and corresponding eigenvectors of the following matrices. Sketch the transformed axes and the eigenvectors in each case.

1 $\begin{pmatrix}2 & -3\\ 1 & -2\end{pmatrix}$ **2** $\begin{pmatrix}3 & -1\\ 0 & 2\end{pmatrix}$ **3** $\begin{pmatrix}-4 & 2\\ -15 & 7\end{pmatrix}$ **4** $\begin{pmatrix}-2 & 2\\ -3 & 5\end{pmatrix}$

5 $\begin{pmatrix}0 & 2\\ -2 & 5\end{pmatrix}$ **6** $\begin{pmatrix}\frac{1}{3} & \frac{1}{6}\\ 0 & \frac{1}{2}\end{pmatrix}$ **7** $\begin{pmatrix}3 & -2\\ -2 & 0\end{pmatrix}$

Do you see any connection between your answers to questions 2 and 6? Do you notice anything about the *eigenvectors* of **A** and **B** above, and of the matrix in question 7? Do you notice anything about the symmetry of the *matrices* **A**, **B**, and that in question 7?

1.5 Transformation of the unit square

We have introduced transformations of the plane as a change of base vectors and have seen the effect of such changes on points and on lines in the plane. If lines are transformed, then so are the regions enclosed by the lines and the most usual approach to the study of transformations is to illustrate the transformation in terms of its *geometrical* effect on a simple figure such as a square, rectangle or triangle. By geometrical effect we mean the way that such things as shape, size and position have changed. We are also interested in the properties which have remained unchanged or invariant.

The simplest figure is the *unit square*, which is bounded by the base vectors $\boldsymbol{i}$ and $\boldsymbol{j}$, with vertices O(0, 0), A(1, 0), C(1, 1) and B(0, 1).

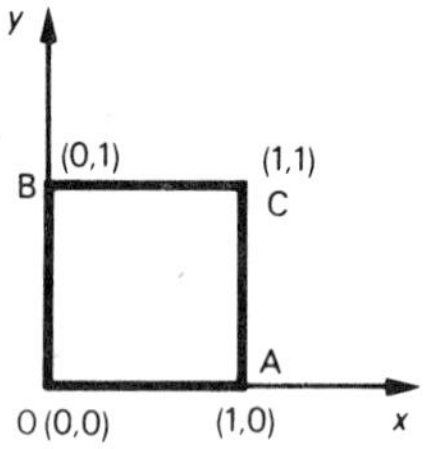

By considering the geometrical effect of a transformation on the unit square, we can see what is happening to the whole plane. Suppose the plane has been transformed by the matrix

$$\mathbf{G} = \begin{pmatrix} -2 & 1 \\ 1 & 1 \end{pmatrix}$$

The origin O has remained *invariant* (as in all transformations of the base vectors that can be represented by a 2×2 matrix).

$$\overset{\text{A}}{\begin{pmatrix} 1 \\ 0 \end{pmatrix}} \to \overset{\text{A}'}{\begin{pmatrix} -2 \\ 1 \end{pmatrix}}, \qquad \overset{\text{B}}{\begin{pmatrix} 0 \\ 1 \end{pmatrix}} \to \overset{\text{B}'}{\begin{pmatrix} 1 \\ 1 \end{pmatrix}} \qquad \text{and} \qquad \overset{\text{C}}{\begin{pmatrix} 1 \\ 1 \end{pmatrix}} \to \begin{pmatrix} -2 & 1 \\ 1 & 1 \end{pmatrix}\begin{pmatrix} 1 \\ 1 \end{pmatrix} = \overset{\text{C}'}{\begin{pmatrix} -1 \\ 2 \end{pmatrix}}$$

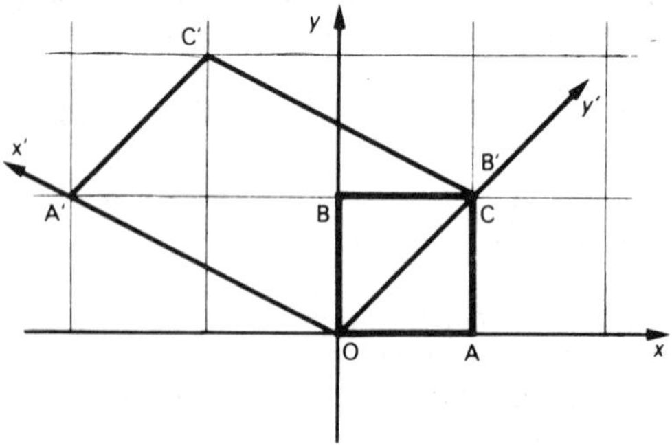

The unit square has been changed into a parallelogram, bounded by the new base vectors

$$\boldsymbol{a} = \begin{pmatrix} -2 \\ 1 \end{pmatrix} \quad \text{and} \quad \boldsymbol{b} = \begin{pmatrix} 1 \\ 1 \end{pmatrix}$$

so the *shape* has changed. The area of the parallelogram can easily be found (by enclosing it in a rectangle, and subtracting the 'corners') and is three square units so the *size* has changed. The figure has also been 'turned over', i.e. its *sense* has changed. Originally, anticlockwise, the square is OACB; now, clockwise, the parallelogram is OA′C′B′. It is not always easy to see from such a small part of the plane whether there are any eigenvectors, but there could be one, or two, or none (real) or else an infinite number.

The area of the transformed unit square

We have just found that when the unit square is transformed by the matrix

$$\mathbf{G} = \begin{pmatrix} -2 & 1 \\ 1 & 1 \end{pmatrix}$$

the area of the transformed figure is 3 square units. The determinant of the matrix

$$\begin{vmatrix} -2 & 1 \\ 1 & 1 \end{vmatrix} = -3$$

and this is no coincidence. In general,

The area of the transformed unit square is equal to the determinant of the transforming matrix. ◀

The sign of the determinant, + or −, indicates whether or not the sense has changed.
For consider the unit square, transformed by the matrix

$$\mathbf{M} = \begin{pmatrix} a_1 & b_1 \\ a_2 & b_2 \end{pmatrix}$$

The vertices of the unit square are transformed as follows. The origin O, is invariant.

$$\underset{\text{A}}{\begin{pmatrix} 1 \\ 0 \end{pmatrix}} \to \underset{\text{A}'}{\begin{pmatrix} a_1 \\ a_2 \end{pmatrix}}, \quad \underset{\text{B}}{\begin{pmatrix} 0 \\ 1 \end{pmatrix}} \to \underset{\text{B}'}{\begin{pmatrix} b_1 \\ b_2 \end{pmatrix}} \quad \text{and} \quad \underset{\text{C}}{\begin{pmatrix} 1 \\ 1 \end{pmatrix}} \to \underset{\text{C}'}{\begin{pmatrix} a_1+b_1 \\ a_2+b_2 \end{pmatrix}}$$

The parallelogram OA′C′B′ has been enclosed in the rectangle ODC′E.

Area of ODC′E $= (a_1+b_1)(a_2+b_2) = a_1a_2+b_1b_2+b_1a_2+a_1b_2$

Area of OFA′ = area C′KB′ $= \tfrac{1}{2}a_1a_2$

Area of OJB′ = area C′GA′ $= \tfrac{1}{2}b_1b_2$

Area of A′GDF = area B′JEK $= a_2b_1 = b_1a_2$

Total unshaded area $= a_1a_2+b_1b_2+2b_1a_2$

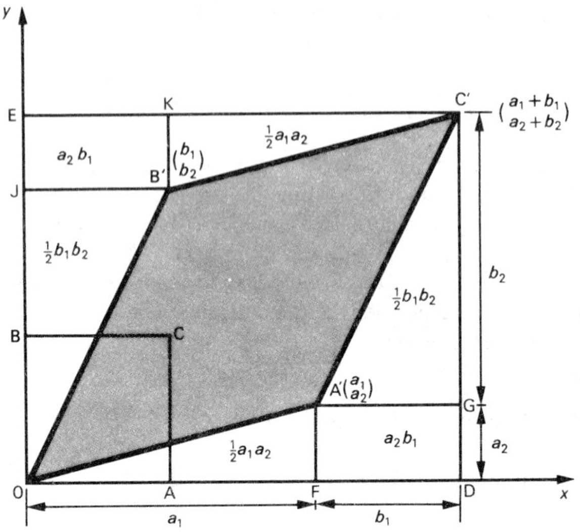

Subtracting this from the area of ODC′E, we find

Area of parallelogram OA′C′B′ $= a_1b_2 - b_1a_2$, the determinant of **M**.

Exercise 1.5

1 On the same axes draw the unit square and the triangle P(2, 0), Q(2, −1), R(0, −1) before and after transformation by the matrix

$$\mathbf{A} = \begin{pmatrix} 2 & 1 \\ 1 & 2 \end{pmatrix}$$

Describe the transformation geometrically and identify any eigenvectors and their corresponding eigenvalues (checking by calculation). Verify that the area of the transformed unit square is equal to the determinant and that the area of the triangle changes with scale factor equal to the determinant.

2 Drawing a separate diagram for each matrix, repeat Question **1** for each of the following:

(a) $\mathbf{C} = \begin{pmatrix} 1 & 3 \\ 1 & -1 \end{pmatrix}$ **(b)** $\mathbf{E} = \begin{pmatrix} 1 & -1 \\ 1 & 1 \end{pmatrix}$ **(c)** $\mathbf{H} = \begin{pmatrix} -2 & 0 \\ 0 & 3 \end{pmatrix}$

(d) $\mathbf{J} = \begin{pmatrix} 0 & -1 \\ 1 & 0 \end{pmatrix}$ **(e)** $\mathbf{K} = \begin{pmatrix} 2 & 0 \\ 0 & 2 \end{pmatrix}$ **(f)** $\mathbf{L} = \begin{pmatrix} 1 & 1 \\ 0 & 1 \end{pmatrix}$

(g) $\mathbf{M} = \begin{pmatrix} 1 & 0 \\ -2 & 1 \end{pmatrix}$ **(h)** $\mathbf{N} = \begin{pmatrix} -1 & 0 \\ 0 & 1 \end{pmatrix}$ **(i)** $\mathbf{P} = \begin{pmatrix} -1 & 0 \\ 0 & -1 \end{pmatrix}$

Keep your answers to this exercise carefully. We shall be referring to them in Section 3.1.

2 Successive, inverse and singular transformations

2.1 One transformation followed by another

Suppose we transform the x, y axes using the matrix

$$\begin{pmatrix} 1 & 3 \\ 0 & 1 \end{pmatrix}$$

into the new x', y' axes

$$\begin{pmatrix} 1 \\ 0 \end{pmatrix} \to \begin{pmatrix} 1 \\ 0 \end{pmatrix}, \qquad \begin{pmatrix} 0 \\ 1 \end{pmatrix} \to \begin{pmatrix} 3 \\ 1 \end{pmatrix}$$

Now transform these new axes x', y' into the axes x'', y'' using the matrix

$$\begin{pmatrix} 2 & 0 \\ 1 & 4 \end{pmatrix}$$

To find the new unit on the x'' axis referred to the original axes

$$\begin{pmatrix} 2 & 0 \\ 1 & 4 \end{pmatrix}\begin{pmatrix} 1 \\ 0 \end{pmatrix} = \begin{pmatrix} 2 \\ 1 \end{pmatrix}$$

and the new unit on the y'' axis, referred to the original axes

$$\begin{pmatrix} 2 & 0 \\ 1 & 4 \end{pmatrix}\begin{pmatrix} 3 \\ 1 \end{pmatrix} = \begin{pmatrix} 6 \\ 7 \end{pmatrix}$$

i.e. for the x units

$$\begin{pmatrix} 1 \\ 0 \end{pmatrix} \to \begin{pmatrix} 1 \\ 0 \end{pmatrix} \to \begin{pmatrix} 2 \\ 1 \end{pmatrix}$$

and for the y units

$$\begin{pmatrix} 0 \\ 1 \end{pmatrix} \to \begin{pmatrix} 3 \\ 1 \end{pmatrix} \to \begin{pmatrix} 6 \\ 7 \end{pmatrix}$$

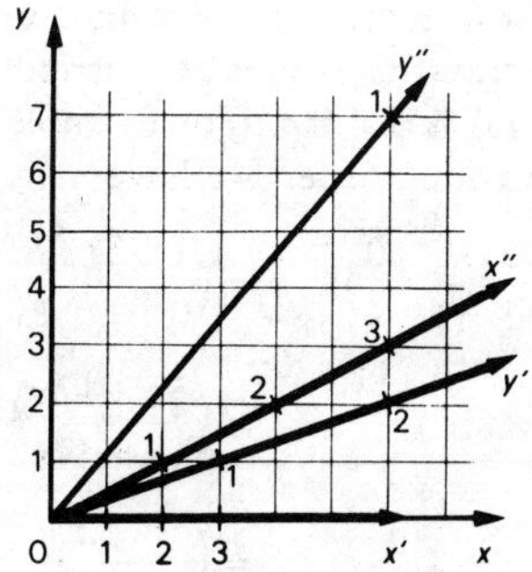

We *could*, however, have made the transformation in a single 'step' using

$$\begin{pmatrix} 2 & 6 \\ 1 & 7 \end{pmatrix}$$

Consider the general point

$$\begin{pmatrix} x \\ y \end{pmatrix}$$

Under the first transformation

$$\begin{pmatrix} 1 & 3 \\ 0 & 1 \end{pmatrix}\begin{pmatrix} x \\ y \end{pmatrix} = x\begin{pmatrix} 1 \\ 0 \end{pmatrix} + y\begin{pmatrix} 3 \\ 1 \end{pmatrix} = \begin{pmatrix} x' \\ y' \end{pmatrix} \quad \text{or} \quad \begin{pmatrix} x' \\ y' \end{pmatrix} = \begin{pmatrix} 1x+3y \\ 0x+1y \end{pmatrix}$$

Under the second transformation

$$\begin{pmatrix} 2 & 0 \\ 1 & 4 \end{pmatrix}\begin{pmatrix} x' \\ y' \end{pmatrix} = x'\begin{pmatrix} 2 \\ 1 \end{pmatrix} + y'\begin{pmatrix} 0 \\ 4 \end{pmatrix} = \begin{pmatrix} x'' \\ y'' \end{pmatrix}$$

or, by substituting for $\begin{pmatrix} x' \\ y' \end{pmatrix}$,

$$\begin{pmatrix} 2 & 0 \\ 1 & 4 \end{pmatrix}\begin{pmatrix} 1 & 3 \\ 0 & 1 \end{pmatrix}\begin{pmatrix} x \\ y \end{pmatrix} = (1x+3y)\begin{pmatrix} 2 \\ 1 \end{pmatrix} + (0x+1y)\begin{pmatrix} 0 \\ 4 \end{pmatrix} = \begin{pmatrix} x'' \\ y'' \end{pmatrix}$$

$$\begin{pmatrix} x'' \\ y'' \end{pmatrix} = \begin{pmatrix} 2x+6y \\ 1x+7y \end{pmatrix}$$

We see that to combine transformations they are arranged in the order

$$\overset{\textit{second}}{\begin{pmatrix} \quad & \quad \end{pmatrix}}\overset{\textit{first}}{\begin{pmatrix} \quad & \quad \end{pmatrix}}\begin{pmatrix} x \\ y \end{pmatrix}$$

and they are combined in the way called 'matrix multiplication'. In general,

$$\begin{pmatrix} c_1 & d_1 \\ c_2 & d_2 \end{pmatrix}\begin{pmatrix} a_1 & b_1 \\ a_2 & b_2 \end{pmatrix} = \left(a_1\begin{pmatrix} c_1 \\ c_2 \end{pmatrix} + a_2\begin{pmatrix} d_1 \\ d_2 \end{pmatrix} \quad b_1\begin{pmatrix} c_1 \\ c_2 \end{pmatrix} + b_2\begin{pmatrix} d_1 \\ d_2 \end{pmatrix}\right)$$

$$= \begin{pmatrix} a_1c_1+a_2d_1 & b_1c_1+b_2d_1 \\ a_1c_2+a_2d_2 & b_1c_2+b_2d_2 \end{pmatrix}$$

You are probably familiar with the process of matrix multiplication and will know that the *order* in which the transformations are carried out is most important, since for matrices **A, B**, in general **AB** $\neq$ **BA**. For example, if we carry out our transformation of the axes in the other order, we have

$$\begin{pmatrix} 1 & 3 \\ 0 & 1 \end{pmatrix}\begin{pmatrix} 2 & 0 \\ 1 & 4 \end{pmatrix}\begin{pmatrix} x \\ y \end{pmatrix} = \begin{pmatrix} 1 & 3 \\ 0 & 1 \end{pmatrix}\begin{pmatrix} 2x+0y \\ 1x+4y \end{pmatrix}$$

$$= \begin{pmatrix} 5x+12y \\ 1x+\ 4y \end{pmatrix}$$

$$= \begin{pmatrix} 5 & 12 \\ 1 & 4 \end{pmatrix}\begin{pmatrix} x \\ y \end{pmatrix}$$

Illustrate this transformation of the axes yourself and compare it with the one given.

NOTE. It is convenient when transforming, for example, the vertices of a quadrilateral, to arrange their position vectors in a 2×4 matrix and premultiply this by the transforming matrix. For instance,

$$\begin{pmatrix} 2 & 1 \\ 0 & 1 \end{pmatrix}\begin{pmatrix} \overset{\text{A}}{1} & \overset{\text{B}}{4} & \overset{\text{C}}{2} & \overset{\text{D}}{0} \\ 0 & 1 & 3 & 2 \end{pmatrix} = \begin{pmatrix} \overset{\text{A}'}{2} & \overset{\text{B}'}{9} & \overset{\text{C}'}{7} & \overset{\text{D}'}{2} \\ 0 & 1 & 3 & 2 \end{pmatrix}$$

Exercise 2.1

1 Transform the triangle with vertices A(2, 0), B(2, 3), and C(1, 0) using first the matrix

$$\mathbf{P} = \begin{pmatrix} 0 & -1 \\ 1 & 0 \end{pmatrix}$$

Call this new position A′B′C′. Now transform A′B′C′ using a second matrix

$$\mathbf{Q} = \begin{pmatrix} -1 & 0 \\ 0 & 1 \end{pmatrix}$$

to the position A″B″C″. Mark these positions on a diagram. Check that the triangle ABC transformed once by the matrix **QP** reaches the same position, A″B″C″. Repeat, using first the matrix **Q** and then the matrix **P**, again showing the new positions on the diagram. Describe each transformation geometrically, i.e. describe any changes in size, shape or position which have occurred.

2 Triangle LMN has coordinates L(1, 1), M(3, 1), N(3, 2). Transform it to L′M′N′ using the matrix

$$\mathbf{A} = \begin{pmatrix} 1 & 1 \\ 0 & 1 \end{pmatrix}$$

Now transform L′M′N′ using the matrix

$$\mathbf{B} = \begin{pmatrix} 1 & 0 \\ 2 & 1 \end{pmatrix}$$

Show the transformations on a diagram and join LL′, MM′, NN′ and L′L″, M′M″, N′N″. Describe the transformations geometrically. Write down the single matrix which would transform LMN to L″M″N″ in one step.

3 OACB is a unit square with A(1, 0), B(0, 1) and C(1, 1). Transform it to OA′C′B′ using first the matrix

$$\mathbf{S} = \begin{pmatrix} 1 & -3 \\ 0 & 1 \end{pmatrix}$$

Now transform OA′C′B′ using the matrix

$$\mathbf{T} = \begin{pmatrix} 0 & 1 \\ 2 & 0 \end{pmatrix}$$

What single matrix is equivalent to **TS**? Describe each transformation geometrically. Repeat, using first **T** and then **S**. (*Reminder*: The transformation **S** followed by the transformation **T** is equivalent to the transformation **TS**. It helps to remember this if you think of **TS** as '**T** *following* **S**'.)

2.2 The inverse transformation

We have seen that under a mapping (represented by a matrix) each point in the plane is mapped onto another (or sometimes the same) point in the plane. We shall frequently need to find the 'opposite' mapping which returns each point to its original point. This is known as the *inverse* mapping and is represented by the 'inverse' matrix of the transformation. The inverse of a matrix **M** is written $\mathbf{M}^{-1}$ and by definition

$$\mathbf{M}^{-1}\mathbf{M} = \mathbf{M}\mathbf{M}^{-1} = \mathbf{I}$$

where I is the identity matrix

For 2 × 2 matrices $\mathbf{I} = \begin{pmatrix} 1 & 0 \\ 0 & 1 \end{pmatrix}$

This means that the result of the mapping represented by **M**, followed by that represented by $\mathbf{M}^{-1}$, is that the plane is left unchanged and is identical with the original plane. For example, consider the mapping or transformation shown below, where the 'black' cartesian grid is transformed into the 'red' grid of the matrix.

$$\mathbf{A} = \begin{pmatrix} 2 & 1 \\ 1 & 2 \end{pmatrix}$$

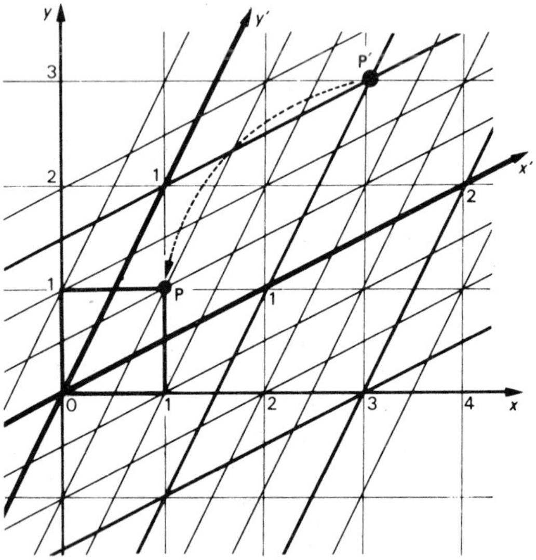

The diagram shows an enlarged portion of the grids, with the 'red' grid shown in bold lines.

Now $\begin{pmatrix} 1 \\ 0 \end{pmatrix}_{\text{Black}} \to \begin{pmatrix} 1 \\ 0 \end{pmatrix}_{\text{Red}} = \begin{pmatrix} 2 \\ 1 \end{pmatrix}_{\text{Black}}$

and $\begin{pmatrix} 0 \\ 1 \end{pmatrix}_{\text{Black}} \to \begin{pmatrix} 0 \\ 1 \end{pmatrix}_{\text{Red}} = \begin{pmatrix} 1 \\ 2 \end{pmatrix}_{\text{Black}}$

The mapping from black to red grid is represented by the black coordinates of points $\begin{pmatrix}1\\0\end{pmatrix}$ and $\begin{pmatrix}0\\1\end{pmatrix}$ on the red grid. The matrix of the transformation is $\begin{pmatrix}2 & 1\\1 & 2\end{pmatrix}$. The inverse mapping is the one which takes us from the red grid back to our original black grid.

$$\begin{pmatrix}1\\0\end{pmatrix}_{\text{Red}} \to \begin{pmatrix}1\\0\end{pmatrix}_{\text{Black}} = \begin{pmatrix}\frac{2}{3}\\-\frac{1}{3}\end{pmatrix}_{\text{Red}}$$

$$\begin{pmatrix}0\\1\end{pmatrix}_{\text{Red}} \to \begin{pmatrix}0\\1\end{pmatrix}_{\text{Black}} = \begin{pmatrix}-\frac{1}{3}\\\frac{2}{3}\end{pmatrix}_{\text{Red}}$$

Hence the matrix representing the inverse mapping is

$$\begin{pmatrix}\frac{2}{3} & -\frac{1}{3}\\-\frac{1}{3} & \frac{2}{3}\end{pmatrix}$$

these being the red coordinates of the points $\begin{pmatrix}1\\0\end{pmatrix}$ and $\begin{pmatrix}0\\1\end{pmatrix}$ on the black grid. Check that

$$\begin{pmatrix}\frac{2}{3} & -\frac{1}{3}\\-\frac{1}{3} & \frac{2}{3}\end{pmatrix}\begin{pmatrix}2 & 1\\1 & 2\end{pmatrix} = \begin{pmatrix}2 & 1\\1 & 2\end{pmatrix}\begin{pmatrix}\frac{2}{3} & -\frac{1}{3}\\-\frac{1}{3} & \frac{2}{3}\end{pmatrix} = \begin{pmatrix}1 & 0\\0 & 1\end{pmatrix}$$

In general, if

$$\begin{pmatrix}x\\y\end{pmatrix} \to \begin{pmatrix}x'\\y'\end{pmatrix} \text{ under } \mathbf{M}\text{, then } \begin{pmatrix}x'\\y'\end{pmatrix} \to \begin{pmatrix}x\\y\end{pmatrix} \text{ under } \mathbf{M}^{-1}$$

or if $\begin{pmatrix}x'\\y'\end{pmatrix} = \mathbf{M}\begin{pmatrix}x\\y\end{pmatrix}$ then $\begin{pmatrix}x\\y\end{pmatrix} = \mathbf{M}^{-1}\begin{pmatrix}x'\\y'\end{pmatrix}$

For example, under $\mathbf{A} = \begin{pmatrix}2 & 1\\1 & 2\end{pmatrix}$

$$\begin{pmatrix}1\\1\end{pmatrix} \to \begin{pmatrix}2 & 1\\1 & 2\end{pmatrix}\begin{pmatrix}1\\1\end{pmatrix} = \begin{pmatrix}3\\3\end{pmatrix}$$

so under $\mathbf{A}^{-1} = \begin{pmatrix}\frac{2}{3} & -\frac{1}{3}\\-\frac{1}{3} & \frac{2}{3}\end{pmatrix}$

$$\begin{pmatrix}3\\3\end{pmatrix} \to \begin{pmatrix}\frac{2}{3} & -\frac{1}{3}\\-\frac{1}{3} & \frac{2}{3}\end{pmatrix}\begin{pmatrix}3\\3\end{pmatrix} = \begin{pmatrix}1\\1\end{pmatrix}$$

To find the inverse matrix algebraically

Suppose $\mathbf{M} = \begin{pmatrix}a_1 & b_1\\a_2 & b_2\end{pmatrix}$

and we have to find $\mathbf{M}^{-1} = \begin{pmatrix}c_1 & d_1\\c_2 & d_2\end{pmatrix}$

such that $\begin{pmatrix}c_1 & d_1\\c_2 & d_2\end{pmatrix}\begin{pmatrix}a_1 & b_1\\a_2 & b_2\end{pmatrix} = \begin{pmatrix}1 & 0\\0 & 1\end{pmatrix}$

Multiplying out, and equating elements, we have four equations:

$$c_1a_1 + d_1a_2 = 1 \qquad \text{I}$$

$$c_1b_1 + d_1b_2 = 0 \qquad \text{II}$$

$$c_2a_1 + d_2a_2 = 0 \qquad \text{III}$$

$$c_2b_1 + d_2b_2 = 1 \qquad \text{IV}$$

Solving simultaneously

$$\text{I} \times b_2: \quad c_1a_1b_2 + d_1a_2b_2 = b_2$$

$$\text{II} \times a_2: \quad c_1a_2b_1 + d_1a_2b_2 = 0$$

$$\text{Subtract:} \quad c_1(a_1b_2 - a_2b_1) = b_2$$

$$c_1 = \frac{b_2}{a_1b_2 - a_2b_1}$$

$$\text{I} \times b_1: \quad c_1a_1b_1 + d_1a_2b_1 = b_1$$

$$\text{II} \times a_1: \quad c_1a_1b_1 + d_1a_1b_2 = 0$$

$$\text{Subtract:} \quad d_1(a_1b_2 - a_2b_1) = -b_1$$

$$d_1 = \frac{-b_1}{a_1b_2 - a_2b_1}$$

Similarly

$$\text{III} \times b_2: \quad c_2a_1b_2 + d_2a_2b_2 = 0$$

$$\text{IV} \times a_2: \quad c_2a_2b_1 + d_2a_2b_2 = a_2$$

$$\text{Subtract:} \quad c_2(a_1b_2 - a_2b_1) = -a_2$$

$$c_2 = \frac{-a_2}{a_1b_2 - a_2b_1}$$

$$\text{III} \times b_1: \quad c_2a_1b_1 + d_2a_2b_1 = 0$$

$$\text{IV} \times a_1: \quad c_2a_1b_1 + d_2a_1b_2 = a_1$$

$$\text{Subtract:} \quad d_2(a_1b_2 - a_2b_1) = a_1$$

$$d_2 = \frac{a_1}{a_1b_2 - a_2b_1}$$

In each case, the denominator is $a_1b_2 - a_2b_1$ which is Det (**M**). Hence

$$\mathbf{M}^{-1} = \frac{1}{a_1b_2 - a_2b_1}\begin{pmatrix} b_2 & -b_1 \\ -a_2 & a_1 \end{pmatrix}$$

'Rule of thumb'

You will probably have learnt how to find $\mathbf{M}^{-1}$ using the 'rule'; i.e. if

$$\mathbf{M} = \begin{pmatrix} a_1 & b_1 \\ a_2 & b_2 \end{pmatrix}$$

interchange a_1 and b_2, change the signs of b_1 and a_2 and divide by the determinant $a_1b_2 - a_2b_1$, so

$$\mathbf{M}^{-1} = \frac{1}{a_1b_2 - a_2b_1}\begin{pmatrix} b_2 & -b_1 \\ -a_2 & a_1 \end{pmatrix} = |\mathbf{M}|\mathbf{N}$$ ◀

NOTE that if $|\mathbf{M}| = 0$, then $\mathbf{M}$ has no inverse. $\mathbf{N}$ is called the *adjoint* of $\mathbf{M}$.

Relationship between a matrix and its inverse

If we write the *top* row of **N** as a column $\begin{pmatrix} b_2 \\ -b_1 \end{pmatrix}$, we see that it is perpendicular to the *second* column of **M**, $\begin{pmatrix} b_1 \\ b_2 \end{pmatrix}$ and if we write the *bottom* row of **N** as a column $\begin{pmatrix} -a_2 \\ a_1 \end{pmatrix}$, we see that it is perpendicular to the *first* column of **M**, $\begin{pmatrix} a_1 \\ a_2 \end{pmatrix}$. Consider for example $\mathbf{P} = \begin{pmatrix} 2 & 5 \\ -1 & 3 \end{pmatrix}$ with base vectors $\boldsymbol{a} = \begin{pmatrix} 2 \\ -1 \end{pmatrix}$ and $\boldsymbol{b} = \begin{pmatrix} 5 \\ 3 \end{pmatrix}$ and determinant $|\mathbf{P}| = 11$. Then $\mathbf{P}^{-1} = \frac{1}{11}\begin{pmatrix} 3 & -5 \\ 1 & 2 \end{pmatrix}$. We now write the top row as the column $\boldsymbol{c} = \begin{pmatrix} 3 \\ -5 \end{pmatrix}$ and the bottom row as $\boldsymbol{d} = \begin{pmatrix} 1 \\ 2 \end{pmatrix}$ and draw them on our diagram.

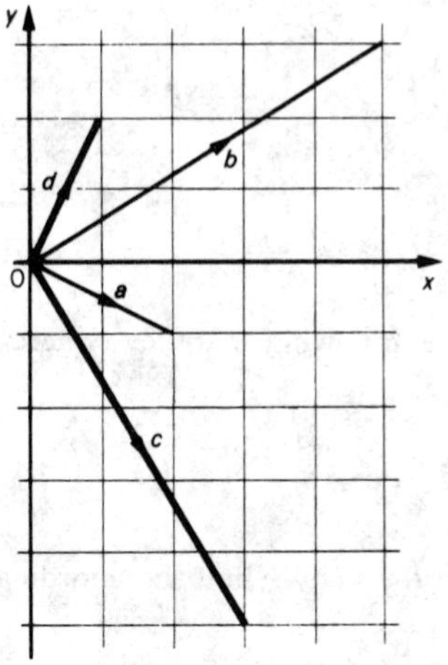

We can see that $\boldsymbol{a} \perp \boldsymbol{d}$ and $\boldsymbol{b} \perp \boldsymbol{c}$. Check that this relationship holds for the matrices

$$\mathbf{A} = \begin{pmatrix} 2 & 1 \\ 1 & 2 \end{pmatrix}, \qquad \mathbf{B} = \begin{pmatrix} 2 & 2 \\ 2 & -1 \end{pmatrix}, \qquad \mathbf{Q} = \begin{pmatrix} 3 & 5 \\ 1 & 2 \end{pmatrix}$$

and their inverses.

This relationship is of great importance when we come to consider 3×3 matrices and their inverses.

Use of the inverse matrix

After a transformation, we may know that a point P(x, y) has coordinates (-5, 1) for example, and we would like to know its original coordinates. Then if the transformation was represented by

$$\mathbf{M} = \begin{pmatrix} -2 & 1 \\ 1 & 1 \end{pmatrix}$$

we have
$$\mathbf{M}\begin{pmatrix} x \\ y \end{pmatrix} = \begin{pmatrix} -5 \\ 1 \end{pmatrix}$$

and hence if $\mathbf{M}$ has an inverse $\mathbf{M}^{-1}$

$$\mathbf{M}^{-1}\mathbf{M}\begin{pmatrix} x \\ y \end{pmatrix} = \mathbf{M}^{-1}\begin{pmatrix} -5 \\ 1 \end{pmatrix}$$

or
$$\mathbf{I}\begin{pmatrix} x \\ y \end{pmatrix} = \mathbf{M}^{-1}\begin{pmatrix} -5 \\ 1 \end{pmatrix} \qquad \text{where } \mathbf{I} \text{ is } \begin{pmatrix} 1 & 0 \\ 0 & 1 \end{pmatrix}$$

and
$$\begin{pmatrix} x \\ y \end{pmatrix} = \mathbf{M}^{-1}\begin{pmatrix} -5 \\ 1 \end{pmatrix}$$

Hence in this case

$$\begin{pmatrix} x \\ y \end{pmatrix} = -\frac{1}{3}\begin{pmatrix} 1 & -1 \\ -1 & -2 \end{pmatrix}\begin{pmatrix} -5 \\ 1 \end{pmatrix}$$

giving
$$\begin{pmatrix} x \\ y \end{pmatrix} = \begin{pmatrix} 2 \\ -1 \end{pmatrix}$$

and finally
$$x = 2, \qquad y = -1$$

Exercise 2.2

1 Find the inverse of the following matrices (where possible) and check your answers by multiplication.

(a) $\begin{pmatrix} 2 & 3 \\ -1 & 5 \end{pmatrix}$ **(b)** $\begin{pmatrix} 3 & -4 \\ 1 & 2 \end{pmatrix}$ **(c)** $\begin{pmatrix} -1 & 3 \\ 1 & 2 \end{pmatrix}$ **(d)** $\begin{pmatrix} 2 & -4 \\ 3 & -6 \end{pmatrix}$

2 Using your answers to the above, find the coordinates (x, y) in the following equations:

(a) $\begin{pmatrix} 2 & 3 \\ -1 & 5 \end{pmatrix}\begin{pmatrix} x \\ y \end{pmatrix} = \begin{pmatrix} 9 \\ 2 \end{pmatrix}$ **(b)** $\begin{pmatrix} 3 & -4 \\ 1 & 2 \end{pmatrix}\begin{pmatrix} x \\ y \end{pmatrix} = \begin{pmatrix} 5 \\ -5 \end{pmatrix}$

(c) $\begin{pmatrix} -1 & 3 \\ 1 & 2 \end{pmatrix}\begin{pmatrix} x \\ y \end{pmatrix} = \begin{pmatrix} -13 \\ -7 \end{pmatrix}$ **(d)** $\begin{pmatrix} 2 & -4 \\ 3 & -6 \end{pmatrix}\begin{pmatrix} x \\ y \end{pmatrix} = \begin{pmatrix} 3 \\ 5 \end{pmatrix}$

3 The line
$$\frac{x-3}{2} = \frac{y-1}{-3}$$

has been transformed using the matrix

$$\begin{pmatrix} 4 & -2 \\ -1 & 1 \end{pmatrix}$$

What was its equation before the transformation?

4 The lines $x = 0$, $y = x$ have been transformed using the matrix $\begin{pmatrix} 2 & -3 \\ -1 & 1 \end{pmatrix}$. What were their equations before the transformation?

5 After a transformation by the matrix $\begin{pmatrix} 1 & -1 \\ 0 & 2 \end{pmatrix}$ the lines $x = 0$ and $y = \frac{3}{4}x$ are the asymptotes of a hyperbola. What were their equations before the transformation?

2.3 The inverse of successive transformations

Consider the transformations by the matrices

$$\mathbf{A} = \begin{pmatrix} 2 & 1 \\ 1 & 2 \end{pmatrix} \quad \text{followed by} \quad \mathbf{B} = \begin{pmatrix} 2 & 2 \\ 2 & -1 \end{pmatrix}$$

Under **A** $\begin{pmatrix} 1 \\ 0 \end{pmatrix} \to \begin{pmatrix} 2 \\ 1 \end{pmatrix}$ and $\begin{pmatrix} 0 \\ 1 \end{pmatrix} \to \begin{pmatrix} 1 \\ 2 \end{pmatrix}$

Under **B** $\begin{pmatrix} 2 \\ 1 \end{pmatrix} \to \begin{pmatrix} 6 \\ 3 \end{pmatrix}$ and $\begin{pmatrix} 1 \\ 2 \end{pmatrix} \to \begin{pmatrix} 6 \\ 0 \end{pmatrix}$

since $\begin{pmatrix} 2 & 2 \\ 2 & -1 \end{pmatrix}\begin{pmatrix} 2 \\ 1 \end{pmatrix} = \begin{pmatrix} 6 \\ 3 \end{pmatrix}$ and $\begin{pmatrix} 2 & 2 \\ 2 & -1 \end{pmatrix}\begin{pmatrix} 1 \\ 2 \end{pmatrix} = \begin{pmatrix} 6 \\ 0 \end{pmatrix}$

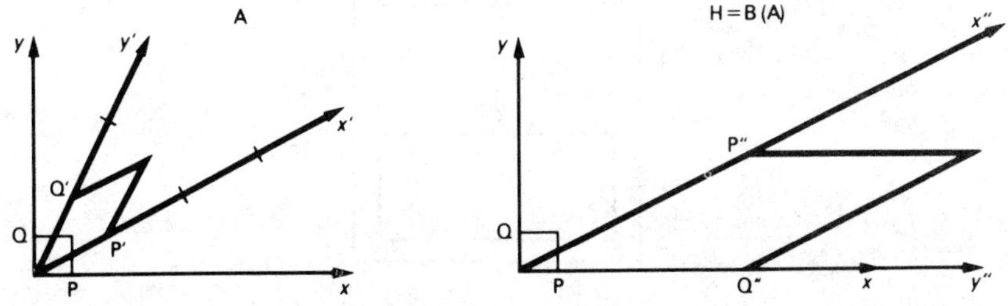

We know that **A** followed by **B** is equivalent to **BA**. Let

$$\mathbf{BA} = \mathbf{H}$$

Then $$\mathbf{H} = \begin{pmatrix} 2 & 2 \\ 2 & -1 \end{pmatrix}\begin{pmatrix} 2 & 1 \\ 1 & 2 \end{pmatrix} = \begin{pmatrix} 6 & 6 \\ 3 & 0 \end{pmatrix}$$

So under **H** $\begin{pmatrix} 1 \\ 0 \end{pmatrix} \to \begin{pmatrix} 6 \\ 3 \end{pmatrix}$ and $\begin{pmatrix} 0 \\ 1 \end{pmatrix} \to \begin{pmatrix} 6 \\ 0 \end{pmatrix}$

—as we have seen above.

We can represent **H** by a flow diagram:

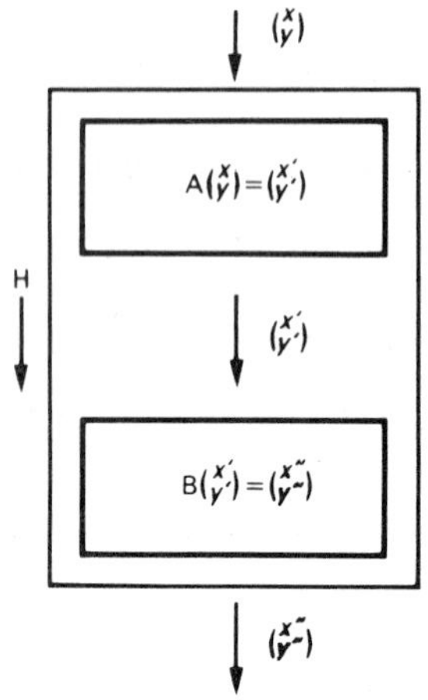

Then the inverse of **H**, which is $\mathbf{H}^{-1}$ can be represented by a second flow diagram:

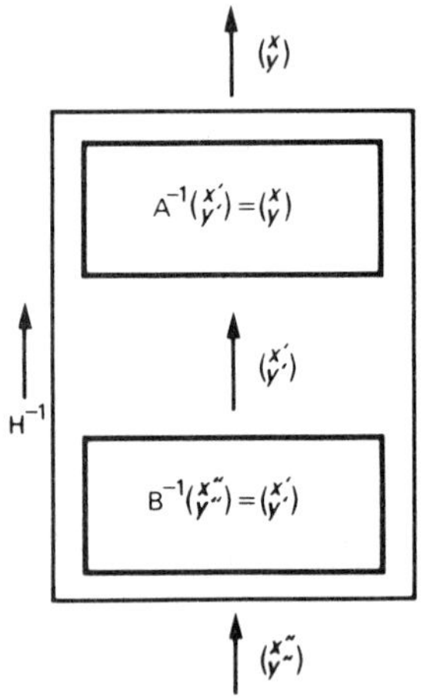

Obviously, we must do the inverse of **B** first, followed by the inverse of **A**. Hence

$$\mathbf{H}^{-1} = \mathbf{A}^{-1}\mathbf{B}^{-1} \qquad (\mathbf{A}^{-1} \text{ following } \mathbf{B}^{-1})$$

but
$$\mathbf{H}^{-1} = (\mathbf{BA})^{-1}$$

so
$$(\mathbf{BA})^{-1} = \mathbf{A}^{-1}\mathbf{B}^{-1}$$ ◀

This result can be checked numerically.

$$(\mathbf{BA})^{-1} = \mathbf{H}^{-1} = \frac{1}{-18}\begin{pmatrix} 0 & -6 \\ -3 & 6 \end{pmatrix}, \quad \mathbf{A}^{-1} = \frac{1}{3}\begin{pmatrix} 2 & -1 \\ -1 & 2 \end{pmatrix}, \quad \mathbf{B}^{-1} = \frac{1}{-6}\begin{pmatrix} -1 & -2 \\ -2 & 2 \end{pmatrix}$$

$$\mathbf{A}^{-1}\mathbf{B}^{-1} = \frac{1}{3}\begin{pmatrix} 2 & -1 \\ -1 & 2 \end{pmatrix}\frac{1}{-6}\begin{pmatrix} -1 & -2 \\ -2 & 2 \end{pmatrix} = \frac{1}{-18}\begin{pmatrix} 0 & -6 \\ -3 & 6 \end{pmatrix}$$

The result $$(\mathbf{BA})^{-1} = \mathbf{A}^{-1}\mathbf{B}^{-1}$$

can also be verified algebraically by post-multiplying both sides by **BA**. Then

$$\text{LHS} = (\mathbf{BA})^{-1}(\mathbf{BA}) = \mathbf{I}$$

$$\begin{aligned}\text{RHS} &= (\mathbf{A}^{-1}\mathbf{B}^{-1})\mathbf{BA} \\ &= \mathbf{A}^{-1}(\mathbf{B}^{-1}\mathbf{B})\mathbf{A}\end{aligned}$$

(assuming the associative law holds)

$$= \mathbf{A}^{-1}\mathbf{IA} = \mathbf{A}^{-1}\mathbf{A} = \mathbf{I}$$

Exercise 2.3

1 Draw the rectangle OPQR, with P(2, 0), Q(2, 1) and R(0, 1)

(a) Show its position after transformation by $\mathbf{F} = \begin{pmatrix} 0 & -1 \\ 1 & 0 \end{pmatrix}$. Write down $\mathbf{F}^{-1}$

(b) Show its second position after transformation by **DF** where $\mathbf{D} = \begin{pmatrix} 2 & 0 \\ 0 & 3 \end{pmatrix}$

Write down $\mathbf{D}^{-1}$ and $(\mathbf{DF})^{-1}$
Check that $(\mathbf{DF})^{-1} = \mathbf{F}^{-1}\mathbf{D}^{-1}$
Repeat using **D** first and then **F**.

2 Draw the rectangle OPQR as in Question 1.
Transform it using the matrices $\mathbf{T} = \begin{pmatrix} 4 & -1 \\ 1 & 2 \end{pmatrix}$ and $\mathbf{S} = \begin{pmatrix} 1 & -2 \\ 1 & -2 \end{pmatrix}$

(a) in the sequence **S** following **T** i.e. **ST**. **(b)** in the sequence **TS**
Is it possible to find $\mathbf{T}^{-1}$, $\mathbf{S}^{-1}$, $(\mathbf{ST})^{-1}$, $(\mathbf{TS})^{-1}$?

2.4 Singular transformations

We have been unable to find the inverse of matrices such as $\begin{pmatrix} 3 & -6 \\ -1 & 2 \end{pmatrix}$ and $\begin{pmatrix} 2 & -4 \\ 3 & -6 \end{pmatrix}$ where the determinant is zero. Moreover, in Exercise 1.2 we found it impossible to draw a grid for the matrix $\begin{pmatrix} 3 & -6 \\ -1 & 2 \end{pmatrix}$. Such matrices are called *singular* matrices, and the transformations they represent, *singular* transformations. We now study them in more detail.

The matrix

$$\mathbf{Z} = \begin{pmatrix} 3 & -6 \\ -1 & 2 \end{pmatrix} \quad \text{maps} \quad \begin{pmatrix} 1 \\ 0 \end{pmatrix} \to \begin{pmatrix} 3 \\ -1 \end{pmatrix} \quad \text{and} \quad \begin{pmatrix} 0 \\ 1 \end{pmatrix} \to \begin{pmatrix} -6 \\ 2 \end{pmatrix}$$

But these two lie in the same line, $y = -\frac{1}{3}x$, and in fact *all* the points in the plane are mapped onto this line. For example,

$$\begin{pmatrix}2\\0\end{pmatrix} \to \begin{pmatrix}3 & -6\\-1 & 2\end{pmatrix}\begin{pmatrix}2\\0\end{pmatrix} = \begin{pmatrix}6\\-2\end{pmatrix}$$

and $$\begin{pmatrix}4\\1\end{pmatrix} \to \begin{pmatrix}3 & -6\\-1 & 2\end{pmatrix}\begin{pmatrix}4\\1\end{pmatrix} = \begin{pmatrix}6\\-2\end{pmatrix}$$ the same point.

Also $$\begin{pmatrix}2\\1\end{pmatrix} \to \begin{pmatrix}3 & -6\\-1 & 2\end{pmatrix}\begin{pmatrix}2\\1\end{pmatrix} = \begin{pmatrix}0\\0\end{pmatrix}$$ the origin

and $$\begin{pmatrix}-4\\-2\end{pmatrix} \to \begin{pmatrix}3 & -6\\-1 & 2\end{pmatrix}\begin{pmatrix}-4\\-2\end{pmatrix} = \begin{pmatrix}0\\0\end{pmatrix}$$ the origin again.

How many points will map onto the origin? If (x, y) is any point which does, then

$$\begin{pmatrix}3 & -6\\-1 & 2\end{pmatrix}\begin{pmatrix}x\\y\end{pmatrix} = \begin{pmatrix}0\\0\end{pmatrix} \qquad \text{which gives us} \qquad \begin{cases}3x-6y=0\\-x+2y=0\end{cases}$$

Hence *all* the points in the line $y = \frac{1}{2}x$ map onto the origin.

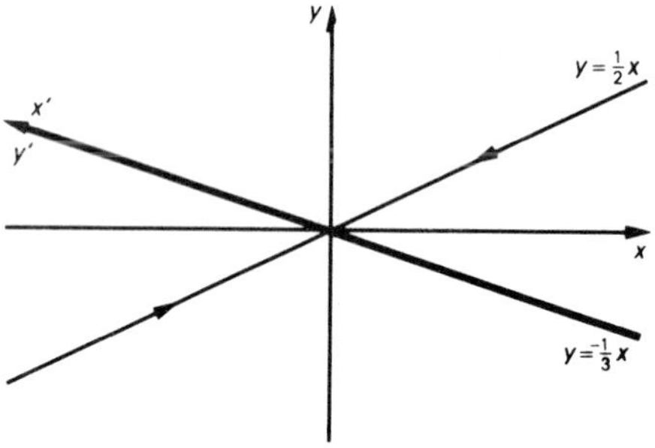

Similarly

$$\begin{pmatrix}3 & -6\\-1 & 2\end{pmatrix}\begin{pmatrix}x\\y\end{pmatrix} = \begin{pmatrix}6\\-2\end{pmatrix} \qquad \text{gives} \qquad \begin{cases}3x-6y=6\\-x+2y=-2\end{cases}$$

and so all the points in the line $y = \frac{1}{2}x - 1$ map onto $(6, -2)$. It follows that every *point* on the line $y = -\frac{1}{3}x$ is the image of a *line* which is parallel to $y = \frac{1}{2}x$. We can find the image, for example, of the line $y = \frac{1}{2}x + 2$:

$$\begin{pmatrix}3 & -6\\-1 & 2\end{pmatrix}\begin{pmatrix}x\\\frac{1}{2}x+2\end{pmatrix} = \begin{pmatrix}3x-3x-12\\-x+\ x+\ 4\end{pmatrix} = \begin{pmatrix}-12\\4\end{pmatrix}$$

We call the line $y = -\frac{1}{3}x$, onto which the whole plane maps, the *image line*. Clearly, it is one of the eigenvectors of the transformation, since points on this line *before* transformation will certainly be on the same line *after* transformation. The other eigenvector is the line $y = \frac{1}{2}x$ which maps onto the origin, with eigenvalue zero.

The set of lines parallel to $y = \frac{1}{2}x$ we call the *projection lines*. If the projection lines are perpendicular to the image line we say the plane maps onto that line *orthogonally*.

Example

Find the matrix which maps the plane orthogonally onto the line $y = 2x$.

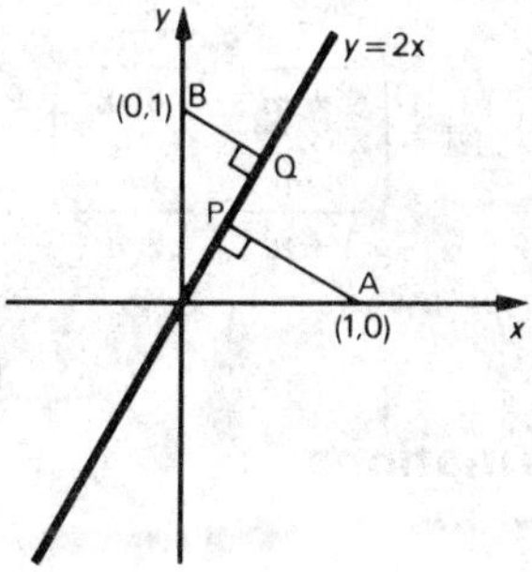

Suppose under the transformation $A(1, 0) \to P$ and $B(0, 1) \to Q$ where $AP \perp PQ$ and $BQ \perp PQ$. Then the position vectors of P and Q are the columns of the required matrix. The direction ratios of the line

$$y = 2x \qquad \text{or} \qquad \frac{x}{1} = \frac{y}{2}$$

are $1:2$ and any point on the line can be expressed parametrically as $(k, 2k)$. Being perpendicular to PQ the direction ratios of both AP and BQ are $2:-1$. So if P is the point $(p, 2p)$ and Q is the point $(q, 2q)$

for AP and for BQ

$$\frac{1-p}{2} = \frac{0-2p}{-1} \qquad \frac{0-q}{2} = \frac{1-2q}{-1}$$

$$-1+p = -4p \qquad q = 2-4q$$

$$5p = 1 \qquad 5q = 2$$

$$p = \tfrac{1}{5} \qquad q = \tfrac{2}{5}$$

P is the point $(\frac{1}{5}, \frac{2}{5})$ and Q is the point $(\frac{2}{5}, \frac{4}{5})$

and the required matrix is

$$\mathbf{M} = \begin{pmatrix} \frac{1}{5} & \frac{2}{5} \\ \frac{2}{5} & \frac{4}{5} \end{pmatrix}$$

Of course $|\mathbf{M}| = 0$ and $\mathbf{M}$ has no inverse.

Exercise 2.4

1 Find the line onto which the plane is mapped by the matrix $\begin{pmatrix} 1 & -1 \\ 0 & 0 \end{pmatrix}$

Which line is mapped onto the origin?

2 Find the matrix which maps the plane orthogonally onto the line $\dfrac{x}{3} = \dfrac{y}{-1}$

3 Find the line which is mapped onto the origin by the transformation $\begin{pmatrix} 4 & 2 \\ 6 & 3 \end{pmatrix}$. Onto which line is the plane mapped?

4 Show that the matrix maps the plane orthogonally onto the line $y = mx$ is

$$\mathbf{M} = \begin{pmatrix} \dfrac{1}{1+m^2} & \dfrac{m}{1+m^2} \\ \dfrac{m}{1+m^2} & \dfrac{m^2}{1+m^2} \end{pmatrix}$$

3 Standard transformations

3.1 Introduction

In Section 1.5 we considered the effect of a transformation of the plane on a particular element of the plane, the unit square, and found that in general its shape changed to a non-square parallelogram, and its size or area changed by a scale factor equal to the determinant of the transforming matrix. In Exercise 1.5 we investigated the effect of particular matrices on both the unit square and on a right angled scalene triangle and found that we could describe the transformations in simple geometrical terms. The matrix $\mathbf{E} = \begin{pmatrix} 1 & -1 \\ 1 & 1 \end{pmatrix}$, for example rotated and enlarged both square and triangle. The matrix $\mathbf{H} = \begin{pmatrix} -2 & 0 \\ 0 & 3 \end{pmatrix}$ stretched the square into a rectangle and 'flipped' it across the y-axis. The matrix $\mathbf{J} = \begin{pmatrix} 0 & -1 \\ 1 & 0 \end{pmatrix}$ rotated the plane anticlockwise about the origin through one right angle and $\mathbf{K} = \begin{pmatrix} 2 & 0 \\ 0 & 2 \end{pmatrix}$ enlarged with linear scale factor 2. $\mathbf{L} = \begin{pmatrix} 1 & 1 \\ 0 & 1 \end{pmatrix}$ and $\mathbf{M} = \begin{pmatrix} 1 & 0 \\ -2 & 1 \end{pmatrix}$ both *sheared* the unit square, $\mathbf{N} = \begin{pmatrix} -1 & 0 \\ 0 & 1 \end{pmatrix}$ reflected it in the y axis and $\mathbf{P} = \begin{pmatrix} -1 & 0 \\ 0 & -1 \end{pmatrix}$ rotated it through a half turn about the origin.

We now study these standard transformations, looking first at transformations in which

(1) the transformed x' and y' axes are perpendicular, and
(2) the new base vectors $\boldsymbol{a}$ and $\boldsymbol{b}$ are of unit length, and hence
(3) the area of the transformed figure is unchanged.

Since the size and shape remain invariant under these transformations they may be described as rotations or reflections (or a combination of these).

We next consider transformations in which size and shape are not invariant, and which may be described as shears and stretches (or a combination of these). For each transformation we state:

(1) the properties which remain invariant and those which change.

(2) the matrix representing the transformation, and that for the inverse transformation.
(3) the characteristic equation of the matrix and hence the eigenvectors and eigenvalues.

Reminders

(i) If under a transformation

$$(1, 0) \to (a_1, a_2) \qquad \text{and} \qquad (0, 1) \to (b_1, b_2)$$

then the matrix representing the transformation is

$$\mathbf{M} = \begin{pmatrix} a_1 & b_1 \\ a_2 & b_2 \end{pmatrix}$$

(ii) The trace of the matrix

$$\text{Tr}\,(\mathbf{M}) = a_1 + b_2$$

The determinant of the matrix

$$\text{Det}\,(\mathbf{M}) = a_1 b_2 - b_1 a_2$$

(iii) The characteristic equation of the matrix is

$$k^2 - (\text{trace})k + \text{determinant} = 0$$

and its solutions, if any, give the eigenvalues, k_1, k_2.

(iv) The eigenvectors $\begin{pmatrix} x \\ y \end{pmatrix}$ are such that

$$\mathbf{M}\begin{pmatrix} x \\ y \end{pmatrix} = k\begin{pmatrix} x \\ y \end{pmatrix} \qquad \text{for } k = k_1, k_2$$

3.2 Rotations, anticlockwise about the origin

Under a rotation of both axes through an angle θ, every point in the plane moves in an arc of a circle, centre O, and the angle swept out by any radius vector, OP, is θ. In fact *every* line in the plane, whether through the origin or not, turns through the same angle, θ.

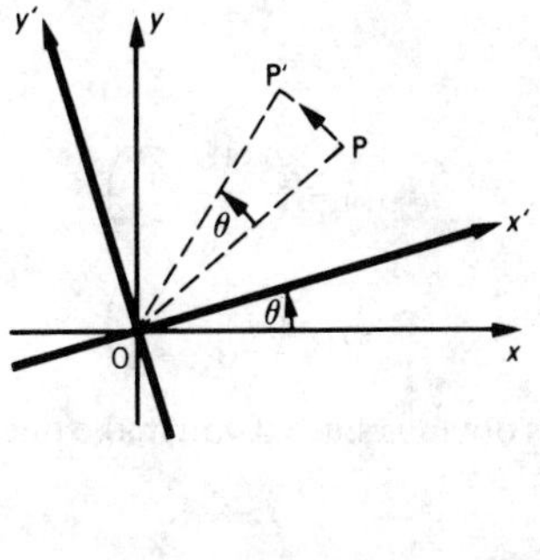

For *all* rotations, shape, size and sense are invariant. The determinant of *every* rotation matrix therefore is $+1$, and the inverse of every anticlockwise rotation is a *clockwise* rotation through the same angle.

Rotation through 90°

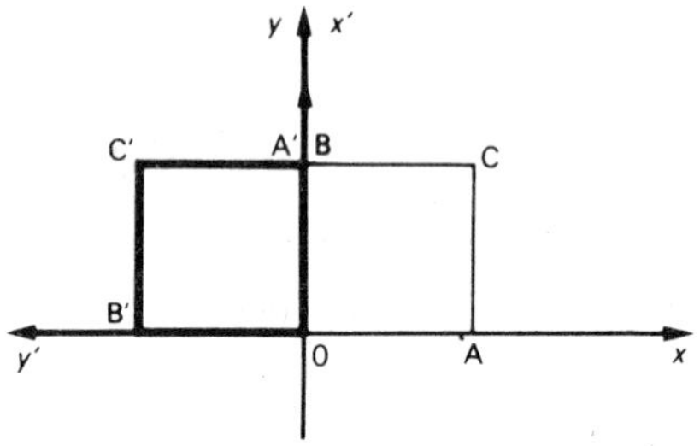

Matrix: $$\mathbf{R}_{90} = \begin{pmatrix} 0 & -1 \\ 1 & 0 \end{pmatrix}$$

Inverse: $$\mathbf{R}_{90}^{-1} = \begin{pmatrix} 0 & 1 \\ -1 & 0 \end{pmatrix}$$

Characteristic equation for $\mathbf{R}_{90}$:

$$k^2+1=0$$

This has *no* real solution and there are no real eigenvalues or eigenvectors. This matrix $\mathbf{R}_{90}$ is often referred to as **J** (see Chapter 11).

Rotation through 180°

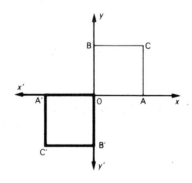

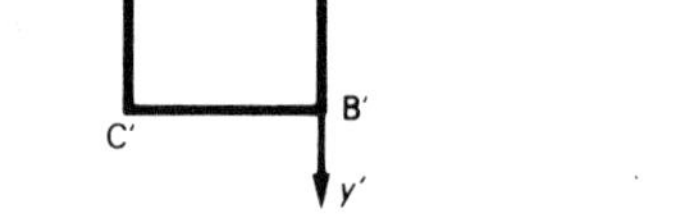

Matrix: $$\mathbf{R}_{180} = \begin{pmatrix} -1 & 0 \\ 0 & -1 \end{pmatrix}$$

Inverse: $$\mathbf{R}_{180}^{-1} = \begin{pmatrix} -1 & 0 \\ 0 & -1 \end{pmatrix}$$

i.e. it is self inverse. (This is obvious since if you make one half turn, another half turn will return you to your starting place). Characteristic equation for $\mathbf{R}_{180}$:

$$k^2-(-2)k+1 = 0$$

$$k^2+2k+1 = 0$$

$$(k+1)^2 = 0$$

Eigenvalues: $k = -1$ (twice)

Eigenvectors: $$\begin{pmatrix}-1 & 0\\ 0 & -1\end{pmatrix}\begin{pmatrix}x\\ y\end{pmatrix} = -1\begin{pmatrix}x\\ y\end{pmatrix}$$

This leads to $x = x$

and $y = y$

These equations are satisfied by every value of x and y and so every vector is an eigenvector. Rotation through 180° is the only rotation which has any eigenvectors and it has an infinite number.

Rotation through 270°

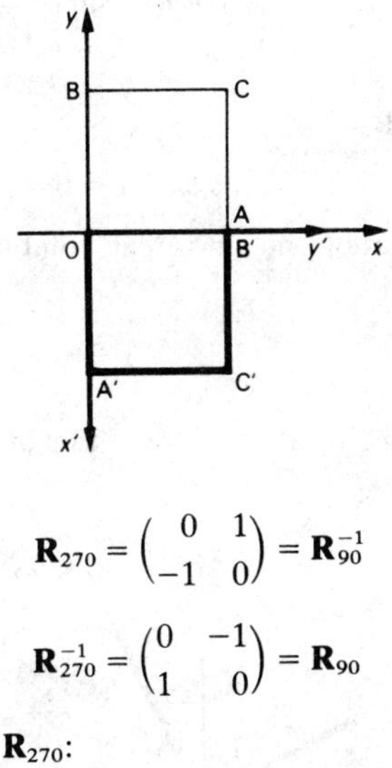

Matrix: $$\mathbf{R}_{270} = \begin{pmatrix}0 & 1\\ -1 & 0\end{pmatrix} = \mathbf{R}_{90}^{-1}$$

Inverse: $$\mathbf{R}_{270}^{-1} = \begin{pmatrix}0 & -1\\ 1 & 0\end{pmatrix} = \mathbf{R}_{90}$$

Characteristic equation for $\mathbf{R}_{270}$:

$$k^2+1=0 \qquad \text{(no real eigenvalues)}$$

Rotation through 45°

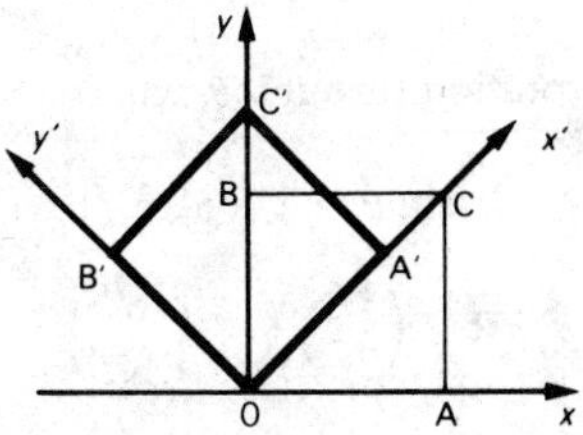

Matrix: $$\mathbf{R}_{45} = \begin{pmatrix} 1/\sqrt{2} & -1/\sqrt{2} \\ 1/\sqrt{2} & 1/\sqrt{2} \end{pmatrix}$$

General case of rotation through $\theta°$

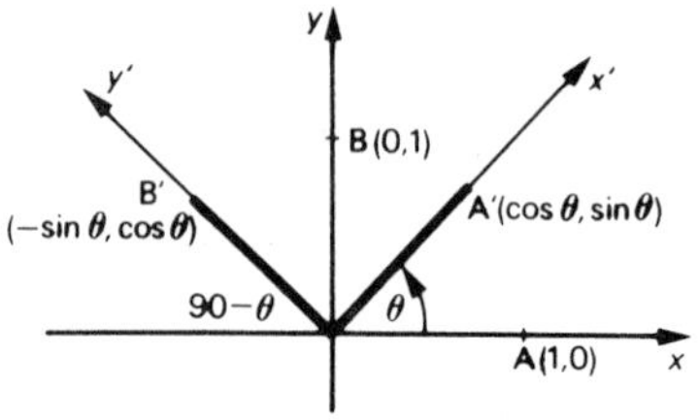

Matrix: $$\mathbf{R}_\theta = \begin{pmatrix} \cos\theta & -\sin\theta \\ \sin\theta & \cos\theta \end{pmatrix}$$

Inverse: $$\mathbf{R}_\theta^{-1} = \begin{pmatrix} \cos\theta & \sin\theta \\ -\sin\theta & \cos\theta \end{pmatrix}$$

Characteristic equation for $\mathbf{R}_\theta$:

$$k^2 - 2\cos\theta k + 1 = 0$$

Since $|\cos\theta| \leqslant 1$, this equation has no real solution ($B^2 < 4AC$) except for $|\cos\theta| = 1$, $\theta = 0°$ or $180°$.

Example

Find the matrix representing a rotation of the x axis onto the line $y = 2x$.

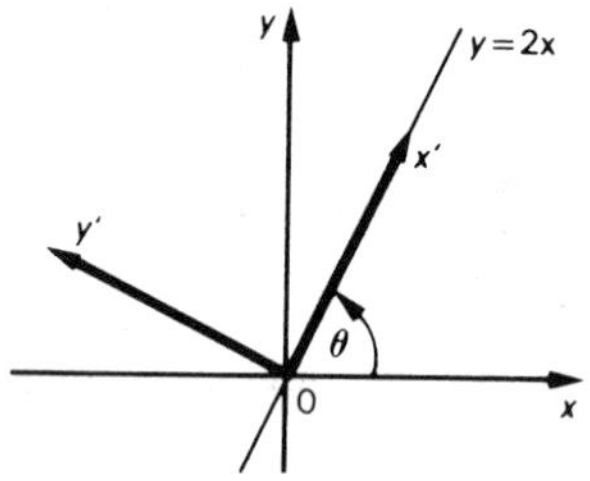

This is an anticlockwise rotation through θ, where

$\tan\theta = 2$, $\sin\theta = 2/\sqrt{5}$, $\cos\theta = 1/\sqrt{5}$

Hence the matrix is: $$\mathbf{R} = \begin{pmatrix} 1/\sqrt{5} & -2/\sqrt{5} \\ 2/\sqrt{5} & 1/\sqrt{5} \end{pmatrix}$$

3.3 Reflections, with the mirror line through the origin

In the transformations described as reflections, the 'mirror line' is a line of invariant points i.e. an eigenvector with eigenvalue 1. This mirror line OM is a line of symmetry, so for any point P and its image P′, PP′ is perpendicular to OM, and PN = P′N.

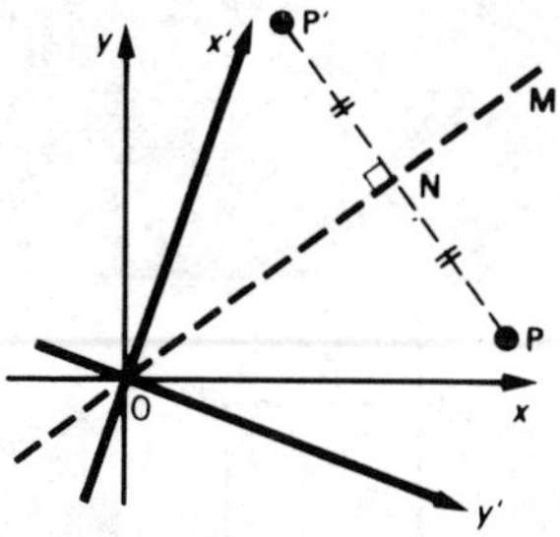

The second eigenvector is therefore perpendicular to the first and has eigenvalue −1. This can be verified algebraically.

In *all* reflections, shape and size are invariant, but the sense is changed. The determinant of every reflection matrix is therefore −1. If a reflection is repeated, every point is transformed back to its original position, so *all* reflections are *self inverse.* This can be verified by finding the inverse of the reflection matrix.

Reflection in the y axis

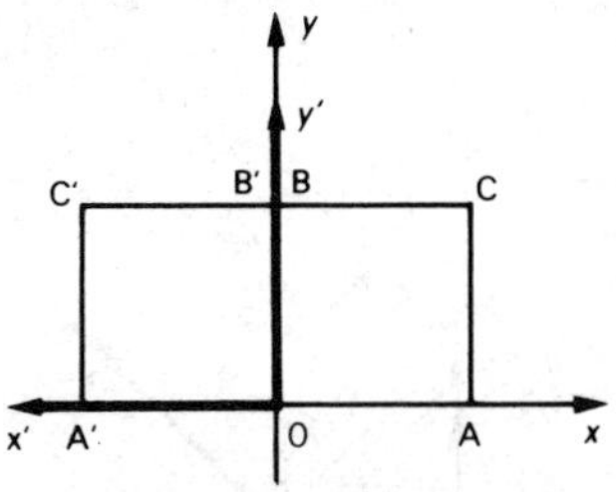

Matrix:

$$\mathbf{M}_y = \begin{pmatrix} -1 & 0 \\ 0 & 1 \end{pmatrix}; \qquad \mathbf{M}_y^{-1} = \frac{1}{-1}\begin{pmatrix} 1 & 0 \\ 0 & -1 \end{pmatrix} = \begin{pmatrix} -1 & 0 \\ 0 & 1 \end{pmatrix} = \mathbf{M}_y$$

Characteristic equation:

$$k^2 - 1 = 0, \qquad k = \pm 1$$

Eigenvectors:

When $k = 1$ $$\begin{pmatrix} -1 & 0 \\ 0 & 1 \end{pmatrix}\begin{pmatrix} x \\ y \end{pmatrix} = 1\begin{pmatrix} x \\ y \end{pmatrix} \quad \text{so} \quad \left.\begin{aligned} -x &= x \\ y &= y \end{aligned}\right\}$$

These are satisfied only by $x = 0$ and all values of y, so the eigenvector is the line $x = 0$, which is the y axis (the mirror line).

When $k = -1$ $\begin{pmatrix} -1 & 0 \\ 0 & 1 \end{pmatrix}\begin{pmatrix} x \\ y \end{pmatrix} = -1\begin{pmatrix} x \\ y \end{pmatrix}$, so $\left.\begin{matrix} x = x \\ y = -y \end{matrix}\right\}$

These are satisfied by $y = 0$ and all x, i.e. the x axis.

Reflection in the x axis

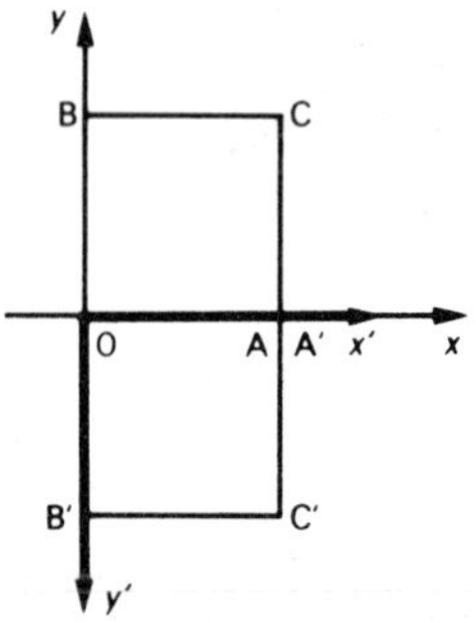

Matrix: $\mathbf{M}_x = \begin{pmatrix} 1 & 0 \\ 0 & -1 \end{pmatrix}$

Reflection in the line $y = x$

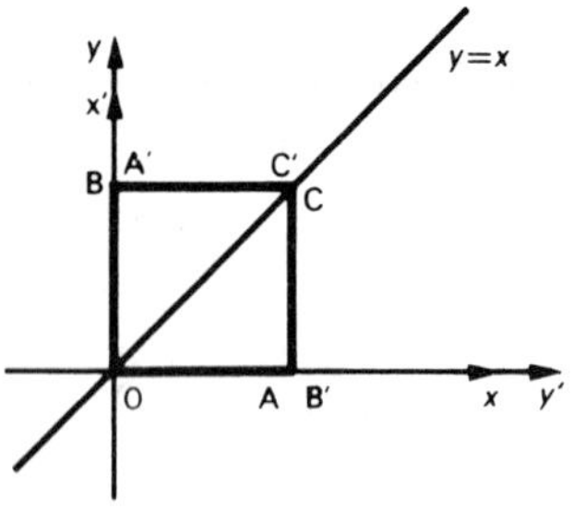

Matrix: $\mathbf{M}_{y=x} = \begin{pmatrix} 0 & 1 \\ 1 & 0 \end{pmatrix}$

Reflection in the line $y = -x$

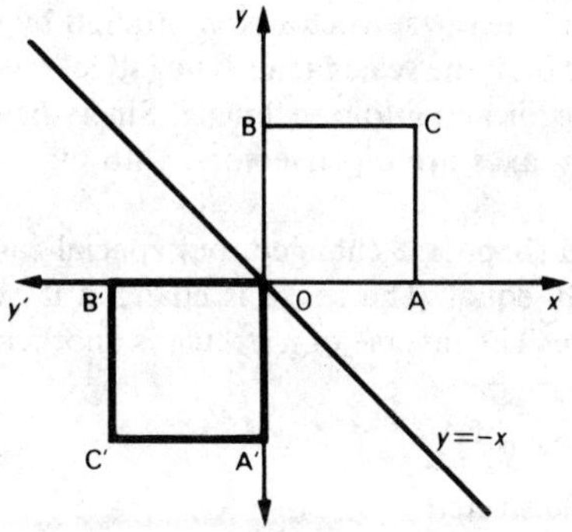

Matrix: $$\mathbf{M}_{y=-x} = \begin{pmatrix} 0 & -1 \\ -1 & 0 \end{pmatrix}$$

In each case the characteristic equation is the same

$$k^2 - 1 = 0, \quad \text{with eigenvalues } k = \pm 1.$$

General case of reflection in the line $y = x \tan \theta$

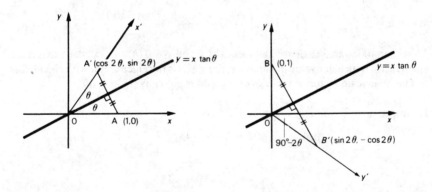

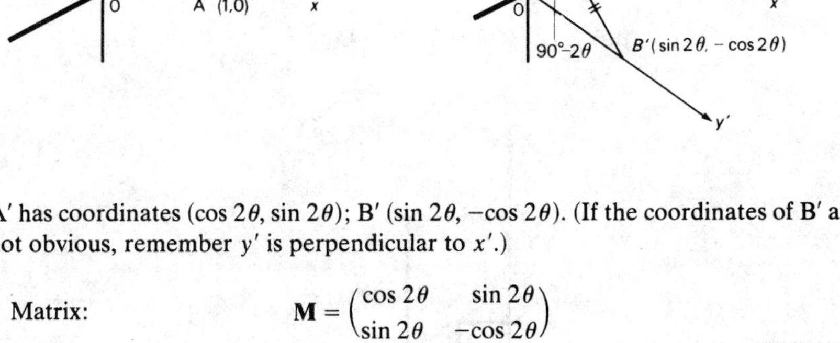

A′ has coordinates (cos 2θ, sin 2θ); B′ (sin 2θ, $-$cos 2θ). (If the coordinates of B′ are not obvious, remember y' is perpendicular to x'.)

Matrix: $$\mathbf{M} = \begin{pmatrix} \cos 2\theta & \sin 2\theta \\ \sin 2\theta & -\cos 2\theta \end{pmatrix}$$

Characteristic equation: $$k^2 - 1 = 0$$

with eigenvalues $k = \pm 1$, as for all reflections.

3.4 Stretch or elongation, parallel to the axes

In this transformation, each base vector is multiplied by some scale factor, but its direction is unchanged or, if the scale factor is negative, reversed. In the general case, the unit square is transformed into a rectangle. Since the directions of the axes are invariant, the x and y axes are eigenvectors, with eigenvalues equal to the scale factors of the stretch.

In general, size and shape are changed, but special cases arise when the eigenvalues are numerically equal. The sense is changed if one (and only one) of the eigenvalues is negative. The inverse of a stretch is another stretch with scale factors the *reciprocals* of the original ones.

General case of double stretch

Matrix: $$\mathbf{D}_{a,b} = \begin{pmatrix} a & 0 \\ 0 & b \end{pmatrix} \qquad (a \neq b)$$

Inverse: $$\mathbf{D}_{a,b}^{-1} = \begin{pmatrix} 1/a & 0 \\ 0 & 1/b \end{pmatrix}$$

Characteristic equation: for $\mathbf{D}_{a,b}$

$$k^2-(a+b)k+ab = 0, \qquad k = a, b$$

Eigenvectors:

When $k = a$ $$\begin{pmatrix} a & 0 \\ 0 & b \end{pmatrix}\begin{pmatrix} x \\ y \end{pmatrix} = a\begin{pmatrix} x \\ y \end{pmatrix} \quad \text{so} \quad \left.\begin{aligned} ax &= ax \\ by &= ay \end{aligned}\right\}$$

These equations are satisfied by all values of x, and $y = 0$ $(b \neq a)$ i.e. the x axis is the eigenvector with eigenvalue a. Similarly, the y axis is the eigenvector with eigenvalue b. The *area* scale factor of the transformation is given by $|\mathbf{D}_{a,b}| = ab$.

Example 1

$$a = 2, \qquad b = 3 \qquad \mathbf{D}_{2,3} = \begin{pmatrix} 2 & 0 \\ 0 & 3 \end{pmatrix}$$

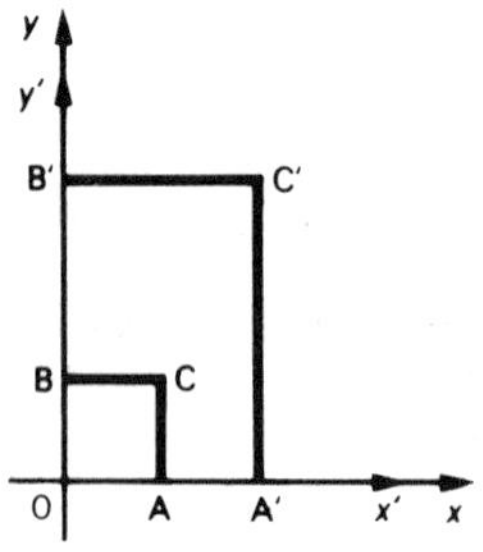

The area of the rectangle is 6 square units; its sense is unchanged.

Example 2

$$a = -2, \qquad b = 3 \qquad \mathbf{D}_{-2,3} = \begin{pmatrix} -2 & 0 \\ 0 & 3 \end{pmatrix}$$

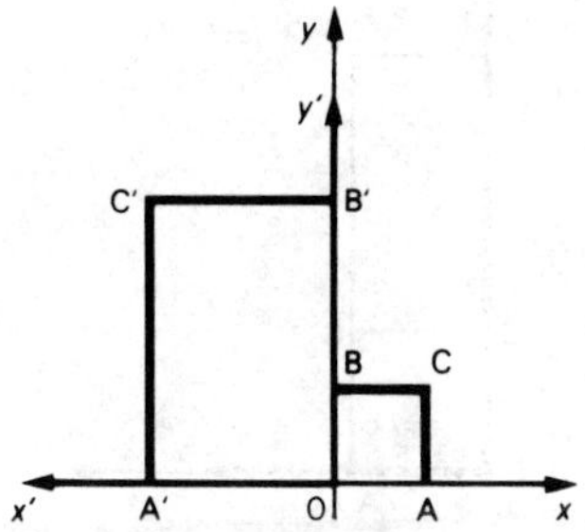

Again the transformed area is 6 square units, but this time the sense is changed, OACB reading anticlockwise, OA′C′B′ clockwise. This could be regarded as $\mathbf{D}_{2,3}$ followed by $\mathbf{M}_y$ (reflection in the y axis), since

$$\begin{pmatrix} -1 & 0 \\ 0 & 1 \end{pmatrix}\begin{pmatrix} 2 & 0 \\ 0 & 3 \end{pmatrix} = \begin{pmatrix} -2 & 0 \\ 0 & 3 \end{pmatrix}$$

One-way stretch

This is a particular case of double stretch with either $a = 1$, or $b = 1$ (but not both).

Example 3

$$a = 2, \qquad b = 1 \qquad \mathbf{D}_{2,1} = \begin{pmatrix} 2 & 0 \\ 0 & 1 \end{pmatrix}$$

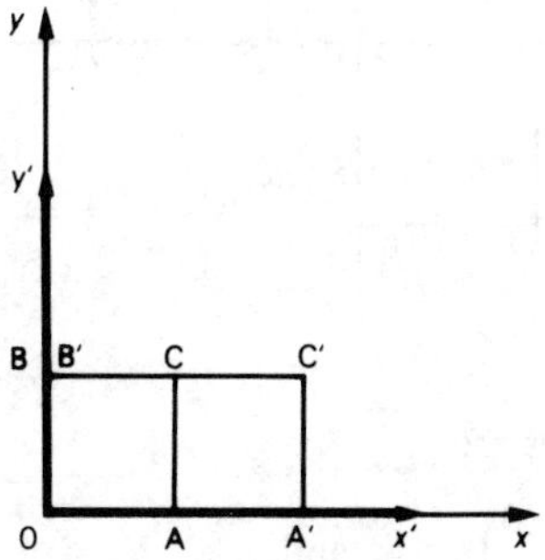

Example 4

$$a = 1, \qquad b = 3 \qquad \mathbf{D}_{1,3} = \begin{pmatrix} 1 & 0 \\ 0 & 3 \end{pmatrix}$$

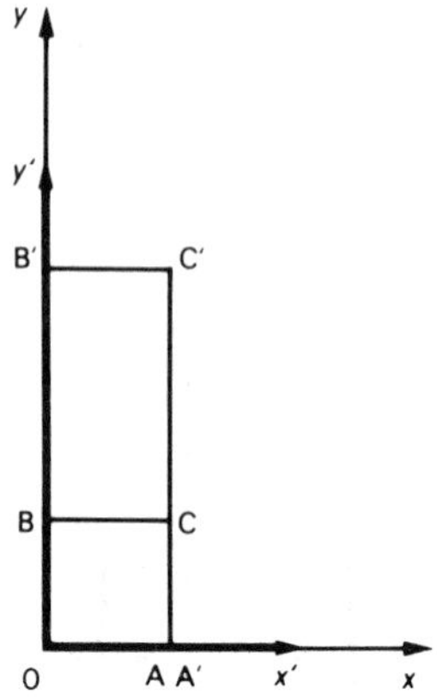

Enlargement

This is the special case of double stretch with $a = b$.

Example 5

$a = b = 3$ transforms the unit square to OA′B′C′

$a = b = -2$ transforms it to OA″B″C″.

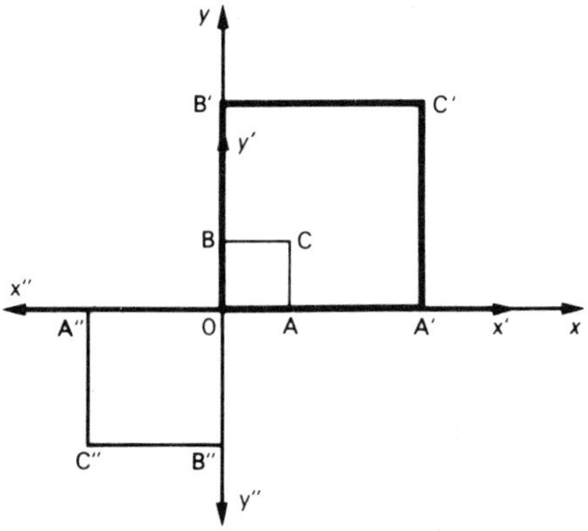

The corresponding matrices are

$$\mathbf{E}_3 = \begin{pmatrix} 3 & 0 \\ 0 & 3 \end{pmatrix} \qquad \text{and} \qquad \mathbf{E}_{-2} = \begin{pmatrix} -2 & 0 \\ 0 & -2 \end{pmatrix}$$

For $\mathbf{E}_3$ the characteristic equation is

$$k^2 - 6k + 9 = 0$$

which gives $k = 3$ (twice).

To find the eigenvectors:

$$\begin{pmatrix}3 & 0\\0 & 3\end{pmatrix}\begin{pmatrix}x\\y\end{pmatrix} = 3\begin{pmatrix}x\\y\end{pmatrix} \qquad \text{gives} \qquad \left.\begin{aligned}3x &= 3x\\3y &= 3y\end{aligned}\right\}$$

These equations are satisfied by all values of x and y so not only the axes, but *all* vectors are eigenvectors.

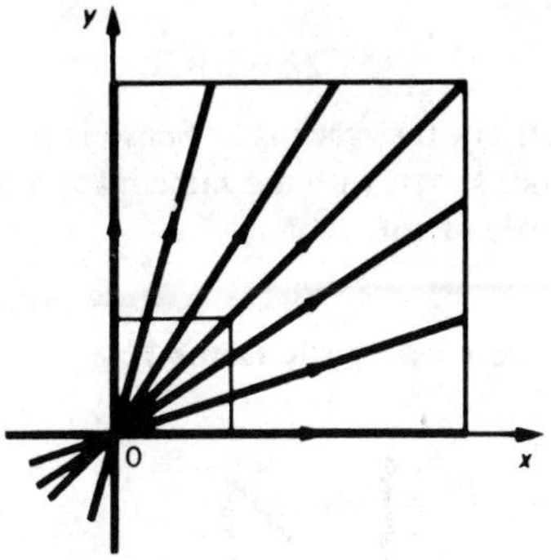

Shape and sense are invariant under enlargement and it is usually introduced as a transformation in its own right rather than as a special double stretch.

Further special cases of double stretch

(1) Reflection in the x axis; $a = 1$, $b = -1$; $\mathbf{M}_x = \begin{pmatrix}1 & 0\\0 & -1\end{pmatrix}$

(2) Reflection in the y axis; $a = -1$, $b = 1$; $\mathbf{M}_y = \begin{pmatrix}-1 & 0\\0 & 1\end{pmatrix}$

(3) Rotation through 180° about the origin; $a = b = -1$; $\mathbf{R}_{180} = \begin{pmatrix}-1 & 0\\0 & -1\end{pmatrix}$

3.5 Shear, with the invariant line through the origin

This transformation has one eigenvector only, with eigenvalue 1, i.e. a line of invariant points through the origin. All other points move parallel to this line, through a distance proportional to their distance from the invariant line.

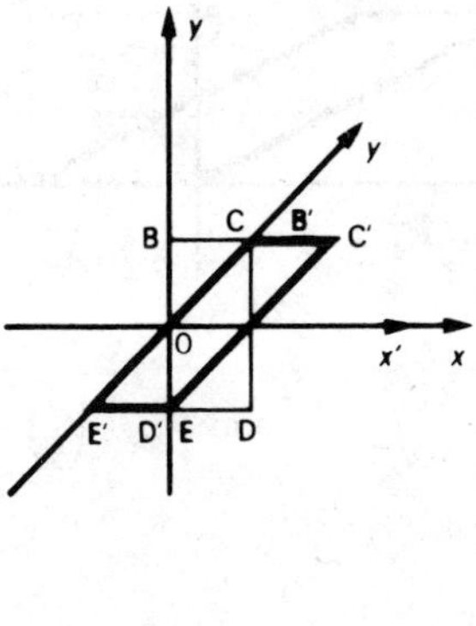

The figure shows the effect of a shear on the two unit squares BCDE which is transformed into the parallelogram B′C′D′E′. In this case the invariant line is the x axis and the scale factor of the shear is 1, since points have moved a distance *equal* to their distance from the x axis; for example, BB′ = OB. As with all shears, area is invariant, so the determinant of any matrix which represents a shear is 1. Since there is only one eigenvector, with eigenvalue 1, the solution to the characteristic equation of a shear matrix must be 1 (twice). Hence all shear matrices have the same characteristic equation:

$$k^2 - 2k + 1 = 0$$

and thus for all shear matrices the trace is 2. Sense is preserved in all shears. The inverse of a shear is another shear, with the same invariant line and scale factor the *negative* of the original scale factor.

Shear with invariant line the y axis, scale factor 1

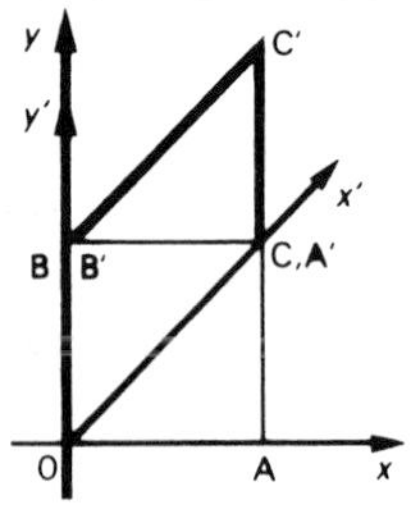

Matrix:

Since $\begin{pmatrix}1\\0\end{pmatrix} \to \begin{pmatrix}1\\1\end{pmatrix}$ and $\begin{pmatrix}0\\1\end{pmatrix} \to \begin{pmatrix}0\\1\end{pmatrix}$

the matrix is $\mathbf{S}_{y,1} = \begin{pmatrix}1 & 0\\1 & 1\end{pmatrix}$; $\mathbf{S}_{y,1}^{-1} = \begin{pmatrix}1 & 0\\-1 & 1\end{pmatrix} = \mathbf{S}_{y,-1}$

Shear with invariant line the x axis, scale factor −2

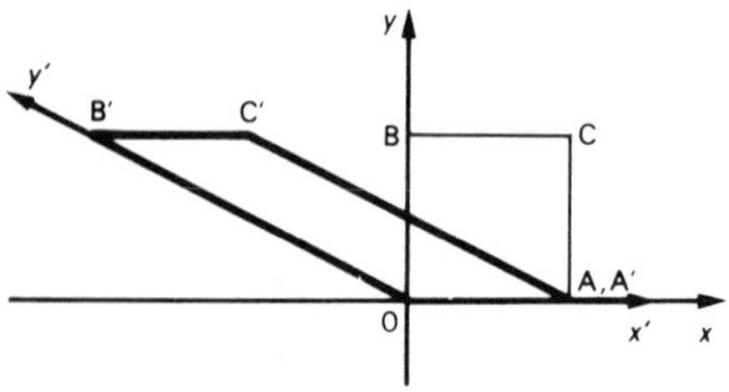

Matrix:

Since $\begin{pmatrix}1\\0\end{pmatrix} \to \begin{pmatrix}1\\0\end{pmatrix}$ and $\begin{pmatrix}0\\1\end{pmatrix} \to \begin{pmatrix}-2\\1\end{pmatrix}$

the matrix is $\mathbf{S}_{x,-2} = \begin{pmatrix} 1 & -2 \\ 0 & 1 \end{pmatrix}$; $\quad \mathbf{S}_{x,-2}^{-1} = \begin{pmatrix} 1 & 2 \\ 0 & 1 \end{pmatrix} = \mathbf{S}_{x,2}$

Shear with invariant line, the line $y = x$, scale factor 2

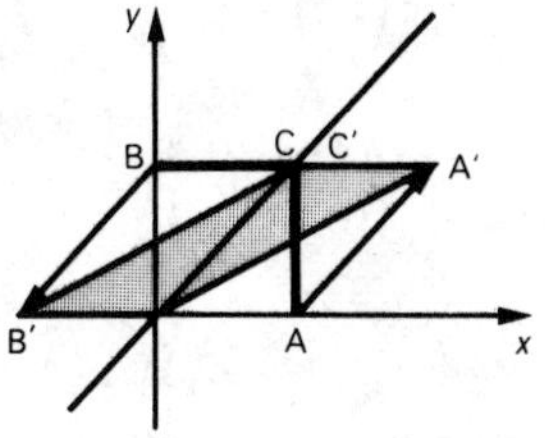

In the figure, the transformed unit square is shown shaded.

Matrix:

Since $\begin{pmatrix} 1 \\ 0 \end{pmatrix} \to \begin{pmatrix} 2 \\ 1 \end{pmatrix}$ and $\begin{pmatrix} 0 \\ 1 \end{pmatrix} \to \begin{pmatrix} -1 \\ 0 \end{pmatrix}$

the matrix is $\mathbf{S} = \begin{pmatrix} 2 & -1 \\ 1 & 0 \end{pmatrix}$

Example

Find the matrix representing a shear about the line through the origin, parallel to $\begin{pmatrix} 2 \\ -1 \end{pmatrix}$, given that $(0, 3) \to (4, 1)$.

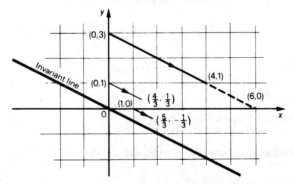

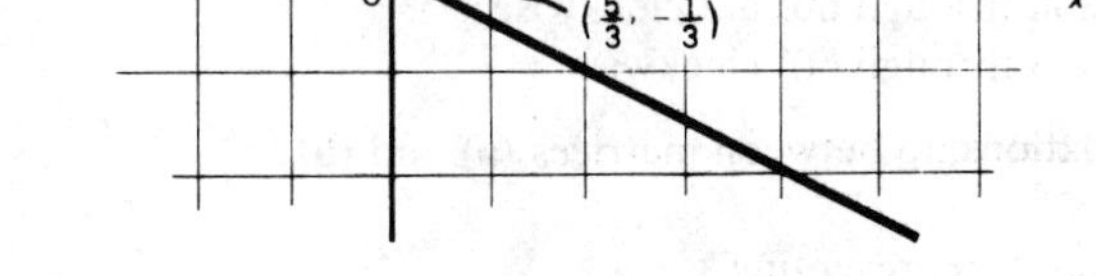

To find the matrix, we must find the effect of the shear on $\begin{pmatrix} 1 \\ 0 \end{pmatrix}$ and $\begin{pmatrix} 0 \\ 1 \end{pmatrix}$. Now the translation $(0, 3) \to (4, 1)$ is $\begin{pmatrix} 4 \\ -2 \end{pmatrix}$ and since $(0, 1)$ is one third the distance that $(0, 3)$ is from the invariant line, $(0, 1)$ will be translated through $\begin{pmatrix} \frac{4}{3} \\ -\frac{2}{3} \end{pmatrix}$, so

$$\begin{pmatrix} 0 \\ 1 \end{pmatrix} \to \begin{pmatrix} \frac{4}{3} \\ \frac{1}{3} \end{pmatrix}$$

Every point on the line through (0, 3) and parallel to $\begin{pmatrix} 2 \\ -1 \end{pmatrix}$ has the same translation $\begin{pmatrix} 4 \\ -2 \end{pmatrix}$ and since (6, 0) lies in this line it too will have a translation $\begin{pmatrix} 4 \\ -2 \end{pmatrix}$. Hence (1, 0) is translated through

$$\begin{pmatrix} \frac{4}{6} \\ -\frac{2}{6} \end{pmatrix} = \begin{pmatrix} \frac{2}{3} \\ -\frac{1}{3} \end{pmatrix}$$

So

$$\begin{pmatrix} 1 \\ 0 \end{pmatrix} \to \begin{pmatrix} \frac{5}{3} \\ -\frac{1}{3} \end{pmatrix}$$

and the required matrix is

$$\mathbf{S} = \begin{pmatrix} \frac{5}{3} & \frac{4}{3} \\ -\frac{1}{3} & \frac{1}{3} \end{pmatrix}$$

Notice, of course, that Tr (**S**) = 2 and Det (**S**) = 1.

The matrix **S** can also be found algebraically.

If $\mathbf{S} = \begin{pmatrix} a & b \\ c & d \end{pmatrix}$, then $\begin{pmatrix} a & b \\ c & d \end{pmatrix}\begin{pmatrix} 3 \\ 0 \end{pmatrix} = \begin{pmatrix} 4 \\ 1 \end{pmatrix}$

Since the transformation is a shear

$$a + d = 2$$

and

$$ad - bc = 1$$

These equations solved simultaneously give

$a = 5/3$ $\quad b = 4/3$ $\quad c = -1/3$ and $d = 1/3$

Exercise 3.5

1 Find the matrix representing

(a) a rotation through 60° anticlockwise
(b) a rotation through 60° clockwise.

What is the relationship between matrices **(a)** and **(b)**?

2 Find the matrix representing

(a) A shear with invariant line $x = 0$ and $(2, 1) \to (2, 0)$.
(b) A shear with invariant line $y = x$ and $(1, 2) \to (0, 1)$.
(c) A shear with invariant line $y = 2x$ and $(-2, 0) \to (-4, -4)$.
(d) A reflection in $y = 2x$.
(e) An anticlockwise rotation to the position where the x axis becomes the line $y = -\frac{1}{2}x$.
(f) An anticlockwise rotation to the position where the y axis becomes the line $y = -\frac{1}{2}x$.

STANDARD TRANSFORMATIONS

	Base vectors	Determinant	Eigenvalues	Characteristic equation	General matrix	Eigenvectors
Rotation (through $\theta°$)	$\boldsymbol{a}, \boldsymbol{b}$ $\boldsymbol{a} \cdot \boldsymbol{b} = 0$ $\lvert\boldsymbol{a}\rvert = \lvert\boldsymbol{b}\rvert = 1$	1	None real (except when $\theta = 180°$)	$k^2 - 2k \cos\theta + 1 = 0$	$\begin{pmatrix} \cos\theta & -\sin\theta \\ \sin\theta & \cos\theta \end{pmatrix}$	None (except when $\theta =$ 180°, when infinite number)
Reflection (in $y = x \tan\theta$)	$\boldsymbol{a}, \boldsymbol{b}$ $\boldsymbol{a} \cdot \boldsymbol{b} = 0$ $\lvert\boldsymbol{a}\rvert = \lvert\boldsymbol{b}\rvert = 1$	-1	± 1	$k^2 - 1 = 0$	$\begin{pmatrix} \cos 2\theta & \sin 2\theta \\ \sin 2\theta & -\cos 2\theta \end{pmatrix}$	$y = (\tan\theta)x$ $y = -(\cot\theta)x$
Stretch	$\boldsymbol{a}, \boldsymbol{b}$ $\boldsymbol{a} = p\boldsymbol{i}$ $\boldsymbol{b} = q\boldsymbol{j}$	pq	p, q	$k^2 - (p+q)k + pq = 0$	$\begin{pmatrix} p & 0 \\ 0 & q \end{pmatrix}$	$x = 0, y = 0$ (except if $p = q$, when infinite number)
Shear	$\boldsymbol{a}, \boldsymbol{b}$ (No simple relationship)	1	1	$k^2 - 2k + 1 = 0$	$\begin{pmatrix} a & b \\ -\dfrac{(a-1)^2}{b} & 2-a \end{pmatrix}$	$y = \dfrac{1-a}{b}x, b \neq 0$ $x = 0, b = 0$
Singular	$\boldsymbol{a}, \boldsymbol{b}$ $c\boldsymbol{a} = \boldsymbol{b}$	0	$0, a_1 + ca_2$	$k[k - (a_1 + ca_2)] = 0$	$\begin{pmatrix} a_1 & ca_1 \\ a_2 & ca_2 \end{pmatrix}$	$y = \dfrac{a_2}{a_1}x$ $y = -\dfrac{1}{c}x$

3 Find the single matrix representing the transformations

(a) $\mathbf{M}_x$ followed by $\mathbf{R}_{90}$.
(b) $\mathbf{R}_{90}$ followed by $\mathbf{M}_x$.
(c) $\mathbf{D}_{2,3}$ followed by $\mathbf{M}_{y=x}$.
(d) $\mathbf{M}_{y=x}$ followed by $\mathbf{D}_{2,3}$.
(e) $\mathbf{E}_{\sqrt{2}}$ followed by $\mathbf{R}_{45}$.
(f) $\mathbf{R}_{45}$ followed by $\mathbf{E}_{\sqrt{2}}$.
(g) $\mathbf{S}_{x,1}$ followed by $\mathbf{R}_{90}$.
(h) $\mathbf{R}_{90}$ followed by $\mathbf{S}_{x,1}$.

4 Find the single matrix representing the sequence of transformations

(a) The x axis maps anticlockwise on to $y = x$ and is stretched by 2 and the y axis maps anticlockwise onto $y = -\frac{1}{2}x$ and is stretched by -3.
(b) A rotation of 90° followed by a shear of one unit with the *new* x axis as invariant line.

5 Find in each case the single matrix representing

(a) a rotation of 90° followed by $\mathbf{D}_{2,3}$.
(b) a rotation of 90° followed by a stretch of the *new* x axis by 2 and of the *new* y axis by 3.

The table on the previous page summarizes the standard transformations.

Miscellaneous examination questions 9

1 Show, with the help of a diagram, that the matrix **P** of the linear transformation which rotates the plane in the counter-clockwise sense through an angle θ about the origin is

$$\begin{pmatrix} \cos\theta & -\sin\theta \\ \sin\theta & \cos\theta \end{pmatrix}$$

Find the matrix **Q** of the linear transformation which reflects the points of the plane in the line $y = x$. Find the values of θ for which $\mathbf{PQ} = \mathbf{QP}$. (L.)

2 The matrix $\begin{pmatrix} -2 & 3 \\ 3 & -2 \end{pmatrix}$ is denoted by **A** and the vector $\begin{pmatrix} x \\ y \end{pmatrix}$ by $\boldsymbol{x}$. It is given that $\mathbf{A}\boldsymbol{x} = k\boldsymbol{x}$ where k is an integer. Form a pair of equations connecting x, y and k and hence two different expressions involving k for the fraction y/x. Find the two possible values of k and the two corresponding values of y/x. (M.E.I.)

3 Show how the matrix

$$\mathbf{A} = \begin{pmatrix} \cos 2\theta & \sin 2\theta \\ \sin 2\theta & -\cos 2\theta \end{pmatrix}$$

can be associated with reflection in the line $y = x \tan\theta$. If **B** is the matrix associated similarly with the line $y = x\sqrt{3}$ find values of θ for which $\mathbf{AB} = \mathbf{BA}$. Describe how these values could be predicted by geometrical argument. (M.E.I.)

4 The transformation with matrix

$$\mathbf{T} = \begin{pmatrix} 4 & 3 \\ 3 & 1 \end{pmatrix}$$

maps the point (x, y) of a plane onto the point (x', y') where

$$\begin{pmatrix} x' \\ y' \end{pmatrix} = \mathbf{T}\begin{pmatrix} x \\ y \end{pmatrix}$$

Find the equation of the line onto which the line $x+2y = 0$ is mapped by the transformation $\mathbf{T}$. Find the values of m for which the line $y = mx$ is mapped onto itself. (M.E.I.)

5 If a and b are non-zero, the matrix $\mathbf{A} = \begin{pmatrix} 1 & a \\ 0 & 1 \end{pmatrix}$ represents a shear with x axis invariant and the matrix $\mathbf{B} = \begin{pmatrix} 1 & 0 \\ b & 1 \end{pmatrix}$ represents a shear with the y axis invariant. Show that the application of these shears is not commutative.

A transformation is effected by pre-multiplying column vectors by the appropriate matrix. Find the two invariant lines in the form $y = mx$ of the transformation represented by $\mathbf{BA}$ when $a = 4$ and $b = 2$. (C.)

6(a) Prove that $\begin{pmatrix} 1 & 0 \\ -1 & 1 \end{pmatrix}\begin{pmatrix} -1 & 0 \\ 0 & 1 \end{pmatrix}\begin{pmatrix} 1 & -1 \\ 0 & 1 \end{pmatrix}\begin{pmatrix} 1 & 0 \\ 1 & 1 \end{pmatrix}\begin{pmatrix} a & b \\ c & d \end{pmatrix} = \begin{pmatrix} c & d \\ a & b \end{pmatrix}$. Deduce that the rows of a 2×2 matrix can be interchanged by operations which add multiples of one row of the matrix to the other, together with operations changing the sign of a row.

Find a 2×2 matrix, $\mathbf{X}$ such that

$$\begin{pmatrix} a & b \\ c & d \end{pmatrix}\mathbf{X} = \begin{pmatrix} b & a \\ d & c \end{pmatrix}$$

(b) Do 2×2 matrices $\mathbf{A}$, $\mathbf{B}$, with integer entries, exist such that

(i) $\mathbf{AB} = \mathbf{0}$, $\mathbf{BA} = \mathbf{0}$?

(ii) $\mathbf{AB} = \mathbf{BA} = \mathbf{0}$, $\mathbf{A} \neq \mathbf{0}$, $\mathbf{B} \neq \mathbf{0}$, $\mathbf{A} \neq \mathbf{B}$?

(iii) $\mathbf{AB} = \mathbf{BA} \neq \mathbf{0}$, $\mathbf{A}$, $\mathbf{B}$, $\neq \mathbf{I}$, $\mathbf{A} \neq \mathbf{B}$?

In each case, if your answer is 'yes', justify it by giving examples of suitable $\mathbf{A}$, $\mathbf{B}$. (M.E.I.)

7 Given that

$$\mathbf{M} = \begin{pmatrix} \cos 2\theta & -\dfrac{1}{k}\sin 2\theta \\ -k\sin 2\theta & -\cos 2\theta \end{pmatrix}$$

where $k \neq 0$ and $\sin 2\theta \neq 0$, find the matrix $\mathbf{M}^2$.

Given that $\mathbf{MX} = \lambda\mathbf{X}$, where λ is a constant and $\mathbf{X}$ is a non-null column matrix with elements x_1, x_2, show, by premultiplying this equation by $\mathbf{M}$, or otherwise, that $\lambda = \pm 1$.

Show also that the values of $\mathbf{X}$ corresponding to these two values of λ are

$$\begin{pmatrix} -c_1\cos\theta \\ kc_1\sin\theta \end{pmatrix} \quad \text{and} \quad \begin{pmatrix} c_2\sin\theta \\ kc_2\cos\theta \end{pmatrix}$$

respectively, where c_1 and c_2 are arbitrary non-zero constants, and find the values of k for which these vectors are orthogonal. (M.E.I.)

8 The position vectors of the vertices A, B, C, D of a square are

$$\boldsymbol{a} = \begin{pmatrix}1\\2\end{pmatrix}, \quad \boldsymbol{b} = \begin{pmatrix}4\\2\end{pmatrix}, \quad \boldsymbol{c} = \begin{pmatrix}4\\5\end{pmatrix}, \quad \boldsymbol{d} = \begin{pmatrix}1\\5\end{pmatrix}$$

They are transformed by the matrix $\mathbf{U} = \begin{pmatrix}0 & 1\\1 & 1\end{pmatrix}$, to the points P, Q, R, S given, in similar notation, by the relations $\boldsymbol{p} = \mathbf{U}\boldsymbol{a}$, $\boldsymbol{q} = \mathbf{U}\boldsymbol{b}$, $\boldsymbol{r} = \mathbf{U}\boldsymbol{c}$, $\boldsymbol{s} = \mathbf{U}\boldsymbol{d}$. Draw a diagram in which the points A, B, C, D and P, Q, R, S are clearly labelled. More generally, points A, B, C, D are now taken to be the vertices of a parallelogram, where $\boldsymbol{a} = \begin{pmatrix}a_1\\a_2\end{pmatrix}$, $\boldsymbol{b} = \begin{pmatrix}b_1\\b_2\end{pmatrix}$, $\boldsymbol{c} = \begin{pmatrix}c_1\\c_2\end{pmatrix}$, $\boldsymbol{d} = \begin{pmatrix}d_1\\d_2\end{pmatrix}$, and the same matrix of transformation $\mathbf{U}$ is again applied to give the vertices P, Q, R, S of a quadrilateral, where

$$\boldsymbol{p} = \mathbf{U}\boldsymbol{a}, \qquad \boldsymbol{q} = \mathbf{U}\boldsymbol{b}, \qquad \boldsymbol{r} = \mathbf{U}\boldsymbol{c}, \qquad \boldsymbol{s} = \mathbf{U}\boldsymbol{d}$$

Prove that PQRS is also a parallelogram. (C.)

9 The transformation with matrix $\mathbf{T} = \begin{pmatrix}3 & 1\\4 & 3\end{pmatrix}$ maps the point (x, y) of a plane onto the point (x', y') where $\begin{pmatrix}x'\\y'\end{pmatrix} = \mathbf{T}\begin{pmatrix}x\\y\end{pmatrix}$. Find the equation of the line onto which the line $y+x = 0$ is mapped by the transformation. Find the values of m for which the line $y = mx$ is mapped onto itself. (J.M.B.)

10(a) A point P has a position vector $\begin{pmatrix}x\\y\end{pmatrix}$. This is transformed by the matrix $\mathbf{M} = \begin{pmatrix}2 & 1\\3 & 4\end{pmatrix}$ and it is found that $\mathbf{M}\begin{pmatrix}x\\y\end{pmatrix} = \begin{pmatrix}x\\y\end{pmatrix}$, i.e. P maps onto itself. Show that P lies on a fixed line p through the origin and find the equation of p.

(b) Another line l, through the origin and distinct from p, has the property that any point Q on l, having a position vector $\begin{pmatrix}x\\y\end{pmatrix}$, is transformed by $\mathbf{M}$ into a point R whose position vector is $\begin{pmatrix}X\\Y\end{pmatrix}$ and R also lies on l. Find the equation of l.

(c) Find the coordinates of the points where the line whose equation is $2x+4y = 3$ meets the axes. Hence, or otherwise, find the equation of the image of this line when it is transformed by $\mathbf{M}$. (O.)

11 The matrix $\mathbf{A} = \begin{pmatrix}1 & 3\\-2 & -6\end{pmatrix}$ represents a transformation $\begin{pmatrix}x\\y\end{pmatrix} \to \mathbf{A}\begin{pmatrix}x\\y\end{pmatrix}$ of two-dimensional space into itself. Find the locus L of all points (x, y) which have image $(1, -2)$ under this transformation.

The point (p, q) is the image of (x, y) under this transformation. Find the locus of (p, q) as (x, y) varies throughout the plane.

Show that any given point P on this locus is the image of just one point on the y axis and explain how the set of all points with image P is related to the locus L. (M.E.I.)

12 The vector joining the origin to any point on the line $x = y$ may be written $\begin{pmatrix}t\\t\end{pmatrix}$.

Find a similar form for the vector joining the origin to any point on the line $2x+y=0$.

M is the matrix $\begin{pmatrix} 4 & -3 \\ -6 & 7 \end{pmatrix}$. Prove that the vector joining the origin to any point on the line $x = y$ is unchanged after being multiplied by **M**. Prove that the vector joining the origin to any point on the line $2x+y=0$ also has its direction unchanged by being multiplied by **M**, but that its length is multiplied by a number λ. Find the value of λ.

Write down the results of each of the products

$$\mathbf{M}^5\begin{pmatrix} 2 \\ 2 \end{pmatrix} \qquad \mathbf{M}^5\begin{pmatrix} -2 \\ 4 \end{pmatrix}$$

(O.)

13 A matrix will be called an M-matrix if the sum of the elements in each of its rows is unity. Thus

$$\begin{pmatrix} 2 & -1 \\ -2 & 3 \end{pmatrix} \quad \text{and} \quad \begin{pmatrix} a & 1-a \\ b & 1-b \end{pmatrix}$$

are M-matrices. Find the 2×2 M-matrix, **A**, such that

$$\mathbf{A}\begin{pmatrix} 4 \\ 2 \end{pmatrix} = \begin{pmatrix} 2 \\ 1 \end{pmatrix}.$$

Prove that, if **B** is a 2×2 M-matrix, then

$$\mathbf{B}\begin{pmatrix} 1 \\ 1 \end{pmatrix} = \begin{pmatrix} 1 \\ 1 \end{pmatrix}$$

Prove also, if **C** is any 2×2 matrix such that

$$\mathbf{C}\begin{pmatrix} 1 \\ 1 \end{pmatrix} = \begin{pmatrix} 1 \\ 1 \end{pmatrix}$$

then **C** is an M-matrix.

Prove that if **D** and **E** are 2×2 M-matrices, then **DE** is also an M-matrix. Prove that, if the inverse of an M-matrix exists, then the inverse is also an M-matrix. (O.)

14
$$\mathbf{M} = \begin{pmatrix} \frac{1}{2} & -\frac{\sqrt{3}}{2} \\ \frac{\sqrt{3}}{2} & \frac{1}{2} \end{pmatrix}$$

is the matrix of a rotation about the origin. Calculate the angle of rotation. Calculate $\mathbf{M}^2$ and $\mathbf{M}^3$ and prove that $\mathbf{M}^3 = \mathbf{AB}$, where

$$\mathbf{A} = \begin{pmatrix} -1 & 0 \\ 0 & 1 \end{pmatrix} \quad \text{and} \quad \mathbf{B} = \begin{pmatrix} 1 & 0 \\ 0 & -1 \end{pmatrix}$$

Interpret the equation $\mathbf{M}^3 = \mathbf{AB}$ geometrically.

$$\mathbf{C} = \begin{pmatrix} 0 & 1 \\ 1 & 0 \end{pmatrix}$$

Find **D** so that $\mathbf{DC} = \mathbf{M}^3$. Interpret this equation geometrically. (O.)

15 **A** is the matrix $\begin{pmatrix} a & b \\ c & d \end{pmatrix}$ where a, b, c, d are all real numbers. The determinant of

A, det **A**, is defined to be $ad-bc$ and the trace of **A**, tr **A**, is defined to be $a+d$.

Given that det $\mathbf{A}=1$, prove that det $(\mathbf{A}^2)=1$, and find the value of tr $(\mathbf{A}^2)$ in terms of a and d. Prove that tr $(\mathbf{A}^2)\geqslant -2$.

M is the matrix $\begin{pmatrix}-1.04 & -0.72\\ -0.72 & -1.46\end{pmatrix}$. Find the value of det **M** and tr **M** and prove that there is no 2×2 matrix **P** with real elements such $\mathbf{P}^2=\mathbf{M}$. (O.)

16 Show that

$$\mathbf{A}=\begin{pmatrix}0 & 1\\ 1 & 0\end{pmatrix} \quad \text{and} \quad \mathbf{B}=\begin{pmatrix}-1 & 0\\ 0 & 1\end{pmatrix}$$

are matrices of reflections and identify the mirror line in each case. Calculate **BA** and identify the single transformation which it represents.

Prove that if

$$\mathbf{C}=\begin{pmatrix}1/\sqrt{2} & -1/\sqrt{2}\\ 1/\sqrt{2} & 1/\sqrt{2}\end{pmatrix}$$

then $\mathbf{C}^2=\mathbf{BA}$ and interpret this equation geometrically.

Find **D** so that $\mathbf{AD}=\mathbf{BA}$. Find also the smallest positive integer value for n for which $(\mathbf{BA})^n=\mathbf{I}$, the identity matrix. (O.)

17(a) The matrix **P** represents the rotation of the point (x, y) anticlockwise through one right angle about the origin. The matrix **Q** represents the reflection of the point (x, y) in the line $y=x$. Write down the 2×2 matrices **P** and **Q**.

Show on a diagram the positions B and C of the images of A(5, 2) under the transformations given by **PQ** and **QP** respectively.

Find the matrix **R** such that $\mathbf{PQ}=\mathbf{RQP}$.

(b) Find the values of x for which the matrix

$$\mathbf{M}=\begin{pmatrix}x^3 & x\\ 4 & 1\end{pmatrix}$$

has no inverse.

Substitute the value of x which is positive into **M** and find the images of the four points (0, 0), (1, 0), (1, 1), and (0, 1) under the transformation represented by the matrix so formed. Comment on the result of applying this transformation to all points of the plane. (C.)

18 Find the two values of λ for which the matrix equation

$$\begin{pmatrix}3 & 2\\ 1 & 4\end{pmatrix}\begin{pmatrix}x\\ y\end{pmatrix}=\lambda\begin{pmatrix}x\\ y\end{pmatrix}$$

has non-trivial solutions for x and y. For each of these values find a corresponding solution for x and y.

If

$$\mathbf{A}=\begin{pmatrix}3 & 2\\ 1 & 4\end{pmatrix}, \quad \mathbf{M}=\begin{pmatrix}x_1 & x_2\\ y_1 & y_2\end{pmatrix}$$

where (x_1, y_1) and (x_2, y_2) are the two solutions just obtained, find a diagonal* matrix **D** such that $\mathbf{AM}=\mathbf{MD}$. (M.E.I.)

* A diagonal matrix is one with non-zero elements on the leading diagonal and zero elements elsewhere.

Chapter 10

Flow Charts and Algorithms

1 Numerical methods and computation

1.1 Introduction

In elementary mathematics we generally have problems to solve in which the numbers involved are fairly easy to deal with. For example, we might have to solve the equation

$$5x = 2 \Rightarrow x = \tfrac{2}{5}$$

Unfortunately, in a 'real' problem the numbers are not necessarily so simple, and we might have this equation:

$$5.0301x = 2.8740 \Rightarrow x = \frac{2.8740}{5.0301}$$

Despite the fact that the numbers themselves are more difficult to handle, the *method* of solution is the same in each case. If $ax = b$ then $x = b/a$. A general method of computation like this is called an *algorithm.*

This elementary example introduces the subject called *numerical analysis,* in which we use 'arithmetic' to solve problems. Usually, however, the problems fall outside what we think of as arithmetic. For instance, we use numerical methods to find the roots of an equation, the sum of a series, or the area under a curve.

The arithmetic involved is usually simple, but long and tedious without the aid of a calculator or computer. Until the late 1940s when the first electronic computers came into service, the word *computer* meant a person engaged in numerical work, usually with the aid of a mechanical calculator. Many people were so employed—by government departments (for example in economic research, ballistics and medical statistics), by scientific institutions such as observatories, by insurance companies, and so on. Nowadays, the human computer has been almost entirely superseded, but many of the sophisticated methods developed by mathematicians over the past 300 years have survived. Some have been modified to suit the rather different demands of the modern electronic computer, and many new ones have been invented. From a practical point of view, there are two main differences between the human computer and his electronic counterpart. The latter is often as much as a million times faster in its calculation time; but it has no judgement, and so is unable to take some of the short-cuts that an experienced mathematician could use to shorten his work.

If an algorithm exists for the solution of any problem, then the answer can be found by substitution followed by the necessary calculation. When there is *no* algorithm, for example for the solution of a polynomial in x^4, numerical methods can be applied to find an approximation to the solution which generally speaking can be as close as we like to it. We discuss such approximations in Chapter 15.

1.2 An algorithm for the solution of quadratic equations

Suppose we have to solve the equation

$$3.12x^2-5.93x+2.71 = 0$$

It is not much use looking for factors, but there is the well-known formula or algorithm for solving quadratic equations.

$$Ax^2+Bx+C = 0 \qquad \text{then} \qquad x = \frac{-B}{2A} \pm \frac{\sqrt{(B^2-4AC)}}{2A}$$

In our equation, $A = 3.12$, $B = -5.93$ and $C = 2.71$. Our thinking runs as follows (although we should probably not write down so many steps, and the exact order of the steps may be different for different calculators).

$$-4AC = -33.8208$$

$$B^2 = 35.1649$$

$$B^2-4AC = 1.3441$$

$$\sqrt{(B^2-4AC)} = 1.1594$$

$$\frac{\sqrt{(B^2-4AC)}}{2A} = 0.1858$$

$$\frac{-B}{2A} = 0.9503$$

$$\frac{-B}{2A}+\frac{\sqrt{(B^2-4AC)}}{2A} = 1.1361$$

$$\frac{-B}{2A}-\frac{\sqrt{(B^2-4AC)}}{2A} = 0.7645$$

Our answers are $x = 1.14$ or $x = 0.76$ to 2D.

This programme of calculation can be carried out once easily enough on a hand calculator, but if a large number of similar equations has to be solved, this can be done at high speed by an electronic computer once a *program* has been drawn up, with the aid of a *flow chart.*

2 Flow charts

2.1 The structure of a flow chart

In a flow chart all the steps needed to carry out an algorithm are broken down into their simplest elements. These simple elements are known as *statements*, and the process represented by a flow chart is called a *program*. A computer programmer uses a flow chart to help him clarify in his own mind the logic required for a program, so that the relationship between a flow chart and the program it represents is much the same as that of an artist's sketch and the final picture. For this reason, there are no set rules for the drawing of flow charts and the same program may often be represented by several different flow charts.

There are six basic types of statement that we shall be using.

1 & 2 BEGIN/END statements

A circular box is used. A flow chart may contain any number of END statements, but only one BEGIN statement.

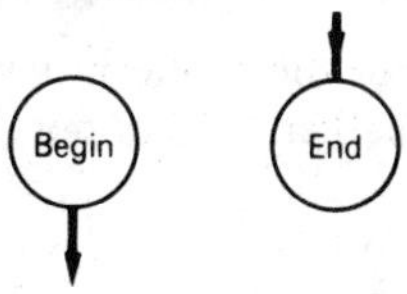

3 Assignment statements

A rectangular box is used. An assignment statement has three parts:

(i) a 'left-part' which can *only* be the name of a variable (in this case x);
(ii) an 'operator' in this case := which means 'becomes equal to'; and
(iii) a 'right-part' which represents the *new* value of the variable in the left-part.

The statement shown below is read 'x becomes -2.7' or 'let $x = -2.7$'

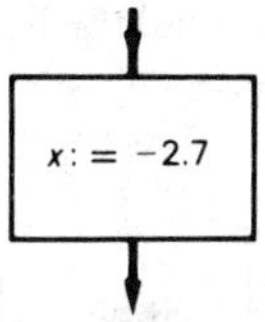

Example

BEGIN $x := 2$ $x := 2+x$ $x := 2+2x$ END

The effect of this program is to give x the values 2, 4, and finally 10. The name of a variable need not be a single letter: often words are used. 'COUNT := COUNT+1' is a valid assignment statement. Notice that $x := y$ is not the same as $y := x$. If the current values of x and y were $\begin{pmatrix} x \\ y \end{pmatrix} = \begin{pmatrix} 2 \\ 3 \end{pmatrix}$, the first statement would give $\begin{pmatrix} x \\ y \end{pmatrix} = \begin{pmatrix} 3 \\ 3 \end{pmatrix}$, and the second $\begin{pmatrix} x \\ y \end{pmatrix} = \begin{pmatrix} 2 \\ 2 \end{pmatrix}$.

4 Conditional statements

A rhomboid box is used. There is no restriction on the left-part and right-part in these statements, which can be *any* expressions. The operator *must* be one of these six:

$$= \qquad \neq \qquad > \qquad \geqslant \qquad < \qquad \leqslant$$

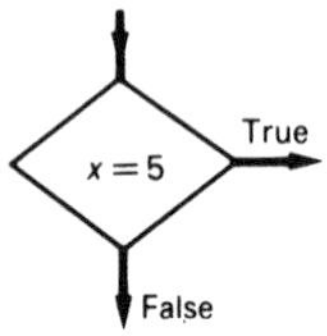

The effect of the statement is to direct the program along one of two branches depending, in this case, upon whether x is 5 or not. The following are all conditional statements.

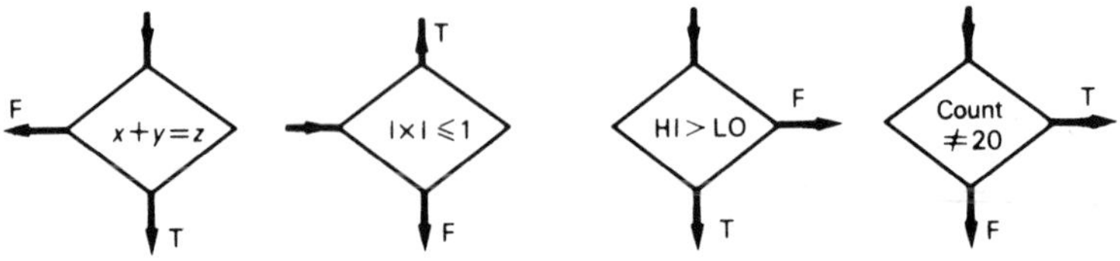

5 READ statements

A rectangular box is used. All computers have a mechanism for receiving data, which might be a punched-card reader, a teletype or paper-tape reader. The READ or INPUT statement is an instruction to read the next number in the data stream and to give its value to a specified variable.

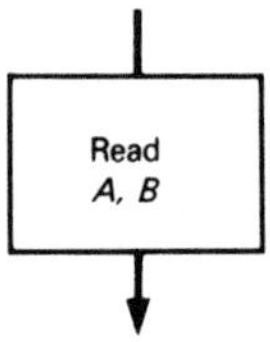

In the example above, the next two numbers are read, and become the values of the variables A and B.

6 PRINT statements

A rectangular box is used. In this instruction the current values of the variables A and B are printed on the computer's output mechanism (perhaps a teletype or a line-printer).

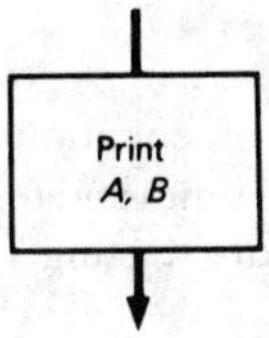

We shall now look at a complete flow chart.

Example

$$Ax^2+Bx+C = 0 \Rightarrow x = \frac{-B}{2A} \pm \frac{\sqrt{(B^2-4AC)}}{2A}$$

A flow chart for the quadratic algorithm would be:

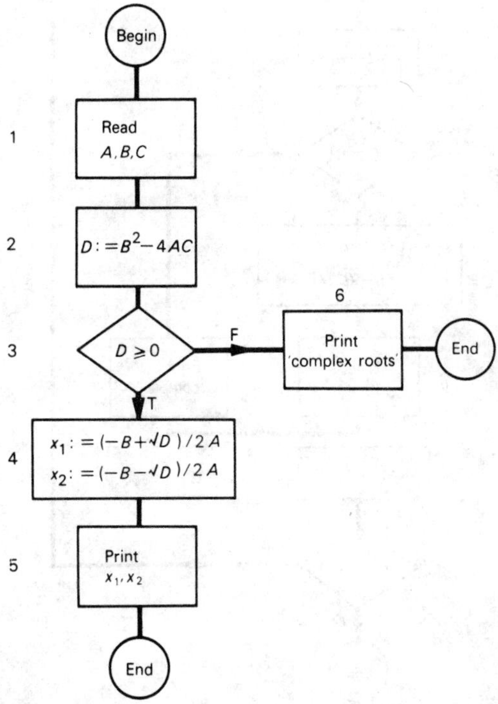

In box 2 a new variable D is introduced. Box 4 contains more than one statement, which is common practice. In box 6 a print statement is used to give an output of words rather than a value. When this is done the text is usually enclosed in inverted commas.

We will now modify the program so that it will solve a number of quadratics, reading in the coefficients of each one in turn. There are two ways of doing this depending on whether or not the number of equations is known—i.e. whether or not we know how many coefficients are present in the input stream.

(*i*) *Counter*

When we do know the number of equations, we can use a *counter* which is incremented (i.e. increased by 1 at a time) and tested after each equation is solved. It is important to zero the counter before starting. In the flow chart below, it is assumed that the number of equations is 10.

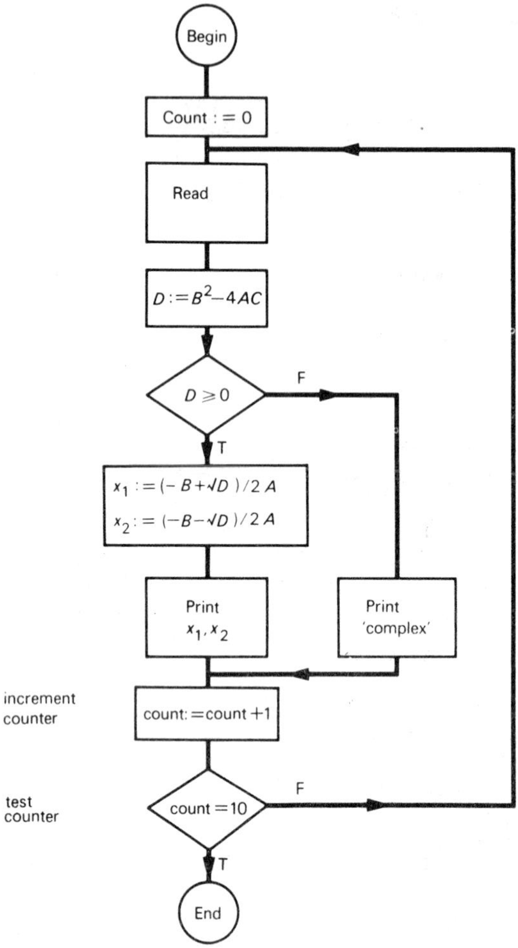

Each time the statement 'READ A, B, C,' is executed, the previous values of these are lost and the next three numbers of the input become the current values.

(*ii*) *Sentinel*

When the number of equations is not known, a different technique is used. The last number of the input stream is followed by what is sometimes called a *sentinel*. This is a number which can be recognized as signalling the end of the input because it is not a valid value of the variable. For example, a list of positive integers might have a negative number as a sentinel. In the quadratic program A is unlikely to have the value zero since the resulting equation $Bx + C = 0$ is not quadratic. Hence we can use $A = 0$ as our sentinel.

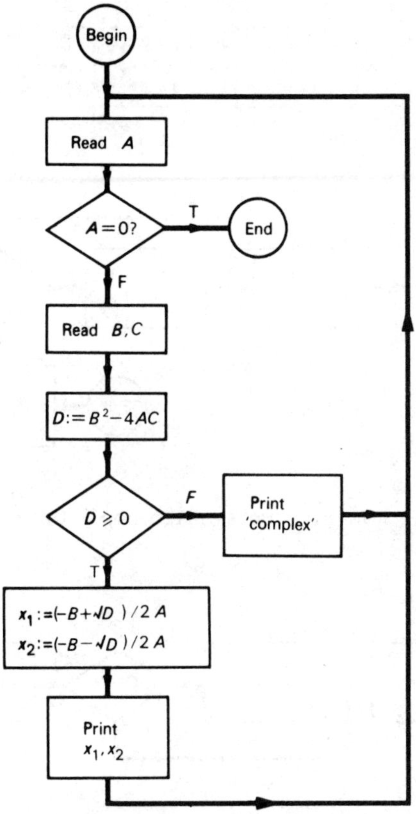

A sample list of data for this program might be:

3 −2.1 −4 1 0 −0.42 0

In this case the two equations $3x^2 - 2.1x - 4 = 0$, and $x^2 - 0.42 = 0$ would be solved, and the program would then halt.

This method of using a sentinel to halt a program is very common. It is more versatile than the counter method since varying amounts of data may be processed by the same program on different occasions.

Exercise 2.1

1 What would be the output from the flow chart above if the data was as follows?

1 −3 2 2 −3 2 2 −8 0 0

2 What are the values of x, y and z when the program below has been executed?

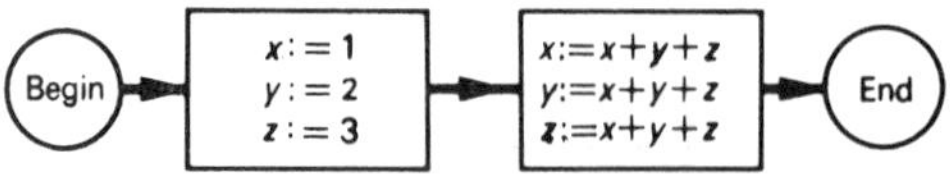

3

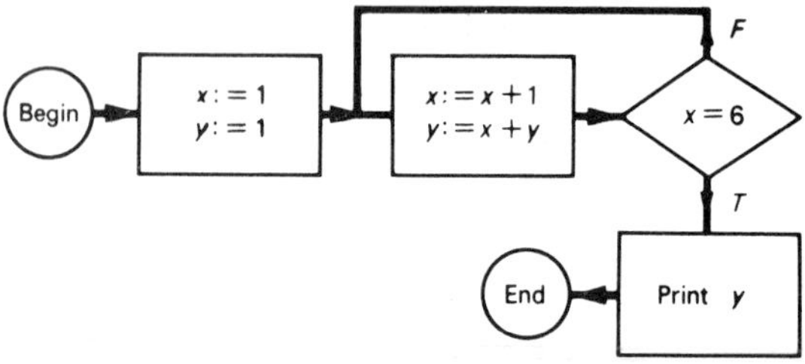

In the flow chart above, how many times will the loop be traversed, and what value of y will be printed?

4

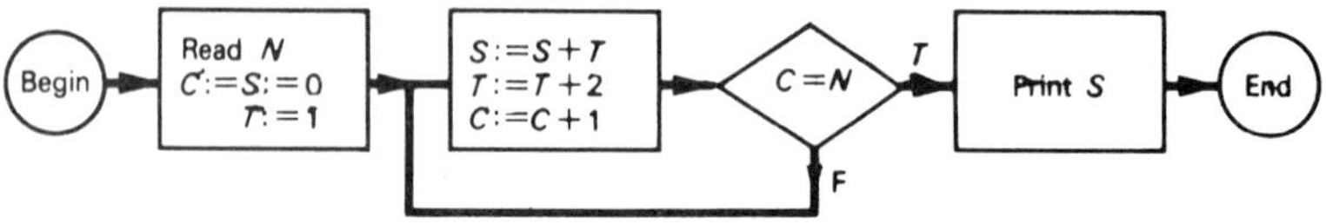

Trace the flow-chart above for $N=4$ and for $N=6$. What is the purpose of the program? What are the functions of the three variables S, T and C? State the algorithm being employed in the form of an algebraic formula.

2.2 Tracing a flow chart

Flow charts often contain loops—groups of statements which are used more than once. Variables which appear as the left-parts of assignment statements inside a loop are liable to change their values many times so when you have written a flow chart to solve a problem, you should make a *trace* of the variables to check that your logic is correct. This may be done by tabulating all the left-part variables *in the order in which they occur within the loop*, and evaluating them for each circuit of the loop.

Example

Trace the flow chart shown below:

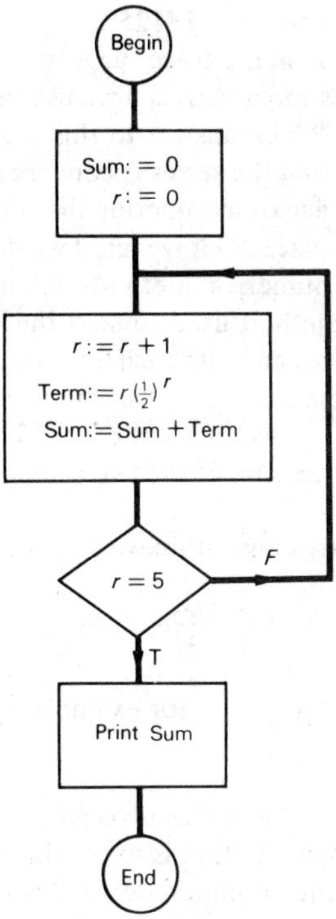

Trace

r	TERM	SUM
0	—	0
1	0.5	0.5
2	0.5	1
3	0.375	1.375
4	0.25	1.625
5	0.15625	1.78125

The initial contents of TERM do not matter.

Summing a series

This flow chart is typical of programs for summing a series. 'r' is a counter, as the conditional statement shows, and is also used to calculate the value of TERM on each circuit of the loop. SUM stores the cumulative total of successive values of TERM. Evidently, the algorithm is:

$$u_r = r \times (\tfrac{1}{2})^r; \qquad \text{SUM} = \sum_1^5 u_r$$

where u_r is the rth term. The series is:

$$(1\times\tfrac{1}{2})+(2\times(\tfrac{1}{2})^2)+(3\times(\tfrac{1}{2})^3)+\ldots$$

and the sum of the first five terms is 1.78125.

A glance at the SUM column in the trace suggests that the series might 'converge' to some number and the question arises: can we use the program to find the 'sum of an infinite number of terms'? The answer to this is not as straightforward as you might think. If we can prove that the series *is* convergent then we can find its sum to any required degree of accuracy (remembering that the sum may not be expressible in a finite number of decimal places). However, if we don't know in advance whether it is convergent or not, then numerical methods will not help us.

In the last example, the method used to sum the series gave the rth term as a function of r. In many series we can write each term as a function of the previous term (or terms) which usually makes the calculation simpler. For example, in the geometric series $a, ab, ab^2, \ldots$ we can write $u_r = b\times u_{r-1}$ while in the Fibonacci series, in which each term is the sum of the two previous terms, $u_r = u_{r-1}+u_{r-2}$ (see recurrence relations, page 5).

As an example of this type of algorithm we shall consider the exponential series:

$$1+1+\frac{1}{2!}+\frac{1}{3!}+\ldots+\frac{1}{n!}+\ldots \quad \text{where e.g. } 3! = 3\times2\times1$$

Here $$u_r = \frac{1}{r}\times u_{r-1} \qquad \left(\text{for example } \frac{1}{5!} = \frac{1}{5}\times\frac{1}{4!}\right)$$

We take the first term as u_0.

As we know in advance that the series is convergent, we can find our answer as accurately as we like. The usual method is to continue adding terms until we reach one which is less than some small number, decided beforehand, called the *tolerance*. In the flow chart we shall work to a tolerance of 10^{-7}.

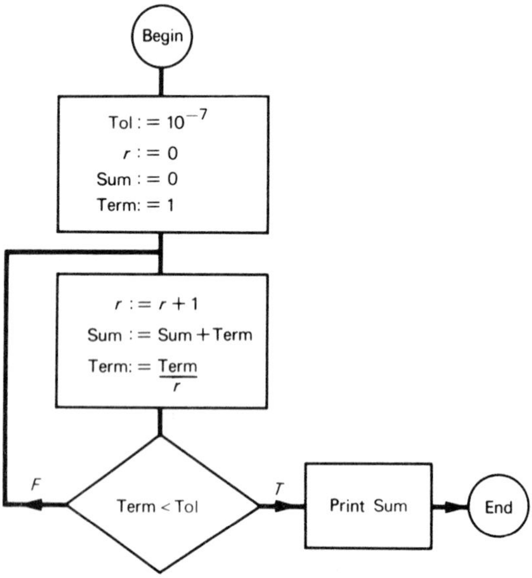

We have written this tolerance in standard form which is a useful way of expressing very small or very large numbers. Numbers are written in the form $N \times 10^e$; where $1 \leq N < 10$, and e, the power or exponent, is a positive or negative integer. For an electronic computer this is written N E e and called 'floating point' notation, but on a hand calculator the E is omitted, leaving a single digit gap in the display if e is positive, but replaced by a minus sign if e is negative. The exponent is usually given as a two digit number.

Examples

$$417 \text{ million} = 4.17 \times 10^8 = 4.17\text{ E}8 = 4.17\ 08$$

$$0.000\ 315 = 3.15 \times 10^{-4} = 3.15\text{ E-}4 = 3.15-04$$

Trace

r	SUM	TERM
0	0	1
1	1	1
2	2	0.5
3	2.5	0.1666667
4	2.666667	0.04166667
5	2.708333	8.333333E−3
6	2.716667	1.388889E−3
7	2.718056	1.984127E−5
8	2.718254	2.480159E−5
9	2.718279	2.755732E−6
10	2.718281	2.755732E−7
11	2.718282	2.505211E−8

Exercise 2.2

In each of the five flow charts below, a series is being summed. Draw up a trace listing the values of all the variables as you follow through the programs. In 1 and 2 name the type of series which is being summed.

1

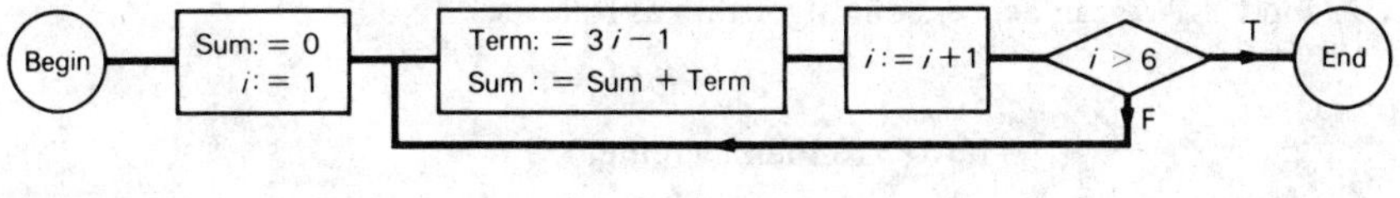

2

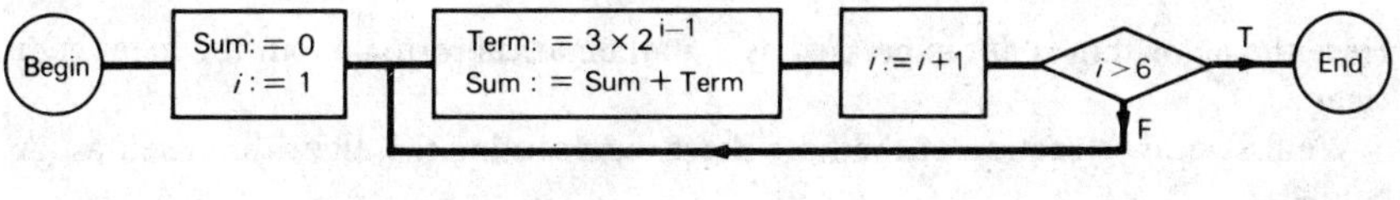

3

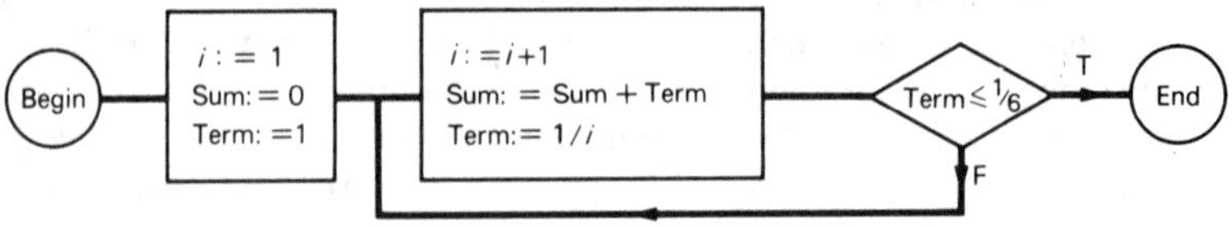

4

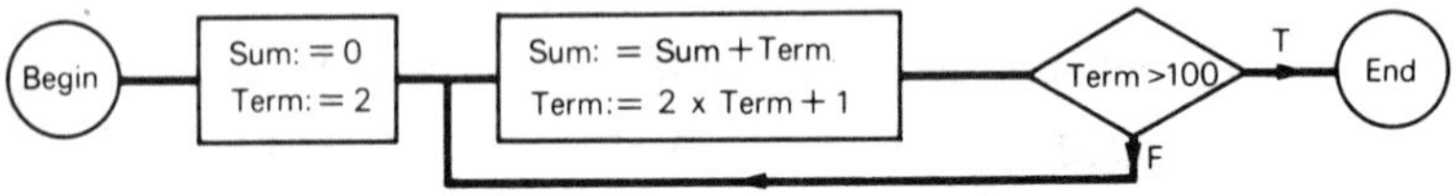

5

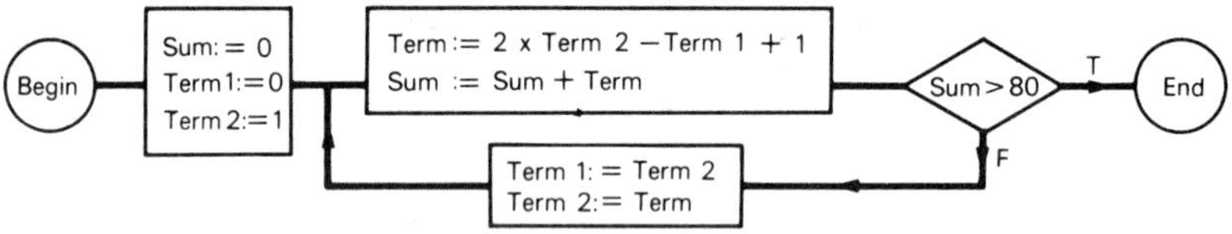

2.3 Constructing a flow chart

When drawing a flow chart for a problem, the first step is always to write down the algorithm. It is not necessary and not always possible to do this in strictly mathematical form. The algorithm will usually be represented by a group of statements somewhere in the middle of the flow chart. These are entered first, and any remaining statements—e.g. input/output instructions and instructions to zero counters and other variables—may be added later.

Example 1

Draw a flow chart for the following problem. Given a list of the length (l), the breadth (b) and the height (h) of a number of rectangular boxes, find the volume (V) of each box and count the number of boxes for which (i) $V < 10$, (ii) $10 \leqslant V < 100$, and (iii) $100 \leqslant V$. The end of the list is marked by a sentinel with $l = 0$.

We shall evidently need three counters for the three volume ranges. Call these C1, C2, and C3. We can express our algorithm as follows:

$$V = lbh$$

If $V < 10$ then increment C1

If $10 \leqslant V < 100$ then increment C2

If $100 \leqslant V$ then increment C3

Here the algorithm is not expressed as a mathematical formula, but the meaning is clear.

We first draw a section of the flow chart representing the algorithm itself as (A) below.

This is the kernel of the flow chart. What else is needed? We need to start the three counters at zero. We must check for the sentinel each time we read a fresh set of *l*, *b* and *h*. Finally, we must include an output instruction. The complete flow chart is as (B) below:

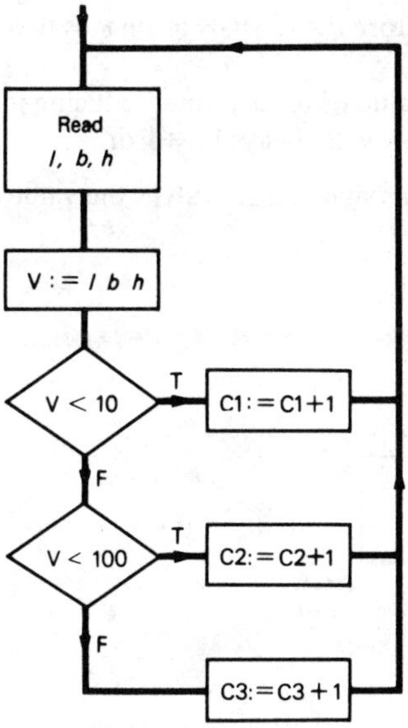

(A)

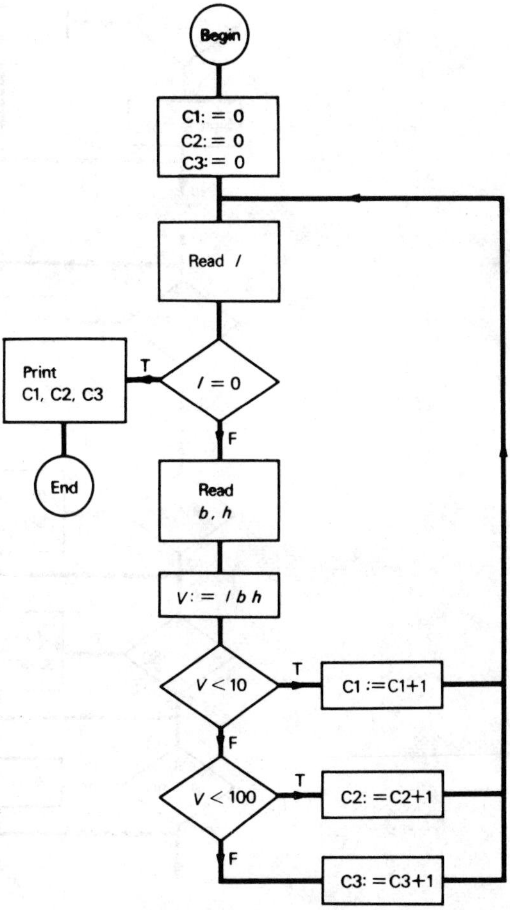

(B)

Example 2

Draw a flow chart to find the sine of an angle, assuming that we only know the values of $\sin\theta$ for $0° \leqslant \theta \leqslant 90°$.

Suppose we are given an angle θ in degrees. θ may be any number, so we must first reduce it to a value in the range $0 \leqslant \theta \leqslant 90$. We will store θ and SIGN of $\sin\theta$ as two separate variables.

The algorithm consists of a series of tests on the value of θ, each time reducing it and changing the value of the SIGN if necessary. SIGN will always be +1 or −1.

(1) $\sin(-\theta) = -\sin\theta$, so if θ is negative, we change its sign and give SIGN the value −1.

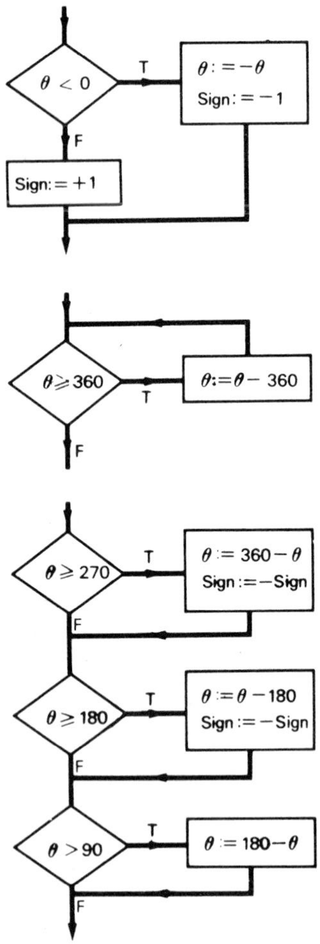

(2) $\sin\theta = \sin(\theta - 360)$ so if $\theta > 360$ we subtract 360 from it, more than once if necessary.

(3) θ is now in the range $0 \leqslant \theta \leqslant 360$. In the next three tests we bring it down into the range $0 \leqslant \theta \leqslant 90$, changing SIGN where necessary (See p. 90.)

(4) The sin of our original angle is SIGN $\times \sin\theta$.

We can now put all the elements of this flow chart together:

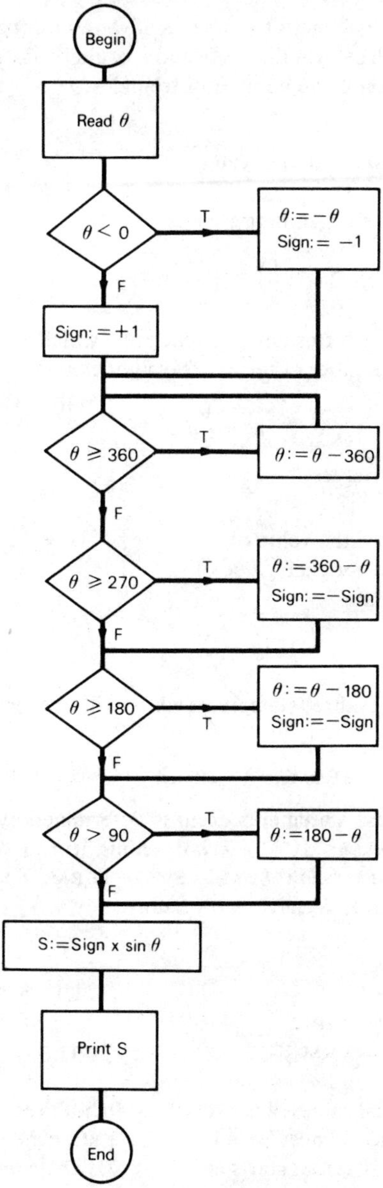

Exercise 2.3a

1 Draw a flow chart for a program to find cos θ where θ is a given angle (in degrees), assuming that we only have the values of cos θ for $0 \leqslant \theta \leqslant 90°$.

2 Pairs of values of the distance s and velocity v for different parts of a journey are read into a computer. The last pair is signalled by a sentinel $s = 0$. Draw a flow chart to find the total time taken and the average velocity for the whole journey.

3 Draw a flow chart which reads twenty sets of values for the three variables a, b, c, and determines for each set whether a, b, and c could be the sides of a triangle. The output from the program is the number of triangles.

Constructing a flow chart to sum a series

As an example we take the geometric series

$$7+7\left(\frac{1}{3}\right)+7\left(\frac{1}{3}\right)^2+7\left(\frac{1}{3}\right)^3+\ldots$$

We shall continue adding terms until we reach one which is less than 10^{-6}, and then print the sum and the number of terms. The algorithm is

$$u_1 = 7, \qquad u_r = \frac{1}{3}u_{r-1}, \qquad S_n = \sum_{r=1}^{n} u_r$$

We shall need three variables:

(1) A counter to record the value of r.
(2) a TERM to hold u_r for each value of r.
(3) a SUM to accumulate

$$\sum_{r=1}^{n} u_r$$

The algorithm requires three statements which will be executed each time the loop is traversed

$r := r+1$ TERM $:= \frac{1}{3}\times$TERM SUM $:=$ SUM+TERM

The order in which these statements occur is determined by the fact that we must always test TERM (TERM $< 10^{-6}$?) *before* adding it into SUM. So the statement TERM $:= \frac{1}{3}\times$TERM must *follow* SUM $:=$ SUM+TERM. The third statement $r := r+1$ may come anywhere. We give two versions:

Version 1	*Version 2*
$r := r+1$	SUM $:=$ SUM+TERM
SUM $:=$ SUM+TERM	$r := r+1$
TERM $:= \frac{1}{3}\times$TERM	TERM $:= \frac{1}{3}\times$TERM

We can now set the initial values of the variables. In both versions these are the same. r must start at zero since it must have the value 1 after the first circuit of the loop. SUM is initially zero and TERM starts at 7 ($u_1 = 7$). The completed flow chart is:

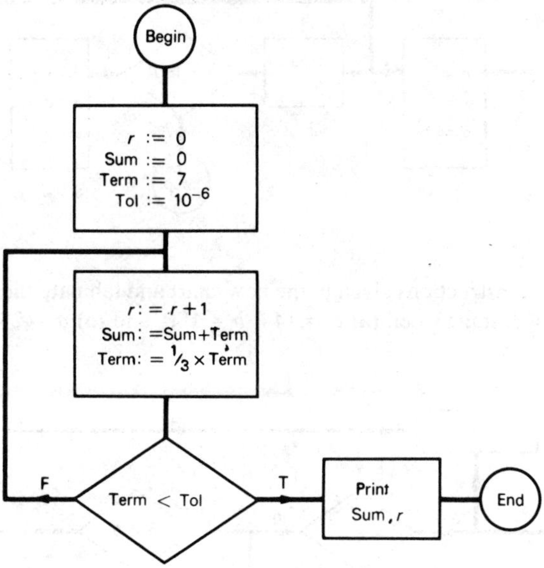

Exercise 2.3b

Draw up flow charts for programs to find the sum of each of the five series below. Your flow chart should take account of the condition listed to the right of each series.

1 $3+\frac{3^2}{2}+\frac{3^3}{3}+\ldots$ to six terms

2 $1+\frac{2}{1}+\frac{2^2}{1\times2}+\frac{2^3}{1\times2\times3}+\ldots$ to six terms

3 $1+\frac{\frac{1}{2}}{1}+\frac{(\frac{1}{2})^2}{1\times2}+\frac{(\frac{1}{2})^3}{1\times2\times3}+\ldots$ until a term less than 0.5E−3 is reached

4 $u_i=\left(1+\frac{8}{100}\right)u_{i-1},\ u_0=100$ until $i=5$

5 $u_i=\frac{1}{2}\left(u_{i-1}+\frac{2}{u_{i-1}}\right),\ u_0=1$ until $|u_i-u_{i-1}|<0.0005$

Miscellaneous examination questions 10

1 List the first four pairs of numbers printed by a computer executing a program described by the flow diagram below. Describe the purposes of the program, and explain the method by which this purpose is achieved. (A.E.B.)

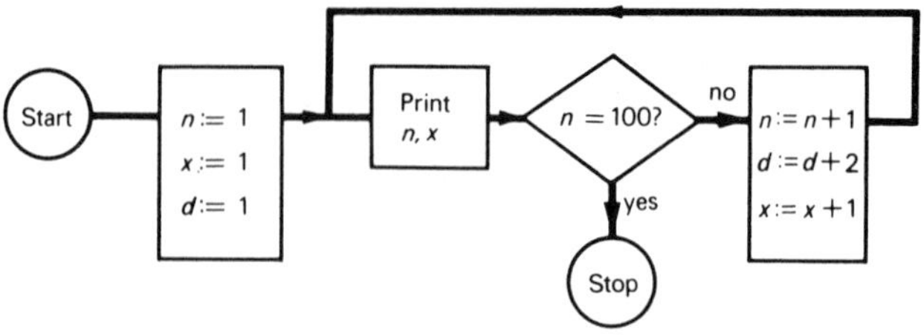

2 Carry out the instructions given in the flow chart and tabulate the current values of a and b at each stage when **(a)** $a = 144$, $b = 180$, and **(b)** $a = 29$, $b = 21$.

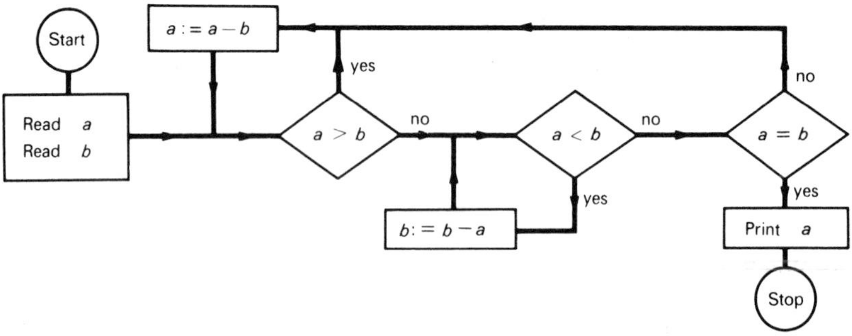

What is the purpose of the program given in the flow chart? Describe how you would modify the flow chart to deal with three numbers a, b, c. (You may do this by writing out a modified flow chart or by showing the additions that would be required.)

(M.E.I.)

3

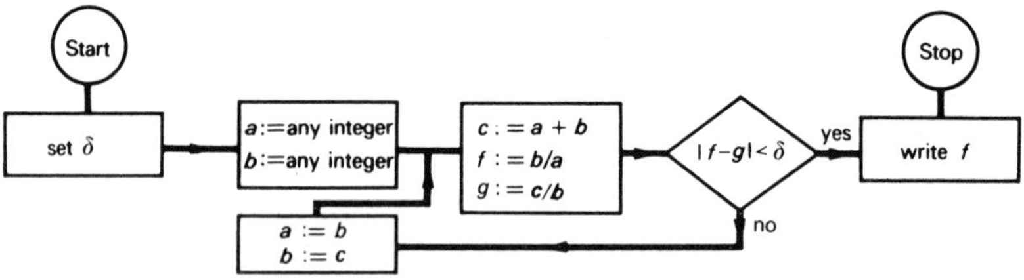

The flow chart represents an algorithm for obtaining an estimate of f (known as Fibonacci's limit). Taking any single-digit positive numbers for a and b (the value of f is independent of a and b), use the flow chart to calculate an estimate of f, taking $\delta = 0.001$.

(C.)

4

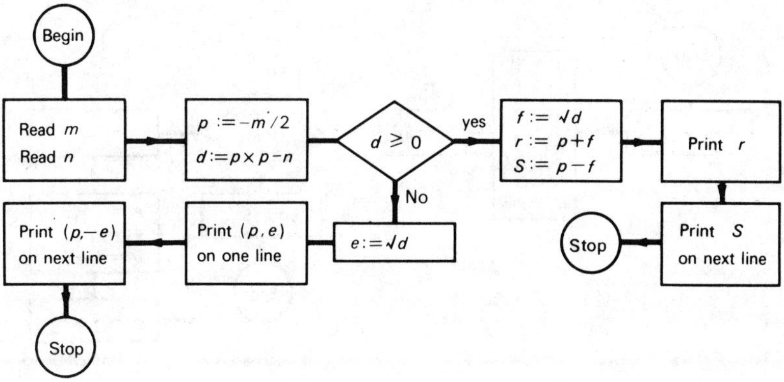

The flow chart shown is for the solution of a certain equation with given coefficients. Correct the error in one instruction in the flow chart and carry out the solution for each set of data below, giving results as accurately as your tables permit.

DATA (read off in pairs m, n): **(a)** −4, 4.25 **(b)** −4, 0.08

The data are treated as exact. If any result is not accurate to 3S use and explain a modified method which determines it to this accuracy. (M.E.I.)

5

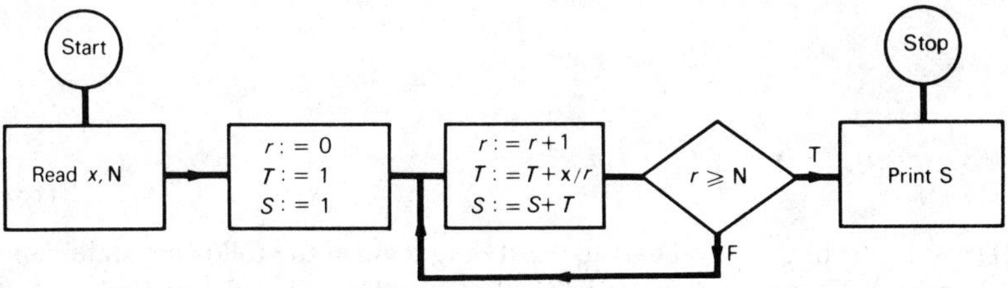

The given flow chart is intended to find, for given values of x and N, the sum S of a certain series. The symbol T is used for a term in the series. Evaluate the number which would be printed if the input numbers x, N were

(a) 3, 4 **(b)** 0.2, 3 **(c)** −0.2, 3

Write down, in terms of x, the first five terms of the series S. (M.E.I.)

6 Show that if

$$f(r) = r(r+1)(r+2)$$

then

$$f(r) - f(r-1) = 3r(r+1)$$

Hence find the sum of the series

$$2+6+12+\ldots+r(r+1)+\ldots+n(n+1)$$

Write a program (i.e. draw a flow chart) to find all the values of n not greater than 1000 for which the sum of the series is either one more or one less than a perfect square. (L.)

7

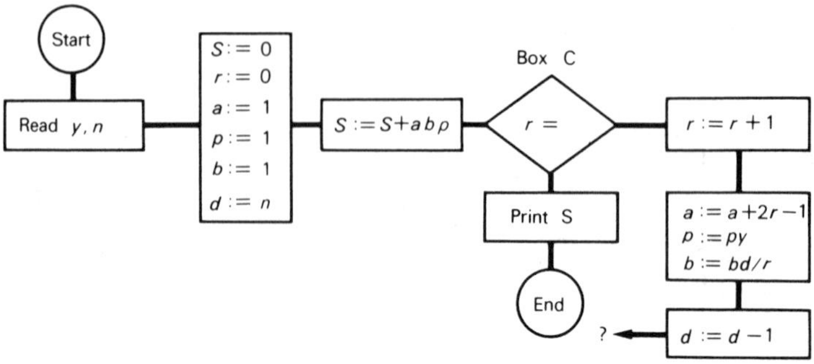

The flow chart is intended to evaluate the sum

$$1+(1+1^2)\binom{n}{1}y+\ldots+(1+r^2)\binom{n}{r}y^r+\ldots+(1+n^2)\binom{n}{n}y^n$$

where y is a given real number and n is a positive integer. Complete the flow chart. Complete the table of values of r, a, p, b, d immediately after the successive decisions in box C have been made, assuming $n = 3$ and $y = 2$.

r	0	1	2	3
a	1			
p	1			
b	1			
d	3			

(J.M.B.)

8 Draw a part of the flow chart to clarify the logic in the following statement: 'If $x < 1$ and $y > 2$, then $z = 0$. If neither of these conditions is satisfied, but $y > 1$, then $z = 1$. Otherwise, $z = 2$, unless x and y are both negative, in which case $z = 3$.' (C.)

9 Draw a flow diagram for a program to find the roots of the quadratic equation

$$x^2+px+q = 0$$

where p and q are real, taking account of the cases
(a) roots real and distinct, **(b)** roots real and equal, **(c)** roots complex,

and show the form of the output obtained in each case. (C.)

Chapter 11

Complex Numbers

1 Manipulation of complex numbers

1.1 Matrices and complex numbers

We have investigated matrix transformations at considerable length and seen that certain matrix transformations give enlargements, e.g. $\begin{pmatrix} 3 & 0 \\ 0 & 3 \end{pmatrix}$ represents an enlargement with a scale factor of 3.

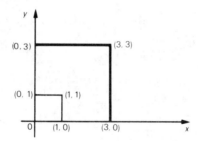

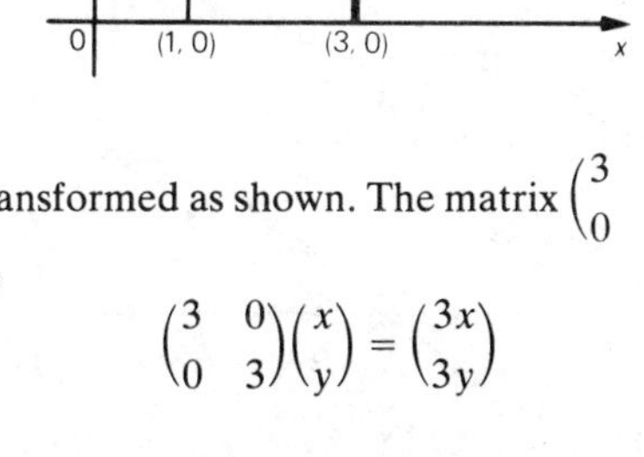

The *unit* square is transformed as shown. The matrix $\begin{pmatrix} 3 & 0 \\ 0 & 3 \end{pmatrix}$ represents, in effect, a change of scale since

$$\begin{pmatrix} 3 & 0 \\ 0 & 3 \end{pmatrix}\begin{pmatrix} x \\ y \end{pmatrix} = \begin{pmatrix} 3x \\ 3y \end{pmatrix}$$

The matrix $\begin{pmatrix} 3 & 0 \\ 0 & 3 \end{pmatrix}$ has the effect of multiplying the column vector $\begin{pmatrix} x \\ y \end{pmatrix}$ by 3. A matrix of the type $\begin{pmatrix} p & 0 \\ 0 & p \end{pmatrix}$ where $p \in \mathbb{R}$ is called a *scalar matrix*, numbers like p often being known as *scalars*.

Now $$\begin{pmatrix} 3 & 0 \\ 0 & 3 \end{pmatrix} + \begin{pmatrix} 2 & 0 \\ 0 & 2 \end{pmatrix} = \begin{pmatrix} 5 & 0 \\ 0 & 5 \end{pmatrix}$$

corresponds to $$3 \quad + \quad 2 \quad = \quad 5$$

and $$\begin{pmatrix} 3 & 0 \\ 0 & 3 \end{pmatrix}\begin{pmatrix} 2 & 0 \\ 0 & 2 \end{pmatrix} = \begin{pmatrix} 6 & 0 \\ 0 & 6 \end{pmatrix}$$

corresponds to $3 \times 2 = 6$

We can see that the scalar matrices satisfy the usual set of rules obeyed by numbers. Here are some examples:

(a)
$$\begin{pmatrix}3 & 0\\0 & 3\end{pmatrix}+\begin{pmatrix}2 & 0\\0 & 2\end{pmatrix}=\begin{pmatrix}5 & 0\\0 & 5\end{pmatrix}=\begin{pmatrix}2 & 0\\0 & 2\end{pmatrix}+\begin{pmatrix}3 & 0\\0 & 3\end{pmatrix}$$
$$3 + 2 = 5 = 2 + 3$$

(b)
$$\begin{pmatrix}3 & 0\\0 & 3\end{pmatrix}+\begin{pmatrix}0 & 0\\0 & 0\end{pmatrix}=\begin{pmatrix}3 & 0\\0 & 3\end{pmatrix}$$
$$3 + 0 = 3$$

(c)
$$\begin{pmatrix}3 & 0\\0 & 3\end{pmatrix}\begin{pmatrix}1 & 0\\0 & 1\end{pmatrix}=\begin{pmatrix}3 & 0\\0 & 3\end{pmatrix}$$
$$3 \times 1 = 3$$

(d)
$$\begin{pmatrix}3 & 0\\0 & 3\end{pmatrix}\left[\begin{pmatrix}2 & 0\\0 & 2\end{pmatrix}+\begin{pmatrix}1 & 0\\0 & 1\end{pmatrix}\right]=\begin{pmatrix}3 & 0\\0 & 3\end{pmatrix}\begin{pmatrix}2 & 0\\0 & 2\end{pmatrix}+\begin{pmatrix}3 & 0\\0 & 3\end{pmatrix}\begin{pmatrix}1 & 0\\0 & 1\end{pmatrix}$$
$$3 \times [2 + 1] = 3 \times 2 + 3 \times 1$$

In fact *all* the rules of numbers are satisfied by the scalar matrices. The two systems are virtually identical. (Two systems like this are said to be *isomorphic*—see page 436.)

The identity matrix $\begin{pmatrix}1 & 0\\0 & 1\end{pmatrix}$ corresponds to 1, and $\begin{pmatrix}-1 & 0\\0 & -1\end{pmatrix}$ corresponds to -1.

Now $\begin{pmatrix}-1 & 0\\0 & -1\end{pmatrix}$ transforms the point (x, y) to $(-x, -y)$ since
$$\begin{pmatrix}-1 & 0\\0 & -1\end{pmatrix}\begin{pmatrix}x\\y\end{pmatrix}=\begin{pmatrix}-x\\-y\end{pmatrix}$$

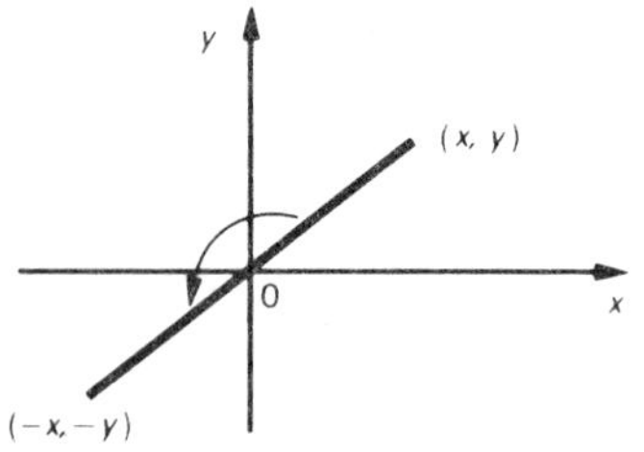

This represents a rotation about the origin of 180°. The rotation can be accomplished by turning through 90° anticlockwise and then turning through another 90°. The matrix representing this rotation through 90° is $\begin{pmatrix}0 & -1\\1 & 0\end{pmatrix} = \mathbf{J}$(say).

Doing this transformation once and then repeating it, we have

$$\mathbf{J}\times\mathbf{J}=\begin{pmatrix}-1 & 0\\0 & -1\end{pmatrix} \qquad \text{i.e.} \qquad \mathbf{J}^2=\begin{pmatrix}0 & -1\\1 & 0\end{pmatrix}^2=\begin{pmatrix}-1 & 0\\0 & -1\end{pmatrix}$$

J has no corresponding number in our scalar number system so we introduce j so that $j^2 = -1$. Numbers like 5j would correspond to

$$\begin{pmatrix} 5 & 0 \\ 0 & 5 \end{pmatrix}\begin{pmatrix} 0 & -1 \\ 1 & 0 \end{pmatrix} = \begin{pmatrix} 0 & -5 \\ 5 & 0 \end{pmatrix}$$

or -2j would correspond to

$$\begin{pmatrix} 0 & +2 \\ -2 & 0 \end{pmatrix}$$

and so on.

In general pj corresponds to

$$\begin{pmatrix} 0 & -p \\ p & 0 \end{pmatrix}$$

We can combine numbers like $2+3$j as follows:

$$\begin{pmatrix} 2 & 0 \\ 0 & 2 \end{pmatrix} + \begin{pmatrix} 0 & -3 \\ 3 & 0 \end{pmatrix} = \begin{pmatrix} 2 & -3 \\ 3 & 2 \end{pmatrix}$$

$$2 \quad + \quad 3\mathrm{j} \quad = 2 + 3\mathrm{j}$$

In general $\begin{pmatrix} p & -q \\ q & p \end{pmatrix}$ corresponds to $p+q\,\mathrm{j}$.

We can also investigate addition of such numbers:

$$\begin{pmatrix} 2 & -3 \\ 3 & 2 \end{pmatrix} + \begin{pmatrix} 3 & -4 \\ 4 & 3 \end{pmatrix} = \begin{pmatrix} 5 & -7 \\ 7 & 5 \end{pmatrix}$$

$$(2 + 3\mathrm{j}) + (3 + 4\mathrm{j}) = (5 + 7\mathrm{j})$$

Similarly for multiplication,

$$\begin{pmatrix} 2 & -3 \\ 3 & 2 \end{pmatrix}\begin{pmatrix} 3 & -4 \\ 4 & 3 \end{pmatrix} = \begin{pmatrix} -6 & -17 \\ 17 & -6 \end{pmatrix}$$

$$(2 + 3\mathrm{j})(3 + 4\mathrm{j}) = (-6 + 17\mathrm{j})$$

In general,

$$\begin{pmatrix} p & -q \\ q & p \end{pmatrix} + \begin{pmatrix} r & -s \\ s & r \end{pmatrix} = \begin{pmatrix} p+r & -q-s \\ +q+s & p+r \end{pmatrix}$$

$$\boldsymbol{(p + q\mathrm{j}) + (r + s\mathrm{j}) = (p+r) + (q+s)\mathrm{j}}$$ ◀

and

$$\begin{pmatrix} p & -q \\ q & p \end{pmatrix}\begin{pmatrix} r & -s \\ s & r \end{pmatrix} = \begin{pmatrix} pr-qs & -ps-qr \\ ps+qr & pr-sq \end{pmatrix}$$

$$\boldsymbol{(p + q\mathrm{j})(r + s\mathrm{j}) = (pr-qs) + (ps+qr)\mathrm{j}}$$ ◀

Notice that this is what we should obtain using ordinary algebra and taking $j^2 = -1$:

$$\begin{aligned}(p+q\mathrm{j})(r+s\mathrm{j}) &= pr + ps\mathrm{j} + qr\mathrm{j} + qs\mathrm{j}^2 \\ &= pr - qs + (ps+qr)\mathrm{j}\end{aligned}$$

Numbers of the type $p+qj$ where $p, q \in \mathbb{R}$ are called *complex numbers*, and we call the set of complex numbers the set $\mathbb{C}$.

Since matrices which are equal have identical entries, if

$$\begin{pmatrix} p & -q \\ q & p \end{pmatrix} = \begin{pmatrix} r & -s \\ s & r \end{pmatrix}$$

then $\qquad p = r \qquad$ and $\qquad q = s$

i.e. if $\qquad p+qj = r+sj$

then $\qquad p = r \qquad$ and $\qquad q = s$

Exercise 1.1

Simplify the following, using the ordinary rules of algebra and remembering that $j^2 = -1$.

1 $3(2-3j)$

2 $5-3j+4+2j$

3 $(3+4j)(2-7j)$

4 $j(2+3j)$

5 $(2+3j)^2$

6 $(3-4j)(3+4j)$

7 $(5-2j)(3+2j)$

8 $(4-5j)(4+5j)$

9 $(2-3j)(3+2j)(4-j)$

10 $(2-4j)(3+4j)(1-j)$

1.2 Complex conjugate numbers

We have seen how to add (or subtract) and multiply complex numbers, but we have not mentioned division. In the algebra of real numbers, if $Ax = b$, then

$$x = b \div A \qquad \text{or} \qquad x = b \times \frac{1}{A}$$

and we can choose which operation we like. In matrix algebra there is no operation of division, so we must use multiplication by the inverse.

For example if we have to solve the equation

$$\mathbf{A}\boldsymbol{x} = \boldsymbol{b}$$

where $\mathbf{A}$ is a matrix and $\boldsymbol{x}$, $\boldsymbol{b}$ are vectors, premultiplying both sides by $\mathbf{A}^{-1}$ we have

$$\boldsymbol{x} = \mathbf{A}^{-1}\boldsymbol{b}$$

If $\qquad \mathbf{A} = \begin{pmatrix} p & -q \\ q & p \end{pmatrix}$

then the adjoint of A $\qquad \text{Adj}(\mathbf{A}) = \begin{pmatrix} p & q \\ -q & p \end{pmatrix}$

and the determinant of A $\qquad \text{Det}(\mathbf{A}) = p^2+q^2$

Hence
$$\mathbf{A}^{-1} = \frac{1}{p^2+q^2}\begin{pmatrix} p & q \\ -q & p \end{pmatrix}$$

Now the complex number corresponding to $\begin{pmatrix} p & -q \\ q & p \end{pmatrix}$ is $p+q\mathrm{j}$, and to $\begin{pmatrix} p & q \\ -q & p \end{pmatrix}$ is $p-q\mathrm{j}$. So

$$\frac{1}{p+q\mathrm{j}} = \frac{1}{p^2+q^2}(p-q\mathrm{j})$$

and division by $p+q\mathrm{j}$ is achieved by multiplication by

$$\frac{1}{p^2+q^2}(p-q\mathrm{j})$$

$p-q\mathrm{j}$ is called the *conjugate* of $p+q\mathrm{j}$;
together they form a *complex conjugate pair.* ◀

We can arrive at the same result directly by multiplying the numerator and denominator by the conjugate of the denominator:

$$\frac{1}{p+q\mathrm{j}} = \frac{1}{p+q\mathrm{j}}\,\frac{p-q\mathrm{j}}{p-q\mathrm{j}} = \frac{p-q\mathrm{j}}{p^2+q^2}$$

We could call this 'realizing' the denominator, analogous to

$$\frac{1}{\sqrt{3}} = \frac{1}{\sqrt{3}}\times\frac{\sqrt{3}}{\sqrt{3}} = \frac{\sqrt{3}}{3}$$

which is called rationalizing the denominator.

Example

Simplify
$$\frac{3+\mathrm{j}}{1+\mathrm{j}}$$

$$\frac{3+\mathrm{j}}{1+\mathrm{j}} = \frac{3+\mathrm{j}}{1+\mathrm{j}}\,\frac{1-\mathrm{j}}{1-\mathrm{j}} = \frac{(3+\mathrm{j})(1-\mathrm{j})}{2} = \frac{4-2\mathrm{j}}{2} = 2-\mathrm{j}$$

Exercise 1.2

Simplify the following:

1 $\dfrac{2+3\mathrm{j}}{4-5\mathrm{j}}$ **2** $\dfrac{1}{5+4\mathrm{j}}$ **3** $\dfrac{2}{3-\mathrm{j}}$

4 $\dfrac{1+3\mathrm{j}}{2-3\mathrm{j}}$ **5** $\dfrac{5\mathrm{j}}{(2+3\mathrm{j})(6-\mathrm{j})}$ **6** $\dfrac{(3-4\mathrm{j})}{(1+\mathrm{j})(4-2\mathrm{j})}$

1.3 Roots of equations with real coefficients

Quadratic equations

Consider the equation $$x^2+2x-4=0$$

This may be solved as follows:

$$(x+1)^2 = 5$$

$$(x+1) = \pm\sqrt{5}$$

giving $x=-1+\sqrt{5}$ or $x=-1-\sqrt{5}$

Suppose $$x^2+2x+4=0$$

$$(x+1)^2 = -3$$

$$(x+1)^2 = -1\times 3$$

$$(x+1)^2 = \mathrm{j}^2 3$$

$$x+1 = \pm\mathrm{j}\sqrt{3}$$

$$x=-1+\mathrm{j}\sqrt{3} \quad \text{or} \quad x=-1-\mathrm{j}\sqrt{3}$$

With this method it is possible to solve *all* quadratic equations with real coefficients. Note that the complex solutions occur as a conjugate pair. If one root is $x=p+q\mathrm{j}$ then the other is $x=p-q\mathrm{j}$.

As we have seen, quadratic equations may have two real different roots, two real equal roots or two complex conjugate roots. If there are complex roots they are always a pair, and always conjugate.

If the equation is

$$Ax^2+Bx+C=0 \qquad (A>0)$$

the roots are shown as

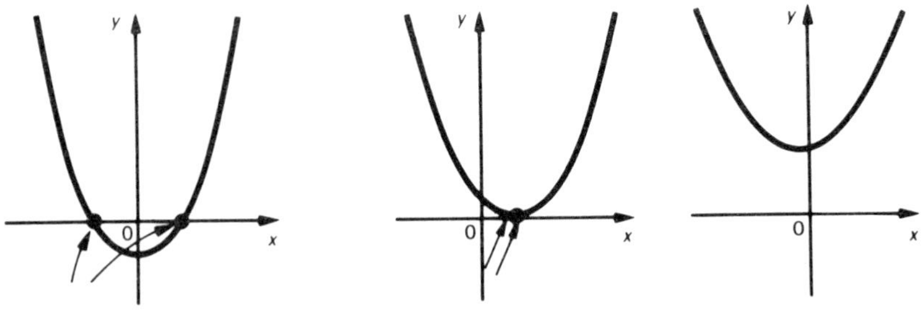

(i) $B^2>4AC$ Two real different roots

(ii) $B^2=4AC$ Two real equal roots

(iii) $B^2<4AC$ Two complex conjugate roots

Cubic equations

For a cubic equation

$$Ax^3+Bx^2+Cx+D=0$$

there are *four* possibilities. There may be three real different roots, two equal and one different real root, three equal real roots, or one real root and a pair of complex conjugate roots. These are shown diagramatically below.

(i) Three real different roots

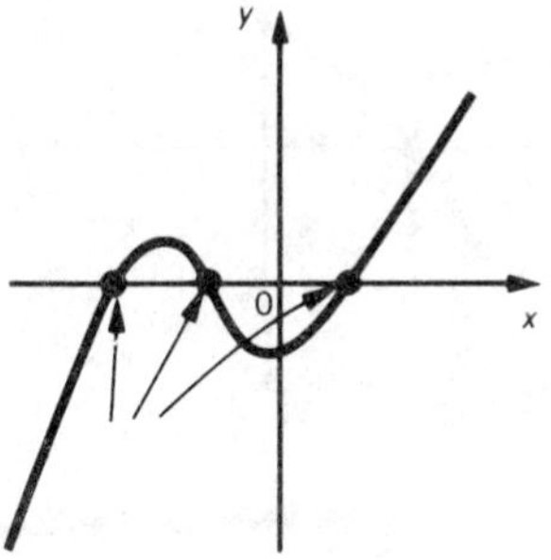

$$y = (x-1)(x+2)(x+4)$$
$$= (x-1)(x^2+6x+8)$$
$$= x^3+5x^2+2x-8$$

(ii) Two equal and one different root

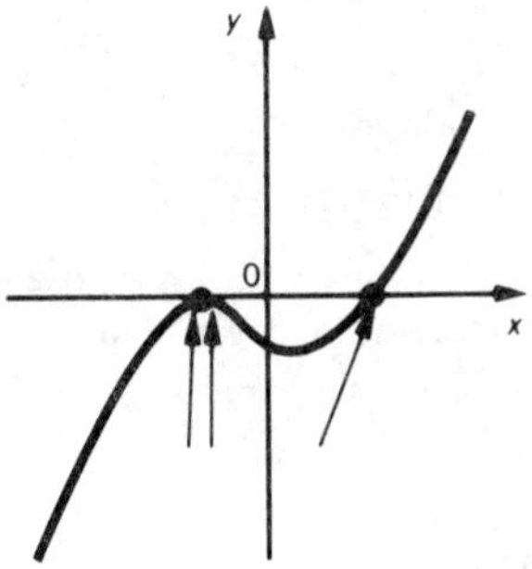

$$y = (x-3)(x+1)(x+1)$$
$$= (x-3)(x^2+2x+1)$$
$$= x^3-x^2-5x-3$$

(iii) Three equal roots

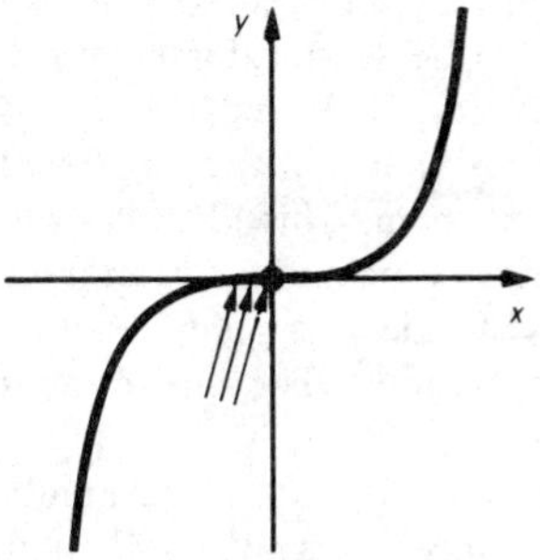

$$y = x^3$$

(iv) One real root and a pair of complex conjugate roots

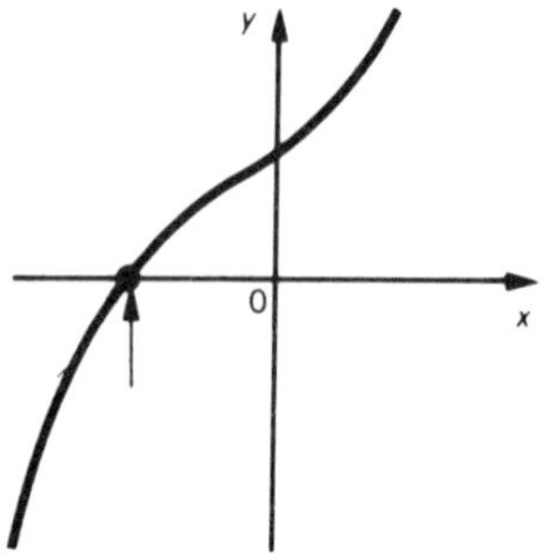

$$y = (x+2)(x^2+3x+8) \qquad (B^2 < 4AC)$$
$$= x^3+5x^2+14x+16$$

Exercise 1.3

Solve the following equations in $\mathbb{C}$:

1 $x^2+4x+9=0$ **4** $3x^3-x+2=0$ **7** $x^3-4x^2+x+6=0$

2 $x^2-2x+5=0$ **5** $2x^2+5=0$ **8** $-x^3+5x^2-8x+4=0$

3 $x^2+3x+1=0$ **6** $5x^2+2x+3=0$ **9** $x^3+2x^2-x+6=0$

10 Given an equation $Ax^2+Bx+C=0$ with A, B and C real numbers, show that if $x = a+b\mathrm{j}$ is one root, then the other *must* be $a-b\mathrm{j}$.

2 The Argand diagram

2.1 Representation of complex numbers in cartesian coordinates

As we have seen, a complex number—z, say—can be written $z = p+q\mathrm{j}$. It is clear that z is specified completely by an ordered pair of numbers (p, q) where the x coordinate corresponds to p, the y coordinate to q. For example $2+3\mathrm{j}$ could be represented by $(2, 3)$, whilst $(5, -4)$ would mean $5-4\mathrm{j}$. As the complex number could be specified by two coordinates, it was suggested that it might be possible to draw a diagram to represent them. This idea was put forward in about 1800 by several mathematicians but a Frenchman, Argand, was the first one to publish it.

Coordinates may be used to locate a point in space, but we cannot *add* points together as we add complex numbers. The clue to the representation is given by the addition of *position* vectors.

When complex numbers were first used, the number j (such that $\mathrm{j}^2 = -1$) was called an *imaginary* number since it was not a *real* number. The x axis is often called the *real* axis and the y axis the *imaginary* axis. If

$$z = x + yj$$

then $$x = \text{Re}(z), \qquad y = \text{Im}(z)$$

which is to be read as 'x is the real part of z' and 'y is the imaginary part of z', where x, $y \in \mathbb{R}$.

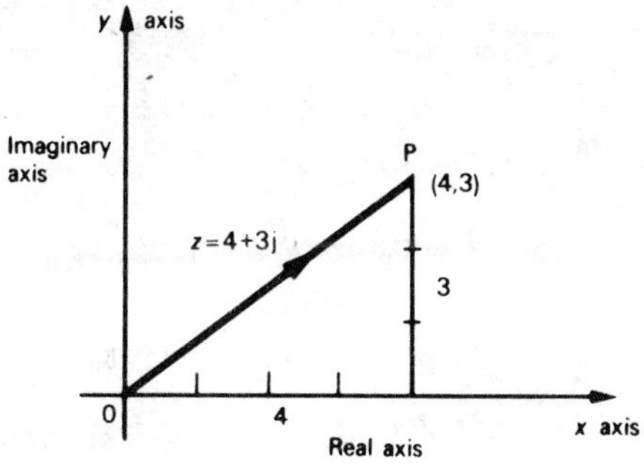

The complex number $z = 4 + 3j$ is represented by the directed line segment OP.

Multiplication by a scalar, *a* (*a* > 0)

Suppose $$z = 2 + 1j$$

Then $$3z = 3(2+1j)$$
$$= 6 + 3j$$

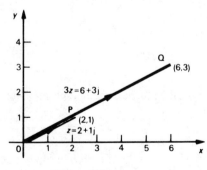

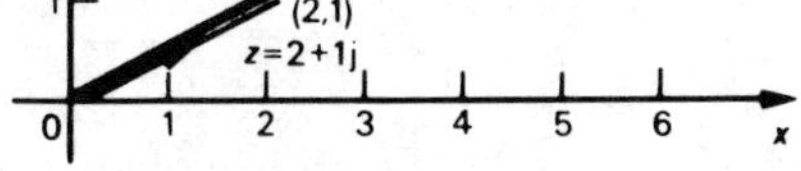

i.e. $$OQ = 3OP$$

In general, if $$z = x + yj$$

and a is a scalar, then $$az = a(x + yj)$$
$$= ax + ayj$$

If a is a fraction, then OQ with be less than OP. In the diagram below, $a = \frac{1}{2}$.

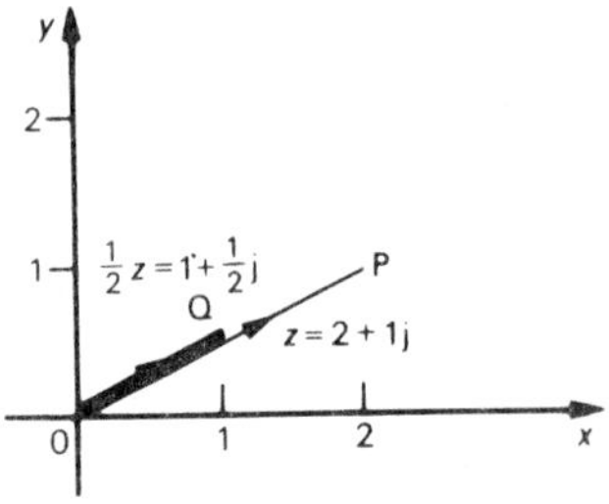

Multiplication by a scalar, a $(a < 0)$

Suppose $z = 3+4j$

Then $-1z = -1(3+4j) = -3-4j$

$-2z = -2(3+4j) = -6-8j$ and so on.

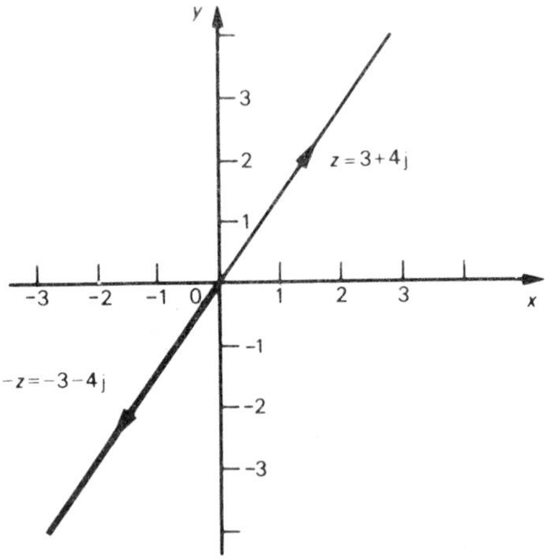

Multiplication by j

From our derivation of j it is obvious that multiplication by j has the effect of rotating OP through 90° anticlockwise about O.

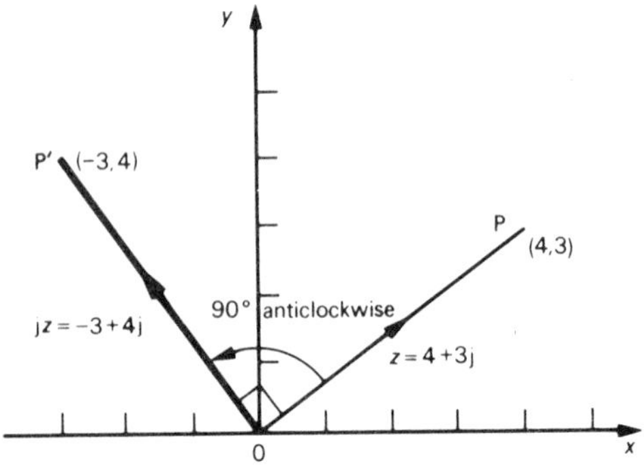

This can be calculated since, if

$$z = 4+3\text{j}$$

then
$$\text{j}z = \text{j}(4+3\text{j})$$
$$= 4\text{j}+3\text{j}^2 \qquad \text{and} \qquad \text{j}^2 = -1$$
$$= -3+4\text{j}$$

Multiplication by 3j, for example, can be thought of as a rotation through 90° anticlockwise followed by a multiplication by the scalar 3. For instance, if

$$z = 2+1\text{j},$$
$$3\text{j}z = 3(-1+2\text{j})$$
$$= -3+6\text{j}$$

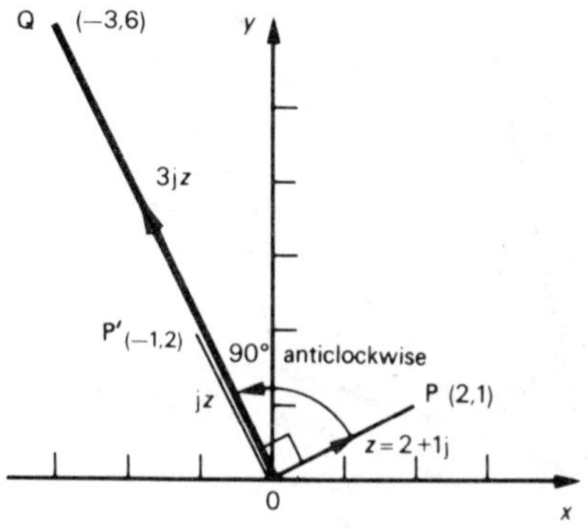

Complex conjugate numbers

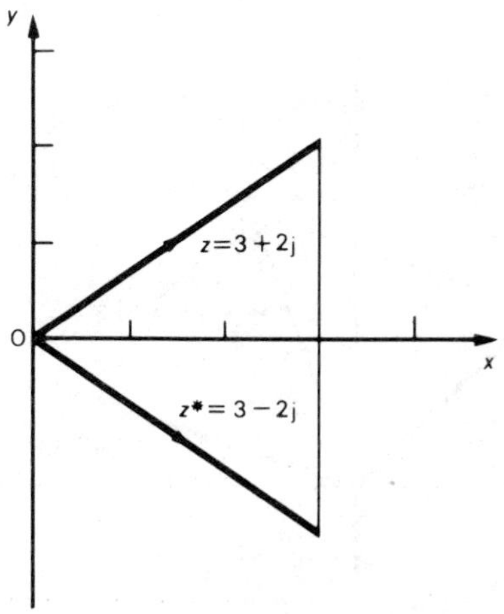

If $z = x + yj$ then the complex conjugate of z written $z^* = x - yj$. z and z^* are reflections in the line $y = 0$. From this definition we have

$$z + z^* = 2x$$

$$z - z^* = 2yj$$

and
$$zz^* = x^2 + y^2$$

Addition of complex numbers, $z = z_1 + z_2$

Example 1

$$(3 + 1j) + (1 + 4j) = (4 + 5j)$$

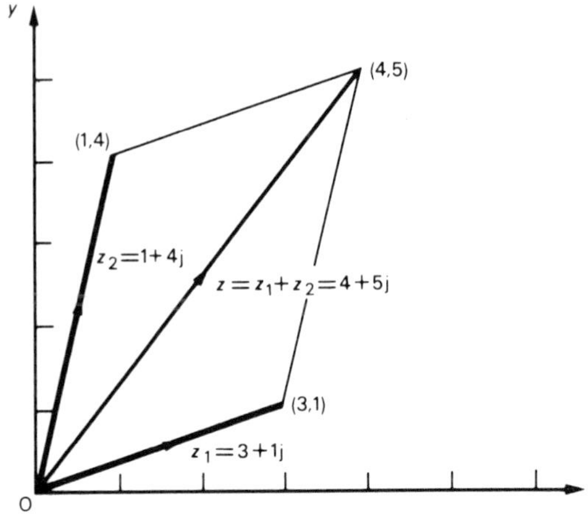

Example 2

$$(3 + 1j) + (-2 + 2j) = (1 + 3j)$$

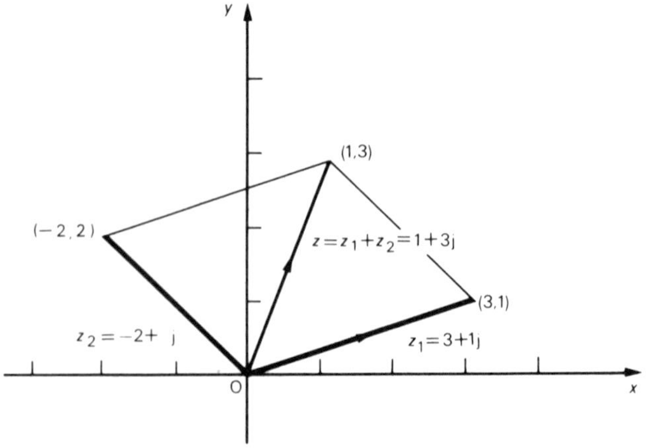

Example 3

$$(3+1j)+(-1-2j) = (2-1j)$$

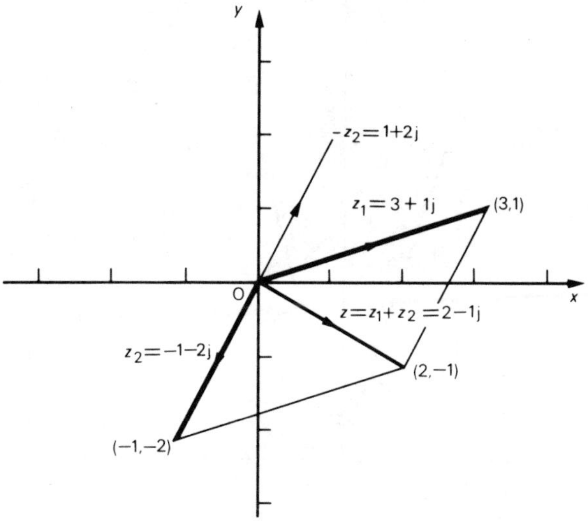

NOTE that $\quad -1(1+2j) = +(-1-2j)$

Subtraction of complex numbers can therefore be carried out as addition of the negative number.

Multiplication of complex numbers

Example

Find $(2+3j)(3+1j)$.

This is equal to $2(3+1j)+3j(3+1j)$ and can be found as follows. See p. 390.
We draw $z = 3+1j$ and hence $2z$. Then jz is found by rotation of z anticlockwise through 90° about 0, and hence $3jz$. The complete multiplication is given by $2z+3jz$.

This is not however, a practical way of multiplying complex numbers. A far easier method is to change from cartesian (x, y) coordinates to polar (r, θ) coordinates, as we shall see in the next section.

Exercise 2.1

Illustrate the following complex numbers on the Argand diagram.

1 $3+4j$
2 $2-3j$
3 $2-4j$
4 $-1+3j$
5 $2(1-3j)$
6 $-3(2-3j)$
7 $5j(2+1j)$
8 $-2j(2+3j)$
9 $-1(2+1j)$
10 $-2-3j$
11 $-2+3j$
12 $3j(2+0j)$

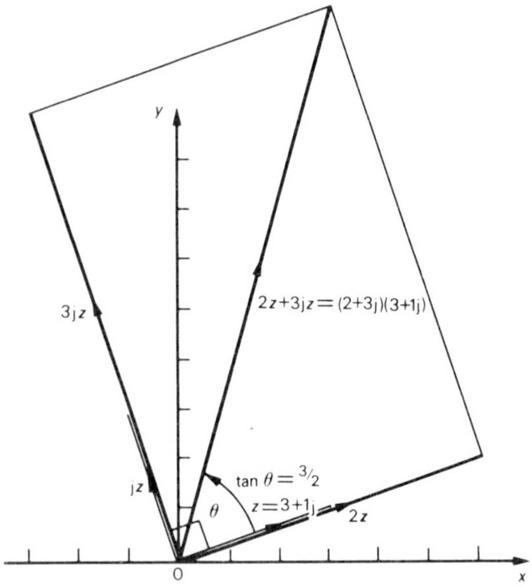

Illustrate the following operations on the Argand diagram.

13 $(2+3j)+(3-2j)$

14 $(-2+1j)+(4+5j)$

15 $(-3-2j)+(-1+2j)$

16 $(4+1j)-(2+3j)$

17 $(2+5j)+(2-5j)$

18 $(3+2j)(1-2j)$

19 $(-1-2j)(3+4j)$

20 $(3+j)(2-3j)$

1.5 Polar coordinates

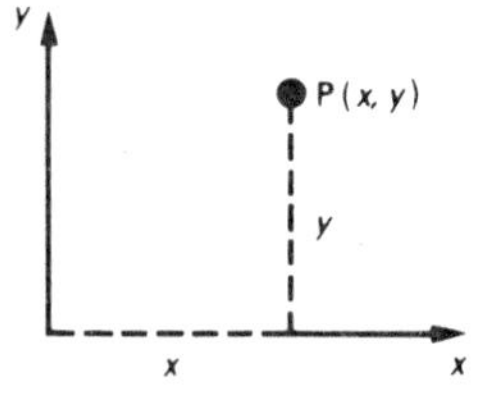

Cartesian coordinates: P is given two coordinates, the distances from the axes.

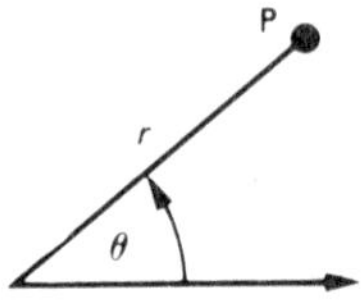

Polar coordinates: P is given two coordinates, the distance from O and the angle measured from a fixed direction.

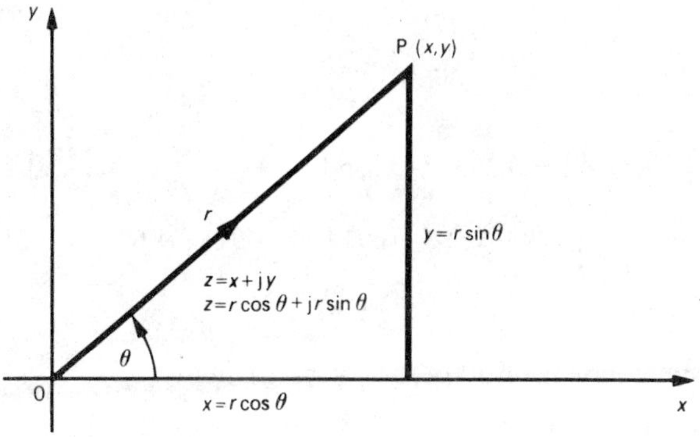

We have seen that

$$x = r\cos\theta, \qquad y = r\sin\theta, \qquad x^2+y^2 = r^2 \qquad \text{and} \qquad \frac{y}{x} = \tan\theta$$

r is the length OP, called the *modulus* of z and written $|z|$. θ is called the *argument* (or *amplitude*) and written arg (z). Using this notation

$$\boldsymbol{z = x + \mathrm{j}y}$$ ◀

becomes

$$z = r\cos\theta + \mathrm{j}r\sin\theta$$

or

$$\boldsymbol{z = r(\cos\theta + \mathrm{j}\sin\theta)}$$ ◀

where $r \geqslant 0$, $-\pi < \theta \leqslant \pi$.

Since $\quad \cos(-\theta) = \cos\theta \quad$ and $\quad \sin(-\theta) = -\sin\theta$

$$r[\cos(-\theta) + \mathrm{j}\sin(-\theta)] = r(\cos\theta - \mathrm{j}\sin\theta)$$

Hence $r(\cos\theta - \mathrm{j}\sin\theta)$ has modulus r, and argument $(-\theta)$. Also since

$$\sin\theta = \cos\left(\frac{\pi}{2}-\theta\right) \qquad \text{and} \qquad \cos\theta = \sin\left(\frac{\pi}{2}-\theta\right)$$

$$r(\sin\theta + \mathrm{j}\cos\theta) = r\left[\cos\left(\frac{\pi}{2}-\theta\right) + \mathrm{j}\sin\left(\frac{\pi}{2}-\theta\right)\right]$$

and has modulus r, and argument $(\pi/2-\theta)$.

Example 1

Express in the form $x+\mathrm{j}y$, the complex numbers

(a) $z_1 = 12\left(\cos\frac{\pi}{6} + \mathrm{j}\sin\frac{\pi}{6}\right)$ **(b)** $z_2 = 5\left(\sin\frac{\pi}{8} + \mathrm{j}\cos\frac{\pi}{8}\right)$

(a) Since
$$\cos\frac{\pi}{6} = \frac{\sqrt{3}}{2} \qquad \text{and} \qquad \sin\frac{\pi}{6} = \frac{1}{2}$$
$$z_1 = 12\left(\frac{\sqrt{3}}{2} + \frac{1}{2}\mathrm{j}\right) = 6\sqrt{3} + 6\mathrm{j}$$

(b) Since
$$\sin\frac{\pi}{8} = \cos\left(\frac{3}{8}\pi\right) = 0.383 \qquad \text{and} \qquad \cos\frac{\pi}{8} = \sin\left(\frac{3}{8}\pi\right) = 0.924$$
$$z_2 = 5(0.383 + 0.924\mathrm{j}) = 1.915 + 4.62\mathrm{j}$$

Example 2

Find the modulus and argument of the complex numbers

(a) $z_1 = 2 - 3\mathrm{j}$ **(b)** $z_2 = -2 + 3\mathrm{j}$ **(c)** $z_3 = -2 - 7\mathrm{j}$ **(d)** $z_2 + z_3$

(a)
$$r_1 = |z_1| = \sqrt{(2^2 + 3^2)} = \sqrt{13} = 3.61$$
$$\theta_1 = \arg(z_1) = \tan^{-1}\left(\frac{-3}{2}\right) = -0.98^c$$

since z_1 is in the fourth quadrant of the Argand diagram.

(b)
$$r_2 = |z_2| = \sqrt{(2^2 + 3^2)} = \sqrt{13} = 3.61, \qquad \text{as before.}$$
$$\theta_2 = \arg(z_2) = \tan^{-1}\left(\frac{3}{-2}\right) = 2.16^c$$

since z_2 is in the second quadrant.

(c)
$$r_3 = |z_3| = \sqrt{(2^2 + 7^2)} = \sqrt{53} = 7.28$$
$$\theta_3 = \arg(z_3) = \tan^{-1}\left(\frac{-7}{-2}\right) = -1.85^c$$

since z_3 is in the third quadrant.

(d)
$$z_2 + z_3 = -2 + 3\mathrm{j} + -2 - 7\mathrm{j} = -4 - 4\mathrm{j}$$
$$|z_2 + z_3| = \sqrt{(4^2 + 4^2)} = \sqrt{32} = 5.66$$
$$\arg(z_2 + z_3) = \tan^{-1}\left(\frac{-4}{-4}\right) = -\frac{3}{4}\pi^c$$

Note that $|z_2| + |z_3| = 3.61 + 7.28 = 10.89$, but $|z_2 + z_3| = 5.66$. This is an illustration of the *triangle inequality* of complex numbers:

$$|\mathbf{z_1}| + |\mathbf{z_2}| \geqslant |\mathbf{z_1} + \mathbf{z_2}|$$ ◀

In the diagram opposite
$$\mathrm{OA} = |z_1| \qquad \text{and} \qquad \mathrm{OB} = \mathrm{AC} = |z_2|$$

Since the sum of two sides of a triangle is always greater than the third side we have
$$\mathrm{OA} + \mathrm{AC} > \mathrm{OC}$$

unless z_1 and z_2 are in the same line, in which case

$$\text{OA}+\text{AC}=\text{OC}$$

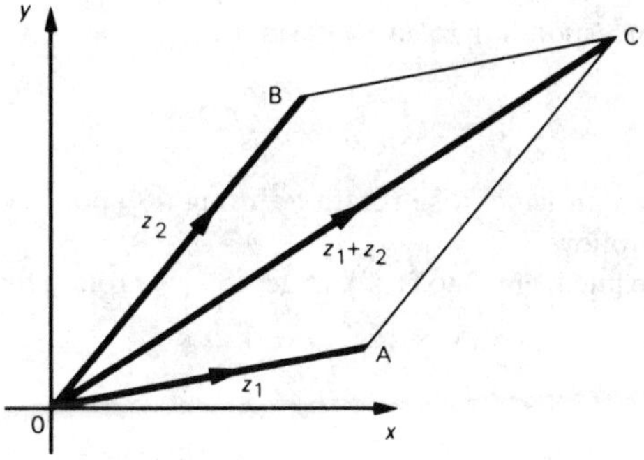

We met the similar triangle inequality of vectors in Chapter 8.

Exercise 2.2

1 Illustrate the following complex numbers in an Argand diagram, and express each in the form $r(\cos\theta+\text{j}\sin\theta)$ where $r>0$, $-\pi<\theta^c\leqslant\pi$

(a) $3+4\text{j}$	**(b)** $-2-\text{j}$	**(c)** $7-24\text{j}$
(d) 1	**(e)** -1	**(f)** -5
(g) 3j	**(h)** $-\sqrt{3}+\text{j}$	**(i)** $2+\sqrt{3}\text{j}$
(j) $-2-\sqrt{2}\text{j}$	**(k)** $\frac{1}{2}-\frac{1}{4}\text{j}$	**(l)** $-\frac{2}{3}+\frac{1}{5}\text{j}$

2 Express in the form $x+\text{j}y$ the following complex numbers:

(a) $4(\cos\frac{5}{6}\pi+\text{j}\sin\frac{5}{6}\pi)$ **(b)** $\sqrt{3}(\cos\frac{5}{4}\pi+\text{j}\sin\frac{5}{4}\pi)$

(c) $2\left(\cos\dfrac{\pi}{3}-\text{j}\sin\dfrac{\pi}{3}\right)$ **(d)** $\sin\dfrac{\pi}{3}+\text{j}\cos\dfrac{\pi}{3}$

3 If $z_1=4+2\text{j}$ and $z_2=-8+\text{j}$, find

(a) $\lvert z_1\rvert$	**(b)** $\lvert z_2\rvert$	**(c)** $\lvert z_1+z_2\rvert$
(d) $\lvert z_1-z_2\rvert$	**(e)** $\lvert z_1z_2\rvert$	**(f)** $\left\lvert\dfrac{z_1}{z_2}\right\rvert$

2.3 Operations on complex numbers in polar coordinates

Multiplication

Consider multiplying $z_1=r_1(\cos\theta+\text{j}\sin\theta)$

by $z_2=r_2(\cos\phi+\text{j}\sin\phi)$

Now remembering that the matrix corresponding to $x+jy$ is

$$\begin{pmatrix} x & -y \\ y & x \end{pmatrix}$$

then the matrix corresponding to $\cos\theta + j\sin\theta$ is

$$\begin{pmatrix} \cos\theta & -\sin\theta \\ \sin\theta & \cos\theta \end{pmatrix}$$

which represents an anticlockwise rotation through θ about O (see page 340). We can think of z_1 as follows.

Starting with the line from O to (1, 0), to get to z_1 we rotate through θ, and enlarge by r_1:

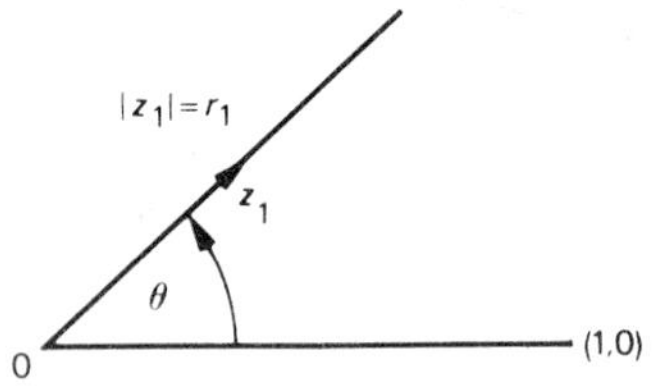

If we then multiply by z_2 this carries out the operation 'rotate through ϕ, enlarge by r_2'.

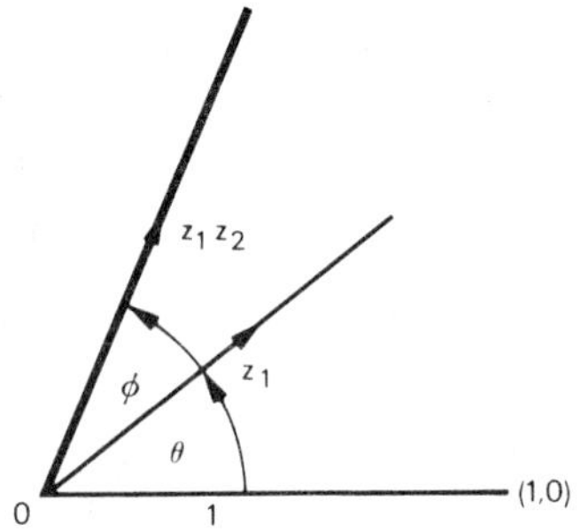

This can also be calculated algebraically:

$$\begin{aligned} z_1 z_2 &= (r_1\cos\theta + jr_1\sin\theta)(r_2\cos\phi + jr_2\sin\phi) \\ &= r_1 r_2[\cos\theta\cos\phi - \sin\theta\sin\phi + j(\sin\theta\cos\phi + \cos\theta\sin\phi)] \end{aligned}$$

$$\boldsymbol{z_1 z_2 = r_1 r_2[\cos(\theta+\phi) + j\sin(\theta+\phi)]}$$

Division

As before we think of division by a complex number as multiplication by its inverse since

$$\frac{z_1}{z_2} = z_1 z_2^{-1} = z_2^{-1} z_1$$

If $\quad z_2 = r_2(\cos\phi + \mathrm{j}\sin\phi), \qquad z_2^{-1} = \frac{1}{r_2}(\cos\phi + \mathrm{j}\sin\phi)^{-1}$

Now
$$\begin{pmatrix} \cos\phi & -\sin\phi \\ \sin\phi & \cos\phi \end{pmatrix}^{-1} = \begin{pmatrix} \cos\phi & \sin\phi \\ -\sin\phi & \cos\phi \end{pmatrix}$$
$$= \begin{pmatrix} \cos(-\phi) & -\sin(-\phi) \\ \sin(-\phi) & \cos(-\phi) \end{pmatrix}$$

So the inverse of a rotation through ϕ anticlockwise, is a rotation through $(-\phi)$ anticlockwise, or through ϕ clockwise (see page 338). Again starting with the line from O to (1, 0), to get z_1 we rotate through θ and enlarge by r_1 as before. Now to divide by z_2, we rotate through $-\phi$ and enlarge by $1/r_2$.

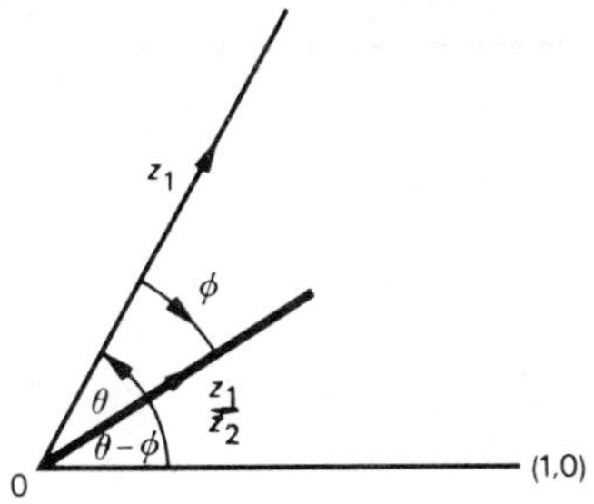

Algebraically,

$$\frac{z_1}{z_2} = \frac{r_1(\cos\theta + \mathrm{j}\sin\theta)}{r_2(\cos\phi + \mathrm{j}\sin\phi)}$$

Multiplying 'top and bottom' by the conjugate of the denominator

$$\frac{z_1}{z_2} = \frac{r_1}{r_2}\frac{(\cos\theta + \mathrm{j}\sin\theta)}{(\cos\phi + \mathrm{j}\sin\phi)} \times \frac{(\cos\phi - \mathrm{j}\sin\phi)}{(\cos\phi - \mathrm{j}\sin\phi)}$$
$$= \frac{r_1}{r_2}\frac{(\cos\theta + \mathrm{j}\sin\theta)(\cos\phi - \mathrm{j}\sin\phi)}{\cos^2\phi + \sin^2\phi}$$

and since $\cos^2\phi + \sin^2\phi = 1$

$$\frac{z_1}{z_2} = \frac{r_1}{r_2}[(\cos\theta\cos\phi + \sin\theta\sin\phi) + \mathrm{j}(\sin\theta\cos\phi - \cos\theta\sin\phi)]$$

$$\boldsymbol{\frac{z_1}{z_2} = \frac{r_1}{r_2}[\cos(\theta - \phi) + \mathrm{j}\sin(\theta - \phi)]} \qquad ◄$$

Multiplication and division of complex numbers in polar coordinate form is very simple, since

$$\boldsymbol{|z_1 z_2| = |z_1||z_2|, \qquad \arg(z_1 z_2) = \arg z_1 + \arg z_2} \qquad ◄$$

and

$$\boldsymbol{\left|\frac{z_1}{z_2}\right| = \frac{|z_1|}{|z_2|}, \qquad \arg\left(\frac{z_1}{z_2}\right) = \arg z_1 - \arg z_2} \qquad ◄$$

Exercise 2.3

1 Illustrate the following complex numbers in an Argand diagram, when $z = 4+3\text{j}$.

(a) $2z$, (b) $z+1$ (c) $3z-1$ (d) $\text{j}z$ (e) $-2\text{j}z$

(f) $2+\text{j}z$ (g) $\text{j}(z-1)$ (h) z^2 (i) $-\text{j}z^3$ (j) z^2+z

(k) $z^2-\text{j}z$ (l) $\dfrac{1}{z}$ (m) $\dfrac{-3}{z}$ (n) $\dfrac{\text{j}}{z}$ (o) $\dfrac{1}{z+1}$

2 Find the modulus and argument of the following complex numbers

(a) $\dfrac{2+3\text{j}}{4+5\text{j}}$ (b) $\dfrac{3-2\text{j}}{3+2\text{j}}$ (c) $\dfrac{-3+2\text{j}}{\text{j}}$

(d) $\dfrac{5-12\text{j}}{2}$ (e) $\dfrac{2-7\text{j}}{-3+\text{j}}$ (f) $\dfrac{1+\frac{1}{2}\text{j}}{1-\frac{1}{2}\text{j}}$

3 If $z_1 = 3(\cos\frac{2}{3}\pi + \text{j}\sin\frac{2}{3}\pi)$ and $z_2 = 5(\cos\frac{1}{4}\pi + \text{j}\sin\frac{1}{4}\pi)$, find

(a) z_1z_2 (b) $\dfrac{z_1}{z_2}$ (c) $\dfrac{z_2}{z_1}$

(d) $(z_1)^2$ (e) $(z_2)^2$ (f) $\left(\dfrac{z_2}{z_1}\right)^2$

4 Simplify the following, giving your answers in the form $M(\cos A \pm \text{j}\sin A)$

(a) $2(\cos 3\theta + \text{j}\sin 3\theta) \times 5(\cos 4\theta + \text{j}\sin 4\theta)$

(b) $(\cos 5\theta + \text{j}\sin 5\theta)) \times (\cos 3\theta - \text{j}\sin 3\theta)$

(c) $(\sin\theta + \text{j}\cos\theta) \times (\cos\theta + \text{j}\sin\theta)$

(d) $(\cos\theta + \text{j}\sin\theta) \times (\cos\theta - \text{j}\sin\theta)$

5 Simplify the following:

(a) $\dfrac{8(\cos 3\theta + \text{j}\sin 3\theta)}{2(\cos 2\theta + \text{j}\sin 2\theta)}$ (b) $\dfrac{\cos 2\phi + \text{j}\sin 2\phi}{\cos\phi - \text{j}\sin\phi}$

(c) $\dfrac{1}{\cos 3\theta + \text{j}\sin 3\theta}$ (d) $\dfrac{\cos 4\theta - \text{j}\sin 4\theta}{\cos 2\theta - \text{j}\sin 2\theta}$

2.4 Equations with complex coefficients

Many of the algebraic methods of dealing with equations which have real coefficients can be used in the solution of equations with complex coefficients. Whereas in 'real' algebra an equation may be represented as a line or a curve, there is no similar representation in 'complex' algebra on the Argand diagram. For example, $y+3x = 8$ represents a line, but $z_1 + 3z_2 = 8$ does not. Equations involving complex numbers are best dealt with algebraically.

Example 1

Solve the simultaneous equations

$$z_1+3z_2=8 \qquad (1)$$

$$4z_1-3jz_2=17+9j \qquad (2)$$

Multiply (1) by j $\qquad jz_1+3jz_2=8j \qquad (3)$

Add (2) and (3) $\qquad (4+j)z_1=17+17j$

$$z_1=\frac{17+17j}{4+j}=\frac{17(1+j)}{(4+j)}.$$

'Real'izing the denominator $\qquad z_1=\frac{17(1+j)}{(4+j)}\times\frac{(4-j)}{(4-j)}$

$$=5+3j \qquad (4)$$

Substituting back (4) in (1)

$$5+3j+3z_2=8$$

$$z_2=1-j$$

The values of z_1 and z_2 satisfying the two equations simultaneously are

$$z_1=5+3j, \qquad z_2=1-j$$

Example 2

Solve the equation

$$6z^2-2(1+2j)z-1=0$$

Using the quadratic formula

$$z=\frac{2(1+2j)\pm\sqrt{[4(1+2j)^2+24]}}{12}$$

$$=\frac{(1+2j)\pm\sqrt{(3+4j)}}{6}$$

To find $\sqrt{(3+4j)}$.

Suppose $(a+bj)^2=3+4j$, where $a, b \in \mathbb{R}$ then

$$a^2-b^2+2abj=3+4j$$

Comparing real and imaginary parts,

$$a^2-b^2=3, \qquad ab=2 \Rightarrow b=\frac{2}{a}$$

$$a^2-\frac{4}{a^2}=3$$

$$a^4-3a^2-4=0$$

$$(a^2-4)(a^2+1)=0$$

$$a=\pm 2, \qquad b=\pm 1 \qquad (\text{since } a, b \in \mathbb{R})$$

Hence the square roots are $2+\mathrm{j}$ and $-2-\mathrm{j}$. Finally

$$z = \frac{1+2\mathrm{j}+2+\mathrm{j}}{6} = \frac{1+\mathrm{j}}{2}$$

or

$$z = \frac{1+2\mathrm{j}-2-\mathrm{j}}{6} = \frac{-1+\mathrm{j}}{6}$$

Note that there is no possibility (usually) of complex conjugate solutions. There may be difficulties in finding the square root using the method shown. However a more general method will be met later in the chapter.

Exercise 2.4

1 Express in the form $a+\mathrm{j}b$ ($a, b \in \mathbb{R}$).
(a) $(1+\mathrm{j})^2$ **(b)** $(1-\sqrt{3}\mathrm{j})^3$ **(c)** $(-1+2\mathrm{j})^5$

2 Describe in the Argand diagram the geometrical effect of (i) squaring and (ii) finding the square root of the complex number $z = 2+\sqrt{5}\mathrm{j}$.
Express in polar coordinate form **(a)** z **(b)** z^2 **(c)** $z^{1/2}$.

3 Find in both polar and cartesian coordinate form
(a) $(-2+3\mathrm{j})^{1/2}$ **(b)** $(1-\mathrm{j})^{1/2}$ **(c)** $\mathrm{j}^{1/2}$

4 Solve simultaneously

$$z_1+z_2 = 5 \qquad \text{and} \qquad 3z_1-2\mathrm{j}z_2 = 9+4j$$

5 Solve the equation

$$z^2-(4+\mathrm{j})z+2\mathrm{j} = 0$$

6 Find the quotient and remainder when $x^3-3\mathrm{j}x^2-3\mathrm{j}$ is divided by $x-\mathrm{j}$.

7 Express the polynomial x^2+4 as the product of two linear complex numbers.

8 Express the following complex numbers in the form $r(\cos\theta+\mathrm{j}\sin\theta)$.
(a) $\cos\alpha-\mathrm{j}\sin\alpha$ **(b)** $1+\cos\beta+\mathrm{j}\sin\beta$
(c) $(1+\cos\gamma+\mathrm{j}\sin\gamma)^2$ **(d)** $(1-\cos\delta-\mathrm{j}\sin\delta)^{-2}$

9 Show that $zz^* = |z|^2$, $z_1^*+z_2^* = (z_1+z_2)^*$, $(z_1z_2)^* = z_1^*z_2^*$.

2.5 Loci in the complex plane

We have seen in Section 1.4 that every complex number can be represented by the position vector of a point in the Argand diagram. For example, if $z = x+\mathrm{j}y$, then the complex number z is represented by OZ where Z is the point (x, y). We now look at *sets* of points whose position vectors represent a variable complex number, z, which is subject to some condition or restriction. Such a set of points is called the locus of Z.

Complex numbers cannot be ordered and a statement like $z_1 > z_2$ is meaningless. But

$$|z_1| > |z_2| \qquad \text{and} \qquad \arg(z_1) < \arg(z_2)$$

are statements about lengths and angles, which can be compared. Hence the conditions we place upon z usually refer either to the modulus or to the argument of z, and this implies a relationship between the real and imaginary parts of z.

If $$z = x + jy$$

then $$|z| \text{ is a constant} \Rightarrow x^2 + y^2 = a^2$$

and $$\arg(z) \text{ is a constant} \Rightarrow y/x = m$$

where m and a are constants.

In polar coordinates, if $$z = r(\cos\theta + j\sin\theta)$$

$$|z| \text{ is a constant} \Rightarrow r = k$$

and $$\arg(z) \text{ is a constant} \Rightarrow \theta = \alpha$$

where k and α are constants.

Clearly if $|z| = 2$, say, the locus of Z is a circle, centre O, radius 2 units and its equation is

$$x^2 + y^2 = 4 \qquad \text{or} \qquad r = 2$$

If $\arg(z) = \pi/6$, the locus of Z is a half line from the origin, making an angle of $\pi/6$ with the positive x axis. Since

$$\tan\frac{\pi}{6} = \frac{1}{\sqrt{3}}$$

its cartesian equation is $$y = \frac{1}{\sqrt{3}}x \qquad (x \geqslant 0)$$

and its polar equation is $$\theta = \frac{\pi}{6} \qquad (r \geqslant 0)$$

If z and p are complex numbers, represented by OZ and OP, then $|z - p|$ represents the *distance* PZ which is equal to the distance OS.

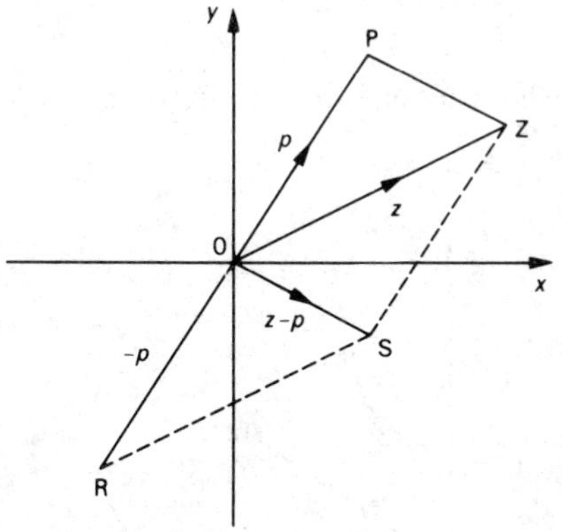

The *direction* which PZ makes with the positive x axis is represented by $\arg(z - p)$. If this angle is θ then $-\pi < \theta \leqslant \pi$, and great care is needed in deciding whether θ is positive or negative, acute or obtuse. It helps if PZ, or its extension in either direction, is marked with an arrow from P to Z.

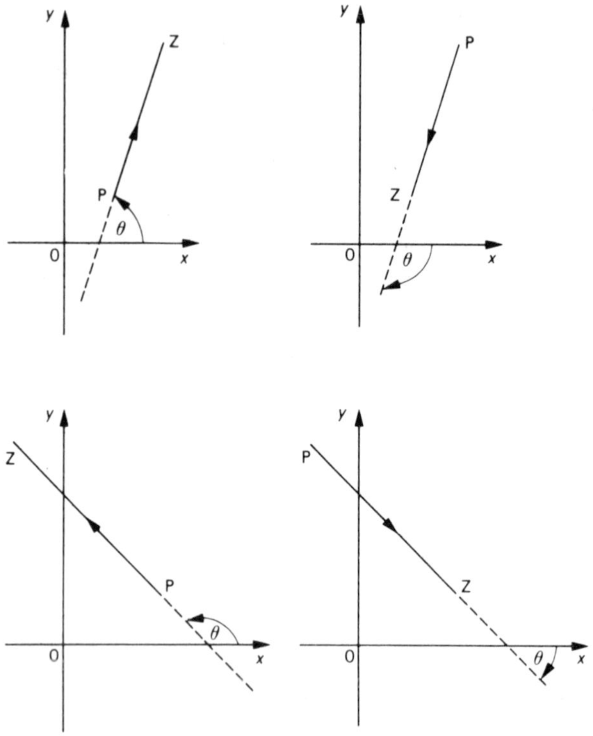

We shall now take z as a variable complex number, and p, q as complex constants and consider the locus of Z subject to certain conditions.

The locus of Z when $|z-p|=k$.

Z is the set of points whose distance from P is fixed, and the locus is a circle, centre P, radius k units.

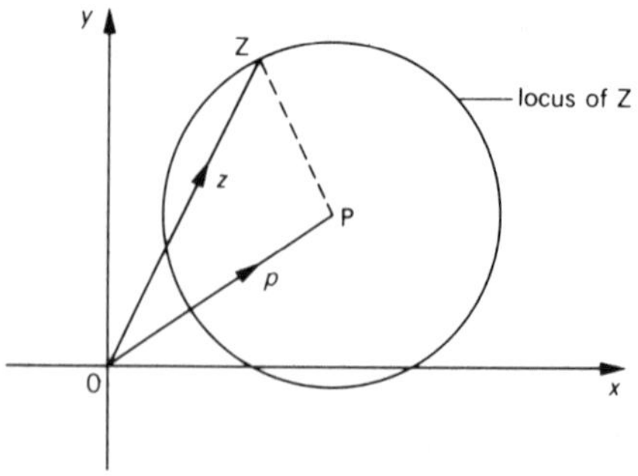

The locus of Z when $|z-p| = |z-q|$

For any one value of the modulus, say

$$|z-p| = |z-q| = k$$

this represents the intersection of two circles, with radius k, and centres P and Q. The locus of Z is therefore the intersection of all pairs of such circles, and is the perpendicular bisector of PQ.

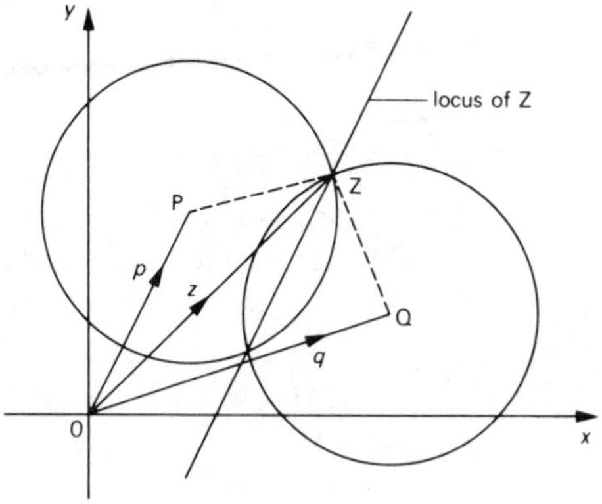

The locus of Z when $|z-p| + |z-q| = k$

This is an ellipse with foci at P and Q.

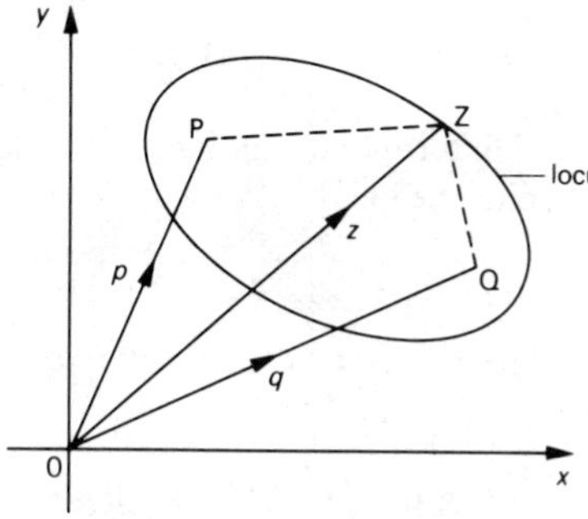

The locus of Z when arg $(z-p) = $ arg (q)

This represents a half line from P parallel to OQ.

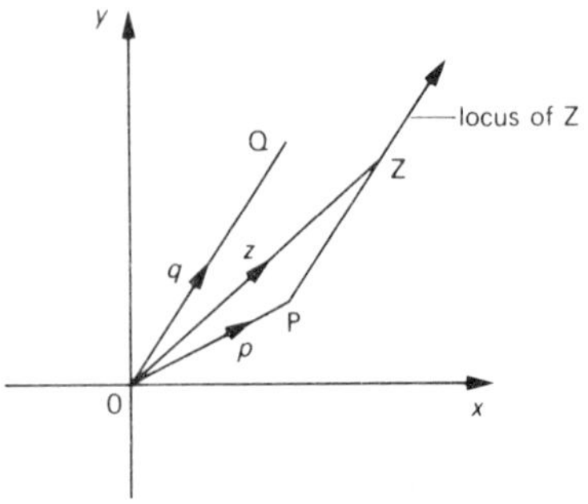

The locus of Z when arg $(z-p) = $ arg $(z-q)$

In this case the direction of PZ is the same as that of QZ, and so Z must lie anywhere in the line of PQ, *except* between P and Q where arg $(z-p)$ differs from arg $(z-q)$ by π^c.

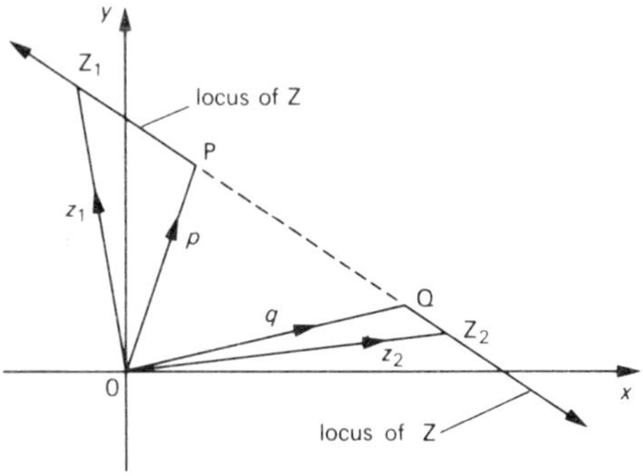

Example 1

Find the locus of Z when **(a)** $|z-1| = 2$ **(b)** arg $(z-1) = \pi/6$.

(a) $|z-1|$ is the distance from the variable point z to the point $p = 1+0\mathrm{j}$ and if this is constant and equal to 2 units, the locus of Z is a circle, centre P(1, 0) radius 2 units.

If $\qquad z = x+\mathrm{j}y, \qquad z-1 = (x-1)+\mathrm{j}y$

and $\qquad |z-1| = 2 \Rightarrow (x-1)^2+y^2 = 4$

which is the equation of the locus. (Figure opposite.)

(b) arg $(z-1)$ is the direction of the line PZ where P is the point P(1, 0). Hence the locus of Z is a half line from P, making an angle of $\pi/6^c$ to the positive x axis.

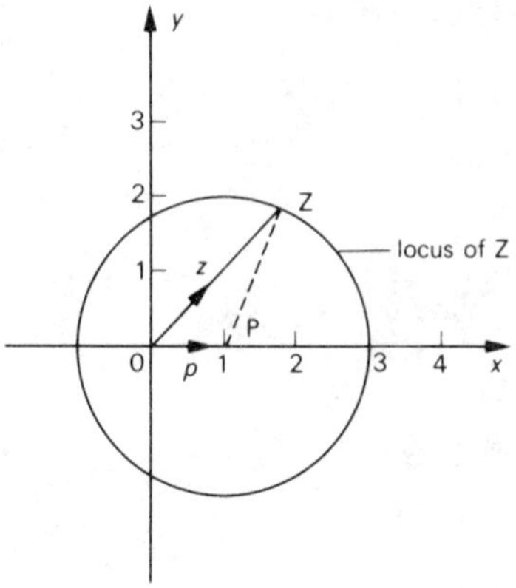

As before, $$z-1=(x-1)+\mathrm{j}y$$

and $$\arg(z-1)=\frac{\pi}{6}\Rightarrow\frac{y}{x-1}=\tan\frac{\pi}{6}=\frac{1}{\sqrt{3}}$$

So $$y=\frac{1}{\sqrt{3}}x-\frac{1}{\sqrt{3}}\qquad(x\geqslant 1/\sqrt{3})$$

is the equation of the locus.

Example 2

Find the locus of Z where $|z-1|+|z+1|=3$.

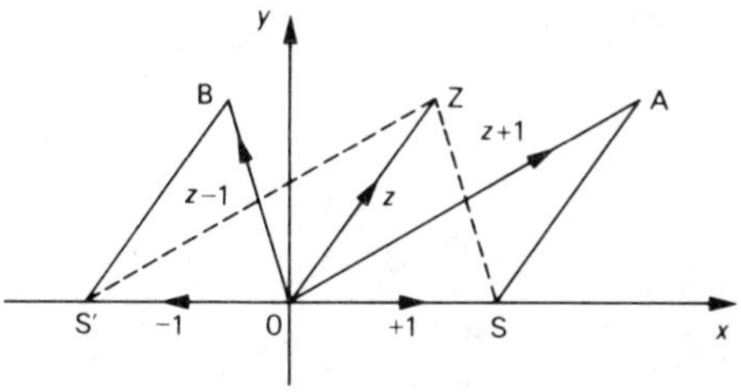

If **OZ** represents z, then **OA** represents $z+1$, and **OB**, $z-1$.

$$|z+1|=\mathrm{OA}=\mathrm{S'Z};\qquad |z-1|=\mathrm{OB}=\mathrm{SZ}$$

Hence $|z-1|+|z+1|=3$ corresponds to

$$\mathrm{SZ}+\mathrm{S'Z}=3$$

The locus of Z is therefore an ellipse with foci at S′ and S and the equation

$$\frac{x^2}{(3/2)^2}+\frac{y^2}{(\sqrt{5}/2)^2}=1$$

Example 3

Find the locus of Z if

$$\arg\left(\frac{z-p}{z-q}\right) = \frac{\pi^c}{4}$$

$$\arg\left(\frac{z-p}{z-q}\right) = \arg(z-p) - \arg(z-q)$$

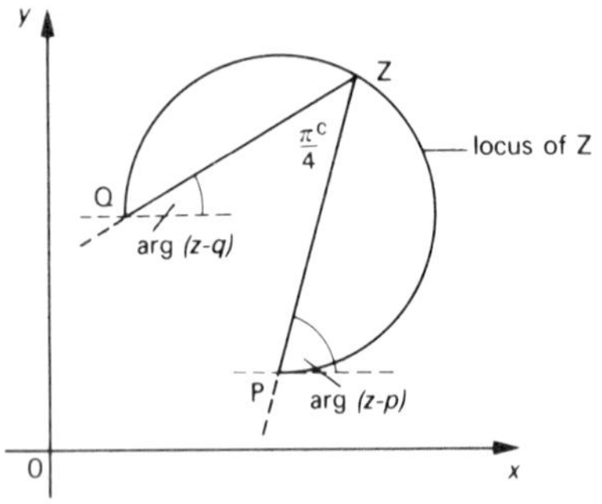

Now arg $(z-p)$ is the angle between PZ and the positive real axis and arg $(z-q)$ is the angle between QZ and the positive real axis. So

$$\arg(z-p) - \arg(z-q) = \angle PZQ$$

and since this is constant and equal to $\pi^c/4$, Z lies on the arc of a circle as shown.

Example 4

Find the locus of Z if

$$\frac{z-3}{z+j}$$

is (a) wholly real and (b) wholly imaginary.

Suppose $$z = x + jy$$

Then
$$\frac{z-3}{z+j} = \frac{(x-3)+jy}{x+j(y+1)} = \frac{[(x-3)+jy][x-j(y+1)]}{[x+j(y+1)][x-j(y+1)]}$$

$$= \frac{x(x-3)+y(y+1)+j[xy-(x-3)(y+1)]}{x^2+(y+1)^2}$$

(a) The expression is wholly real if

$$xy - (x-3)(y+1) = 0$$

$$xy - (xy + x - 3y - 3) = 0$$

$$x - 3y = 3$$

The locus of Z is therefore the line which cuts the real axis at $x = 3$ and the imaginary axes at $y = -1$.

(b) The expression is wholly imaginary if

$$x(x-3)+y(y+1) = 0$$

$$x^2-3x+\tfrac{9}{4}+y^2+y+\tfrac{1}{4} = \tfrac{10}{4}$$

$$(x-\tfrac{3}{2})^2+(y+\tfrac{1}{2})^2 = \tfrac{5}{2}$$

The locus of Z is the circle, centre $(\tfrac{3}{2}, -\tfrac{1}{2})$ and radius $\sqrt{\tfrac{5}{2}}$.

Exercise 2.5

1 Sketch the locus of Z and find its equation in each of the following:

(a) $|z-3+2\text{j}| = 5$

(b) $|z-3+2\text{j}| = |z-2-3\text{j}|$

(c) $|z-3+2\text{j}| = 2|z-2-3\text{j}|$

(d) $|z-2|+|z+2| = 8$

2 Shade the region in the Argand diagram represented by

(a) $|z+2\text{j}| \leqslant 2$

(b) $|z-4| \geqslant 4$

(c) $|z-3\text{j}| \leqslant |z+2|$

3 Find the locus of Z if

(a) $\arg(z+1) = \tfrac{3}{4}\pi$

(b) $\arg(z-2\text{j}) = \tfrac{1}{3}\pi$

(c) $\arg\left(\dfrac{z+1}{z-2\text{j}}\right) = \dfrac{\pi}{2}$

(d) $\arg(z+1) = \arg(z-2\text{j})$

2.6 Transformations of the complex plane

Suppose the complex number z is mapped into the number w, where $w = 2z$. Then the position vector OW, representing w, will lie in the same direction as OZ, and be twice as long. But if $w = -3\text{j}z$, then OW is three times as long as OZ, and rotated clockwise through a quarter turn about O. We now consider the mapping of a set of points Z, corresponding to a variable complex number which is subject to some restriction, into the set W, where w is related to z in some such way. Usually, w will be a function of z.

Example 1

Find the locus of W if $w = z+3\text{j}$ and **(a)** $|z| = 2$ **(b)** $\arg(z) = \pi/6$.

(a) The locus of Z is a circle, centre the origin and radius 2 units. Under the mapping $z \to w$, each point is translated 3 units in the direction of the positive y axis and hence the locus of W is a circle, centre (0, 3) radius 2 units.

(b) The locus of Z is a half line from the origin at an angle of $\pi/6$ to the positive x axis. Under the mapping this is similarly translated and the locus of W is a parallel half line, starting from (0, 3), in the same direction.

Example 2

Find the locus of W if $w = 2/z$ when **(a)** $|z| = 2$ and **(b)** $\arg(z) = \pi/6$.

(a) It is easier to see how the locus of W is related to that of Z if only values of z lying in the first quadrant are considered, and we think of Z tracing a path in the quadrant of a circle from the x axis to the y axis.

If $w = 2/z$, then

$$|w| = \frac{2}{|z|} \qquad \text{and} \qquad \arg(w) = -\arg(z)$$

Since $|z| = 2$, $|w| = 1$ and the locus of W is a circle centre O, radius 1 unit, traced clockwise.

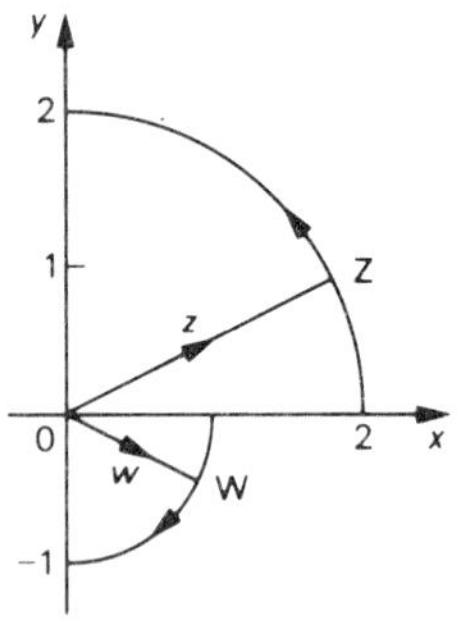

(b) Since $\arg(w) = -\arg(z)$, the locus of W, when $\arg(z) = \pi/6$ is a line through the origin inclined at an angle of $-\pi/6$ to the positive x axis. It could be described as the reflection of the locus of Z, in the x axis.

Exercise 2.6

1 Find the locus of W (i) when $|z| = 4$ and (ii) when $\arg(z) = \pi/3$ in each of the following cases:

(a) $w = z$ **(b)** $w = z + 3 - 2j$ **(c)** $w = jz$

(d) $w = z^*$ **(e)** $w = z^2$ **(f)** $w = z^{1/2}$

(g) $w = \dfrac{1}{z+1}$ **(h)** $w = \dfrac{j}{z+1}$ **(i)** $w = \dfrac{j}{z+j}$

2 Repeat Question **1**, when (i) $|z| = 1$ and (ii) $\arg(z) = \pi/3$. In each case describe the transformation geometrically and find the equation of the locus of W algebraically.

3 De Moivre's theorem

3.1 De Moivre's theorem and matrices

The matrix

$$\begin{pmatrix} \cos\theta & -\sin\theta \\ \sin\theta & \cos\theta \end{pmatrix}$$

which corresponds to the complex number $\cos\theta + \text{j}\sin\theta$, represents an anticlockwise rotation of θ about the origin. We call this $\mathbf{R}_\theta$. Then

$$\mathbf{R}_{2\theta} = \mathbf{R}_\theta\mathbf{R}_\theta = (\mathbf{R}_\theta)^2$$

so

$$\begin{aligned} \cos 2\theta + \text{j}\sin 2\theta &= (\cos\theta + \text{j}\sin\theta)^2 \\ &= (\cos\theta + \text{j}\sin\theta)(\cos\theta + \text{j}\sin\theta) \\ &= \cos^2\theta - \sin^2\theta + 2\text{j}\sin\theta\cos\theta \end{aligned}$$

Equating real and imaginary parts,

$$\cos 2\theta = \cos^2\theta - \sin^2\theta$$

and

$$\sin 2\theta = 2\sin\theta\cos\theta$$

Similarly

$$\mathbf{R}_{3\theta} = \mathbf{R}_\theta\mathbf{R}_\theta\mathbf{R}_\theta = (\mathbf{R}_\theta)^3$$

so

$$\begin{aligned} \cos 3\theta + \text{j}\sin 3\theta &= (\cos\theta + \text{j}\sin\theta)^3 \\ &= (\cos\theta + \text{j}\sin\theta)(\cos\theta + \text{j}\sin\theta)(\cos\theta + \text{j}\sin\theta) \\ &= (\cos^2\theta - \sin^2\theta + 2\text{j}\sin\theta\cos\theta)(\cos\theta + \text{j}\sin\theta) \\ &= \cos^3\theta - 3\cos\theta\sin^2\theta + \text{j}(3\cos^2\theta\sin\theta - \sin^3\theta) \end{aligned}$$

Again, equating real and imaginary parts,

$$\cos 3\theta = \cos^3\theta - 3\cos\theta\sin^2\theta$$

and

$$\sin 3\theta = 3\cos^2\theta\sin\theta - \sin^3\theta$$

(see page 227)

It seems reasonable that for $n \in \mathbb{Z}^+$

$$(\cos n\theta + \text{j}\sin n\theta) = (\cos\theta + \text{j}\sin\theta)^n$$

with the corresponding matrix equation

$$\begin{pmatrix} \cos n\theta & -\sin n\theta \\ \sin n\theta & \cos n\theta \end{pmatrix} = \begin{pmatrix} \cos\theta & -\sin\theta \\ \sin\theta & \cos\theta \end{pmatrix}^n$$

This is known as *De Moivre's theorem*. For example

$$(\cos\theta + \text{j}\sin\theta)^7 = \cos 7\theta + \text{j}\sin 7\theta$$

$$(\cos\theta + \text{j}\sin\theta)^{15} = \cos 15\theta + \text{j}\sin 15\theta$$

... and so on.

Since rotations about the origin can be anticlockwise ($\mathbf{R}_\theta$) or clockwise ($\mathbf{R}_{-\theta}$) it may be assumed that the formulae will be true if n is a negative integer. Now algebraically

$$\frac{1}{\cos\theta+\mathrm{j}\sin\theta}=\frac{1}{\cos\theta+\mathrm{j}\sin\theta}\times\frac{\cos\theta-\mathrm{j}\sin\theta}{\cos\theta-\mathrm{j}\sin\theta}$$

$$=\frac{\cos\theta-\mathrm{j}\sin\theta}{\cos^2\theta+\sin^2\theta}$$

$$=\cos\theta-\mathrm{j}\sin\theta$$

This is exactly what we should obtain using De Moivre's theorem for $n=-1$; i.e.

$$(\cos\theta+\mathrm{j}\sin\theta)^{-1}=\cos(-\theta)+\mathrm{j}\sin(-\theta)$$

$$=\cos\theta-\mathrm{j}\sin\theta$$

corresponding to a rotation $(-\theta)$ about the origin.

It can be proved by induction that

$$\boldsymbol{\cos n\theta+\mathrm{j}\sin n\theta=(\cos\theta+\mathrm{j}\sin\theta)^n,\qquad n\in\mathbb{Z}}$$ ◀

Exercise 3.1

Express the following in the form $\cos A\pm\mathrm{j}\sin A$.

1 $(\cos\theta+\mathrm{j}\sin\theta)^4$

2 $(\cos\theta-\mathrm{j}\sin\theta)^5$

3 $\dfrac{1}{(\cos\theta+\mathrm{j}\sin\theta)^3}$

4 $(\cos\theta-\mathrm{j}\sin\theta)^{-2}$

5 $(\sin\theta+\mathrm{j}\cos\theta)^4$

6 $\dfrac{(\cos\theta-\mathrm{j}\sin\theta)^4}{(\cos\theta+\mathrm{j}\sin\theta)^5}$

7 $\dfrac{(\cos 3\theta-\mathrm{j}\sin 3\theta)^4}{(\cos 4\theta+\mathrm{j}\sin 4\theta)^3}$

8 $\dfrac{(\cos\theta+\mathrm{j}\sin\theta)^3(\cos 2\theta+\mathrm{j}\sin 2\theta)^5}{(\cos 2\theta+\mathrm{j}\sin 2\theta)^4(\cos 3\theta-\mathrm{j}\sin 3\theta)^2}$

3.2 De Moivre's theorem and powers of trigonometrical functions

If $$z=\cos\theta+\mathrm{j}\sin\theta \qquad (1)$$

then $$\frac{1}{z}=\cos\theta-\mathrm{j}\sin\theta \qquad (2)$$

Add (1) and (2): $$z+\frac{1}{z}=2\cos\theta$$

Subtracting (2) and (1), $$z-\frac{1}{z}=2\mathrm{j}\sin\theta$$

Similarly $$z^2=\cos 2\theta+\mathrm{j}\sin 2\theta$$

and $$\frac{1}{z^2} = \cos 2\theta - \text{j} \sin 2\theta$$

which give $$z^2 + \frac{1}{z^2} = 2 \cos 2\theta$$

and $$z^2 - \frac{1}{z^2} = 2\text{j} \sin 2\theta$$ . . . and so on.

Finally $$z^n = \cos n\theta + \text{j} \sin n\theta$$

and $$\frac{1}{z^n} = \cos n\theta - \text{j} \sin n\theta$$

give $$z^n + \frac{1}{z^n} = 2 \cos n\theta$$

and $$z^n - \frac{1}{z^n} = 2\text{j} \sin n\theta$$

This idea can be used in finding formulae as follows.

Example 1

Express $\cos^3 \theta$ in terms of $\cos 3\theta$ and $\cos \theta$.

$$(2 \cos \theta)^3 = \left(z + \frac{1}{z}\right)^3$$

$$= z^3 + 3z^2 \times \frac{1}{z} + 3z \times \frac{1}{z^2} + \frac{1}{z^3}$$

$$= \left(z^3 + \frac{1}{z^3}\right) + 3\left(z + \frac{1}{z}\right)$$

Hence $$8 \cos^3 \theta = 2 \cos 3\theta + 6 \cos \theta$$

and $$\cos^3 \theta = \tfrac{1}{4}(\cos 3\theta + 3 \cos \theta)$$

Similarly $$(2\text{j} \sin \theta)^4 = \left(z - \frac{1}{z}\right)^4$$

$$= z^4 - 4z^3 \times \frac{1}{z} + 6z^2 \times \frac{1}{z^2} - 4z \times \frac{1}{z^3} + \frac{1}{z^4}$$

$$= \left(z^4 + \frac{1}{z^4}\right) - 4\left(z^2 + \frac{1}{z^2}\right) + 6$$

$$16 \sin^4 \theta = 2 \cos 4\theta - 8 \cos 2\theta + 6$$

$$\sin^4 \theta = \tfrac{1}{8}(\cos 4\theta - 4 \cos 2\theta + 3)$$

Sometimes the problem is set the other way around:

Example 2

Find $\cos 5\theta$ in terms of powers of $\cos\theta$.

$$(\cos\theta + \mathrm{j}\sin\theta)^5 = \cos 5\theta + \mathrm{j}\sin 5\theta \quad \text{(De Moivre's theorem)}$$

Expanding, we have

$$\cos 5\theta + \mathrm{j}\sin 5\theta = \cos^5\theta + 5\mathrm{j}\cos^4\theta\sin\theta + 10\mathrm{j}\ \cos^3\theta\sin^2\theta$$
$$+10\mathrm{j}^3\cos^2\theta\sin^3\theta + 5\mathrm{j}^4\cos\theta\sin^4\theta + \mathrm{j}^5\sin^5\theta$$

Equating real parts,

$$\begin{aligned}\cos 5\theta &= \cos^5\theta - 10\cos^3\theta\sin^2\theta + 5\cos\theta\sin^4\theta \\ &= 5\cos^5\theta - 10\cos^3\theta(1-\cos^2\theta) + 5\cos\theta(1-2\cos^2\theta+\cos^4\theta) \\ &= 16\cos^5\theta - 20\cos^3\theta + 5\cos\theta\end{aligned}$$

Example 3

Find an expression for $\sin 4\theta$ in terms of powers of $\sin\theta$ and $\cos\theta$.

Now $\quad \cos 4\theta + \mathrm{j}\sin 4\theta = (\cos\theta + \mathrm{j}\sin\theta)^4$

$$= \cos^4\theta + 4\cos^3\theta(\mathrm{j}\sin\theta) + 6\cos^2\theta(\mathrm{j}\sin\theta)^2$$
$$+4\cos\theta(\mathrm{j}\sin\theta)^3 + (\mathrm{j}\sin\theta)^4$$

Equating the imaginary parts,

$$\sin 4\theta = 4\cos^3\theta\sin\theta - 4\cos\theta\sin^3\theta$$

Exercise 3.2

In questions **1** to **5** find formulae for the given functions in terms of multiple angles; in questions **6** and **8** in terms of powers of $\sin\theta$; in questions **7** and **9** in terms of powers of $\cos\theta$, and in question **10** in mixed powers of $\sin\theta$ and $\cos\theta$.

1 $\sin^3\theta$ **2** $\cos^4\theta$ **3** $\sin^5\theta$ **4** $\cos^5\theta$ **5** $\sin^6\theta$

6 $\sin 3\theta$ **7** $\cos 4\theta$ **8** $\sin 5\theta$ **9** $\cos 6\theta$ **10** $\sin 6\theta$

3.3 De Moivre's theorem and equations

Cos θ and sin θ are periodic functions: that is, after a certain angle (360° or $2\pi^c$), their values are repeated.

$$\cos\theta = \cos(\theta + 360°), \qquad \sin\theta = \sin(\theta + 360°)$$

or

$$\cos\theta = \cos(\theta + 2\pi^c), \qquad \sin\theta = \sin(\theta + 2\pi^c)$$

Not only are these true, but adding any multiple of $2\pi^c$, (or 360°) does not alter their value. If k is any integer then

$$\cos\theta = \cos(\theta + 2k\pi^c)$$

and

$$\sin\theta = \sin(\theta + 2k\pi^c)$$

Consider, for example, the equation

$$z^2 = \cos\theta + \mathrm{j}\sin\theta$$

or

$$z = (\cos\theta + \mathrm{j}\sin\theta)^{1/2}$$

Now if we assume that we can apply De Moivre's theorem for n being a fraction then $z = \cos\frac{1}{2}\theta + \mathrm{j}\sin\frac{1}{2}\theta$—unfortunately only one answer. ('Unfortunately' since we should like two! Quadratic equations have *two* solutions, cubic equations *three*, quartic equations *four*, and so on. Of course, the solutions may be real or complex—see page 51.) We can, however, overcome the problem easily, since

$$\cos\theta = \cos(\theta + 2k\pi^c), \qquad \sin\theta = \sin(\theta + 2k\pi^c)$$

Hence

$$\begin{aligned} z &= (\cos\theta + \mathrm{j}\sin\theta)^{1/2} \\ &= [\cos(\theta + 2k\pi^c) + \mathrm{j}\sin(\theta + 2k\pi^c)]^{1/2} \\ &= \cos\left(\frac{\theta}{2} + k\pi^c\right) + \mathrm{j}\sin\left(\frac{\theta}{2} + k\pi^c\right) \end{aligned}$$

We can now run through values of k to give us our solutions.

If

$$k = 0 \qquad z = \cos\frac{\theta}{2} + \mathrm{j}\sin\frac{\theta}{2} \tag{1}$$

$$k = 1 \qquad z = \cos\left(\frac{\theta}{2} + \pi^c\right) + \mathrm{j}\sin\left(\frac{\theta}{2} + \pi^c\right) \tag{2}$$

$$k = 2 \qquad z = \cos\left(\frac{\theta}{2} + 2\pi^c\right) + \mathrm{j}\sin\left(\frac{\theta}{2} + 2\pi^c\right) \tag{3}$$

$$k = 3 \qquad z = \cos\left(\frac{\theta}{2} + 3\pi^c\right) + \mathrm{j}\sin\left(\frac{\theta}{2} + 3\pi^c\right) \tag{4}$$

and so on. In this section we take $0 < \arg z \leqslant 2\pi^c$.

Now (3) is identical with (1), and (4) is identical with (2), as we can show on the Argand diagram. No matter what values we take for k, we only obtain *two* different solutions.

This idea can be extended, so that, for example if we wish to find $(\cos\theta + \mathrm{j}\sin\theta)^{2/3}$ we use De Moivre's theorem and our results are given by

$$[\cos(\theta + 2k\pi^c) + \mathrm{j}\sin(\theta + 2k\pi^c)]^{2/3} = \cos\tfrac{2}{3}(\theta + 2k\pi^c) + \mathrm{j}\sin\tfrac{2}{3}(\theta + 2k\pi^c)$$

for $k = 0, 1, 2$.

There are three values for k since we are finding the *cube* root. If we were finding the fifth root, we should use five values for k, $k = 0, 1, 2, 3, 4$.

In general, the values of $(\cos\theta + \mathrm{j}\sin\theta)^{p/q}$ are given by

$$\boldsymbol{\cos\frac{p}{q}(\theta + 2k\pi^c) + \mathrm{j}\sin\frac{p}{q}(\theta + 2k\pi^c)} \qquad ◀$$

with k having the values $k = 0, 1, 2, \ldots q-1$.

Example 1

Solve the equation $z^3 = 1$.

Now $\qquad 1 = \cos 0 + \mathrm{j} \sin 0$

hence $\qquad z^3 = (\cos 0 + \mathrm{j} \sin 0)$

$$z = (\cos 0 + \mathrm{j} \sin 0)^{1/3}$$

$$z = \cos \tfrac{1}{3}(0 + 2k\pi^c) + \mathrm{j} \sin \tfrac{1}{3}(0 + 2k\pi^c)$$

for $k = 0, 1, 2$, so

$z_1 = \cos 0 + \mathrm{j} \sin 0$ $\qquad$ corresponding to $k = 0$

or $\qquad z_2 = \cos \tfrac{2}{3}\pi^c + \mathrm{j} \sin \tfrac{2}{3}\pi^c$ $\qquad$ corresponding to $k = 1$

or $\qquad z_3 = \cos \tfrac{4}{3}\pi^c + \mathrm{j} \sin \tfrac{4}{3}\pi^c$ $\qquad$ corresponding to $k = 2$

These solutions can be shown on the Argand diagram like this:

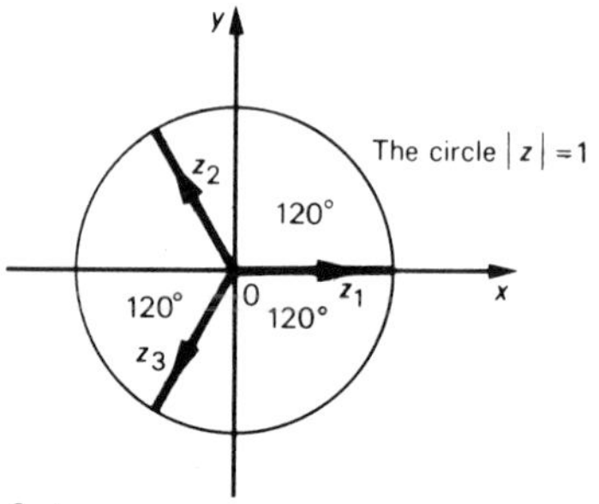

The roots of $z^3 = 1$

Example 2

Solve the equation $z^4 = -16\mathrm{j}$ and show the roots on an Argand diagram.

$$z^4 = -16\mathrm{j} = 16(-\mathrm{j})$$

$$-\mathrm{j} = \cos \tfrac{3}{2}\pi^c + \mathrm{j} \sin \tfrac{3}{2}\pi^c$$

hence $\qquad z^4 = +16(\cos \tfrac{3}{2}\pi^c + \mathrm{j} \sin \tfrac{3}{2}\pi^c)$

$$z = 16^{1/4}(\cos \tfrac{3}{2}\pi^c + \mathrm{j} \sin \tfrac{3}{2}\pi^c)^{1/4}$$

$$z = 2[\cos \tfrac{1}{4}(\tfrac{3}{2}\pi^c + 2k\pi^c) + \mathrm{j} \sin \tfrac{1}{4}(\tfrac{3}{2}\pi^c + 2k\pi^c)]$$

for $k = 0, 1, 2, 3$. So

$z_1 = 2(\cos \tfrac{3}{8}\pi^c + \mathrm{j} \sin \tfrac{3}{8}\pi^c)$, $\qquad z_2 = 2(\cos \tfrac{7}{8}\pi^c + \mathrm{j} \sin \tfrac{7}{8}\pi^c)$

$z_3 = 2(\cos \tfrac{11}{8}\pi^c + \mathrm{j} \sin \tfrac{11}{8}\pi^c)$, $\qquad z_4 = 2(\cos \tfrac{15}{8}\pi^c + \mathrm{j} \sin \tfrac{15}{8}\pi^c)$

Again these solutions can be illustrated on the Argand diagram. This time the points representing the complex numbers will be on the circle $|z| = 2$.

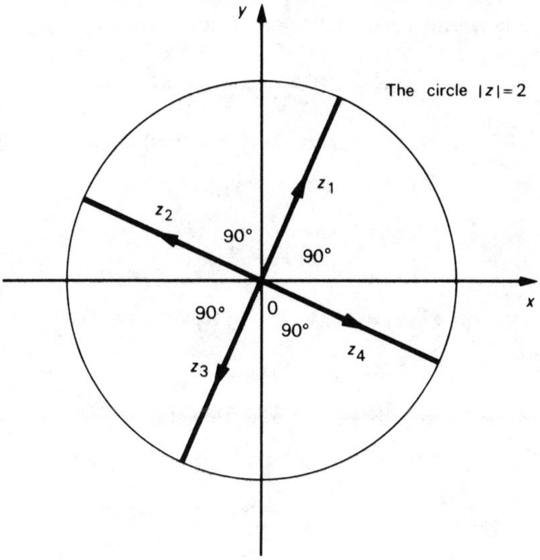

Exercise 3.3

Solve the following equations, illustrating your answers on the Argand diagram if possible.

1 $z^3 = -27$ **2** $z^{4/3} = \mathrm{j}$ **3** $z^5 = 3+4\mathrm{j}$

4 $(x+\mathrm{j})^3+(x-\mathrm{j})^3 = 0$ **5** If $w^3 = 1$, and $w \neq 1$ show that $w^2+w+1 = 0$

6 $z = (1+\mathrm{j})^{3/5}$ **7** $x^8+x^4-1 = 0$ **8** $z^3 = 1+\sqrt{3}\mathrm{j}$

9 $x^{2n}-2x^n \cos n\theta+1 = 0$ **10** $(x+1)^n = x^n$

3.4 Complex numbers and series

This section depends on a knowledge of Maclaurin's theorem, which states that

$$f(x) = f(0)+xf^{\mathrm{I}}(0)+\frac{x^2}{2!}f^{\mathrm{II}}(0)+\frac{x^3}{3!}f^{\mathrm{III}}(0)+\ldots$$

This is extremely useful in enabling any reasonable function of x to be written as an infinite series of powers of x.

Now suppose that

$$f(x) = \cos x \qquad f(0) = 1$$

then

$$f^{\mathrm{I}}(x) = -\sin x \qquad f^{\mathrm{I}}(0) = 0$$

$$f^{\mathrm{II}}(x) = -\cos x \qquad f^{\mathrm{II}}(0) = -1$$

$$f^{\mathrm{III}}(x) = \sin x \qquad f^{\mathrm{III}}(0) = 0$$

$$f^{\mathrm{IV}}(x) = \cos x \qquad f^{\mathrm{IV}}(0) = 1$$

and the sequence continues as repetitions of this. Hence

$$\cos x = 1 - \frac{x^2}{2!} + \frac{x^4}{4!} - \frac{x^6}{6!} + \ldots \tag{1}$$

Similarly if

$$\begin{aligned} f(x) &= \sin x & f(0) &= 0 \\ f^{\mathrm{I}}(x) &= \cos x & f^{\mathrm{I}}(0) &= 1 \\ f^{\mathrm{II}}(x) &= -\sin x & f^{\mathrm{II}}(0) &= 0 \\ f^{\mathrm{III}}(x) &= -\cos x & f^{\mathrm{III}}(0) &= -1 \\ f^{\mathrm{IV}}(x) &= \sin x & f^{\mathrm{IV}}(0) &= 0 \end{aligned}$$

. . . and so on. So

$$\sin x = x - \frac{x^3}{3!} + \frac{x^5}{5!} - \frac{x^7}{7!} + \ldots \tag{2}$$

Finally consider

$$\begin{aligned} f(x) &= e^x & &\text{and} & f(0) &= 1 \\ f^{\mathrm{I}}(x) &= e^x & &\text{and} & f^{\mathrm{I}}(0) &= 1 \\ f^{\mathrm{II}}(x) &= e^x & &\text{and} & f^{\mathrm{II}}(0) &= 1 \\ f^{\mathrm{III}}(x) &= e^x & &\text{and} & f^{\mathrm{III}}(0) &= 1 \end{aligned}$$

and

$$e^x = 1 + x + \frac{x^2}{2!} + \frac{x^3}{3!} + \frac{x^4}{4!} + \frac{x^5}{5!} + \ldots \tag{3}$$

We now add together (1) and (2) in order to compare the result with (3):

$$\cos x + \sin x = 1 + x - \frac{x^2}{2!} - \frac{x^3}{3!} + \frac{x^4}{4!} + \frac{x^5}{5!} - \frac{x^6}{6!} - \frac{x^7}{7!} + \ldots$$

$$e^x = 1 + x + \frac{x^2}{2!} + \frac{x^3}{3!} + \frac{x^4}{4!} + \frac{x^5}{5!} + \frac{x^6}{6!} + \frac{x^7}{7!} + \ldots$$

We can see that the two series are very similar. Several of the terms in each are equal (ringed), the others match apart from the signs. E.g. we have $-x^2/2!$ in the first series, $+x^2/2!$ in the second.

Now $\mathrm{j}^2x^2 = -x^2$ so we consider the series

$$e^{\mathrm{j}x} = 1 + \mathrm{j}x + \frac{\mathrm{j}^2x^2}{2!} + \frac{\mathrm{j}^3x^3}{3!} + \frac{\mathrm{j}^4x^4}{4!} + \frac{\mathrm{j}^5x^5}{5!} + \ldots$$

We know that

$$\mathrm{j}^2 = -1,\ \mathrm{j}^3 = \mathrm{j}^2\mathrm{j} = -\mathrm{j},\ \mathrm{j}^4 = \mathrm{j}^2 \times \mathrm{j}^2 = +1$$

and so on, so

$$e^{\mathrm{j}x} = 1 + \mathrm{j}x - \frac{x^2}{2!} - \frac{\mathrm{j}x^3}{3!} + \frac{x^4}{4!} + \frac{\mathrm{j}x^5}{5!} - \ldots$$

$$e^{\mathrm{j}x} = \left(1 - \frac{x^2}{2!} + \frac{x^4}{4!} - \ldots\right) + \mathrm{j}\left(x - \frac{x^3}{3!} + \frac{x^5}{5!} - \ldots\right)$$

$$= \quad \cos x \quad + \mathrm{j} \quad \sin x$$

This is a very important relation, often used.

$$\boldsymbol{e^{\mathrm{j}x} = \cos x + \mathrm{j} \sin x}$$

◀

It leads to one of the strangest equations in mathematics. If we substitute $x = \pi^c$ we have

$$e^{j\pi} = -1$$

Why strange? Well, $e = 2.718\,28\ldots$ and $\pi = 3.141\,59\ldots$, both transcendental; j is some 'imaginary' number and $e^{j\pi} = -1$, -1 being a common or garden everyday real number. Think! What *does* 'equals' mean in this equation?

Application to trigonometrical formulae and De Moivre's theorem

Returning to θ as our variable,

$$e^{j\theta} = \cos\theta + j\sin\theta \qquad (1)$$

$$e^{-j\theta} = \cos\theta - j\sin\theta \qquad (2)$$

Thus we can mark $z = e^{j\theta}$ or $z = e^{-j\theta}$ on the Argand diagram.
Adding (1) and (2)

$$e^{j\theta} + e^{-j\theta} = 2\cos\theta$$

So

$$\boldsymbol{\cos\theta = \tfrac{1}{2}(e^{j\theta} + e^{-j\theta})} \quad ◀$$

Similarly, subtracting (2) from (1)

$$e^{j\theta} - e^{-j\theta} = 2j\sin\theta$$

$$\boldsymbol{\sin\theta = \frac{1}{2j}(e^{j\theta} - e^{-j\theta})} \quad ◀$$

The relation $e^{j\theta} = \cos\theta + j\sin\theta$

gives an easy derivation of the formulae for the sine or cosine of the sum of two angles.

Since $e^{jA} = \cos A + j\sin A$ and $e^{jB} = \cos B + j\sin B$

$$e^{jA}\times e^{jB} = (\cos A + j\sin A)(\cos B + j\sin B)$$

$$= \cos A\cos B - \sin A\sin B + j(\sin A\cos B + \cos A\sin B) \qquad (3)$$

But $e^{jA}\times e^{jB} = e^{j(A+B)}$

and $e^{j(A+B)} = \cos(A+B) + j\sin(A+B) \qquad (4)$

Comparing equations (3) and (4) we see that

$$\cos(A+B) = \cos A\cos B - \sin A\sin B$$

and

$$\sin(A+B) = \sin A\cos B + \cos A\sin B$$

The relation also gives a very simple expression of De Moivre's theorem since

$$(\cos\theta + j\sin\theta)^n = \cos n\theta + j\sin n\theta$$

is now seen to correspond to

$$\boldsymbol{(e^{j\theta})^n = e^{jn\theta}} \quad ◀$$

Exercise 3.4

1 Express in the form $X + \mathrm{j}Y$

(a) $e^{1-\mathrm{j}\pi}$ **(b)** $e^{\mathrm{j}} + e^{-\mathrm{j}}$

(c) $e^{a+\mathrm{j}b}\,e^{a-\mathrm{j}b}$ **(d)** $e^{r\cos\theta + \mathrm{j}r\sin\theta} \times e^{s\cos\phi + \mathrm{j}s\sin\phi}$

2 If $X + \mathrm{j}Y = e^{a+\mathrm{j}b}$, find a relationship between X and Y
(a) if a is constant and is equal to c, and
(b) if b is constant and is equal to k.

3 If $X + \mathrm{j}Y = (u + \mathrm{j}v)^2$, find X and Y in terms of u and v. On the Argand diagram for X and Y sketch the curves corresponding to
(a) u constant and equal to c, and
(b) v constant and equal to k.

4 If $\sin(X + \mathrm{j}Y) = u + \mathrm{j}v$ prove that $u^2\operatorname{cosec}^2 X - v^2\sec^2 X = 1$.

5 If $z = x + \mathrm{j}y$ and $w = u + \mathrm{j}v$, find the relation between u and v with x and y when $w = z + 1/z$. Investigate the transformation when $z = \cos\theta + \mathrm{j}\sin\theta$.

Miscellaneous examination questions 11

1(a) If $z = \dfrac{2+\mathrm{j}}{1-\mathrm{j}}$ find the real and imaginary parts of $z + \dfrac{1}{z}$.

(b) If $z = \cos\theta + \mathrm{j}\sin\theta$, show that

$$z - \frac{1}{z} = 2\mathrm{j}\sin\theta \qquad \text{and} \qquad z^n - \frac{1}{z^n} = 2\mathrm{j}\sin n\theta$$

Express $\sin^5\theta$ in the form

$$a\sin 5\theta + b\sin 3\theta + c\sin\theta$$

and hence solve completely the equation

$$16\sin^5\theta = \sin 5\theta$$

(M.E.I.)

2(a) Express

$$p = \frac{5+\mathrm{j}}{2+3\mathrm{j}} \qquad \text{and} \qquad q = \frac{2\sqrt{2}}{1-\mathrm{j}\sqrt{3}}$$

in the form $x + \mathrm{j}y$, where x and y are real. Find also the modulus and the argument of p and of q, and hence write down the argument of $p + q$.

(b) State De Moivre's theorem for an integral exponent. Show that if

$$z = \cos\theta + \mathrm{j}\sin\theta$$

then $\sin\theta = \dfrac{1}{2\mathrm{j}}\left(z - \dfrac{1}{z}\right)$, $\quad \cos\theta = \dfrac{1}{2}\left(z + \dfrac{1}{z}\right)$, $\quad \cos n\theta = \dfrac{1}{2}\left(z^n + \dfrac{1}{z^n}\right)$

Express $\sin^2\theta\cos^4\theta$ in the form

$$\sum_{r=0}^{n} a_r \cos 2r\theta \qquad \text{(M.E.I.)}$$

3(a) Given that one root of the equation

$$z^4-4z^3+12z^2+4z-13=0$$

is $2-3j$ find the other three roots.

(b) If z is a complex number $x+jy$ where x and y are real, then the complex number $x-jy$ is denoted by z^*. Given

$$z=2\left(\cos\frac{\pi}{6}+j\sin\frac{\pi}{6}\right)$$

illustrate on an Argand diagram the points representing the complex numbers

$$z, \qquad z^*, \qquad (z^*)^2, \qquad \frac{(z^*)^2}{|z|}$$

S is the set of points in the first quadrant which lie on the circumference of the circle $|z|=2$. Find the image of S under the mapping

$$z \to \frac{(z^*)^2}{|z|} \qquad \text{(M.E.I.)}$$

4(a) Find the value of the complex numbers z_1 and z_2 which satisfy the simultaneous equations

$$z_1-2jz_2=-1, \qquad 2z_1-5z_2=23j$$

expressing your results in the form $a+jb$ where a and b are real.

(b) The points A, B on an Argand diagram represent

$$z_1=\cos\theta+j\sin\theta, \qquad z_2=1+\cos\theta+j\sin\theta$$

respectively, and O is the origin. Show the triangle OAB in a diagram and prove that it is isosceles.

Find the modulus and the argument of z_2.

Write down the modulus and the argument of each of the complex numbers

$$\left(1+\cos\frac{\pi}{3}+j\sin\frac{\pi}{3}\right), \qquad \left(1+\cos\frac{\pi}{3}+j\sin\frac{\pi}{3}\right)^6 \qquad \text{(M.E.I.)}$$

5(a) Find the quadratic equation with real coefficients which has

$$2j\left(\cos\frac{\pi}{6}+j\sin\frac{\pi}{6}\right)$$

as one root.

If the roots of this quadratic equation are denoted by α and β, show that $\alpha^6+\beta^6=2^7$. Mark on an Argand diagram the points representing the complex numbers α and β.

(b) Show that there is a unique value of z for which

$$\arg(z+j)=\frac{\pi^c}{4} \qquad \text{and} \qquad |z+1|=2$$

and that this value is real. (M.E.I.)

6 Define the modulus and argument of a complex number with reference to an Argand diagram. Find the modulus and argument of each of the roots of the equation $z^3+64 = 0$ and show these roots on the diagram.

If $z_1 = 2+\mathrm{j}$, $z_2 = 4+3\mathrm{j}$ and A, B are the points representing z_1 and z_2 on the Argand diagram, find the complex numbers represented by C and C′ where ABC, ABC′ are equilateral triangles. (O. & C.)

7(a) If points A and B represent the complex numbers z_1 and z_2 respectively on an Argand diagram give geometrical constructions to find points C and D representing z_1+z_2 and z_1-z_2 respectively.

(b) Find the modulus and amplitude of

$$\frac{(2-3\mathrm{j})^2}{(1-\mathrm{j})^2}$$

(c) Prove that if

$$\frac{z-8\mathrm{j}}{z+6}$$

is purely imaginary, the locus of z in the Argand diagram is a circle with centre at the point $4\mathrm{j}-3$ and radius 5. (O. & C.)

8 Write down the product of the complex numbers $x_1+\mathrm{j}y_1$ and $x_2+\mathrm{j}y_2$. Show that this product has a modulus r_1r_2 and amplitude $\theta_1+\theta_2$ where r_1, r_2 are moduli and θ_1, θ_2 the amplitudes of the given complex numbers.

Solve the equation

$$\frac{z}{3+4\mathrm{j}}+\frac{z-1}{5\mathrm{j}}=\frac{5}{3-4\mathrm{j}}$$

Show that if $\dfrac{z-2}{z-\mathrm{j}}$ is real, the point corresponding to z in the Argand diagrams lies on a straight line through the points 2 and j, and find the equation relating x and y when the ratio is purely imaginary. (O. & C.)

9 The roots of the equation $x^2+2ax+b = 0$ are $p+\mathrm{j}q$ and $p-\mathrm{j}q$, where a, b, p, q are real numbers and $\mathrm{j}^2 = -1$. Express p and q in terms of a and b and find the equation whose roots are $p^2+\mathrm{j}q^2$ and $p^2-\mathrm{j}q^2$, proving any formulae used. (O & C.)

10(a) Find the modulus and argument of each root of the equation $z^2+4z+8=0$. If the roots are denoted by α and β, simplify the expression

$$\frac{\alpha+\beta+4\mathrm{j}}{\alpha\beta+8\mathrm{j}}$$

(b) If $z_1 = -1+\mathrm{j}\sqrt{3}$ and $z_2 = \sqrt{3}+\mathrm{j}$, show in an Argand diagram points representing the complex numbers z_1, z_2, z_1+z_2 and z_1/z_2. (L.)

11 Shade on a diagram the region in the complex plane where the following inequalities are simultaneously satisfied:

$$|z-4| \leqslant |z-6\mathrm{j}|$$

$$|z-4| \leqslant 5$$

$$\frac{\pi^c}{4} \leqslant \arg(z+3\mathrm{j}) \leqslant \frac{\pi^c}{2}$$

(J.M.B.)

12(a) By means of a diagram in the complex plane, or otherwise, prove that, for any two complex numbers z_1, z_2,

$$|z_1+z_2| \leqslant |z_1|+|z_2|$$

The complex number z is such that

$$z^2+2z = 8e^{j\alpha}$$

where α is real. Prove that $|z| \geqslant 2$.

(b) Mark in an Argand diagram points A, B, C, representing the complex numbers

$$e^{j\alpha}, \qquad 1+e^{j\alpha}, \qquad 1-e^{j\alpha}$$

assuming that α lies between 0 and $\pi^c/2$. Given that

$$\frac{1+e^{j\alpha}}{1-e^{j\alpha}} = r\,e^{j\theta} \qquad (r,\, \theta \text{ real})$$

express r and θ in term of OB, OC and $\angle$BOC where O is the origin. Hence, or otherwise, find θ and show that

$$r = \cot\frac{\alpha}{2}$$ (J.M.B.)

13 If z_1 and z_2 are complex numbers, show that

$$(z_1+z_2)^* = z_1^*+z_2^*$$

and

$$(z_1z_2)^* = z_1^*z_2^*$$

Hence or otherwise, prove that if a, b, c and d are real numbers and z is a root of the equation

$$z^4+az^3+bz^2+cz+d = 0$$

then z^* is also a root of the equation.

Show that the equation

$$z^4-4z^3+14z^2-4z+13 = 0$$

has a purely imaginary root and find all the roots of the equation. (J.M.B.)

14 If $z = x+jy$ and $z' = (1+j)z$ obtain an expression for z' in the form $x'+jy'$ and write down the values of x' and y' in terms of x and y.

Find the algebraic relation between x' and y' as z varies in each of the following cases:

(a) z has a constant real part equal to 2.
(b) z has a constant modulus r.
(c) z has a constant argument θ. (C.)

15(a) Express the complex number $(3+4j)^2$ in the form $a+bj$ where a and b are real numbers.

If $x+jy = (3+jt)^2$ where t is a real variable, find, in simplified form the x, y equation of the locus of points representing the number $x+jy$ on an Argand diagram.

(b) Given that

$$x + \mathrm{j}y = \frac{1}{u + 3\mathrm{j}}$$

where u is real, express x and y each in terms of u. (C.)

16(a) If $z_1 = 1 - \mathrm{j}$ and $z_2 = 7 + \mathrm{j}$ find the modulus of

(i) $z_1 - z_2$ (ii) $z_1 z_2$ (iii) $\dfrac{z_1 - z_2}{z_1 z_2}$

(b) Sketch on an Argand diagram the locus of a point P representing the complex number z where

$$|z - 1| = |z - 3\mathrm{j}|$$

and find z when $|z|$ has its least value on this locus. (L.)

17(a) Given two complex numbers $z_1 = 4 + 3\mathrm{j}$ and $z_2 = 3 - \mathrm{j}$ express the numbers

$$z_1 - 2z_2, \qquad z_1^2 - z_2^2, \qquad \frac{z_1}{z_2 + 2j}$$

in the form $a + b\mathrm{j}$.

(b) Expand

$$\left(z + \frac{1}{z}\right)^4 \quad \text{and} \quad \left(z - \frac{1}{z}\right)^4.$$

By putting $z = \cos\theta + \mathrm{j}\sin\theta$ deduce that

$$\cos^4\theta + \sin^4\theta = \tfrac{1}{4}(\cos 4\theta + 3)$$ (L.)

18(a) Express each of the complex numbers

$$z_1 = (1 - \mathrm{j})(1 + 2\mathrm{j}), \qquad z_2 = \frac{2 + 6\mathrm{j}}{3 - \mathrm{j}}, \qquad z_3 = \frac{-4\mathrm{j}}{1 - \mathrm{j}}$$

in the form $a + b\mathrm{j}$ where a and b are real.

Show that $|z_2 - z_1| = |z_1 - z_3|$ and that for principal values of the arguments

$$\arg(z_2 - z_1) - \arg(z_1 - z_3) = \frac{\pi^c}{2}$$

If z_1, z_2, z_3 are represented by points P_1, P_2, P_3 respectively in an Argand diagram, prove that P_1 lies on the circle with $P_2 P_3$ as diameter.

(b) Using De Moivre's theorem, or otherwise, find an expression for $\cos 6\theta$ in ascending powers of $\cos\theta$. (L.)

19 Given that

$$z = \cos\theta + \mathrm{j}\sin\theta$$

show that

$$z + \frac{1}{z} = 2\cos\theta$$

Use De Moivre's theorem to prove that

$$z^n + z^{-n} = 2\cos n\theta$$

Hence or otherwise, solve the equation

$$2z^4+3z^3+5z^2+3z+2=0$$ (J.M.B.)

20 Prove that when n is a positive integer

$$(\cos\theta+\mathrm{j}\sin\theta)^n=\cos n\theta+\mathrm{j}\sin n\theta$$

Find the modulus and argument of

$$\frac{[\sqrt{3}(\cos\theta+\mathrm{j}\sin\theta)]^4}{\cos 2\theta-\mathrm{j}\sin 2\theta}$$ (J.M.B.)

21(a) Prove that, if $z=\pm(\cos\frac{1}{4}\pi+\mathrm{j}\sin\frac{1}{4}\pi)$

where $\mathrm{j}^2=-1$ then $z^2=\dfrac{1+\mathrm{j}}{1-\mathrm{j}}$

(b) Sketch in an Argand diagram the sets of complex numbers z such that

(i) $-\frac{1}{3}\pi<\arg z<\frac{1}{3}\pi$ (ii) $|z-1|+|z+1|=2$ (M.E.I.)

22(a) If $Z_1=1+3\mathrm{j}$ and $Z_2=3-\mathrm{j}$ mark on an Argand diagram the points representing Z_1, Z_2, $Z_1\times Z_2$, Z_1/Z_2.

(b) Define the modulus and the argument of a complex number.

Prove that, if $|z_1+z_2|=|z_1-z_2|$, then the arguments of z_1 and z_2 differ by $\frac{1}{2}\pi^c$ or $\frac{3}{2}\pi^c$.

(c) State De Moivre's theorem for a positive integral exponent. Show that $(1-\mathrm{j})^{16}$ is a real number. (M.E.I.)

Chapter 12

Algebraic Structure

1 Sets and operations

1.1 Binary operations

For generations mathematicians solved problems involving numbers and operations without giving much thought to the *rules* governing the ways in which the numbers or operations were combined. Solving a problem is similar to playing a game. A game is played with a variety of pieces (or elements) together with a method of play. There are also a number of subsidiary rules which govern the game. For example, in Snakes and Ladders, we have the counters (the elements) which are moved according to the score thrown on a die (the method of play). The subsidiary rules are

1 If we land on a ladder we go to the top of it.
2 When we land on a snake's head we go to its tail.
3 For a six we have two turns.
4 We must stay on the board finishing with the exact required number.

In mathematics, when we have to solve certain problems we are given a set of *elements*, all different, and a method of *combining* the elements *two* at a time. Such a method is called a *binary operation*—typical ones being addition and multiplication. For example, if we have more than two numbers to add, we add two of them, and then add on the next to our first total, and so on. A different type of binary operation is 'followed by' where we 'perform' one 'instruction' after another.

We call the 'game' played in mathematics *structure*. It is 'played' with a set (or sets) of elements which are combined by one or more binary operations. These sets may have a finite or infinite number of elements. The method of combining the elements may be an 'active' one such as addition and multiplication or the 'passive' one—'followed by'—where the elements *themselves* are operations such as rotations, rearrangements or substitutions. In this case, the effect of doing one operation followed by another is (usually) equivalent to doing a single operation which may or may not belong to the original set of elements.

The rules governing the 'game'

In the structures we are considering the rules are of the following types:

(*1*) *Closure*

Any two elements in the set combine to give another one in the set.

(2) *Associativity*

This is best explained as the 'bracketing' law. If a, b, c are three elements, then

$$a+(b+c) = (a+b)+c$$

and

$$a(bc) = (ab)c$$

This illustrates the law for the operations of addition and multiplication.

(3) *Identity*

In the set there is a unique element which when combined with any other element leaves it unchanged.

(4) *Inverses*

It is possible to find, in the set, a unique element corresponding to each element, which combines with it to give the identity element.

(5) *Commutativity*

If the operation (or way of combining the elements) is commutative, then the order in which the elements are combined (two at a time) does not alter the result, e.g.

$$a+b = b+a$$

$$ab = ba$$

These are the most common rules involving *one* method of combination of the elements.

Just as a game like Monopoly is more complicated than Snakes and Ladders, so in mathematics, it is possible to have much more complicated systems with several different kinds of elements and operations. We shall meet some of these later.

1.2 Combination tables

The result of combining sets of elements can be set out in a Cayley table. Clearly it is only possible to draw up a complete table if the set contains no more than a few elements. We give a number of examples of the combinations of sets of two elements. In these Cayley tables, a symbol standing for the rule of combination is placed in the top left-hand corner and the elements of the set are listed in the left-hand column and the top row.

*	A	B
A	A * A	A * B
B	B * A	B * B

Each figure in the body of the table gives the result of combining the element at the left-hand end of its row, with that at the top of its column, in that order. Since many combinations are not commutative it is important to distinguish between $A * B$ and $B * A$. The symbol $*$ can stand for any rule of combination, but in the following example it usually means 'follows' when the elements in the set are themselves operations. The *right*-hand element is therefore the operation performed first.

Active combinations

Example 1

Odd and even numbers under addition.

		RIGHT	
	+	O	E
LEFT	O	E	O
	E	O	E

Example 2

Odd and even numbers under multiplication.

		RIGHT	
	×	O	E
LEFT	O	O	E
	E	E	E

Example 3

The sets A, ∅ under the operation of union (⋃).

		RIGHT	
	⋃	A	∅
LEFT	A	A	A
	∅	A	∅

Example 4

The sets A, ∅ under the operation of intersection (⋂).

		RIGHT	
	⋂	A	∅
LEFT	A	A	∅
	∅	∅	∅

Example 5

The matrices $\begin{pmatrix}1 & 0\\0 & 1\end{pmatrix}, \begin{pmatrix}-1 & 0\\0 & -1\end{pmatrix}$ under multiplication.

	×	RIGHT $\begin{pmatrix}1 & 0\\0 & 1\end{pmatrix}$	$\begin{pmatrix}-1 & 0\\0 & -1\end{pmatrix}$
LEFT	$\begin{pmatrix}1 & 0\\0 & 1\end{pmatrix}$	$\begin{pmatrix}1 & 0\\0 & 1\end{pmatrix}$	$\begin{pmatrix}-1 & 0\\0 & -1\end{pmatrix}$
	$\begin{pmatrix}-1 & 0\\0 & -1\end{pmatrix}$	$\begin{pmatrix}-1 & 0\\0 & -1\end{pmatrix}$	$\begin{pmatrix}1 & 0\\0 & 1\end{pmatrix}$

Passive combinations

In constructing these tables, the entry represents the single operation which is equivalent to the two given operations (elements).

Example 6

The elements I ('leave it alone') and X ('reflect in the x axis') under the rule of combination $*$ ('follows').

	*	RIGHT (1st) I	X
LEFT (2nd)	I	I	X
	X	X	I

Example 7

The rotations R_0, R_{180} under the rule of 'follows'.

	*	RIGHT (1st) R_0	R_{180}
LEFT (2nd)	R_0	R_0	R_{180}
	R_{180}	R_{180}	R_0

These tables illustrate in a simple way the various rules which we have discussed:

1 All the tables are closed, i.e. they contain only the elements we started with.
2 All the tables are associative. For instance, in Example 6

$$I * (X * X) = (I * X) * X$$

3 Each example contains a unique identity element; e.g.

$$\begin{pmatrix}1 & 0\\0 & 1\end{pmatrix}, \mathrm{I}, \mathrm{R}_0$$

4 Where the identity element appears in the 'body' of the table we can find inverses. E.g. the inverse of

$$\begin{pmatrix}-1 & 0\\0 & -1\end{pmatrix} \quad \text{is} \quad \begin{pmatrix}-1 & 0\\0 & -1\end{pmatrix} \quad \text{since} \quad \begin{pmatrix}-1 & 0\\0 & -1\end{pmatrix}\begin{pmatrix}-1 & 0\\0 & -1\end{pmatrix} = \begin{pmatrix}1 & 0\\0 & 1\end{pmatrix}$$

The inverse of X is X, since $X * X = I$. Similarly the inverse of R_{180} is R_{180}. (All these are *self*-inverse, in fact.)

There are very few tables involving *three* elements which illustrate these rules, one being the rotations R_0, R_{120}, R_{240} under the rule 'follows':

	*	RIGHT (1st) R_0	R_{120}	R_{240}
LEFT (2nd)	R_0	R_0	R_{120}	R_{240}
	R_{120}	R_{120}	R_{240}	R_0
	R_{240}	R_{240}	R_0	R_{120}

Here the identity is R_0, the inverse of R_0 is R_0, the inverse of R_{120} is R_{240} and the inverse of R_{240} is R_{120}.

There are several sets of *four* elements, some of which we meet in the next exercise.

Exercise 1.2a (active rules of combination)

1(a) A number modulo n is the *remainder* that is left when a number is divided by n. Find (i) 23 mod 10 (ii) 999 mod 37 (iii) 1 mod 5.

(b) Copy and then complete the multiplication table below for these numbers:

mod 10, in the set $A = \{1, 3, 7, 9\}$

	×	RIGHT (1st) 1	3	7	9
LEFT (2nd)	1				
	3		9		
	7			9	
	9				

(i) Find the number e such that for any other number a

$$e \times a = a \times e = a \qquad \text{where } a, e \in A.$$

(ii) Find the inverse of each of the elements.

2 Repeat Question 1(b) for the set B = {2, 4, 6, 8} under multiplication, mod 10.

Draw up combination tables for the following sets of elements and rules of combination:

3 {1, j, −1, −j} under multiplication, where $j^2 = 1$.

4 $\left\{\begin{pmatrix}1 & 0\\0 & 1\end{pmatrix}, \begin{pmatrix}0 & -1\\1 & 0\end{pmatrix}, \begin{pmatrix}-1 & 0\\0 & -1\end{pmatrix}, \begin{pmatrix}0 & 1\\-1 & 0\end{pmatrix}\right\}$ under multiplication.

5 $\left\{\begin{pmatrix}1 & 0\\0 & 1\end{pmatrix}, \begin{pmatrix}1 & 0\\0 & -1\end{pmatrix}, \begin{pmatrix}-1 & 0\\0 & -1\end{pmatrix}, \begin{pmatrix}-1 & 0\\0 & 1\end{pmatrix}\right\}$ under multiplication.

NOTE. Keep all these tables, as we refer to them later.

Exercise 1.2b (passive rule of combination)

Make up Cayley tables for the following:

1 The operations on a rectangle shown in the diagram:

where the combination law is to do first one operation then the other.

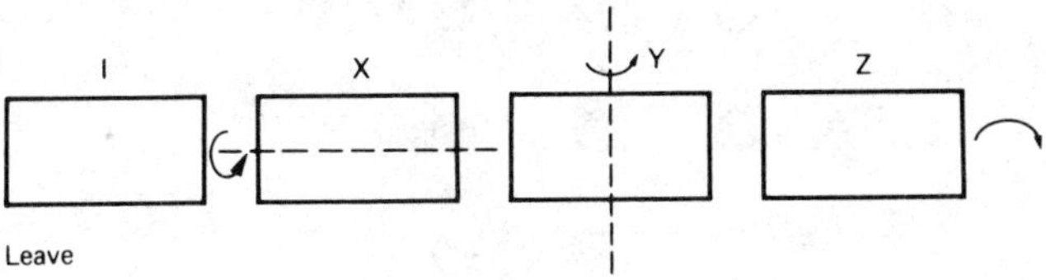

2 The operations of turning clockwise: I, stay put; R, clockwise through 90°; R^2, clockwise through 180°; R^3, clockwise through 270° and the combination law 'do first one rotation then the other'.

3 Consider again the operations of Question 1. These can be performed with any shape (not just a rectangle), where I means 'leave it as it is' and X, Y and Z represent half rotations (i.e. through 180°) about the x, y and z axes respectively.

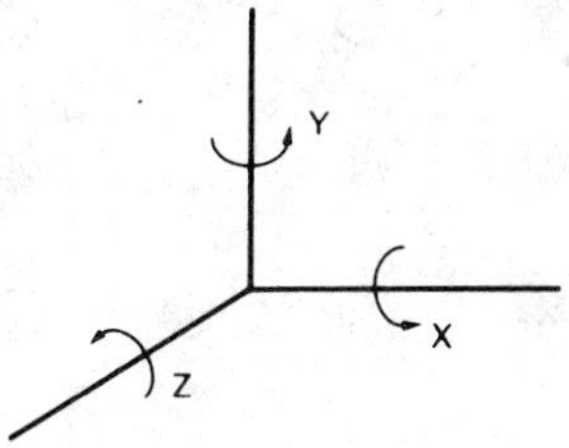

Check that the same table applies as in Question 1.

4 The operations given in a car servicing manual for changing wheels, with the combination rule 'follows'.

Initially		*Operation*	*Result*	
A	B	I (leave them alone)	A	B
C	D		C	D
A	B	P (diagonal change)	D	C
C	D		B	A
A	B	Q (side-by-side change)	B	A
C	D		D	C
A	B	R (back-to-front change)	C	D
C	D		A	B

Pattern

We have now made up several tables of combination for sets of four elements. If we shade the elements in each table (for example, in Question 4 above, shade I white, P grey, Q striped and R black) we shall see clearly a certain pattern—one of the two below.

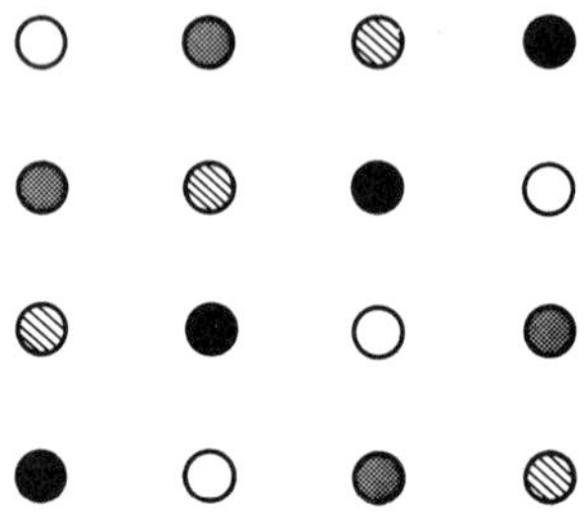

This is a *cyclic* pattern: the elements occur in a 'circular' pattern one after the other.

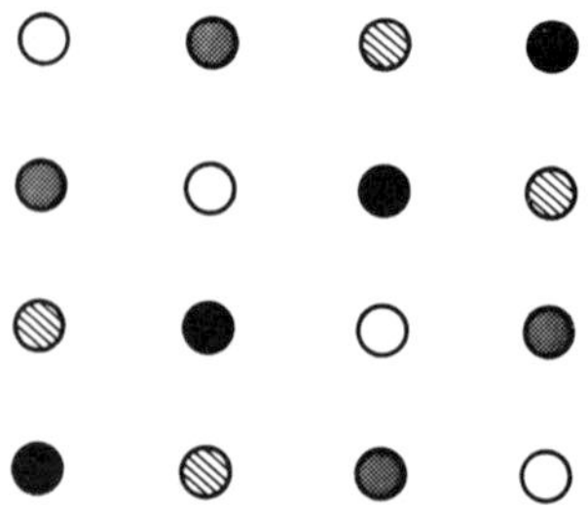

This is known as the *Klein* pattern after a famous mathematician.

Look back at the tables you have made and determine the pattern in each case.

2 Groups

2.1 Definition

By far the most important, basic structure of mathematics is the *group*. A group contains one set of elements which are combined by one binary operation.

► **A set of elements form a group G, under a rule of combination $*$, if:**

1 For all elements $a, b \in G$, then $a * b \in G$ (closure).

2 For all elements $a, b, c \in G$

$$(a * b) * c = a * (b * c) \text{ (associativity)}$$

3 There is a unique identity element e so that

$$a * e = e * a = a \text{ (identity)}$$

4 To each element $a \in G$ there corresponds a unique element a^{-1} (called the inverse of a under $*$) so that

$$a * a^{-1} = a^{-1} * a = e \text{ (inverses)}$$ ◄

If the rule of combination is also commutative then the set is called an *Abelian* group. This leads to an easy way of remembering the group laws of Closure Associativity Inverses Neutral (CAIN—ABEL); (the Americans call the identity the *neutral* element).

The tables which you have constructed are all group tables except for three of those on page 424. Can you see which they are?

A first glance at a group table shows that each element occurs once and only once in each row and in each column. This is not sufficient evidence that the elements form a group but it is a quick way of noticing if they do not.

Exercise 2.1a (involving modular arithmetics)

Draw up group tables for the following sets of elements. In each case find the identity element and give the inverse of each element in the set.

1 {2, 4, 8, 10, 14, 16} multiplication mod 18

2 {2, 4, 6, . . . 20} multiplication mod 22

3 {2, 4, 6, 8, 10, 12} multiplication mod 14

4 {3, 6, 9, 12} multiplication mod 15

Exercise 2.1b (involving operations)

1(a) We define operations on an equilateral triangle as in the diagram below, with the axes of rotation fixed in the *triangle*.

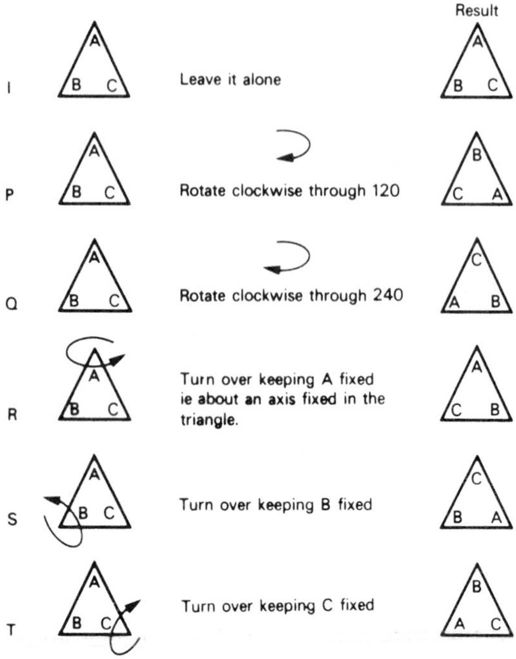

Make a table of combination under the rule, 'do first one operation then the other'. Check your table carefully for associativity.

(b) We now redefine some of our operations. Suppose we have new operations R, S and T, each defined (as in the diagram) as 'turn about an axis fixed in space'.

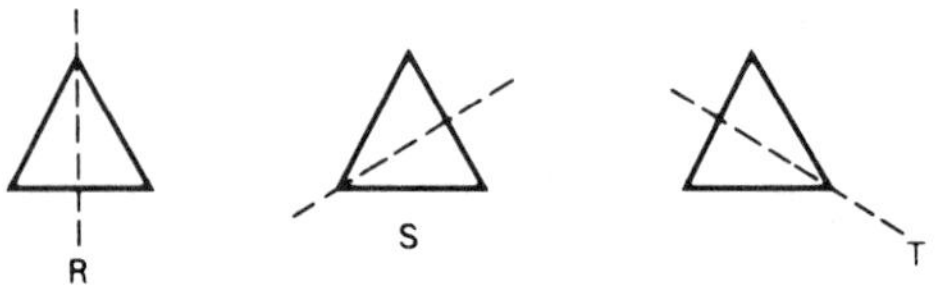

Make out the new table of combination for I, P, Q, R, S, T and show that this time the operations form a group.

2 An equilateral triangular prism as shown stands on a table. The following are two of the symmetry operations which can be carried out upon it.

(i) a rotation through 120° clockwise (as seen from above) about its axis. This operation will be denoted by R.

(ii) interchanging the positions A and A′ by rotation which leaves the prism standing on the same triangular portion of the table-top. This operation will be denoted by U.

Show that there are four other symmetry operations and write them in terms of R and U (e.g. one might be RU—but the meaning of this must be explained). Show that the operations form a group.

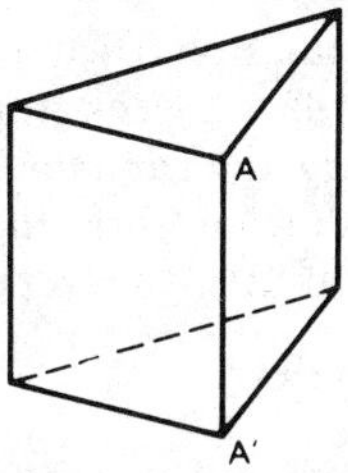

Exercise 2.1c (groups involving a rearrangement in order—or permutation)

1 Consider the following operations where (1 2 3) is changed as shown.

$$I\begin{pmatrix}1&2&3\\1&2&3\end{pmatrix}\quad J\begin{pmatrix}1&2&3\\2&3&1\end{pmatrix}\quad K\begin{pmatrix}1&2&3\\3&1&2\end{pmatrix}$$

$$L\begin{pmatrix}1&2&3\\1&3&2\end{pmatrix}\quad M\begin{pmatrix}1&2&3\\3&2&1\end{pmatrix}\quad N\begin{pmatrix}1&2&3\\2&1&3\end{pmatrix}$$

The operations are combined as follows: $K * M$ means 'do M first, then K'. Then

$$\text{M takes}\begin{pmatrix}1&2&3\\&\text{into}&\\3&2&1\end{pmatrix}\qquad\text{K then takes}\begin{pmatrix}3&2&1\\&\text{into}&\\2&1&3\end{pmatrix}$$

so that $$K * M \text{ takes}\begin{pmatrix}1&2&3\\&\text{into}&\\2&1&3\end{pmatrix}\qquad\text{or } K * M = N$$

Make up the table for yourself and show that {I, J, K, L, M, N} form a group under the operation illustrated.

2 The back row of the St Snatsnud's pack in a rugby football team consists of Matthews, Field and Ring. In a practice game the coach shouts 'A' if he wants Matthews to be replaced by Field, Field to be replaced by Ring and Ring to be replaced by Matthews. This could be represented symbolically by

$$A = \begin{Bmatrix}\text{mfr}\\\text{frm}\end{Bmatrix}$$

Other changes are indicated by

$$B = \begin{Bmatrix}\text{mfr}\\\text{fmr}\end{Bmatrix}\quad C = \begin{Bmatrix}\text{mfr}\\\text{rfm}\end{Bmatrix}\quad D = \begin{Bmatrix}\text{mfr}\\\text{rmf}\end{Bmatrix}\quad E = \begin{Bmatrix}\text{mfr}\\\text{mrf}\end{Bmatrix}\quad\text{and}\quad I = \begin{Bmatrix}\text{mfr}\\\text{mfr}\end{Bmatrix}$$

indicates that no changes are to take place.

(a) If BA means change A followed by change B, which symbol is equal to BA?

(b) Show that (AB)C = A(BC).

(c) Does AB = BA?

(d) Which instruction following D will restore the back row to the positions which each player occupied before the interchange D was ordered?

(e) Determine X such that DX = B and Y such that YC = D. (M.E.I.)

3 Three pairs, Alf (A) and Art (a), Bob (B) and Bill (b), Chris (C) and Charles (c), work shifts round the clock, five days a week from midnight at the end of Sunday. They work two machines, the Ligger (L) and the Tenny (T). Bob always takes over from Alf, Chris from Bob and Alf from Chris, the shift times being 0.00–08.00 (I), 08.00–16.00 (II), and 16.00–00.00 (III). The six possible schedules for arranging the work are shown in this table:

SCHEDULE	No. 1			No. 2			No. 3		
Shift	I	II	III	I	II	III	I	II	III
Ligger	A	B	C	B	C	A	C	A	B
Tenny	a	b	c	b	c	a	c	a	b

SCHEDULE	No. 4			No. 5			No. 6		
Shift	I	II	III	I	II	III	I	II	III
Ligger	a	b	c	b	c	a	c	a	b
Tenny	A	B	C	B	C	A	C	A	B

A change in plan in which every man changes over machines without altering shifts, e.g. schedule 1 to schedule 4, is called M; one in which all shift times are advanced by 8 hours, except for the first pair which goes to be last, but all stay on the same machine, e.g. schedule 1 to schedule 2, is called P.

Find whether all allowable changes can be obtained from M and P and combinations of them. Investigate whether these changes form a group of order 6, and, if so, whether it is commutative. (M.E.I.)

Exercise 2.1d (groups involving substitutions)

1 The elements are four functions,

$$p(x) = x \qquad q(x) = -x$$

$$r(x) = \frac{1}{x} \qquad s(x) = -\frac{1}{x}$$

These can be more easily understood as being (starting with x in each case)

$$p\,[\text{For } x \text{ put } x] \qquad q\,[\text{For } x \text{ put } -x]$$

$$r\left[\text{For } x \text{ put } \frac{1}{x}\right] \qquad s\left[\text{For } x \text{ put } -\frac{1}{x}\right]$$

The law of combination is denoted by $*$, where $q * r$ would mean 'do r first then q'.

First replace x by $\frac{1}{x}$ and then replace $\frac{1}{x}$ by $-\frac{1}{x}$. Thus $q * r = s$.

	*	FIRST OPERATION p	q	r	s
	p	p	q	r	s
SECOND	q			s	
OPERATION	r				
	s				

Complete the table above and show that $\{p, q, r, s\}$ form a group under $*$.

2 Four functions are defined as follows:

$$p: x \to x \qquad q: x \to \frac{2}{2-x} \qquad r: x \to \frac{x-2}{x-1} \qquad s: x \to \frac{2(x-1)}{x}$$

Their law of combination, denoted by $*$, is as follows where $r * q$ is determined: the process q is performed first on x to give $q(x)$ and then r is performed on $q(x)$ to give $r[q(x)]$ which is

$$\frac{q(x)-2}{q(x)-1} \quad \text{and reduces to} \quad \frac{2(x-1)}{x}$$

—which is s. Assuming associativity, show that the four functions form a group under this law of composition and give the group table.

3 With functions defined as follows,

$$f \equiv 1-x \qquad g \equiv \frac{1}{x} \qquad p \equiv fg = 1-\frac{1}{x} = \frac{x-1}{x}$$

$$q \equiv gf = \frac{1}{1-x} \qquad r \equiv gp = \frac{x}{x-1} \qquad i \equiv x$$

compose the combination table. For example

$$p * g = \frac{\frac{1}{x}-1}{\frac{1}{x}} = 1-x = f$$

4 The symbol A indicates the transformation $x \to 1-x$, i.e. x is replaced by $1-x$; similarly B indicates the transformation $x \to 1/x$. C indicates the transformation AB (A after B); D is BA; E is the identity and F is ABA.

Show that of the six transformations A, B, C, D, E, F, four are their own inverses and the other two are inverses of each other. (The associative law may be assumed to hold for these transformations.)

Show that CCC = E and BAB = F.

Simplify DAD and FACE, in each case to a single letter.

2.2 Demonstrating group properties

It is often required to show that a set of elements form a group, and this raises various problems. These include

1 We should show that *every* pair of elements in G combine to give another element in G.
2 We should show that *every* triple of elements in G is associative.
3 We should show that the identity element *is* the identity for *every* element in G.
4 We should show that *every* element has a unique inverse in G.

These four problems would make the task of demonstrating group properties very tedious or, if the group contained an infinite number of elements, impossible. Hence we show that the laws are true for a 'general' set of elements of G, and look for any counter-examples—one is quite sufficient to show that the set does not form a group.

Example

The matrices of the type $\begin{pmatrix} 1 & 0 \\ n & 1 \end{pmatrix}$ where $n \in \mathbb{Z}$ represent a shearing of the plane (see page 347). They also form an infinite group under multiplication, since:

(1) $\begin{pmatrix} 1 & 0 \\ r & 1 \end{pmatrix}\begin{pmatrix} 1 & 0 \\ s & 1 \end{pmatrix} = \begin{pmatrix} 1 & 0 \\ r+s & 1 \end{pmatrix}$ showing closure.

(2) $\begin{pmatrix} 1 & 0 \\ r & 1 \end{pmatrix}\left[\begin{pmatrix} 1 & 0 \\ s & 1 \end{pmatrix}\begin{pmatrix} 1 & 0 \\ t & 1 \end{pmatrix}\right] = \left[\begin{pmatrix} 1 & 0 \\ r & 1 \end{pmatrix}\begin{pmatrix} 1 & 0 \\ s & 1 \end{pmatrix}\right]\begin{pmatrix} 1 & 0 \\ t & 1 \end{pmatrix}$

$= \begin{pmatrix} 1 & 0 \\ r+s+t & 1 \end{pmatrix}$ showing associativity.

(3) The identity element is $\begin{pmatrix} 1 & 0 \\ 0 & 1 \end{pmatrix}$.

(4) For each element $\begin{pmatrix} 1 & 0 \\ r & 1 \end{pmatrix}$ there is a unique inverse $\begin{pmatrix} 1 & 0 \\ -r & 1 \end{pmatrix}$; (see page 348).

Exercise 2.2

1 S denotes the set of matrices of the form $\begin{pmatrix} x & y \\ y & x \end{pmatrix}$ where x and y are real numbers. Investigate whether, for the operation of matrix multiplication **(a)** S is closed **(b)** the identity belongs to S **(c)** every element of S has an inverse.

2(a) Show that matrices of the form $\begin{pmatrix} \cos\theta & -\sin\theta \\ \sin\theta & \cos\theta \end{pmatrix}$ form a group under matrix multiplication.

(b) Show that all numbers which can be written in the form 10^n where $n \in \mathbb{Z}$ form an infinite group under multiplication. State the identity element and give the inverse of 10^{-13}.

3 Let G be the set of all matrices of the form $\begin{pmatrix} 1 & x \\ 0 & 1 \end{pmatrix}$ with x a real number.

(a) Show that G does not form a group under matrix addition.

(b) Show that G does form a group under matrix multiplication. (You may assume associativity.)

4 Show that the vectors $\begin{pmatrix} a_1 \\ a_2 \end{pmatrix}$ where $a_1, a_2 \in \mathbb{R}$ form an infinite group under addition. Explain why they do not form a group under the rule of combination 'dot product'.

3 Rings and fields

3.1 Systems involving a set of elements and two binary operations

The simplest sets to investigate under *two* binary operations are the modular arithmetics under addition and multiplication. Study of their tables will reveal most of the 'rules' applicable to some of the more complicated mathematical 'games'.

Modulo 2 arithmetic

+	0	1
0	0	1
1	1	0

×	0	1
0	0	0
1	0	1

Modulo 3 arithmetic

+	0	1	2
0	0	1	2
1	1	2	0
2	2	0	1

×	0	1	2
0	0	0	0
1	0	1	2
2	0	2	1

Modulo 4 arithmetic

+	0	1	2	3
0	0	1	2	3
1	1	2	3	0
2	2	3	0	1
3	3	0	1	2

×	0	1	2	3
0	0	0	0	0
1	0	1	2	3
2	0	2	0	2
3	0	3	2	1

Modulo 5 arithmetic

+	0	1	2	3	4
0	0	1	2	3	4
1	1	2	3	4	0
2	2	3	4	0	1
3	3	4	0	1	2
4	4	0	1	2	3

×	0	1	2	3	4
0	0	0	0	0	0
1	0	1	2	3	4
2	0	2	4	1	3
3	0	3	1	4	2
4	0	4	3	2	1

Modulo 6 arithmetic

+	0	1	2	3	4	5
0	0	1	2	3	4	5
1	1	2	3	4	5	0
2	2	3	4	5	0	1
3	3	4	5	0	1	2
4	4	5	0	1	2	3
5	5	0	1	2	3	4

×	0	1	2	3	4	5
0	0	0	0	0	0	0
1	0	1	2	3	4	5
2	0	2	4	0	2	4
3	0	3	0	3	0	3
4	0	4	2	0	4	2
5	0	5	4	3	2	1

At first glance the addition and multiplication patterns seem to be quite different, probably because the multiplication tables contain one row and one column entirely composed of zeros. In the multiplication patterns let us ignore these particular rows and columns for the moment.

We can see at once that the addition patterns are all of the same type. The rows and columns contain each element once and once only; the elements are in order in each row and column and follow a cyclic pattern.

The multiplication patterns vary considerably but break down into two categories (ignoring the first row and the first column of zeros): (a) Modulo 2, modulo 3 and modulo 5 under multiplication have each element in each row and column once only; The elements are not necessarily in cyclic order in the rows and columns. (b) Modulo 4 and modulo 6 under multiplication contain elements two or three times in some rows.

We can compare some of the patterns:

+	0	1
0	0	1
1	1	0

mod 2

×	1	2
1	1	2
2	2	1

mod 3

and see that there is a correspondence between the elements of the first pattern and the elements of the second pattern, such that

$$\text{First} \begin{matrix} 0 \leftrightarrow 1 \\ 1 \leftrightarrow 2 \end{matrix} \text{Second}$$

Two patterns like these are said to be *isomorphic*; they have the same shape and are the same pattern, in fact.

Provided:

1 there is a one-to-one correspondence between the elements in each set, and
2 the result of combining two elements in the second set is the image of the result of combining the corresponding elements in the first set,

then the patterns are said to be *isomorphic*.

Now consider

+	0	1	2	3
0	0	1	2	3
1	1	2	3	0
2	2	3	0	1
3	3	0	1	2

mod 4

×	1	2	3	4
1	1	2	3	4
2	2	4	1	3
3	3	1	4	2
4	4	3	2	1

mod 5

As the two patterns stand they are not isomorphic (look at the 0's in the first pattern, the 1's in the second). However, we can rearrange the elements in our second pattern—

+	0	1	2	3
0	0	1	2	3
1	1	2	3	0
2	2	3	0	1
3	3	0	1	2

mod 4

×	1	2	4	3
1	1	2	4	3
2	2	4	3	1
4	4	3	1	2
3	3	1	2	4

mod 5

—and find that the two patterns *are* isomorphic and that there is a correspondence between the elements.

	$0 \leftrightarrow 1$	
First	$1 \leftrightarrow 2$	Second
pattern	$2 \leftrightarrow 4$	pattern
	$3 \leftrightarrow 3$	

The arithmetics under addition all form cyclic groups and by extending the idea we say that all arithmetics whose modulus is an integer will form a group under addition. Under multiplication (ignoring the first row and first column of zeros) only certain arithmetics form groups: modulos 2, 3, 5, . . . (can you continue the sequence?). In fact, all arithmetics modulo *prime numbers* under multiplication form groups (ignoring zeros). Here, then, we have sets of elements combined under two rules of combination (addition and multiplication).

We can now discuss two more systems informally; the first, an almost double group (i.e. a group under addition and a group under multiplication but without a row and column of zeros), is called a *field*, whilst the other, a group under addition but without all four group laws under multiplication, is called a *ring*.

There is, however, one further rule needed, which enables us to combine the *operations*. This is the *distributive law*. We say, for example, that multiplication is distributive over addition since

$$a \times (b+c) = (a \times b) + (a \times c)$$

In general $\circ$ is distributive over $*$ if

$$a \circ (b * c) = (a \circ b) * (a \circ c)$$

Here are definitions of the two systems.

Ring

A set of elements together with two laws of combination is called a *ring* if the laws of combination are defined for the set so that

1 Both laws of combination are associative.
2 The system is a commutative group with respect to one law of combination called addition and given the symbol +.

$$a+b = b+a$$

3 The other law of combination is distributive with respect to addition. I.e.

$$a * (b+c) = a * b + a * c.$$

Field

A set of elements is called a *field* if it forms a ring and there is also an identity element and a unique inverse element, under $*$, for every element except zero.

Vector spaces

Many systems involve *two* sets of elements and have at least two operations defined on them. Typical of these is the set of vectors and the set of real numbers under addition and scalar multiplication. Other similar examples are the set of matrices and the set of real numbers under addition and scalar multiplication; the set of n-ordered numbers, and the set of real numbers under the same operations. These operations are usually those of + and ×, although in $\boldsymbol{a}+\boldsymbol{b}$, and in $2+3$, the operation written + has different meanings (—in the first we are adding vectors, in the second adding numbers). We must always say clearly what we mean by + and × on the two elements.

The table below summarizes the laws of the structures we have met.

Elements	*Operations*	*Laws*	*Structure*
One set	One	Closure Associativity Identity Inverse	GROUP
One set	Two(+, ×)	+ Closure Associativity Identity Inverse Commutative × Closure Associativity Distributive law	RING

Elements	*Operations*	*Laws*	*Structure*
One set	Two (+, ×)	+ Closure Associativity Identity Inverse Commutative × Closure Associativity Identity Inverse (except for zero) Distributive law	FIELD
Two sets (vectors, scalars)	Two(+, ×)	Vectors form an Abelian group under +. Scalars form a field Several mixed laws: e.g. $\lambda \boldsymbol{a}$ is a vector $\lambda(\boldsymbol{a}+\boldsymbol{b}) = \lambda\boldsymbol{a}+\lambda\boldsymbol{b}$ $(\lambda+\mu)\boldsymbol{a} = \lambda\boldsymbol{a}+\mu\boldsymbol{a}$ $(\lambda\mu)\boldsymbol{a} = \lambda(\mu\boldsymbol{a})$ where λ, μ are scalars $\boldsymbol{a}, \boldsymbol{b}$ are vectors.	VECTOR SPACE

Exercise 3.1

Classify the following number systems as either a ring or a field.

1 {Integers} under + and ×.

2 Modulo 6 arithmetic under + and ×.

3 Modulo 71 arithmetic under + and ×.

4 {Rational numbers} under + and ×.

5 {All 2×2 matrices} under + and ×.

6 $\left\{\text{All } 2\times 2 \text{ matrices of the form } \begin{pmatrix}\cos\theta & -\sin\theta\\ \sin\theta & \cos\theta\end{pmatrix}\right\}$ under + and ×.

7 {All real numbers} under + and ×.

8 {All irrational numbers} under + and ×.

9 $\left\{\text{All column vectors } \begin{pmatrix}x\\ y\end{pmatrix}\right\}$ under + and scalar ×.

10 {All subsets of a set} under $\cap$ and $\cup$.

3.2 The need for algebraic structure

The ideas of structure are most important. When we meet a problem, we have to decide whether the elements and operations belong to a known structure. If they do, then we shall know whether the problem can be solved and if so how many solutions may be possible. (These ideas have been successfully adapted to elementary particle physics and were responsible for the discovery of a new particle, the Ω^-).

In our first example we show the need of group structure in solving even the simplest equations.

Example 1

Solve in $\mathbb{Z}$ the equation $$^+3+x = {}^+7$$

We know that the integers form a group under addition so we use the four laws of a group to solve our problem.

The first step is to add to both sides of our equation the inverse under addition of $^+3$. This is easily found since the identity element under addition is 0. Hence

$$^+3+(\text{inverse of } {}^+3) = 0$$

$$(\text{inverse of } {}^+3) = {}^-3$$

so

$$^-3+({}^+3+x) = {}^-3+{}^+7$$

$$({}^-3+{}^+3)+x = {}^-3+{}^+7 \qquad \text{(associative law)}$$

$$0+x = {}^-3+{}^+7 \qquad \text{(inverses)}$$

$$x = {}^-3+{}^+7 \qquad \text{(identity)}$$

$$x = 4 \qquad \text{(closure)}$$

Note that each of the four laws is essential if we are to solve the equation.

In our second example we require the laws of a field.

Example 2

Solve in $\mathbb{Q}$ the equation

$$^+3+4\times x = {}^+5$$

$$^-3+({}^+3+4\times x) = {}^-3+{}^+5$$

$$({}^-3+{}^+3)+4\times x = {}^-3+{}^+5 \qquad \text{(associative law under +)}$$

$$0+4\times x = {}^-3+{}^+5 \qquad \text{(inverses under +)}$$

$$+4\times x = {}^-3+{}^+5 \qquad \text{(identity under +)}$$

$$+4\times x = 2 \qquad \text{(closure)}$$

$$\tfrac{1}{4}\times(4\times x) = \tfrac{1}{4}\times 2$$

$$(\tfrac{1}{4}\times 4)\times x = \tfrac{1}{4}\times 2 \qquad \text{(associative law under } \times\text{)}$$

$$1\times x = \tfrac{1}{4}\times 2 \qquad \text{(inverses under } \times\text{)}$$

$$x = \tfrac{1}{4}\times 2 \qquad \text{(identity under } \times\text{)}$$

$$x = \tfrac{1}{2} \qquad \text{(closure)}$$

Exercise 3.2

1 If $x \in \mathbb{Q}$, solve the following equations putting in reasons for each step.

(a) $-4+x = -3$ **(b)** $+3+x = +1$ **(c)** $+2\times x = +5$
(d) $+3-5x = +2$ **(e)** $+2-x = +3$ **(f)** $-3-\frac{1}{5}x = +\frac{1}{2}$

2 Solve the following equations where possible in the number system indicated.

(a) $4x = 2 \pmod 6$ **(b)** $2x+1 = 2 \pmod 3$ **(c)** $2x+1 = 3 \pmod 4$
(d) $3x+1 = 2 \pmod 6$ **(e)** $2x+1 = 2 \pmod 4$
(f) $5x+2x = 1 \pmod 6$

3 A binary operation $*$ is defined on the real numbers by the formula $a * b = a+b-2$

(a) State whether the operation $*$ is commutative, giving reasons.
(b) (i) Calculate $3 * 4$ and $(3 * 4) * 4$.
(ii) Write down clearly and evaluate another combination of the numbers 3 and 4 which, together with your answer to (a) will suggest whether or not the operation $*$ is associative.
(c) Find the neutral (identity) element e such that $e * y = y$ for *every* possible value of y.
(d) Find the inverse of the number 6, that is, the number x such that $x * 6 = e$, where e is the number found in **(c)** above.

4 An operation $*$ is defined on the *non-negative* real numbers by the formula $a * b = \sqrt{(a^2+b^2)}$

(a) Calculate (i) $3 * 4$ (ii) $(3 * 4) * 12$ (iii) $3 * (4 * 12)$
(b) What property do your results to **(a)** illustrate?
(c) Find an element e such that for every element x, $e * x = x$
(d) Show that just one non-negative real number has an inverse with respect to this operation.

5 We define $a \sim b$ to mean the positive (or zero) difference between a and b. We consider this operation in the set $\{0, 1, 2, 3, 4, 5, \dots\}$. For example $2 \sim 7 = 5$, $10 \sim 1 = 9$.

(a) Find numbers a, b, c such that

$$a \sim (b \sim c) \neq (a \sim b) \sim c$$

showing clearly that the numbers that you have given have this property.
(b) Show that there is an identity element.
(c) What can you say about the inverses of the numbers in this set?
(d) Find the solution sets of each of the following equations
(i) $x \sim x = 4$
(ii) $6 \sim x = 3$
(iii) $6 \sim (y \sim 5) = 3$

6 The notation $a * b$ will be used to mean the average of two numbers a and b, that is $a * b = \dfrac{a+b}{2}$

(a) Solve the following equations
(i) $x * 5 = 7$
(ii) $(2 * y) * 7 = 5$
(iii) $z * (3 * 8) = -2$

(b) Is it possible to find an identity element for this operation? If so, state its value, or if not, explain why an identity does not exist.

(c) If $(a * b) * c = a * (b * c)$, what can you deduce about a, b and c?

7 A set P is $\{2, 4, 6, 8, 10, 12\}$. The operation $*$ is defined as follows: if a and b are any elements of P, then $a * b$ denotes the remainder when the result of multiplying a by b is divided by 14; for example

$$6 * 12 = 2$$

(a) Find the identity element of P, that is, the element e such that $e * a = a$ for every element a of the set.

(b) Find the inverse of 10, that is, the element y such that $y * 10 = e$ where e is the identity element.

(c) Solve the equation $10 * x = 4$ by multiplying both sides of the equation by the value of y found above.

(d) Use a similar technique to solve the equation $6 * x = 2$

(e) Find two solutions of the equation $x * x = 4$

3.3 Worked examples

We have been studying systems in which we have been given the elements and the various rules of combination. In most cases we have used either numerical examples (e.g. modular arithmetics) or geometric examples (e.g. operations on an equilateral triangle). However, in the examinations, the questions appear to have a more abstract look and tend to be concerned with whether or not a certain set of elements do, or do not form a group (ring, field and so on) given a rule (or rules) of combination. In this case, we look carefully to see whether any group laws are violated. In fact, the law which is often the cause of trouble is the one saying that there must be a *unique* identity for the system.

Example 1

Three distinct elements a, b, c are subject to a law of combination $*$ for which

$$a * c = c * a = a, \qquad b * c = c * b = b, \qquad a * a = c.$$

Prove that they do not form a group: Keeping the first two relations, suggest an alternative value for $a * a$ under which the elements would form a group.

Since there are only three elements in the set, it is an easy matter to make up the table of combination and fill in the values given.

			1st	
	$*$	a	b	c
	a	c		a
2nd	b			b
	c	a	b	

We know that in a group table, the elements in a row (or column) are all different. Hence we require the top row to contain b. But in this case, the second column would contain two bs which is not allowed. Hence the elements under this rule do not form a group (since if $b * a = b$ and $b * c = b$, then $a = c$, but a, c are distinct—given). The only group containing three elements is the cyclic group so given

		1st		
	$*$	a	b	c
	a			a
2nd	b			b
	c	a	b	

We know that $c * c$ must be c, then $b * b = a$ and $a * a = b$.

Example 2

The binary operation $*$ on the set $\mathbb{R}$ of all real numbers is defined by $a * b = a+b+2$. Determine whether the operation is
(i) commutative **(ii)** associative **(iii)** Investigate also the existence of a neutral element and an inverse element to a.

Another binary operation $\circ$ is defined on $\mathbb{R}$ by $a \circ b = \frac{1}{2}(a+b)$. Investigate whether
(a) $\circ$ is distributive over $*$ **(b)** $*$ is distributive over $\circ$. (M.E.I.)

(i) If the operation $*$ is commutative, then $a * b = b * a$. Now

$$a * b = a+b+2, \qquad b * a = b+a+2$$

Since in $\mathbb{R}$ $a+b = b+a$, then $a * b = b * a$.

(ii) If the operation is associative $a * (b * c) = (a * b) * c$. Now

$$\begin{aligned} a * (b * c) &= a * (b+c+2) \\ &= a+b+c+2+2 \\ &= a+b+c+4 \\ (a * b) * c &= (a+b+2) * c \\ &= a+b+2+c+2 \\ &= a+b+c+4 \end{aligned}$$

Hence the operation is associative.

(iii) If there is a neutral element e then $a * e = e * a = a$. Now

$$a * e = a+e+2 = a, \qquad \text{so } e = -2$$

The inverse of a, a^{-1} is such that $a * a^{-1} = a^{-1} * a = e$. I.e.

$$a * a^{-1} = a+a^{-1}+2 = e = -2$$

so

$$a^{-1} = -a-4$$

(a) If $\circ$ is distributive over $*$, then

$$a \circ (b * c) = (a \circ b) * (a \circ c)$$

Now $$a \circ (b+c+2) = \tfrac{1}{2}(a+b+c+2)$$

$$a \circ b = \tfrac{1}{2}(a+b), \qquad a \circ c = \tfrac{1}{2}(a+c)$$

therefore $$(a \circ b) * (a \circ c) = \tfrac{1}{2}(a+b)+\tfrac{1}{2}(a+c)+2$$

This is not equal to $a \circ (b * c)$. Hence $\circ$ is not distributive over $*$.

(b) If $*$ is distributive over $\circ$ we have

$$a * (b \circ c) = (a * b) \circ (a * c)$$

Now $$a * (b \circ c) = a * [\tfrac{1}{2}(b+c)]$$
$$= a+\tfrac{1}{2}(b+c)+2$$

$$(a * b) \circ (a * c) = (a+b+2) \circ (a+c+2)$$
$$= \tfrac{1}{2}[a+b+2+a+c+2]$$
$$= a+\tfrac{1}{2}(b+c)+2$$

Hence $*$ is distributive over $\circ$.

Example 3

The set R consists of all ordered pairs of integers with the second integer even, i.e. all pairs $(m, 2n)$ where m and n are integers. The subset S of R consists of all pairs $(m, 0)$ where m is an integer. Operations of addition and multiplication on R are defined by setting

$$(m_1, 2n_1)+(m_2, 2n_2) = (m_1-m_2, 2n_1+2n_2)$$

$$(m_1, 2n_1)\times(m_2, 2n_2) = (m_1m_2, 4n_1n_2)$$

for all $(m_1, 2n_1), (m_2, 2n_2) \in$ R.

(i) Is the system (R, +, $\times$) closed, associative, commutative with respect to each operation?

(ii) Is multiplication distributive over addition in (R, +, $\times$)?

(iii) Does (R, +, $\times$) have an identity element with respect to multiplication?

Answer the same questions for the subsystem (S, +, $\times$).

(i) Since combination (either + or $\times$) of even numbers gives another even number, and subtraction or multiplication of integers gives another integer, the system (R, +, $\times$) is closed.

If the system is associative under +

$$(m_1, 2n_1)+[(m_2, 2n_2)+(m_3, 2n_3)] = [(m_1, 2n_1)+(m_2, 2n_2)]+(m_3, 2n_3)$$

Now $$(m_1, 2n_1)+[(m_2, 2n_2)+(m_3, 2n_3)] = (m_1, 2n_1)+(m_2-m_3, 2n_2+2n_3)$$
$$= (m_1-m_2+m_3, 2n_1+2n_2+2n_3)$$

Also $$[(m_1, 2n_1)+(m_2, 2n_2)]+(m_3, 2n_3) = (m_1-m_2, 2n_1+2n_2)+(m_3, 2n_3)$$
$$= (m_1-m_2-m_3, 2n_1+2n_2+2n_3)$$

Hence the system is not associative under +.

If the system is associative under ×

$$(m_1, 2n_1)\times[(m_2, 2n_2)\times(m_3, 2n_3)] = (m_1, 2n_1)\times(m_2m_3, 4n_2n_3)$$
$$= (m_1m_2m_3, 8n_1n_2n_3)$$

which is clearly equal to

$$[(m_1, 2n_1)\times(m_2, 2n_2)]\times(m_3, 2n_3)$$

so the system is associative under ×.

If the system is commutative under +

$$(m_1, 2n_1)+(m_2, 2n_2) = (m_2, 2n_2)+(m_1, 2n_1)$$

Now $$(m_1, 2n_1)+(m_2, 2n_2) = (m_1-m_2, 2n_1+2n_2)$$

and $$(m_2, 2n_2)+(m_1, 2n_1) = (m_2-m_1, 2n_2+2n_1)$$

Hence the operation is not commutative under +.

If the system is commutative under ×

$$(m_1, 2n_1)\times(m_2, 2n_2) = (m_1m_2, 4n_1n_2) = (m_2, 2n_2)\times(m_1, 2n_1)$$

and so the operation is commutative under ×.

(ii) *If multiplication is distributive over addition*

$$(m_1, 2n_1)[(m_2, 2n_2)+(m_3, 2n_3)] = (m_1, 2n_1)(m_2, 2n_2)+(m_1, 2n_1)(m_3, 2n_3)$$

Now

$$(m_1, 2n_1)[(m_2, 2n_2)+(m_3, 2n_3)] = (m_1, 2n_1)(m_2-m_3, 2n_2+2n_3)$$
$$= (m_1m_2-m_1m_3, 4n_1n_2+4n_1n_3)$$

Also

$$(m_1, 2n_1)(m_2, 2n_2)+(m_1, 2n_1)(m_3, 2n_3) = (m_1m_2, 4n_1n_2)+(m_1m_3, 4n_1n_3)$$
$$= (m_1m_2-m_1m_3, 4n_1n_2+4n_1n_3)$$

So multiplication is distributive over addition.

(iii) *Suppose the identity is* $(e, 2f)$

then $$(m_1, 2n_1)\times(e, 2f) = (m_1, 2n_1)$$

i.e. $$(m_1e, 4n_1f) = (m_1, 2n_1)$$
$$e = 1, \quad f = \tfrac{1}{2}$$

i.e. the identity would be (1, 1) but this does *not* belong to R, so there is no identity.

If we consider the system (S, +, ×)

(a) it is closed under + and ×
(b) it is not associative under +
(c) it is associative under ×
(d) it is not commutative under +
(e) it is commutative under ×
(f) Multiplication is distributive over addition

Finally, (1, 0) will be the identity, since $(m_1, 0)\times(1, 0) = (m_1, 0)$.

Miscellaneous examination questions 12

1 The set of ordered pairs (a, b) where a, b are real numbers and $a \neq 0$, forms a group under the operation $*$ defined by

$$(a_1, b_1) * (a_2, b_2) = (a_1a_2, a_1b_2 + b_1)$$

Find **(a)** the identity element, and **(b)** the inverse of (a, b). (S.M.P.)

2 The operations $\circ$ and $*$ are defined by the tables

	$\circ$	RIGHT a	b	c	d
LEFT	a	a	c	d	a
	b	b	a	c	d
	c	d	b	a	c
	d	c	d	b	a

	$*$	RIGHT a	b	c	d
LEFT	a	b	c	d	a
	b	c	d	a	b
	c	d	a	b	c
	d	a	b	c	d

(For example, $a \circ d = a$)

Give the complete solution set for x in each of the following:

(a) $b \circ x = c$ **(b)** $(a \circ x) * c = a$

(c) $(a \circ x) * b = c$ **(d)** $[a * (x \circ b)] \circ c = b$ (S.M.P.)

3 a and b are elements of a group with identity element e. If

$$a^3 = b^2 = e \qquad \text{and} \qquad ba = a^2b$$

(a) prove that $(ba)^2 = e$, and **(b)** find the simplest form of $(bab)^{-1}$. (S.M.P.)

4 A law of combination for two vectors $\boldsymbol{a}$ and $\boldsymbol{b}$ is defined by $\boldsymbol{a} \circ \boldsymbol{b} = ab \sin\theta$ where a, b are the magnitudes of $\boldsymbol{a}, \boldsymbol{b}$ and where θ is the angle between the vectors. Assuming that $\circ$ is distributive over addition show by combining $\boldsymbol{a} + \boldsymbol{b}$ with itself, that $\circ$ is not commutative. Suggest a suitable convention for measuring θ. (S.M.P.)

5 Compile operation tables for

(a) $\{1, 2\}$ under multiplication, mod 3

(b) $\{0, 1\}$ under addition mod 2

Write down all possible ordered pairs whose first element belongs to the set $\{1, 2\}$ and whose second element belongs to the set $\{0, 1\}$. Compile an operation table for these ordered pairs under the operation defined by

$$(x_1y_1) * (x_2y_2) = (x_1x_2, y_1 + y_2)$$

State the identity element and give a general proof of the associativity of the operation $*$. (S.M.P.)

6 Define an isomorphism of two groups. Prove that all groups consisting of two elements are isomorphic. (S.M.P.)

7 A binary operation $\otimes$ is defined on the set of all ordered pairs (x, y) of real numbers such that $y \neq 0$ by setting

$$(x_1y_1) \otimes (x_2y_2) = (x_1 + y_1x_2, y_1y_2)$$

Prove that the set of pairs with this operation forms a group. Is this group Abelian?

Does the subset consisting of all pairs of the form $(0, y)$ with $y \neq 0$ form a subgroup? (M.E.I.)

8 Show that all groups of order 3 are isomorphic. Prove that the set of permutations of three letters forms a group of order 6 under a law of composition to be stated explicitly. Find a subgroup of order 3. (C.)

9 Prove that the set $\{1, 2, 4, 7, 8, 11, 13, 14\}$ (consisting of numbers less than 15 and prime to it) forms a group under multiplication modulo 15.

There are three subgroups each consisting of 1, 4 and two other elements. Identify these subgroups and prove that two of them are isomorphic. (C.)

10(a) The set $\{e, a, b, c\}$ forms a group under the binary operation $*$ and e is the neutral element. Prove, explaining your reasoning carefully, that if $a * a = b * b = e$, then $c * c = e$ also, and give the combination table in full. Show also how to build up the combination table of the group for which $a * a = e$, but neither $b * b$ nor $c * c$ is equal to e.

(b) Find the values of the real numbers x and y so that $\{1, x + jy, x - jy\}$ form a group under the operation of multiplication of complex numbers.

11(a) The operation $\circ$ is defined on the set $\mathbb{R}'$ of non-negative real numbers by $m \circ n = \sqrt{(m^2 + n^2)}$. Determine whether the operation (i) is commutative (ii) is associative, and (iii) has an identity in $\mathbb{R}'$.

If the operation is applied to the set $\mathbb{Z}^+$ of positive integers, show that $m \circ n \in \mathbb{Z}^+$ if $n = \frac{1}{2}(m^2 - 1)$ and state the condition this imposes on m. Find the relation between the integers p, q, r if $m = p + q$, $n = q + r$ and $m \circ n = p + q + r$.

(b) Let A be the set of all numbers of the form $a + b\sqrt{2}$ where a and b are non-negative integers. Determine whether A is closed under the operations of subtraction, multiplication and division. Investigate also the operation of finding the positive square root. (M.E.I.)

12 Let e be a left-identity element of a group G with the operation of multiplication (i.e. an element such that $ea = a$ for every a in G) and, for each a in G let a_L be a left inverse of a in G (i.e. an element of G such that $a_L a = e$).

By considering the expression $b(a_L a a_L)$ where b is the left inverse of a_L show that $a a_L = e$. Deduce that e is also a right identity element (i.e. that $ae = a$ for every a in G).

Show further that

(a) e is unique

(b) e is the only idempotent element of the group (i.e. the only element x satisfying $xx = x$).

(c) if $(ab)^n = e$ for some natural number n, then $(ba)^n = e$ (J.M.B.)

13 The elements of the set of all positive integers $\{1, 2, 3, \ldots\}$ are subjected to a binary operation $*$ for which $a * b$ means the greater of a or b or the integer a itself when $a = b$. Determine whether the binary operation on this set satisfies the conditions of

(a) closure **(b)** associativity **(c)** existence of an identity element **(d)** existence of an inverse for each element of the set.

Determine also the corresponding results when the set is replaced by the set $\{1, \frac{1}{2}, \frac{1}{3} \ldots\}$ of the reciprocals of the positive integers. (C.)

14 The set $\mathbb{Z}$ consists of all integers (positive, zero and negative). Operations of 'addition' $\oplus$ and 'multiplication' $\otimes$ are defined on $\mathbb{Z}$ as follows

$$m \oplus n = m+n+1, \qquad m \otimes n = m+n-mn$$

Show that the system $(\mathbb{Z}, \oplus, \otimes)$ is closed, commutative and associative with respect to each operation, and that 'multiplication' is distributive over 'addition'. Show also that each operation has an identity element in $\mathbb{Z}$ and find them. Determine whether each element of $\mathbb{Z}$ has an inverse with respect to each operation. (M.E.I.)

15 The operation $\circ$ is defined on the number pairs

$$A \equiv (a_1, a_2) \qquad \text{and} \qquad B \equiv (b_1, b_2)$$

so that $A \circ B = (a_1+b_2, a_2+b_1)$ and $A = B$ if and only if $a_1 = b_1$ and $a_2 = b_2$. Find whether the operation is associative.

Find P such that $A \circ P = A$, and Q such that $Q \circ A = A$, and determine whether I, J can be found such that for all A, $A \circ I = A$ and $J \circ A = A$.

Given that $A^* = (-a_2, -a_1)$ discuss the following:

$$B \circ A = C \circ A$$
$$\Rightarrow B \circ A \circ A^* = C \circ A \circ A^*$$
$$\Rightarrow B \circ (0, 0) = C \circ (0, 0)$$
$$\Rightarrow B = C$$

(M.E.I.)

16 An operation $\circ$ is defined on the set of ordered pairs of real numbers so that if $A = (a_1, a_2)$ and $B = (b_1, b_2)$ then

$$A \circ B = (a_1b_1 - a_2b_2, a_1b_2 + a_2b_1)$$

From this definition, stating any properties of the real numbers that you use, prove that the operation $\circ$ is commutative and associative. Find the identity element for $\circ$, and the inverse of A.

Determine the pair (p_1, p_2) such that

$$(-a_2, a_1) \circ (p_1, p_2) = A \circ A$$

(M.E.I.)

17 An operation $\circ$ is defined on the set of positive real numbers $\mathbb{R}^+$, by setting $x \circ y = \sqrt{(xy)}$ for all $x, y \in \mathbb{R}^+$.

(a) Is the system $(\mathbb{R}^+, \circ)$ closed with respect to the operation $\circ$?
(b) Is the operation $\circ$ commutative?
(c) Is the operation associative?
(d) Does the system $(\mathbb{R}^+, \circ)$ have an 'identity element'?

Give reasons for your answers with counter-examples where appropriate. (M.E.I.)

18 Let $\mathbb{R}$ be the set of real numbers and let S be the subset of $\mathbb{R}$ consisting of all real numbers except 1. A commutative operation $*$ is defined by the rule $a * b = a+b-ab$.

(a) Is the system $(\mathbb{R}, *)$ closed and associative?
(b) Does $(\mathbb{R}, *)$ have an identity element?
(c) Does every element of $(\mathbb{R}, *)$ have an inverse?

Answer the same three questions for the sub-system $(S, *)$.

Solve the equation

$$2 * (x * (5 * x)) = 2 * x \text{ in the system } (S, *)$$

(M.E.I.)

Chapter 13

Coordinate Geometry—3D

1 Lines in space

1.1 Points and lines

To describe a point in space

In space we fix a point by giving it three coordinates, x, y and z. If P is the point (2, 3, 1) we are showing
an 'x step' of two units
a 'y step' of three units, and
a 'z step' of one unit
from the origin (0, 0, 0), which can be illustrated like this:

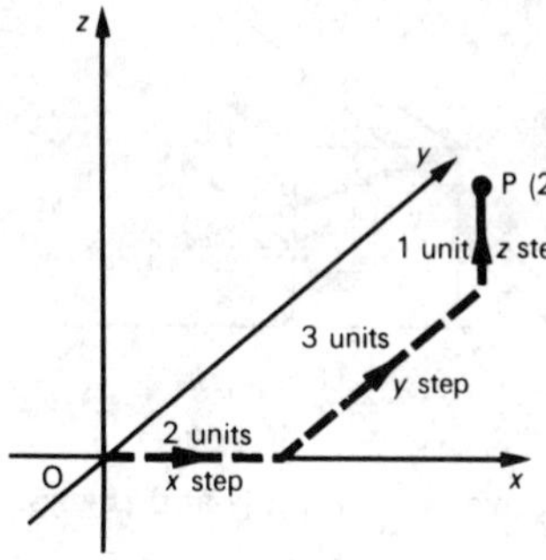

NOTE that we always show the axes in the order shown. *Do not*, by mistake, interchange the x and y axes.

The distance between points in space

Distance of a point from the origin

The distance of P(2, 3, 1) from O(0, 0, 0), using Pythagoras' theorem, is given by

$$OP^2 = OR^2 + RP^2$$
$$= (2^2 + 3^2) + 1^2$$
$$OP = \sqrt{14}$$

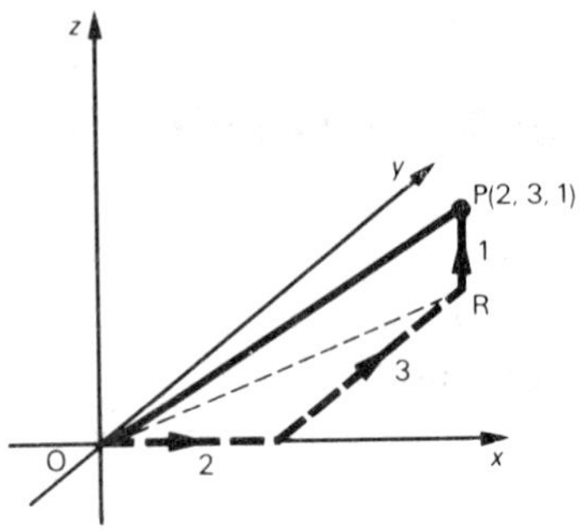

Distance between two points

Consider, for example, the distance between S(1, 3, 2) and T(5, 6, −2):
the '$x$step' is $5-1=4$,
the 'y step' is $6-3=3$ and
the 'z step' is $-2-2=-4$.

$$ST^2 = 4^2+3^2+(-4)^2$$

so $$ST = \sqrt{41}$$

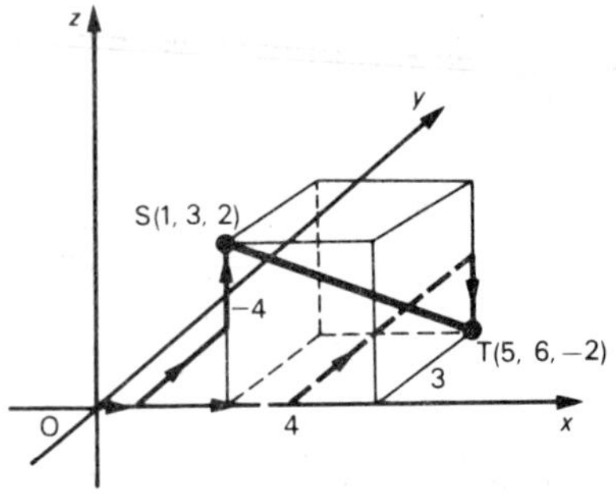

In general, the distance d between (x_1, y_1, z_1) and (x_2, y_2, z_2) is

$$\boldsymbol{d = \sqrt{[(x_1-x_2)^2+(y_1-y_2)^2+(z_1-z_2)^2]}}$$ ◀

Directions

(a) In the plane, the direction of one point from another is given by the *ratio* of the x step : y step. For instance, we say that OR in the diagram above has *direction ratio* 2 : 3.

(b) In space we extend this idea and say that the direction of one point from another, or of the line joining these points, is given by the ratios x step : y step : z step. The direction of OP is given in this case by the *direction ratios* 2 : 3 : 1. (The abbreviation DR can be used for both 'direction ratio' and the plural, 'direction ratios'.)

Example

Find the direction ratios of a line joining two points S(1, 3, 2) and T(5, 6, −2).

The 'x step' from S to T is	$5-1=4$
The 'y step' is	$6-3=3$
The 'z step' is	$-2-2=-4$

So the direction ratios of ST are $4:3:-4$.

In general, the DR of a line joining (x_1, y_1, z_1) to (x_2, y_2, z_2) are

$$(x_2-x_1):(y_2-y_1):(z_2-z_1)$$

Equations

(a) For the line OP

Consider a point K(x, y, z) on the line. There are several equal ratios (from pairs of similar triangles); i.e.

$$\frac{x}{2}=\frac{y}{3}=\frac{z}{1}$$

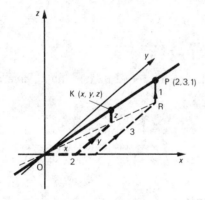

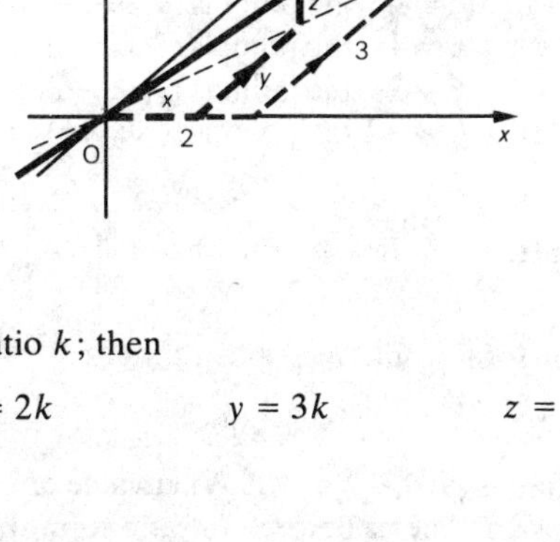

Suppose we call this ratio k; then

$$x = 2k \qquad y = 3k \qquad z = 1k$$

(b) For the line ST

Check that the direction ratios of the line were $4:3:-4$. Consider a line parallel to ST through O. It would have equation

$$\frac{x}{4}=\frac{y}{3}=\frac{z}{-4}=k$$

or $\qquad x = 4k \qquad y = 3k \qquad z = -4k$

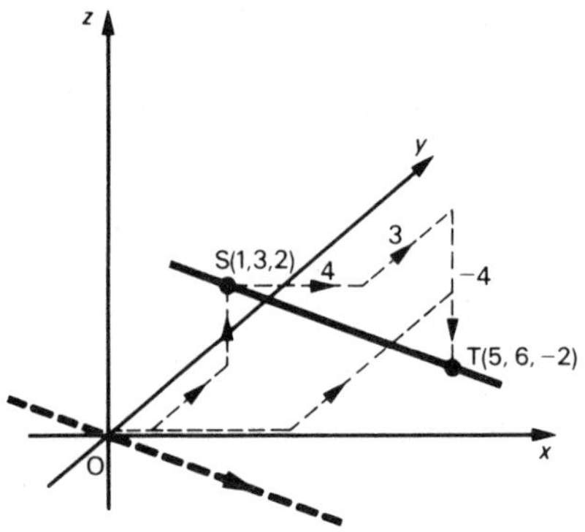

The line ST has been 'shifted' by the vector $\begin{pmatrix}1\\3\\2\end{pmatrix}$ to start at S so

$$\begin{aligned} x \text{ becomes } x &= 4k+1 \\ y \text{ becomes } y &= 3k+3 \\ z \text{ becomes } z &= -4k+2 \end{aligned}$$

or in ratio form

$$\frac{x-1}{4} = \frac{y-3}{3} = \frac{z-2}{-4} = k \tag{1}$$

Other points on the line are found by substituting different values for k. For example,

when $k = 0$ the point is (1, 3, 2) . . . S
$k = 1$ the point is (5, 6, −2) . . . T
$k = 2$ the point is (9, 9, −6)
$k = -1$ the point is (−3, 0, 6)

Suppose we had 'shifted' the line by the vector $\begin{pmatrix}5\\6\\-2\end{pmatrix}$ to start at T. The new equations in parametric form would have been

$$x = 4k+5 \qquad y = 3k+6 \qquad z = -4k-2$$

Now when $k = 0$ the point is (5, 6, −2) . . . T. What value of k would give us S? Have we the equation of the same line as before? In ratio form the line is

$$\frac{x-5}{4} = \frac{y-6}{3} = \frac{z+2}{-4} = k \tag{2}$$

NOTE. It is not obvious that the two sets of equations (1) and (2) represent identical lines. We deal with this later (page 458).

The meaning of a 'zero' direction ratio

(a) Consider the line with DR 1:0:0. This is a line parallel to the x axis. A particular line through (0, 2, 0) with DR 1:0:0 is written

$$\frac{x}{1} = \frac{y-2}{0} = \frac{z}{0} = k$$

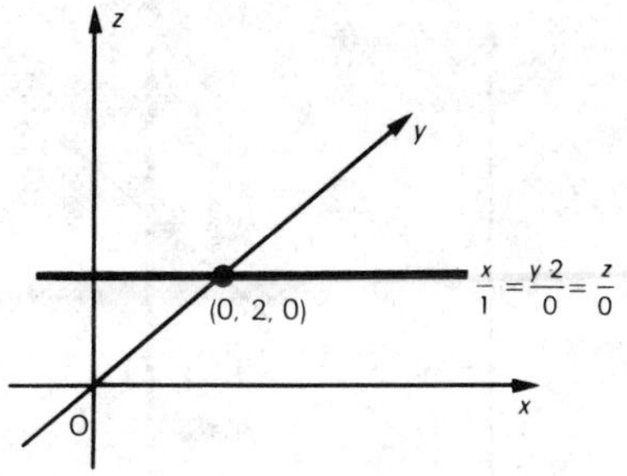

In parametric form the equations would be

$$x = k \qquad y = 2 \qquad z = 0$$

This (for different values of k) would give a line in the plane containing the x and y axes. A particular value of k gives a point on this line.

(b) Consider a line with DR 0:1:0. This is parallel to the y axis. A particular line through (0, 2, 3), for example, can be written

$$\frac{x}{0} = \frac{y-2}{1} = \frac{z-3}{0} = l$$

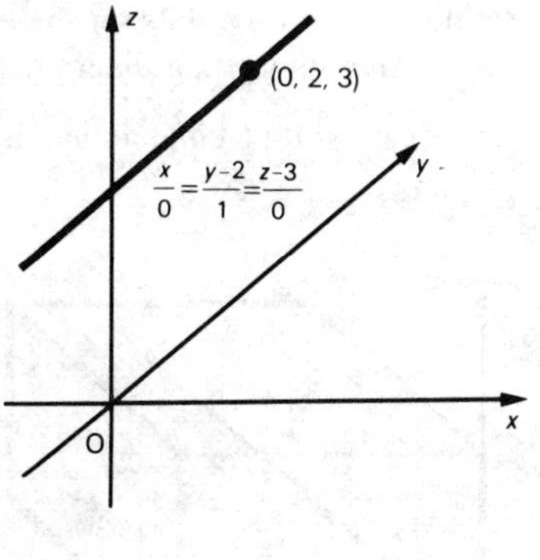

In parametric form

$$x = 0 \qquad y = l + 2 \qquad z = 3$$

This line is in the plane containing the y and z axes and is parallel to the y axis.

(c) Consider a line with DR 0:0:1. This is parallel to the z axis. Consider a particular line through (2, 3, 4) with these DR:

$$\frac{x-2}{0}=\frac{y-3}{0}=\frac{z-4}{1}=m$$

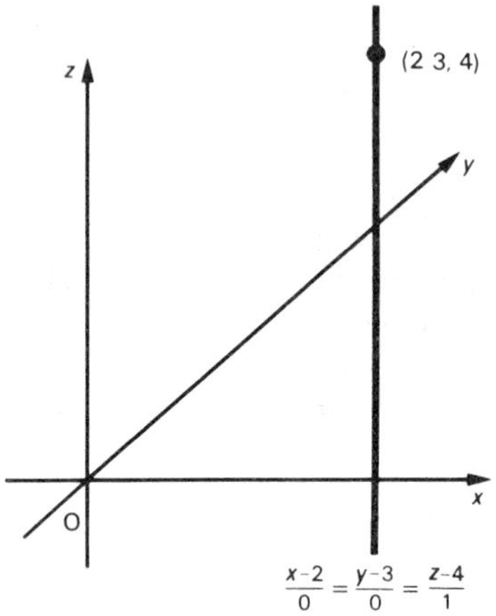

Parametrically

$$x=2 \qquad y=3 \qquad z=m+4$$

This line is in a plane parallel to the z axis.

Exercise 1.1

1 Write down the coordinates of the six points on the axes each of which is at a distance one unit from O. Show the points on a diagram.

2 A rectangular box, length 8 cm, width 6 cm, and height 5 cm, has the axes along the edges as shown.

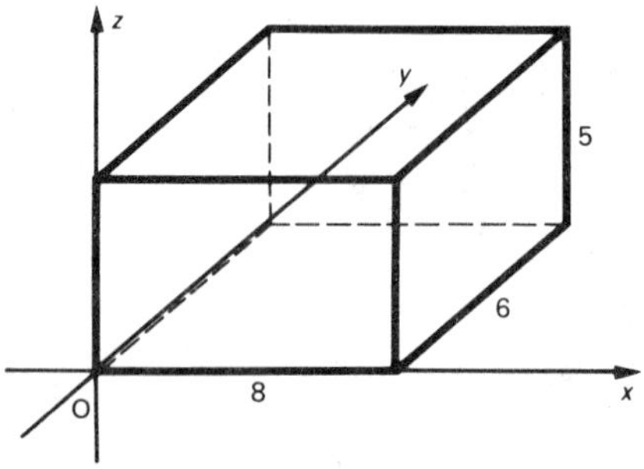

(a) Write down the coordinates of each corner of the box.
(b) Give the coordinates of the centre of each face.
(c) Write down the equation of each edge of the box.

3 ABCD is a square-based pyramid with axes as shown. AB = 2 and VO = 3.

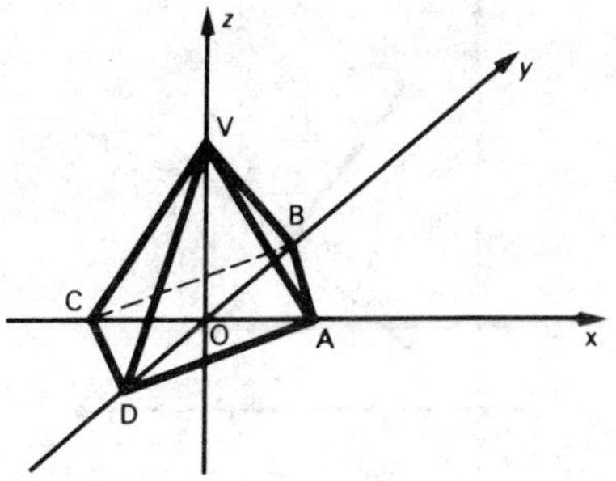

(a) Write down the coordinates of V, A. B, C and D.
(b) Write down the equation of each edge of the pyramid.

4(a) A is the point (1, 2, 3). If OA : OB : OC = 1 : 2 : 5 and O, A, B and C are collinear, find the coordinates of B and C.

(b) A is (1, 2, 3) and P is (1, 3, 5). Find the coordinates of Q and R if AP : AQ : AR = 1 : 2 : 5 and A, P, Q and R are collinear. In each case, illustrate your answer with a diagram.

5 Find the direction ratios of the lines joining

(a) (3, 0, −1) to (1, −3, 2) **(b)** (1, 3, 0) to (−4, 1, −2)

6 Find the distance between the following points, leaving your answer in square root form.

(a) (5, 1, 3) and (−1, 0, −2) **(b)** (0, 1, −2) and (3, −4, 2)

7 Write down *two* equations in ratio form for each of the lines joining

(a) (−1, 2, 0) to (3, −1, 1) **(b)** (0, 2, 3) to (−2, 2, 1)

8 Write down *two* equations in parametric form for each of the lines joining

(a) (2, 1, 3) to (−1, 2, −2) **(b)** (0, −1, 2) to (−1, −3, 2)

9 Write down the coordinates of three points on each of the following lines

(a) $\dfrac{x-1}{2}=\dfrac{y+3}{4}=\dfrac{z+1}{-1}$ **(b)** $\dfrac{x}{-3}=\dfrac{y+1}{0}=\dfrac{z-5}{2}$

(c) $x=3k-1, \quad y=2k+4, \quad z=-k+1$

(d) $x=2, \quad y=-3k+2, \quad z=k$

1.2 Two lines in space

Diagrammatically, the lines may be

(i) intersecting

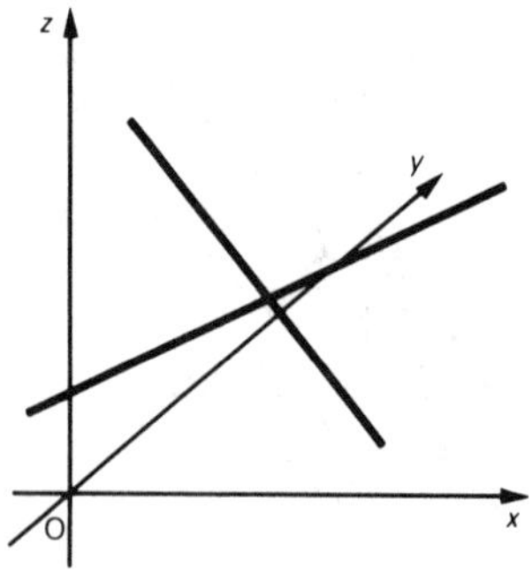

(ii) parallel

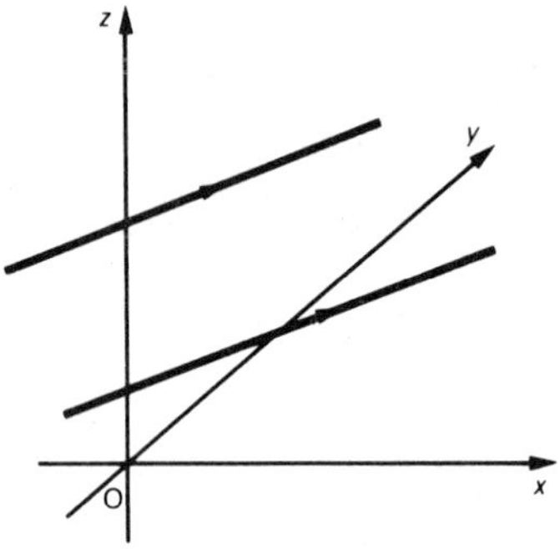

(iii) identical

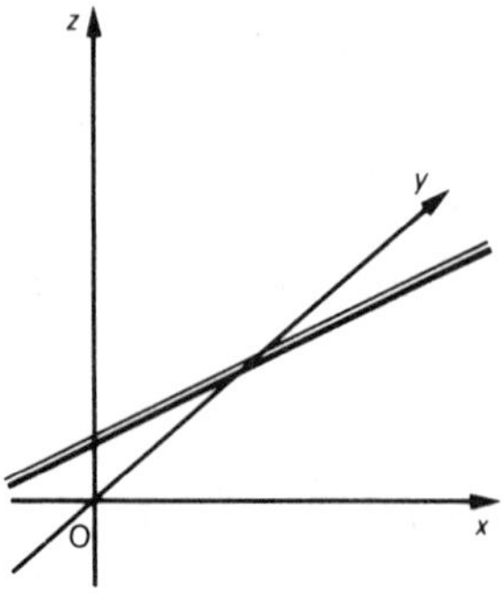

(iv) skew

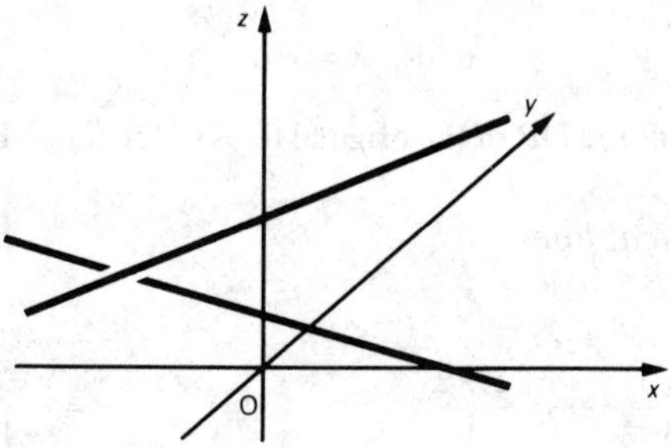

We consider parallel lines first.

Case (ii): parallel lines

Here are two lines:

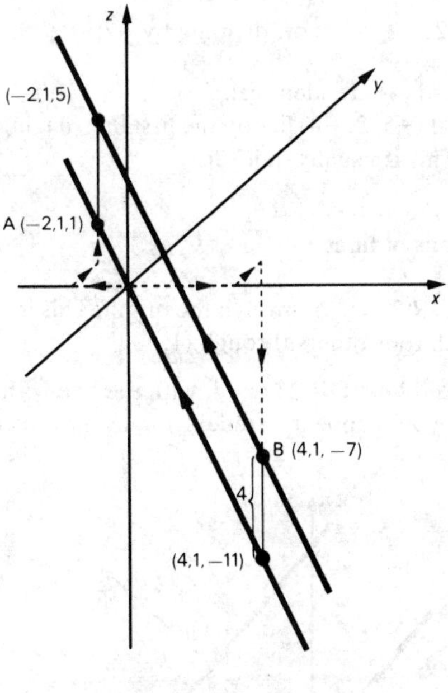

(1) $\dfrac{x+2}{-1}=\dfrac{y-1}{0}=\dfrac{z-1}{2}$ (2) $\dfrac{x-4}{2}=\dfrac{y-1}{0}=\dfrac{z+7}{-4}$

The DR of the lines are $-1:0:2$ and $2:0:-4$

Multiply the first DR by -2 (which does not change the ratio) and we have the second. Hence the lines are either parallel or identical.

There are 'obvious' points on each line:

on (1) A(−2, 1, 1) on (2) B(4, 1, −7)

The DR of AB are $6:0:-8 = 3:0:-4$

This is not the same as the DR of the original lines so the lines (1) and (2) are parallel.

Case (iii): identical lines

Consider two lines

$$(3)\quad \frac{x-1}{3}=\frac{y}{-1}=\frac{z+2}{1} \qquad (4)\quad \frac{x+5}{3}=\frac{y-2}{-1}=\frac{z+4}{1}$$

They both have the same DR: $3:-1:1$

An obvious point on (3) is

C (1, 0, −2) and on (4) D is (−5, 2, −4)

The DR of CD are

$-6:2:-2$ or, dividing by −2, $3:-1:1$

Hence the lines (3) and (4) are identical.

Or we can show that (−5, 2, −4) lies on the first line, having noticed that both lines have the same DR. This is usually quicker.

Digression: Projections of lines

Consider a line with DR $2:1:-4$ through the origin. This is our 'fixed' line. We now compare this line with four others through (1, 1, 1).

(1) Compare the fixed line, DR $2:1:-4$, with the line with DR $6:3:-12$ through (1, 1, 1). These lines would appear parallel from every direction.

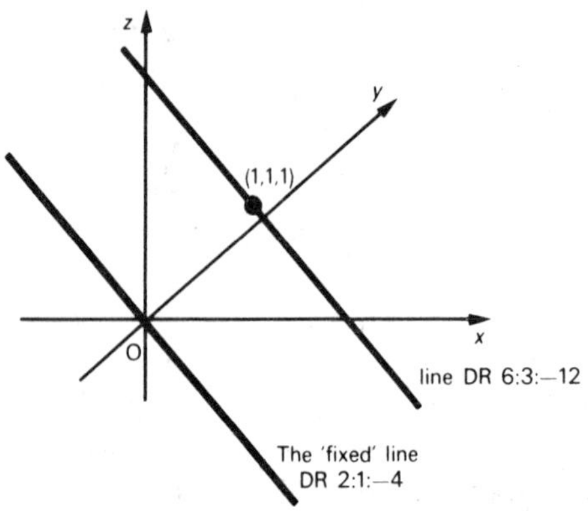

(2) Compare the fixed line DR $6:3:-12$ with a non-parallel line through $(1, 1, 1)$ with DR $6:3:-8$. Seen from vertically above, these lines would appear parallel, i.e. their 'shadows' on the x, y plane are parallel.

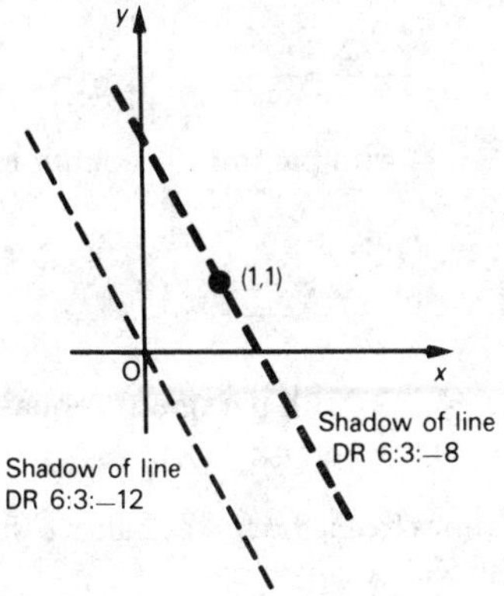

(3) Compare the fixed line DR $6:3:-12$ with a line through $(1, 1, 1)$, DR $6:2:-12$. These lines would appear parallel if viewed in the direction of the y axis, i.e. the 'shadows' in the x, z plane are parallel.

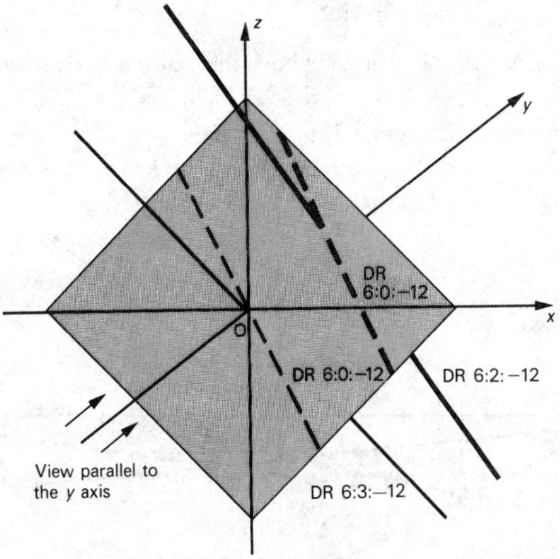

(4) A fourth line with DR $4:3:-12$ compared with the fixed line $6:3:-12$ would look parallel if viewed in the direction of the x axis.

We use these ideas when we investigate whether lines in space intersect.

Cases (i) and (iv): Intersecting lines and skew lines

We assume that you know how to deal with intersecting lines in a plane by solving the pair of simultaneous equations representing the two lines. Here we are interested in lines in space.

Consider the lines

(a) $$\frac{x-2}{3}=\frac{y+4}{1}=\frac{z-1}{-1}=k$$

This passes through (2, −4, 1) with parametric equations

$$x=3k+2, \qquad y=k-4, \qquad z=-k+1$$

and (b) $$\frac{x+1}{2}=\frac{y+4}{1}=\frac{z+2}{-2}=l$$

This passes through (−1, −4, −2) with parametric equations

$$x=2l-1, \qquad y=l-4, \qquad z=-2l-2$$

If we look at these two lines from above we shall see their shadows (or projections) on the $z=0$ plane. These will be given by

$$\frac{x-2}{3}=\frac{y+4}{1}\Rightarrow x-3y=14$$

and $$\frac{x+1}{2}=\frac{y+4}{1}\Rightarrow x-2y=7$$

These two projections intersect when

$$\left.\begin{aligned}x-3y&=14\\x-2y&=7\end{aligned}\right\}\Rightarrow x=-7, \qquad y=-7$$

The z value (or height) of each line above this point is derived as follows:

In line (a) when $x=-7$, $y=-7$, then $k=-3$ and so $z=4$
In line (b) when $x=-7$, $y=-7$, then $l=-3$ and $z=4$ again.

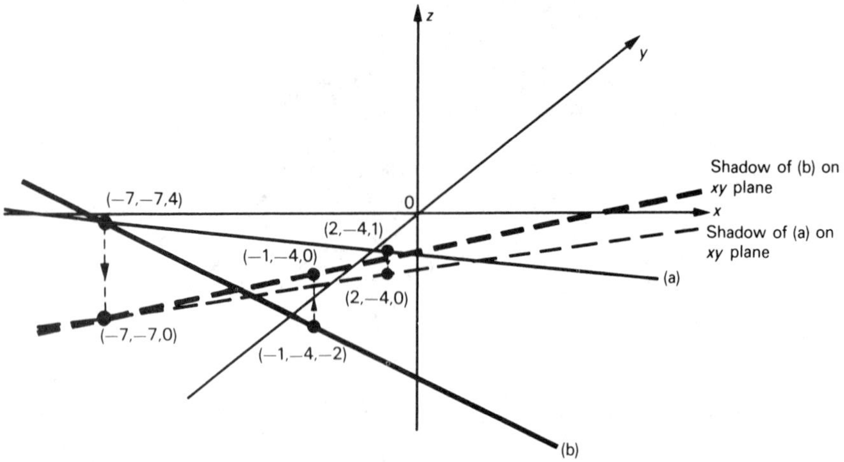

Intersecting lines and their projections

These two lines intersect at $(-7, -7, 4)$. The complete diagram is on the previous page. Below is the view of the lines from above.

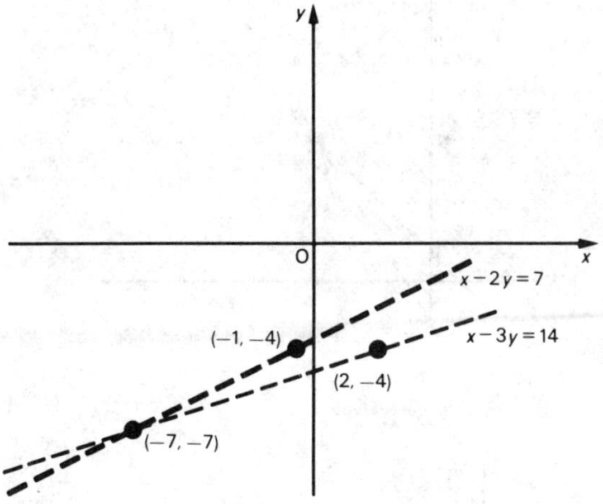

Shadow on *xy* plane

As a second example consider the lines given by

(c)
$$\frac{x-1}{1}=\frac{y+1}{2}=\frac{z+2}{3}=p \text{ (say)} \Rightarrow \left.\begin{aligned} x &= p+1 \\ y &= 2p-1 \\ z &= 3p-2 \end{aligned}\right\}$$

and (d)
$$\frac{x+1}{1}=\frac{y}{1}=\frac{z-1}{1}=q \text{ (say)} \Rightarrow \left.\begin{aligned} x &= q-1 \\ y &= q \\ z &= q+1 \end{aligned}\right\}$$

The lines are not parallel since the DR of (c) are $1:2:3$ and the DR of (d) are $1:1:1$. The projections of the lines in the plane $z = 0$ are given by

$$\left.\begin{aligned} &\frac{x-1}{1}=\frac{y+1}{2} \Rightarrow 2x-y=3 \\ \text{and} \quad &\frac{x+1}{1}=\frac{y}{1} \quad \Rightarrow x-y=-1 \end{aligned}\right\}$$

These two projections meet at (4, 5). The z value of line (c) at $x=4$, $y=5$ is given when $p = 3$, i.e. $z = 7$. For line (d) when $x = 4$, $y = 5$, $q = 5$, so z is 6. As the two z values are different, the lines do not intersect—they are *skew* lines.

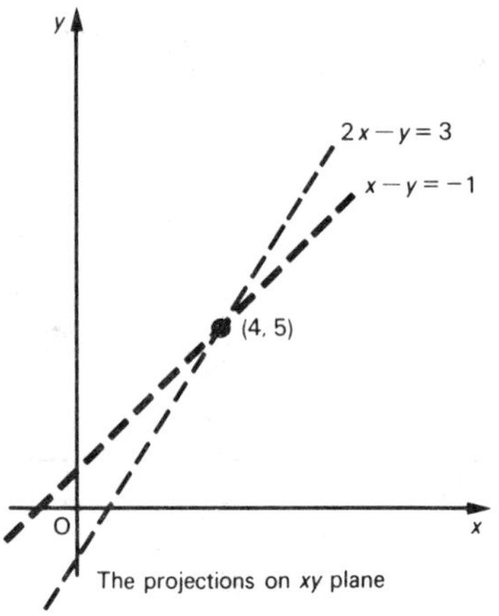

The projections on xy plane

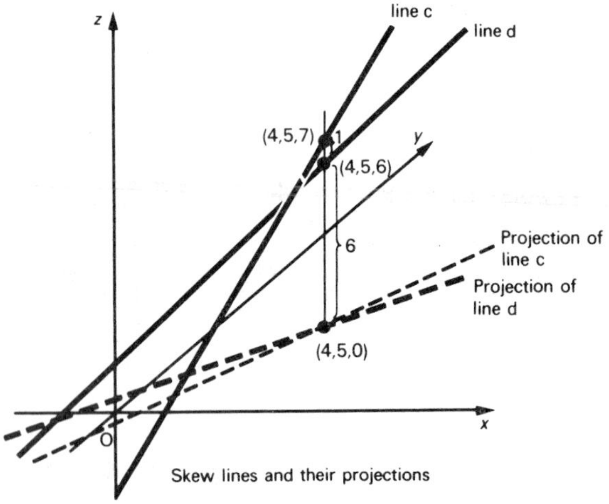

Skew lines and their projections

Exercise 1.2

1 Check whether the following three equations refer to the same or different lines

(a) $\dfrac{x-1}{2}=\dfrac{y+3}{-1}=\dfrac{z}{1}$ **(b)** $\dfrac{x}{2}=\dfrac{y-1}{-1}=\dfrac{z+1}{1}$ **(c)** $\dfrac{x+1}{2}=\dfrac{y-2}{-1}=\dfrac{z-1}{1}$

2 Write down the equation of the line through $(-1, 2, 3)$ parallel to

$$\frac{x}{-1}=\frac{y+1}{2}=\frac{z-1}{3}$$

Find the coordinates of three points on the line.

3 Find the point of intersection of the two lines

$$\frac{x-5}{4}=\frac{y-7}{4}=\frac{z+3}{-5} \quad \text{and} \quad \frac{x-8}{7}=\frac{y-4}{1}=\frac{z-5}{3}$$

4 Show that the following two lines do not intersect

$$\frac{x-10}{1}=\frac{y-9}{3}=\frac{z+2}{-2} \quad \text{and} \quad \frac{x+1}{2}=\frac{y-12}{4}=\frac{z-5}{1}$$

5 Find the equation of the line through the origin and through the point of intersection of the lines joining (0, 1, 1) to (3, 7, 10) and (−3, 1, 0) to (3, 4, 6).

1.3 Perpendicular lines in space

Remembering that two lines, in a plane, with DR $l_1 : m_1$ and $l_2 : m_2$, are perpendicular if $l_1 l_2 + m_1 m_2 = 0$, it would seem likely that if the perpendicular lines in space had DR $l_1 : m_1 : n_1$ and $l_2 : m_2 : n_2$ then the condition for them to be at right angles would be $l_1 l_2 + m_1 m_2 + n_1 n_2 = 0$. We shall show later on that this is true.

A model

We first of all discuss easy ideas of perpendicular lines (in space). We found the work simpler to understand using a model—a knitting needle and several discs cut from stiff paper.

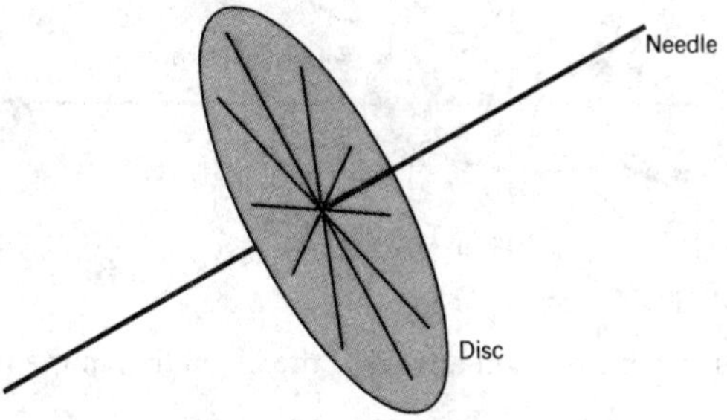

If the disc is arranged at right angles to the needle then *all lines* on the disc and through its centre are perpendicular to the needle. We shall call the lines on the disc 'spokes' whilst the needle represents a line. The disc can slide along the line as required. For example, if we wish to find the perpendicular to a given line passing through a given point, we can imagine sliding the disc until it passes through the given point and then drawing in the line:

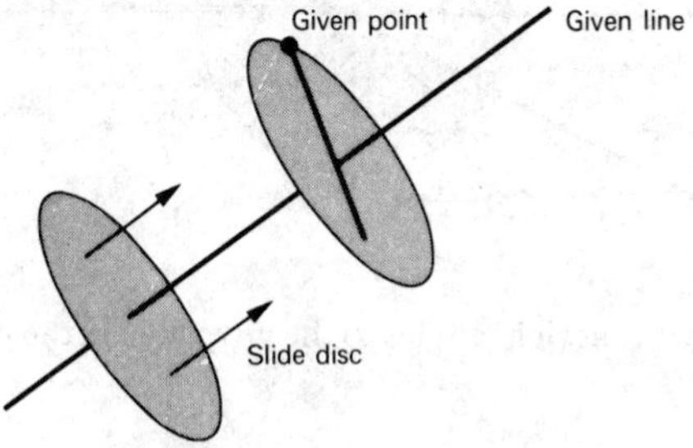

Quite often we shall need to pick out a special line on our disc; for example, visualize the line on our disc which is *horizontal*. This can be done by using two half-discs.

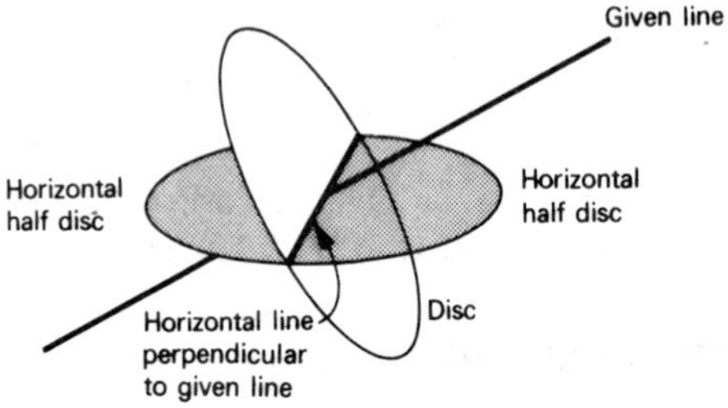

To find out more about the DR of the spokes we consider an example. Suppose our given line has DR 3 : 2 : 1, we then consider the spokes in the planes $z = 0$, $y = 0$ and $x = 0$. The diagrams are as follows, with the disc's centre being the origin.

The line AB is the line at right angles to the given line in the plane $z = 0$. Its DR are 2 : −3 : 0.

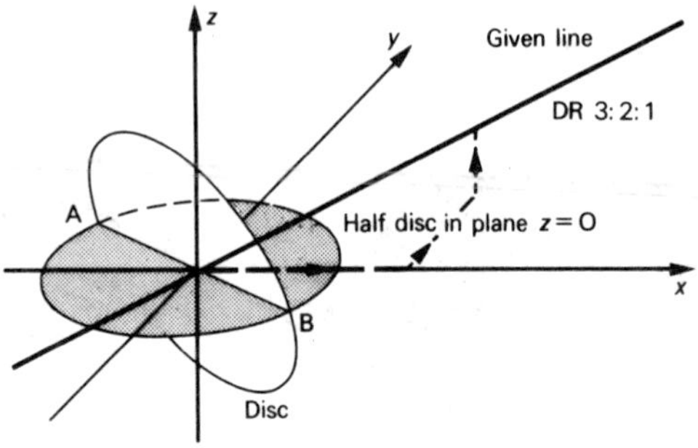

The line CD is the line at right angles to the given line in the plane $y = 0$. Its DR are 1 : 0 : −3.

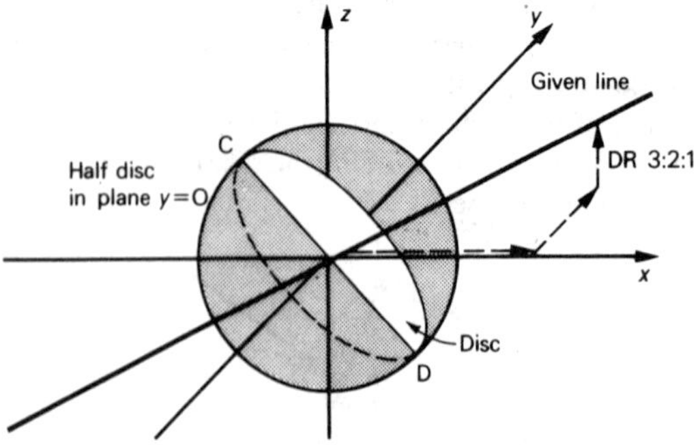

The line EF is the line at right angles to the given line in the plane $x = 0$. Its DR are 0 : 1 : −2.

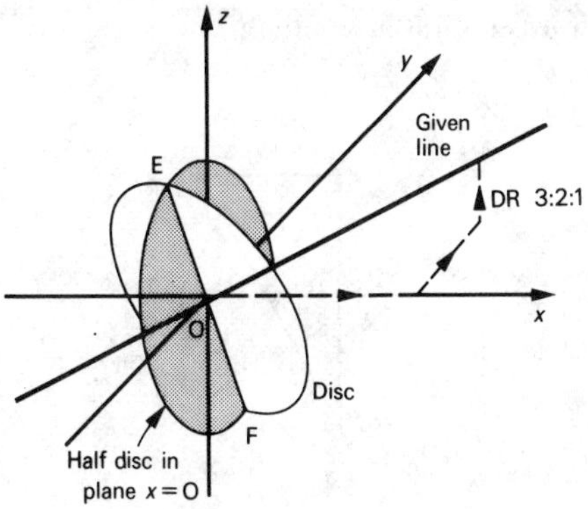

We have seen that the line with DR 3 : 2 : 1 is perpendicular to the lines with DRs

$$2:-3:0 \qquad 1:0:-3 \qquad 0:1:-2$$

It seems that if the line is perpendicular to a line with DR $l:m:n$ then

$$3l+2m+1n = 0$$

Would it matter if our disc had not been at the origin? No, the *position* of the lines would alter, but not their DR. We now investigate this further in the general case.

Perpendicular lines

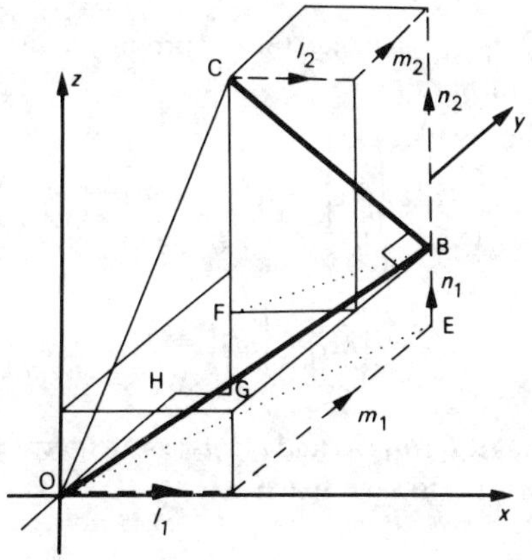

Suppose OB (DR $l_1:m_1:n_1$) is perpendicular to BC (DR $l_2:m_2:n_2$). Let B be (l_1, m_1, n_1), and C be $(l_1+l_2, m_1+m_2, n_1+n_2)$. Then in $\triangle$OBE

$$OB^2 = l_1^2+m_1^2+n_1^2$$

In $\triangle$BCF

$$BC^2 = l_2^2+m_2^2+n_2^2$$

So

$$OC^2 = l_1^2+m_1^2+n_1^2+l_2^2+m_2^2+n_2^2$$

Continue CF downwards until it meets the plane $z = 0$ at G. Draw in the triangle OHG:

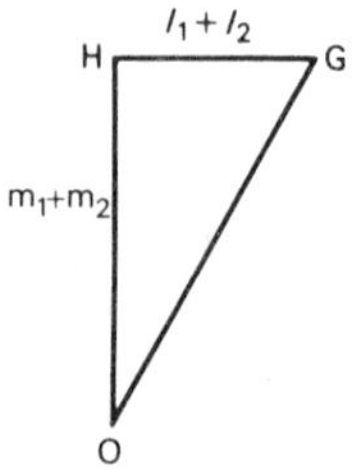

$$\mathrm{OG}^2 = (m_1+m_2)^2+(l_1+l_2)^2$$

In △OCG

$$\mathrm{OC}^2 = (m_1+m_2)^2+(l_1+l_2)^2+(n_1+n_2)^2$$

so

$$l_1^2+m_1^2+n_1^2+l_2^2+m_2^2+n_2^2 = l_1^2+2l_1l_2+l_2^2+m_1^2+2m_1m_2+m_2^2+n_1^2+2n_1n_2+n_2^2$$

and hence $$\boldsymbol{l_1l_2+m_1m_2+n_1n_2 = 0}$$ ◀

NOTE In the diagram l_2 and m_2 are negative.

The dot product

The number $l_1l_2+m_1n._2+n_1n_2$ is called the dot product of the DR and can be written with the DR in vector form as

$$\begin{pmatrix} \boldsymbol{l_1} \\ \boldsymbol{m_1} \\ \boldsymbol{n_1} \end{pmatrix} \cdot \begin{pmatrix} \boldsymbol{l_2} \\ \boldsymbol{m_2} \\ \boldsymbol{n_2} \end{pmatrix} = \boldsymbol{l_1l_2+m_1m_2+n_1n_2}$$ ◀

If
$$\begin{pmatrix} l_1 \\ m_1 \\ n_1 \end{pmatrix} \cdot \begin{pmatrix} l_2 \\ m_2 \\ n_2 \end{pmatrix} = 0$$

then the two lines with DR $l_1:m_1:n_1$ and $l_2:m_2:n_2$ are perpendicular. We may write this $(l_1:m_1:n_1)\cdot(l_2:m_2:n_2)$ to save space.

Examples

(1) Suppose two lines have DR $1:-1:3$ and $2:0:-1$. Then

$$\begin{pmatrix} 1 \\ -1 \\ 3 \end{pmatrix} \cdot \begin{pmatrix} 2 \\ 0 \\ -1 \end{pmatrix} = 1\times2+(-1)\times0+3\times(-1) = -1$$

and so the lines are *not* perpendicular.

(2) Suppose the lines have DR $1:-1:3$ and $3:9:2$. Then

$$\begin{pmatrix}1\\-1\\3\end{pmatrix}\cdot\begin{pmatrix}3\\9\\2\end{pmatrix} = 1\times3+(-1)\times9+3\times2 = 0$$

and this time the lines *are* perpendicular.

To find the condition that a line should be perpendicular to two other lines in space

Consider two intersecting lines with DR $l_1:m_1:n_1$ and $l_2:m_2:n_2$.

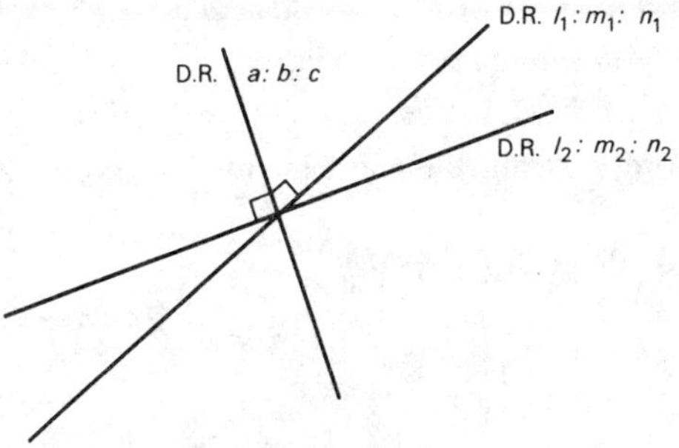

The line we are interested in has been given DR $a:b:c$ and we hope to find some condition satisfied by a, b, c. Now our line is perpendicular to each of the other lines and so

$$l_1a+m_1b+n_1c = 0 \qquad \text{and} \qquad l_2a+m_2b+n_2c = 0$$

We only have two equations to find a, b and c but we are really interested in the ratio $a:b:c$ so we rewrite the equations are

$$l_1A+m_1B+n_1 = 0 \qquad\qquad l_2A+m_2B+n_2 = 0$$

where $A = a/c$ and $B = b/c$. Solving the equations simultaneously gives

$$A = \frac{m_1n_2-m_2n_1}{l_1m_2-l_2m_1} \qquad \text{and} \qquad B = \frac{n_1l_2-n_2l_1}{l_1m_2-l_2m_1}$$

and hence the ratios $a:b:c$ are given by

$$a:b:c = (m_1n_2-m_2n_1):(n_1l_2-n_2l_1):(l_1m_2-l_2m_1)$$

The cross product

The direction of the line which is perpendicular to two other lines is extremely important, being the basis of much of the more advanced work on vectors and mechanics, besides being used in coordinate geometry in 3D. The direction of the line is given by the *cross product* of the DR, which is defined by

$$\begin{pmatrix} l_1 \\ m_1 \\ n_1 \end{pmatrix} \times \begin{pmatrix} l_2 \\ m_2 \\ n_2 \end{pmatrix} = \begin{pmatrix} \begin{vmatrix} m_1 & m_2 \\ n_1 & n_2 \end{vmatrix} \\ \\ \begin{vmatrix} n_1 & n_2 \\ l_1 & l_2 \end{vmatrix} \\ \\ \begin{vmatrix} l_1 & l_2 \\ m_1 & m_2 \end{vmatrix} \end{pmatrix}$$

where $\begin{vmatrix} m_1 & m_2 \\ n_1 & n_2 \end{vmatrix}$ is the *determinant* of the matrix $\begin{pmatrix} m_1 & m_2 \\ n_1 & n_2 \end{pmatrix}$ and equals $m_1n_2 - m_2n_1$.

Notice the cyclic order! Again, this may be written $(l_1 : m_1 : n_1) \times (l_2 : m_2 : n_2)$ to save space. For example

$$\begin{pmatrix} 2 \\ -1 \\ 0 \end{pmatrix} \times \begin{pmatrix} 1 \\ 3 \\ -1 \end{pmatrix} = \begin{pmatrix} 1-0 \\ 0+2 \\ 6+1 \end{pmatrix} = \begin{pmatrix} 1 \\ 2 \\ 7 \end{pmatrix} \Rightarrow (2:-1:0) \times (1:3:-1) = 1:2:7$$

It is advisable to check, using the dot product, that this is perpendicular to each of the other lines in turn:

$$\begin{pmatrix} 2 \\ -1 \\ 0 \end{pmatrix} \cdot \begin{pmatrix} 1 \\ 2 \\ 7 \end{pmatrix} = 0 \qquad \text{and} \qquad \begin{pmatrix} 1 \\ 3 \\ -1 \end{pmatrix} \cdot \begin{pmatrix} 1 \\ 2 \\ 7 \end{pmatrix} = 0$$

Exercise 1.3

1 Find the direction ratios of the line perpendicular to the lines with DR $1:2:-1$ and $3:0:2$.

2 Find the DR of the line perpendicular to the lines joining $(1, 0, 3)$ to $(-1, 1, 0)$ and $(-3, 1, 2)$ to $(2, 0, 0)$.

3 Find the equation of the line through the origin and perpendicular to the lines with DR $2:1:-1$ and $3:1:0$.

4 Find the equation of the line through $(2, 1, -1)$ and perpendicular to the x and y axes.

5 Find the equation of the line through the origin and perpendicular to $x = y = z$ and the z axis.

1.4 Distances between points and lines

Perpendicular distances

The distance from the origin to a line

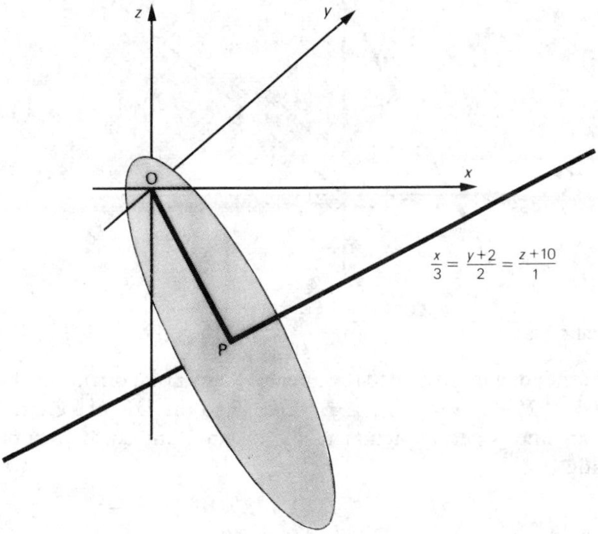

Suppose the line is $$\frac{x}{3} = \frac{y+2}{2} = \frac{z+10}{1} = k$$

It has DR 3:2:1 and passes through (0, −2, −10). Any point on the line has coordinates

$$x = 3k \qquad y = 2k-2 \qquad z = k-10$$

Think of arranging our disc so that it passes through the origin. DR of OP are $3k:2k-2:k-10$. Now OP is perpendicular to our line so

$$3\times 3k + 2\times(2k-2) + 1(k-10) = 0 \quad \text{(The dot product of the DR is zero.)}$$

$$9k + 4k - 4 + k - 10 = 0$$

$$14k = 14$$

$$k = 1$$

hence P is (3, 0, −9) and

$$\text{OP}^2 = 3^2 + 0^2 + 9^2$$

$$\text{OP} = \sqrt{90}$$

The distance from any point to any line in space

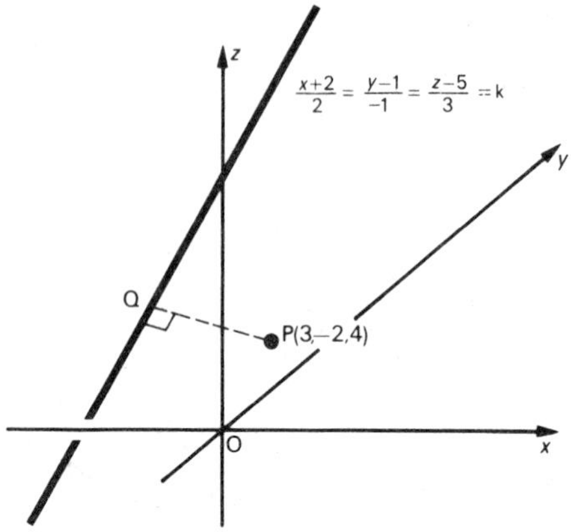

Suppose the line is $\frac{x+2}{2}=\frac{y-1}{-1}=\frac{z-5}{3}=k$ and the point P (3, −2, 4). Let Q be the foot of the perpendicular from P to the line. Now any point on the line has parametric coordinates $x = 2k-2$, $y = -k+1$, $z = 3k+5$ so the DR of PQ are $2k-5:-k+3:3k+1$. This line is perpendicular to the original line so the dot product of the direction ratios is zero, i.e.

$$2\times(2k-5)-1\times(-k+3)+3(3k+1) = 0$$
$$4k-10+k-3+9k+3 = 0$$
$$14k-10 = 0$$
$$k = \tfrac{5}{7}$$

Hence Q is the point $(-\frac{4}{7}, \frac{2}{7}, \frac{50}{7})$ and

$$PQ = \sqrt{((3\tfrac{4}{7})^2+(-2\tfrac{2}{7})^2+(-3\tfrac{1}{7})^2)}$$
$$\approx 5.28$$

Distance between skew lines

Consider the line

$$\frac{x-3}{1}=\frac{y-2}{1}=\frac{z-4}{3}=p$$

This passes through (3, 2, 4) with DR 1:1:3. A point P on this line will have coordinates

$$x = p+3 \qquad y = p+2 \qquad z = 3p+4$$

Suppose we have a second line

$$\frac{x}{1}=\frac{y+1}{0}=\frac{z+1}{1}=q$$

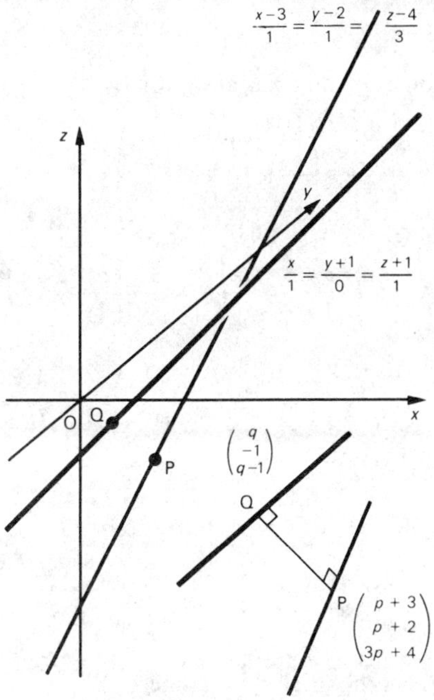

This passes through $(0, -1, -1)$ with DR $1:0:1$. Q has coordinates

$$x = q \qquad y = -1 \qquad z = q - 1$$

P and Q are the ends of the common perpendicular, and the DR of PQ are

$$p+3-q:p+2+1:3p+4-q+1$$

or

$$p-q+3:p+3:3p-q+5$$

Now PQ is perpendicular to each of the lines so the dot products are zero, i.e.

$$1\times(p-q+3)+1\times(p+3)+3\times(3p-q+5)=0$$

and

$$1\times(p-q+3)+0\times(p+3)+1\times(3p-q+5)=0$$

Simplifying we have $\qquad 11p-4q+21=0$

and $\qquad 4p-2q+8=0$

These two equations give $p=-\frac{5}{3}$ and $q=\frac{2}{3}$

Hence P is $(1\frac{1}{3}, \frac{1}{3}, -1)$ and Q $(\frac{2}{3}, -1, -\frac{1}{3})$

$$PQ^2 = (1\tfrac{1}{3}-\tfrac{2}{3})^2+(\tfrac{1}{3}+1)^2+(-1+\tfrac{1}{3})^2$$

$$PQ = \tfrac{1}{3}\sqrt{(4+16+4)} = \tfrac{2}{3}\sqrt{6}$$

Alternatively

The DR of the common perpendicular are given by

$$\begin{pmatrix}1\\1\\3\end{pmatrix} \times \begin{pmatrix}1\\0\\1\end{pmatrix} = \begin{pmatrix}1\\2\\-1\end{pmatrix}$$

$$\frac{p-q+3}{1} = \frac{p+3}{2} = \frac{3p-q+5}{-1}$$

Hence $2(p-q+3) = 1(p+3)$ so $p-2q+3=0$

and $-1(p+3) = 2(3p-q+5)$ so $7p-2q+13=0$

Subtracting,

$$6p+10=0, \qquad p=-\tfrac{5}{3}, \qquad q=\tfrac{2}{3} \qquad \text{(as before)}$$

Exercise 1.4

1 Find the distance from the origin to the line

$$\frac{x-1}{1} = \frac{y+2}{-1} = \frac{z}{3}$$

2 Find the distance of the point (2, 1, 0) from the lines

(a) $\dfrac{x}{2} = \dfrac{y}{1} = \dfrac{z}{-1}$

(b) $\dfrac{x}{2} = \dfrac{y-3}{1} = \dfrac{z+2}{-1}$

3 Find the distance between the parallel lines

(a) $\dfrac{x+1}{2} = \dfrac{y}{-3} = \dfrac{z+2}{0}$ and $\dfrac{x}{2} = \dfrac{y-3}{-3} = \dfrac{z+1}{0}$

(b) $\dfrac{x+1}{2} = \dfrac{y}{1} = \dfrac{z}{-1}$ and $\dfrac{x+3}{2} = \dfrac{y}{1} = \dfrac{z+2}{-1}$

4 Find the shortest distance between the two skew lines

(a) $y = z = 0$ and $\dfrac{x-2}{2} = \dfrac{y}{-1} = \dfrac{z+1}{3}$

(b) $\dfrac{x-1}{2} = \dfrac{y+2}{3} = \dfrac{z}{-1}$ and $\dfrac{x+2}{1} = \dfrac{y-2}{2} = \dfrac{z+1}{-1}$

2 Planes

2.1 The direction of a plane

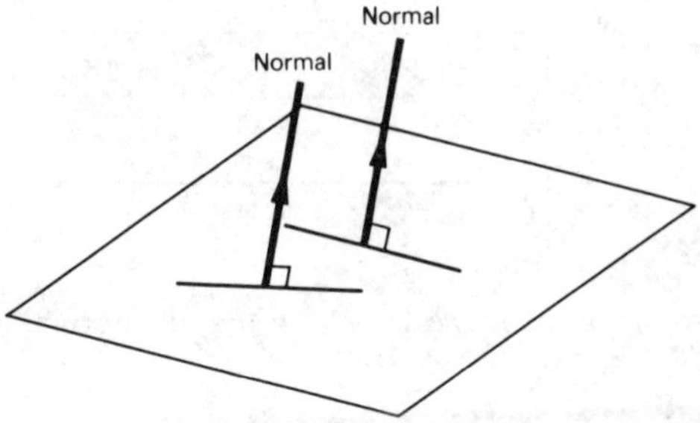

A plane contains an infinite number of lines in various directions. However, it is clear that the *normal* to the plane is always in a fixed direction and so we can use the direction of the normal to specify our plane. For example, we know that the normal must be perpendicular to all the lines in the plane so we can write down the direction ratios of the normals to some 'well-known' planes.

Plane	*Plane-direction*	*Direction ratios of the normal*
$x = 0$	contains the y and z axes	1:0:0
$y = 0$	contains the x and z axes	0:1:0
$z = 0$	contains the x and y axes	0:0:1
$1x+1y = n$	parallel to the z axis	1:1:0
$1y+1z = n$	parallel to the x axis	0:1:1
$1x+1z = n$	parallel to the y axis	1:0:1

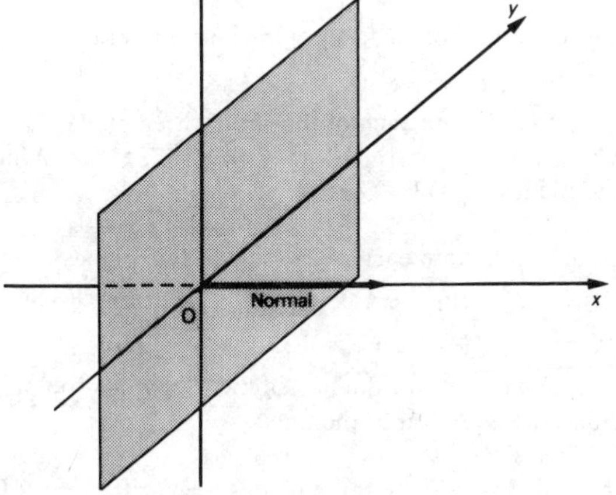

Part of the plane $x = 0$ and the normal along the x axis.

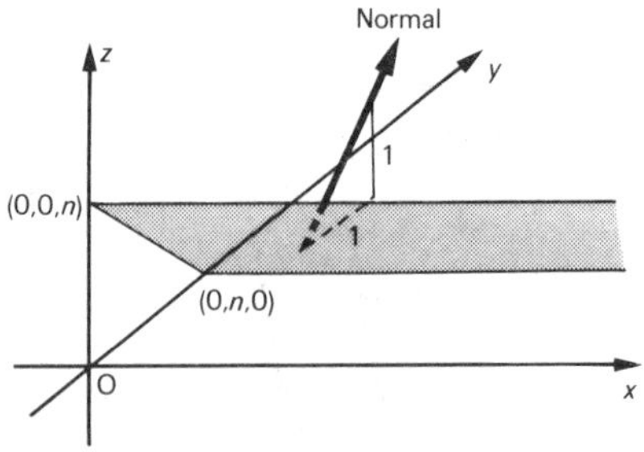

Part of the plane $1y + 1z = n$ and a normal.

From these results, abbreviated below—

Plane	*DR normal*	*Plane*	*DR normal*
$1x = 0$	$1:0:0$	$1x + 1y = n$	$1:1:0$
$1y = 0$	$0:1:0$	$1y + 1z = n$	$0:1:1$
$1z = 0$	$0:0:1$	$1x + 1z = n$	$1:0:1$

—we should expect that if the DR normal of a plane were $1:1:1$ then the plane would be $1x + 1y + 1z = D$. The value of D determines the *position* of the plane.

Exercise 2.1a

1 Write down the equations of the faces of the box in Exercise 1.1, question 2, page 454.

2 Draw a diagram to illustrate each of the set of three planes **(a)** $x = 0$, $y = 2$, $z = -3$ and **(b)** $y = 0$, $x = 7$, $z = 4$. What is the point of intersection of the planes in **(a)**?

3 Draw a diagram to illustrate each of the sets of two planes

(a) $x = 1, y = 2$ **(b)** $z = 0, y = -3$ **(c)** $x + y = 0, z = 3$

(d) $x + y = 0, x = 6$ **(e)** $z + y = 1, x = 1$ **(f)** $x + z = 2, y = 1$

In each case write down the coordinates of two 'obvious' points on the line of intersection and find the equation of the line.

4 Draw a diagram to illustrate the three planes $x + y = 0$, $y + z = 0$ and $x = z + 1$. Comment.

The equation of a plane

(a) We investigate, for example, the equation $1x + 1y + 1z = 6$.

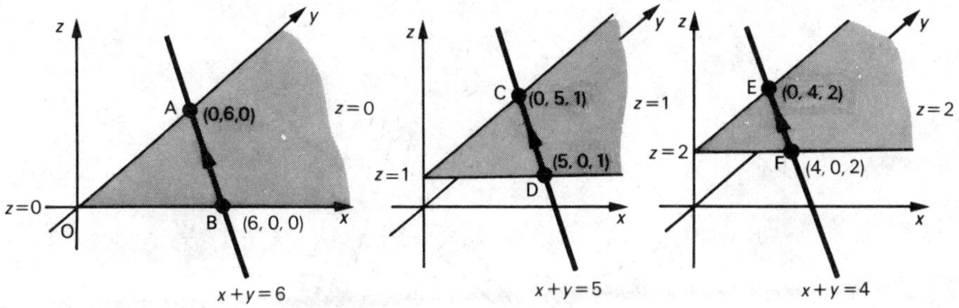

To build up the plane $1x+1y+1z=6$

We can imagine the intermediate steps (e.g. $z = 1\frac{1}{2}$) and see that we are building up a plane as a series of parallel lines. This is illustrated below.

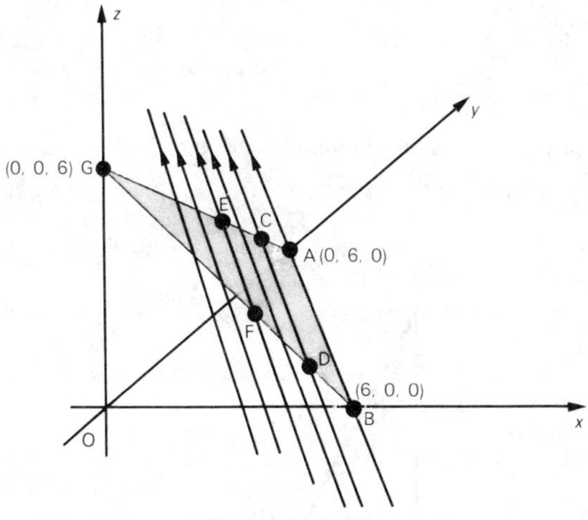

Plane $1x+1y+1z=6$

The parallel lines are 'building' the plane $x+y+z = 6$.We know that the normal must be perpendicular to AB with DR $6:-6:0$, CD with DR $5:-5:0$ and EF with DR $4:-4:0$. Since these are all parallel we require further information. When $x = 0$, $y+z = 6$ and the normal must also be perpendicular to GA (with DR $0:6:-6$).

The *direction ratios of the normal* (henceforward to be abbreviated to DRN) can be taken as $l:m:n$. The normal is perpendicular to AB and GA, so $l:m:n$ will be given by the cross product of the DR of AB and GA, i.e.

$$\begin{pmatrix} 1 \\ -1 \\ 0 \end{pmatrix} \times \begin{pmatrix} 0 \\ 1 \\ -1 \end{pmatrix} = \begin{pmatrix} 1 \\ 1 \\ 1 \end{pmatrix}$$

hence $l:m:n = 1:1:1$, and the DRN of the plane $1x + 1y + 1z = 6$ are $1:1:1$.

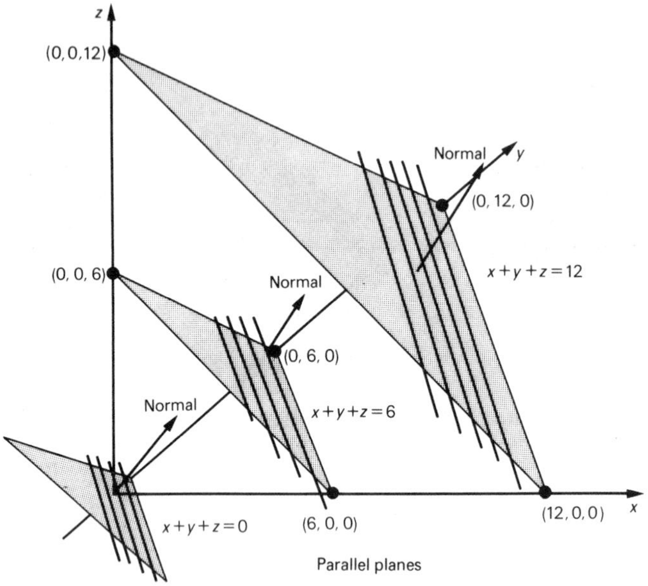

Parallel planes

(b) Suppose the equation is more complicated, e.g. $3x + 2y + z = 6$. The points

A(2, 0, 0) B(0, 3, 0) and C(0, 0, 6)

are on the plane.

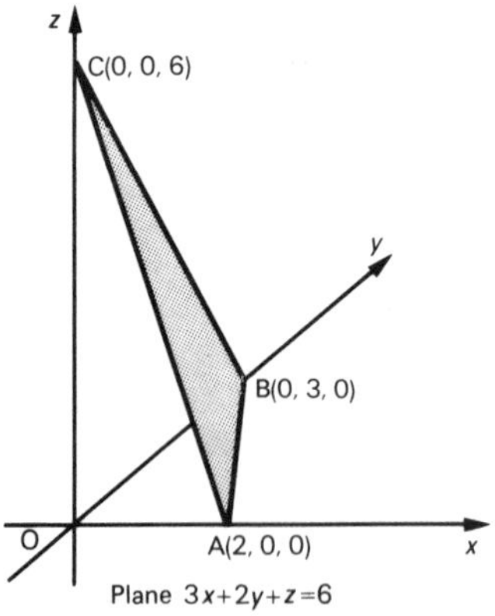

Plane $3x+2y+z=6$

The DR of AB are $2:-3:0$; the DR of BC are $0:3:-6$; the DRN of the mutual perpendicular to AB and BC is given by

$$\begin{pmatrix} 2 \\ -3 \\ 0 \end{pmatrix} \times \begin{pmatrix} 0 \\ 3 \\ -6 \end{pmatrix} = \begin{pmatrix} 18 \\ 12 \\ 6 \end{pmatrix} = 6\begin{pmatrix} 3 \\ 2 \\ 1 \end{pmatrix}$$

Hence the DRN to the plane is $3:2:1$.

In general

If the equation of the plane is $Ax + By + Cz = D$ then the DRN to the plane is A : B : C. ◀

The equation of a plane with given DRN

Consider a plane through the origin with DRN A : B : C and any point P(x, y, z) in the plane. Then OP has DR $x : y : z$. Since OP is perpendicular to the normal PQ the dot product of their direction ratios is zero. Hence $Ax + By + Cz = 0$ is the equation of a plane through the origin.

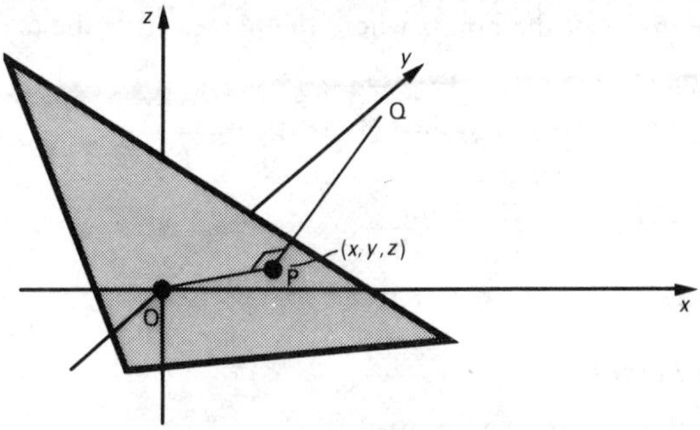

Consider a plane not through the origin with DRN A: B: C passing through a known point R(a, b, c) and any other point P(x, y, z) in the plane.

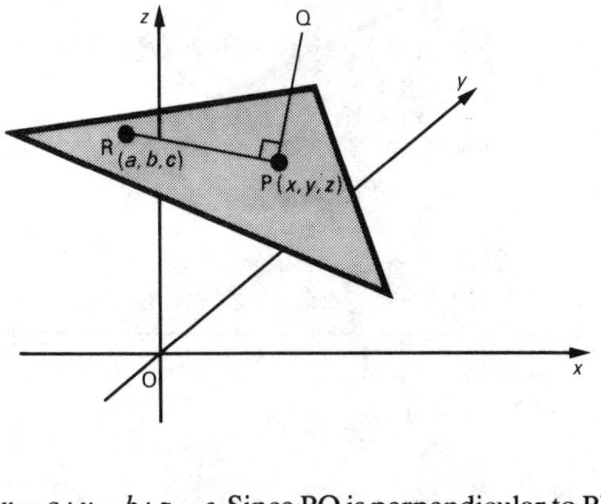

Then PR has DR $x-a : y-b : z-c$. Since PQ is perpendicular to PR, the dot product of their direction ratios is zero. Hence

$$A(x-a)+B(y-b)+C(x-c) = 0$$

$$Ax + By + Cz = Aa + Bb + Cc$$

$$= D \text{ (say)}$$

Hence $Ax + By + Cz = D$ is the equation of a plane not passing through the origin, but parallel to $Ax + By + Cz = 0$.

Exercise 2.1b

1 Write down the equation of the plane with DRN $1:3:-1$ which passes through the origin. Give the coordinates of any three points on the plane.

2 Write down the coordinates of the points where the plane $2x-3y-z=12$ crosses the axes. Find the coordinates of the foot of the perpendicular from O to the plane. What is the distance of the plane from O?

3 Find the distance from the origin of the two planes
(a) $x+2y-5z=-10$ and **(b)** $x+2y-5z=20$
Show the two planes on a sketch and the normal to the planes passing through O. Mark in the coordinates of the points where the planes cross the axes.

4 Sketch the planes $-2x-y+3z=-6$ and $-x+8y+2z=16$. Draw in the normals through O and prove that they are perpendicular.

2.2 Defining a plane

Through the origin

(a) Given three points

For example O(0, 0, 0), B(2, 3, 0), A(0, 0, 4).

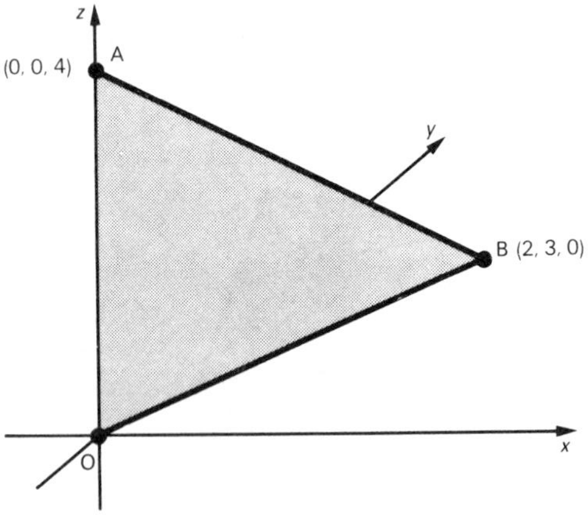

The DR of OA are $0:0:4$ and of OB $2:3:0$, so the DRN (which is perpendicular to both) is given by the cross product

$$(0:0:4)\times(2:3:0) = -12:8:0 \qquad \text{or} \qquad -3:2:0$$

Hence the equation of the plane is of the form

$$-3x+2y+0z = D$$

but the plane passes through O, so $D=0$.

(*b*) *Given a point and a line in the plane*

For example P(0, 2, 1) and the x axis,

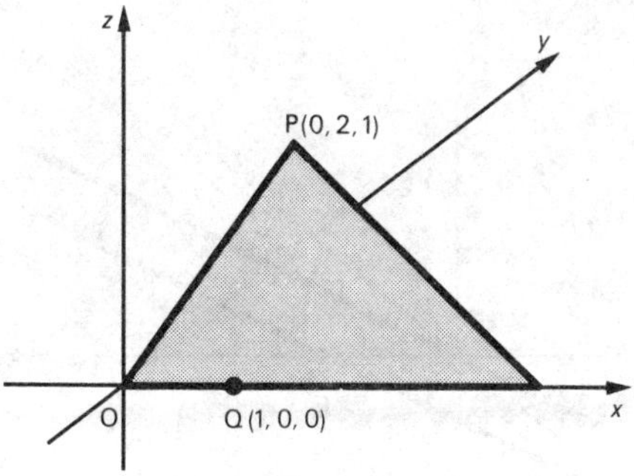

Choose any two points on the line, e.g. O (0, 0, 0) and Q (1, 0, 0). We now know three points in space and the problem is the same as (*a*). The DR of OP are 1 : 0 : 0, and of PQ are −1 : 2 : 1. The DRN are (1 : 0 : 0) × (−1 : 2 : 1) = 0 : −1 : 2. The equation of the plane is $0x - 1y + 2z = D$ and it passes through (0, 0, 0) hence $D = 0$.

(*c*) *Given two intersecting lines in the plane*

Consider $\frac{x}{3} = \frac{y}{2} = \frac{z}{1}$ and $\frac{x}{1} = \frac{y}{-1} = \frac{z}{1}$

The normal to the plane is perpendicular to both lines (which intersect at O)

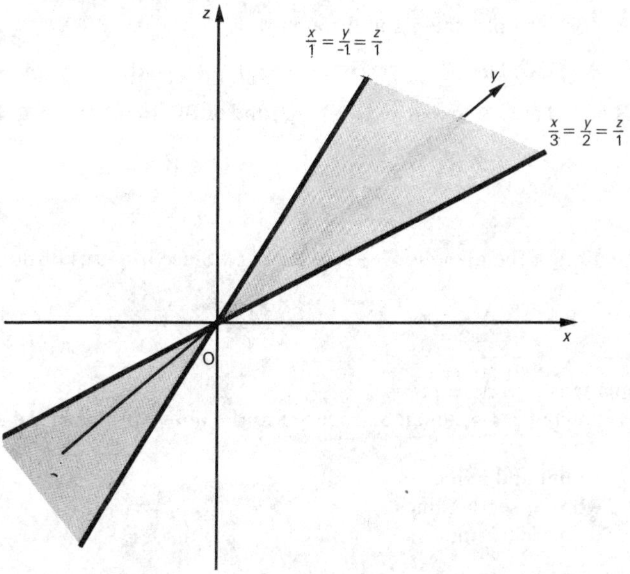

The DRN are $(3:2:1)\times(1:-1:1) = 3:-2:-5$. The equation of the plane is $3x-2y-5z = D$ and since the line passes through O, $D=0$.

(*d*) *Given two parallel lines*

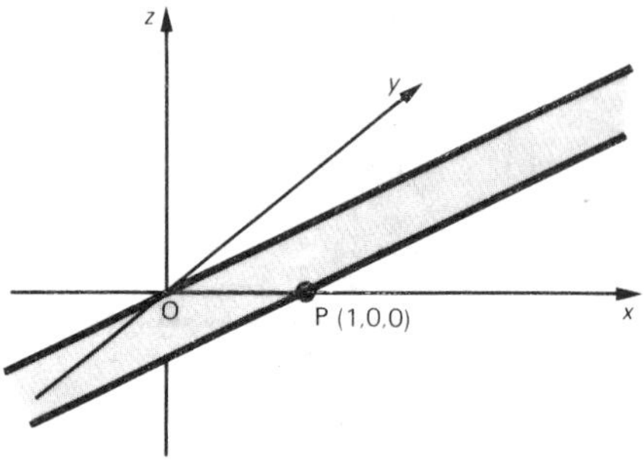

For example $\quad \dfrac{x}{3}=\dfrac{y}{2}=\dfrac{z}{1} \quad$ and $\quad \dfrac{x-1}{3}=\dfrac{y}{2}=\dfrac{z}{1}$

Choose a point on each line, O(0, 0, 0) and P(1, 0, 0). The DR of OP are $1:0:0$ hence the DRN are $(1:0:0)\times(3:2:1) = 0:1:-2$. The equation of the plane is $0x+1y-2z = D$ and again $D=0$.

Defining a plane not through the origin

(*a*) *Given three points*

Consider for example, the plane through

A(−1, 3, 1), B(1, −3, −3) and C(3, −1, 5)

The DR of AB are $2:-6:-4 = 1:-3:-2$, and of BC are $2:2:8 = 1:1:4$. The DRN are

$$(1:-3:-2)\times(1:1:4) = -10:-6:4$$
$$= 5:3:-2$$

The equation of the plane is $5x+3y-2z = D$. Since it passes through (−1, 3, 1).

$$5\times(-1)+3\times 3-2\times 1 = D$$
$$2 = D$$

so the plane is $5x+3y-2z = 2$.

The following cases can all be reduced to the above problem and solved accordingly:

(*b*) A point and a line
(*c*) Two intersecting lines
(*d*) Two parallel lines.

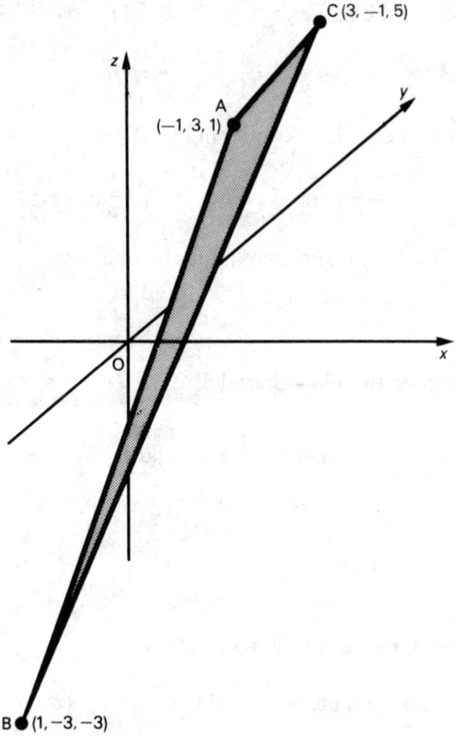

Exercise 2.2

1 Find the equation of the plane through the origin, (2, −1, 1) and (5, 0, 2).

2 Find the equation of the plane through (1, 0, −1) and containing the line

$$\frac{x}{1}=\frac{y}{-1}=\frac{z}{2}$$

3 Find the equation of the plane containing the two lines

$$\frac{x}{3}=\frac{y}{-2}=\frac{z}{1}$$

and the z axis.

4 Find the equation of the plane containing the two parallel lines

$$\frac{x}{1}=\frac{y}{-1}=\frac{z}{2} \qquad \text{and} \qquad \frac{x+1}{1}=\frac{y-2}{-1}=\frac{z}{2}$$

5 Find the equation of the plane through the three points

(1, 2, 1), (−1, 0, 3) and (0, 5, −1)

6 Find the equation of the plane through (1, 0, −3) and containing the line

$$\frac{x}{2} = \frac{y}{1} = \frac{z+1}{-1}$$

7 Find the equation of the plane containing the lines

$$\frac{x-1}{3} = \frac{y}{-1} = \frac{z+2}{1} \qquad \text{and} \qquad \frac{x-1}{4} = \frac{y}{-2} = \frac{z+2}{3}$$

8 Find the equation of the plane containing the lines

$$\frac{x+1}{-1} = \frac{y}{3} = \frac{z+1}{2} \qquad \text{and} \qquad \frac{x}{-1} = \frac{y}{3} = \frac{z+4}{2}$$

9 Find the equation of the plane parallel to $x - 2y + z = 5$ and passing through (1, −3, 2).

10 Find the equation of the plane perpendicular to the line

$$\frac{x-1}{2} = \frac{y}{-1} = \frac{z}{3}$$

and passing through (1, −3, 2).

2.3 The distance from a point to a plane

Distance from the origin to a plane

As an example, find the distance of the origin from the plane

$$3x + 2y - 1z = 12$$

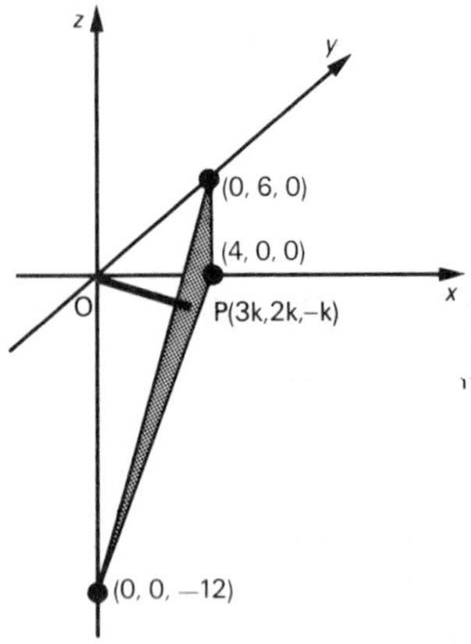

The plane cuts the axes at (4, 0, 0), (0, 6, 0) and (0, 0, −12) (which helps us to visualize it). OP is the normal from the plane and passing through the origin. The DRN of this plane are 3 : 2 : −1. Hence OP has DR 3 : 2 : −1 and any point on OP can be expressed as $(3k, 2k, -k)$. The distance OP is $k\sqrt{[3^2 + 2^2 + (-1)^2]}$.

Now P lies on the line Op and is also in the plane, so its coordinates, $(3k, 2k, -k)$, must satisfy the equation of the plane. Hence

$$3(3k)+2(2k)-1(-k) = 12$$
$$9k+4k+k = 12$$
$$14k = 12$$
$$k = \tfrac{6}{7}$$

so P is $(\frac{18}{7}, \frac{12}{7}, \frac{-6}{7})$ and

$$OP = \tfrac{6}{7}\sqrt{[3^2+2^2+(-1)^2]}$$
$$= \tfrac{6}{7}\sqrt{14}$$

Distance of a point from a plane through the origin

Suppose we wish to know the distance of P(1, 5, 3) from the plane $2x+y-z=0$. First check that P does not lie on the plane by substituting the values (1, 5, 3). $2.1+5-3 = 4 \neq 0$, so P does not lie on the plane.

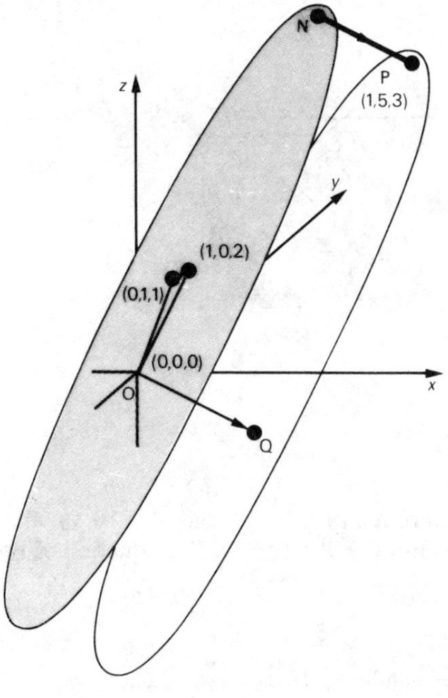

Now the required distance PN is equal to the distance OQ from the origin to a parallel plane through P. This has equation $2x+y-z = D$ and, since P lies on it, $D = 4$, i.e. $2x+y-z = 4$. Then as above OQ has DR $2:1:-1$, any point on it can be expressed $(2k, k, -k)$ and the distance $OQ = k\sqrt{[2^2+1^2+(-1)^2]}$.

Since $Q(2k, k, -k)$ lies on the plane $2x+y-z=4$

$$2(2k)+k-(-k)=4$$
$$k=\tfrac{2}{3}$$

So Q is $(\tfrac{4}{3}, \tfrac{2}{3}, -\tfrac{2}{3})$ and

$$OQ = \tfrac{2}{3}\sqrt{[2^2+1^2+(-1)^2]}$$
$$=\tfrac{2}{3}\sqrt{6}$$

Distance of a point from a plane not through the origin

For example, let us find the distance from a point $P(-1, 7, 5)$ to the plane $5x-y-z=10$.

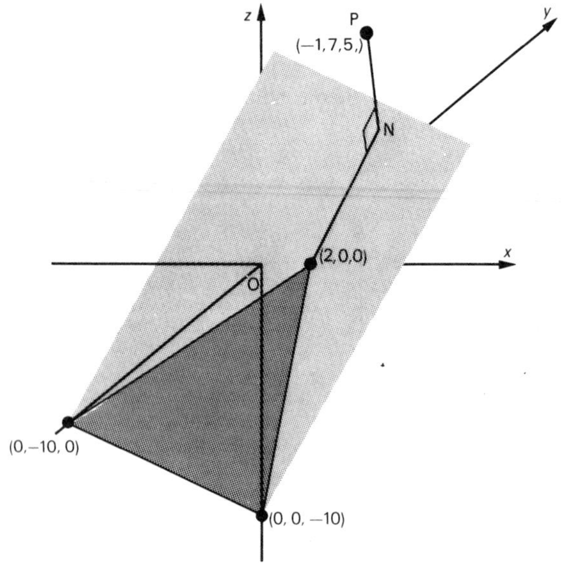

The plane passes through $(0, 0, -10)$, and $(0, -10, 0)$, and $(2, 0, 0)$. PN has DR $5:-1:-1$ and passes through $P(-1, 7, 5)$. The equation of PN is

$$\frac{x+1}{5}=\frac{y-7}{-1}=\frac{z-5}{-1}=k$$

The coordinates of N can be taken as

$$x=5k-1, \qquad y=-k+7, \qquad z=-k+5$$
$$PN=\sqrt{[(5k-1-(-1))^2+(-k+7-7)^2+(-k+5-5)^2]}$$
$$=k\sqrt{[5^2+(-1)^2+(-1)^2]}$$

Now N lies on the plane so

$$5(5k-1)-1(-k+7)-1(-1k+5) = 10$$
$$25k-5+k-7+k-5 = 10$$
$$27k = 27$$
$$k = 1$$
$$PN = 1\sqrt{[5^2+(-1)^2+(-1)^2]}$$
$$= \sqrt{27} = 3\sqrt{3}$$

Distance between parallel planes

For example, let us find the distance between the planes $3x+2y-z = 7$ and $3x+2y-z = -14$.

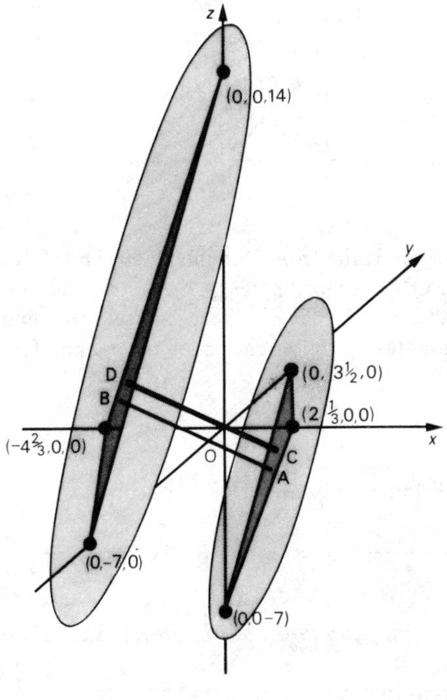

The perpendicular distance between the planes AB is the same as the distance CD. Consider C on the first plane and D on the second. DR of CD are 3:2:−1. The coordinates of any point on CD are given by $x = 3k$, $y = 2k$, $z = -1k$.

For C
$$3(3k)+2(2k)-1(-1k) = 7$$
$$9k+4k+1k = 7$$
$$k = \tfrac{1}{2}$$

Hence C is $(\frac{3}{2}, 1, -\frac{1}{2})$

For D

$$3(3k)+2(2k)-1(-1k) = -14$$
$$14k = -14$$
$$k = -1$$

Hence D is $(-3, -2, 1)$. Distance CD is given by

$$CD^2 = (-3-\tfrac{3}{2})^2+(-2-1)^2+(1+\tfrac{1}{2})^2$$
$$CD = \tfrac{3}{2}\sqrt{14}$$

In general

To find the distance from the origin to the plane $Ax+By+Cz = D$

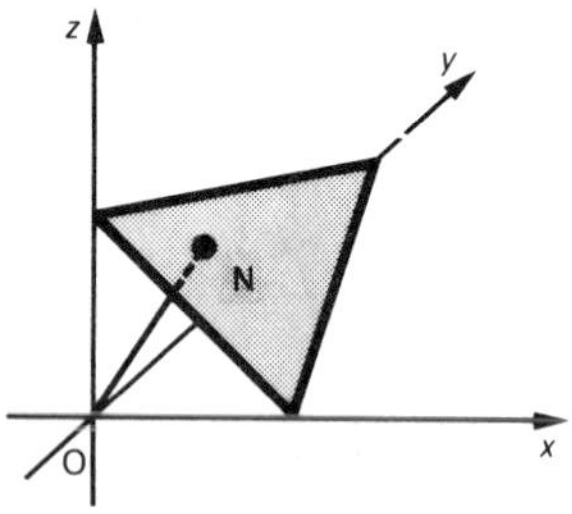

N is the foot of the perpendicular from O to the plane. Thus ON has DR $A:B:C$, and any point P on the line ON has coordinates (Ak, Bk, Ck). Its distance from the origin, $OP = k\sqrt{(A^2+B^2+C^2)}$. Since N is on the plane, we can find the value of k by substituting its coordinates in the equation of the plane. Thus $A(Ak)+B(Bk)+C(Ck) = D$ and

$$k = \frac{D}{(A^2+B^2+C^2)}$$

so it follows that its distance from the origin must be

$$ON = \frac{D}{(A^2+B^2+C^2)} \times \sqrt{(A^2+B^2+C^2)} = \frac{D}{\sqrt{(A^2+B^2+C^2)}}$$

To find the distance from any point to the plane $Ax+By+Cz = D$

P is any point with coordinates (a, b, c)
Let N be the foot of the perpendicular from P to the plane.

The DR of PN = DRN of the plane = $A:B:C$

PN has equations $\frac{x'}{A} = \frac{y'}{B} = \frac{z'}{C}$ referred to new axes through P and since $x' = x-a$, $y' = y-b$, $z' = z-c$ we have

$$\frac{x-a}{A} = \frac{y-b}{B} = \frac{z-c}{C} = k$$

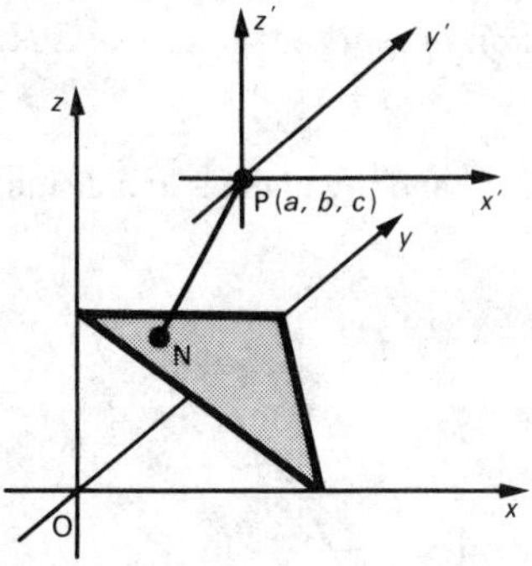

so the parametric coordinates of N are $(Ak+a, Bk+b, Ck+c)$ and

$$PN = k\sqrt{(A^2+B^2+C^2)}$$

Now N lies on the plane, so

$$A(Ak+a)+B(Bk+b)+C(Ck+c) = D$$

$$k(A^2+B^2+C^2) = D-(Aa+Bb+Cc)$$

$$k = \frac{D-(Aa+Bb+Cc)}{A^2+B^2+C^2}$$

and
$$\mathbf{PN} = \frac{\boldsymbol{D-(Aa+Bb+Cc)}}{\boldsymbol{\sqrt{(A^2+B^2+C^2)}}}$$ ◀

This gives us a quick way of finding the distances.

To write down the equation of a plane, given the DRN and its distance from the origin

Suppose the DRN are 3 : 2 : 1 and the distance of the plane from the origin is 5 units. Then the equation of the plane is $Ax+By+Cz = D$ where $A = 3, B = 2, C = 1$ and

$$\frac{D}{\sqrt{(A^2+B^2+C^2)}} = \frac{D}{\sqrt{14}} = 5$$

i.e. $D = \pm 5\sqrt{14}$ and the required equation is

$$3x+2y+z = \pm 5\sqrt{14}$$

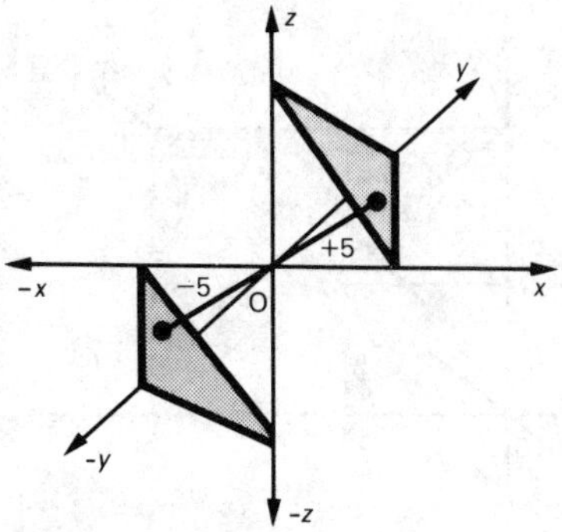

To write down the equation of a plane, given the DRN and its distance from a point (a, b, c)

Suppose the DRN are $3:2:1$, and the plane is at a distance from $P(a, b, c)$ of 6 units towards the origin.

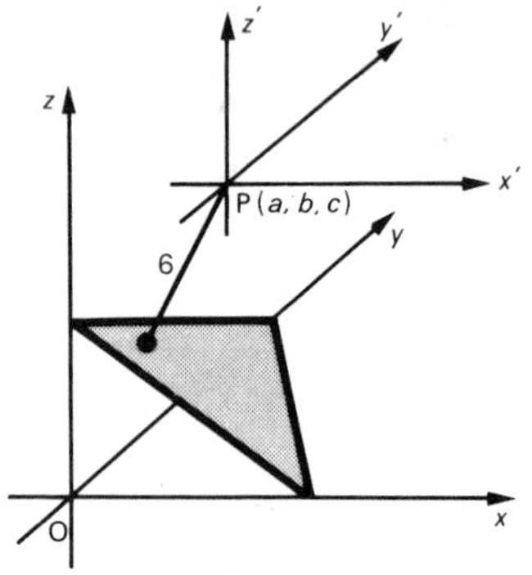

Think of the origin at P, then the equation of the plane is

$$3x'+2y'+z' = -6\sqrt{14}$$

Translate the axes to their original positions and the equation of the plane becomes

$$3(x-a)+2(y-b)+1(z-c) = -6\sqrt{14}$$

Exercise 2.3

1(a) Write down the equation of the plane with DRN $1:1:1$ at a distance of 6 units from the origin.

(b) If the plane cuts the axes at X, Y, Z, find the volume of the tetrahedron OXYZ.

(c) Write down the equation of the plane parallel to XYZ at a distance of 4 units from it, and further from the origin.

(d) What is the volume of the frustum of the pyramid XYZLMN?

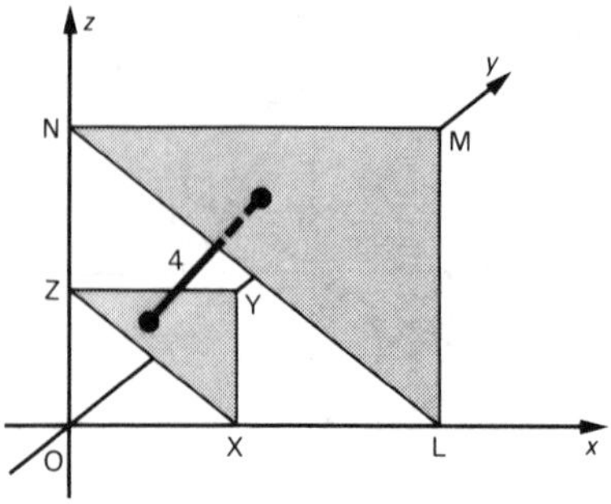

2 Write down the equations of the two planes at a distance of 5 units from the point (3, 1, 0) with DRN $0:2:1$.

3 Find the distance from $(-2, 1, -1)$ to the plane $5x-7y+3z=0$.

4 Find the distance from $(0, -1, 1)$ to the plane $2x-y=3$.

5 Show that the points $(1, -1, 3)$ and $(3, 3, 3)$ are equidistant from the plane $5x+2y-7z=-9$ and are on opposite sides of it.

6 Find the distance between the parallel planes

$$3x+2y-z=-4 \qquad \text{and} \qquad 3x+2y-z=-6$$

7 Find the equations of the planes through (a) $(-5, 3, 4)$ and (b) $(4, 1, -2)$ parallel to the plane $x+2y-z=0$. What is the distance between them?

2.4. Intersection of lines and planes

Intersection of a line and a plane

Either a line is parallel to the plane or it will intersect it at a point. If it is parallel to the plane, it will either be in the plane or not intersect it at all.

A line will be parallel to a plane if the line is perpendicular to the normal. Consider, for example, the plane $2x-3y+z=4$ with DRN $2:-3:1$ and the line

$$\frac{x-3}{1}=\frac{y+1}{1}=\frac{z}{1} \quad \text{with DR } 1:1:1$$

Now the dot product $(2:-3:1)\cdot(1:1:1)=0$, so the line is parallel to the plane.

If we wish to check whether the line is in the plane, we choose any point on the line and substitute the coordinates into the equation of the plane. Now $(3, -1, 0)$ is on the line but $2\times3-3\times(-1)+4\times0\neq4$ so the line is not in the plane.

To find the point of intersection of a line with a plane, we use the parametric form of the line and substitute in the equation of the plane. For example, to find the point of intersection of the line

$$\frac{x-2}{3}=\frac{y+1}{-2}=\frac{z-1}{2}=k$$

and the plane $\qquad 2x-3y+4z=21$

The parametric equations of the line are

$$x=3k+2, \qquad y=-2k-1, \qquad z=2k+1$$

Substituting these in the equation of the plane,

$$\begin{aligned} 2(3k+2)-3(-2k-1)+4(2k+1) &= 21 \\ 6k+4+6k+3+8k+4 &= 21 \\ 20k &= 10 \\ k &= \tfrac{1}{2} \end{aligned}$$

Hence the point of intersection is $(3\frac{1}{2}, -2, 2)$.

Intersection of two planes

(a) *Two planes through the origin*

Consider for example the two planes

$$2x+3y-z=0$$

and
$$2x-y+3z=0$$

The two planes are not parallel, so they must intersect in a line which passes through the origin (since both the planes pass through O). Consider the intersection of each plane with $z=1$:

$$2x+3y-z=0 \text{ intersects this plane when } 2x+3y=1$$

$$2x-y+3z=0 \text{ intersects the plane when } 2x-y=-3$$

The two lines $2x+3y=1$ and $2x-y=-3$

meet on the $z=1$ plane at $x=-1$, $y=1$.

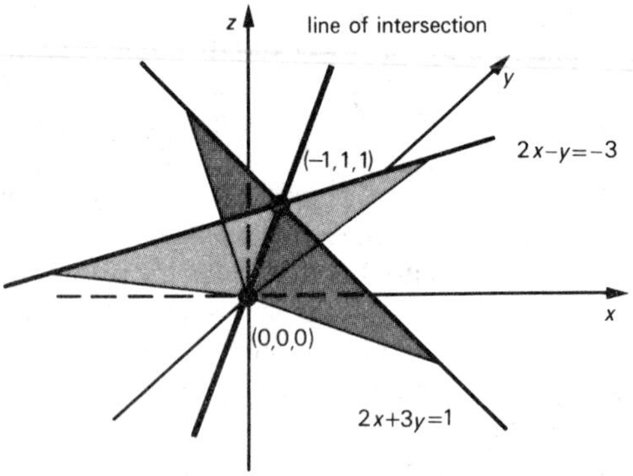

Hence the line of intersection passes through $(-1, 1, 1)$ and $(0, 0, 0)$. The DR of the line of intersection are $-1:1:1$ and since it passes through $(0, 0, 0)$ its equation is

$$\frac{x}{-1}=\frac{y}{1}=\frac{z}{1}$$

(b) *Two planes not through the origin*

Consider for example the two planes

$$3x-y-z=2$$

$$x-2y+3z=-6$$

Consider the intersection of these planes with the $z = 0$ plane

$$\left.\begin{aligned} 3x - y &= 2 \\ x - 2y &= -6 \end{aligned}\right\} \quad \text{meet at } (2, 4, 0)$$

Now find the intersection on the $z = 1$ plane

$$\left.\begin{aligned} 3x - y &= 3 \\ x - 2y &= -9 \end{aligned}\right\} \quad \text{meet at } (3, 6, 1)$$

Hence the line of intersection passes through (2, 4, 0) and (3, 6, 1) with DR 1:2:1 so the equation of the line is $\dfrac{x-2}{1} = \dfrac{y-4}{2} = \dfrac{z-0}{1}$.

(*c*) *The plane $z = 0$ with other planes*

Consider the intersections of the plane $3x + 2y + z = 6$ with the plane $z = 0$. The intersection is the line $3x + 2y = 6$ which is in the x, y plane.

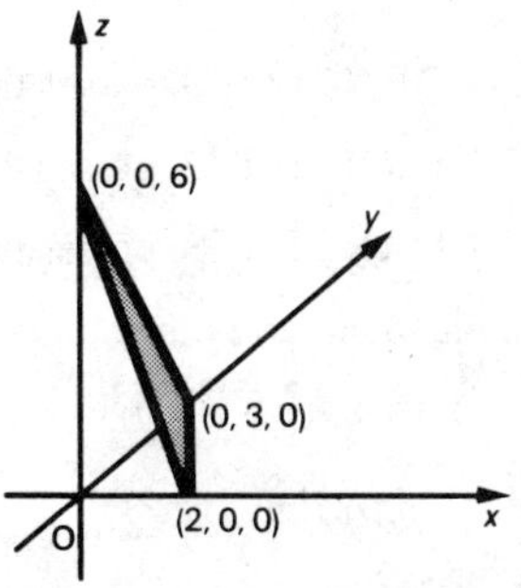

The line $3x + 2y = 6$ is the line of intersection of the plane $z = 0$ with planes with equations of the form $3x + 2y + kz = 6$ where k has any value. In particular when $k = 0$, $3x + 2y = 6$, which is the vertical plane. *In general* plane $Ax + By + Cz = D$ intersects the $z = 0$ plane in the line $Ax + By = D$. Thus the distance to the line of intersection, RQ, is ON $= \dfrac{D}{\sqrt{(A^2 + B^2)}}$

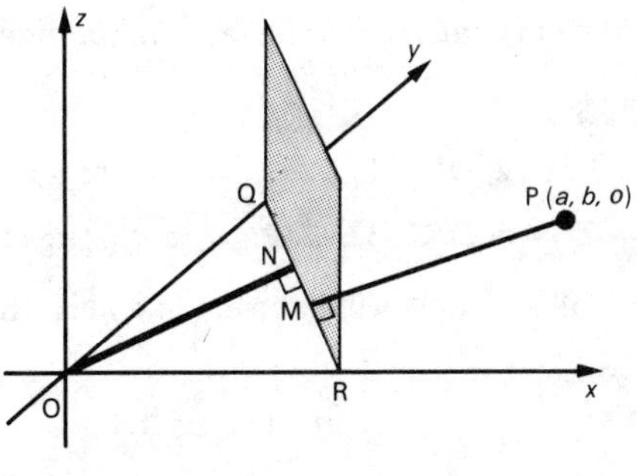

and the distance from P$(a, b, 0)$ to the line is

$$PM = \frac{D-(Aa+Bb)}{\sqrt{(A^2+B^2)}}$$

The intersection of any plane with the planes $x = 0$ and $y = 0$ can be treated similarly.

Intersection of three planes

There are several possible configurations for the intersection of three planes. We consider the obvious possibilities in detail, but mention the others.

(*a*) *The three planes may be coincident*

Consider the three planes:

$$2x+y-3z = 5, \quad \text{DRN } 2:1:-3, \text{ passes through } (0, 0, -\tfrac{5}{3})$$
$$6x+3y-9z = 15, \quad \text{DRN } 2:1:-3, \text{ passes through } (0, 0, -\tfrac{5}{3})$$
$$-4x-2y+6z = -10, \text{ DRN } 2:1:-3, \text{ passes through } (0, 0, -\tfrac{5}{3})$$

Hence the three planes are coincident, and our intersection is the original plane.

(*b*) *The three planes may be parallel*

Consider:

$$2x-8y-4z = 10, \text{ DRN } 1:-4:-2, \text{ passes through } (0, 0, -\tfrac{5}{2})$$
$$-x+4y+2z = 6, \quad \text{DRN } 1:-4:-2, \text{ passes through } (0, 0, 3)$$
$$3x-12y-6z = 48, \text{ DRN } 1:-4:-2, \text{ passes through } (0, 0, -8)$$

Since the normals are in the same direction the planes are parallel but not coincident as they pass through different points on the z axis. There is no intersection.

(*c*) *The three planes may intersect in a line like the pages of a book*

Consider the two planes:

$$x+y-z = 2, \text{ DRN } 1:1:-1, \text{ passes through } (0, 0, -2)$$

and
$$3x-2y+2z = 5, \text{ DRN } 3:-2:2, \text{ passes through } (0, 0, \tfrac{5}{2})$$

The planes are not parallel so they will intersect in a line. They meet on the $z = 0$ plane where

$$\left.\begin{aligned} x+y &= 2 \\ 3x-2y &= 5 \end{aligned}\right\} \quad \text{i.e.} \quad (\tfrac{9}{5}, \tfrac{1}{5}, 0)$$

They intersect on the $z = 1$ plane where

$$\left.\begin{array}{r} x+y=3 \\ 3x-2y=3 \end{array}\right\} \quad \text{i.e.} \quad (\tfrac{9}{5}, \tfrac{6}{5}, 1)$$

The line of intersection has DR $0:1:1$ and passes through $(\frac{9}{5}, \frac{1}{5}, 0)$ so its equation is

$$\frac{x-\frac{9}{5}}{0} = \frac{y-\frac{1}{5}}{1} = \frac{z}{1} = k,$$

or parametrically

$$x = \tfrac{9}{5} \qquad y = k + \tfrac{1}{5} \qquad z = k$$

Now consider the third plane

$$7x - 3y + 3z = 12, \text{ DRN } 7:-3:3, \text{ passes through } (0, 0, 4)$$

This intersects the line when

$$7(\tfrac{9}{5}) - 3(k + \tfrac{1}{5}) + 3(k) = 12$$

which leads to the identity $12 \equiv 12$. This means that the line lies in the third plane since it satisfies the equation of the third plane. All three planes therefore intersect in the same line.

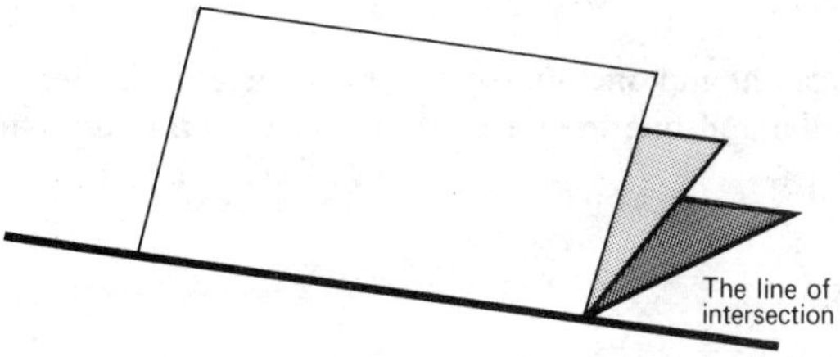

(*d*) *The three planes may form a prism*

Consider again the two planes $x+y-z = 2$ and $3x-2y+2z = 5$ whose line of intersection has DR, $0:1:1$, and passes through $(\frac{9}{5}, \frac{1}{5}, 0)$.

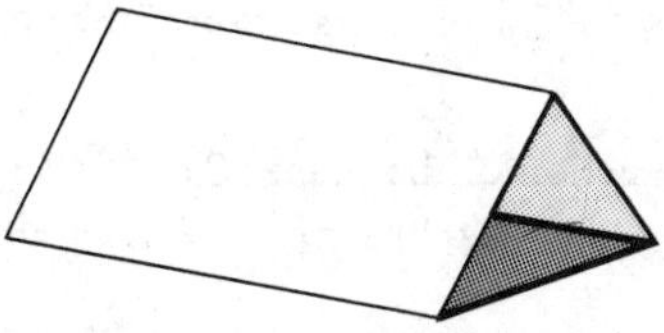

Now consider a third plane $7x - 3y + 3z = 4$. The line intersects this plane if we can find k to satisfy $7(\frac{9}{5}) - 3(k + \frac{1}{5}) + 3(k) = 4$. But this leads to the inconsistency $12 = 4$ which can never be true. Hence there is no point of intersection and so the plane must be parallel to the line. This can be checked, since if the plane's normal is perpendicular to the line, the dot product of DR is zero.

DRN plane $7:-3:3$ DR line $0:1:1$ and $(7:-3:3)\cdot(0:1:1) = 0$

In this case there are no intersections of all three planes, each pair of planes meeting in parallel lines.

(e) The three planes may meet in a point

Consider again the two planes

$$\left.\begin{aligned} x+y-z &= 2 \\ 3x-2y+2z &= 5 \end{aligned}\right\} \quad \text{meeting in the line} \quad x = \tfrac{9}{5}, \quad y = k+\tfrac{1}{5}, \quad z = k$$

Suppose we have a third plane $-x+3y+z = 0$. The line meets this plane where

$$-\tfrac{9}{5}+3(k+\tfrac{1}{5})+k = 0$$

$$k = \tfrac{3}{10}$$

Hence the line meets the plane at $(\frac{9}{5}, \frac{1}{2}, \frac{3}{10})$. The intersection of the three planes is thus the point $(\frac{9}{5}, \frac{1}{2}, \frac{3}{10})$. We now mention three other possibilities:
(f) Two coincident and one parallel plane have no intersection common to all three.
(g) Two coincident and one intersecting plane meet in a line.
(h) Two parallel and one intersecting plane have no intersection common to all three.

Exercise 2.4a

1 Show that the line joining $(4, 3, 5)$ to $(7, -4, 6)$ is parallel to the plane $5x+2y-z = 10$ and not lying in the plane.

2 Find the coordinates of the point where the line joining $(1, 2, 3)$ to $(2, 3, 4)$ meets the plane $2x+3y+z = 1$.

3 Find the line of intersection of the planes $x-3y-z = -8$ and $x-y+z = 2$. Find the coordinates of the point where this line cuts the plane containing the x and y axes.

4 Illustrate on a diagram the line of intersection of the planes $z = 1$ and $2y+z = 7$. Find its equation.

5 Find the line of intersection of the planes $2x-y+5z = 7$ and $5x+3y-z = 4$. Find the value of D if the plane $3x+4y-6z = D$ contains the line.

Exercise 2.4b

In each question three planes are given. Find their intersection, where it exists and give a sketch of your solutions. Each set of equations gives a different type of solution.

1
$$\begin{aligned} 3x-y+2z &= 6 \\ -6x+2y-4z &= -12 \\ 9x-3y+6z &= 18 \end{aligned}$$

2
$$\begin{aligned} x+2y-3z &= 6 \\ 2x+4y-6z &= 24 \\ -x-2y+3z &= 6 \end{aligned}$$

3
$$\begin{aligned} x+y-2z &= 4 \\ 3x-y+z &= 3 \\ 5x+y-3z &= 11 \end{aligned}$$

4
$$\begin{aligned} -x+y-z &= 3 \\ 2x-y+z &= 4 \\ -x+2y-2z &= 10 \end{aligned}$$

5
$$\begin{aligned} -x+4y+3z &= 1 \\ 2x-7y-5z &= -1 \\ -3x+11y+7z &= 1 \end{aligned}$$

6
$$\begin{aligned} x+2y-z &= 4 \\ 3x+6y-3z &= 12 \\ -2x-4y+2z &= 8 \end{aligned}$$

7
$$\begin{aligned} 3x-6y+3z &= 12 \\ x-2y+z &= 4 \\ x+y-z &= 3 \end{aligned}$$

8
$$\begin{aligned} 2x+3y-z &= 6 \\ -2x-3y+z &= 12 \\ x+y+z &= 3 \end{aligned}$$

2.5 Angles between lines and planes

To describe the direction of a line

(a) In a plane, we give the direction of a line by specifying the angle between the line and a known direction—usually the positive x axis. Here $0 \leqslant \theta \leqslant 90°$ and is measured anti-clockwise:

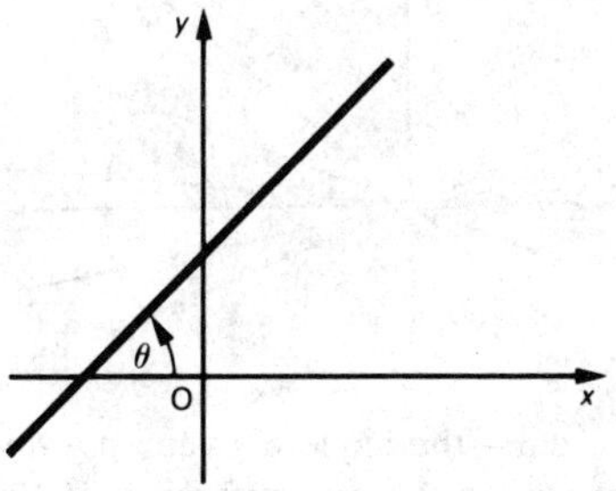

In this diagram θ is obtuse:

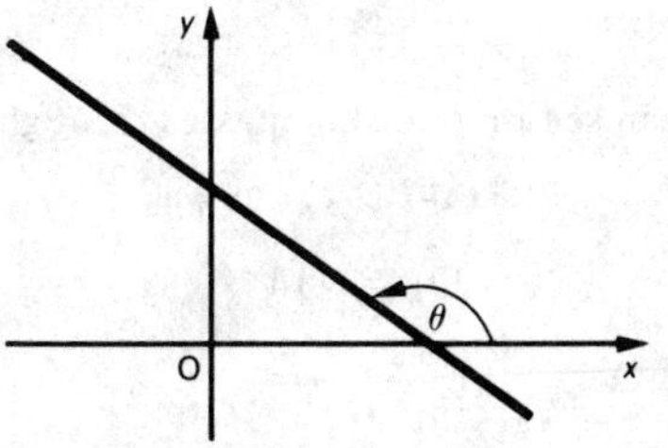

Clearly, in a plane one angle is sufficient to determine direction (but this is not sufficient to enable us to position the line).

(b) In space, consider a line such as

$$\frac{x}{3} = \frac{y}{2} = \frac{z}{1}$$

This passes through (0, 0, 0) and has DR 3 : 2 : 1. To specify its direction in space we need *two* angles. (One angle would only tell us that the line lies on the surface of a cone—see diagram below.)

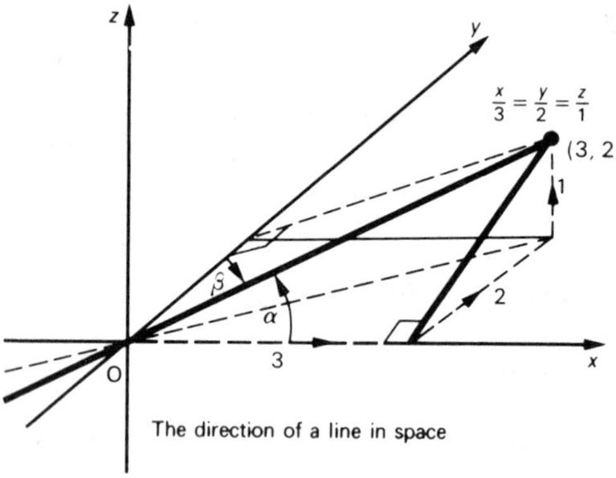

The direction of a line in space

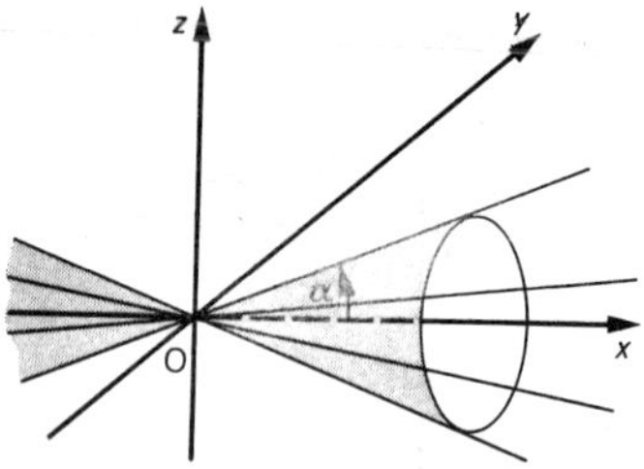

The two angles we use are α—the angle between *positive* x axis and the line, and β—the angle between the *positive* y axis and the line. For the sake of symmetry a third angle γ is introduced—this is the angle between the *positive* z axis and the line.

Direction cosines

From its equation we can see that our line passes through P(3, 2, 1).

$$\mathrm{OP}^2 = 3^2 + 2^2 + 1^2$$

so

$$\mathrm{OP} = \sqrt{14}$$

Hence

$$\cos\alpha = \frac{3}{\sqrt{14}}, \qquad \cos\beta = \frac{2}{\sqrt{14}} \qquad \text{and} \qquad \cos\gamma = \frac{1}{\sqrt{14}}$$

These values are called the *direction cosines* of the line.

Example

OLM is the end of a roof with L(4, 1, 2) being at the top.

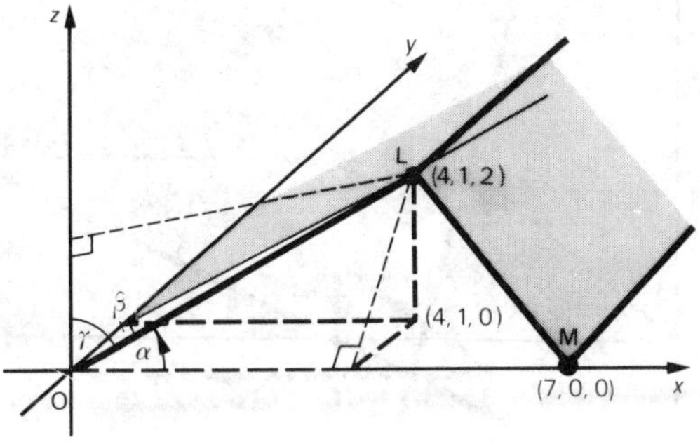

Find (i) the direction cosines (now to be abbreviated to DC) of OL, and (ii) the DC of LM.

(i) Now $OL^2 = 4^2+1^2+2^2$ so $OL = \sqrt{21}$. The DR of OL are $4:1:2$ and

$$\cos\alpha = \frac{4}{\sqrt{21}}, \qquad \cos\beta = \frac{1}{\sqrt{21}}, \qquad \cos\gamma = \frac{2}{\sqrt{21}}$$

(ii) Also $LM^2 = (4-7)^2+1^2+2^2$ so $LM = \sqrt{14}$. LM has DR $-3:1:2$ so

$$\cos\alpha_1 = \frac{-3}{\sqrt{14}}, \qquad \cos\beta_1 = \frac{1}{\sqrt{14}}, \qquad \cos\gamma_1 = \frac{2}{\sqrt{14}}$$

where α_1, β_1, γ_1 are the angles between LM and the positive x, y and z axes.

NOTE that the direction cosines can always be found from the direction ratios. If the direction ratios are $a:b:c$ then the direction cosines are given by

$$\frac{a}{\sqrt{(a^2+b^2+c^2)}}, \qquad \frac{b}{\sqrt{(a^2+b^2+c^2)}} \qquad \text{and} \qquad \frac{c}{\sqrt{(a^2+b^2+c^2)}}$$

The angle between two lines in space

Consider the lines

$$\frac{x-2}{3} = \frac{y-1}{2} = \frac{z+1}{1} \qquad \text{and} \qquad \frac{x-2}{-1} = \frac{y-1}{2} = \frac{z+1}{-3}$$

The two lines intersect at $(2, 1, -1)$ and have DR $3:2:1$ and $-1:2:-3$ respectively. From our previous formula in 2D (p. 154) we might expect

$$\cos\theta = \frac{l_1l_2+m_1m_2+n_1n_2}{\sqrt{(l_1^2+m_1^2+n_1^2)}\sqrt{(l_2^2+m_2^2+n_2^2)}}$$

$$= \frac{3\times-1+2\times2+1\times-3}{\sqrt{(3^2+2^2+1^2)}\sqrt{[(-1)^2+2^2+(-3)^2]}}$$

$$= \frac{-2}{14} = \frac{-1}{7}$$

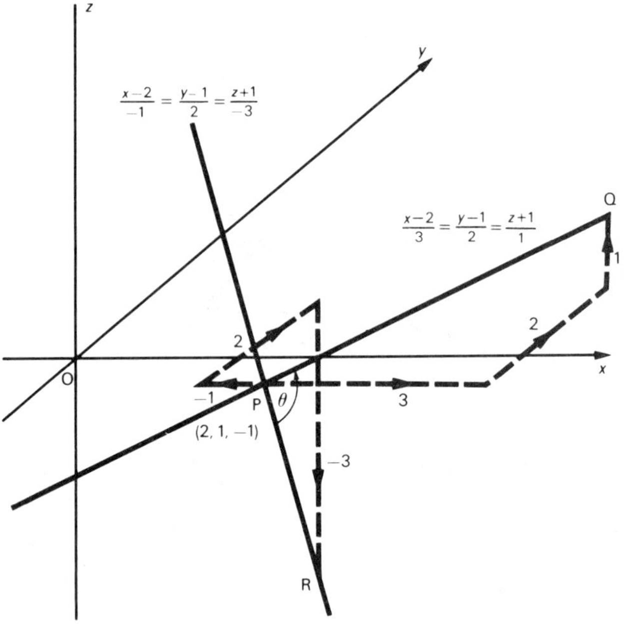

We now show that this formula is true in general. Suppose the two lines intersect at P and have DR $l_1:m_1:n_1$ and $l_2:m_2:n_2$. Suppose Q and R have coordinates (l_1, m_1, n_1) and (l_2, m_2, n_2) relative to P.

Then
$$PQ^2 = l_1^2+m_1^2+n_1^2$$
$$PR^2 = l_2^2+m_2^2+n_2^2$$
$$RQ^2 = (l_1-l_2)^2+(m_1-m_2)^2+(n_1-n_2)^2$$

If we use the cosine formula for the triangle PQR we have

$$\cos\theta = \frac{PQ^2+PR^2-RQ^2}{2PQ\cdot PR}$$

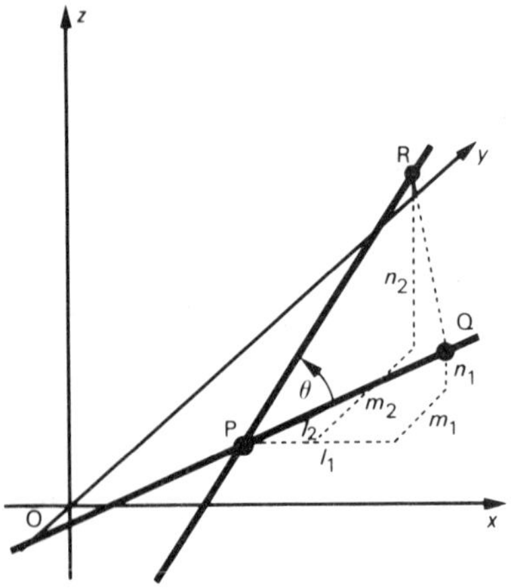

$$\cos\theta = \frac{l_1^2+m_1^2+n_1^2+l_2^2+m_2^2+n_2^2 - (l_1^2+l_2^2-2l_1l_2+m_1^2+m_2^2-2m_1m_2+n_1^2+n_2^2-2n_1n_2)}{2\sqrt{(l_1^2+m_1^2+n_1^2)}\sqrt{(l_2^2+m_2^2+n_2^2)}}$$

$$= \frac{2l_1l_2+2m_1m_2+2n_1n_2}{2\sqrt{(l_1^2+m_1^2+n_1^2)}\sqrt{(l_2^2+m_2^2+n_2^2)}}$$

$$\boldsymbol{\cos\theta = \frac{l_1l_2+m_1m_2+n_1n_2}{\sqrt{(l_1^2+m_1^2+n_1^2)}\sqrt{(l_2^2+m_2^2+n_2^2)}}}$$ ◀

Angle 'between' skew lines

We have seen that the cosine of the angle between two intersecting lines is given in terms of the dot product of the DR divided by suitable lengths (which also depend on the DR).

If the lines are in the same direction, the lines are parallel and the DR of each will be identical and $\cos\theta = 1$, i.e. $\theta = 0$.

If the two lines are not in the same direction and are skew, then it is still possible to calculate $\cos\theta$ (although θ cannot be measured using the given lines).

For example, consider again the skew lines

$$\frac{x-1}{1} = \frac{y+1}{2} = \frac{z+2}{3} \quad \text{through } (1, -1, -2), \text{ DR } 1:2:3$$

and

$$\frac{x+1}{1} = \frac{y}{1} = \frac{z-1}{1} \quad \text{through } (-1, 0, 1), \text{ DR } 1:1:1$$

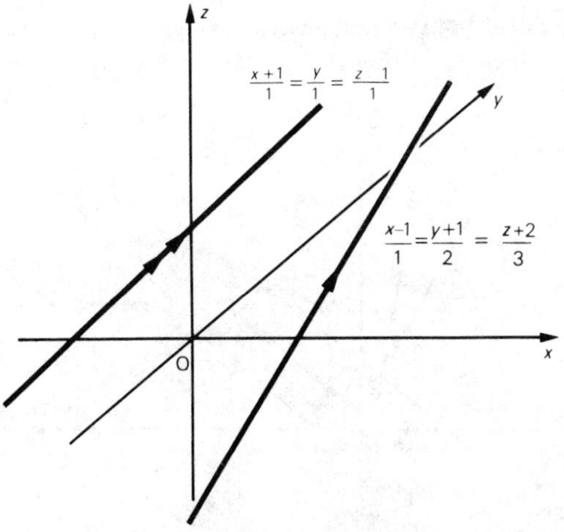

We can calculate $\cos\theta$ using

$$\cos\theta = \frac{1\times1+1\times2+1\times3}{\sqrt{(1^2+1^2+1^2)}\sqrt{(1^2+2^2+3^2)}}$$

$$= \frac{6}{\sqrt{3}\sqrt{14}} = \frac{\sqrt{6}}{\sqrt{7}}$$

The angle is the same as that between two *intersecting* lines parallel to the given *skew* lines. For example, θ is the angle between

$$\frac{x}{1} = \frac{y}{2} = \frac{z}{3} \qquad \text{DR } 1:2:3$$

and

$$\frac{x}{1} = \frac{y}{1} = \frac{z}{1} \qquad \text{DR } 1:1:1$$

which both pass through the origin.

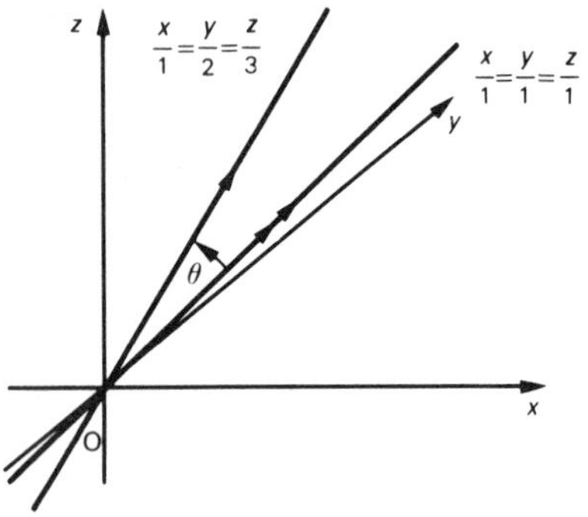

Angle between two planes

Consider, for example, the planes

$$x+y-4z = -1 \qquad \text{and} \qquad 2x-3y+4z = -5$$

The first plane has DRN $1:1:-4$ and passes through $(0, 0, \frac{1}{4})$. The second has DRN $2:-3:4$ and passes through $(0, 0, -\frac{5}{4})$.

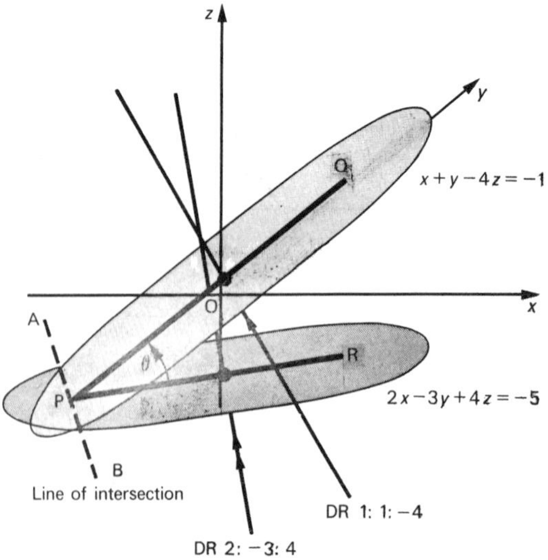

Choose a point P on the line of intersection of the two planes AB. Construct PQ perpendicular to AB where Q lies in the first plane. Construct PR perpendicular to AB where R lies in the second plane. The angle between the two planes, θ, is defined as the angle between PQ and PR.

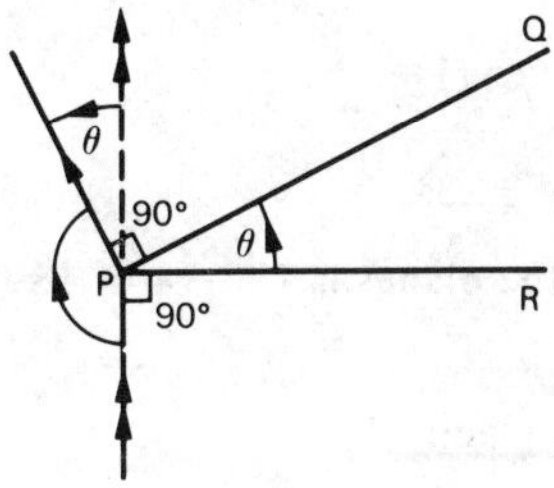

Construct the normals to the two planes at P as shown. These four lines lie in a plane so the acute angle between the two normals is θ. In this case the acute angle between the normals is given by

$$\cos\theta = \left|\frac{1\times 2+1\times -3+-4\times 4}{\sqrt{[1^2+1^2+(-4)^2]}\sqrt{[2^2+(-3)^2+4^2]}}\right|$$

$$= \frac{17}{\sqrt{18}\sqrt{29}}$$

$$\theta = 41.92^\circ$$

Perpendicular planes

We know that vertical planes are perpendicular to horizontal ones. e.g. $Ax+By = D$ with DRN $A:B:0$ is perpendicular to $Cz = E$ with DRN $0:0:C$. It is clear that the dot product of DRN is zero. *In general* if the normals to two planes are perpendicular then so are the planes. For example $2x-3y+z = 5$ will be perpendicular to $3x+y-3z = 2$ since $2\times 3-3\times 1+1\times -3 = 0$.

Example

Two adjacent sides of a roof, whose horizontal bases meet at right angles, slope at 30° and 45° to the horizontal. At what angle do the sides of the roof intersect?

The normal to the front face is at 60° to the horizontal with DR $0:1:-\sqrt{3}$

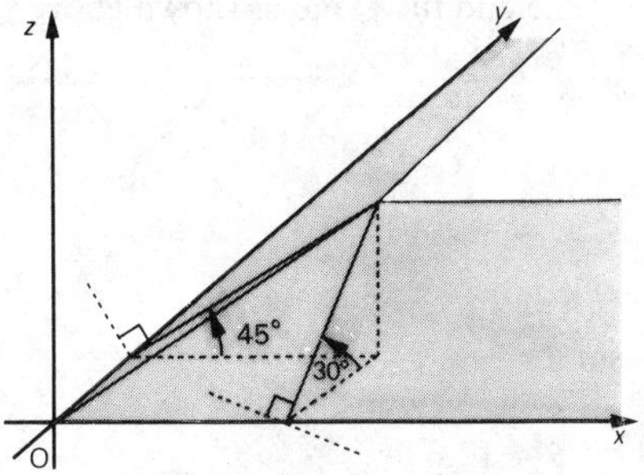

Adjacent sides of a roof

The normal to the side face is at 45° to the horizontal as shown with DR 1 : 0 : −1. The acute angle between the planes ϕ, is equal to the angle between the normals.

$$\cos\phi = \left|\frac{1\times 0+0\times 1+-1\times -\surd 3}{\surd[1^2+0^2+(-1)^2]\surd[0^2+1^2+(\surd 3)^2]}\right|$$

$$= \frac{\surd 3}{\surd 2\surd 4} = \frac{\surd 6}{4}$$

$$\phi = 52.23°$$

The obtuse angle between the planes is $180-\phi = 180°-52.23° = 127.77°$.

Angle between a line and a plane

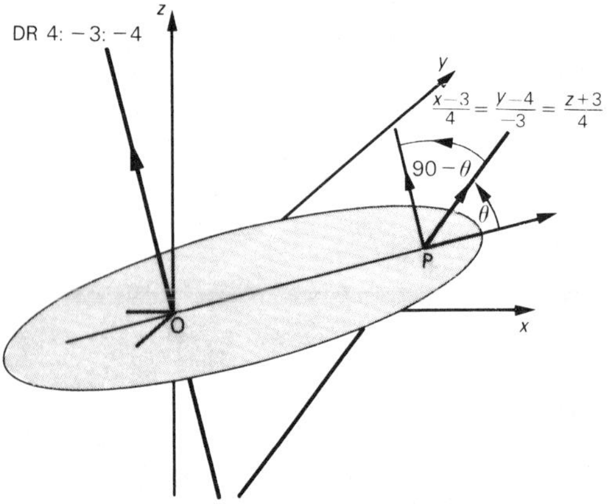

For example, to find the angle between the line

$$\frac{x-3}{4} = \frac{y-4}{-3} = \frac{z+3}{4}$$

and the plane $4x-3y-4z = 0$. The line passes through (3, 4, −3) with DR 4 : −3 : 4, whilst the plane passes through (0, 0, 0) with DRN 4 : −3 : −4. We see that the line and the plane are not parallel and so they will intersect at some point P. Construct the normal to the plane at P. The angle between the normal and the line is $90°-\theta$ where θ is the angle between the line and the plane as shown above.

$$\cos(90°-\theta) = \frac{4\times 4+-3\times -3+4\times -4}{\surd[4^2+(-3)^2+4^2]\surd[4^2+(-3)^2+(-4)^2]}$$

$$= \frac{9}{41}$$

Hence $$\sin\theta = \frac{9}{41}$$

$$\theta = 12.68°$$

Exercise 2.5

1 Find the direction cosines of the line PQ in each of the following cases

(a) P(2, 0, 1) Q(3, 1, 2) **(b)** P(−1, 1, 0) Q(1, 2, −3)
(c) P(a, $2a$, 0) Q(0, $-a$, a)

2 Find the angles of the triangle with vertices (0, 1, −1), (2, 3, 1), (1, 2, 3).

3 Find the cosine of the angle between the two lines

$$\frac{x}{2} = \frac{y-1}{-3} = \frac{z+1}{-1} \quad \text{and} \quad \frac{x-1}{1} = \frac{y+2}{0} = \frac{z-1}{-2}$$

4 Show that the two skew lines

$$\frac{x-1}{2} = \frac{y+1}{3} = \frac{z+1}{2} \quad \text{and} \quad \frac{x+1}{1} = \frac{y-2}{2} = \frac{z}{-4}$$

are perpendicular.

5 A tetrahedron has vertices A(0, 1, 0), B(0, 0, 2), C(1, 1, 0), D(−1, 0, −1). Find the acute angle between the opposite edges AB and CD.

6 Find the cosine of the acute angle between the planes

$$2x - y = 0 \quad \text{and} \quad x + y + z = 0$$

7 Find the cosine of the acute angle between the line

$$\frac{x-2}{2} = \frac{y-1}{2} = \frac{z}{1}$$

and the plane $3x - 2y + 2z + 4 = 0$

8 Find the equation of the plane passing through (3, 1, 1) and perpendicular to the line with DR $-1:2:3$.

9 DRN to a plane are $-1:2:3$. It is at a distance of 8 units from 0. Find the equation of the plane.

10 The equation of a plane is $3x + 2y - z = 5$. Find

(a) its perpendicular distance from the origin, and
(b) the angles its normal makes with the axes.

Miscellaneous examination questions 13

(J.M.B. unless stated otherwise)

1 Two lines L and M are given respectively by the parametric equations

$$x = 1 + t, \quad y = -3 + 2t, \quad z = 6 - 2t$$

and $$x = -u, \quad y = 1 + u, \quad z = -4 + 5u$$

Given that P and Q are points on L and M respectively such that PQ is perpendicular to L, show that the parameters of P and Q satisfy the equation $t+u = 3$. Given that PQ is perpendicular to both L and M find the coordinates of P and Q and the length of PQ.

2
$$\begin{pmatrix} a_1 \\ a_2 \\ a_3 \end{pmatrix}, \quad \begin{pmatrix} b_1 \\ b_2 \\ b_3 \end{pmatrix} \quad \text{etc.}$$

are position vectors of four points A, B, C, D which form the vertices of a tetrahedron.

(a) Write down the position vectors of P, Q, R, S, the mid-points of AB, BC, CD, DA respectively.

(b) Find PQ and RS.

(c) Find the direction ratios of PQ and SR.

(d) What can you deduce about the quadrilateral PQRS? Give your reasons.

3 Prove that the lines

$$\frac{x-2}{1} = \frac{y-3}{4} = \frac{z-10}{8}$$

$$\frac{x-3}{2} = \frac{y+4}{-3} = \frac{z-8}{6}$$

$$\frac{x-2}{1} = \frac{y-1}{2} = \frac{z-4}{2}$$

are concurrent and find the coordinates of their point of intersection P.

The coordinates of the points A, B, C are (2, 3, 10), (3, −4, 8), (2, 1, 4) respectively. Prove that

(a) The area of the parallelogram having PB, PC as sides is $21 \sin \theta$, where $\cos \theta = \frac{8}{21}$

(b) the distance of A from the plane containing PB and PC is $46/\sqrt{377}$.

Deduce the volume of a parallelopiped having PA, PB, PC as edges. (L.)

4 A regular tetrahedron ABCO has vertices A, B and O which lie in the plane $z = 0$, where O is the origin and A is a point (4, 0, 0). If the coordinates of C are all positive, find the coordinates of B and C. Determine the direction cosines of the straight line through B and C and write down equations for this line. Find also the equation for the plane which contains BC and is parallel to OA. (L.)

5 (a) AA′, BB′, CC′ and DD′ are edges of a cube perpendicular to the face ABCD. The edges of the cube are of length a. Find

(i) the perpendicular distance of D′ from the diagonal AC′,

(ii) the shortest distance between the edge DD′ and the diagonal AC′.

(b) A plane is drawn through the line $x+y = 2$, $z = 0$ to make an angle $\cos^{-1}\left(\frac{2\sqrt{2}}{3}\right)$ with the plane $x+y+z = 0$. Prove that two such planes can be drawn and find their equations.

6 Find the equation of the plane which contains the points P$(1, -3, -4)$ and Q$(-1, 0, 5)$ and is perpendicular to the plane $3x+7y-2z+5=0$. Find parametric equations for the locus of points in the plane $3x+7y-2z+5=0$ equidistant from P and Q. (L.)

7 (a) Prove that the three lines through the origin whose direction cosines are proportional to $(1, -1, 1)$, $(1, -3, 2)$ and $(2, 0, 1)$ are coplanar and write down the equation of the plane which contains them.

(b) Prove that the points $(1, 3, 2)$, $(-1, 2, 3)$ and $(5, 5, 0)$ are collinear and find the equation of the line on which they lie.

(c) Find the angle between the line of part **(b)** and the plane of part **(a)**.

8 The points A, B, C have position vectors ***a***, ***b***, ***c*** given by

$$\boldsymbol{a} = \begin{pmatrix} 2 \\ 0 \\ 0 \end{pmatrix}, \qquad \boldsymbol{b} = \begin{pmatrix} 0 \\ 5 \\ 0 \end{pmatrix}, \qquad \boldsymbol{c} = \begin{pmatrix} 3 \\ 2 \\ 9 \end{pmatrix}$$

and O is the origin.

(a) Find the perpendicular distance of C from the plane OAB and hence or otherwise the volume of the tetrahedron OABC.

(b) Show that the Cartesian equation of the plane through A, B, C is $5x+2y-z=10$.

(c) Find the direction cosines of the line drawn from O perpendicular to and towards the plane ABC, and the coordinates of the foot of this perpendicular. (M.E.I.)

9 A plane π is perpendicular to each of the planes $3x+y+z=0$ and $4x-2y+3z=0$ and passes through the point A$(2, 1, 3)$. Find the equation of the plane π and determine the direction cosines of OM where M is the foot of the normal drawn to π from the origin O. Obtain the equations of the line through B$(1, 1, 1)$ which is perpendicular to π.

10(a) Find the equation of the plane β which contains the point P$(0, 4, 3)$ and the line q whose equations are

$$\frac{x+1}{2} = \frac{y-6}{-1} = \frac{z-1}{-2}$$

Find also the coordinates of the point in which the line through A$(-2, 5, -3)$ and B$(4, 2, 3)$ meets the plane β.

(b) Show that the point $(2, 3, 1)$ is equidistant from the point P and the line q.

11 Prove that the two lines

$$\frac{x+1}{1} = \frac{y}{1} = \frac{z-5}{-1} \quad \text{and} \quad \frac{x-3}{2} = \frac{y-1}{-1} = \frac{z-4}{1}$$

intersect and find the coordinates of their point of intersection.

(b) Find the equation of the plane passing through the point $(1, 2, 1)$ and containing the line

$$\frac{x+2}{3} = \frac{y+1}{1} = \frac{z+1}{2}$$

Show that the plane is parallel to the y axis and find the volume of the prism enclosed by it and the planes $x = 0$, $z = 0$, $y = 0$, and $y = 3$.

12 Show that the equations of the line of intersection of planes $4x+4y-5z = 12$ and $8x+12y-13z = 32$ may be written as

$$\frac{x-1}{2} = \frac{y-2}{3} = \frac{z}{4}$$

Obtain the equation of the plane through the origin perpendicular to the given planes and find the point of intersection of the three planes.

13(a) If l, m, n are the direction cosines of a straight line, prove that

$$l^2+m^2+n^2 = 1$$

(b) A plane P is perpendicular to the plane $x+y+3z = 0$ and the plane $3x-2y+4z = 0$ and passes through the point (1, 1, 1). Find

(i) the direction ratios of the normal to P,

(ii) the equation of P,

(iii) the foot of the perpendicular to P from the origin.

14 Show that the lines whose equations are

$$\frac{x+5}{2} = \frac{y+4}{2} = \frac{z+9}{4} \quad \text{and} \quad \frac{x+1}{2} = \frac{y-1}{1} = \frac{z-2}{1}$$

intersect and find their point of intersection. Find the equation of the plane in which both lines lie. Find also the equations of the planes which are parallel to both of the above lines and distant $\sqrt{11}$ units from them.

15(a) The equations of a line and plane are

$$\frac{x-2}{1} = \frac{y-2}{2} = \frac{z-3}{2}$$

and $2x+y+4z = 9$ respectively. P is the point on the line where x is 3. N is the foot of the perpendicular from the point P to the plane. Find

(i) the coordinates of N

(ii) The cosine of the angle between NP and the line.

(b) Find the coordinates of the points where the line of intersection of the planes $x-2y+z = -2$ and $2x-y+3z = 1$ cuts the sphere $x^2+y^2+z^2 = 9$.

16 The equations of the lines p, q, r are respectively

$$x-2 = \frac{y-2}{3} = z-3$$

$$x-2 = \frac{y-3}{4} = \frac{z-4}{2}$$

$$\frac{x-5}{2} = \frac{y+1}{-3} = z-2$$

Show that p and q intersect and find the equation of their plane, π. Determine the coordinates of the point C at which r meets π and deduce that r meets neither p nor q.

Find the equation of the plane which contains r and is perpendicular to π.

17 Find the equations of the line through the origin perpendicular to the plane with the equation $3x+2y-4z = 3$. Find the shortest distance from the origin to the plane. (A.E.B.)

18 Find the distance of the point (2, 4, 7) from the plane determined by the points (3, 4, 4), (4, 5, 7), and (6, 8, 9).

19 Find the equations of the line through A(−1, 4, 2) meeting both the lines

$$\frac{x-1}{1} = \frac{y-2}{2} = \frac{z-3}{-1} \quad \text{and} \quad \frac{x+2}{-1} = \frac{y-1}{2} = \frac{z+3}{-3}$$

Find also the equation of the plane through the first of the given lines and parallel to the second.

Find the perpendicular distance from A to the plane through the origin containing the first of the given lines. (L.)

20 Two adjacent portions of the roof of a building are parts of the planes whose equations are $z = \frac{1}{2}x+12$, $z = \frac{2}{3}y+12$; and the z axis is vertical, the origin is a point on the horizontal ground and distances are measured in metres. The line L of intersection of the planes meets the ground at P.

(i) Find the coordinates of P.

(ii) Express the equation of L in the form

$$\frac{x-a}{p} = \frac{y-b}{q} = \frac{z-c}{r}$$

(iii) Write down the direction cosines $\cos\theta_1$, $\cos\theta_2$, $\cos\theta_3$ of the line L and interpret the angles θ_1, θ_2, θ_3 in relation to the building.

(iv) Calculate to the nearest half degree, the angles between each of the given planes and the ground. Show that the angle inside the roof space between the two given planes is an obtuse angle (you are not required to calculate the value of the angle). (M.E.I.)

21 The cross section of a right prism is an equilateral triangle. The rectangular face ABCD of the prism lies in the plane $x+y+5z = \sqrt{2}$ where A and B are the points $(0, \sqrt{2}, 0)$ and $(\sqrt{2}, 0, 0)$ respectively. EF is the edge in which the other two rectangular faces ADEF and BCEF meet. Prove that the equation of the plane containing A, B, F is $5x+5y-2z = 5\sqrt{2}$. If the origin lies inside the prism, determine the equations of the edge EF. (L.)

22 To find the position of an underground rock layer, a number of trial borings are made at points on horizontal ground which form a coordinate grid. Results are as follows, units being 1000 ft.

Grid Pair:	(0, 0)	(2, 0)	(0, 2)	(2, 2)
Depth:	(0.270)	(0.225)	(0.162)	(0.117)

Show that these results are consistent with this part of the rock layer being a plane. Find the x, y equation of the line in which this plane when produced would meet the ground, and show that the plane would be inclined at about $3\frac{1}{3}°$ to the ground.

What would you conclude if a boring at (1, 1) gave a depth of about 0.18?

Chapter 14

Errors

Introduction

This chapter is not concerned with the errors that are mistakes or blunders, but with the unavoidable inexactness or inaccuracy of all measurements, most calculations and many formulae. Blunders can be eliminated with careful checking. Errors are inevitable and must be taken into account and, as far as possible, kept within bounds.

1 Inexact numbers

1.1 Types of errors in numbers

As all irrational and most rational numbers are non-terminating decimals, it is usually necessary to *round* them. There are two well-known rounding techniques: *decimal places* (abbreviated to D) and *significant figures* (abbreviated to S). Several different ways have been adopted to deal with the case in which the final digit is a 5. We shall always round such numbers *upwards*.

Example 1

$$
\begin{aligned}
11.6955 &= 11.696 && \text{rounded to 5S or 3D}\\
&= 11.70 && \text{rounded to 4S or 2D}\\
&= 11.7 && \text{rounded to 3S or 1D}\\
&= 12 && \text{rounded to 2S}\\
&= 10 && \text{rounded to 1S}
\end{aligned}
$$

Most computers do not round but chop (or truncate). This is because the accuracy that would be gained by rounding is usually not worth the extra time involved.

Example 2

$$
\begin{aligned}
11.6955 &= 11.695 && \text{chopped to 5S}\\
&= 11.6 && \text{chopped to 3S}\\
&= 10 && \text{chopped to 1S}
\end{aligned}
$$

As a result of rounding or chopping there is a *round-off error* in most of the numbers we use. This is not the only source of error, however. There may be *inherent errors* in the data we are working with, especially if these are measurements. These can never be exact, but will depend on the precision of the measuring instrument. There is a third type of error known as a *truncation error* which occurs when we use only the first few terms of an infinite series in the evaluation of a function.

In numerical work errors are unavoidable. It is therefore essential to investigate the size of the error resulting from a calculation involving inexact numbers and to specify the *error bounds* for the number we have calculated. These are the limits between which the error lies. For example, if we know that the number 2.51 has been rounded, we know that the exact value lies between 2.505 and 2.515. This is usually expressed as

$$2.51 \pm 0.005$$

and the error bounds in this number are ± 0.005. Again, a man's height may be measured as 183 cm to the nearest centimetre. It therefore lies between 182.5 and 183.5 cm and may be given as

$$183 \pm 0.5 \text{ cm}$$

with error bounds ± 0.5. If a physical quantity such as the density of a substance is determined by experiment, its value may be given as

$$4.32 \pm 0.13 \text{ g cm}^{-3}$$

where the calculated error bounds are ± 0.13 and the true value lies between 4.19 and 4.45 g cm^{-3}.

Notation

We use capital letters for exact numbers (numbers without error), small letters corresponding to inexact numbers. Thus x is an approximation to X. The error in x we denote δx, with $\text{X} = x + \delta x$, so that δx may be positive or negative. Then

the absolute error in x is defined as $|\delta x|$. ◀

Suppose, for example, that X is the sum of the three angles in a triangle and when measuring the angles with a protractor, we arrive at the sum of 181°. Then

$$\text{X} = 180°, \ x = 181°, \ \delta x = -1° \qquad \text{and the absolute error in } x \text{ is } 1°.$$

We take the *modulus* or absolute value of the error as we are interested more in its size than its sign. If a number X has been rounded to 3D and $x = 0.034$ then $0.0335 \leqslant \text{X} < 0.0345$. The error bounds are ± 0.0005 or in other words the maximum absolute error is 0.0005.

We can generalize this result as follows:

The maximum absolute error when a number has been rounded to nD is $\frac{1}{2} \times 10^{-n}$ or 5E$-(n+1)$. ◀

1.2 Absolute errors in simple arithmetic calculations

Suppose we have two inexact numbers with known error bounds and we wish to find their sum and its error bounds. It is an easy matter, with an electronic calculator, to find the maximum and the minimum value of the sum. We shall call the mean of the maximum and minimum values the *mid-value*, and the answer when the calculation is carried out on the inexact numbers the *working value.*

Example 1

If $a = 2.41$, $b = 3.37$ and both numbers are rounded, find $A+B$ stating the error bounds of the answer.

$$\text{The working value of } a+b = 2.41 \quad +3.37 \quad = 5.78$$

$$\text{The maximum value of } a+b = 2.415+3.375 = 5.79$$

$$\text{The minimum value of } a+b = 2.405+3.365 = 5.77$$

Hence $\quad$ the mid-value $= \frac{1}{2}(5.79+5.77) = 5.78$

and $\quad$ the error bound $= \frac{1}{2}(5.79-5.77) = 0.01$

In this simple example, the working value and the mid-value are the same, and

$$A+B = 5.78 \pm 0.01$$

Example 2

If $a = 4.63$ and $b = 7.35$, both rounded to 2D, find AB and give the error bounds.

$$\text{The working value of } ab = 4.63 \quad \times 7.35 \quad = 34.030\,5$$

$$\text{The maximum value of } ab = 4.635\times 7.355 = 34.090\,425$$

$$\text{The minimum value of } ab = 4.625\times 7.345 = 33.970\,625$$

Hence $\quad$ the mid-value $= \frac{1}{2}(34.090\,425+33.970\,625) = 34.030\,525$

and $\quad$ the error bound $= \frac{1}{2}(34.090\,425-33.970\,625) = \quad 0.059\,9$

In this example, the working value and the mid-value differ slightly. However it is usual to round the absolute error to 2S and then to round the answer to the same number of decimal places as in the rounded error. Here the error bounds are ± 0.060 (3D) and to 3D both working value and mid-value are equal to 34.031. Hence

$$AB = 34.031 \pm 0.060$$

which means that the true value of AB lies between $34.031-0.060$ and $34.031+0.060$ or

$$33.971 \leqslant AB \leqslant 34.091$$

In more complicated calculations a little thought is necessary to decide whether the maximum or minimum values of the inexact numbers must be substituted to give the maximum value of the answer.

Example 3

Evaluate the expression

$$\frac{17.24}{0.52}-\frac{11.69}{3.18}$$

where all numbers are rounded.

$$\text{Working value} = \frac{17.24}{0.52}-\frac{11.69}{3.18} = 29.477\,745$$

$$\text{Maximum value} = \frac{17.245(\text{max})}{0.515(\text{min})}-\frac{11.685(\text{min})}{3.185(\text{max})} = 29.816\,677$$

$$\text{Minimum value} = \frac{17.235(\text{min})}{0.525(\text{max})}-\frac{11.695(\text{max})}{3.175(\text{min})} = 29.145\,106$$

$$\text{Mid-value} = \tfrac{1}{2}(29.816\,677+29.145\,106) = 29.480\,892$$

$$\text{Maximum absolute error} = \tfrac{1}{2}(29.816\,677-29.145\,106) = 0.335\,785\,5$$

Rounding the error to 2S and either the working or the mid-value to 2D we arrive at

$$29.48 \pm 0.34$$

Exercise 1.2

1 Express to 4D the numbers
(a) 0.128 451 **(b)** 0.129 E-2 **(c)** $0.\dot{8}0\dot{8}$ **(d)** 12.50

2 Express to 4S the numbers
(a) $0.00\dot{3}\dot{5}$ **(b)** 37 519 **(c)** $\frac{8}{9}$ **(d)** $0.00\dot{0}\dot{8}$

3 Express the following inexact numbers in the form

$$a \leqslant x \leqslant b$$

(a) 1.23 (rounded) **(b)** 5740 (rounded to 3S) **(c)** 14.05 (rounded)
(d) 19.3 ± 0.4 **(e)** 27.542 ± 0.087 **(f)** $0.004\,62 \pm 0.000\,24$

4 Give the maximum and minimum values, the mid-value and the error bounds for the following expressions when $p = 1231.5 \pm 0.05$, $q = 439.6 \pm 0.05$

(a) $p+q$ **(b)** $p-q$ **(c)** $q-p$

(d) pq **(e)** $\dfrac{p}{q}$ **(f)** $\dfrac{q}{p}$

5 Evaluate the following expressions, giving the mid values and the error bounds, where $p = 38.12$, $q = 48.35$, $r = 89.06$, $s = 20.58$

(a) $pq+rs$ **(b)** $pq-rs$ **(c)** $\dfrac{p}{q}+\dfrac{r}{s}$ **(d)** $\dfrac{p}{q}-\dfrac{r}{s}$

1.3 Relative errors in numbers

It is often useful to express the error as a proportion. In the example about the sum of the angles of a triangle, where the absolute error is 1°, the proportionate error is 1 in 180 or $1/180 = 0.00\dot{5}$. We define

the relative error in X as $\left|\frac{\delta x}{X}\right|$ or if X is not known (as is usually the case) as $\left|\frac{\delta x}{x}\right|$. ◀

Sometimes the error is given as a percentage. This will be the relative error multiplied by 100, i.e. $\left|\frac{\delta x}{x}\right| \times 100$. If a number is given with its error in *percentage* form, for example

$$85 \pm 2\%$$

this means

$$\begin{aligned} &85 \pm (2\% \text{ of } 85) \\ &= 85 \pm \left(\frac{2}{100} \times 85\right) \\ &= 85 \pm 1.7 \end{aligned}$$

It is important to distinguish between $85 \pm 2\%$ (relative error) and 85 ± 2 (absolute error).

Relative errors often mean more than absolute errors. Here is an illustration. We are more upset if we are 'short-changed' by 5p when buying a newspaper (price 15p) than we would be if we were buying a watch (price £50). The shop keeper's absolute error is the same in each case, 5p, but his relative errors are $0.\dot{3}(33\frac{1}{3}\%)$ and $0.001(0.1\%)$ respectively.

Example 1

In an experiment to verify Boltzmann's Constant (1.380E-23 Joules per degree Kelvin to 4S) the result was 1.41E-23. What are the absolute and relative errors?

Here $X = 1.380\text{E-}23$ and $x = 1.41\text{E-}23$

Since $X = x + \delta x$, $\delta x = 1.380\text{E-}23 - 1.41\text{E-}23$

$$\begin{aligned} &= -0.03\text{E-}23 \\ &= -3\text{E-}25 \text{ J K}^{-1} \end{aligned}$$

Hence the absolute error $= |\delta x| = 3\text{E-}25$

and the relative error $= \left|\frac{\delta x}{X}\right| = 0.022 = 2.2\%$ (to 2S)

This example illustrates two important points.

(1) The absolute error is extremely small, but the relative error is not. Evidently the experiment was not very successful in verifying the value of Boltzmann's Constant for it is the relative error that measures the degree of success—the smaller the relative error the more successful the experiment.
(2) The absolute error is in units of $\mathrm{J\,K^{-1}}$. If it was expressed in $\mathrm{MJ\,K^{-1}}$, for example, it would become 3E-31, if in $\mathrm{mJ\,K^{-1}}$ it would be 3E-19. In other words, the size of the absolute error depends on the units employed. The relative error, on the other hand, is a dimensionless quantity and does not depend on the units employed.

1.4 Absolute and relative errors in calculations

Errors in addition and subtraction

Example 1

If $a = 243.7$, $b = 187.5$, and both numbers are rounded, find (i) $A+B$ (ii) $A-B$ stating their error bounds.

(i) Working value $= 243.7 + 187.5 = 431.2$

Max value $= 243.75 + 187.55 = 431.3$

Min value $= 243.65 + 187.45 = 431.1$

Mid-value and error bounds $= 431.2 \pm 0.1$

$A+B = 431.2 \pm 0.023\%$

(ii) Working value $= 243.7 - 187.5 = 56.2$

Max value $= 243.75 - 187.45 = 56.3$

Min value $= 243.65 - 187.55 = 56.1$

Mid-value and error bounds $= 56.2 \pm 0.1$

$A-B = 56.2 \pm 0.18\%$

We notice that in both (i) and (ii) the absolute error is equal to 0.1, which is the *sum* of the absolute errors in the two numbers being added *or* subtracted. The relative errors, on the other hand, are different, being considerably greater for subtraction than for addition. In extreme cases of the subtraction of nearly equal numbers, this can give rise to very large errors indeed and must be avoided (see Section 2.5).

Errors in multiplication and division

Example 2

Given $c = 57.4$, $d = 29.8$, and both numbers are rounded find (i) CD (ii) C/D stating their error bounds.

(i)

$$\begin{aligned}
\text{Working value} &= 57.4 \times 29.8 &&= 1710.52\\
\text{Max value} &= 57.45 \times 29.85 &&= 1714.8825\\
\text{Min value} &= 57.35 \times 29.75 &&= 1706.1625
\end{aligned}$$

$$\text{Mid-value} = \tfrac{1}{2}(1714.8825 + 1706.1625) = 1710.5225$$

$$\text{Error bound} = \tfrac{1}{2}(1714.8825 - 1706.1625) = 4.36$$

$$CD = 1710.5 \pm 4.4$$

$$= 1710.5 \pm 0.25\%$$

(ii)

$$\begin{aligned}
\text{Working value} &= 57.4 \div 29.8 &&= 1.926\,174\,5\\
\text{Max value} &= 57.45 \div 29.75 &&= 1.931\,092\,4\\
\text{Min value} &= 57.35 \div 29.85 &&= 1.921\,273\,0\\
\text{Mid-value} & &&= 1.926\,182\,7\\
\text{Error bound} & &&= 0.004\,909\,7
\end{aligned}$$

$$C/D = 1.9262 \pm 0.0049$$

$$= 1.9262 \pm 0.25\%$$

The absolute errors in the product and the quotient of c and d are different, but their relative errors are the same. Is this relative error of 0.25% connected with the separate relative errors in c and d?

$$\text{Relative error in } c = \frac{0.05}{57.4} \times 100 = 0.0871$$

$$\text{Relative error in } d = \frac{0.05}{29.8} \times 100 = 0.1678$$

$$\text{Sum of the relative error in } c \text{ and } d = 0.2549\%$$

It seems that when adding or subtracting numbers we can add their *absolute* errors and when multiplying or dividing numbers we can add their *relative* errors. Is this always true?

Example 3

If $e = 4.2 \pm 0.8$ and $f = 2.3 \pm 0.5$ find (i) $E+F$ (ii) $E-F$ (iii) EF (iv) E/F

It is convenient to set the calculations out in a table.

	e	f	$e+f$	$e-f$	ef	e/f
Working value	4.2	2.3	6.5	1.9	9.66	1.8261
Max value	5.0	2.8	7.8	3.2	14	2.7778
Min value	3.4	1.8	5.2	0.6	6.12	1.2143
Mid-value	4.2	2.3	6.5	1.9	10.06	1.9960
Absolute error	0.8	0.5	1.3	1.3	3.94	0.7817
Relative error	19%	22%	20%	68%	39%	39%

We see that it is still true that in addition and subtraction the absolute error in the answers (1.3) is equal to the sum of the absolute errors in the terms $(0.8+0.5)$ but for multiplication and division the relative error in the answers (39%) is only approximately equal to the sum of the relative errors of the factors $(19+22=41)$. The effect that the errors in the constituent numbers of a calculation have on the answer to the calculation is called the *propagation* of errors and we analyze this more formally in the next section.

We also see that when the errors are rounded to 2S and the answers to the same number of decimal places, the working values differ from the mid-values in multiplication and division. We shall take the mid-values for our answers when using this maximum and minimum method.

(i) $E+F = 6.5\pm1.3 = 6.5\pm20\%$ (ii) $E-F = 1.9\pm1.3 = 1.9\pm68\%$
(iii) $EF = 10.1\pm3.9 = 10.1\pm39\%$ (iv) $E/F = 2.00\pm0.78 = 2.0\pm39\%$

Exercise 1.4

1 The numbers below have either been rounded or stated together with their error bounds. In each case give the maximum absolute and relative errors, stating the relative error both as a fraction and as a percentage.

(a) 2.5 **(b)** 2.50 **(c)** 2.500
(d) 1.25×10^{-2} **(e)** 1.250×10^{4} **(f)** 0.05 ± 0.005
(g) $0.05\pm5\%$ **(h)** $1.75\times10^{-6}\pm10\%$ **(i)** $2400\pm2\frac{1}{2}\%$

2 Find the relative error in p and q in Question **4** of Exercise 1.2, and also the relative error in your answer to each part of the question. Check to see if the following rules hold, (i) the absolute error of a sum or difference is equal to the sum of the absolute errors and (ii) the relative error of a product or quotient is approximately equal to the sum of the relative errors.

3 Express your answer to each part of Question **5** in Exercise 1.2 in the form

$$A\pm P\%$$

1.5 Analysis of error propagation

We now consider in general terms the errors arising from addition, subtraction, multiplication and division of inexact numbers.

Addition

Let $z = x+y$ where x and y are inexact

Then if $Z = X+Y$ is the exact result

$$z+\delta z = x+\delta x+y+\delta y$$

Subtracting $\delta z = \delta x+\delta y$

Hence, since δx and δy can be either positive or negative

$$|\boldsymbol{\delta z}| \leqslant |\boldsymbol{\delta x}|+|\boldsymbol{\delta y}|$$ ◄

Subtraction

A similar argument leads to the conclusion

$$\delta z = \delta x - \delta y$$

and so to the same result as for addition

$$|\boldsymbol{\delta z}| \leqslant |\boldsymbol{\delta x}| + |\boldsymbol{\delta y}|$$ ◀

The absolute error in addition or subtraction is less than or equal to the sum of the absolute errors in the terms. ◀

We have met this 'triangle' inequality before on page 277 and it can, of course, be extended to three or more terms:

If $$z = w + x + y$$

$$|\delta z| \leqslant |\delta w| + |\delta x| + |\delta y|$$

Exact multiples

Suppose $$z = \lambda x \qquad \text{where } \lambda \text{ is an exact number}$$

$$z + \delta z = \lambda(x + \delta x)$$

$$\delta z = \lambda \delta x$$

Example 1

Evaluate $A + 2B - 3C$ where $a = 4.5$, $b = 2.3$, and $c = 1.25$ (all rounded) and analyze the errors involved.

Let $$x = a + 2b - 3c = 4.5 + 2(2.3) - 3(1.25) = 5.25$$

$$\delta a = \delta b = 0.05, \text{ and } \delta c = 0.005$$

$$|\delta x| \leqslant |\delta a| + |2\delta b| + |3\delta c|$$

$$|\delta x| \leqslant 0.05 + 0.1 + 0.015 = 0.165$$

Hence $$X = 5.25 \pm 0.17 \qquad \text{or} \qquad 5.08 \leqslant X \leqslant 5.42$$

This gives the *maximum* error bounds; the true error is most unlikely to be as large as 0.165.

Multiplication

If $$z = xy$$

and $$Z = XY \qquad \text{is the exact result}$$

$$z + \delta z = (x + \delta x)(y + \delta y)$$

$$= xy + y\,\delta x + x\,\delta y + \delta x\,\delta y$$

then $$\delta z = y\,\delta x + x\,\delta y + \delta x\,\delta y$$

But if δx and δy are small, $\delta x\,\delta y$ is very small and may be ignored. So

$$\delta z \approx y\,\delta x + x\,\delta y$$

Dividing on the left by z and on the right by xy

$$\frac{\delta z}{z} \approx \frac{\delta x}{x} + \frac{\delta y}{y}$$

Taking moduli

$$\left|\frac{\delta \boldsymbol{z}}{\boldsymbol{z}}\right| \leqslant \left|\frac{\delta \boldsymbol{x}}{\boldsymbol{x}}\right| + \left|\frac{\delta \boldsymbol{y}}{\boldsymbol{y}}\right|$$ ◀

Division

If $z = x/y$

and $Z = X/Y$

$$z + \delta z = (x + \delta x)(y + \delta y)^{-1}$$

$$= (x + \delta x)y^{-1}\left(1 + \frac{\delta y}{y}\right)^{-1}$$

$$\approx \left(\frac{x}{y} + \frac{\delta x}{y}\right)\left(1 - \frac{\delta y}{y}\right) \qquad \text{ignoring terms in } (\delta y)^2 \ldots$$

then $$z + \delta z \approx \frac{x}{y} + \frac{\delta x}{y} - \frac{x}{y}\frac{\delta y}{y} \qquad \text{ignoring the term in } \delta x\,\delta y$$

Subtracting $$\delta z \approx \frac{x}{y}\left(\frac{\delta x}{x} - \frac{\delta y}{y}\right)$$

$$\frac{\delta z}{z} \approx \frac{\delta x}{x} - \frac{\delta y}{y} \qquad \text{dividing by } z \text{ and by } \frac{x}{y}$$

As before, taking moduli

$$\left|\frac{\delta \boldsymbol{z}}{\boldsymbol{z}}\right| \leqslant \left|\frac{\delta \boldsymbol{x}}{\boldsymbol{x}}\right| + \left|\frac{\delta \boldsymbol{y}}{\boldsymbol{y}}\right|$$ ◀

The relative error in multiplication or division is less than or equal to the sum of the relative errors in the factors, (so long as these relative errors are small) ◀

Example 2

If the numbers a, b, c, and d are subject to small errors δa, δb, δc, and δd, find the error bounds for

$$\frac{AB}{C + D}$$

The work is best arranged in three columns:

Quantity	Absolute error	Relative error
a	$\lvert\delta a\rvert \longrightarrow$	$\left\lvert\frac{\delta a}{a}\right\rvert$
b	$\lvert\delta b\rvert \longrightarrow$	$\left\lvert\frac{\delta b}{b}\right\rvert$
ab (product: add relative errors)		$\left\lvert\frac{\delta a}{a}\right\rvert + \left\lvert\frac{\delta b}{b}\right\rvert$
c	$\lvert\delta c\rvert$	
d	$\lvert\delta d\rvert$	
$c+d$ (sum: add absolute errors)	$\lvert\delta c\rvert + \lvert\delta d\rvert \longrightarrow$	$\left\lvert\frac{\delta c+\delta d}{c+d}\right\rvert$
$\frac{ab}{c+d}$ (quotient: add relative errors)	$\left(\frac{ab}{c+d}\right)\left(\left\lvert\frac{\delta a}{a}\right\rvert + \left\lvert\frac{\delta b}{b}\right\rvert + \left\lvert\frac{\delta c+\delta d}{c+d}\right\rvert\right) \longleftarrow$	$\left\lvert\frac{\delta a}{a}\right\rvert + \left\lvert\frac{\delta b}{b}\right\rvert + \left\lvert\frac{\delta c+\delta d}{c+d}\right\rvert$

The error bounds are

$$\pm\left(\frac{ab}{c+d}\right)\left(\left|\frac{\delta a}{a}\right| + \left|\frac{\delta b}{b}\right| + \left|\frac{\delta c+\delta d}{c+d}\right|\right)$$

This general result can be applied to particular cases.

If $a = 4.5$, $b = 2.3$, $c = 1.25$, $d = 0.12$ (all rounded) then

$$\frac{ab}{c+d} = \frac{4.5\times 2.3}{1.25+0.12} = 7.554\,744\,5$$

$$\text{Error bound} = 7.5547\left(\frac{0.05}{4.5} + \frac{0.05}{2.3} + \frac{0.005+0.005}{1.25+0.12}\right)$$

$$= 7.5547(0.011\,11 + 0.021\,74 + 0.007\,299)$$

$$= 7.5547 \times 0.040\,149 \approx 0.3033$$

Hence $$\frac{AB}{C+D} = 7.55 \pm 0.30 = 7.55 \pm 4.0\%$$

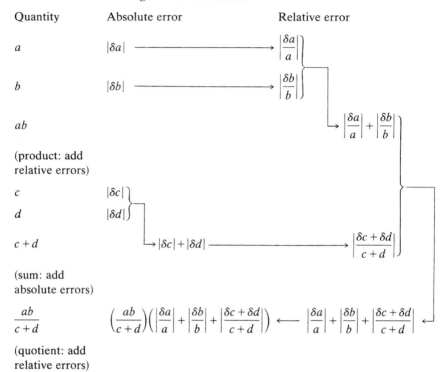

We can compare this result with that obtained by the maximum and minimum method.

$$\text{Working value} = \frac{4.5 \times 2.3}{1.25 + 0.12} = 7.554\ 744\ 5$$

$$\text{Max value} = \frac{4.55 \times 2.35}{1.245 + 0.115} = 7.862\ 132\ 4$$

$$\text{Min value} = \frac{4.45 \times 2.25}{1.255 + 0.125} = 7.255\ 434\ 8$$

$$\text{Mid-value} = 7.558\ 783\ 6$$

$$\text{Error bound} = 0.303\ 348\ 8$$

$$\text{Hence } \frac{AB}{C+D} = 7.56 \pm 0.30 = 7.56 \pm 4.0\%$$

The answers given by the two methods differ by 0.0040 (4D) which is approximately 0.05%.

Rule of thumb

The rule concerning the sum of relative errors for a product or quotient gives a quick method for finding the error bounds (commonly used by physicists).

Example 3

Find $\frac{AB}{C}$ and state its error bounds, when

$a = 3.8 \pm 1.4\%$, $b = 75.2 \pm 2.5\%$, and $c = 9.34 \pm 3.8\%$

$$\frac{AB}{C} = \frac{3.8 \times 75.2}{9.34} \pm (1.4 + 2.5 + 3.8)\%$$

$$= 30.595 \pm 7.7\%$$

$$= 30.6 \pm 7.7\%$$

Exercise 1.5

1 In the expression $a + b - c$ all three numbers have been rounded, with maximum absolute errors of δa, δb and δc. Find a general expression for the maximum relative error and hence evaluate it in the following cases

(a) $a = 0.79$, $b = 0.83$, $c = 0.62$
(b) $a = 0.126$, $b = 11.13$, $c = 1.256$
(c) $a = 2.18 \times 10^{-3}$, $b = 3.14 \times 10^{-4}$, $c = 4.94 \times 10^{-4}$

2 Repeat Question **1** for the expression $\dfrac{ab}{c}$

3 The numbers a, b, c, and d are subject to small errors, δa, δb, δc, and δd. Find error bounds for the expressions

(a) $a+b$ **(b)** bc **(c)** $a+bc$ **(d)** $(a-b)c$

(e) $\dfrac{a+b}{c}$ **(f)** $\dfrac{a}{b}+\dfrac{c}{d}$ **(g)** $a-\dfrac{b}{c}$

4 Using your results in Question **3**, evaluate the expressions when $a = 5.8, b = 2.4$, $c = 1.31$, $d = 0.86$ giving your answers in the form

$$A \pm P\%$$

2 Functions of inexact numbers

2.1 The differential method of error analysis

The methods that we have met so far for finding the error bounds in a calculation, i.e. the maximum and minimum method and the sum of absolute and/or relative errors method, are limited in their scope. The former is of no use in non-numerical problems such as Example 2 on page 517 and the latter would not help if we had to find the error bounds for an expression involving for example $\sin x$, $\ln x$ or e^x. The sum of errors method cannot be applied to the evaluation of expressions in which the terms or factors are not independent. For example, in evaluating

$$z = a + \frac{1}{a}$$

a positive error δa in a will make the first term too large and the second term too small, and the errors therefore tend to cancel out so that the *maximum* error bound will be *less* than the sum of the absolute errors. Also, in evaluating such a function of a, it is not possible to tell at a glance whether the maximum or the minimum value of a will give the maximum value of x. This will depend on whether the function is increasing or decreasing in the neighbourhood of the particular value of a. This difficulty becomes more acute if we have an expression in which several inexact numbers must be substituted, such as the familiar

$$x = \frac{-b}{2a} \pm \frac{\sqrt{(b^2-4ac)}}{2a}$$

We need a method that will cope with all of these difficulties and fortunately help is at hand in the calculus method of small changes.

An algorithm for the error bounds in a differentiable function of x

Suppose we require the value of a function, $f(x)$, for the argument X. The exact value of X is not known, but we have an approximation, x, with a known error bound, δx, so that

$$X = x + \delta x$$

Let $Z = f(X)$ be the exact result

$$z + \delta z = f(x + \delta x)$$

and $z = f(x)$

Using Taylor's Theorem

$$f(x+\delta x) = f(x) + f'(x)\delta x + \frac{f''(x)}{2!}(\delta x)^2 + \cdots$$

Ignoring terms in $(\delta x)^2$ and higher powers of δx (being very small)

$$z + \delta z \approx f(x) + f'(x)\,\delta x$$

and subtracting

$$\delta z \approx f'(x)\,\delta x$$

Taking moduli, we have the absolute error in the function

$$|\boldsymbol{\delta z}| \approx |\boldsymbol{f'(x)\,\delta x}|$$ ◀

and dividing on the left by z and on the right by $f(x)$ we have the relative error in the function

$$\left|\frac{\boldsymbol{\delta z}}{\boldsymbol{z}}\right| \approx \left|\frac{\boldsymbol{f'(x)}}{\boldsymbol{f(x)}}\,\boldsymbol{\delta x}\right|$$ ◀

The relative error takes a simple form when the function is a root or a power, for if

$$f(x) = x^n, \qquad \text{then} \qquad f'(x) = nx^{n-1}$$

and

$$\left|\frac{\delta z}{z}\right| \approx \left|n\frac{x^{n-1}}{x^n}\,\delta x\right| = \left|n\frac{\delta x}{x}\right|$$

Thus

the relative error in x^n is n times the relative error in x ◀

We now apply this last result to the functions x^2, $\sqrt{x}$, and $\dfrac{1}{x}$

(i) If $z = x^2$

$$\text{absolute error} = |\delta z| \approx 2|x\,\delta x|$$

$$\text{relative error} = \left|\frac{\delta z}{z}\right| \approx \left|\frac{2x\,\delta x}{x^2}\right| = 2\left|\frac{\delta x}{x}\right|$$

(ii) If $z = \sqrt{x}$

$$\text{absolute error} = |\delta z| \approx \frac{1}{2}\left|\frac{\delta x}{\sqrt{x}}\right|$$

$$\text{relative error} = \left|\frac{\delta z}{z}\right| = \left|\frac{1}{2\sqrt{x}}\frac{\delta x}{\sqrt{x}}\right| = \frac{1}{2}\left|\frac{\delta x}{x}\right|$$

(iii) If $z = \frac{1}{x}$

$$\text{absolute error} = |\delta z| = \left|-\frac{1}{x^2}\,\delta x\right|$$

$$\text{relative error} = \left|\frac{\delta z}{z}\right| = \left|-\frac{1}{x^2}\,\delta x \Big/ \frac{1}{x}\right| = \left|\frac{\delta x}{x}\right|$$

When using an electronic calculator to evaluate such functions it is important to consider the error bounds in the value given when the argument is inexact. The value is only accurate to a particular number of significant figures.

Let $x = 28.3$ when rounded, so that the absolute error in x is 0.05 and the relative error in x is $\frac{0.05}{28.3} = 0.001\,77$ to 3S. We tabulate the results

Function	*Inexact value*	*Relative error*	*Absolute error*	*Exact value*
x^2	800.89	0.003 54	2.835	800.9 ± 2.8
$\sqrt{x}$	5.319 774 4	0.000 885	0.004 71	5.3198 ± 0.0047
$\frac{1}{x}$	0.035 335	0.001 77	0.000 062 5	$0.035\,335 \pm 0.000\,063$

The 'inexact value' is that given by the calculator and the 'exact value' column in fact gives a *range* of values within which the exact value lies.

For x^2 this is 798.1 to 803.7

For $\sqrt{x}$ this is 5.3151 to 5.3245

For $\frac{1}{x}$ this is 0.035 272 to 0.035 398

In each case, although the calculator gives up to 8 figures, we can only be sure that the first *two* significant figures are correct.

Example 1

Find the value of $V = 2\pi r^2 h$ and its error bounds when $r = 28.5 \pm 0.05$ and $h = 12.3 \pm 0.05$.

Now the relative error in a product is the sum of the relative errors.

Relative error in $r = 0.001\,75$

relative error in $r^2 = 0.003\,50$

relative error in $h = 0.004\,07$

Hence $r^2h = 9990.675$ with relative error 0.007 57

Therefore absolute error in $r^2h = 75.63$

absolute error in $2\pi r^2 h = 475.21$

Hence $$2\pi r^2 h = 62\,773 \pm 475$$

$$= 62\,770 \pm 480 \qquad \text{(rounding the error to 2S)}$$

Example 2

Find the value of $T = 2\pi\sqrt{(l/g)}$ and its error bounds when $l = 28.5 \pm 0.05$ and $g = 980 \pm 5$

Relative error in $l = 0.001\,75$

therefore relative error in $\sqrt{l} = 0.000\,875$

relative error in $g = 0.005\,1$

and relative error in $\sqrt{g} = 0.002\,55$

Hence $T = 1.071\,49$ with relative error $0.003\,425$

i.e. $$T = 1.071\,49 \pm 0.003\,669\,8$$

$$= 1.0715 \pm 0.0037$$

Example 3

Find the value of f if $1/f = 1/u + 1/v$ and $u = 12.3 \pm 0.05$ and $v = 28.5 \pm 0.05$

Relative error in $u = 0.004\,07$

so relative error in $\dfrac{1}{u} = 0.004\,07$

Similarly relative error in $v = 0.001\,75$

Therefore absolute error in $\dfrac{1}{u} = 0.000\,33$

and absolute error in $\dfrac{1}{v} = 0.000\,061$

so absolute error in $\dfrac{1}{u} + \dfrac{1}{v} = 0.000\,391$ relative error $= 0.003\,359$

Hence $f = 8.591\,91$ with relative error $0.003\,359$

$$= 8.591\,91 \pm 0.028\,86$$

$$= 8.592 \pm 0.029$$

Exercise 2.1

1 Write down the error in z where $z = f(a)$ and a is subject to a small error δa, in the following cases

(a) a^3 **(b)** $3a^2$ **(c)** $\dfrac{2}{a}$ **(d)** $\sqrt{a}$ **(e)** $\dfrac{5}{a^2}$

Hence evaluate each expression, with its error bounds when a is rounded and equal to
(i) 3.7 (ii) 370 (iii) 0.037
Give your answers in the form

$$z \pm P\%$$

2 Evaluate $A = 2\pi(rh + r^2)$ with its error bounds when $r = 5.7$ and $h = 19.8$, both rounded.

3 Evaluate $A = \pi rl + \pi r^2$ when $r = 4.32$, and $l = 6.78$, both rounded.

4 Evaluate $d = \sqrt{(b^2 - 4ac)}$ when $a = 8.4 \pm 0.5$, $b = 6.3 \pm 0.4$, $c = -4.7 \pm 0.3$ and give the error bounds.

5 Find the volume of air in a football of external diameter 23.0 cm to the nearest mm, if the thickness of the leather is 2 mm to the nearest $\frac{1}{2}$ mm.

6 In an experiment to determine g, the acceleration due to gravity, the time of 20 swings of a simple pendulum of length l cm is measured. From this the time of 1 swing (T) is calculated and g evaluated from

$$g = \frac{4\pi^2 l}{T^2}$$

The time of 20 swings was 17.3 s, $l = 18.5$ cm (both rounded). Find g and state the error bounds.

2.2 Errors in the values of circular, exponential and logarithmic functions due to inexact values of the argument

We have shown that if

$$z = f(x)$$

then

$$|\delta z| \approx |f'(x)\,\delta x|$$

and

$$\left|\frac{\delta z}{z}\right| \approx \left|\frac{f'(x)}{f(x)}\,\delta x\right|$$

For the usual calculator functions we have

$f(x)$	$f'(x)$
$\sin x$	$\cos x$
$\cos x$	$-\sin x$
$\tan x$	$\sec^2 x$
e^x	e^x
$\ln x$	$\dfrac{1}{x}$
$\log_{10} x$	$\dfrac{1}{x}\log_{10} e = \dfrac{0.4343}{x}$
a^x	$a^x \ln a$

These may be used in determining the errors in $f(x)$ where x is inexact.

Example 1

An angle x is measured as $32.6° \pm 0.05°$. Evaluate $\sin x$. Now

$$|\delta z| \approx |\cos x \delta x| \qquad \text{where } \delta x \text{ is in radians}$$

$$\approx |\cos 32.6° \times 0.000\,872\,66|$$

$$\approx 0.000\,735$$

Hence $\sin 32.6° = 0.538\,77 \pm 0.000\,74$

An alternative method is to use the maximum and minimum values, i.e.

$$\sin 32.65° = 0.539\,506$$

$$\sin 32.55° = 0.538\,035$$

From this we conclude that $\sin 32.6° = 0.538\,77 \pm 0.000\,74$.

Example 2

We have to find 4^x where $x = 2.7 \pm 0.05$. Now

$$|\delta z| = |4^{2.7} \times \ln 4| \times 0.05$$

$$= 2.927$$

Hence $4^x = 42.2 \pm 2.9$

Alternatively using the maximum and minimum we have

$$4^{2.75} = 45.254\,834$$

$$4^{2.65} = 39.396\,621$$

Hence, using the mid-value $4^{2.7} = 42.3 \pm 2.9$

Exercise 2.2

1 Write down expressions for the absolute and relative errors in z for each of the following functions where the error bound for x is δx.

(a) $z = 3 \sin x$ **(b)** $z = 2 \ln x$ **(c)** $z = 4 \cos^2 x$
(d) $z = 2e^x$ **(e)** $z = 2x\,e^x$ **(f)** $z = 5 \log_{10} x$
(g) $z = x^2 \tan x$ **(h)** $z = 10^{2x}$ **(i)** $z = e^{4x}$

2 Use your answers for Question 1 to evaluate z together with its absolute and relative error when $x = 1.42$ (rounded).

2.3 Errors in algebraic functions of one variable

We can now find the error bounds in evaluating *any* differentiable function of a single variable when the argument is inexact.

Example 1

Obtain an expression for the error in

$$z = a+\frac{1}{a}$$

Use this expression to evaluate Z, and give the error bounds when
(i) $a = 0.24$ (ii) $a = 2.4$ (both rounded).

Now $$\delta z \approx f'(a)\,\delta a$$

and $$f(a) = a+\frac{1}{a}$$

so $$f'(a) = 1-\frac{1}{a^2}$$

Hence the absolute error in z is given by

$$|\delta z| = \left|\left(1-\frac{1}{a^2}\right)\delta a\right|$$

(i) When

$$a = 0.24$$

$$z = 0.24+\frac{1}{0.24} \qquad = 4.40\dot{6}$$

and $$\delta z = \left(1-\frac{1}{0.24^2}\right)0.005 = -0.0818$$

$$Z = 4.407 \pm 0.082$$

(ii) When

$$a = 2.4$$

$$z = 2.4+\frac{1}{2.4} \qquad = \quad 2.81\dot{6}$$

and $$\delta z = \left(1-\frac{1}{2.4^2}\right)0.05 \quad = \quad 0.0413$$

$$Z = 2.817 \pm 0.041$$

These results can be checked by the max-min method.

(i) Value of z corresponding to $a_{\text{max}} = 0.245+\dfrac{1}{0.245} = 4.326\,632\,7$

$$\text{to } a_{\text{min}} = 0.235+\frac{1}{0.235} = 4.490\,319\,1$$

$$\text{Mid-value} = \tfrac{1}{2}(4.326\,632\,7+4.490\,319\,1) = 4.408\,475\,9$$

$$\text{Error bound} = \tfrac{1}{2}(4.490\,319\,1-4.326\,632\,7) = 0.081\,843\,2$$

$$Z = 4.408 \pm 0.082$$

(ii) Value of z corresponding to $a_{max} = 2.858\,163\,3$

$$\text{to } a_{min} = 2.775\,531\,9$$

$$\text{Mid-value} = 2.816\,847\,6$$

$$\text{Error bound} = 0.041\,315\,7$$

$$Z = 2.817 \pm 0.041$$

These results agree very closely with those obtained by the method of differentials, but we note that in (i) the maximum value of a gives the minimum value of z since the function is decreasing in the neighbourhood of 0.24, whereas in (ii) the maximum value of a gives the maximum value of z, since the function is then increasing.

Example 2

Obtain an expression for the error bound in

$$f(x) = \frac{x}{(1-x)^2}$$

If $z = f(x)$, we have to find $\delta z \approx f'(x)\,\delta x$

$$f'(x) = \frac{(1-x)^2 - 2x(1-x)(-1)}{(1-x)^4}$$

$$= \frac{1 - 2x + x^2 + 2x - 2x^2}{(1-x)^4}$$

$$= \frac{1-x^2}{(1-x)^4} = \frac{1+x}{(1-x)^3}$$

Hence, the maximum absolute error is given by

$$|\delta z| = \left|\frac{(1+x)}{(1-x)^3}\,\delta x\right|$$

Evaluation of polynomial functions

If we are required to find the error bounds for z where

$$z = 2.45x^3 - 1.40x^2 + 3.22x + 7.11$$

when all the coefficients are exact and $x = 2.15$ (rounded) we must evaluate both z and δz where

$$\delta z = (3 \times 2.45x^2 - 2 \times 1.40x + 3.22)0.005$$

Using a calculator it is much quicker to evaluate such polynomials if they are first arranged in *nested* forms

$$f(x) = [(2.45x - 1.40)x + 3.22]x + 7.11$$

This eliminates the need to use the memory on the calculator and it also reduces the number of multiplications, so fewer rounding errors are introduced in the course of the calculation. If some of the coefficients of the polynomial are zero, care must be taken to allow for this when nesting. For example

$$f(x) = 3.12x^5 + 11.20x^3 - 0.51x + 1$$

becomes
$$f(x) = [(3.12x^2 + 11.20)x^2 - 0.51]x + 1$$

Example 3

Evaluate $f(x) = 1.34x^4 - 2.87x^2 + 3.15x - 4.63$ for $x = 1.23 \pm 0.005$, stating the error bounds.

Nested
$$f(x) = [(1.34x^2 - 2.87)x + 3.15]x - 4.63$$

$$f(1.23) = -2.030\,442$$

$$f'(x) = 5.36x^3 - 5.74x + 3.15$$

which, nested, means

$$f'(x) = (5.36x^2 - 5.74)x + 3.15 \qquad f'(1.23) = 6.064\,047\,1$$

If $z = f(x)$ then $\delta z \approx f'(x)\,\delta x$

Hence
$$\delta z = 6.064\,047\,1 \times 0.005 = 0.030\,32$$

and
$$f(x) = -2.030 \pm 0.030$$

Alternatively, the max and min method may be used

$$f(1.235) = -1.999\,888\,6$$

$$f(1.225) = -2.060\,530\,7$$

$$\text{Mid-value} = -2.030\,209\,7$$

$$\text{Error bound} = 0.030\,321$$

Hence
$$f(x) = -2.030 \pm 0.030$$

Exercise 2.3

1 Use the nesting procedure to evaluate the polynomial

$$2x^2 + 3x - 11$$

(a) at $x = 3$ **(b)** at $x = 3.11$ **(c)** at $x = 0.011$
Find the error bounds in each case if x is rounded.

2 Evaluate, by nesting, the polynomial

$$0.51x^3 - 3.18x^2 - 2.40x + 17.15$$

for $x = 0.44$ (rounded).

3 Tabulate the function

$$2x^4 - 13x^3 + 2x^2 - 5x - 12$$

for $x = 3.0(0.1)3.5$, which means that x takes values $3.0, 3.1, \ldots, 3.5$ i.e. x is increased or *incremented* from 3.0 to 3.5 in steps of 0.1.

4 In evaluating the polynomial $a_3x^3 + a_2x^2 + a_1x + a_0$ on a calculating machine, powers are calculated by repeated multiplication e.g. $x^3 \equiv x \cdot x \cdot x$. Assuming that all the coefficients are non-zero, how many arithmetic operations (multiplications and additions) are needed (a) for direct evaluation, (b) when nesting is used?

Find an expression in terms of n for the number of operations in each method when the polynomial is of degree n.

5 The number a is subject to a small error δa. Find the error bounds for the expression

$$z = a^2 + \frac{4}{a}$$

Hence find the error bounds for z when $a = 2.50 \pm 1\%$ and verify these by direct calculation.

6 Obtain an expression for the error in z in each of the following cases

(a) $z = x^2 - \dfrac{1}{x^2}$ **(b)** $z = \dfrac{(2+x)^3}{x}$ **(c)** $z = \dfrac{x^2}{3-x}$

Hence find the error bounds for z when $x = 0.76$ (rounded).

2.4 Errors in functions of more than one variable

We have met many functions of more than one variable. The very first example in the chapter involved a and b and in Section 1.5, Example 2 we found the error function for the expression $\dfrac{ab}{c+d}$ with four variables. So long as the variables are separable and the function can be arranged so that the error in each term or factor is independent, then the method of the sum of the relative or the absolute errors can be used.

Example 1

If the numbers u and v are subject to small errors δu and δv, find an expression for the error bounds for the harmonic mean,

$$\frac{uv}{u+v}$$

As it stands, the errors in the numerator and the denominator are not independent, since the same variables appear in both. However the expression may be rearranged as

$$\frac{1}{\dfrac{1}{u} + \dfrac{1}{v}}$$

and the errors are then independent.

Quantity	*Absolute error*	*Relative error*
u	$\|\delta u\|$	$\|\delta u/u\|$
$1/u$	$\|\delta u/u^2\|$	$\|\delta u/u\|$ (the same as in u)
$1/v$	$\|\delta v/v^2\|$ (similarly)	
$1/u+1/v$	$\|\delta u/u^2\|+\|\delta v/v^2\|$	$(\|\delta u/u^2\|+\|\delta v/v^2\|)/(1/u+1/v)$
$\dfrac{1}{1/u+1/v}$		the same as in $1/u+1/v$

Hence
$$\text{error bound} = \pm\left(\frac{1}{1/u+1/v}\right)\left(\frac{|\delta u/u^2|+|\delta v/v^2|}{1/u+1/v}\right)$$
$$= \pm\left(\frac{uv}{u+v}\right)\left(\frac{|v\,\delta u/u|+|u\,\delta v/v|}{u+v}\right)$$
$$= \pm\left(\frac{v^2|\delta u|+u^2|\delta v|}{(u+v)^2}\right)$$

This can also be arranged as
$$\pm\frac{uv}{u+v}\left(\left|\frac{\delta u}{u}\right|+\left|\frac{\delta v}{v}\right|-\left|\frac{\delta u+\delta v}{u+v}\right|\right)$$

This result should be compared with that obtained in Example 2 on page 517, where the error bounds for the expression
$$\frac{ab}{c+d}$$
were found to be
$$\pm\frac{ab}{c+d}\left(\left|\frac{\delta a}{a}\right|+\left|\frac{\delta b}{b}\right|+\left|\frac{\delta c+\delta d}{c+d}\right|\right)$$

Notice the difference in sign. As we would expect the error in $\dfrac{uv}{u+v}$ is less than in $\dfrac{ab}{c+d}$, since a high value of either u or v would make *both* numerator and denominator high, thus affecting the quotient less than would high values of a and b together with low values of c and d.

Functions in which the variables cannot be treated separately

It is not always possible to arrange things so that the errors in all the variables are independent. For example, the expressions
$$a+\frac{1}{a} \qquad \text{and} \qquad \frac{a}{b}+\frac{1}{a+b}$$

cannot be treated in this way. The following example introduces a technique for dealing with such expressions.

Example 2

The numbers a and b are subject to small errors δa and δb, and x is calculated from the formula

$$x = \frac{a}{b} + \frac{1}{a+b}$$

Find the error bounds for x.

We first suppose that b is exact and consider the effect of an error in a.

Then $$x = f(a) = \frac{a}{b} + \frac{1}{a+b}$$

and $$f'(a) = \frac{1}{b} - \frac{1}{(a+b)^2} \qquad \text{(treating } b \text{ as constant)}$$

So the error in x due to the error δa in a is

$$|f'(a)\,\delta a| = \left\{\frac{1}{b} - \frac{1}{(a+b)^2}\right\}\delta a$$

Now suppose that a is exact and consider the effect of an error in b.

Then $$x = g(b) = \frac{a}{b} + \frac{1}{a+b}$$

and $$g'(b) = -\frac{a}{b^2} - \frac{1}{(a+b)^2} \qquad \text{(treating } a \text{ as constant)}$$

So the error in x due to the error δb in b is

$$|g'(b)\,\delta b| = \left\{\frac{a}{b^2} + \frac{1}{(a+b)^2}\right\}\delta b$$

If a and b both contain errors, the absolute error in x will be the *sum* of the absolute errors due to a and b separately, so the error bounds for x are

$$\pm\left[\left\{\frac{1}{b} - \frac{1}{(a+b)^2}\right\}\delta a + \left\{\frac{a}{b^2} + \frac{1}{(a+b)^2}\right\}\delta b\right]$$

NOTE. The technique we have used for differentiating a function of two variables, by treating each variable in turn as a constant, is called *partial differentiation*. It can be extended to three or more variables. Suppose x is a function of a, b and c then the partial derivative of x with respect to a (keeping b and c constant) is written $\partial x/\partial a$. Similarly the partial derivative of x with respect to b (keeping a and c constant) is $\partial x/\partial b$ and of x with respect to c (keeping a and b constant) is $\partial x/\partial c$. We then use the formula

$$\delta x \approx \frac{\partial x}{\partial a}\delta a + \frac{\partial x}{\partial b}\delta b + \frac{\partial x}{\partial c}\delta c$$

to find the absolute error in x.

Example 3

If
$$x = \frac{-b+\sqrt{b^2-4ac}}{2a}$$

where $a = 0.61 \pm 0.006$, $b = 1.20 \pm 0.04$, and $c = 0.49 \pm 0.01$ find the relative error in x.

The absolute error in x, δx, depends on the error δa in a, δb in b and δc in c and

$$|\delta x| \leqslant \left|\frac{\partial x}{\partial a}\delta a\right| + \left|\frac{\partial x}{\partial b}\delta b\right| + \left|\frac{\partial x}{\partial c}\delta c\right|$$

$$\frac{\partial x}{\partial a} \approx \frac{2a[\frac{1}{2}(b^2-4ac)^{-1/2}(-4c)]-2[-b+(b^2-4ac)^{1/2}]}{4a^2} = -0.6767$$

$$\frac{\partial x}{\partial b} \approx \frac{-1+\frac{1}{2}(b^2-4ac)^{-1/2}2b}{2a} = 1.1699$$

$$\frac{\partial x}{\partial c} \approx \frac{\frac{1}{2}(b^2-4ac)^{-1/2}(-4a)}{2a} = 2.0228$$

$$|\delta x| \leqslant 0.6767 \times 0.006 + 1.1699 \times 0.04 + 2.0228 \times 0.01$$
$$\leqslant 0.071 \qquad \text{to 2S}$$

By direct substitution

$$x = \frac{-1.20+\sqrt{(1.20^2-4\times 0.61 \times 0.49)}}{2\times 0.61} = -0.5784$$

So

$$x = -0.578 \pm 0.071 \qquad = -0.578 \pm 12\%$$

We see that although the percentage errors in a (1%), b (3%) and c (2%) are fairly small, the relative error in x is 12%.

NOTE that this solution is not the same as that obtained using maximum and minimum values.

The value x_{max} is given when we take a_{min}, b_{max}, c_{min} and with $a = 0.604$, $b = 1.24$, $c = 0.48$, $x_{max} = -0.517\,589\,4$. Similarly x_{min} is found when a_{max}, b_{min}, c_{max} are chosen and with $a = 0.616$, $b = 1.16$, $c = 0.50$, $x_{min} = -0.667\,982\,2$. Using these values we obtain the mid-value and the error bounds

$$x = -0.593 \pm 0.075$$

or

$$x = -0.593 \pm 12.7\%$$

The difference between the two solutions given is due to the fact that the errors are comparatively large.

Exercise 2.4

1 The numbers a, b and c are subject to small errors δa, δb, δc. Find the error bounds for the following expressions

(a) $\dfrac{a+b}{a}$ **(b)** $\dfrac{a}{a+b}$ **(c)** $\dfrac{abc}{bc+ca+ab}$

(Use the method of Example 1, page 529.)

Hence evaluate the expressions for $a = 4.5$, $b = 2.3$, $c = 1.2$, rounded.

2 The numbers a and b and the angle θ radians are subject to small errors δa, δb and $\delta\theta$. Find error bounds for the following expressions

(a) $c = ab\cos\theta$ **(b)** $c = e^a \sin\theta$ **(c)** $c = a^2 + \ln b$

(d) $c = a\,e^{-a} + b\tan\theta$ **(e)** $c = a^3 - ab$ **(f)** $c = a + \dfrac{b}{a}$

(g) $c = a\sin\theta + b\cos\theta$ **(h)** $c = \dfrac{e^{ab}}{a+b}$

3 If $x = 0.82$ and $y = 0.97$, both rounded, evaluate the following expressions, giving their maximum absolute errors

(a) $\cos(x+y)$ **(b)** $\tan(y-x)$ **(c)** $\log_{10} xy$

(d) $\log_{10}(xy)^5$ **(e)** $\ln(xy)^5$ **(f)** x^y

4 In the formula

$$A = \frac{x}{y}\left(y + \frac{z}{xy}\right)$$

x, y and z are the results of experimental observations and have the values $x = 12.04 \pm 0.005$, $y = 6.66 \pm 0.0025$, $z = 4.82 \pm 0.0075$. Express A as accurately as possible, quoting the maximum error to 2S.

2.5 Minimization of errors

Errors in the data

We have seen that errors are inevitable in any calculation and so before giving any result it is important to determine the error bounds and then to round the result to the number of significant figures justified by those error bounds. For example, if a young experimenter, determining the density of lead, weighs a piece and finds its mass to be 103 g $\pm$ 1 g and calculates its volume as 9 cm^3 $\pm$ 1 cm^3, he should not be over jubilant. His calculation

$$\text{density} = \frac{\text{mass}}{\text{volume}} = \frac{103}{9} = 11.\dot{4}\ \text{g cm}^{-3}$$

gives an answer close to the true value. But he should go on

$$\text{Maximum value} = \frac{104}{8} = 13$$

$$\text{minimum value} = \frac{102}{10} = 10.2$$

$$\text{Mid-value} = 11.6$$

$$\text{Error bound} = 1.4$$

$$\text{Density of lead} = 11.6 \pm 1.4 \text{ g cm}^{-3}$$

His relative error is 12%—rather high!

This large error in the result is due to large errors in his data and he must improve his experimental technique.

Sometimes however, relatively small errors in the data lead to much larger errors in the result, particularly if the calculation has involved the subtraction of nearly equal numbers. An example may be taken from Statistics.

Example 1

A working formula for the covariance of x and y is

$$\text{cov}(x, y) = \frac{\Sigma xy}{n} - \frac{\Sigma x}{n}\frac{\Sigma y}{n}$$

The correct sums for a set of seven pairs of values of (x, y) were

$$\Sigma(xy) = 448.5, \qquad \Sigma x = 350, \qquad \Sigma y = 8.56$$

but an error was made in Σxy and the value 487.7 was taken instead. Find the percentage error in the value of $\Sigma(xy)$ and in the calculated covariance.

$$\text{The percentage error in } \Sigma(xy) = \frac{487.7 - 448.5}{448.5} \times 100 = 8.7\%$$

The correct value for the covariance is

$$\text{cov}(x, y) = \frac{448.5}{7} - \frac{350}{7} \times \frac{8.56}{7} = 2.93 \quad (3S)$$

The incorrect value is

$$\frac{487.7}{7} - \frac{350}{7} \times \frac{8.56}{7} = 8.53 \quad (3S)$$

The percentage error in the covariance is

$$\frac{8.53 - 2.93}{2.93} \times 100 = 190\%$$

The error in the value of Σxy in this case was a mistake or blunder, but the loss of significant figures due to the subtraction magnified it enormously.

Example 2

Find the absolute and relative error in x, if $x = (542 \times 136) - (712 \times 102)$ and the numbers are rounded.

$$\begin{aligned}
\text{Working value} &= (542 \times 136) - (712 \times 102) \\
&= 73\,712 - 72\,624 \qquad = 1088 \\
\text{Maximum value} &= (542.5 \times 136.5) - (711.5 \times 101.5) \\
&= 74\,051.25 - 72\,217.25 = 1834 \\
\text{Minimum value} &= (541.5 \times 135.5) - (712.5 \times 102.5) \\
&= 73\,373.25 - 73\,031.25 = 342 \\
\text{Mid-value} &= \tfrac{1}{2}(1834 + 342) \qquad = 1088 \\
\text{Error bound} &= \tfrac{1}{2}(1834 - 342) \qquad = 746
\end{aligned}$$

Hence $\qquad X = 1088 \pm 746$

or $\qquad X = 1088 \pm 69\%$

This illustrates clearly how, even though the largest relative error in any of the numbers is $\dfrac{0.5}{102} \approx 0.5\%$, the answer has the huge error of 69%.

Errors due to rounding during the calculation

So far we have been dealing with errors in the result of a calculation due to errors in the data, but there will usually be rounding errors in a result even if the data is exact.

Example 3

Evaluate $(5426 \times 1358) - (7122 \times 1034)$ where the numbers are exact.

An 8-digit calculator (or long multiplication) gives the exact answer

$$7\,368\,508 - 7\,364\,148 = 4360$$

But if four figure tables are used so that each step in the calculation is rounded to 4S we have

$$7\,369\,000 - 7\,364\,000 = 5000$$

The relative error is 15% and the result is not even correct to 1S. Had we been adding instead of subtracting, the exact and rounded answers would have been 14 732 656 and 14 733 000 respectively, with relative error 0.0023%.

Returning to the statistical example, Example 1 opposite, we note that rounding errors can be serious in the calculation of the covariance by the working formula quoted, and in the calculation of variance by the similar formula

$$\operatorname{var}(x) = \frac{\Sigma x^2}{n} - \left(\frac{\Sigma x}{n}\right)^2$$

They can be avoided usually by transforming or coding the variable or by the use of the definitive formula

$$\text{var}(x) = \frac{\Sigma(x-\bar{x})^2}{n}$$

but the calculation is then more tedious.

Every stage in any calculation that results in a recurring decimal involves a rounding error and if the calculation involves many operations these can accumulate considerably, particularly if every stage is calculated to 4S only, as in logarithm tables. With the electronic calculator, rounding errors are very small and are usually far outweighed by the errors due to inexact data. Rounding errors can be minimized by arranging the calculation so that the minimum number of operations are carried out, but this is not usually worthwhile with a calculator when the rounding errors are so very small.

The smaller root of a quadratic equation

Loss of accuracy can also occur in the solution of quadratic equations when one root is numerically very much smaller than the other. This is the case when, in the equation

$$Ax^2+Bx+C=0, \qquad B^2 \gg 4AC$$

Example 3

Solve the equation

$$x^2-40.12x+1.3=0 \quad \text{(taking the coefficients as exact)}$$

Using the quadratic algorithm and an electronic calculator we find

$$x = \frac{40.12 \pm \sqrt{(40.12^2 - 4\times 1.3)}}{2}$$

$$= \frac{40.12 \pm \sqrt{1\,604.414\,4}}{2}$$

$$= \frac{40.12 \pm 40.055\,142}{2}$$

$$= 40.087\,571 \qquad \text{or} \qquad 0.032\,429$$

The larger root is given to 8S, and the smaller to 5S, a loss of three significant figures.

Had we been limited to 4S at every step in the calculation (for example, using four figure logarithm tables) the solution would be

$$x = \frac{40.12 \pm \sqrt{(40.12^2 - 4\times 1.3)}}{2}$$

$$= \frac{40.12 \pm \sqrt{(1610-5.2)}}{2}$$

$$= \frac{40.12 \pm \sqrt{1605}}{2}$$

$$= \frac{40.12 \pm 40.06}{2}$$

$$= 40.09 \qquad \text{or} \qquad 0.03$$

This time the larger root is given to 4S and the smaller to 1S—again a loss of three significant figures. The percentage error in the larger root is 0.006%, but in the smaller root it is 7.5%, which is unacceptably large.

The accuracy of the smaller root can be increased, even though limited to 4S during the calculation, using the fact that the product of the roots of the equation $Ax^2+Bx+C = 0$ is C/A. In this equation

$$C/A = 1.3$$

so

$$\text{larger root} \times \text{smaller root} = 1.3$$

The larger root is 40.09 to 4S so the smaller root is $1.3 \div 40.09 = 0.032\,42$ (4S). The error in the smaller root is now only 0.03%.

Exercise 2.5

1 Let $\alpha = \sqrt{1241} - \sqrt{1240}$

(a) Evaluate α, rounding each stage in the calculation to 4S.

(b) Using a calculator, evaluate α as accurately as you can. What is the percentage error in your answer to part **(a)**? What is the source of this error?

(c) Show that

$$\alpha = \frac{1}{\sqrt{1241}+\sqrt{1240}}$$

and use this expression to evaluate α, working to 4S throughout. What is the percentage error in this value? Explain why this expression gives a more accurate value.

2 A table of values of the function

$$f(x) = \sqrt{(x^2+1)} - \sqrt{(x^2-1)}$$

is required for $x = 20(1)25$. If only four figure tables are available and $f(x)$ is evaluated directly, to how many significant figures can the values be calculated?

By multiplying by

$$\frac{\sqrt{(x^2+1)}+\sqrt{(x^2-1)}}{\sqrt{(x^2+1)}+\sqrt{(x^2-1)}}$$

obtain a formula for $f(x)$ which does not involve subtraction of nearly equal numbers. Working to 4S, obtain the required table of values, correct to 3S.

3 Working to 4S, find the roots of the following quadratic equations, correct to 3S.

(a) $x^2+98x-1=0$ **(b)** $2x^2-3200x+3=0$ **(c)** $x^2+(7\times 10^{20})x-5=0$

4 Evaluate

$$f(x) = \frac{1-\cos x}{\sin x}$$

when $x = 0.03$ radians, working to 4S. Obtain an equivalent formula for $f(x)$ that avoids subtraction, and hence obtain a more accurate value for $f(0.03)$, still working to 4S.

5 Evaluate $\sin 82° - \sin 80°$, working to 4S. By first applying the formula

$$\sin P - \sin Q = 2 \cos \frac{P+Q}{2} \sin \frac{P-Q}{2}$$

obtain a more accurate value, still working to 4S.

6 The standard deviation σ of a set of numbers $x_1, x_2, \ldots, x_n$ can be calculated using the formula

$$\sigma = \sqrt{\left\{\frac{\sum_{i=1}^{i=n} x_i^2}{n} - \left(\frac{\sum_{i=1}^{i=n} x_i}{n}\right)^2\right\}}$$

Find the standard deviation of the numbers 851, 853, 854, 859, 867, 872, working to 4S throughout. How many significant figures in your answer are reliable?

The standard deviation of a set of numbers is not affected if a constant is added to, or subtracted from, all the numbers. By first subtracting 850 from all the numbers, obtain a more accurate value for the standard deviation, still working to 4S.

2.6 Statistical accumulation of errors

(This section may be omitted at a first reading)

Suppose that z is a function of many variables $x_1, x_2, \ldots, x_n$, each of which is subject to an error. Using the methods described earlier, we can find the maximum possible error in z. But as there are many variables, some with positive errors and some negative, then the errors will tend to cancel each other out to some extent. So it is most unlikely that the error in z will be anything near the maximum possible error. We can use a statistical method to find the largest error that is likely to occur in practice.

We shall only consider the case $z = x_1 + x_2 + \cdots + x_n$ where each value x_i is subject to the same error $\pm h$. Then the maximum possible error in z is $\pm nh$. If δx_i is the actual error in x_i, then δx_i may be any number between $-h$ and h, so we may regard δx_i as a random variable having the uniform distribution on the interval $[-h, h]$. Now, if the random variable X has the uniform distribution on $[a, b]$ the expected (mean) value of X is $\mathrm{E}[X] = \frac{1}{2}(a+b)$, and the variance of X is $\mathrm{var}(X) = \frac{1}{12}(b-a)^2$. So

$$\mathrm{E}[\delta x_i] = 0$$

and

$$\mathrm{var}(\delta x_i) = \tfrac{1}{12}(2h)^2 = \tfrac{1}{3}h^2$$

If δz is the error in z then

$$z+\delta z = (x_1+\delta x_1)+(x_2+\delta x_2)+\cdots+(x_n+\delta x_n)$$
$$= x_1+x_2+\cdots+x_n+\delta x_1+\delta x_2+\cdots+\delta x_n$$

and so
$$\delta z = \delta x_1+\delta x_2+\cdots+\delta x_n$$

Now the mean of a sum of random variables is equal to the sum of the individual means, and the variance of a sum of independent random variables is equal to the sum of the variances. So

$$\mathrm{E}[\delta z] = \mathrm{E}[\delta x_1]+\mathrm{E}[\delta x_2]+\cdots+E[\delta x_n] = 0$$
$$\mathrm{var}\,(\delta z) = \mathrm{var}\,(\delta x_1)+\mathrm{var}\,(\delta x_2)+\cdots+\mathrm{var}\,(\delta x_n) = \tfrac{1}{3}h^2+\tfrac{1}{3}h^2+\cdots+\tfrac{1}{3}h^2 = \tfrac{1}{3}nh^2$$

Therefore, the error in z is distributed with mean value 0 and standard deviation $\sqrt{(\tfrac{1}{3}nh^2)} = h\sqrt{(\tfrac{1}{3}n)}$.

A random variable is most unlikely to be more than 3 standard deviations from its mean so

$$\text{maximum likely error in } z = \pm 3h\sqrt{(\tfrac{1}{3}n)}$$
$$= \pm h\sqrt{(3n)}$$

This compares favourably with the (non-statistical) maximum error of $\pm nh$.

Example 1

The mean is calculated from a grouped frequency table as follows:

Weight kg	*Frequency* f	*Mid-interval value* X	$x = \dfrac{X-22.5}{5}$	xf
0–5	7	2.5	−4	−28
5–10	18	7.5	−3	−54
10–15	25	12.5	−2	−50
15–20	33	17.5	−1	−33
20–25	37	22.5	0	0
25–30	31	27.5	1	31
30–35	22	32.5	2	44
35–40	16	37.5	3	48
40–45	11	42.5	4	44
	200			2

$$\text{mean} = \frac{2}{200}\times 5+22.5 = 22.55$$

What is the maximum likely error in this value?

For the purpose of the calculation, the 25 weights in the 10–15 kg class, for example, are replaced by 25 equal weights each of 12.5 kg, and this approximation is the source of error. (Changing the origin to 22.5 and using units of 5 merely simplifies the arithmetic and does not affect the result.) In calculating the mean of the 200 weights,

$$m = \frac{x_1 + x_2 + \cdots + x_{200}}{200}$$

each value has been approximated to the nearest number in the set {2.5, 7.5, 12.5, ...} and is therefore subject to an error of 2.5. Thus the maximum *possible* error in the mean is ± 2.5, but this could only occur if all the values were at the upper (or lower) ends of their classes and this is most unlikely in practice. To find the maximum likely error we use the statistical analysis of errors.

$$\text{Maximum likely error in } x_1 + x_2 + \cdots + x_{200} = \pm h\sqrt{(3n)}$$

$$= \pm 2.5\sqrt{(3 \times 200)}$$

$$= \pm 61.24$$

and so

$$\text{maximum likely error in } m = \pm\frac{61.24}{200}$$

$$= \pm 0.306$$

So

$$\text{the mean, } m = 22.55 \pm 0.31$$

If the standard deviation is calculated from the table, this too will be subject to an error, but finding the error in this case requires more advanced techniques.

3 Finite differences

3.1 Difference tables

In Exercise 2.3 we drew up tables of values of a function of x, taken at equal intervals of x, using the efficient method of nesting. Such tables of values are needed when drawing a graph of a function, and, as we shall see in Chapter 15, when finding a definite integral numerically. It is possible to work in reverse, that is, given a table of values we can find the equation of the function. The method used depends on finding the difference between adjacent (or successive) values in the table and is called the method of finite differences. It can also be used to correct possible errors in the table and to find the first and higher derivatives (dy/dx, d^2y/dx^2, etc.) of the function.

It is easy to see the importance of such methods. Many experiments in Physics and Chemistry where simultaneous readings of two variables are taken provide the basis for such a table; so too do the statistics obtained in Geography and Economics.

Table 1 shows the difference table for the function $f(x) = x^3 - 2x$ for integral values of x from 0 to 6, usually written $x = 0(1)6$—the figure in brackets being the constant increment.

Table 1
Difference table for $f(x) = x^3 - 2x$

x	$f(x)$	1	2	3
0	0			
		−1		
1	−1		6	
		5		6
2	4		12	
		17		6
3	21		18	
		35		6
4	56		24	
		59		6
5	115		30	
		89		
6	204			

The numbers in the column headed 1, called the *first differences*, give the difference between successive values of the function. Thus $f(1)-f(0) = -1$, $f(2)-f(1) = 5$ etc. The next column gives the *second differences* which represent the difference between the successive first differences, e.g. $5-(-1) = 6$ etc. It can be seen that the third differences are constant, so that all further differences would be zero. All polynomial functions will have a column of constant differences, provided they are tabulated for values of x with a constant increment, and this may be used to extend the table without calculating the function. In Table 2 we find the value of $f(7)$ by extending Table 1.

Table 2

x	f	1	2	3
⋮	⋮			
				6
5	115		30 ← +	↓
		89 ← +	↓ =	6
6	204 ← +	↓ =	36	
	↓ =	125		
7	329			

When drawing up a difference table, each column of differences should be checked for accuracy. This is a simple matter as the diagram illustrates.

n^{th} difference	$(n+1)^{\text{th}}$ difference
a	$b-a$
b	$c-b$
c	$d-c$
d	$e-d$
e	
	Total $e-a$

Add the sum of the differences to the initial difference in the preceding column. The total should equal the final difference in the preceding column.

Errors in the table

A single error (which might be a mistake) in the tabulated function is usually easy to find if the function values are exact. The effect of such an error is shown in Table 3. Often the *fan* pattern shows up clearly. Another useful pointer is the fact that the largest error in an *even* order difference column is opposite the function value which contains the mistake.

Table 3
Propagation of an error

x	Error in f	1	2	3	4
x_0	0				
		0			
x_1	0		0		
		0		0	
x_2	0		0		e
		0		e	
x_3	0		e		$-4e$
		e		$-3e$	
x_4	e		$-2e$		$6e$
		$-e$		$3e$	
x_5	0		e		$-4e$
		0		$-e$	
x_6	0		0		e
		0		0	
x_7	0		0		
		0			
x_8	0				

If the mistake is a small one and neither of these methods helps to find it, the following procedure must be adopted. It can be shown that the order of the difference column which is constant is the same as the degree of the polynomial. A quadratic function has constant second differences, a cubic constant third difference and so on. If the polynomial is known to be of degree n, then the $(n+1)^{\text{th}}$ differences should be zero and this enables us to detect the error immediately. If the order is not known, the function is differenced until the differences are seen to *increase*. Each column is then averaged and the column with the least average difference should be the zero column. (Notice that this need not always be true. If the value of f that contains an error is near the top or the bottom of the table, not all of the fan will be present in the difference columns, and the error will be much more difficult to find.) It is then necessary to recognize the pattern of the coefficients of e in this column. A glance at Table 3 shows that the coefficients of e in the column of nth differences are equal to the coefficient of x in $(1-x)^n$.

Example

Write down the first three orders of differences for the following table of values. Locate and correct a probable error in the table and suggest how this type of error may occur.

x	7	8	9	10	11	12	13	14
y	103.32	110.62	118.04	125.62	133.04	141.42	149.72	158.34

Table 4

x	$y=f(x)$	1	2	3	4
7	103.32				
		730			
8	110.62		12		
		742		04	
9	118.04		16		(−36)
		758		−32	
10	125.62		−16		(144)
		742		112	
11	133.04		96		(−216)
		838		−104	
12	141.42		−08		(144)
		830		40	
13	149.72		32		
		862			
14	158.34				

The number 96 in the second differences points to $f(11)$ (the function value opposite) and the fan has been drawn in accordingly. This is confirmed by the 4th differences which are shown in brackets and which contain the large difference −216, also opposite $f(11)$. We now look for the patterns 1, −2, 1; 1, −3, 3, −1; 1, −4, 6, −4, 1 in the second, third and fourth differences. The fourth differences may be written −36, −4(−36), 6(−36), −4(−36). This indicates that the error is −36 and that the function is a cubic, since the fourth column will be zero after the error has been corrected. Finally, we subtract the error from $f(11)$

$$133.04-(-0.36) = 133.40$$

The likely cause of the mistake is evidently a transposition of 40 into 04. Notice how in the above table the decimal point has been left out in the difference columns. This is standard practice.

Notation

To refer to specific entries in a difference table we use a notation based on the *difference operator*, Δ. If y_0 and y_1 are consecutive values of the function, we write

$$\Delta y_0 = y_1 - y_0$$

Similarly

$$\Delta(\Delta y_0) = \Delta(y_1 - y_0) = \Delta y_1 - \Delta y_0$$

$$= (y_2 - y_1) - (y_1 - y_0) = y_2 - 2y_1 + y_0$$

$\Delta(\Delta y_0)$ is written $\Delta^2 y_0$ and represents a second difference. It is easily verified that

$$\Delta^3 y_0 = y_3 - 3y_2 + 3y_1 - y_0$$

and in general

$$\mathbf{\Delta^r y_0 = y_r - \binom{r}{1} y_{r-1} + \binom{r}{2} y_{r-2} - \cdots + (-1)^r y_0}$$ ◀

Table 5 shows how this notation applies to the difference table.

Table 5

x	f	Δf	$\Delta^2 f$	$\Delta^3 f$	$\Delta^4 f$
x_0	y_0				
		Δy_0			
x_1	y_1		$\Delta^2 y_0$		
		Δy_1		$\Delta^3 y_0$	
x_2	y_2		$\Delta^2 y_1$		$\Delta^4 y_0$
		Δy_2		$\Delta^3 y_1$	
x_3	y_3		$\Delta^2 y_2$		
		Δy_3			
x_4	y_4				

Exercise 3.1

1 Draw up the difference table for $f(x) = x^2 - 2x + 3$ for $x = 0(1)7$. Use the table to find $f(8)$ and verify your result.

2 Draw up difference tables for the following functions, in each case taking $x = -2(1)3$

(a) $f(x) = x^2 + x + 1$ **(b)** $f(x) = x^3 - 7x^2$ **(c)** $f(x) = x^4 - 5x^2 + 5$

Find a relationship between the degree of the polynomial and the order of the constant difference column.

3 Tabulate the function $f(x) = x^3 - x$ for $x = 1(0.1)1.6$ and verify that the third differences are constant provided that exact arithmetic is used.

4

x	f	Δf	$\Delta^2 f$	$\Delta^3 f$
0.5	−0.375			
		0.311		
0.6	−0.064		0.076	
		0.387		0.006
0.7	0.323		0.082	
		0.469		
0.8	0.792			

Given that the third differences of the function tabulated above are constant find $f(0.9)$ and $f(1.0)$.

5 The cubic polynomial $y = f(x)$ is differenced for $x = 1(0.1)1.3$ with the following results:

$$f(1) = -1, \qquad \Delta f(1) = -0.099, \qquad \Delta^2 f(1) = \Delta^3 f(1) = 0.006$$

Construct a difference table, and find $f(1.1)$, $f(1.2)$, $f(1.3)$. Extend the table to find $f(1.4)$.

6 The quadratic function $y = f(x)$ is incorrectly tabulated as follows:

x	1.0	1.2	1.4	1.6	1.8	2.0
y	−4.00	−4.56	−5.04	−5.36	−5.76	−6.00

Find and correct the mistake in the table.

7 Find and correct the mistake in the following table:

x	1	1.1	1.2	1.3	1.4	1.5	1.6
y	0	0.231	0.582	0.897	1.344	1.875	2.496

8 Show that

$$(\Delta+1)y_n = y_{n+1}$$

Find an expression for

$$(\Delta+1)^2 y_n$$

and deduce a corresponding result for

$$(\Delta+1)^r y_n$$

9 The *shift operator* E is defined by $\mathrm{E}y_n = y_{n+1}$. Show that

$$\mathrm{E}^2 y_n [= \mathrm{E}(\mathrm{E}y_n)] = y_{n+2}$$

$$\mathrm{E}^r y_n = y_{n+r}$$

$$\Delta \mathrm{E} y_n = \mathrm{E}\Delta y_n$$

$$\Delta y_n = (\mathrm{E}-1)y_n$$

By writing $\Delta = \mathrm{E}-1$ and expanding, find an expression for $\Delta^4 y_n$.

10 Tabulate the first three orders of differences of the function $y = 2^x$ for $x = 0(1)6$. Will there ever be a column of constant differences?

3.2 Finding the equation of a polynomial

A common problem is to find the equation of a polynomial given its tabulated function. To do this, first write the polynomial in the form

$$f(x) = a_0 + a_1 x + a_2 x(x-1) + a_3 x(x-1)(x-2) + \ldots + a_n x(x-1)\ldots(x-n+1) \qquad \text{I}$$

Substituting successive integral values of x, we have

$$f(0) = a_0$$

$$f(1) = a_0 + a_1$$

$$f(2) = a_0 + 2a_1 + 2a_2$$

$$f(3) = a_0 + 3a_1 + 6a_2 + 6a_3 \quad \text{etc.}$$

Now

$$\Delta y_0 = f(1) - f(0) = a_1$$

$$\Delta^2 y_0 = f(2) - 2f(1) + f(0) = 2a_2$$

$$\Delta^3 y_0 = f(3) - 3f(2) + 3f(1) - f(0) = 6a_3$$

and in general

$$\boldsymbol{\Delta^r y_0 = r!a_r}$$ ◀

Hence we can express the coefficients of equation I in terms of differences

$$\boldsymbol{f(x) = y_0 + \Delta y_0 x + \frac{\Delta^2 y_0}{2!}x(x-1) + \ldots + \frac{\Delta^n y_0}{n!}x(x-1)\ldots(x-n+1)} \qquad \text{II}$$ ◀

Example 1

Find the equation of the polynomial tabulated below

x	0	1	2	3	4	5
y	1	2	9	22	41	66

We first form the difference table.

Table 6

x	y	Δy	$\Delta^2 y$
0	1		
		1	
1	2		6
		7	
2	9		6
		13	
3	22		6
		19	
4	41		6
		25	
5	66		

It is clear that the polynomial is a quadratic. From the table

$$y_0 = 1 \qquad \Delta y_0 = 1 \qquad \Delta^2 y_0 = 6$$

Hence, using equation II, we have

$$f(x) = 1 + x + \tfrac{6}{2}x(x-1)$$

or

$$f(x) = 3x^2 - 2x + 1$$

Example 2

Find the equation of the cubic polynomial whose difference table is given below.

Table 7

x	y	Δy	$\Delta^2 y$	$\Delta^3 y$
7	103.32			
		730		
8	110.62		12	
		742		4
9	118.04		16	
		758		4
10	125.62		20	
		778		4
11	133.40		24	
		802		
12	141.42			

This is the same function that we corrected in an example in the previous section (Table 4). The difficulty here is that y is not tabulated from $x = 0$. We can overcome this by making the transformation $z = x - 7$. From the table

$$y_0 = 103.32 \qquad \Delta y_0 = 7.3 \qquad \Delta^2 y_0 = 0.12 \qquad \Delta^3 y_0 = 0.04$$

Hence

$$f(z) = 103.32 + 7.3z + \frac{0.12}{2}z(z-1) + \frac{0.04}{6}z(z-1)(z-2)$$

$$f(x) = 103.32 + 7.3(x-7) + 0.06(x-7)(x-8) + 0.0067(x-7)(x-8)(x-9)$$

Simplifying

$$f(x) = 52.2032 + 7.6797x - 0.1008x^2 + 0.0067x^3 \quad \text{(coefficients to 4D)}$$

These somewhat artificial examples illustrate the method. Any actual table of values derived from, for example, an experiment in Physics would only approximate to a polynomial and the final difference would only be approximately constant.

Exercise 3.2

1 The following table gives pairs of values of x and $f(x)$. It is known that $f(x)$ is a polynomial function of degree 3. Find an expression for $f(x)$.

x	0	1	2	3
$f(x)$	1	0	−1	7

2 The following table gives values of $f(x)$ for various values of x. A mistake has been made in writing down the numbers $f(x)$. Given that $f(x)$ is a third degree polynomial expression, locate and correct the mistake.

x	−3	−2	−1	0	1	2	3	4	5	6	7
$f(x)$	−61	−25	−7	−1	−1	5	−1	23	59	119	209

3 Show that if tabular values are given for $x = 0, 1, 2, 3$ of the function

$$f(x) = a + bx + cx(x-1) + dx(x-1)(x-2)$$

then the values of a, b, c, d can be obtained from the differences derived from the table, e.g. b from $f(1) - f(0)$.

Given the following table for a cubic polynomial $g(x)$, find and check the values of a, b, c, d required to express it in the form given above. Hence or otherwise evaluate $g(5)$, $g(6)$, $g(7)$, $g(8)$.

x	0	1	2	3	4
$g(x)$	87.25	89.37	91.49	96.85	108.69

4 Find and correct the mistakes in the following table and derive the equation of this function tabulated

x	0	1	2	3	4	5	6	7	8
$f(x)$	-1	-1	1	5	23	59	119	209	335

Miscellaneous examination questions 14

1 Find the values of x between $-90°$ and $+90°$, which satisfy the equation

$$2\cos^2 x = b\sin x + c$$

The values of b and c are only known with an error of ± 0.01 so that $b = -1 \pm 0.01$ and $c = 2 \pm 0.01$. Find the bounds within which the larger value of x must lie.

(M.E.I.)

2 Find the percentage error in calculating $ab/\sqrt{c}$ when a and b are overestimated by 1% and c is underestimated by 1%. (S.)

3 Explain why accuracy to 3S is impossible if 4 figure tables are used to compute the expression $(x^2+2)^{1/2} - (x^2+1)^{1/2}$ directly for $x = 24$. Recast the expression so that an answer correct to 3S can be found using 4 figure tables and find it. (W.)

4 The horizontal range of a gun is $R = v^2 \sin 2a/g$, where v is the muzzle velocity and a the angle of elevation. If the intended values of v and a are 400 ms^{-1} and 30°, estimate the greatest possible percentage error in R if errors of 0.5% in v and 1° in a are possible. (W.)

5 In order to calculate the volume V and the total surface area A of a solid cone of given semi-vertical angle x, the slant height S of the cone is measured. If there is a small error s in the measurement of S, show that, if powers of s greater than the first are neglected, then the resulting error v in V is given approximately by

$$v = \pi S^2 s \sin^2 x \cos x$$

Find also an expression for the approximate error a in A.

Taking $S = 21$ mm and $x = 45°$, calculate the values of V and A. If the value of S is only correct to the nearest mm, whereas x is exact, estimate the maximum errors in your calculated values of V and A. (C.)

6 The side a of a triangle ABC is calculated from $a^2 = b^2 + c^2 - 2bc\cos A$. If small errors β and γ occur in b and c, show that if β^2, γ^2 and $\beta\gamma$ are neglected, then the resulting small error α in a is given approximately by

$$a\alpha = (b - c\cos A)\beta + (c - b\cos A)\gamma$$

Find also an expression for the approximate error δ in the area of the triangle calculate from the formula $\Delta = \frac{1}{2}bc\sin A$. If the sides b and c are given as 42 mm and 24 mm, each to the nearest mm, and A is 60° exactly, calculate values for a and Δ and establish in each case the maximum error in the value obtained. (C.)

7 If the logarithm of x to base e is known to lie between $l+d$ and $l-d$, derive a value for the maximum relative error in taking x to be e^l. Show that if $\log_{10} x$ is known to within 5×10^{-6}, the maximum relative error in x is about 1.2×10^{-5}.
(M.E.I.)

8 Three quantities x, y and z are measured and found to be 1.61, 2.23 and 4.66 respectively, correct to two places of decimals. Find x^2, $(y-z)^2$ and $x^2-(y-z)^2$ to two places of decimals and in each case calculate the maximum possible error involved.
(M.E.I.)

9 A scout tries to estimate the height h metres of a hill due north of his position P by first measuring roughly the angle of elevation $\alpha°$ of the line from P to the top of the hill, and then the corresponding angle $\beta°$ from a position Q, d km east of P.

Assuming the hill and the positions P and Q to be on a plane, using elementary trigonometry he applies the formula

$$h = \frac{1000d}{\sqrt{(\cot^2\beta° - \cot^2\alpha°)}}$$

to calculate h. If $\alpha = 20\pm1$, $\beta = 10\pm1$, $d = 1\pm0.01$, find to the nearest metre the limits within which the scout's estimate of h will lie.

Advise the scout how to narrow the limits within which his estimate of h will lie, given that he is unable to improve the accuracy of his measurement (i.e. angles are given to within 1 degree, distances to within 1%).
(M.E.I.)

10 The position of a point P in relation to a base-line AB of known length is found by calculation from the observed angles $\hat{PAB} = \theta$ and $\hat{PBA} = \phi$. Show by logarithmic differentiation or otherwise that the percentage error in the length PA due to a small error μ degrees in ϕ, (where θ is exact) is given by

$$k\mu\{\cot\phi - \cot(\theta+\phi)\} \qquad \text{where } k \approx 1.75.$$
(M.E.I.)

11 Two radio stations C and D are 200 km apart, with D east of C. A man navigating a small craft in fog checks his position by taking radio bearings. He estimates the bearing of C to be between 240° and 245°, and of D between 125° and 130°. His most northerly possible position based on these data is N, his most easterly possible position is E, and so on. Determine an exact formula for the distance WS as a percentage of SD, evaluate it to three significant figures, and compare with the estimate obtained by a suitable adaptation of the formula given in Question 10.
(M.E.I.)

12(a) Assuming that third differences of the polynomial f are constant, find $f(2)$ from the data

x	4	5	6	7	8
$f(x)$	0.35	0.88	1.71	2.90	4.51

(b) Find the cubic polynomial in x which takes the values 1, −3, −1, 13 when $x = 1, 2, 3, 4$ respectively.
(M.E.I.)

13 The time T of a pendulum of length l is given by

$$T = 2\pi\sqrt{\frac{l}{g'}} \qquad \text{where} \qquad g' = g\left(\frac{r}{r+h}\right)^2$$

Find the maximum possible percentage error in T due to small errors of a, b, c and d per cent in h, l, g and r respectively. (M.E.I.)

14 The differences of a polynomial $f(x)$ are formed from its values at x_{-3}, x_{-2}, x_{-1}, x_0, x_1, x_2, x_3. Show, by calculating the fourth differences, how an error of E in the value of $f(x_0)$ will affect the table of differences of the function. Estimate the maximum possible error in the fifth differences if E is a rounding off error in the least significant digit.

Tables of values for two quartic polynomials $g(x)$ and $h(x)$ are given to three significant figures as

x	1.0	1.1	1.2	1.3	1.4	1.5	1.6
$g(x)$	1.00	1.13	1.35	1.76	2.10	2.69	3.46
$h(x)$	4.00	4.87	5.91	7.15	8.60	10.3	12.3

Correct any errors other than those attributable to rounding off, in either table. (M.E.I.)

15(a) The following table contains an error. By contructing a difference table, locate the error and correct the original table.

x	1	2	3	4	5	6	7	8	9	10
y	7	12	21	34	51	70	97	126	159	196

(b) Show that the equation $x^3 - 3x + 1 = 0$ has a root lying between 0.3 and 0.4. *Either* find this root correct to four significant figures *or* write a flow diagram for Newton's or some other iterative method for calculation by a digital computer of this root to six significant figures. (M.E.I.)

16 Explain, by reference to a general cubic polynomial, the method of *nested multiplication* for the evaluation of a polynomial.

Show that, for the polynomial

$$A_n x^n + A_{n-1}x^{n-1} + \cdots + A_0$$

where n is a positive integer and A_n, A_{n-1}, . . . , A_0 are real numbers, evaluation by the method of nested multiplication requires a smaller number of multiplication operations than evaluation term-by-term.

Draw a flow diagram for the evaluation of this polynomial by the method of nested multiplication. (M.E.I.)

Chapter 15

Approximations

Introduction

This chapter might have been entitled 'Deliberate Errors' for in it we investigate methods of *approximation* that are used (a) to evaluate functions (b) to evaluate definite integrals and differentials of a function and (c) to solve equations in one variable. Approximation necessarily involves inexactness or error and we must be aware of the sources of error, whether in the data, in the method of approximation, in the calculation, or in all three, and must make sure that the errors are kept within tolerable limits.

1 Evaluation of a function

1.1 Evaluation of a function using a series expansion

The values of a function given in a book of tables or by an electronic calculator have been found by means of a series expansion. The Binomial Theorem, Maclaurin's or Taylor's theorem is used to express a function of x, $f(x)$, as an infinite series of powers of x (or power series of x) and, provided this series converges, any required degree of accuracy can be obtained by taking sufficient terms of the series. The infinite series is thus cut short or truncated and the error involved in neglecting the terms in the higher powers of x is accordingly known as a *truncation error.* Evaluation of the truncation error is in general beyond our scope, but if the series is converging rapidly it is usually sufficient to take the *principal* truncation error which is the first term not included.

Example 1

By means of a series expansion, evaluate $\sin x$ to 5D when $x = \frac{1}{2}^c$ (exact).

Maclaurin's series gives

$$\sin x = x - \frac{x^3}{3!} + \frac{x^5}{5!} - \frac{x^7}{7!} + \cdots$$

The recurrence relation is

$$u_i = -\frac{x^2}{(2i-1)(2i-2)}u_{i-1}$$

It is advisable to keep two guarding figures, that is, two more decimal places than required, so we calculate successive terms to 7D.

$$u_1 = 0.5$$

$$u_2 = -0.020\,833\,3$$

$$u_3 = 0.000\,260\,4$$

$$u_4 = -0.000\,001\,6$$

$$u_5 = 0 \quad (7D)$$

It is clear that further terms will not affect the fifth decimal place.

So $\sin \frac{1}{2}^c \approx \sum_{i=1}^{4} u_i = 0.479\,425\,5 = 0.479\,43$ to 5D.

Example 2

By means of a series expansion evaluate the fourth root of 1.1 to 5D.

Using the Binomial series

$$(1.1)^{1/4} = 1 + \tfrac{1}{4}(0.1) + \frac{(\frac{1}{4})(-\frac{3}{4})}{2!}(0.1)^2 + \frac{(\frac{1}{4})(-\frac{3}{4})(-\frac{7}{4})}{3!}(0.1)^3 + \cdots$$

This time, the recurrence relation is

$$u_i = -(0.1)\frac{(4i-9)}{4(i-1)}u_{i-1}$$

$$u_1 = 1$$

$$u_2 = 0.025$$

$$u_3 = -\tfrac{3}{8} \times 0.1 \times u_2 = -0.000\,937\,5$$

$$u_4 = -\tfrac{7}{12} \times 0.1 \times u_3 = 0.000\,054\,6$$

$$u_5 = -\tfrac{11}{16} \times 0.1 \times u_4 = -0.000\,003\,8$$

Later terms will not affect the fifth place

$$(1.1)^{1/4} \approx \sum_{i=1}^{5} u_i = 1.024\,113\,3 = 1.024\,11 \quad \text{to 5D}$$

Exercise 1.1

Check all your results in this exercise with your calculator functions.

1 The series for $\ln(1+x)$ is

$$\ln(1+x) = x - \frac{x^2}{2} + \frac{x^3}{3} - \frac{x^4}{4} + \cdots \qquad (-1 < x \leqslant 1)$$

Verify the recurrence relation

$$u_i = -x\frac{(i-1)}{i}u_{i-1}, \qquad u_1 = x$$

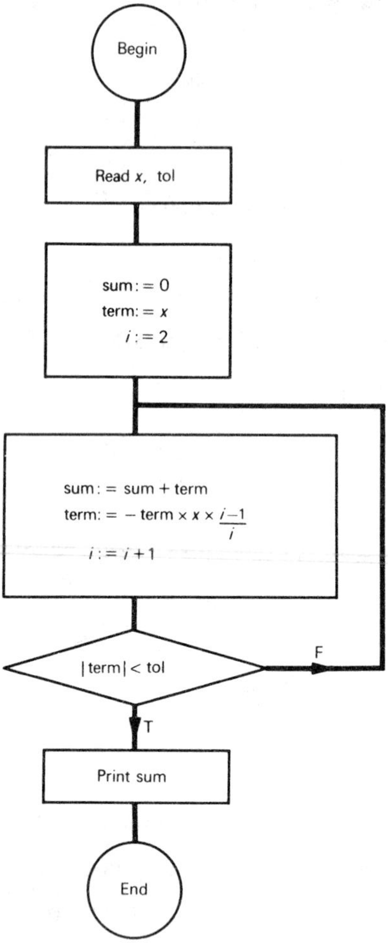

The figure shows a flow chart that uses this algorithm to evaluate ln $(1+x)$. Assuming that the next two numbers in the input stream are 0.1, 0.000 005, find ln 1.1 correct to 5D.

2 The series for e^x is

$$e^x = 1 + x + \frac{x^2}{2!} + \frac{x^3}{3!} + \cdots$$

Verify that the recurrence relation is

$$u_{i+1} = \frac{x}{i}u_i, \qquad u_1 = 1$$

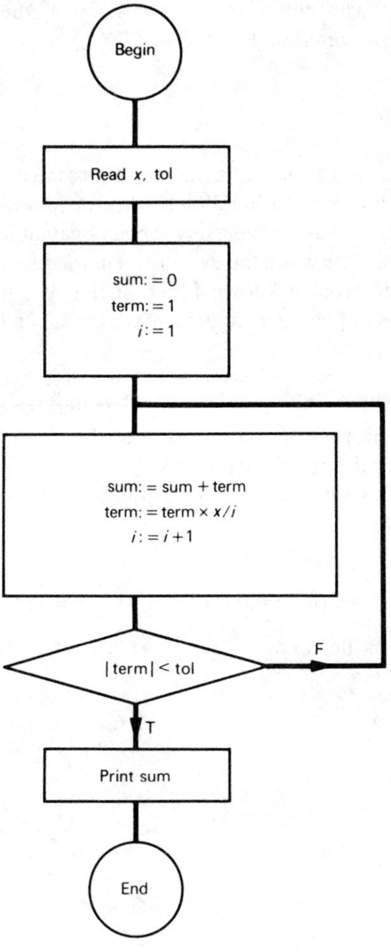

The flow chart is based on this algorithm. Taking $x = 0.5$, tol $= 0.000\,001$, find a value for $e^{1/2}$.

3 Find algorithms and draw up flow charts for summing each of the following series. Test your flow chart for $x = 0.2$, tol $= 0.000\,001$.

(a) $\ln(1-2x) = -\left(2x + \frac{(2x)^2}{2} + \frac{(2x)^3}{3} + \frac{(2x)^4}{4} + \cdots\right)$

(This series is valid for $|x| < \frac{1}{2}$.)

(b) $e^{-3x} = 1 - 3x + \frac{(3x)^2}{2!} - \frac{(3x)^3}{3!} + \frac{(3x)^4}{4!} - \cdots$

(c) $\cos x = 1 - \frac{x^2}{2!} + \frac{x^4}{4!} - \frac{x^6}{6!} + \cdots$

4 Expand $(1-x^2)^{1/2}$ as a power series in x as far as the term in x^6. By putting $x=0.1$, obtain an approximation for $\sqrt{11}$ to 5D.

1.2 Interpolation

Sometimes we need to find a value of a function for some value of x that lies between two values for which those of the function are known. These known values might be (a) from a book of tables (having themselves been evaluated numerically as we have seen), (b) experimental data when the exact form of the function will not in general be known, or (c) derived from a known function that is complicated or difficult to calculate. The process of finding an approximate value of a function between known values is called *interpolation*.

In *linear* interpolation we approximate to the curve between the two points by treating it as if it were a straight line. It is obvious that the error in the interpolated value will depend in part on the actual shape of the curve between the two points, being an overestimate if it is concave upwards and an underestimate if it is convex upwards. There will also be an error if the known values themselves are inexact.

Example 1

Estimate tan 80.43°, given that tan 80.4° = 5.912 36 and tan 80.5° = 5.975 76.

We only draw part of the curve $y = \tan x$. At A (and at D) $y = 5.912\ 36$ and at E $y = 5.975\ 76$.

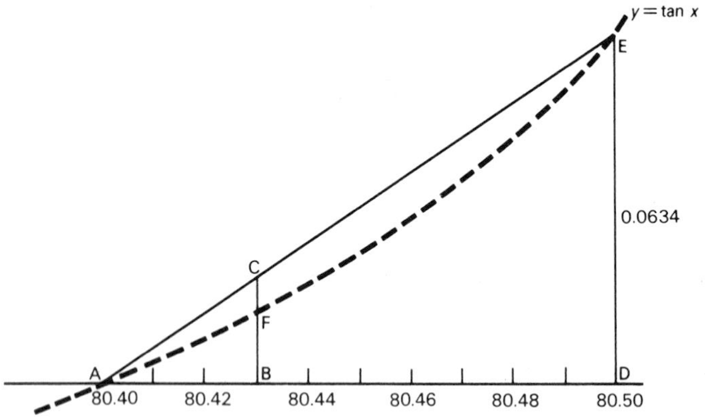

The triangles ABC and ADE are similar. Hence

$$\frac{AB}{AD} = \frac{BC}{DE}$$

$$\frac{3}{10} = \frac{BC}{0.0634}$$

so

$$BC = 0.019\ 02$$

and the value of tan x when $x = 80.43°$ is approximately

$$5.912\,36+0.019\,02 = 5.931\,38$$

This is in fact the value at the point C on the line, not at the point F on the curve and we should expect it to be higher than the true value. A calculator gives tan 80.43° = 5.931 239 9.

Graphical method

If great accuracy is not required the interpolated value can be found very quickly by plotting on some large and simple scale the points (80.4, 5.912) and (80.5, 5.976) and reading off the y value corresponding to $x = 80.43$.

General expression for linear interpolation

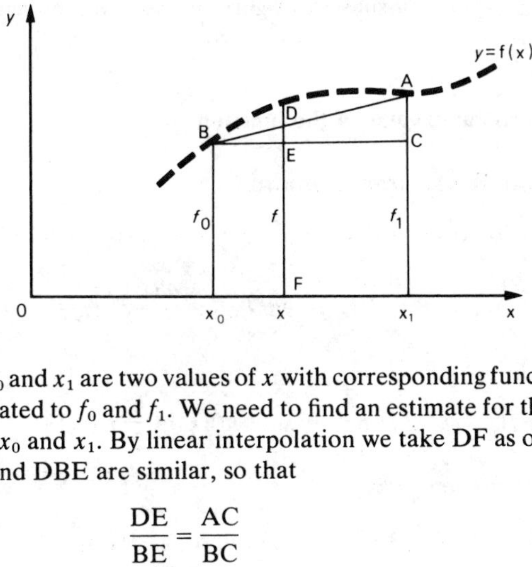

In the diagram, x_0 and x_1 are two values of x with corresponding function values $f(x_0)$ and $f(x_1)$ abbreviated to f_0 and f_1. We need to find an estimate for the value of f at a point x between x_0 and x_1. By linear interpolation we take DF as our estimate of f. Triangles ABC and DBE are similar, so that

$$\frac{\text{DE}}{\text{BE}} = \frac{\text{AC}}{\text{BC}}$$

$$\frac{f-f_0}{x-x_0} = \frac{f_1-f_0}{x_1-x_0}$$

$$f-f_0 = \frac{(x-x_0)}{(x_1-x_0)}(f_1-f_0)$$

$$\boldsymbol{f = f_0+\frac{(x-x_0)}{(x_1-x_0)}(f_1-f_0)}$$ ◄

We shall refer to the fraction $\dfrac{x-x_0}{x_1-x_0}$ as θ, to the step (x_1-x_0) as h, and (as when we studied the method of finite differences) to (f_1-f_0) as Δf_0. Then

$$\boldsymbol{f_\theta = f_0+\theta\,\Delta f_0}$$ ◄

Example 2

Tables of the normal probability distribution function give

$$\Phi(1.36) = 0.9131 \qquad \text{and} \qquad \Phi(1.37) = 0.9147$$

Find by linear interpolation an approximation to $\Phi(1.367)$

$$\Delta f_0 = 0.9147 - 0.9131 = 16 \times 10^{-4}$$

$$\theta = \frac{1.367 - 1.36}{1.37 - 1.36} = \frac{7}{10}$$

$$\Phi(1.367) = 0.9131 + \tfrac{7}{10} \times 16 \times 10^{-4} = 0.9131 + 0.001\,12$$

$$= 0.914\,22$$

In many tables of the normal distribution, the difference between successive values of the function is given as a subscript figure to speed the process of linear interpolation.

Errors in the interpolated value of the function

(a) Error due to linear approximation

The Taylor series for any function $f(x)$ at $x = x_0 + \theta h$ is

$$f(x_0 + \theta h) = f(x_0) + \theta h f'(x_0) + \frac{(\theta h)^2}{2!} f''(x_0) + \dots \tag{1}$$

and at $x_1 = x_0 + h$

$$f(x_1) = f(x_0 + h) = f(x_0) + h f'(x_0) + \frac{h^2}{2!} f''(x_0) + \dots$$

The linear approximation gives

$$f(x_0 + \theta h) \approx f(x_0) + \theta[f(x_1) - f(x_0)]$$

Substituting for $f(x_1)$

$$f(x_0 + \theta h) \approx f(x_0) - \theta f(x_0) + \theta\left[f(x_0) + h f'(x_0) + \frac{h^2}{2!} f''(x_0) + \dots\right]$$

$$\approx f(x_0) + \theta h f'(x_0) + \frac{\theta h^2}{2!} f''(x_0) + \dots \tag{2}$$

Subtracting (2) from (1) we have the error, ε, due to the linear approximation where

$$\varepsilon = \tfrac{1}{2}\theta h^2 f''(x_0)(\theta - 1) \qquad \text{plus terms in higher powers of } h.$$

Providing h is sufficiently small, this is a satisfactory estimate of the error due to approximating to the curve by a linear instead of a polynomial function. It is a truncation error.

(b) Error due to inexact values of the given data

If the known values are experimentally determined, they are likely to be subject to about the same absolute error, and again, if they are tabulated values, they will be rounded to the same number of significant figures. The interpolated value will therefore also be subject to a maximum absolute error less than or equal to that in the known values of the function.

Quadratic and higher order interpolation

If the truncation error is unacceptably large, then we must use one of the interpolation formulae based on the method of differences, to whatever degree is required. The best known of these, given here without proof is the Gregory–Newton formula (sometimes called the Newton forward difference interpolation formula).

$$f(x_0+\theta h) \approx f(x_0)+\theta\,\Delta f(x_0)+\frac{1}{2!}\theta(\theta-1)\,\Delta^2 f(x_0)+\dots$$
$$+\frac{1}{n!}\theta(\theta-1)\dots(\theta-n+1)\,\Delta^n f(x_0) \quad ◀$$

We can now see that the general expression for linear interpolation is given by the first two terms in this formula. If quadratic (or higher order) interpolation is to be used the values of the function between which a value is to be interpolated must be known to sufficient significant figures for the second (and higher) differences still to have two or more significant figures.

Example 2

Estimate tan 80.43° given that tan 80.4° = 5.912 36, tan 80.5° = 5.975 76 and tan 80.6° = 6.040 51.

The work is best arranged in columns

x_n	$f(x_n)$	$\Delta f(x_n)$	$\Delta^2 f(x_n)$
80.4	5.912 36	0.063 40	0.001 35
80.5	5.975 76	0.064 75	
80.6	6.040 51		

$$h = 0.1 \qquad \text{and} \qquad \theta = \tfrac{3}{10}$$

$$\tan 80.43° = 5.912\,36+\tfrac{3}{10}(0.063\,40)+\tfrac{1}{2}(\tfrac{3}{10})(-\tfrac{7}{10})(0.001\,35)$$
$$= 5.912\,36+0.019\,02-0.000\,14$$
$$= 5.931\,24$$

Exercise 1.2

1 Use four figure tables and linear interpolation to evaluate the following functions and check your results on your calculator.

(a) log sin 5.55° **(b)** log sin 5.84° **(c)** log cos 86.17°
(d) tan 80.42° **(e)** sec 78.36° **(f)** sec 78.475°

2 The curve $y = f(x)$ passes through the points (3, 1.92) and (5, 1.84). Interpolate the values of

(a) $f(4)$ **(b)** $f(4.5)$ **(c)** $f(4.6)$

3 The curves $y = x^2$ and $y = \sqrt{x}$ both pass through the points (0, 0) and (1, 1). Use linear interpolation to find y when $x = 0.49$ and compare this with the values of the two functions at $x = 0.49$. Sketch the curves and interpret the difference in sign of the two errors.

4 Given the data

x	0.10	0.11	0.12	0.13	0.14	0.15
$f(x)$	0.801	0.969	1.156	1.361	1.584	1.826

use the quadratic interpolation formula to obtain an approximation to 4S for $f(0.136)$.

2 Numerical integration and differentiation

2.1 The area under a curve

One of the most useful applications of numerical mathematics is in the calculation of definite integrals by finding areas. There are three types of problem that need a numerical solution.

(1) The function under consideration may not be integrable analytically. That is to say there is no simple function that differentiates to give the required function. An example from mechanics arises in the oscillation of a simple pendulum making *large* swings. The time taken between two points on the path requires the integration of $(1 - k\sin^2\theta)^{-1/2}$ and this can only be done numerically. In statistics, the Normal probability function $k\,e^{-\frac{1}{2}x^2}$ likewise cannot be integrated analytically except between $-\infty$ and $+\infty$.

(2) It may be possible to integrate the function, but the evaluation of the integral presents such difficulties that it is quicker to find a numerical solution.

e.g. $$\int_0^x \frac{t}{a^3+t^3}\,dt = \frac{1}{6a}\ln\frac{x^2-ax+a^2}{(x+a)^2} + \frac{1}{a\sqrt{3}}\tan^{-1}\frac{x\sqrt{3}}{2a-x} \qquad (-a < x < 2a)$$

(3) We may know the value of the function at a number of points without knowing its explicit form. This is often the case in scientific experiments. We might, for example, have made a series of measurements of the temperature in an experiment, without knowing precisely how the temperature varies with the time elapsed.

Consider the integral $I = \int_a^b f(x)\,dx$. This may be represented as the area under the curve $y = f(x)$ between $x = a$ and $x = b$.

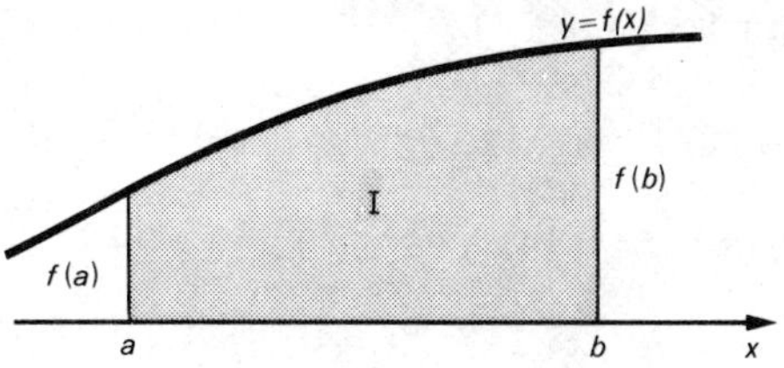

There are several methods of finding the area numerically, but in most of them the first step is to divide the area into a number (n) of equally spaced vertical strips. If h is the width of each strip, then $h = \dfrac{(b-a)}{n}$.

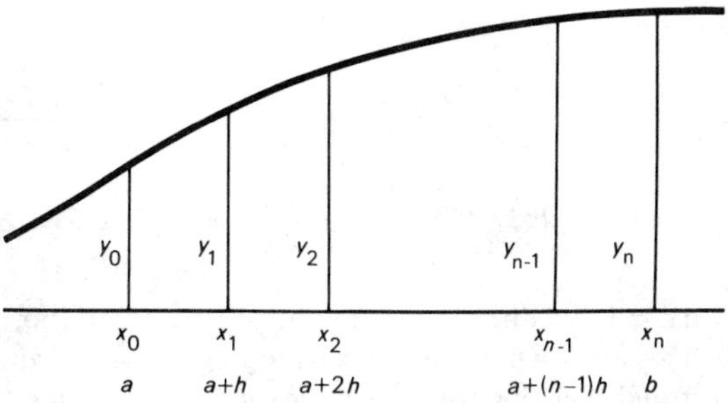

It is clear from the figure that $x_i = a + ih$, and $y_i = f(a + ih)$, and that the ith strip is bounded by y_{i-1} and y_i.

The next step is to find an expression for the area of each strip by replacing the curve at the top of the strip by a curve of simpler form. The various methods of numerical integration differ in their choice of this approximating curve.

The trapezium rule

In this rule the curve is replaced by a *straight line* as in the figure.

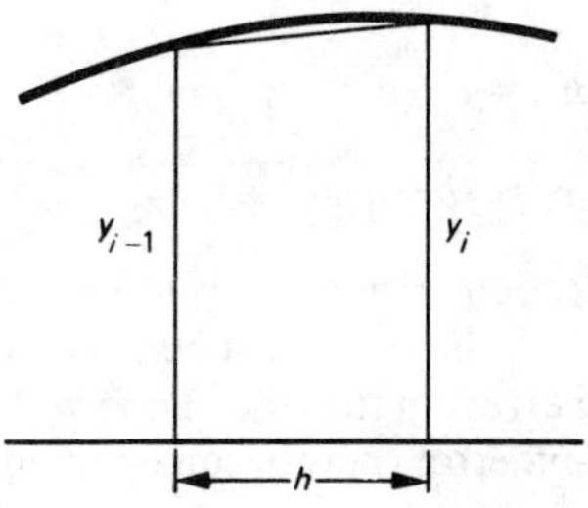

The area of the ith strip is $\frac{1}{2}h(y_{i-1}+y_i)$

$$I \approx \sum_{i=1}^{n} \tfrac{1}{2}h(y_{i-1}+y_i) = \tfrac{1}{2}h(y_0+y_1)+\tfrac{1}{2}h(y_1+y_2)+\cdots+\tfrac{1}{2}h(y_{n-1}+y_n)$$

$$\mathbf{I \approx h(\tfrac{1}{2}y_0+y_1+y_2+\cdots+y_{n-1}+\tfrac{1}{2}y_n)}$$ ◀

Example

Estimate to 3D $\int_0^{\pi/2} \cos x \, dx$ using six strips ($n = 6$)

i	0	1	2	3	4	5	6
x_i	0	$\frac{1}{12}\pi$	$\frac{2}{12}\pi$	$\frac{3}{12}\pi$	$\frac{4}{12}\pi$	$\frac{5}{12}\pi$	$\frac{6}{12}\pi$
y_i	1	0.9659	0.8660	0.7071	0.5000	0.2588	0

$$h = \frac{\pi}{12} = 0.2618, \qquad \tfrac{1}{2}(y_0+y_6) = 0.5, \qquad \sum_1^5 y_i = 3.2978$$

$$\int_0^{\pi/2} \cos x \, dx \approx 0.2618(0.5+3.2978) = 0.9943 = 0.994 \quad \text{(3D)}$$

In fact $\int_0^{\pi/2} \cos x \, dx = 1$ by direct integration, so the error (both absolute and relative) is 0.006. This error will be due in part to the method of approximation (in this case taking a straight line instead of a curve) and in part to inexact data (in this case the values of the function are calculated to 4D, so each will be subject to a rounding error with bound $\pm 5\times 10^{-5}$).

It is apparent from the figure that the trapezium rule will give an underestimate of the area under parts of the curve that are convex upwards and an overestimate where the curve is concave. As with linear interpolation this is a truncation error and it can be shown that for most functions the truncation error is proportional to h^2 and so inversely proportional to n^2. It may therefore be expected to decrease rapidly as the number of steps is increased. The round-off error in the area due to inexact data, however, is independent of n. If each y value is subject to a maximum absolute error, ε, then the error in the integral will be ε_I where

$$\varepsilon_I \leqslant h(\tfrac{1}{2}\varepsilon+\varepsilon+\varepsilon+\cdots+\tfrac{1}{2}\varepsilon)$$

$$= hn\varepsilon$$

But $\qquad hn = b-a$

Hence $\qquad \varepsilon_I \leqslant (b-a)\varepsilon$

When n is small the truncation error is likely to be dominant since if the y values are found with the aid of a calculator the round-off errors in the data will be very small and also the rounding errors in the calculation will be very small. But for very large values of n, the round-off errors may become dominant and further subdivision will not improve the result.

Flow chart for the trapezium rule

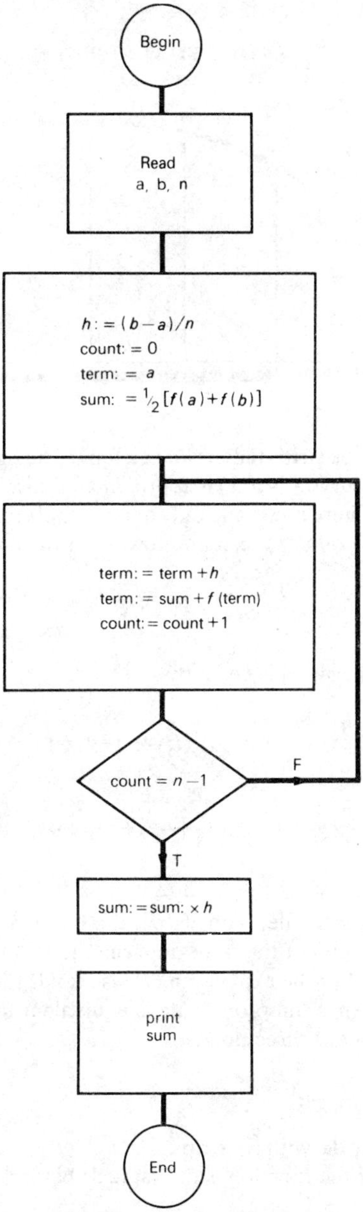

The first and last terms, $\frac{1}{2}f(a)$ and $\frac{1}{2}f(b)$, are found first (not being typical members of the series) and their sum is assigned to the variable sum. The remaining terms are computed using the algorithm

$$f(t_i) = f(t_{i-1} + h)$$

Finally the accumulated *sum* is multiplied by *h* to give the required result.

2.2 Simpson's rule

For this rule, the number of strips, n, must be even.

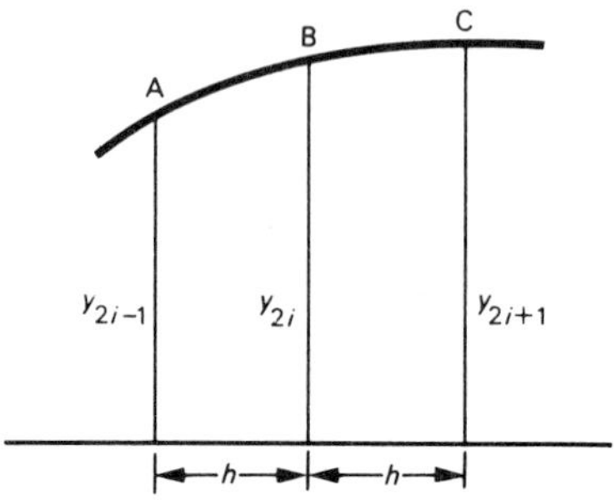

We estimate the area of the strips taken two at a time. The figure shows the $(2i)^{th}$ and the $(2i+1)^{th}$ strips. The curve $y = f(x)$ is approximated to a *parabola* drawn through the points A, B and C. (There is one and only one parabola that can be drawn through any three non-collinear points.) It can be shown that the area of the double strip is

$$\frac{h}{3}(y_{2i-1}+4y_{2i}+y_{2i+1}) \qquad (1)$$

so the total area of all the strips is given by

$$I = \frac{h}{3}(y_0+4y_1+y_2)+\frac{h}{3}(y_2+4y_3+y_4)+\cdots$$

$$\mathbf{I = \frac{h}{3}(y_0+4y_1+2y_2+4y_3+\cdots+4y_{n-1}+y_n)} \quad ◀$$

Notice the pattern of the coefficients—14242 . . . 241.

It is clear that Simpson's rule, with its parabolic segments, should give better results than the straight lines of the trapezium rule. In fact it is even more powerful than might be expected. For the expression (1) also holds for any cubic curve drawn through A, B and C. Hence Simpson's rule is equivalent to drawing a cubic curve through each adjacent set of three points.

Example

Consider again $\int_0^{\pi/2} \cos x \, dx$ with six strips.

The table of values of the function is the same as before.

i	0	1	2	3	4	5	6
x_i	0	$\frac{1}{12}\pi$	$\frac{2}{12}\pi$	$\frac{3}{12}\pi$	$\frac{4}{12}\pi$	$\frac{5}{12}\pi$	$\frac{6}{12}\pi$
y_i	1	0.9659	0.8660	0.7071	0.5000	0.2588	0

Now

$$\tfrac{1}{3}h = \tfrac{1}{36}\pi = 0.0873, \qquad 4(y_1+y_3+y_5) = 7.7272,$$

$$2(y_2+y_4) = 2.7320, \qquad \text{and} \qquad y_0+y_6 = 1$$

$$\int_0^{\pi/2} \cos x \, dx \approx 0.0873(1+7.7272+2.7320) = 1.0004 = 1.000 \quad \text{(3D)}$$

Rounded to 3D, this gives the correct result, which demonstrates a gain in accuracy over the previous method.

The error in Simpson's rule is inversely proportional to n^4 for most functions so that convergence is much faster than for the trapezium rule. As a rough comparison, Simpson's rule with n points gives about the same order of accuracy as the trapezium rule with $2n$ points.

The effect of the round-off error in the values of the function is the same as for the trapezium rule. Suppose the error in each y value is ε. Then the error in the integral is

$$\varepsilon_I = \tfrac{1}{3}h(\varepsilon+4\varepsilon+2\varepsilon+\cdots+4\varepsilon+\varepsilon)$$

There are $\frac{1}{2}n$ terms with multiple 4, $\frac{1}{2}n-1$ terms with multiple 2

So

$$|\varepsilon_I| \leqslant \tfrac{1}{3}h(1+4\times\tfrac{1}{2}n+2(\tfrac{1}{2}n-1)+1)|\varepsilon|$$

$$= \tfrac{1}{3}h(2+2n+n-2)|\varepsilon|$$

$$= nh|\varepsilon|$$

$$|\varepsilon_I| \leqslant (b-a)|\varepsilon|$$

Flow chart for Simpson's rule

The flow chart, which appears on the next page, is similar to the previous one.

Again, the first and last terms are evaluated first. The coefficients 4242 etc. are derived using the variable *coeff*. This is initially zero and then alternates between 2 and 0 as the assignment statement *coeff*: = 2 − *coeff* is executed on each circuit of the loop so that the expression (4 − *coeff*) takes the value 4 and 2 alternately. When the series,

$$f(a)+4f(a+h)+2f(a+2h)\cdots+f(b)$$

has been accumulated in the variable sum, it is multiplied by $\frac{1}{3}h$ to give the required result.

Exercise 2.2

1 Use the trapezium rule with six intervals to evaluate the following integrals

(a) $\int_0^{1.2} \sqrt{(1+x)}\, dx$ **(b)** $\int_0^{\pi/2} \sin x\, dx$ **(c)** $\int_0^{1.8} x\, e^x\, dx$

(d) $\int_1^4 (5x-x^2-4)\, dx$

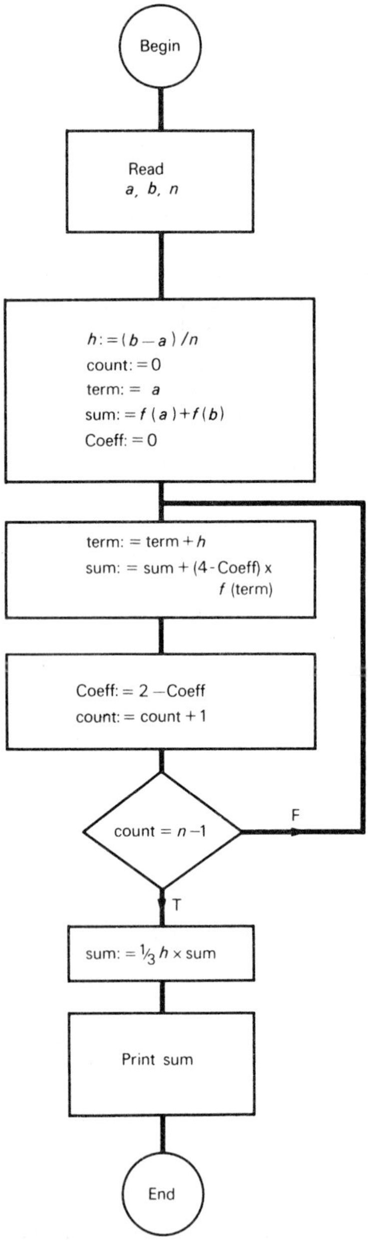

2 Evaluate the integrals in question **1**, using Simpson's rule, with 6 intervals.

3 Find an approximation to the value of

$$\int_0^{\pi/6} \ln(1+\sin x)\,dx$$

(a) by using Simpson's rule with 6 strips.

(b) by expanding ln $(1+\sin x)$ in ascending powers of x up to and including x^3 and integrating.

4 Use **(a)** the trapezium rule, and **(b)** Simpson's rule, each with 7 ordinates, to estimate

$$\int_0^{\pi} x \sin x \, dx$$

By integrating the equation

$$\frac{d(x \cos x)}{dx} = \cos x - x \sin x$$

show that the exact value of the integral is π.

5 Use the trapezium rule to find an approximation for

$$\int_0^1 \frac{dx}{1+x}$$

by dividing the range of integration into 5 equal parts. Hence obtain an approximate value for ln 2.

6 Evaluate

$$\int_0^{1/2} (1-x^2)^{-1/2} \, dx$$

by Simpson's rule, using 4 strips. Use your result to obtain a numerical estimate of the value of π.

2.3 Numerical differentiation

(This section could be left for a second reading)

We cannot hope for such good results from numerical differentiation as can be achieved by numerical integration. Given, say, three points on a curve, we can usually find a good approximation to the definite integral by assuming linearity (the trapezium rule) or by fitting the points to a quadratic or cubic curve (Simpson's rule). Unfortunately, in numerical differentiation the approximations lead to differential coefficients that are not as accurate as we should like since they usually involve the subtraction of nearly equal numbers (see page 534). However, numerical differentiation is the method by which we obtain approximate solutions to differential equations and which enables us to deal with tabulated functions (where the actual form of the function is unknown).

Consider a curve as shown in the diagram at the top of the next page. When $x = -h$, $y = y_{-1}$, when $x = 0$, $y = y_0$ and when $x = h$, $y = y_1$. Suppose that the curve can be represented as a power series in x, then by Maclaurin's theorem

$$f(-h) = y_{-1} = y_0 - hy_0^{\mathrm{I}} + \frac{h^2}{2!}y_0^{\mathrm{II}} - \frac{h^3}{3!}y_0^{\mathrm{III}} + \frac{h^4}{4!}y_0^{\mathrm{IV}} - \cdots$$

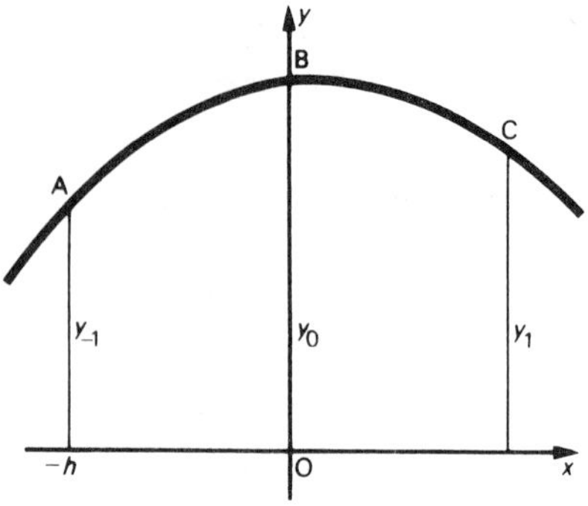

and $$f(h) = y_1 = y_0 + hy_0^{\text{I}} + \frac{h^2}{2!}y_0^{\text{II}} + \frac{h^3}{3!}y_0^{\text{III}} + \frac{h^4}{4!}y_0^{\text{IV}} + \cdots$$

subtracting $$y_1 - y_{-1} = 2hy_0^{\text{I}} + 2\left(\frac{h^3}{3!}y_0^{\text{III}} + \frac{h^5}{5!}y_0^{\text{V}} + \cdots\right)$$

If h is small and y_0^{III} is also small, then we have

$$\boldsymbol{y_0^{\text{I}} \approx \frac{y_1 - y_{-1}}{2h}}$$ ◀

with a truncation error of $\frac{h^2}{3!}y_0^{\text{III}} + \frac{h^4}{5!}y_0^{\text{V}} + \cdots$. Graphically, this approximation corresponds to using the slope of the chord AC as the slope of the tangent at B.

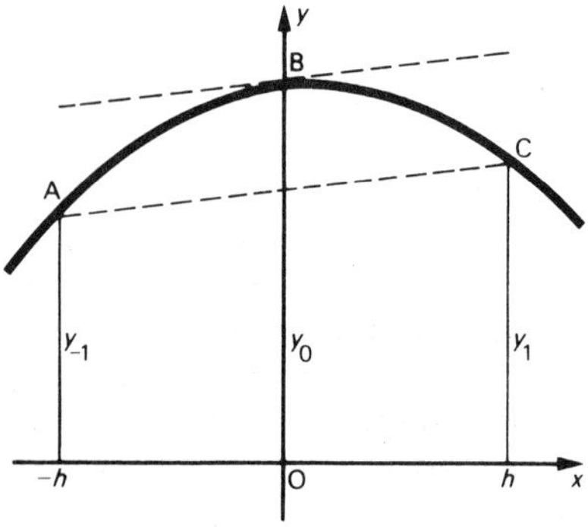

Since we usually require dy/dx at some other point than when $x = 0$, we can easily adapt the formula (using Taylor's theorem rather than Maclaurin's theorem to give the series). This can be done by considering the value of y when $x = a - h$ to be y_{n-1}, when $x = a$, $y = y_n$ and when $x = a + h$, $y = y_{n+1}$. This gives the approximation as

$$y_n^{\text{I}} \approx \frac{y_{n+1} - y_{n-1}}{2h}$$

with truncation error

$$\frac{h^2}{3!}y_n^{\text{III}}+\frac{h^4}{5!}y_n^{\text{V}}+\cdots$$

If we use the difference notation

$$\Delta y_n = y_{n+1}-y_n$$

then

$$y_{n+1}-y_{n-1} = (y_{n+1}-y_n)+(y_n-y_{n-1})$$
$$= \Delta y_n+\Delta y_{n-1}$$

and

$$\mathbf{y_n^{I} \approx \frac{(\Delta y_n+\Delta y_{n-1})}{2h}}$$ ◄

with the same truncation error as before.

We shall note that in practice the errors due to the subtraction of the two nearly equal rounded values of the function usually swamp any truncation error due to the approximation to the differential at the point.

Approximation for the second derivative

Consider again the power series representing the function (page 567)

$$f(-h)=y_{-1} = y_0-hy_0^{\text{I}}+\frac{h^2}{2!}y_0^{\text{II}}-\frac{h^3}{3!}y_0^{\text{III}}+\frac{h^4}{4!}y_0^{\text{IV}}-\cdots$$

and

$$f(h)=y_1 = y_0+hy_0^{\text{I}}+\frac{h^2}{2!}y_0^{\text{II}}+\frac{h^3}{3!}y_0^{\text{III}}+\frac{h^4}{4!}y_0^{\text{IV}}+\cdots$$

Adding

$$y_{-1}+y_1 = 2y_0+h^2y_0^{\text{II}}+\frac{2h^4}{4!}y_0^{\text{IV}}+\frac{2h^6}{6!}y_0^{\text{VI}}+\cdots$$

Now if the terms containing h^4 and higher powers of h are so small that they may be neglected then

$$y_{-1}+y_1 \approx 2y_0+h^2y_0^{\text{II}}$$

and

$$\mathbf{y_0^{II} \approx \frac{y_1-2y_0+y_{-1}}{h^2}}$$ ◄

with a truncation error of

$$2\frac{h^4}{4!}y_0^{\text{IV}}+2\frac{h^6}{6!}y_0^{\text{VI}}+\cdots$$

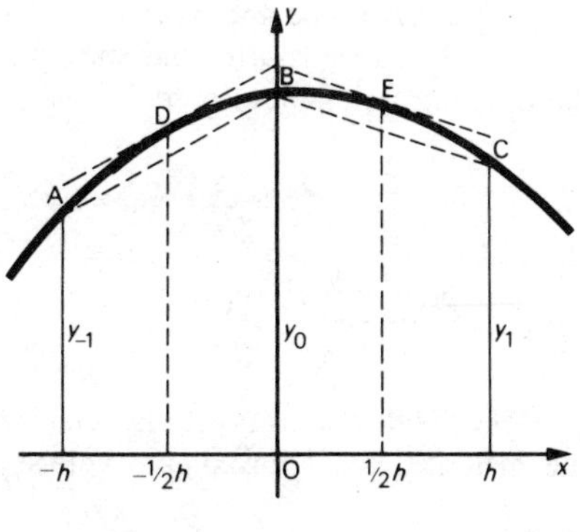

This approximation can be seen graphically where the second differential at B,

$$y_0^{\mathrm{II}} = \frac{(\text{gradient at E}) - (\text{gradient at D})}{h}$$

$$\approx \frac{\left(\frac{y_1 - y_0}{h} - \frac{y_0 - y_{-1}}{h}\right)}{h} \quad \text{i.e.} \quad \left(\frac{\text{Gradient of BC} - \text{Gradient of AB}}{h}\right)$$

As previously, we generalize the approximation so that we can use it at any point on the curve as

$$y_n^{\mathrm{II}} \approx \frac{y_{n+1} - 2y_n + y_{n-1}}{h^2}$$

with a truncation error of

$$2\frac{h^4}{4!}y_n^{\mathrm{IV}} + 2\frac{h^6}{6!}y_n^{\mathrm{VI}} + \cdots$$

Using the difference notation we have

$$\Delta y_n = y_{n+1} - y_n$$

$$\Delta y_{n-1} = y_n - y_{n-1}$$

and

$$\begin{aligned} \Delta^2 y_{n-1} &= \Delta y_n - \Delta y_{n-1} \\ &= y_{n+1} - y_n - (y_n - y_{n-1}) \\ &= y_{n+1} - 2y_n + y_{n-1} \end{aligned}$$

and so the approximation can be written

$$\boldsymbol{y_n^{\mathrm{II}} \approx \frac{\Delta^2 y_{n-1}}{h^2}}$$ ◀

with the same truncation error as before.

Again, the truncation error is likely to be swamped by errors due to the rounding in the original values of y_{-1}, y_0 and y_1 and in the subsequent calculations.

Example 1

A particle is moving along a straight line and its distance x cm from the origin O is noted at times $t = 0, 1, \ldots, 10$ seconds after the start. Estimate its velocity and acceleration during the time it is being monitored.

The velocity,

$$\frac{dx}{dt} \approx \frac{\Delta x_n + \Delta x_{n-1}}{2h} \qquad \text{where } h = 1$$

and the acceleration,

$$\frac{d^2x}{dt^2} \approx \frac{\Delta^2 x_{n-1}}{h^2} \qquad \text{where } h = 1$$

In the table we list the velocity and acceleration obtained from these approximations and in the figures the distance, the approximate velocity and the acceleration respectively are plotted against time. (The last two columns of the table are explained after the figures.)

Time t	*Distance* x	Δx_n	*Acceleration* $\Delta^2 x_{n-1}$	*Velocity* $\frac{1}{2}(\Delta_n+\Delta_{n-1})$	*Acceleration*	*Velocity*
0	0				14	18
		25				
1	25		5	27.5	8	29
		30				
2	55		5	32.5	2	34
		35				
3	90		−5	32.5	−4	33
		30				
4	120		−10	25.0	−10	26
		20				
5	140		−15	12.5	−16	13
		5				
6	145		−25	−7.5	−22	−6
		−20				
7	125		−25	−32.5	−28	−31
		−45				
8	80		−35	−62.5	−34	−62
		−80				
9	0		−40	−100	−40	−99
		−120				
10	−120					

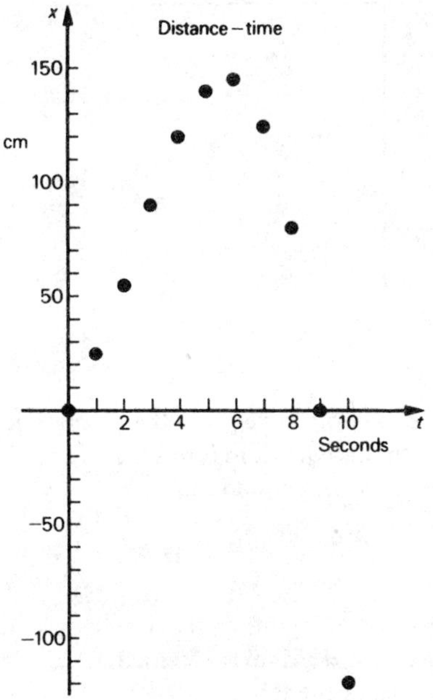

In the last figure overleaf the points lie on or near a straight line whose equation is

$$\frac{d^2x}{dt^2} = -6t + 14 \qquad \text{(from the slope and intercept of the line)}$$

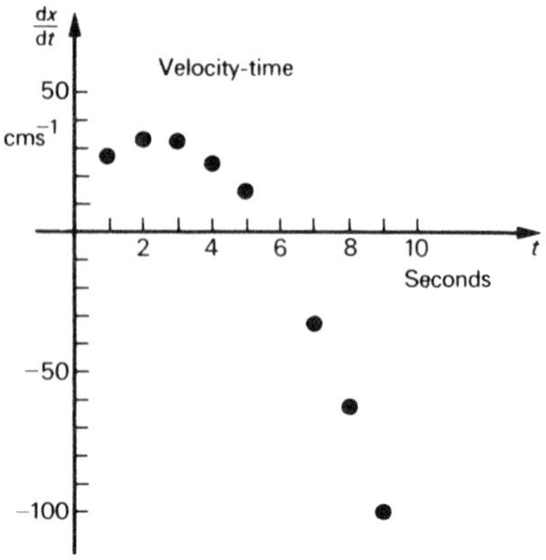

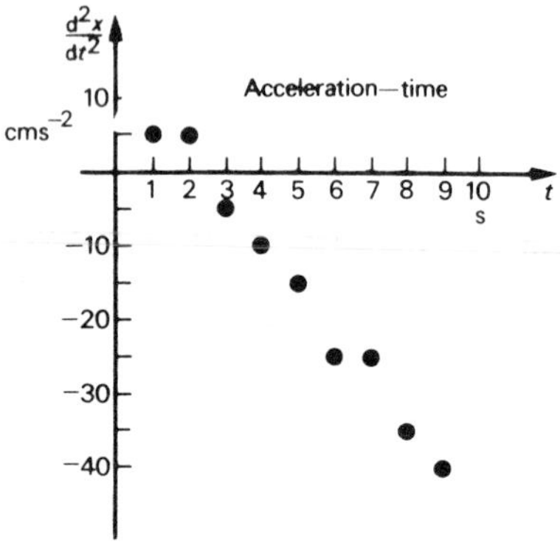

In the sixth column of the table we have given the acceleration, assuming that it is a linear function of time, with this equation. If this is so, the points in the velocity-time graph should lie in a parabola with equation

$$\frac{\mathrm{d}x}{\mathrm{d}t} = -3t^2 + 14t + 18$$

(We obtain this equation by integrating the previous equation and noting the intercept of the parabola on the $\mathrm{d}x/\mathrm{d}t$ axis.) Velocities calculated from this equation are given in the final column of the table.

Example 2

Given the differential equation

$$100\frac{\mathrm{d}^2y}{\mathrm{d}x^2} = 1 + (y-3)^2$$

with conditions $y(0) = 4$ and $y(1) = 4$, use the approximation

$$y^{\text{II}}(x_r) \approx \frac{1}{h^2}\{y(x_{r+1}) - 2y(x_r) + y(x_{r-1})\}$$

where $$y^{\text{II}}(x_r) = \left(\frac{d^2y}{dx^2}\right)_{x=x_r} \quad \text{and} \quad h = 1$$

to estimate $y(4)$ working to SD.

Given that a similar computation with conditions $y(0) = 4$ and $y(1) = 4.1$ gives $y(4) = 4.545$, use linear interpolation to estimate to 3S the value of $y(1)$ for which $y(4) = 4.3$.

Since $y(x)$ satisfies the differential equation, we have

$$y^{\text{II}}(x_r) = \tfrac{1}{100}\{1 + (y(x_r) - 3)^2\}$$

and so $$\frac{y(x_{r+1}) - 2y(x_r) + y(x_{r-1})}{h^2} \approx \tfrac{1}{100}\{1 + (y(x_r) - 3)^2\}$$

Working with the step length $h = 1$, and taking $x_r = 1$

$$\frac{y(2) - 2y(1) + y(0)}{1^2} \approx \tfrac{1}{100}\{1 + (y(1) - 3)^2\}$$

i.e. $$\frac{y(2) - 2\times 4 + 4}{1} \approx \tfrac{1}{100}\{1 + (4 - 3)^2\}$$

so $$y(2) \approx 4.02$$

Taking $x_r = 2$ $$\frac{y(3) - 2y(2) + y(1)}{1^2} \approx \tfrac{1}{100}\{1 + (y(2) - 3)^2\}$$

i.e. $$\frac{y(3) - 2\times 4.02 + 4}{1} \approx \tfrac{1}{100}\{1 + (4.02 - 3)^2\}$$

so $$y(3) \approx 4.060\,40 \quad \text{(5D)}$$

Taking $x_r = 3$ $$\frac{y(4) - 2y + y(2)}{1^2} \approx \tfrac{1}{100}\{1 + (y(3) - 3)^2\}$$

i.e. $$\frac{y(4) - 2\times 4.060\,40 + 4.02}{1} \approx \tfrac{1}{100}\{1 + (4.060\,40 - 3)^2\}$$

so $$y(4) \approx 4.122\,04 \quad \text{(5D)}$$

So, when $y(1) = 4$, $y(4) = 4.122$ (3D) and we are given that, when $y(1) = 4.1$, $y(4) = 4.545$. We may regard $y(4)$ as a function of $y(1)$ and we require the value of $y(1)$ when $y(4) = 4.3$. When $y(1) = 4 + 0.1\theta$, linear interpolation gives

$$y(4) \approx 4.122 + \theta(4.545 - 4.122) = 4.122 + 0.423\theta$$

So $$y(4) = 4.3 \quad \text{when} \quad \theta = \frac{4.3 - 4.122}{0.423} \approx 0.42$$

$$\text{i.e. when} \quad y(1) = 4 + 0.1\times 0.42 = 4.042$$

Exercise 2.3

In questions 1 to 3 tabulate the given functions $f(x)$ to 4 decimal places for the given range of values of x. Use the approximations of this section to estimate the values of $f'(x)$ and $f''(x)$ for these values of x (excluding the end values). In each case check the accuracy of some of your results by differentiating, and comment on them.

1 $f(x) = e^{2x}$ for $x = 0.0(0.1)1.1$
2 $f(x) = 3 \sin x$ for $x = 1.00(0.01)1.11$
3 $f(x) = \ln(1+x)$ for $x = 0.0(0.1)1.1$

4 The following table gives the distance y cm of a particle from an origin 0 at time t seconds. Use the approximations of this section to estimate its speed v and acceleration a at these times.

Sketch the $y-t$, $v-t$, and $a-t$ curves and comment on the justification of joining up the points on these curves.

t	0	0.1	0.2	0.3	0.4	0.5	0.6	0.7	0.8	0.9	1.0	1.1
y	0	0.5	1.1	1.3	1.7	2.5	4.1	7.3	13.7	26.5	52.1	100

5 If $f(x)$ has a continuous second derivative in the interval $a-h<x<a+h$, then, when h is small, show that the value of d^2f/dx^2 when $x = a$ is approximately equal to

$$\{f(a+h)-2f(a)+f(a-h)\}/h^2$$

Given that $f(x)$ satisfies the differential equation

$$\frac{d^2f}{dx^2} = 16f-12$$

and that $f(0) = 0$ and $f(1) = 0$, use the above result to find an approximation to the value of $f(0.5)$

(a) by taking $h = 0.5$
(b) by taking $h = 0.25$ (M.E.I.)

3 Solution of equations by iteration

3.1 Introduction—trial and error

Equations have to be solved in every branch of mathematics, and the various methods of solution have a long and interesting history. There are basically two methods of solution, direct and indirect. In a direct method, the correct procedure gives the exact root; in an indirect method, the result is an approximate answer which may, however, be as accurate as we like. Linear and quadratic equations can be solved directly. Here are some equations:

(1) $3x+5=0$ (2) $2^x-5=0$ (3) $x^2+x-1=0$
(4) $\sin x+\cos x-\frac{1}{2}=0$ (5) $e^x+e^{-x}-2=0$

(1) can be solved by inspection. (2) may be transformed into a linear equation by rearranging and using logarithms. (3) is solved using the quadratic algorithm, and (4) and (5) can both be transformed into quadratic equations by appropriate substitutions.

Algorithms exist for the solution of both cubic and quartic equations, but they are complicated, and in practice indirect methods are used. Polynomial equations of the fifth degree and higher cannot normally be solved by direct methods, and there is a class of equations (called *transcendental*) which by their very nature cannot be solved by direct methods. Examples of these are $\cos x - x = 0$, and $x e^x - 1 = 0$. With the aid of a calculator, many such equations can be solved by 'trial and error' and we consider this method before going on to study more systematic indirect methods.

Trial and error

This can be explained as

(a) Guess an answer within the sort of range we expect.
(b) Check.
(c) Guess another answer, that we hope will be nearer to a solution.
(d) Check . . . and so on.

Example 1

Solve the equation $\cos x = x$, for $x \geqslant 0$.

We know that
(i) $0 \leqslant |\cos x| \leqslant 1$, so we need only try values of x between 0 and 1.
(ii) $\cos x$ decreases as x increases.

Number of guess	*Guess for x*	*Value of* $\cos x$	*Comment*
1	0.5	0.877	x too small
2	0.75	0.732	x too large
3	0.74	0.738	

Each time we narrow the difference between x and $\cos x$ by approximately halving to obtain our next guess. Already with three guesses we have obtained a solution, $x = 0.74$ (2S).

Example 2

Solve $x e^x = 1$ $\left(\text{or } e^x = \dfrac{1}{x}\right)$

We know that
(i) e^x is increasing as x increases.
(ii) $\dfrac{1}{x}$ is decreasing as x increases.

No. of guess	*Guess for x*	e^x	$\frac{1}{x}$	*Comment*
1	1	2.72	1	x too large
2	0.5	1.65	2	x too small
3	0.75	2.12	1.33	x too large
4	0.625	1.87	1.6	x too large
5	0.5625	1.755	1.77	x too small
6	0.57	1.768	1.75	x too large
7	0.565	1.759	1.770	x too small
8	0.567	1.7629	1.7636	x too small
9	0.5671	1.7631	1.7634	
				and so on

A solution is

$$x = 0.567 \qquad \text{(3D)}$$

Notice that in each case we have found one solution only, the smallest positive solution, and have not considered any others.

Exercise 3.1

In each of the following use your calculator with 'trial and error' methods to find the smallest positive root to 3D.

1 $4x = e^x$
2 $x^2 = x + 1$
3 $x^2 = \sin x$
4 $\log_{10} x = 2 - x$
5 $4^x = 2\cos x$
6 $x^3 = 2x + 1$
7 $x^4 = 2 + \ln x$
8 $x = 7.5 \log_{10} x$

3.2 Introduction to iterative methods

Next we deal with indirect methods of solution of the type known as *iterative*. These are the methods most commonly used.

A root of the equation $F(x) = 0$ is a number a such that $F(a) = 0$. In an iterative method we find a sequence of numbers $x_0, x_1, x_2, x_3, \ldots$, each one closer to the root, that is $x_i \to a$ as $i \to \infty$. Each approximation or *iterate* is found from the one before it by a relation of the form $x_i = f(x_{i-1})$. The more rapidly the sequence converges, the better the method. Most methods depend for their success on the initial value x_0 being a good approximation to a root. This means that before we can start, the roots have to be found approximately so the solution falls into two parts—first, finding an initial value and, second, improving on this value by the iterative method.

The principle of iteration is illustrated in the figure at the top of the next page.

As an example, we take the algorithm

$$x_i = \frac{1}{2 - x_{i-1}} \qquad x_0 = 0$$

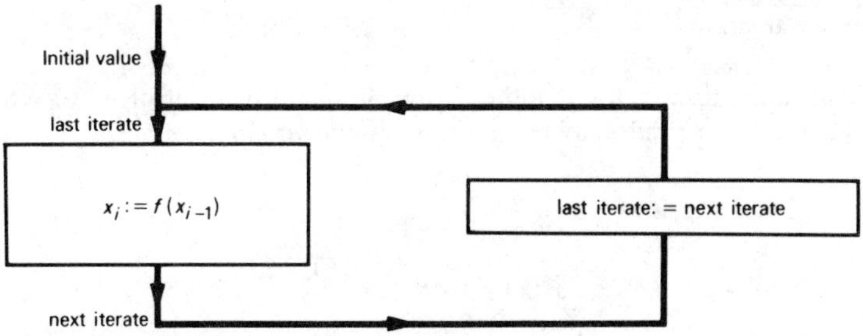

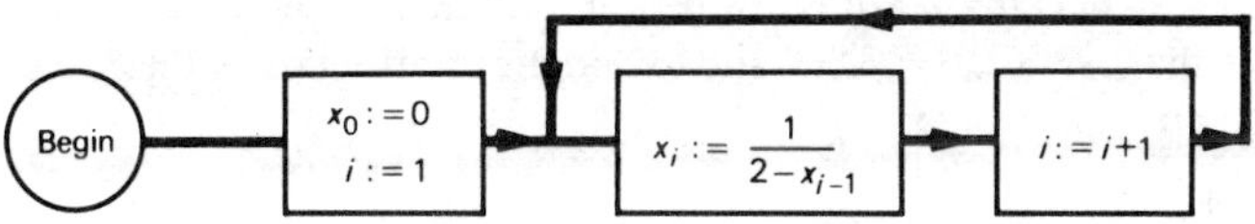

Tracing the flow chart for the first 5 iterates we have

$$x_0 = 0$$

$i = 1$	$x_1 = \frac{1}{2}$	$= 0.5$
$i = 2$	$x_2 = \dfrac{1}{1.5}$	$= 0.67$
$i = 3$	$x_3 = \dfrac{1}{1.33}$	$= 0.75$
$i = 4$	$x_4 = \dfrac{1}{1.25}$	$= 0.8$
$i = 5$	$x_5 = \dfrac{1}{1.2}$	$= 0.83$

Evidently the iterates are getting larger, but we can see that the difference between successive iterates is getting smaller. The process appears to be *converging*, that is to say if we continued iterating for long enough we would come to the stage where two successive iterates were equal (to a given number of significant figures).

Looking again at the flow chart we can see that the counter i does not play a very significant role, since it is not the *number* of iterations that matters but the *difference* between successive iterates (although of course the time involved *is* important). The process is represented more clearly if we denote the *last* iterate at any stage by x and the *next* iterate by y.

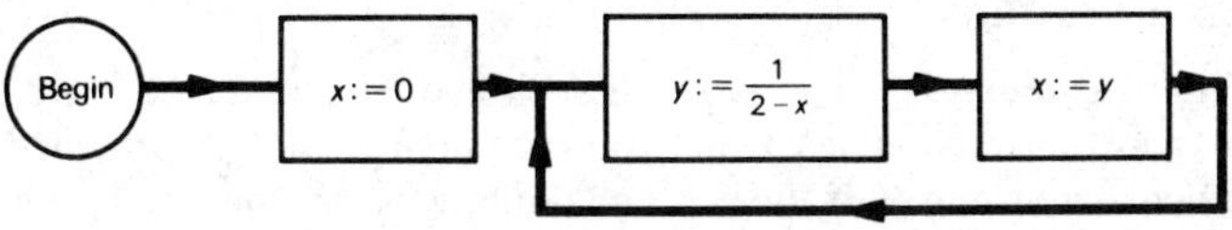

Finding initial values

The initial values may be found either from a graph or by using algebra. Whichever method is used, the result may be improved by *linear interpolation.*

(a) Graphical method

$$F(x) = 0 \Leftrightarrow \begin{cases} y = F(x) \\ y = 0 \end{cases}$$

The graph of $y = F(x)$ is plotted and the real roots of the equation occur at points where the curve cuts the x axis. However, it is often more practical to rearrange the equation in the form $f_1(x) = f_2(x)$, and to find the intersection of the curves $y = f_1(x)$ and $y = f_2(x)$.

Example 1

Investigate the roots of the equation $\cos x - x = 0$

Rearranging: $x = \cos x$. Plot $y = \cos x$ and $y = x$.

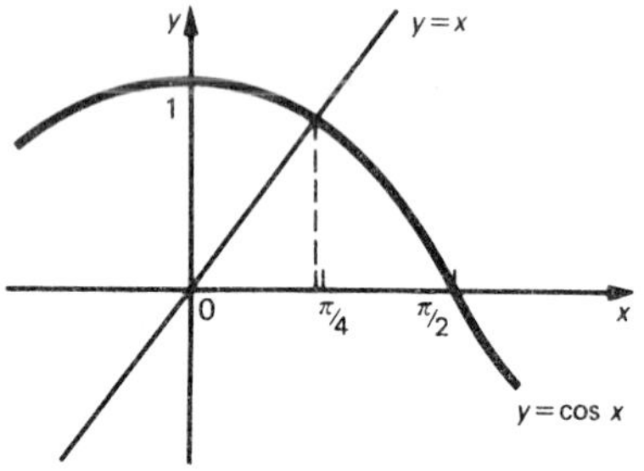

It is clear that the equation has only one root. This is just less than $\pi/4$. $\pi/4 \approx 0.785$, so the solution probably lies between 0.7 and 0.8.

Example 2

Investigate the roots of the equation $x^3 - 2.55x^2 - 2.35x + 3 = 0$.

Rearranging: $x^3 = 2.55x^2 + 2.35x - 3$. $y = x^3$ and $y = 2.55x^2 + 2.35x - 3$ can both be easily plotted.

The figure at the top of the opposite page shows that there are three points of intersection giving three real roots with approximate values -1.25, 0.75, 3.0.

(b) Algebraic method

If we can find two values of x, $x = \alpha$, $x = \beta$ such that $F(\alpha)$ and $F(\beta)$ have different signs, then there must be at least one root between α and β, provided $F(x)$ is continuous between α and β. If there is any doubt whether the number of roots in

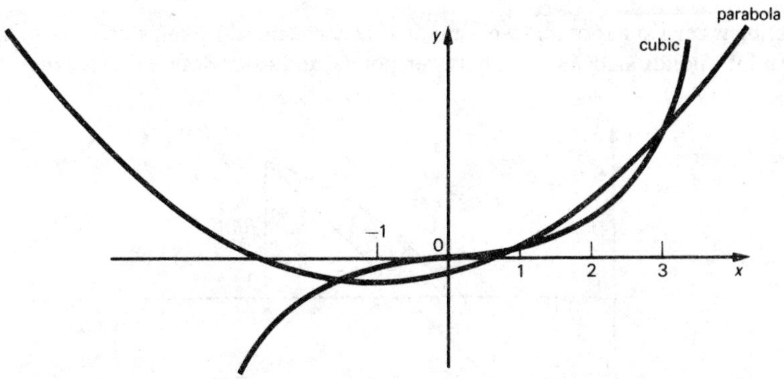

between is one or more, then we must sketch a graph of the function. If α and β are close together, their mean x_0 could be taken as the initial value, but it is always better to use linear interpolation.

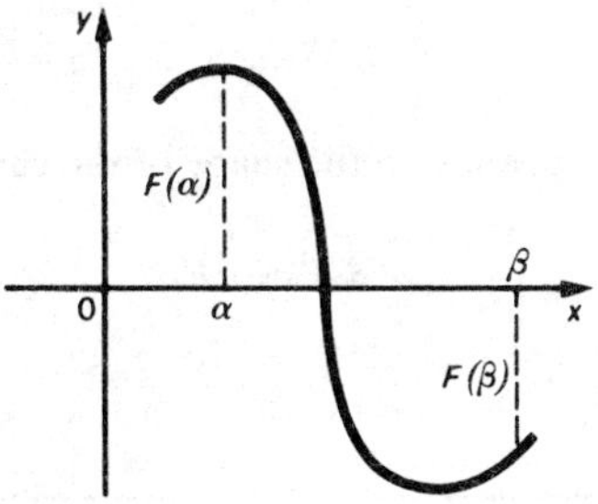

Example 1 (continued)

Solve $F(x) = \cos x - x = 0$.

We know that $x = 0.7$ is an approximate solution. We therefore evaluate the function for $x = 0.6, 0.7, 0.8$

x	0.6	0.7	0.8
$F(x)$	0.225	0.065	−0.1

Since $F(0.7)$ is positive and $F(0.8)$ is negative, there *is* a root between 0.7 and 0.8.

Linear interpolation

Once we have found an interval in which a root lies, we use linear interpolation to find an initial value. The method is similar to that on page 556, but whereas there we were estimating the value of the function for a given value of x, here we know that the function is zero at a root and we estimate the corresponding value of x. As we know, linear interpolation means 'line between points' and so we draw a line between them.

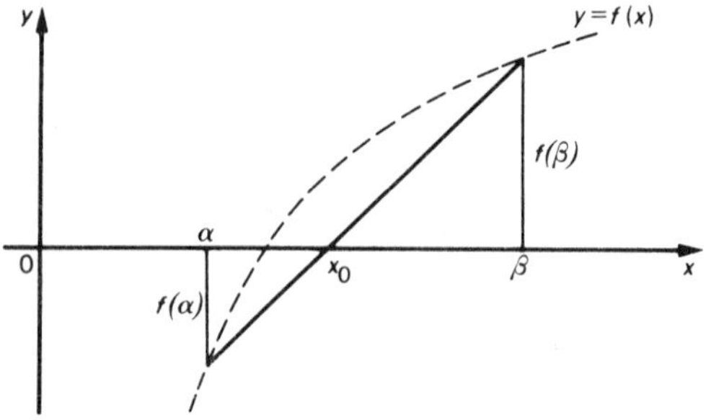

Using similar triangles we have

$$\frac{x_0 - \alpha}{\beta - x_0} = \frac{|f(\alpha)|}{|f(\beta)|}$$

and

$$x_0 = \frac{\alpha|f(\beta)| + \beta|f(\alpha)|}{|f(\alpha)| + |f(\beta)|}$$

Any error in the method depends on the shape of the curve.

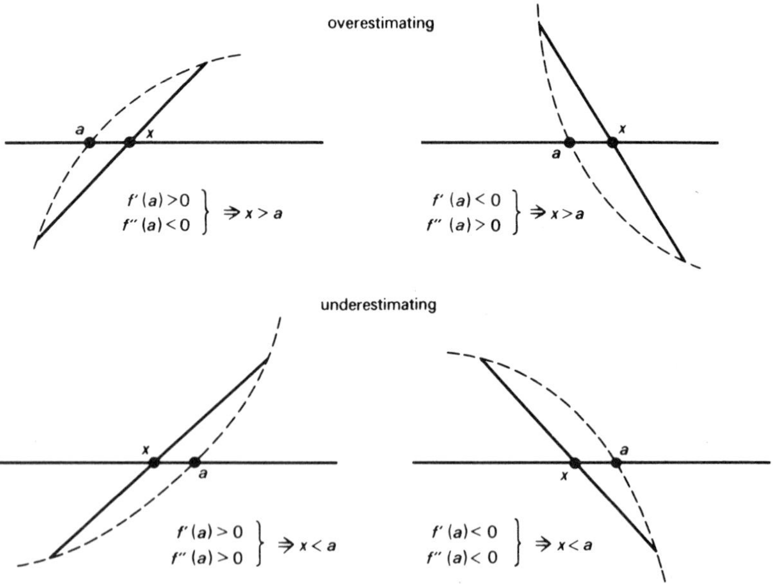

In practice we could either use the formula, or read off x_0 from a scale drawing or make a sketch and use the similar triangles.

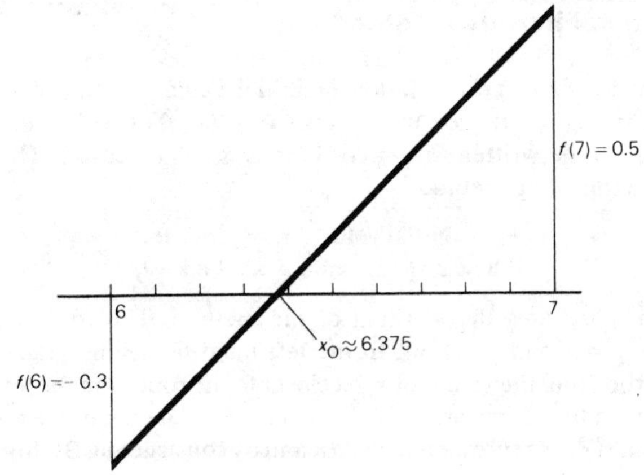

For example, if $f(6) = -0.3$, $f(7) = 0.5$ and $x_0 - 6 = d$, then

$$\frac{d}{1} = \frac{0.3}{0.3+0.5} \qquad \text{and} \qquad d = 0.375$$

Example 1 (continued)

In the last section we found that the equation $f(x) = \cos x - x = 0$ has a root between $x = 0.7$ and $x = 0.8$. Here

$$f(0.7) = \cos(0.7) - 0.7 = 0.065$$

$$f(0.8) = \cos(0.8) - 0.8 = -0.1$$

A quick sketch will give $x_0 \approx 0.74$.

Exercise 3.2

1 Use graphical methods to find initial values for the iterative solution of the following equations

(a) $x^3 - x - 1 = 0$ (rearrange as $x^3 = x + 1$)
(b) $x^4 - 2x - 1 = 0$ (two real roots)
(c) $e^x - 3x = 0$

2 In each of the following equations, tabulate $F(x)$ for integral values of x in the range $-2 \leqslant x \leqslant 2$. Having located a root, use linear interpolation to find an initial value for the iterative solution of the equation

(a) $F(x) = x^4 - 5x - 5 = 0$ (2 real roots)
(b) $F(x) = x^3 - 2x^2 + 3x - 1 = 0$
(c) $F(x) = \cos\left(\frac{\pi x}{3}\right) - 4x = 0$

3.3 The general iterative method

Having obtained a first approximation or initial value for one of the roots, the equation $F(x) = 0$ is rearranged in the form $x = f(x)$. For example, the equation $\cos x - x = 0$ might be written as $x = \cos x$ or as $x = \frac{1}{2}(x + \cos x)$. The root is then found using the following method:

$$\mathbf{x_0 = (initial\ value);\ x_i = f(x_{i-1});}$$
$$\mathbf{When\ x_i \approx x_{i-1}\ take\ x_i\ as\ the\ root.}$$ ◀

The diagram illustrates the working of the method. The root is given by the intersection of $y = x$ and $y = f(x)$. In the left hand figure the gradient of $f(x)$ is positive at the root, and the values of x get closer to the root from the left. In the right hand figure the gradient is negative and the values oscillate about the root. OA is the initial value (x_0). $f(x_0)$ is represented by AB, and by constructing BC horizontally, we ensure that $x_1 = f(x_0)$ i.e. OD = DC.

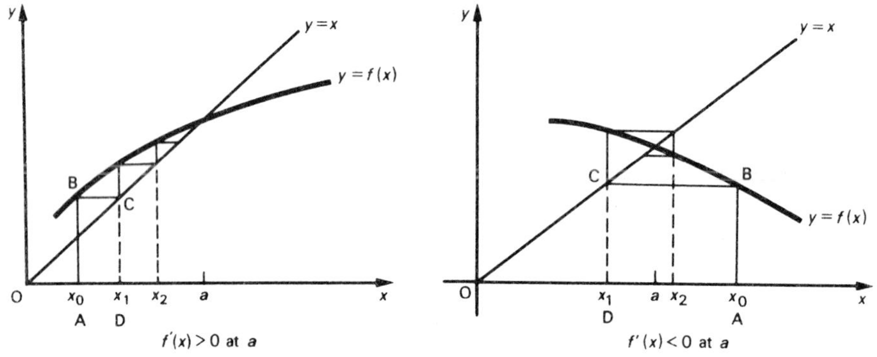

The process works for the two functions illustrated, but this is not always so. If the absolute error in the ith iterate is e_i, so that

$$a\,(\text{the root}) = x_i + e_i = x_{i-1} + e_{i-1}$$

then $$x_i = f(x_{i-1}) \Rightarrow a - e_i = f(a - e_{i-1})$$

$$\Rightarrow a - e_i = f(a) - e_{i-1}f'(a) + \tfrac{1}{2}e_{i-1}^2 f''(a) - \cdots$$

(using Taylor's theorem)

Now unless $f''(a)$ is very large, the third and subsequent terms on the RHS can be ignored, and we have

$$a - e_i = f(a) - e_{i-1}f'(a)$$

and since $$a = f(a)$$

$$\boldsymbol{e_i = e_{i-1}f'(a)} \qquad \text{I}$$ ◀

For convergence

$$|e_i| < |e_{i-1}| \Rightarrow |f'(a)| < 1$$

Of course a is unknown at the outset, but provided the initial value is a good approximation, $f'(x_0)$ will not differ greatly from $f'(a)$, and we may take as our *condition for convergence*

$$|f'(x_0)| < 1$$

Equation I shows, too, that the smaller (numerically) $f'(a)$ is, the more rapid will be the convergence. Since the error at any stage is proportional to the error at the previous stage, the process is said to have *first order convergence.*

Example 3

Find an algorithm for solving the equation

$$x^3 - x^2 - 6 = 0$$

given the initial value, $x_0 = 2$.

The equation may be rearranged in five different ways.

(1)
$$x = (x^2+6)^{1/3}$$
$$f'(x) = \tfrac{1}{3}(x^2+6)^{-2/3} \times 2x$$
$$f'(2) = 0.287$$

(2)
$$x = (x^3-6)^{1/2}$$
$$f'(x) = \tfrac{1}{2}(x^3-6)^{-1/2} \times 3x^2$$
$$f'(2) = 4.243$$

(3)
$$x = \sqrt{6}(x-1)^{-1/2}$$
$$f'(x) = \sqrt{6} \times -\tfrac{1}{2}(x-1)^{-3/2}$$
$$f'(2) = -1.224$$

(4)
$$x = (x+6/x)^{1/2}$$
$$f'(x) = \tfrac{1}{2}(x+6/x)^{-1/2}(1-6/x^2)$$
$$f'(2) = -0.112$$

(5)
$$x = x^2 - 6/x$$
$$f'(x) = 2x + 6/x^2$$
$$f'(2) = 5.5$$

Of these five, only (1) and (4) satisfy the criterion for convergence. In (1), $f'(x_0)$ is positive and the iterates form an increasing sequence (as in the left hand diagram on page 582) whereas (4) leads to an oscillating sequence, since $f'(x_0)$ is negative (as in the right hand diagram on page 582). But (4) will converge faster since $|f'(x_0)|$ is smaller than in (1).

In case (3) the criterion for convergence, that $|f'(x_0)| < 1$, is apparently not met, but in fact this sequence does converge very slowly. This is because the slope of $y = f(x)$ is increasing in the neighbourhood of the root of $x = f(x)$ from -1.224 when $x = 2$ to -0.667 when $x = 2.5$, and at the root the slope is just greater than -1. A suitable algorithm, which converges quickly, is therefore

$$x_i = (x_{i-1} + 6/x_{i-1})^{1/2} \qquad x_0 = 2$$

One final point has to be settled before we can start. We have to decide on a method for stopping! Each iterate is closer to the root, but there is no simple relationship between the difference between successive values and the number of places of decimals that can be relied on. If we need to be accurate to nD, a useful rule is to continue until the difference between successive iterates is less than $\frac{1}{2}\times 10^{-n}$. This rule is the same as that for round-off error and gives good results except in cases where convergence is very slow, e.g. when $|f'(x_0)| > \frac{1}{2}$.

We can now draw a flow chart for the process.

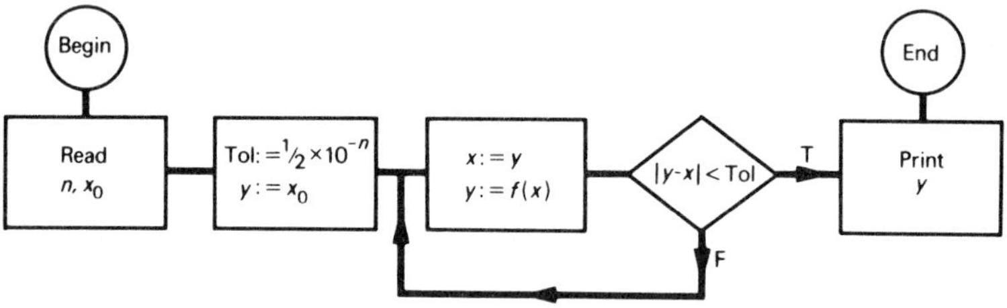

Example 1 (continued)

Solve the equation $\cos x - x = 0$, working to 6D.

(1) Initial value. $x = 0.74$ (found in Section 3.2, page 581)
(2) Tolerance $= \frac{1}{2}\times 10^{-6}$
(3) Algorithm

First try

$$\cos x - x = 0 \Leftrightarrow x = \cos x$$

$$f(x) = \cos x \Rightarrow f'(x) = -\sin x$$

$$f'(x_0) = -0.674$$

So convergence will be slow and oscillatory (see trace).

Trace for $f(x) = \cos x$

x	y
0.74	0.738 646 86
0.738 646 86	0.739 500 3
0.739 500 3	0.738 805 4
0.738 805 4	0.739 273 6
0.739 273 6	0.738 958 2
0.738 958 2	0.739 170 6
0.739 170 6	0.739 027 6
0.739 027 6	0.739 123 9
0.739 123 9	0.739 059 0
0.739 059 0	0.739 102 7

x	y
0.739 102 7	0.739 073 3
0.739 073 3	0.739 093 1
0.739 093 1	0.739 079 8
0.739 079 8	0.739 088 7
0.739 088 7	0.739 082 7
0.739 082 7	0.739 086 8
0.739 086 8	0.739 084 0
0.739 084 0	0.739 085 9
0.739 085 9	0.739 084 6
0.739 084 6	0.739 085 5
0.739 085 5	0.739 084 9
0.739 084 9	0.739 085 3

$$x = 0.739\,085 \qquad (6D)$$

Second try

$$\cos x - x = 0 \Leftrightarrow x = \tfrac{1}{2}(x + \cos x)$$

$$f(x) = \tfrac{1}{2}(x + \cos x) \Rightarrow f'(x) = \tfrac{1}{2}(1 - \sin x)$$

$$f'(x_0) = 0.162$$

So the convergence will be faster.

Trace for $f(x) = \frac{1}{2}(x + \cos x)$

x	y
0.74	0.739 234 3
0.739 234 3	0.739 109 5
0.739 109 5	0.739 089 1
0.739 089 1	0.739 085 8
0.739 085 8	0.739 085 3

$$x = 0.739\,085 \qquad (6D)$$

The traces show the importance of finding a rapidly converging sequence. The first try needed 22 iterations, whilst the second took only five and would be quite quick using a calculator. As a rough guide, an algorithm for this method should have $|f'(x_0)| < \frac{1}{2}$.

Exercise 3.3

1 It is known that the equation $x^3 - x - 1 = 0$ has a root in the region of $x = 1.3$. The equation may be rearranged as follows:

(a) $x^3 - x - 1 = 0 \Rightarrow x = x^3 - 1 \qquad f_1(x) = x^3 - 1$

(b) $x^3 - x - 1 = 0 \Rightarrow x(x^2 - 1) = 1 \Rightarrow x = \dfrac{1}{x^2 - 1} \qquad f_2(x) = \dfrac{1}{x^2 - 1}$

(c) $x^3 - x - 1 = 0 \Rightarrow x^3 = x + 1 \Rightarrow x = (x+1)^{1/3} \qquad f_3(x) = (x+1)^{1/3}$

In each case, find $f'(1.3)$ and state which of the three functions could be used as an iterative algorithm.

2 The equation $x^4-2x^2-7=0$ has a root near $x=2$. Find a suitable rearrangement of the equation, in the form $x=f(x)$, such that $|f'(2)|<1$.

3 The equation $x\,e^x=4$ has a root in the neighbourhood of $x=1.2$. Show that $x=4\,e^{-x}$ would not be a suitable algorithm for an iterative solution, and find a better one.

4 Sketch the curve $y=\log_{10}x$ for values of x between 0 and 1. Use the graph to show that the equation $10x+\log_{10}x=4$ has only one real root, and find this root approximately from the graph. Evaluate the root correct to 3D by iteration using the equation in the form $x=(4-\log_{10}x)/10$. Explain the meaning of the statement that this iterative method has first order convergence.

5 An equation can be written in the form $x=F(x)$ and it is known that it has a root in the neighbourhood of $x=x_1$. Explain with the aid of a diagram how the iterative formula $x_{r+1}=F(x_r)$ may give the root to whatever degree of accuracy is required and state a condition for convergence. The cubic equation $x^3-2x-5=0$ has one real root that is near $x=2$. The equation can be written in any one of the forms

(a) $x=\frac{1}{2}(x^3-5)$ **(b)** $x=5(x-2)^{-1}$ **(c)** $x=(2x+5)^{1/3}$

Choose the form for which the previous iterative formula to find this root will converge, and find the root to 4S.

3.4 The Newton–Raphson method

Here the algorithm for solving $F(x)=0$ is

$$\boldsymbol{x_0=\text{(initial value)};\qquad x_i=x_{i-1}-\frac{F(x_{i-1})}{F'(x_{i-1})}}$$ ◀

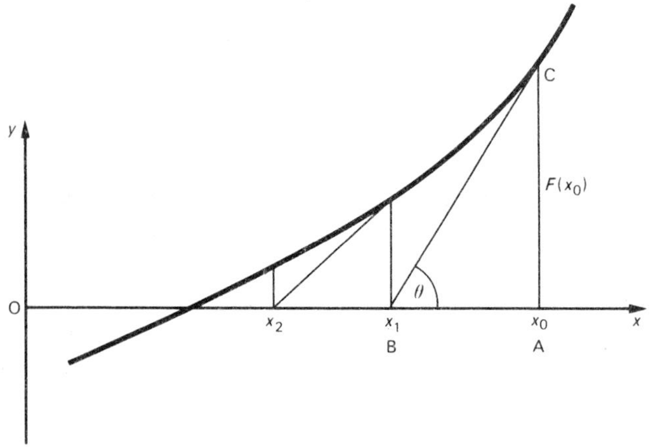

In the diagram OA is the initial value, x_0, and AC represents $F(x_0)$. The tangent to the curve at C meets the axis at B, and OB is taken as the first iterate, x_1

$$x_1=\text{OA}-\text{BA}=\text{OA}-\text{AC}\cot\theta=x_0-\frac{F(x_0)}{F'(x_0)}$$

Similarly
$$x_i = x_{i-1} - \frac{F(x_{i-1})}{F'(x_{i-1})}$$

Conditions for convergence

The values of x_i will converge if
(i) x_0 is sufficiently close to a root.
(ii) $F'(x_0)$ is not too close to zero.
(iii) $F''(x_i)$ does not become very large for any i.
The second of these conditions means that difficulties may arise if the equation has two nearly equal roots. In such cases, great accuracy in choosing the initial value is necessary. The figures show some cases of failure.

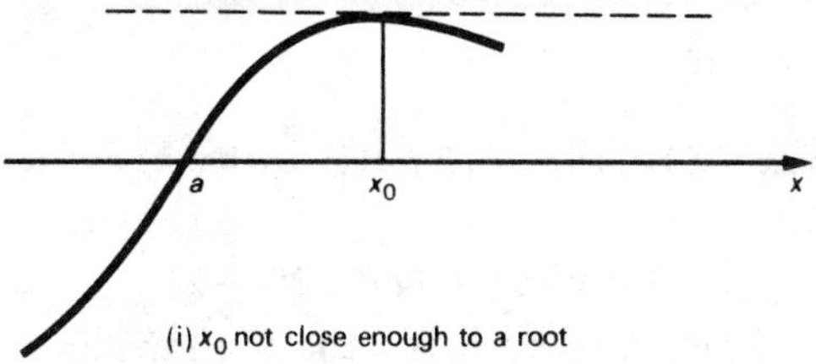

(i) x_0 not close enough to a root

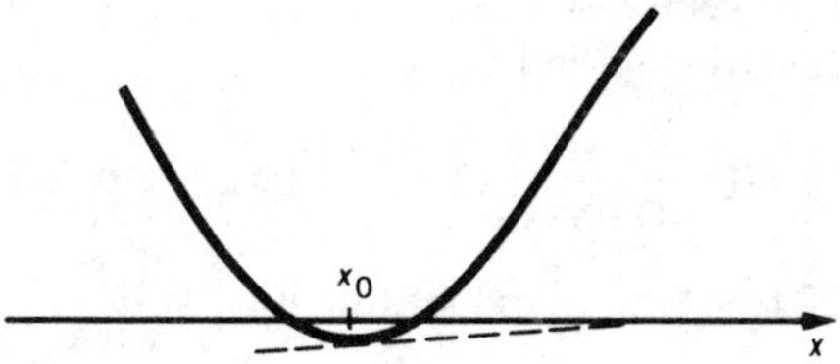

(ii) $f'(x_0)$ very small
(two nearly equal roots)

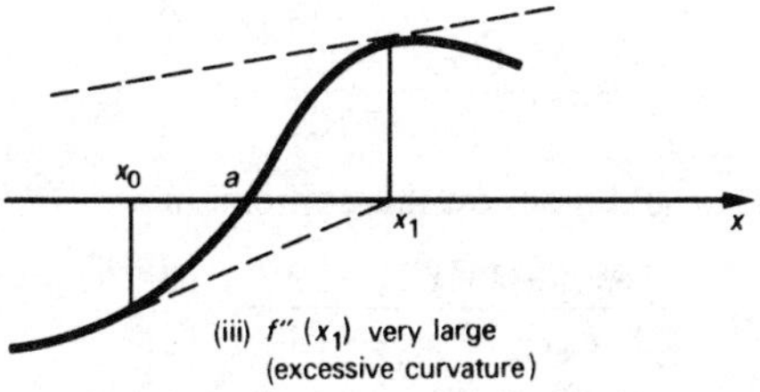

(iii) $f''(x_1)$ very large
(excessive curvature)

The values x_i found by Newton's algorithm converge faster than by the general method. It can be shown that

$$e_i \approx k e_{i-1}^2 \qquad \text{II} \blacktriangleleft$$

where k is a constant depending on $F'(a)$ and $F''(a)$. The *error* at each stage is proportional to the *square* of the *previous* error. By comparison with the corresponding relation for the general method (equation I, page 582), Newton's method is said to have 'second order' or 'quadratic' convergence. In practical terms, this means that the number of accurate significant figures is approximately doubled with each iteration. We adopt the same stopping method as before, that is to say a tolerance of $\frac{1}{2}\times 10^{-n}$ for nD.

The flow chart is almost the same as for the general method.

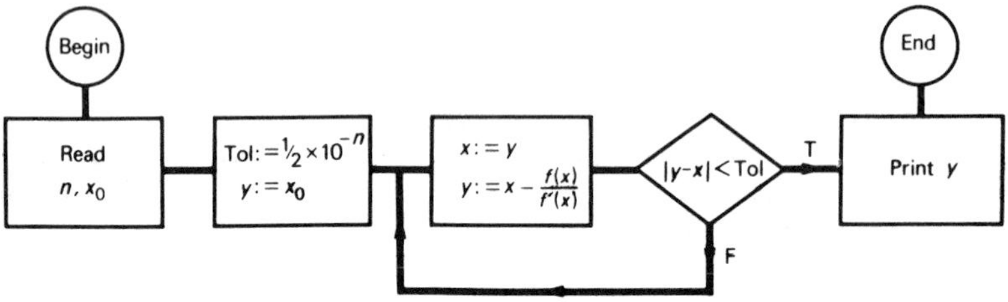

Example 4

Solve the equation $9x^3-11x^2+18x-22 = 0$ given that it has one real root. Work to 4S.

Writing $$F(x) = 9x^3-11x^2+18x-22$$

we have $$F(0) = -22 \qquad F(1) = -6 \qquad F(2) = 42$$

Hence there is a root between $x = 1$ and $x = 2$.

We use linear interpolation to find x_0

$$x_0 = 1-\frac{-6}{42-(-6)}(2-1) = 1.125$$

Now $F'(x) = 27x^2-22x+18$, so our algorithm is

$$x_i = x_{i-1}-\frac{9x_{i-1}^3-11x_{i-1}^2+18x_{i-1}-22}{27x_{i-1}^2-22x_{i-1}+18}$$

or rearranged

$$x_i = \frac{18x_{i-1}^3-11x_{i-1}^2+22}{27x_{i-1}^2-22x_{i-1}+18}$$

Using a calculator, we would first nest this expression as

$$x_1 = \frac{(18x_{i-1}-11)x_{i-1}^2+22}{(27x_{i-1}-22)x_{i-1}+18}$$

Then
$$x_0 = 1.125$$
$$x_1 = 1.229\,202\,3$$
$$x_2 = 1.222\,256\,2$$
$$x_3 = 1.222\,222\,2$$
$$x_4 = 1.222\,222\,2$$

In fact the exact solution is $x = 1.\dot{2}$.

Example 5

By applying Newton's method to the function defined by $f(x) = 1-(7/x^2)$, develop an iterative formula for calculating $\sqrt{7}$. Hence using 2 as a first approximation to $\sqrt{7}$, calculate $\sqrt{7}$ correct to 2D. Show that if x_n, the nth approximation to $\sqrt{7}$, has a small error e_n, then the next approximation, e_{n+1}, has an error of magnitude about $0.6e_n^2$.

(M.E.I.)

Now
$$f(x) = 1-\frac{7}{x^2}$$

Clearly
$$f(x) = 0 \Leftrightarrow x^2 = 7$$

We need to simplify the function $x - \dfrac{f(x)}{f'(x)}$

$$f'(x) = \frac{14}{x^3}$$

Hence
$$x - \frac{f(x)}{f'(x)} = x - \frac{1-7/x^2}{14/x^3} = \frac{21x-x^3}{14}$$

Our algorithm is
$$x_i = \frac{21x_{i-1}-x_{i-1}^3}{14}; \qquad x_0 = 2$$

Working to 4S, we find

$$x_1 = 2.429$$
$$x_2 = 2.620$$
$$x_3 = 2.645$$
$$x_4 = 2.646$$

As $|x_3-x_4| < \frac{1}{2}\times 10^{-2}$ we may take x_4 as our result, i.e. $\sqrt{7} \approx 2.65$. (This method of finding square roots was popular before the advent of electronic calculators.)

If the error in x_n is e, we have

$$x_{n+1} = \frac{21(\sqrt{7}+e)-(\sqrt{7}+e)^3}{14} = \frac{21(\sqrt{7}+e)-(7\sqrt{7}+21e+3\sqrt{7}\,e^2+e^3)}{14}$$
$$= \sqrt{7} - \frac{3\sqrt{7}}{14}e^2 - \frac{e^3}{14}$$

e being small, we may ignore the term in e^3. Now

$$\frac{3\sqrt{7}}{14} \approx 0.6$$

and hence
$$x_{n+1} \approx \sqrt{7} - 0.6\,e^2$$

giving
$$|e_{n+1}| \approx 0.6\,e_n^2$$

Example 1 (continued again!)

Use Newton's method to solve the equation

$$\cos x - x = 0, \qquad \text{with} \quad x_0 = 0.74$$

$$F(x) = \cos x - x$$

$$\Rightarrow F'(x) = -\sin x - 1$$

The algorithm is

$$x_i = x_{i-1} + \frac{\cos x - x}{\sin x + 1}$$

Trace

x	y
0.74	0.739 085 3
0.739 085 3	0.739 085 1
0.739 085 1	0.739 085 1

The trace is the result of working to 7D (Tol $= \frac{1}{2}$E-7). 6D is achieved in two iterations (as compared with five by the general method) and 7D on the next iterate.

Why do we ever use the general method since it is clearly less efficient than the Newton–Raphson method? The answer is that the rapid convergence has to be paid for in computation time. Both $F(x_i)$ and $F'(x_i)$ have to be evaluated on each iteration, and with some functions the general method is in fact quicker.

Exercise 3.4

1 Use Newton's method to solve the equation $x^2 - 2.2x + 1.21 = 0$. Work to 4S taking an initial value $x_0 = 1$.

2 Use the Newton–Raphson iteration procedure to find to 4S the only real solution of the equation $x^3 + x + 1 = 0$.

3 Use Newton's method to find the real root of $x^3 - 2x + 2 = 0$ to 3S taking $x = -2$ as the first approximation. Justify that the number of iterations gives the required degree of accuracy.

4 Find the larger real root of the equation $x^2 - 2 - \ln x = 0$, to 4S using Newton's method. Find the smaller root of the same equation to 3S.

5 By applying Newton's method to the function f defined by $f(x) = 1 - 5/x^2$ develop an iterative formula for calculating $\sqrt{5}$, and show that if x_n is in error by a small quantity, d_n, then the next approximation x_{n+1} is in error by about $0.7d_n^2$.

6 Show that the equation $2 \tan x = 3x$ has a root between $\pi^c/6$ and $\pi^c/3$. Using $x = 1$ as a first approximation, obtain a second approximation to the root. (C.)

7 Find the positive root of the equation $x = \ln(x + 2)$ giving your answer correct to 4S. (C.)

8 Show that one root of the equation $x^3+x=5$ lies between 1 and 2, and find this root correct to 3D. (C.)

3.5 An iterative algorithm to find the smaller root of a quadratic equation

We have seen in the last chapter, page 537, how to find the smaller root of a quadratic equation by finding first the larger root and then using the relation

$$x_1x_2 = \frac{c}{a}$$

where x_1, x_2 are the roots of the equation $ax^2+bx+c=0$. We can also use the two relations $x_1+x_2=-b/a$ and $x_1x_2=c/a$ to solve the quadratic iteratively. When one root is much larger than the other, i.e. when $b^2 \gg 4ac$, the larger root is approximately $-b/a$.

Calling the two roots l and s, we have

$$l+s = -\frac{b}{a} \qquad ls = \frac{c}{a}$$

Taking

$$l_0 = -\frac{b}{a} \quad \Rightarrow \quad s_0 = \frac{c}{a} \div l_0$$

$$l_1 = -\frac{b}{a} - s_0 \quad \Rightarrow \quad s_1 = \frac{c}{a} \div l_1$$

$$l_2 = -\frac{b}{a} - s_1 \quad \Rightarrow \quad s_2 = \frac{c}{a} \div l_2 \qquad \text{etc.}$$

Example 1

Solve the equation $x^2+10x+\frac{1}{10}=0$

$l+s=-10 \qquad ls=0.1$

$l_0=-10 \qquad s_0=0.1\div(-10)=-0.01$

$l_1=-10+0.01=-9.99 \qquad s_1=0.1\div(-9.99)=-0.010\,01$

$l_2=-10+0.010\,01=-9.989\,99 \qquad s_2=0.1\div(-9.989\,99)=-0.010\,01$ (5D)

Further iterations will not improve the result to 5D, so we may take the roots as l_2 and s_2.

In the next example we make use of both methods.

Example 2

Solve the equation $x^2-10.2x+0.125=0$ giving the roots to 4S.

We first use the formula

$$x = \frac{10.2 \pm \sqrt{103.54}}{2}$$

This gives, with four figure tables

$$l \approx 10.185 \quad \text{and} \quad s \approx 0.015$$

We will iterate to find the smaller root to 4S

$$l = 10.2 - s \qquad s = 0.125 \div l$$

$$l_0 = 10.2 \qquad s_0 = 0.012\,254$$

$$l_1 = 10.187\,745 \qquad s_1 = 0.012\,269$$

$$l_2 = 10.187\,730 \qquad s_2 = 0.012\,269$$

We cannot improve on this result using an 8 digit calculator, so $l = 10.19$ and $s = 0.012\,27$ (4S). We could, in fact, have obtained the results to the same accuracy by direct application of the formula and a calculator, but the method is important and a computer would give the roots to as many significant figures as it can display.

Exercise 3.5

Solve the following quadratic equations, giving the roots to 4S, using an iterative method.

1 $x^2 - 40.04x + 1.60 = 0$ **2** $10x^2 - 5001x + 500 = 0$
3 $100x^2 - 28198x - 564 = 0$ **4** $81x^2 + 8091x - 900 = 0$

In each case notice that $b^2 \gg 4ac$.

Miscellaneous examination questions 15

1 Evaluate the integral

$$\int_0^4 \exp(\sqrt{x})\,dx$$

(a) by Simpson's rule, **(b)** by the trapezium rule, using the values below. Give your answers to 3D.

x	0	1	2	3	4
$\exp\sqrt{x}$	1	2.7183	4.1132	5.6522	7.3891

By using a suitable substitution to evaluate the integral, determine which of these numerical answers is nearer to the exact value. (L.)

2 Taking 4 intervals and working to 4D, use Simpson's rule to find an approximate value of

$$\int_0^1 \frac{dx}{1+x^2}$$

Hence find an approximate value of π to 4S, given that

$$\int \frac{dx}{1+x^2} = c + \tan^{-1} x$$

Determine a second approximation, also to 4S, calculated from the integral by expanding $\dfrac{1}{1+x^2}$ by the binomial theorem and integrating the first six non-zero terms. What is the percentage error in the second result taking $\pi = 3.142$? (A.E.B.)

3 Use Simpson's rule with 6 equal strips to calculate the integral of $\sqrt{x}$ over the interval $4 \leqslant x \leqslant 16$, using values of x from 4 figure tables and giving your answer to 2D. The absolute error in Simpson's rule is not greater than $Mh^5/90$, where h is the strip width and M is the greatest magnitude of the fourth derivative of the integrand in the interval. Show that the error in your result from this source is less than 0.003. (L.)

4 Use Simpson's rule with interval 0.2, and also with interval 0.4 to calculate the integral

$$\int_{0.1}^{0.9} (1-x^3)^{1/2}\,\mathrm{d}x$$

Using these values, and assuming that the error resulting from Simpson's rule with interval width h is equal to Ah^4, where A is a constant, show that when $h = 0.2$ the error is less than 0.0003. With the same assumption, find a value of h which would give an error less than 0.0001. (W.)

5 Tabulate values of $f(x) = \{64+(x-4)^3\}^{1/2}$ for integral values of x from 0 to 8 inclusive and sketch the graph of $f(x)$ over this domain.

Given that $F(t) = \int_0^t f(x)\,\mathrm{d}x$, use Simpson's rule and the calculated values of $f(x)$ to compute $F(2)$, $F(4)$ and $F(6)$. Verify that $\frac{1}{4}[F(6)-F(2)]$ is very nearly equal to $f(4)$ and comment on this result. (M.E.I.)

6 Given that it is required to use Simpson's rule to evaluate

$$\int_0^6 f(x)\,\mathrm{d}x \qquad \text{where } f(x) = (400+x^2)^{1/2}-20$$

show that it is preferable when using tables to obtain values of $f(x)$, to use $f(x)$ in the equivalent form

$$f(x) = \frac{x^2}{(400+x^2)^{1/2}+20}$$

Use Simpson's rule with three ordinates to evaluate the integral, giving the result to 4S. An alternative method uses the approximation $f(x) \approx x^2/40$ and direct integration. Show that the two methods give results differing by less than 2%. (M.E.I.)

7 Use Simpson's rule to find an approximation to

$$\int_0^{\pi/4} \log_{10}(\sec x)\,\mathrm{d}x$$

taking 6 intervals. Find an estimate of the error, indicating clearly the formula you are using. (W.)

8 Show that the approximation

$$\int_{a-h}^{a+h} f(x)\,dx \approx \tfrac{1}{3}h[f(a+h)+4f(a)+f(a-h)]$$

is exact if $f(x)$ is a cubic polynomial, and show that the error is $4h^5/15$ when it is used in the case $f(x) = x^4$.

Find an approximate value for

$$\int_{-1/2}^{1/2} (3+x^2)\,e^{-x^2}\,dx$$

using Simpson's rule with three ordinates. Estimate the error in your calculation.

9 The value of $\int_1^3 1/x\,dx$ is estimated using the trapezium rule with n intervals. Show that an estimate for the absolute error bound due to the use of the trapezium rule is $2/(3n)$. If in addition each ordinate is evaluated correct to $\pm\varepsilon$, find an absolute error bound for the result.

Find a value of n which will ensure that the result is accurate to two places of decimals if $\varepsilon = 0.0005$. (M.E.I.)

10 The following data define a cubic polynomial $f(x)$, the difference being expressed in terms of 10^{-4}.

$x_0 = 1.0, \quad h = 0.1, \quad f_0 = 2.6344, \quad \Delta_0 = 7775, \quad \Delta_0^2 = 1650, \quad \Delta_0^3 = 150$

By means of Newton's forward difference interpolation formula (i.e. the Gregory–Newton formula), determine the coefficients of the polynomial. Find f_4 by forming a difference table, and check your answer by means of direct evaluation. (A.E.B.)

11 From the following table of values of a function $f(x)$, calculate
(a) $f(0.48)$ by linear interpolation
(b) $\int_{0.1}^{0.5} f(x)\,dx$ by Simpson's rule
giving your results to three places of decimals.

x	0.1	0.2	0.3	0.4	0.5
$f(x)$	1.2840	1.3499	1.4191	1.4918	1.5683

If it is known that the errors in the tabulated values of $f(x)$ are exactly kx at each point, where k is a constant, find expressions, in the terms of k, for the errors in the calculated values of $f(0.48)$ and $\int_{0.1}^{0.5} f(x)\,dx$ resulting from these errors in tabulation. (M.E.I.)

12 The values of a polynomial u at $x = a, a+h, \ldots, a+nh$ are denoted by $u_a, u_{a+h}, \ldots, u_{a+nh}$ respectively. Prove that

$$u_{a+nh} = u_a + \binom{n}{1}\Delta u_a + \binom{n}{2}\Delta^2 u_a + \cdots + \binom{n}{r}\Delta^r u_a + \cdots + \Delta^n u_a$$

where

$$\Delta u_a \equiv u_{a+h} - u_a,$$

$$\Delta^r u_a \equiv \Delta^{r-1}u_{a+h} - \Delta^{r-1}u_a \qquad (r = 2, 3, \ldots, n)$$

The following table gives the values u_x of a polynomial of the fourth degree for certain integral values of x:

x	5	6	7	8	9
u_x	6.195	5.919	5.630	5.326	5.006

Calculate the value of the polynomial when $x = 7.5$. (M.E.I.)

13 The equation $f(x) = 0$ can be solved by rearranging it as $x = g(x)$, and setting up an iterative procedure $x_{n+1} = g(x_n)$. The iteration converges if $|g'(x)| < 1$ in the region of the root. In a particular example, where $f(x) = x^3 - 2x - 2$, show that two possible forms for $g(x)$ are $2/(x^2-2)$ and $(2+2/x)^{1/2}$. Determine which of the two forms will give an iteration which will converge to the root between $x = 1$ and $x = 2$. Hence find this root correct to 2D. (C.)

14 The roots of the quadratic equation $x^2 - 7x + 1 = 0$ are to be calculated by use of the recurrence relation $x_{r+1} = 1/(7-x_r)$. Sketch the graphs of $y = x$ and $y = 1/(7-x)$, and hence show **(a)** that the equation has two roots, which lie between 0 and 7, and **(b)** that if x_1 has a value lying between these roots, then the recurrence relation will always yield an approximation to the smaller root. Taking $x_1 = 1$, find the smaller root correct to 3D. Obtain the value of the larger root to the same degree of accuracy. (C.)

15 State without proof the condition for convergence of the method of successive substitution in which a root of the equation $x = f(x)$ is found by iteration, using the relation $x_{n+1} = f(x_n)$.

Taking a suitable initial approximation, use this method to calculate correct to 2D the positive root of the equation $x^4 = 2x + 10$, by writing this equation in the form $x = (2x+10)^{1/4}$. Show that it is not possible to calculate this root by using the form $x = \frac{1}{2}(x^4 - 10)$. Draw up a program (i.e. draw a flow chart) to evaluate to 2D for $c = 1, 2, \ldots, 10$ the positive root of the equation $x^4 = 2x + c$. (L.)

16 By investigating the turning values of $f(x) = x^3 + 3x^2 + 6x - 38$, or otherwise, show that the equation $f(x) = 0$ has only one real root. Find two consecutive integers n and $n+1$ that enclose the root. Describe a method by which successive approximations to the root can be obtained. Starting with the value of n as a first approximation, calculate two further successive approximations to the root. Give your answers correct to 3S. (C.)

17 Show by a sketch that for a given value of k (where $k > 1$) there is just one root of $\tan x - kx = 0$ in the interval $0 < x < \pi^c/2$. It is required to tabulate values of this root for $k = 1.4, 1.5, \ldots, 2.0$. Draw a graph of $(\tan x)/x$ for $0.82 \leqslant x \leqslant 1.22$ and so find the approximate values of the root. Calculate the value of the root to 3S when $k = 1.6$, and write a flow chart for computing the whole series of values to this degree of accuracy. (M.E.I.)

18 It is required to tabulate the root, lying between 1 and 10, of the equation $1 + \ln x = kx$ for $k = 0.5(0.1)0.9$. Using any method or combination of methods, form such a table. More credit will be given for a complete table with moderate accuracy than for fewer results with higher accuracy. The accuracy claimed should in each case be stated and substantiated. (M.E.I.)

19 It is required to find the positive root of the equation $2\cos x - x = 0$ using Newton's method. The figure shows part of a flow diagram for this purpose. Complete the diagram and explain the reasons for boxes 2, 5, and 6.

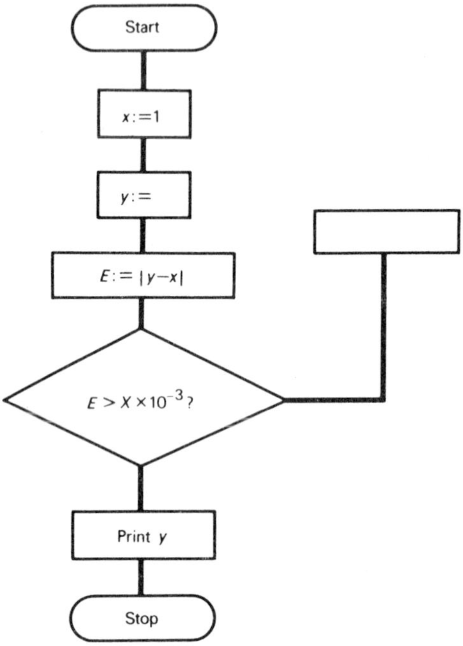

Calculate the required root, using this flow diagram. (M.E.I.)

20 Show that if x_1 and x_2 are roots of the equation $ax^2 + bx + c = 0$ then

$$x_1 = -\frac{b}{a} - x_2 \qquad \text{and} \qquad x_2 = \frac{c}{ax_1}$$

These results can be used to obtain sequences of approximations to the roots of the equation $2x^2 + 10x + 3 = 0$. Starting with the approximation $x_2 = 0$, calculate the first three approximations to x_1 and x_2. (M.E.I.)

Chapter 16

Vectors 2

1 Vectors in three dimensions

1.1 Review of ideas

Summary of vectors in a plane

First of all, we summarize the ideas we met in Chapter 8 (Vectors 1), and then we show how to extend these concepts into three dimensions.

Representation

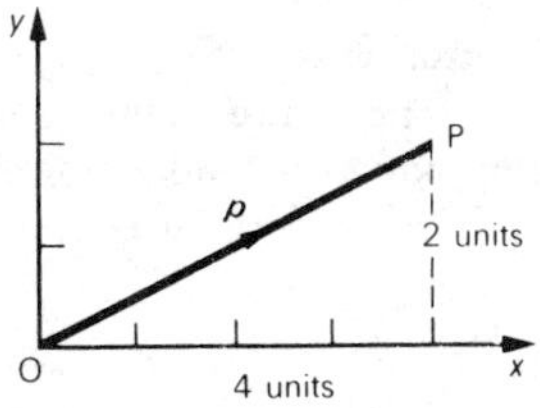

We have described the vector route from O to P in several different ways.

1 As the position vector OP with its 'tail' at the origin.

2 As a representative of the equivalence class of free vectors $\boldsymbol{p}$.

3 In coordinate form $\begin{pmatrix} x \\ y \end{pmatrix}$ with the $\begin{pmatrix} x \text{ step} \\ y \text{ step} \end{pmatrix}$; here $\boldsymbol{p} = \begin{pmatrix} 4 \\ 2 \end{pmatrix}$.

4 In terms of the base vectors $\boldsymbol{i}$ and $\boldsymbol{j}$ where

$$\boldsymbol{i} = \begin{pmatrix} 1 \\ 0 \end{pmatrix} \quad \text{and} \quad \boldsymbol{j} = \begin{pmatrix} 0 \\ 1 \end{pmatrix}$$

so $$\boldsymbol{p} = 4\boldsymbol{i} + 2\boldsymbol{j}$$

5 In terms of *any* other two (non-parallel) base vectors in the plane. E.g. if

$$\boldsymbol{e} = \begin{pmatrix} 1 \\ 1 \end{pmatrix} \quad \text{and} \quad \boldsymbol{f} = \begin{pmatrix} -1 \\ 1 \end{pmatrix}$$

then $$\boldsymbol{p} = 3\boldsymbol{e} + (-1)\boldsymbol{f}$$

Remember that any vector in the plane can be represented by a unique combination of the base vectors.

Length

The length (or modulus) of $\boldsymbol{p}$ is written $|\boldsymbol{p}|$ (or p). It can be calculated using Pythagoras' theorem.

$$|\boldsymbol{p}| = \sqrt{(4^2+2^2)} = \sqrt{20} = 2\sqrt{5}$$

Unit vectors

The vector of unit length in the direction of $\boldsymbol{p}$ is written

$$\hat{\boldsymbol{p}} = \frac{1}{|\boldsymbol{p}|}\boldsymbol{p}$$

Vector addition

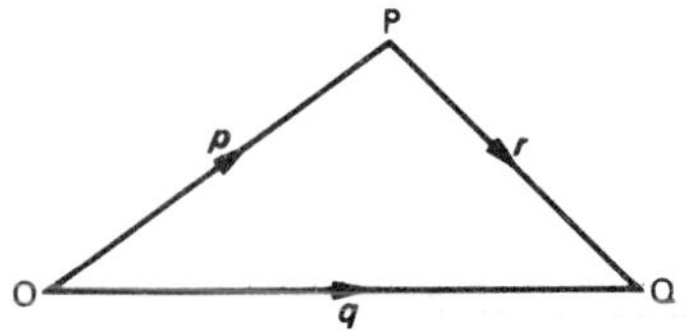

The route from P to Q can be described as **PQ** or $\boldsymbol{r} = -\boldsymbol{p}+\boldsymbol{q}$; that from O to Q can be described as **OQ** or $\boldsymbol{q} = \boldsymbol{p}+\boldsymbol{r}$. The figure defines vector addition with the lines representing the vectors being added, $\boldsymbol{p}$ and $\boldsymbol{r}$, joined tip to tail. It is clear that $|\boldsymbol{q}| < |\boldsymbol{p}|+|\boldsymbol{r}|$, unless $\boldsymbol{p}$ and $\boldsymbol{r}$ are in the same direction, when $|\boldsymbol{q}| = |\boldsymbol{p}|+|\boldsymbol{r}|$.

Equation of a line

Any point X on OP can be described in terms of a parameter λ, as $\mathbf{OX} = \boldsymbol{x} = \lambda\boldsymbol{p}$. If $\lambda = 0$, $\boldsymbol{x} = \boldsymbol{0}$; if $\lambda = 1$, $\boldsymbol{x} = \boldsymbol{p}$.

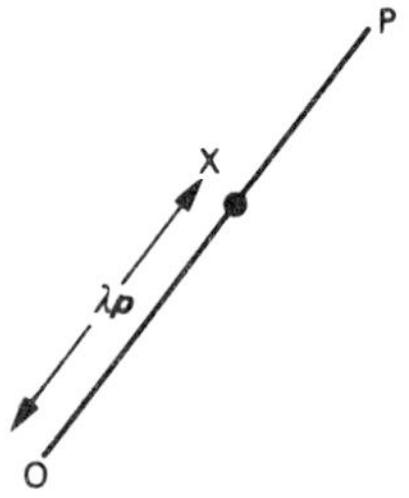

Similarly any point X on PQ is given by

$$\boldsymbol{x} = \boldsymbol{p}+\mu\boldsymbol{r} = \boldsymbol{p}+\mu(-\boldsymbol{p}+\boldsymbol{q}) = (1-\mu)\boldsymbol{p}+\mu\boldsymbol{q}$$

If $\mu = 0$, $\boldsymbol{x} = \boldsymbol{p}$; if $\mu = 1$, $\boldsymbol{x} = \boldsymbol{q}$; if $\mu = \frac{1}{2}$, X is the midpoint of PQ, when

$$\boldsymbol{x} = (1-\tfrac{1}{2})\boldsymbol{p}+\tfrac{1}{2}\boldsymbol{q} = \tfrac{1}{2}(\boldsymbol{p}+\boldsymbol{q}).$$

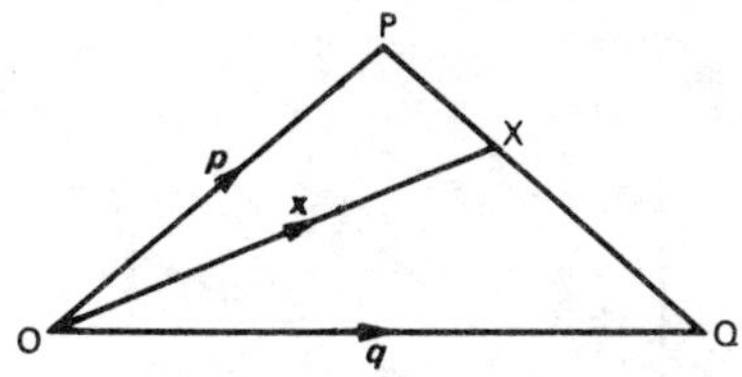

If PX:XQ = $l:m$ and $\mu = \dfrac{l}{l+m}$, then

$$x = p + \frac{l}{l+m}(-p+q)$$

$$x = \frac{mp + lq}{l+m} \qquad \text{which is the section formula.}$$

Collinear points

Suppose that P, Q, R are three points in a plane, with position vectors $\boldsymbol{p}$, $\boldsymbol{q}$, $\boldsymbol{r}$ respectively. The condition that P, Q, R are collinear is that if $\boldsymbol{r} = \lambda \boldsymbol{p} + \mu \boldsymbol{q}$, then $\lambda + \mu = 1$.

Geometry

Many geometrical conditions can be concisely stated in vector terms (and can often be proved by a consideration of symmetry).

(i)

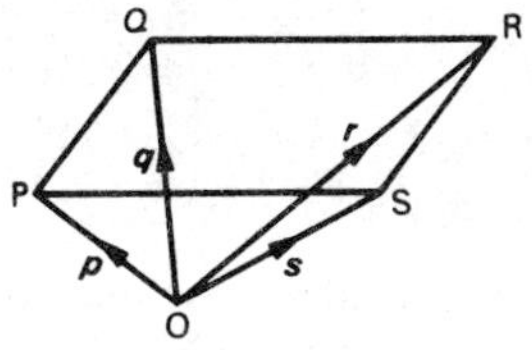

If $\boldsymbol{p}+\boldsymbol{r} = \boldsymbol{q}+\boldsymbol{s}$, then PQRS is a parallelogram.

(ii) The medians of the triangle ABC intersect at the centroid G, where

$$\boldsymbol{g} = \tfrac{1}{3}(\boldsymbol{a}+\boldsymbol{b}+\boldsymbol{c})$$

(iii) The bisector of the angle AOB has equation

$$\boldsymbol{x} = \lambda(\hat{\boldsymbol{a}} + \hat{\boldsymbol{b}})$$

Extension to three dimensions

Much of Chapter 8, Vectors 1, is a restatement in vector terms of Chapter 4, Coordinate geometry 1. In a similar way much of the content of Chapter 13, Coordinate geometry—3D, can be restated in vector terms. Here we are dealing with points in *space*, requiring *three* coordinates to define them.

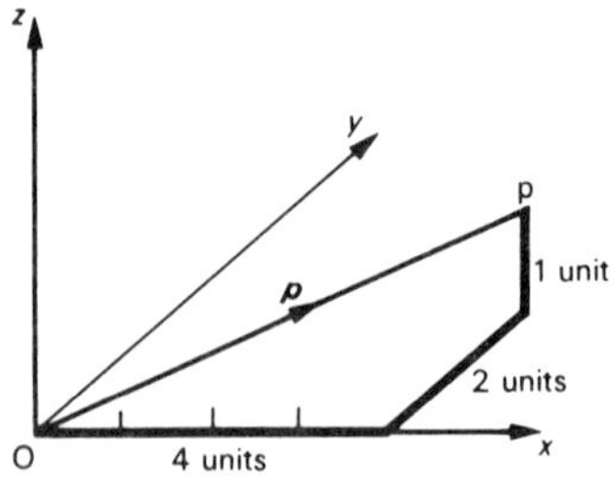

Thus, for example, in space

$$\mathbf{OP} = \boldsymbol{p} = \begin{pmatrix} x \text{ step} \\ y \text{ step} \\ z \text{ step} \end{pmatrix} = \begin{pmatrix} 4 \\ 2 \\ 1 \end{pmatrix}$$

$$= 4\boldsymbol{i} + 2\boldsymbol{j} + 1\boldsymbol{k}$$

where $\boldsymbol{i} = \begin{pmatrix} 1 \\ 0 \\ 0 \end{pmatrix}, \quad \boldsymbol{j} = \begin{pmatrix} 0 \\ 1 \\ 0 \end{pmatrix}, \quad \boldsymbol{k} = \begin{pmatrix} 0 \\ 0 \\ 1 \end{pmatrix}$

The length of $\boldsymbol{p}$

$$|\boldsymbol{p}| = \sqrt{(4^2 + 2^2 + 1^2)}$$
$$= \sqrt{21}$$

The unit vector, $\hat{\boldsymbol{p}}$ is given by

$$\hat{\boldsymbol{p}} = \frac{1}{|\boldsymbol{p}|}\boldsymbol{p} = \begin{pmatrix} 4/\sqrt{21} \\ 2/\sqrt{21} \\ 1/\sqrt{21} \end{pmatrix}$$

Any vector in space can be described as a unique combination of any three base vectors (which must not be parallel or in the same plane). So here, if

$$\boldsymbol{p} = l\boldsymbol{i} + m\boldsymbol{j} + n\boldsymbol{k}$$

and also $\boldsymbol{p} = 4\boldsymbol{i} + 2\boldsymbol{j} + 1\boldsymbol{k}$

then $l = 4$, $m = 2$ and $n = 1$ and no other values of l, m, n will give $\boldsymbol{p}$.

Dot product

The dot product of two vectors $\boldsymbol{a} = \begin{pmatrix} a_1 \\ a_2 \\ a_3 \end{pmatrix}$ and $\boldsymbol{b} = \begin{pmatrix} b_1 \\ b_2 \\ b_3 \end{pmatrix}$ is defined as

$$\boldsymbol{a} \cdot \boldsymbol{b} = a_1 b_1 + a_2 b_2 + a_3 b_3 = |\boldsymbol{a}||\boldsymbol{b}| \cos \theta$$

where θ is the angle between $\boldsymbol{a}$ and $\boldsymbol{b}$ and $0 \leqslant \theta \leqslant \pi$. If $\boldsymbol{a} \perp \boldsymbol{b}$, then $\boldsymbol{a} \cdot \boldsymbol{b} = 0$.

Cross product

The cross product of two vectors $\boldsymbol{a}$ and $\boldsymbol{b}$ is defined as

$$\boldsymbol{n} = \boldsymbol{a} \times \boldsymbol{b} = \begin{pmatrix} \begin{vmatrix} a_2 & b_2 \\ a_3 & b_3 \end{vmatrix} \\ \begin{vmatrix} a_3 & b_3 \\ a_3 & b_1 \end{vmatrix} \\ \begin{vmatrix} a_1 & b_1 \\ a_2 & b_2 \end{vmatrix} \end{pmatrix} = \begin{pmatrix} a_2b_3 - a_3b_2 \\ a_3b_1 - a_1b_3 \\ a_1b_2 - a_2b_1 \end{pmatrix}$$

This is a vector normal to the plane containing $\boldsymbol{a}$ and $\boldsymbol{b}$, its direction being given by the right hand rule. That is if the middle finger of the right hand is held perpendicular to the thumb and forefinger, then they represent $\boldsymbol{n}$, $\boldsymbol{a}$, and $\boldsymbol{b}$ respectively *in that order.*

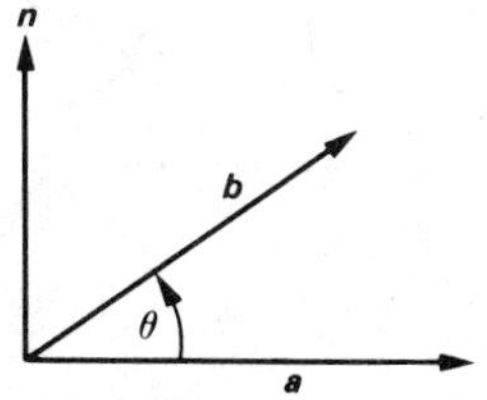

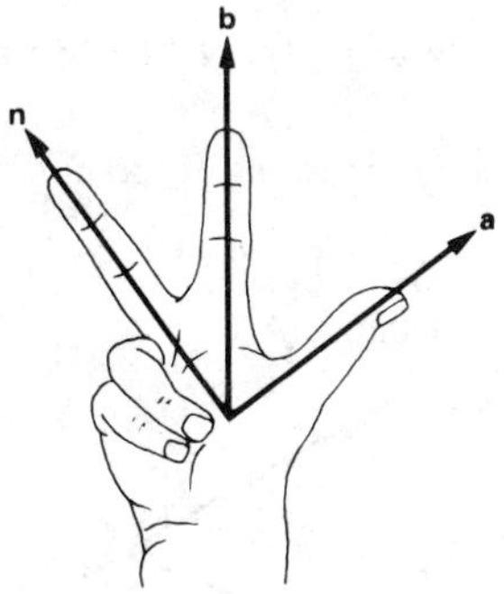

We show later (page 623) that this vector has length $|\boldsymbol{a}||\boldsymbol{b}| \sin \theta$.

Projections

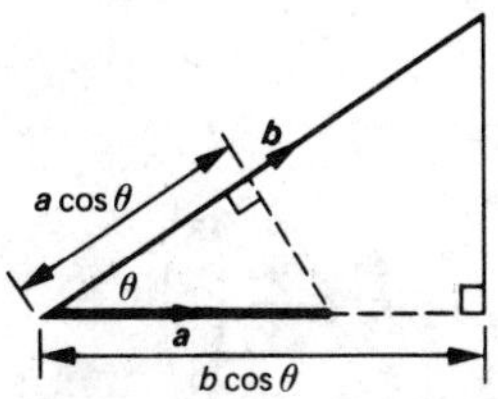

The length of the projection of $\boldsymbol{b}$ on $\boldsymbol{a}$ is

$$b \cos \theta = \frac{\boldsymbol{b} \cdot \boldsymbol{a}}{|\boldsymbol{a}|}$$

and of $\boldsymbol{a}$ on $\boldsymbol{b}$ is

$$a \cos \theta = \frac{\boldsymbol{a} \cdot \boldsymbol{b}}{|\boldsymbol{b}|}$$

The vector equation of a line in space

A line can be defined by one point on it and its direction in space, so

$$\boldsymbol{x} = \boldsymbol{a} + t\boldsymbol{l}$$

is the equation of a line through A in the direction of $\boldsymbol{l}$

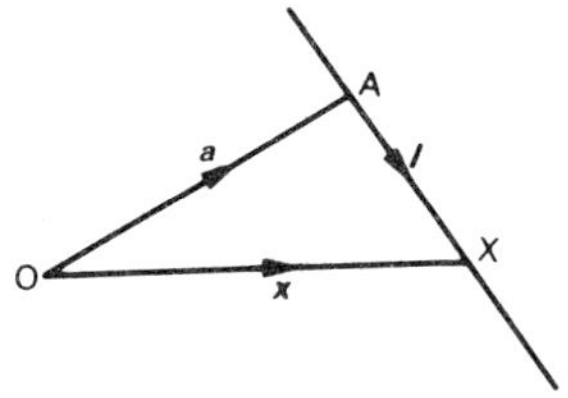

For example the line through A $(1, 2, -1)$ parallel to $\boldsymbol{l} = \begin{pmatrix} 0 \\ 1 \\ 2 \end{pmatrix}$ has the equation

$$\boldsymbol{x} = 1\boldsymbol{i} + 2\boldsymbol{j} - 1\boldsymbol{k} + t(0\boldsymbol{i} + 1\boldsymbol{j} + 2\boldsymbol{k})$$

in cartesian vector form.

We can also write the equation in terms of the unit vector $\hat{l}$ as

$$\boldsymbol{x} = \boldsymbol{a} + t\hat{\boldsymbol{l}}$$

where $t = |t\hat{\boldsymbol{l}}|$ gives the actual distance AX.

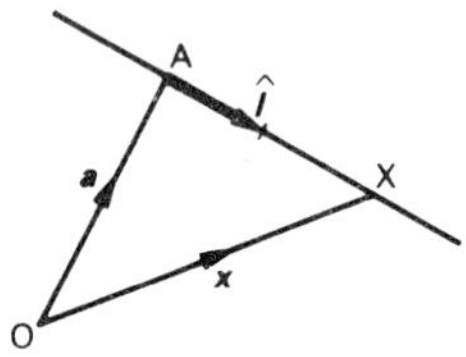

Example

What is the position vector of a point 4 units distant from A $(1, -1, 2)$ along the vector $\boldsymbol{l} = \begin{pmatrix} 3 \\ 1 \\ 1 \end{pmatrix}$? Here

$$\hat{\boldsymbol{l}} = \frac{1}{\sqrt{11}} \begin{pmatrix} 3 \\ 1 \\ 1 \end{pmatrix}$$

and $$x = \begin{pmatrix} 1 \\ -1 \\ 2 \end{pmatrix} + 4\begin{pmatrix} 3/\sqrt{11} \\ 1/\sqrt{11} \\ 1/\sqrt{11} \end{pmatrix} = \begin{pmatrix} 1+12/\sqrt{11} \\ -1+4/\sqrt{11} \\ 2+4/\sqrt{11} \end{pmatrix}$$

Exercise 1.1

1 Write down in column vector form an equation for a line through A, in the direction of $\boldsymbol{l}$ and find the points corresponding to $t = -1, 1, 2$ where

(a) $\boldsymbol{a} = \begin{pmatrix} 3 \\ 1 \\ -1 \end{pmatrix}$ and $\boldsymbol{l} = \begin{pmatrix} 1 \\ 2 \\ 3 \end{pmatrix}$

(b) $\boldsymbol{a} = \begin{pmatrix} 0 \\ 3 \\ 1 \end{pmatrix}$ and $\boldsymbol{l} = \begin{pmatrix} 0 \\ -2 \\ -4 \end{pmatrix}$

(c) $\boldsymbol{a} = \begin{pmatrix} 1 \\ 2 \\ -1 \end{pmatrix}$ and $\boldsymbol{l} = \begin{pmatrix} 2 \\ -1 \\ 0 \end{pmatrix}$

2 Rewrite each of the equations in Question 1 in cartesian vector form.

3 Find the position vectors of the following points

(a) 5 units distant from A (3, 1, 2) in the direction of $\boldsymbol{l} = \begin{pmatrix} 1 \\ -2 \\ 2 \end{pmatrix}$.

(b) 3 units distant from B where $\boldsymbol{b}^T = (1\ 0\ 3)$ and in the direction of $\boldsymbol{l}^T = (2\ -1\ --1)$

4 Write down cartesian vector equations of the lines

(a) Through A, $\boldsymbol{a} = \boldsymbol{i}+5\boldsymbol{j}-3\boldsymbol{k}$, and B, $\boldsymbol{b} = 3\boldsymbol{i}-3\boldsymbol{j}-\boldsymbol{k}$.

(b) Through C, $\boldsymbol{c} = 4\boldsymbol{j}-\boldsymbol{k}$, and D, $\boldsymbol{d} = 3\boldsymbol{i}+\boldsymbol{j}-5\boldsymbol{k}$.

In each case find three other points on the lines, and find the unit vectors, $\hat{\boldsymbol{l}}$ where $\boldsymbol{l} = -\boldsymbol{a}+\boldsymbol{b}$, and $\hat{\boldsymbol{m}}$ where $\boldsymbol{m} = -\boldsymbol{c}+\boldsymbol{d}$.

5 Find the position vector of any point on the following lines

(a) Through E (3, −5, 6) in the direction of $-3\boldsymbol{i}+2\boldsymbol{j}-\boldsymbol{k}$.

(b) Through points F and G with position vectors $2\boldsymbol{i}-\boldsymbol{j}+2\boldsymbol{k}$ and $4\boldsymbol{i}-2\boldsymbol{j}+\boldsymbol{k}$ respectively.

(c) Through points H (2, −1, 5) and L (12, 2, −10).

(d) Through point M with position vector $3\boldsymbol{i}+10\boldsymbol{j}-9\boldsymbol{k}$ parallel to the direction of $\boldsymbol{i}-\boldsymbol{j}+\boldsymbol{k}$. Find also the point on this line which has $5\boldsymbol{i}$ as one component of its position vector.

(e) Through N $(3\boldsymbol{i}-4\boldsymbol{j}-\boldsymbol{k})$ parallel to the line $\boldsymbol{x} = 2\boldsymbol{i}-26\boldsymbol{j}+\lambda(\boldsymbol{i}+2\boldsymbol{j})$.

1.2 The vector equation of a plane

A plane is defined by
(a) two lines, intersecting or parallel or
(b) three non-collinear points or
(c) the direction of the normal to the plane and one point on the plane.
There are other ways of defining a plane but these are the most important.

Equations of a plane in parametric form

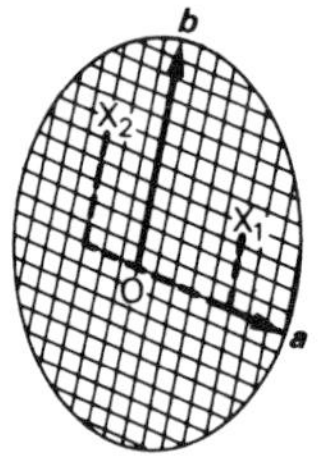

The hatched portion of the diagram represents part of the plane through the origin containing the vectors $\boldsymbol{a}$ and $\boldsymbol{b}$. X_1 and X_2 are two points in the plane and the position vector of *any* such point, X, in the plane, is given by

$$\boldsymbol{x} = \lambda\boldsymbol{a} + \mu\boldsymbol{b}$$

which is therefore the vector equation of the plane.

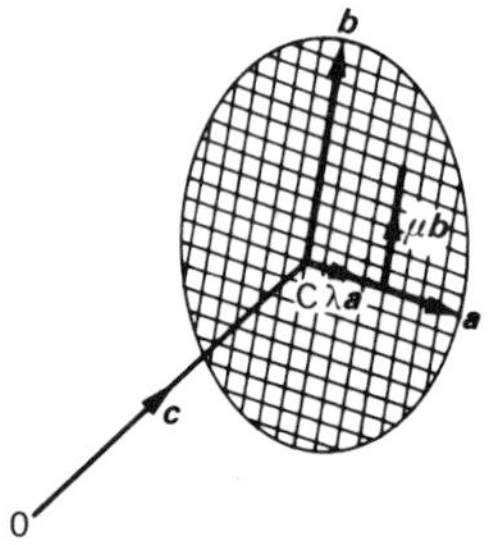

The equation of the plane through any point C, with position vector $\boldsymbol{c}$, and containing vectors parallel to $\boldsymbol{a}$ and $\boldsymbol{b}$ is

$$\boldsymbol{x} = \boldsymbol{c} + \lambda\boldsymbol{a} + \mu\boldsymbol{b}$$

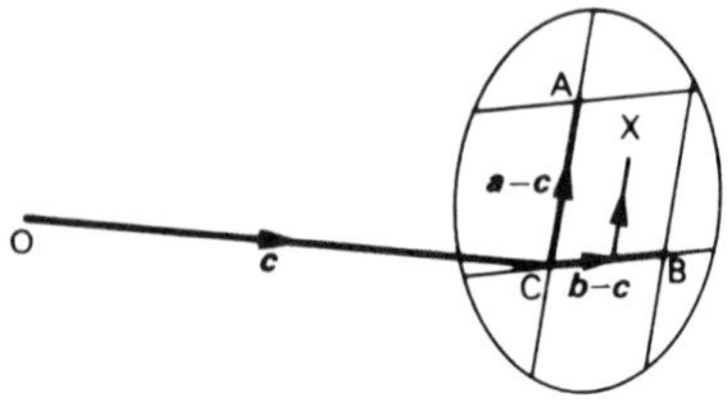

The equation of the plane through any three points A, B, C with position vectors $\boldsymbol{a}$, $\boldsymbol{b}$, $\boldsymbol{c}$ is found by choosing any two vectors in the plane as base vectors, for example $-\boldsymbol{c}+\boldsymbol{a}$ and $-\boldsymbol{c}+\boldsymbol{b}$. Then

$$\boldsymbol{x} = \boldsymbol{c}+\lambda(-\boldsymbol{c}+\boldsymbol{a})+\mu(-\boldsymbol{c}+\boldsymbol{b})$$

or

$$\boldsymbol{x} = \lambda\boldsymbol{a}+\mu\boldsymbol{b}+(1-\lambda-\mu)\boldsymbol{c} \qquad \text{I} \blacktriangleleft$$

Coplanar points

Equation I corresponds to the condition for four points to be coplanar.

Suppose $\boldsymbol{x} = \lambda\boldsymbol{a}+\mu\boldsymbol{b}+\nu\boldsymbol{c}$ (λ, μ, ν unique)

If X is on the plane of A, B, C
then $\lambda+\mu+\nu = 1$

Equations of a plane in dot product form

Our equations so far have been in terms of base vectors in the plane or of the position vectors of points in the plane, and have used two parameters, λ and μ. The equation of a plane can also be given in a form involving the dot product of vectors. If $\boldsymbol{n}$ is a vector normal to the plane, then we can find a simple expression for the equation of the plane.

Equation of a plane through O, given $\hat{\boldsymbol{n}}$.

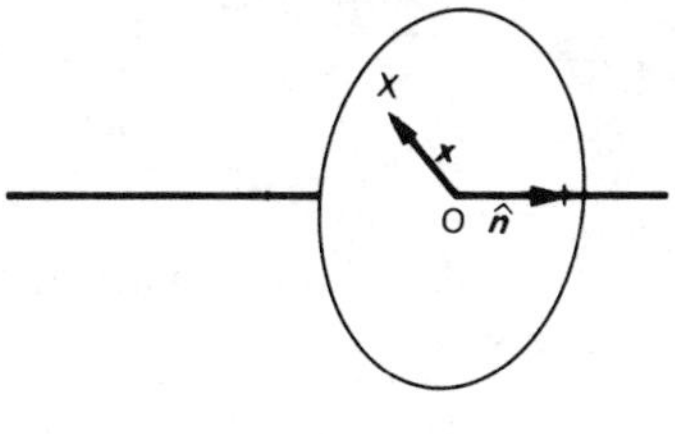

Any point X on the plane has position vector $\boldsymbol{x}$ and, since this is perpendicular to the unit normal vector $\hat{\boldsymbol{n}}$,

$$\boldsymbol{x}\cdot\hat{\boldsymbol{n}} = 0$$

This simple equation is the vector equation of the plane in dot-product form.

Equation of a plane, given $\hat{\boldsymbol{n}}$ and distance d from O

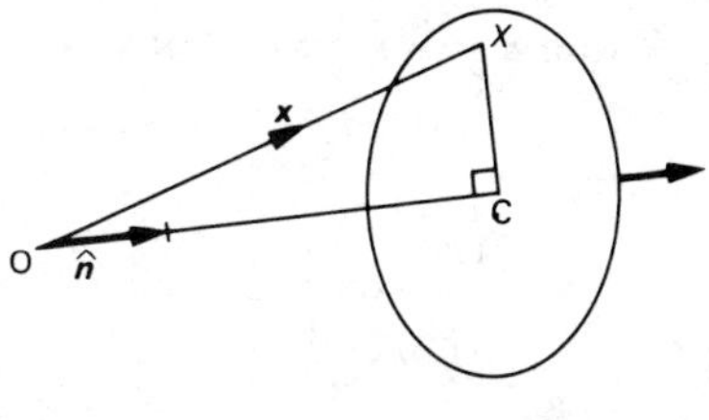

If C is the foot of the perpendicular from the origin to the plane, then OC = d. The projection of $\boldsymbol{x}$ in the direction of $\hat{\boldsymbol{n}}$ is d, hence

$$\boldsymbol{x} \cdot \hat{\boldsymbol{n}} = d$$ ◀

Since $\hat{\boldsymbol{n}} = \dfrac{\boldsymbol{n}}{|\boldsymbol{n}|}$, the equation is often written as

$$\boldsymbol{x} \cdot \boldsymbol{n} = e \qquad \text{where} \qquad e = |\boldsymbol{n}|d$$

Suppose $\boldsymbol{n} = \begin{pmatrix}1\\2\\2\end{pmatrix}$ and $d = 4$. Then $|\boldsymbol{n}| = \surd(1^2+2^2+2^2) = 3$ and $e = 3\times 4 = 12$. The equation of the plane is

$$\boldsymbol{x} \cdot \boldsymbol{n} = e$$

or
$$\begin{pmatrix}x\\y\\z\end{pmatrix} \cdot \begin{pmatrix}1\\2\\2\end{pmatrix} = 12 \qquad \text{or} \qquad x+2y+2z = 12$$

This looks familiar.

Equation of a plane through A, given $\hat{\boldsymbol{n}}$

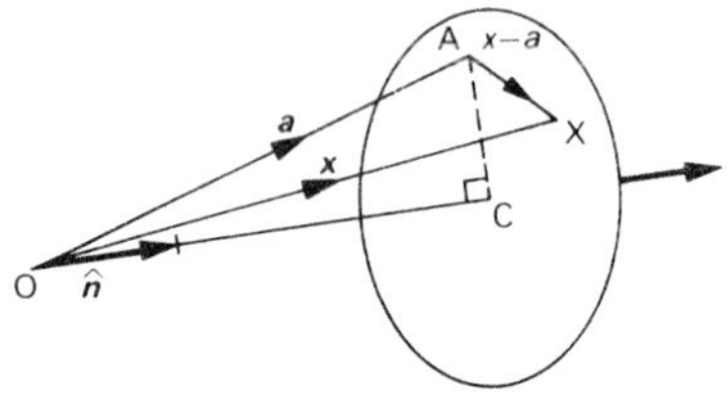

The plane contains $\boldsymbol{AX} = -\boldsymbol{a}+\boldsymbol{x}$ which is perpendicular to $\hat{\boldsymbol{n}}$. Hence

$$(-\boldsymbol{a}+\boldsymbol{x}) \cdot \hat{\boldsymbol{n}} = 0$$

or

$$\boldsymbol{x} \cdot \hat{\boldsymbol{n}} = \boldsymbol{a} \cdot \hat{\boldsymbol{n}}$$ ◀

Again we find that $\boldsymbol{a} \cdot \hat{\boldsymbol{n}} = d$, the projection of $\boldsymbol{a}$ in the direction $\boldsymbol{n}$. As before in multiplying by $|\boldsymbol{n}|$ we have $\boldsymbol{x} \cdot \boldsymbol{n} = \boldsymbol{a} \cdot \boldsymbol{n}$. The equation $\boldsymbol{x} \cdot \hat{\boldsymbol{n}} = \boldsymbol{a} \cdot \hat{\boldsymbol{n}} = d$ can be used to find the distance of a plane from the origin.

Example 1

A plane passes through A with $\boldsymbol{a} = \begin{pmatrix}3\\1\\-2\end{pmatrix}$ with DRN, $\boldsymbol{n} = \begin{pmatrix}1\\-1\\2\end{pmatrix}$. Find its distance from O. Now

$$\hat{\boldsymbol{n}} = \begin{pmatrix}1/\surd 6\\-1/\surd 6\\2/\surd 6\end{pmatrix}$$

The perpendicular distance, $d = \boldsymbol{a} \cdot \hat{\boldsymbol{n}}$. Hence

$$d = \begin{pmatrix} 3 \\ 1 \\ -2 \end{pmatrix} \cdot \begin{pmatrix} 1/\sqrt{6} \\ -1/\sqrt{6} \\ 2/\sqrt{6} \end{pmatrix} = \frac{-2}{\sqrt{6}}$$

Example 2

A plane is 7 units from O; the DRN is given by $\boldsymbol{n} = \begin{pmatrix} 1 \\ 3 \\ -1 \end{pmatrix}$. Find l if $\begin{pmatrix} l+2 \\ 2l-2 \\ 3l \end{pmatrix}$ lies on the plane.

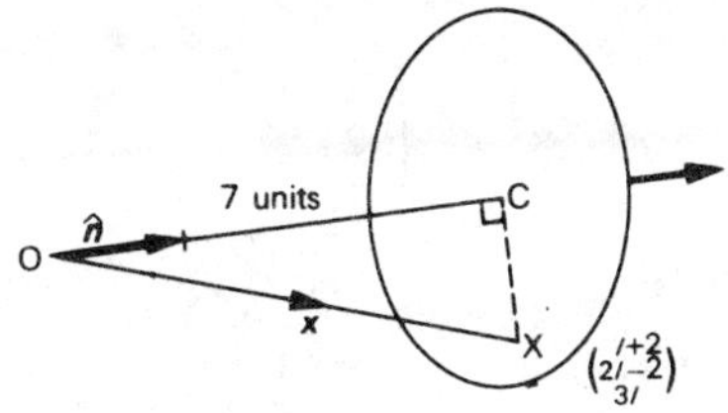

Now $\qquad \boldsymbol{x} \cdot \hat{\boldsymbol{n}} = d$

so
$$\begin{pmatrix} l+2 \\ 2l-2 \\ 3l \end{pmatrix} \cdot \begin{pmatrix} 1/\sqrt{11} \\ 3/\sqrt{11} \\ -1/\sqrt{11} \end{pmatrix} = 7$$

$$\frac{1}{\sqrt{11}}(l+2+6l-6-3l) = 7$$

$$4l-4 = 7\sqrt{11}$$

$$l = \frac{7\sqrt{11}+4}{4}$$

Equivalence of the equations of a plane

We have found the equation of a plane, distance d from O, perpendicular to $\boldsymbol{n}$, as $\boldsymbol{x} \cdot \hat{\boldsymbol{n}} = d$. We have also found the equation of a plane through C, containing the vectors $\boldsymbol{a}$ and $\boldsymbol{b}$ as $\boldsymbol{x} = \boldsymbol{c} + \lambda\boldsymbol{a} + \mu\boldsymbol{b}$. How can we tell if these two equations represent the same plane?

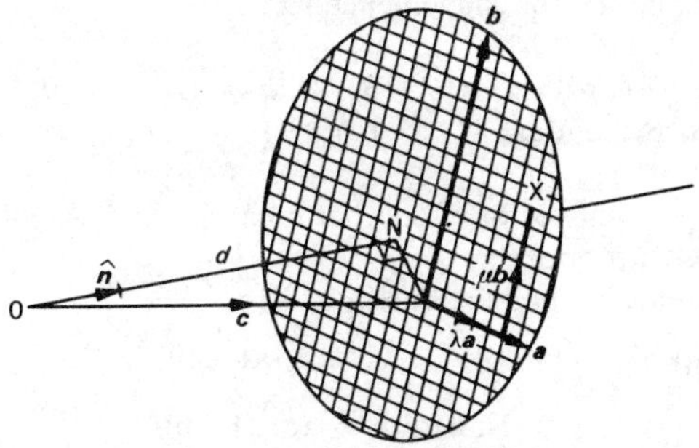

If the planes are identical
then (i) $\boldsymbol{c} \cdot \hat{\boldsymbol{n}} = d$
and (ii) $\boldsymbol{a} \cdot \hat{\boldsymbol{n}} = 0 \quad (\boldsymbol{a} \perp \hat{\boldsymbol{n}})$
and (iii) $\boldsymbol{b} \cdot \hat{\boldsymbol{n}} = 0 \quad (\boldsymbol{b} \perp \hat{\boldsymbol{n}})$

Example 3

Do the equations

$$\boldsymbol{x} = \begin{pmatrix} 1 \\ 2 \\ 3 \end{pmatrix} + \lambda \begin{pmatrix} 2 \\ -3 \\ -2 \end{pmatrix} + \mu \begin{pmatrix} 0 \\ -2 \\ -1 \end{pmatrix} \qquad \text{I}$$

and

$$\boldsymbol{x} \cdot \begin{pmatrix} 1 \\ -2 \\ 4 \end{pmatrix} = 9 \qquad \text{II}$$

represent the same plane?

The point (1, 2, 3) lies on I (put $\lambda = \mu = 0$).

$$\begin{pmatrix} 1 \\ 2 \\ 3 \end{pmatrix} \cdot \begin{pmatrix} 1 \\ -2 \\ 4 \end{pmatrix} = 1 - 4 + 12 = 9 \Rightarrow (1, 2, 3) \text{ also lies on II.}$$

Vectors $\begin{pmatrix} 2 \\ -3 \\ -2 \end{pmatrix}$ and $\begin{pmatrix} 0 \\ -2 \\ -1 \end{pmatrix}$ lie in I and $\begin{pmatrix} 1 \\ -2 \\ 4 \end{pmatrix}$ is the DRN of II.

$$\begin{pmatrix} 2 \\ -3 \\ -2 \end{pmatrix} \cdot \begin{pmatrix} 1 \\ -2 \\ 4 \end{pmatrix} = 2 + 6 - 8 = 0 \qquad \text{and} \qquad \begin{pmatrix} 0 \\ -2 \\ -1 \end{pmatrix} \cdot \begin{pmatrix} 1 \\ -2 \\ -4 \end{pmatrix} = 0 + 4 - 4 = 0$$

i.e. the normal to II is mutually perpendicular to two vectors which lie on I so it is also normal to II. Since the planes have the same DRNs, and have one point in common, they are identical.

Exercise 1.2

(Vector **a** is written as $\boldsymbol{a}^{\mathrm{T}}$ for convenience.)

1 Using $\boldsymbol{x} = \lambda \boldsymbol{a} + \mu \boldsymbol{b}$, with $\boldsymbol{a}^{\mathrm{T}} = (1 \quad 3 \quad 1)$, $\boldsymbol{b}^{\mathrm{T}} = (2 \quad -1 \quad 0)$

(a) Find P, corresponding to $\lambda = 1$, $\mu = 1$ and find Q corresponding to $\lambda = 3$, $\mu = -1$.

(b) Find the position vector of another point R which is in line with PQ and on the plane, $\boldsymbol{x} = \lambda \boldsymbol{a} + \mu \boldsymbol{b}$.

(c) Are the following points on the plane?

L, with $\boldsymbol{l}^{\mathrm{T}} = (1 \quad -4 \quad -1)$; M, with $\boldsymbol{n}^{\mathrm{T}} = (5 \quad 1 \quad 1)$;

N, with $\boldsymbol{n}^{\mathrm{T}} = (6 \quad 1 \quad 0)$.

2 Using $\boldsymbol{x} = \boldsymbol{c} + \lambda\boldsymbol{a} + \mu\boldsymbol{b}$, with $\boldsymbol{a}^{\mathrm{T}} = (3 \quad 1 \quad -1)$, $\boldsymbol{b}^{\mathrm{T}} = (2 \quad 1 \quad 0)$, $\boldsymbol{c}^{\mathrm{T}} = (1 \quad 0 \quad 2)$.

(a) Find $\boldsymbol{p}$, corresponding to $\lambda = 2$, $\mu = 1$

(b) Find $\boldsymbol{q}$ where $\boldsymbol{q} = -\boldsymbol{p} + \boldsymbol{c}$

(c) Find the length of **PC** $= \boldsymbol{q}$ and find another point on the plane at the same distance from C.

(d) Are the following points on the plane: L, with $\boldsymbol{l}^{\mathrm{T}} = (3 \quad 1 \quad 2)$; M, with $\boldsymbol{m}^{\mathrm{T}} = (7 \quad 2 \quad 0)$; N, with $\boldsymbol{n}^{\mathrm{T}} = (8 \quad 1 \quad 4)$?

3 Using $\boldsymbol{x} = \lambda\boldsymbol{a} + \mu\boldsymbol{b} + (1 - \lambda - \mu)\boldsymbol{c}$, with $\boldsymbol{a}^{\mathrm{T}} = (1 \quad 0 \quad 1)$, $\boldsymbol{b}^{\mathrm{T}} = (0 \quad -1 \quad 2)$, $\boldsymbol{c}^{\mathrm{T}} = (3 \quad 1 \quad -2)$.

(a) Find P, corresponding to $\lambda = 1$, $\mu = 2$ and Q corresponding to $\lambda = -1$ and $\mu = 3$.

(b) Are the following points on the plane: L, with $\boldsymbol{l}^{\mathrm{T}} = (4 \quad 1 \quad -3)$; M, with $\boldsymbol{m}^{\mathrm{T}} = (2 \quad 1 \quad 0)$?

In questions 4–6 give your answers in parametric form. They will not be unique.

4 Write down an equation of the plane through the points with position vectors $(2\boldsymbol{i} - 3\boldsymbol{j} + 1\boldsymbol{k})$, $(1\boldsymbol{i} + 2\boldsymbol{j} - 5\boldsymbol{k})$ and $(-1\boldsymbol{i} + 1\boldsymbol{j} - 2\boldsymbol{k})$.

5 (a) Write down an equation of the plane through O, and containing the vectors $\boldsymbol{a} = (1\boldsymbol{i} + 3\boldsymbol{j} + 1\boldsymbol{k})$ and $\boldsymbol{b} = (-1\boldsymbol{i} + 4\boldsymbol{j} - 1\boldsymbol{k})$

(b) Write down an equation of the plane through C, where $\boldsymbol{c} = (4\boldsymbol{i} - 1\boldsymbol{j} + 2\boldsymbol{k})$, containing vectors parallel to $\boldsymbol{a}$ and $\boldsymbol{b}$.

6 Find an equation of the plane through the points with position vectors $(3\boldsymbol{i} - 2\boldsymbol{j})$ $(2\boldsymbol{i} + 3\boldsymbol{k})$ and $(\boldsymbol{i} - \boldsymbol{j} + \boldsymbol{k})$.

7 Write down the equation of the plane through P with $\boldsymbol{p} = 4\boldsymbol{i} - 2\boldsymbol{j} - 2\boldsymbol{k}$ and normal to $\boldsymbol{i} + \boldsymbol{j} - 3\boldsymbol{k}$. What is its distance from O?

8 A plane is 5 units from O and perpendicular to $3\boldsymbol{i} + \boldsymbol{j} - 2\boldsymbol{k}$. Find m if $(3m, 2m - 1, -m + 2)$ lies on the plane.

9 Write down the equations of the plane parallel to the plane

$$\boldsymbol{x} \cdot (2\boldsymbol{i} + 3\boldsymbol{j} - \boldsymbol{k}) = 5$$

and **(a)** at twice the distance from the origin and on the same side.

(b) at the same distance but on the opposite side of the origin.

1.3 Intersections of lines and planes

Intersection of lines

Consider two lines in space $\boldsymbol{x}_1 = \boldsymbol{a} + s\boldsymbol{l}$ and $\boldsymbol{x}_2 = \boldsymbol{b} + t\boldsymbol{m}$. Often these lines will be skew, but if they do intersect at X say, then $\boldsymbol{x} = \boldsymbol{x}_1 = \boldsymbol{x}_2$ and $\boldsymbol{a} - \boldsymbol{b} = t\boldsymbol{m} - s\boldsymbol{l}$ and we must find values of s and t which will satisfy the equation. If we cannot find s and t, i.e. the equations are inconsistent, then the lines do *not* intersect.

Example 1

Suppose $\boldsymbol{x}_1 = \begin{pmatrix}1\\0\\-1\end{pmatrix} + s\begin{pmatrix}1\\1\\1\end{pmatrix}$ and $\boldsymbol{x}_2 = \begin{pmatrix}2\\-1\\3\end{pmatrix} + t\begin{pmatrix}4\\6\\1\end{pmatrix}$. If these lines intersect

$$\begin{pmatrix}1\\0\\-1\end{pmatrix} - \begin{pmatrix}2\\-1\\3\end{pmatrix} = t\begin{pmatrix}4\\6\\1\end{pmatrix} - s\begin{pmatrix}1\\1\\1\end{pmatrix}$$

$$\begin{pmatrix}-1\\1\\-4\end{pmatrix} = \begin{pmatrix}4t-s\\6t-s\\t-s\end{pmatrix}$$

$$\left.\begin{aligned}-1 &= 4t-s\\ 1 &= 6t-s\end{aligned}\right\} \Rightarrow t = 1,\ s = 5$$

These values satisfy the third equation $-4 = t-s$ and so the equations are consistent.

The lines meet at $\boldsymbol{x} = \begin{pmatrix}6\\5\\4\end{pmatrix}$.

Example 2

Suppose $\boldsymbol{x}_1 = s\begin{pmatrix}1\\1\\0\end{pmatrix}$ and $\boldsymbol{x}_2 = \begin{pmatrix}1\\3\\1\end{pmatrix} + t\begin{pmatrix}2\\2\\1\end{pmatrix}$. If the lines intersect

$$s\begin{pmatrix}1\\1\\0\end{pmatrix} = \begin{pmatrix}1\\3\\1\end{pmatrix} + t\begin{pmatrix}2\\2\\1\end{pmatrix}$$

giving $\begin{pmatrix}s-2t\\s-2t\\-t\end{pmatrix} = \begin{pmatrix}1\\3\\1\end{pmatrix}$ and $\begin{aligned}s-2t &= 1\\ s-2t &= 3\\ t &= 1\end{aligned}$

Now the first two equations are inconsistent and so the lines do not intersect, i.e. they are *skew*.

Intersection of a line and a plane

Find the intersection of the line $\boldsymbol{x} = \boldsymbol{a} + t\boldsymbol{b}$ with the plane $\boldsymbol{x} \cdot \hat{\boldsymbol{n}} = d$.
Suppose they intersect at R. Now $\boldsymbol{r} = \boldsymbol{a} + t\boldsymbol{b}$ since R lies on the line and $\boldsymbol{r} \cdot \hat{\boldsymbol{n}} = d$ since R lies on the plane. Hence

$$(\boldsymbol{a} + t\boldsymbol{b}) \cdot \hat{\boldsymbol{n}} = d$$

$$\boldsymbol{a} \cdot \hat{\boldsymbol{n}} + t\boldsymbol{b} \cdot \hat{\boldsymbol{n}} = d$$

$$t = \frac{d - \boldsymbol{a} \cdot \hat{\boldsymbol{n}}}{\boldsymbol{b} \cdot \hat{\boldsymbol{n}}}$$

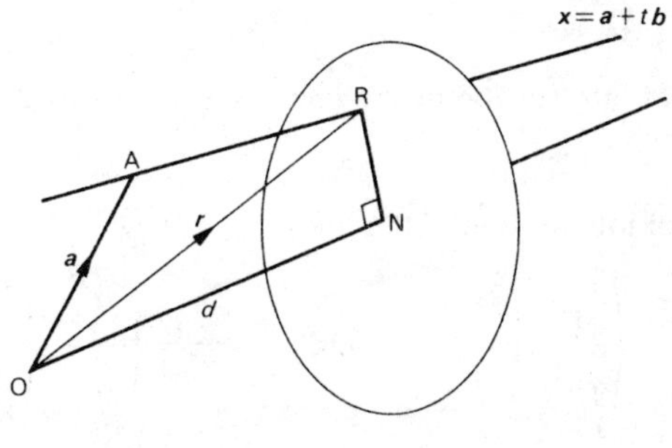

Hence $$r = a + \frac{(d - a \cdot \hat{n})}{b \cdot \hat{n}} b$$

Example 3

Consider the line $x = s\begin{pmatrix}0\\3\\5\end{pmatrix}$ and the plane $\left[x - \begin{pmatrix}6\\1\\14\end{pmatrix}\right] \cdot \begin{pmatrix}1\\1\\-2\end{pmatrix} = 0$. If these two intersect at R then

$$r = s\begin{pmatrix}0\\3\\5\end{pmatrix} \qquad \text{since R is on the line}$$

and $$\left[r - \begin{pmatrix}6\\1\\14\end{pmatrix}\right] \cdot \begin{pmatrix}1\\1\\-2\end{pmatrix} = 0 \qquad \text{since R is on the plane}$$

so $$r \cdot \begin{pmatrix}1\\1\\-2\end{pmatrix} - \begin{pmatrix}6\\1\\14\end{pmatrix} \cdot \begin{pmatrix}1\\1\\-2\end{pmatrix} = 0$$

and $$r \cdot \begin{pmatrix}1\\1\\-2\end{pmatrix} = -21$$

Thus $$s\begin{pmatrix}0\\3\\5\end{pmatrix} \cdot \begin{pmatrix}1\\1\\-2\end{pmatrix} = -21$$

$$-7s = -21, \qquad s = 3$$

Hence the line and plane intersect at R, with $r = \begin{pmatrix}0\\9\\15\end{pmatrix}$.

Exercise 1.3

1 Find the point of intersection of the line $\boldsymbol{x} = -3\boldsymbol{i}+4\boldsymbol{j}+t(3\boldsymbol{i}-2\boldsymbol{j})$ with the line $\boldsymbol{x} = 2\boldsymbol{i}+\boldsymbol{j}+s(\boldsymbol{i}-\boldsymbol{j})$.

2 Find the point of intersection of the lines

$$\boldsymbol{x} = \begin{pmatrix}3\\3\\4\end{pmatrix}+t\begin{pmatrix}2\\4\\1\end{pmatrix} \quad \text{and} \quad \boldsymbol{x} = \begin{pmatrix}3\\3\\2\end{pmatrix}+s\begin{pmatrix}1\\2\\2\end{pmatrix}$$

3 Determine whether the lines

$$\boldsymbol{x} = \begin{pmatrix}1\\2\\3\end{pmatrix}+t\begin{pmatrix}1\\-1\\1\end{pmatrix} \quad \text{and} \quad \boldsymbol{x} = \begin{pmatrix}3\\2\\1\end{pmatrix}+s\begin{pmatrix}2\\-1\\-3\end{pmatrix}$$

are intersecting or skew.

4 Show that the lines

$$\boldsymbol{x} = \begin{pmatrix}-2\\0\\6\end{pmatrix}+s\begin{pmatrix}1\\2\\-1\end{pmatrix} \quad \text{and} \quad \boldsymbol{x} = \begin{pmatrix}-5\\0\\0\end{pmatrix}+t\begin{pmatrix}1\\-1\\2\end{pmatrix}$$

do not intersect.

5 Show that the lines

$$\boldsymbol{x} = \begin{pmatrix}4\\2\\-6\end{pmatrix}+s\begin{pmatrix}-8\\1\\-2\end{pmatrix} \quad \text{and} \quad \boldsymbol{x} = \begin{pmatrix}-2\\1\\-2\end{pmatrix}+t\begin{pmatrix}-9\\2\\-5\end{pmatrix}$$

intersect at $(-20, 5, -12)$.

6 Find the point of intersection of $\boldsymbol{x} = \begin{pmatrix}2\\0\\5\end{pmatrix}+t\begin{pmatrix}3\\12\\4\end{pmatrix}$ with the plane $\boldsymbol{x}\cdot\begin{pmatrix}-1\\2\\2\end{pmatrix} = 66$.

7 Find the point of intersection of the line $\boldsymbol{x} = \begin{pmatrix}2\\1\\1\end{pmatrix}+s\begin{pmatrix}2\\3\\-1\end{pmatrix}$ with the plane $\boldsymbol{x}\cdot\begin{pmatrix}1\\2\\-1\end{pmatrix} = 12$.

8 Find where the line $\boldsymbol{x}-2\boldsymbol{i}+6\boldsymbol{j}-3\boldsymbol{k}+t(3\boldsymbol{i}-2\boldsymbol{j}+\boldsymbol{k})$ meets the plane $\boldsymbol{x}2\boldsymbol{i}+3\boldsymbol{j}-4\boldsymbol{k}+\lambda(-3\boldsymbol{i}+2\boldsymbol{j}-4\boldsymbol{k})+\mu(-\boldsymbol{i}+\boldsymbol{j}-\boldsymbol{k})$.

9 Find where the line through the points with position vectors $\boldsymbol{r}_1 = 2\boldsymbol{i}+3\boldsymbol{j}+4\boldsymbol{k}$ and $\boldsymbol{r}_2 = 3\boldsymbol{i}-2\boldsymbol{j}+5\boldsymbol{k}$ meets the plane $\boldsymbol{p} = \boldsymbol{i}+\boldsymbol{j}+\boldsymbol{k}+\lambda(\boldsymbol{i}-\boldsymbol{j}+2\boldsymbol{k})+\mu(3\boldsymbol{i}-4\boldsymbol{j}+5\boldsymbol{k})$.

1.4 Intersection of two planes

Consider the planes $\boldsymbol{x}\cdot\hat{\boldsymbol{a}} = k$ and $\boldsymbol{x}\cdot\hat{\boldsymbol{b}} = l$ with $\boldsymbol{a}, \boldsymbol{b}$ not parallel.

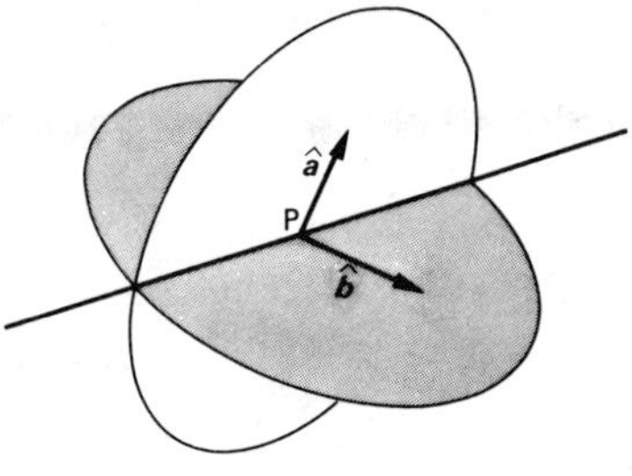

(i) The planes have a common point P.
(ii) They intersect in a line through P.
(iii) The line is perpendicular to $\boldsymbol{a}$ and to $\boldsymbol{b}$.
(iv) Its direction is $\boldsymbol{a}\times\boldsymbol{b}$.

Hence the equation of the line is given by $\boldsymbol{x} = \boldsymbol{p}+s(\boldsymbol{a}\times\boldsymbol{b})$.

Example 1

The two planes $\boldsymbol{x}\cdot\begin{pmatrix}2\\1\\3\end{pmatrix} = k$ and $\boldsymbol{x}\cdot\begin{pmatrix}-1\\0\\1\end{pmatrix} = l$ pass through P with $\boldsymbol{p} = \begin{pmatrix}5\\0\\-1\end{pmatrix}$. Find the equation of the line of intersection of the planes.

Now $$\begin{pmatrix}2\\1\\3\end{pmatrix}\times\begin{pmatrix}-1\\0\\+1\end{pmatrix} = \begin{pmatrix}1\\-5\\1\end{pmatrix}$$

Hence the line is given by

$$\boldsymbol{x} = \begin{pmatrix}5\\0\\-1\end{pmatrix}+s\begin{pmatrix}1\\-5\\1\end{pmatrix}$$

Example 2

Two planes $\boldsymbol{x}\cdot\boldsymbol{a} = 5$ and $\boldsymbol{x}\cdot\boldsymbol{b} = 1$ intersect. If $\boldsymbol{a} = \begin{pmatrix}1\\2\\2\end{pmatrix}$, $\boldsymbol{b} = \begin{pmatrix}-2\\2\\1\end{pmatrix}$, find the equation of the line of intersection.

$$\boldsymbol{a}\times\boldsymbol{b} = \begin{pmatrix}1\\2\\2\end{pmatrix}\times\begin{pmatrix}-2\\2\\1\end{pmatrix} = \begin{pmatrix}-2\\-5\\6\end{pmatrix}$$

so
$$\boldsymbol{x} = \boldsymbol{p}+s\begin{pmatrix}-2\\-5\\6\end{pmatrix}$$

We must now find a point through which the two planes pass. Their equations are

$$\begin{pmatrix}x\\y\\z\end{pmatrix}\cdot\begin{pmatrix}1\\2\\2\end{pmatrix} = 5 \qquad \text{or} \qquad x+2y+2z = 5$$

and
$$\begin{pmatrix}x\\y\\z\end{pmatrix}\cdot\begin{pmatrix}-2\\2\\1\end{pmatrix} = 1 \qquad \text{or} \qquad -2x+2y+z = 1$$

When $z = 0$,

$$\left.\begin{aligned}x+2y &= 5\\ -2x+2y &= 1\end{aligned}\right\}\Rightarrow x = \tfrac{4}{3}, \qquad y = \tfrac{11}{6}$$

Hence the planes pass through P with $\boldsymbol{p} = \begin{pmatrix}\frac{4}{3}\\ \frac{11}{6}\\ 0\end{pmatrix}$. Thus the line is

$$\boldsymbol{x} = \begin{pmatrix}\frac{4}{3}\\ \frac{11}{6}\\ 0\end{pmatrix}+s\begin{pmatrix}-2\\-5\\6\end{pmatrix}$$

Example 3

A plane contains the line $\boldsymbol{x} = \begin{pmatrix}1\\2\\1\end{pmatrix}+t\begin{pmatrix}1\\-1\\2\end{pmatrix}$ and is parallel to $\begin{pmatrix}1\\2\\3\end{pmatrix}$. Find its equation.

The normal to the plane is given by $\begin{pmatrix}1\\-1\\2\end{pmatrix}\times\begin{pmatrix}1\\2\\3\end{pmatrix} = \begin{pmatrix}-7\\-1\\3\end{pmatrix}$ and it passes through $\begin{pmatrix}1\\2\\1\end{pmatrix}$.

Its equation can be written

$$\boldsymbol{x}\cdot\begin{pmatrix}-7\\-1\\3\end{pmatrix} = \begin{pmatrix}1\\2\\1\end{pmatrix}\cdot\begin{pmatrix}-7\\-1\\3\end{pmatrix} = -6 \qquad (\boldsymbol{x}\cdot\boldsymbol{n} = \boldsymbol{a}\cdot\boldsymbol{n})$$

or
$$-7x-y+3z = -6$$

Exercise 1.4

1 Find the equation of the line of intersection of the planes $\boldsymbol{x}\cdot\begin{pmatrix}1\\3\\-1\end{pmatrix}=4$ and $\boldsymbol{x}\cdot\begin{pmatrix}2\\-1\\1\end{pmatrix}=10$.

2 Find the equation of the plane containing the line

$\boldsymbol{x}=\begin{pmatrix}-1\\2\\-4\end{pmatrix}+t\begin{pmatrix}1\\1\\2\end{pmatrix}$ and parallel to $\begin{pmatrix}2\\3\\1\end{pmatrix}$.

3 A plane is parallel to the two lines $\boldsymbol{x}=\begin{pmatrix}1\\0\\1\end{pmatrix}+t\begin{pmatrix}2\\3\\4\end{pmatrix}$ and $\boldsymbol{x}=\begin{pmatrix}-1\\0\\0\end{pmatrix}+s\begin{pmatrix}-1\\2\\1\end{pmatrix}$ and it passes through $(1, 0, -1)$. Find its equation.

4 Find the vector equation of the plane containing the two parallel lines $\boldsymbol{r}_1=\boldsymbol{a}_1+s\boldsymbol{b}$, and $\boldsymbol{r}_2=\boldsymbol{a}_2+t\boldsymbol{b}$.

5 If $\boldsymbol{u}=\boldsymbol{i}+2\boldsymbol{j}$, $\boldsymbol{v}=2\boldsymbol{i}-\boldsymbol{j}+3\boldsymbol{k}$ and $\boldsymbol{w}=-\boldsymbol{i}+13\boldsymbol{j}-9\boldsymbol{k}$, show that $\boldsymbol{w}$ is coplanar with $\boldsymbol{u}$ and $\boldsymbol{v}$.

6 Show that vector $\boldsymbol{a}=-\boldsymbol{i}-4\boldsymbol{j}+7\boldsymbol{k}$ is coplanar with vectors $\boldsymbol{u}=2\boldsymbol{i}+3\boldsymbol{j}-\boldsymbol{k}$ and $\boldsymbol{r}=4\boldsymbol{i}+\boldsymbol{j}+11\boldsymbol{k}$. Find a vector that is coplanar with these three vectors and perpendicular to $\boldsymbol{a}$.

7 Write down the equation of the plane through the point $-2\boldsymbol{i}+3\boldsymbol{j}-4\boldsymbol{k}$ which is parallel to the lines

$$l_1=2\boldsymbol{i}-6\boldsymbol{j}+5\boldsymbol{k}+\lambda_1(3\boldsymbol{i}-2\boldsymbol{j}-5\boldsymbol{k})$$
$$l_2=-3\boldsymbol{i}+2\boldsymbol{j}-3\boldsymbol{k}+\lambda_2(2\boldsymbol{i}+2\boldsymbol{j}-3\boldsymbol{k})$$

2 Vector methods applied

2.1 Distances between points, lines and planes

Distance of a point from a plane

Example 1

Find the distance of P with $\boldsymbol{p}=\begin{pmatrix}3\\3\\1\end{pmatrix}$ from the plane

$$\left[\boldsymbol{x}-\begin{pmatrix}-1\\-1\\0\end{pmatrix}\right]\cdot\begin{bmatrix}1\\-1\\1\end{bmatrix}=0$$

Let d be the distance PQ from the point P to the plane through A with $\boldsymbol{a} = \begin{pmatrix} -1 \\ -1 \\ 0 \end{pmatrix}$ and let the unit normal vector to the plane be $\hat{\boldsymbol{n}} = \frac{1}{\sqrt{3}}\begin{pmatrix} 1 \\ -1 \\ 1 \end{pmatrix}$. Now we know that

$$d = (-\boldsymbol{a} + \boldsymbol{p}) \cdot \hat{\boldsymbol{n}}$$

$$= \left[-\begin{pmatrix} -1 \\ -1 \\ 0 \end{pmatrix} + \begin{pmatrix} 3 \\ 3 \\ 1 \end{pmatrix} \right] \cdot \frac{1}{\sqrt{3}} \begin{pmatrix} 1 \\ -1 \\ 1 \end{pmatrix}$$

$$= \frac{1}{\sqrt{3}} \begin{pmatrix} 4 \\ 4 \\ 1 \end{pmatrix} \cdot \begin{pmatrix} 1 \\ -1 \\ 1 \end{pmatrix} = \frac{1}{\sqrt{3}}$$

The required distance is $1/\sqrt{3}$ units.

Projections

The projection of a line on a plane can be thought of as the 'shadow' of the line on the plane.

Example 2

Find the equation of the projection of the line $\boldsymbol{x} = \begin{pmatrix} 5 \\ 0 \\ 4 \end{pmatrix} + t\begin{pmatrix} 3 \\ 1 \\ 1 \end{pmatrix}$ on the plane $\boldsymbol{x} \cdot \begin{pmatrix} 1 \\ 2 \\ 1 \end{pmatrix} = 3$.

Consider any point P on the line parametrically as $(5 + 3t, 0 + 1t, 4 + 1t)$. Q is the foot of the perpendicular from P to the plane.

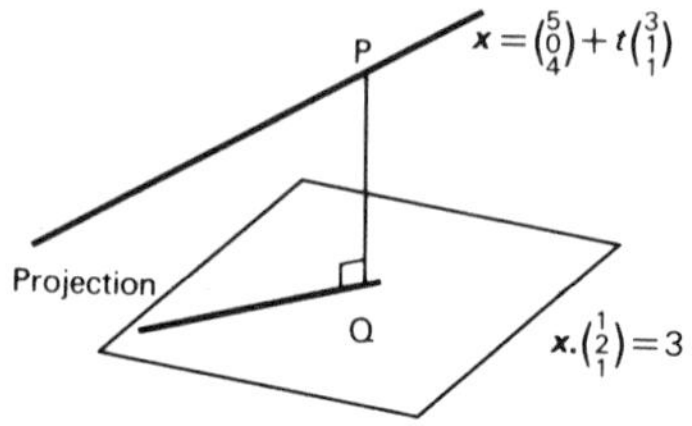

PQ is parallel to the normal to the plane. Hence $\boldsymbol{PQ} = \begin{pmatrix} k \\ 2k \\ k \end{pmatrix}$. Now

$$\boldsymbol{OQ} = \boldsymbol{OP} + \boldsymbol{PQ}$$

$$\boldsymbol{q} = \begin{pmatrix} 5+3t+k \\ 0+t+2k \\ 4+t+k \end{pmatrix}$$

Since Q lies on the plane,

$$\boldsymbol{q} \cdot \begin{pmatrix} 1 \\ 2 \\ 1 \end{pmatrix} = 3$$

so

$$\begin{pmatrix} 5+3t+k \\ 0+t+2k \\ 4+t+k \end{pmatrix} \cdot \begin{pmatrix} 1 \\ 2 \\ 1 \end{pmatrix} = 3$$

$$5+3t+k+2t+4k+4+t+k = 3$$

$$9+6t+6k = 3$$

$$k = -t-1$$

Hence

$$\boldsymbol{q} = \begin{pmatrix} 5+3t-t-1 \\ t-2t-2 \\ 4+t-t-1 \end{pmatrix} = \begin{pmatrix} 4+2t \\ -2-t \\ 3 \end{pmatrix}$$

and the equation of the projection is

$$\boldsymbol{x} = \begin{pmatrix} 4 \\ -2 \\ 3 \end{pmatrix} + t\begin{pmatrix} 2 \\ -1 \\ 0 \end{pmatrix}$$

Distance between skew lines

These are lines which do not intersect and are in different planes. However, at some point they are closest together, in fact they have a *common perpendicular* which is the shortest distance between the two lines.

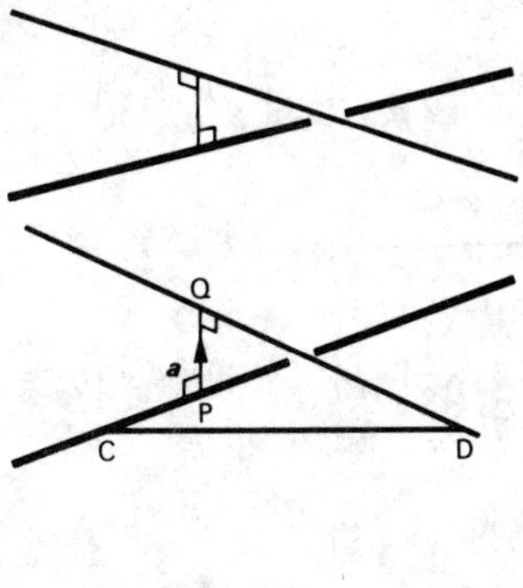

This common perpendicular is the projection in the direction of the perpendicular, of the line joining *any* point on one line to *any* point on the other, i.e. the length of PQ is $\mathbf{CD}\cdot\hat{\boldsymbol{a}}$ or

$$(-\boldsymbol{c}+\boldsymbol{d})\cdot\hat{\boldsymbol{a}}$$

Thus if $\hat{\boldsymbol{a}} = \frac{1}{\sqrt{18}}\begin{pmatrix}4\\1\\1\end{pmatrix}$, $\boldsymbol{c} = \begin{pmatrix}2\\1\\-4\end{pmatrix}$, and $\boldsymbol{d} = \begin{pmatrix}6\\0\\-1\end{pmatrix}$, so $(-\boldsymbol{c}+\boldsymbol{d}) = \begin{pmatrix}4\\-1\\3\end{pmatrix}$ then the shortest distance between the lines is given by

$$\mathbf{CD}\cdot\hat{\boldsymbol{a}} = \begin{pmatrix}4\\-1\\3\end{pmatrix}\cdot\frac{1}{\sqrt{18}}\begin{pmatrix}4\\1\\1\end{pmatrix} = \frac{1}{\sqrt{18}}(18) = \sqrt{18}$$

Example 3

Find the shortest distance between the two lines

$$\boldsymbol{x} = \begin{pmatrix}2\\3\\-5\end{pmatrix} + t\begin{pmatrix}3\\2\\-4\end{pmatrix} = \boldsymbol{a}+t\boldsymbol{l}$$

and

$$\boldsymbol{x} = \begin{pmatrix}3\\-1\\4\end{pmatrix} + s\begin{pmatrix}5\\-2\\-4\end{pmatrix} = \boldsymbol{b}+s\boldsymbol{m}$$

The common perpendicular $\boldsymbol{e}$ is given by

$$\boldsymbol{e} = \begin{pmatrix}3\\2\\-4\end{pmatrix}\times\begin{pmatrix}5\\-2\\-4\end{pmatrix} = \begin{pmatrix}-16\\-8\\-16\end{pmatrix} = 8\begin{pmatrix}-2\\-1\\-2\end{pmatrix}$$

and

$$\hat{\boldsymbol{e}} = \frac{1}{3}\begin{pmatrix}-2\\-1\\-2\end{pmatrix}$$

The line joining any point on the first line to any point on the second line can be taken as

$$\boldsymbol{AB} = -\boldsymbol{a}+\boldsymbol{b} = \begin{pmatrix}1\\-4\\9\end{pmatrix}$$

Hence the shortest distance is

$$\begin{pmatrix}1\\-4\\9\end{pmatrix}\cdot\frac{1}{3}\begin{pmatrix}-2\\-1\\-2\end{pmatrix} = \tfrac{1}{3}(-2+4-18) = -\tfrac{16}{3}$$

Exercise 2.1

1 Find the distances of the points P(5, 2, −1) and Q(−5, 1, 3) from the plane through R(1, 1, 1) with DRN $\begin{pmatrix} 2 \\ -1 \\ 2 \end{pmatrix}$. Explain the difference in sign.

2 Find the distance of the point P(1, 1, 1) from the line

$$\boldsymbol{x} = \begin{pmatrix} 2 \\ -1 \\ 3 \end{pmatrix} + t\begin{pmatrix} 4 \\ 1 \\ -2 \end{pmatrix}$$

3 Four points in space have position vectors $\boldsymbol{a}$, $\boldsymbol{b}$, $\boldsymbol{c}$ and $\boldsymbol{d}$ with

$$\boldsymbol{a}^{\mathrm{T}} = (1\ \ 1\ \ 0), \qquad \boldsymbol{b}^{\mathrm{T}} = (3\ \ 0\ \ 1), \qquad \boldsymbol{c}^{\mathrm{T}} = (1\ \ 0\ \ 2), \qquad \boldsymbol{d}^{\mathrm{T}} = (1\ \ 1\ \ 3).$$

Find the equations of two parallel planes, of which one contains A and B, and the other contains C and D. Deduce the shortest distance between the planes.

4 Find the projection of the line

$$\boldsymbol{x} = \begin{pmatrix} 10 \\ 4 \\ 2 \end{pmatrix} + t\begin{pmatrix} 9 \\ -1 \\ 0 \end{pmatrix}$$

on the plane

$$\boldsymbol{x} \cdot \begin{pmatrix} 3 \\ -1 \\ 2 \end{pmatrix} = 2$$

5 Find the equation of the projection on the plane

$$\boldsymbol{x} \cdot \begin{pmatrix} 6 \\ -3 \\ 2 \end{pmatrix} = 6$$

of the line of intersection of the two planes

$$\boldsymbol{x} \cdot \begin{pmatrix} 1 \\ 1 \\ 2 \end{pmatrix} = 3 \qquad \text{and} \qquad \boldsymbol{x} \cdot \begin{pmatrix} 3 \\ 1 \\ 3 \end{pmatrix} = 4$$

6 Find the distance of P, (3, 1, −1) from the line

$$\boldsymbol{x} = \begin{pmatrix} 1 \\ 0 \\ 3 \end{pmatrix} + t\begin{pmatrix} -1 \\ 2 \\ 0 \end{pmatrix}$$

7 Find the distance of Q, (2, 1, −2) from the plane

$$\left[x - \begin{pmatrix} 2 \\ 0 \\ -1 \end{pmatrix}\right] \cdot \begin{pmatrix} 1 \\ 2 \\ 1 \end{pmatrix} = 0$$

8 Find the shortest distance between the two lines

$$x = \begin{pmatrix} 3 \\ 3 \\ -4 \end{pmatrix} + t\begin{pmatrix} 1 \\ -2 \\ -3 \end{pmatrix} \quad \text{and} \quad x = \begin{pmatrix} -3 \\ -1 \\ 2 \end{pmatrix} + s\begin{pmatrix} -2 \\ 1 \\ 3 \end{pmatrix}$$

9 Find the shortest distances between the pairs of skew lines in Exercise 1.3, page 612.

2.2 Angles between lines and planes

The angle between two vectors can be found from their dot product since

$$\boldsymbol{a} \cdot \boldsymbol{b} = |\boldsymbol{a}||\boldsymbol{b}| \cos \theta \qquad \text{and so} \qquad \cos \theta = \frac{\boldsymbol{a} \cdot \boldsymbol{b}}{|\boldsymbol{a}||\boldsymbol{b}|}$$

There are *two* angles between a line and a plane or between two planes, one acute and the other obtuse (except in the special case of perpendicularity). Normally, the *acute* angle is given, so we use

$$\cos \theta = \left|\frac{\boldsymbol{a} \cdot \boldsymbol{b}}{|\boldsymbol{a}||\boldsymbol{b}|}\right|$$

We can find the angle between two lines, or a line and a plane or between two planes, given their vector equations.

Example 1

Find the angle between the line

$$x = \begin{pmatrix} 1 \\ 2 \\ 3 \end{pmatrix} + t\begin{pmatrix} 2 \\ 3 \\ 1 \end{pmatrix}$$

and the plane

$$x = \lambda\begin{pmatrix} 2 \\ -1 \\ 0 \end{pmatrix} + \mu\begin{pmatrix} 1 \\ 0 \\ 2 \end{pmatrix}$$

The line has DR $\begin{pmatrix} 2 \\ 3 \\ 1 \end{pmatrix}$ and the plane contains the vectors $\begin{pmatrix} 2 \\ -1 \\ 0 \end{pmatrix}$ and $\begin{pmatrix} 1 \\ 0 \\ 2 \end{pmatrix}$ and therefore its DRN is given by their cross product

$$\begin{pmatrix}2\\-1\\0\end{pmatrix} \times \begin{pmatrix}1\\0\\2\end{pmatrix} = \begin{pmatrix}-2\\-4\\1\end{pmatrix}$$

The angle between the line and the *normal* to the plane is θ, where

$$\cos\theta = \frac{\begin{pmatrix}2\\3\\1\end{pmatrix}\cdot\begin{pmatrix}-2\\-4\\1\end{pmatrix}}{\sqrt{(2^2+3^2+1^2)}\sqrt{(2^2+4^2+1^2)}} = \frac{-4-12+1}{\sqrt{14}\sqrt{21}}$$

$$\cos\theta = \frac{-15}{7\sqrt{6}}$$

so $$\theta = 29°$$

The angle between the line and the plane is then $90-\theta = 61°$.

Exercise 2.2

1 Find the angle between the lines

$$\boldsymbol{x} = \begin{pmatrix}3\\3\\4\end{pmatrix} + t\begin{pmatrix}2\\4\\1\end{pmatrix} \quad \text{and} \quad \boldsymbol{x} = \begin{pmatrix}0\\0\\2\end{pmatrix} + s\begin{pmatrix}1\\2\\2\end{pmatrix}$$

2 Find the angle between the skew lines

$$\boldsymbol{x} = \begin{pmatrix}-2\\0\\6\end{pmatrix} + s\begin{pmatrix}1\\2\\-1\end{pmatrix} \quad \text{and} \quad \boldsymbol{x} = \begin{pmatrix}-5\\0\\0\end{pmatrix} + t\begin{pmatrix}1\\-1\\2\end{pmatrix}$$

3 Find the angle between the line

$$\boldsymbol{x} = \begin{pmatrix}2\\0\\5\end{pmatrix} + t\begin{pmatrix}3\\12\\4\end{pmatrix} \quad \text{and the plane} \quad \boldsymbol{x}\cdot\begin{pmatrix}-1\\2\\2\end{pmatrix} = 66$$

4 Find the angle between the planes

$$\boldsymbol{x}\cdot\begin{pmatrix}1\\3\\-1\end{pmatrix} = 4 \quad \text{and} \quad \boldsymbol{x}\cdot\begin{pmatrix}2\\-1\\1\end{pmatrix} = 10$$

5 Find two unit vectors in the plane $z = 0$ which make an angle of $\cos^{-1}(2/\sqrt{5})$ with the vector $2\boldsymbol{i}-\boldsymbol{j}$.

6 Find the equations of the two planes which intersect the $z = 0$ plane in the line $y = x$ and make an angle of 60° with it.

7 Find the equation of the plane through the origin and the point (0, 1, 0) which makes an angle of 30° with the plane $\boldsymbol{x} \cdot \begin{pmatrix}1\\1\\1\end{pmatrix} = 3$.

8 Show that the three planes $\boldsymbol{x} \cdot \begin{pmatrix}0\\1\\-1\end{pmatrix} = 1$, $\boldsymbol{x} \cdot \begin{pmatrix}1\\0\\-1\end{pmatrix} = -1$ and $\boldsymbol{x} \cdot \begin{pmatrix}1\\-1\\0\end{pmatrix} = 1$ intersect the plane $\boldsymbol{x} \cdot \begin{pmatrix}1\\1\\1\end{pmatrix} = 0$ in three lines which are the sides of an equilateral triangle.

2.3 Areas and volumes

The area of a parallelogram

From the definition of cross product (page 601) we know that if

$$\boldsymbol{r} = \boldsymbol{p} \times \boldsymbol{q} = \begin{pmatrix}p_1\\p_2\\p_3\end{pmatrix} \times \begin{pmatrix}q_1\\q_2\\q_3\end{pmatrix} = \begin{pmatrix}p_2q_3-p_3q_2\\p_3q_1-p_1q_3\\p_1q_2-p_2q_1\end{pmatrix}$$

then **OR** is perpendicular to both **OP** and **OQ**

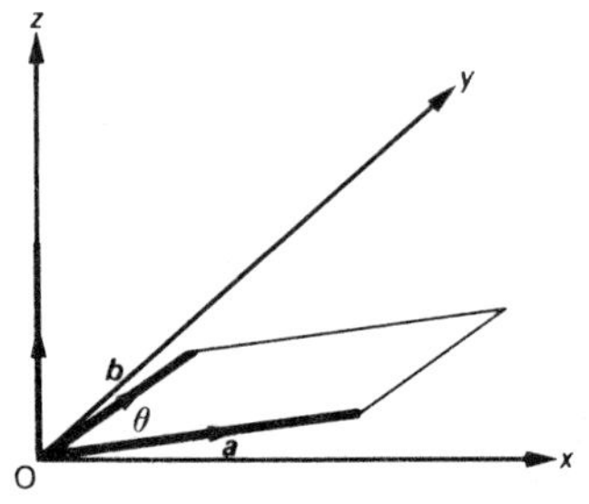

Now if $\boldsymbol{a}$ and $\boldsymbol{b}$ are in the plane $z = 0$, the area of the parallelogram formed by them is given by the determinant of the matrix

$$(\boldsymbol{a} \quad \boldsymbol{b}) = \begin{pmatrix}a_1 & b_1\\a_2 & b_2\end{pmatrix}$$

$$\det(\boldsymbol{a} \quad \boldsymbol{b}) = \begin{vmatrix}a_1 & b_1\\a_2 & b_2\end{vmatrix} = a_1b_2 - a_2b_1$$

NOTE. The symbol for the determinant of a matrix (the pair of vertical lines) is similar to that for the length or modulus of a vector, but the context should make the meaning clear in each case.

However, the area of the parallelogram is also $ab \sin\theta$ and hence

$$ab \sin\theta = a_1b_2 - a_2b_1$$

If $$\boldsymbol{a} = \begin{pmatrix} a_1 \\ a_2 \\ 0 \end{pmatrix} \text{ and } \boldsymbol{b} = \begin{pmatrix} b_1 \\ b_2 \\ 0 \end{pmatrix} \text{ then } \boldsymbol{a}\times\boldsymbol{b} = \begin{pmatrix} 0 \\ 0 \\ a_1b_2 - a_2b_1 \end{pmatrix}$$

so $$|\boldsymbol{a}\times\boldsymbol{b}| = a_1b_2 - a_2b_1 = ab\sin\theta$$

i.e. $\boldsymbol{a}\times\boldsymbol{b}$ is a vector perpendicular to the plane of $\boldsymbol{a}$ and $\boldsymbol{b}$ whose length is equal to the area of the parallelogram.

We consider now whether $|\boldsymbol{a}\times\boldsymbol{b}| = ab\sin\theta$ is still true if $\boldsymbol{a}$ and $\boldsymbol{b}$ are not in the plane $z = 0$.

For example, suppose $\boldsymbol{a} = \begin{pmatrix} 3 \\ 1 \\ 2 \end{pmatrix}$, $\boldsymbol{b} = \begin{pmatrix} 2 \\ -1 \\ 0 \end{pmatrix}$

$$\boldsymbol{a}\times\boldsymbol{b} = \begin{pmatrix} 3 \\ 1 \\ 2 \end{pmatrix} \times \begin{pmatrix} 2 \\ -1 \\ 0 \end{pmatrix} = \begin{pmatrix} 2 \\ 4 \\ -5 \end{pmatrix}$$

This vector has a length

$$|\boldsymbol{a}\times\boldsymbol{b}| = \sqrt{(4+16+25)} = \sqrt{45}$$

$$|\boldsymbol{n}| = \sqrt{45}$$

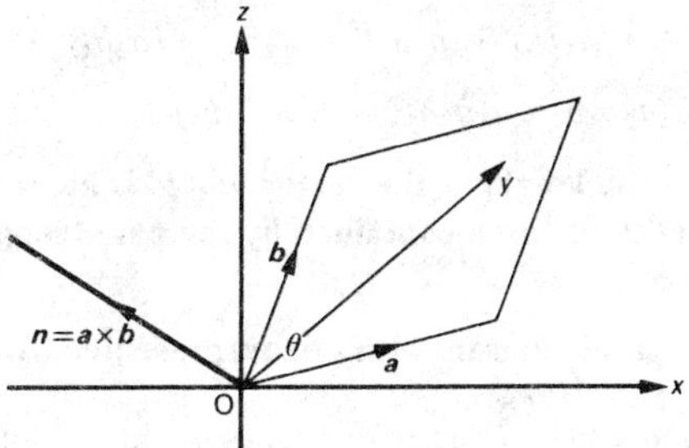

We hope to show that the area of the parallelogram is $\sqrt{45}$. Since the area is $ab\sin\theta$ and

$$a = |\boldsymbol{a}| = \sqrt{(3^2+1^2+2^2)} = \sqrt{14},$$
$$b = |\boldsymbol{b}| = \sqrt{(2^2+(-1)^2+0)} = \sqrt{5}$$

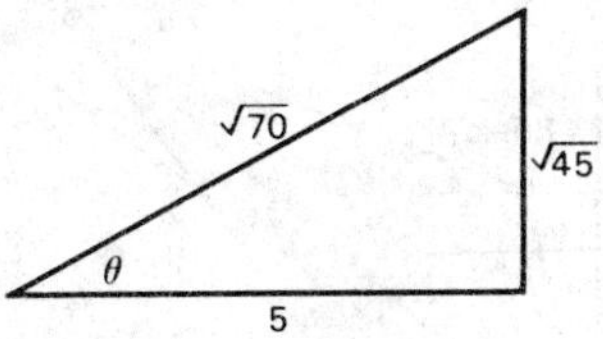

$$\cos\theta = \frac{\boldsymbol{a}\cdot\boldsymbol{b}}{\sqrt{14}\sqrt{5}} = \frac{3\times2+1\times-1+2\times0}{\sqrt{70}} = \frac{5}{\sqrt{70}}$$

so $$\sin\theta = \frac{\surd 45}{\surd 70} \qquad \text{(since } \sin^2\theta + \cos^2\theta = 1\text{)}$$

The area is $$\surd 14 \surd 5 \frac{\surd 45}{\surd 70} = \surd 45$$

So again $|\boldsymbol{a}\times\boldsymbol{b}|$ = area of the parallelogram = $ab \sin\theta$ and in general this is true, as we now show. The length of the vector squared is given by

$$\begin{aligned}|\boldsymbol{a}\times\boldsymbol{b}|^2 &= (a_2b_3 - a_3b_2)^2 + (a_3b_1 - a_1b_3)^2 + (a_1b_2 - a_2b_1)^2\\ &= (a_2b_3)^2 + (a_3b_2)^2 + (a_3b_1)^2 + (a_1b_3)^2 + (a_1b_2)^2 + (a_2b_1)^2\\ &\quad - 2(a_2a_3b_2b_3 + a_3a_1b_1b_3 + a_1a_2b_1b_2)\end{aligned}$$

Also the area, squared is

$$\begin{aligned}a^2b^2\sin^2\theta &= a^2b^2(1-\cos^2\theta)\\ &= (a_1^2+a_2^2+a_3^2)(b_1^2+b_2^2+b_3^2)\left[1 - \frac{(a_1b_1+a_2b_2+a_3b_3)^2}{a^2b^2}\right]\end{aligned}$$

$$\text{since } \cos\theta = \frac{a_1b_1+a_2b_2+a_3b_3}{ab}$$

$$\begin{aligned}&= (a_1b_1)^2 + (a_2b_2)^2 + (a_3b_3)^2 + (a_1b_2)^2 + (a_1b_3)^2 + (a_2b_1)^2 + (a_2b_3)^2\\ &\quad + (a_3b_1)^2 + (a_3b_2)^2 - [(a_1b_1)^2 + (a_2b_2)^2 + (a_3b_3)^2\\ &\quad + 2(a_1a_2b_1b_2 + a_1a_3b_1b_3 + a_2a_3b_2b_3)]\\ &= (a_1b_2)^2 + (a_1b_3)^2 + (a_2b_1)^2 + (a_2b_3)^2 + (a_3b_1)^2 + (a_3b_2)^2\\ &\quad - 2(a_1a_2b_1b_2 + a_1a_3b_1b_3 + a_2a_3b_2b_3)\end{aligned}$$

Hence the length of the vector $|\boldsymbol{a}\times\boldsymbol{b}|$ is numerically equal to the area contained by the parallelogram. ◀

To recap,

(i) the area of the parallelogram with sides represented by $\boldsymbol{a}$, $\boldsymbol{b}$ can be calculated as $|\boldsymbol{a}\times\boldsymbol{b}|$

(ii) $(\boldsymbol{a}\times\boldsymbol{b})$ has a length equal to the area of the parallelogram and is perpendicular to the plane of it. I.e. $\boldsymbol{a}\times\boldsymbol{b} = ab\sin\theta\hat{\boldsymbol{n}}$ where $\hat{\boldsymbol{n}}$ is the unit vector perpendicular to the plane of $\boldsymbol{a}$ and $\boldsymbol{b}$.

The area of a triangle formed by joining three points not coplanar with the origin

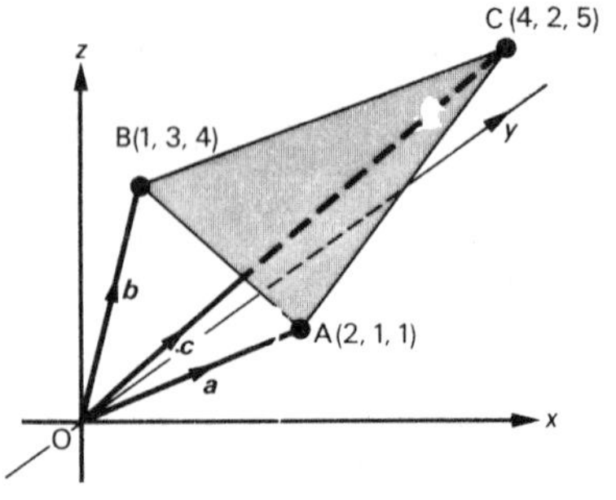

The area of the triangle ABC, for example,

$$= \tfrac{1}{2}\text{AB} \times \text{AC} \sin \text{CAB}$$

$$= \tfrac{1}{2}|\boldsymbol{AB} \times \boldsymbol{AC}|$$

$$= \tfrac{1}{2}|(\boldsymbol{b} - \boldsymbol{a}) \times (\boldsymbol{c} - \boldsymbol{a})|$$

Here

$$\boldsymbol{a} = \begin{pmatrix} 2 \\ 1 \\ 1 \end{pmatrix}, \boldsymbol{b} = \begin{pmatrix} 1 \\ 3 \\ 4 \end{pmatrix}, \boldsymbol{c} = \begin{pmatrix} 4 \\ 2 \\ 5 \end{pmatrix},$$

$$\boldsymbol{b} - \boldsymbol{a} = \begin{pmatrix} -1 \\ 2 \\ 3 \end{pmatrix} \text{ and } \boldsymbol{c} - \boldsymbol{a} = \begin{pmatrix} 2 \\ 1 \\ 4 \end{pmatrix}.$$

So the area of the triangle is

$$\frac{1}{2}\left|\begin{pmatrix} -1 \\ 2 \\ 3 \end{pmatrix} \times \begin{pmatrix} 2 \\ 1 \\ 4 \end{pmatrix}\right| = \frac{1}{2}\left|\begin{pmatrix} 5 \\ 10 \\ -5 \end{pmatrix}\right| = \frac{5}{2}\sqrt{6}$$

Also the normal to the plane of the triangle ABC is given by

$$\boldsymbol{n} = (\boldsymbol{b} - \boldsymbol{a}) \times (\boldsymbol{c} - \boldsymbol{a})$$

So $$\tfrac{1}{2}\boldsymbol{n} = \frac{1}{2}\begin{pmatrix} 5 \\ 10 \\ -5 \end{pmatrix}$$

which is a vector of length equal to the area of the triangle.

The volume of a parallelepiped

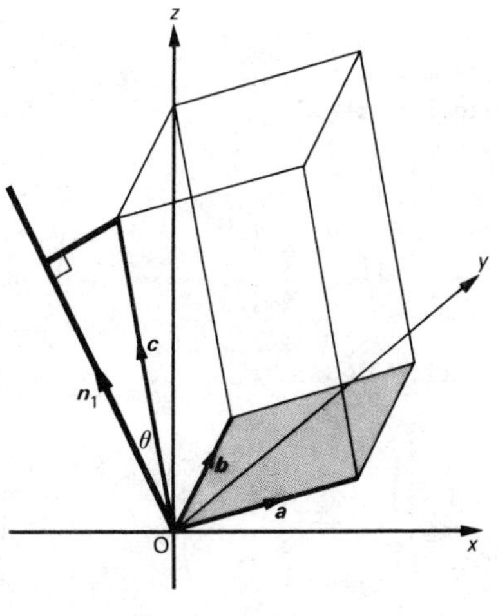

Consider the parallelepiped with sides represented by $\boldsymbol{a}$, $\boldsymbol{b}$ and $\boldsymbol{c}$, and suppose $\boldsymbol{a} = \begin{pmatrix} 1 \\ 2 \\ 1 \end{pmatrix}$, $\boldsymbol{b} = \begin{pmatrix} 0 \\ 1 \\ 1 \end{pmatrix}$, $\boldsymbol{c} = \begin{pmatrix} -4 \\ 6 \\ 3 \end{pmatrix}$. The volume is given by

$$\text{base area} \times \text{perpendicular height.}$$

Now the area of the base parallelogram formed by $\boldsymbol{a}$ and $\boldsymbol{b}$ and shaded in the figure is $|\boldsymbol{a} \times \boldsymbol{b}| = |\boldsymbol{n}|$ where

$$\boldsymbol{n} = \boldsymbol{a} \times \boldsymbol{b} = \begin{pmatrix} 1 \\ 2 \\ 1 \end{pmatrix} \times \begin{pmatrix} 0 \\ 1 \\ 1 \end{pmatrix} = \begin{pmatrix} 1 \\ -1 \\ 1 \end{pmatrix}$$

If θ is the angle between $\boldsymbol{c}$ and $\boldsymbol{n}$, then the perpendicular height of the prism is $|\boldsymbol{c}| \cos \theta$. Hence the volume is

$$\begin{aligned} \mathrm{V} &= |\boldsymbol{n}||\boldsymbol{c}| \cos \theta \\ &= \boldsymbol{n} \cdot \boldsymbol{c} \\ &= (\boldsymbol{a} \times \boldsymbol{b}) \cdot \boldsymbol{c} \\ &= \begin{pmatrix} 1 \\ -1 \\ 1 \end{pmatrix} \cdot \begin{pmatrix} -4 \\ 6 \\ 3 \end{pmatrix} = -7 \end{aligned}$$

We could equally well have found the volume by considering $\boldsymbol{b}$ and $\boldsymbol{c}$, or $\boldsymbol{a}$ and $\boldsymbol{c}$ as the base. Hence

$$\textbf{Volume} = (\boldsymbol{a} \times \boldsymbol{b}) \cdot \boldsymbol{c} = (\boldsymbol{b} \times \boldsymbol{c}) \cdot \boldsymbol{a} = (\boldsymbol{c} \times \boldsymbol{a}) \cdot \boldsymbol{b}$$ ◀

Exercise 2.3

1 Find the area of triangle OAB where

$$\boldsymbol{a} = \begin{pmatrix} 4 \\ 3 \\ -1 \end{pmatrix} \quad \text{and} \quad \boldsymbol{b} = \begin{pmatrix} -2 \\ 4 \\ 1 \end{pmatrix}.$$

2 Find the area of triangle ABC where

$$\boldsymbol{a} = \begin{pmatrix} 4 \\ 3 \\ -1 \end{pmatrix}, \quad \boldsymbol{b} = \begin{pmatrix} -2 \\ 4 \\ 1 \end{pmatrix}, \quad \boldsymbol{c} = \begin{pmatrix} 3 \\ 1 \\ 2 \end{pmatrix}$$

3

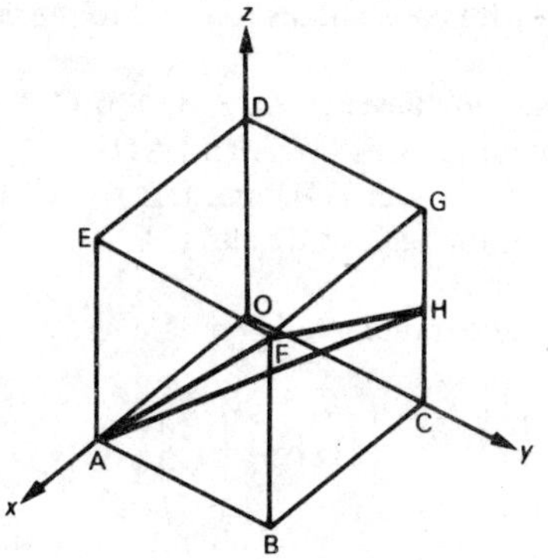

The diagram shows a cube of side 2 units. H is the mid point of GC.

(a) By forming the cross product of AF and AH, calculate the area of the triangle AFH.

(b) What is the angle $F\hat{H}A$?

4

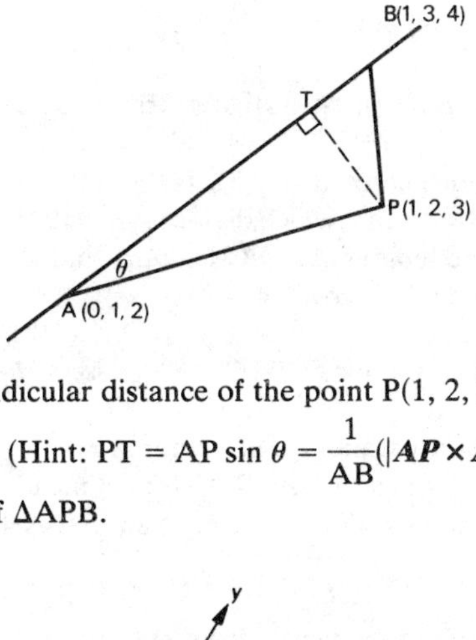

(a) Find the perpendicular distance of the point P(1, 2, 3) from the line joining A(0, 1, 2) to B(1, 3, 4). (Hint: $\text{PT} = \text{AP} \sin\theta = \frac{1}{\text{AB}}(|\boldsymbol{AP} \times \boldsymbol{AB}|)$.

(b) Find the area of ΔAPB.

5

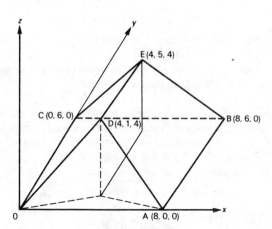

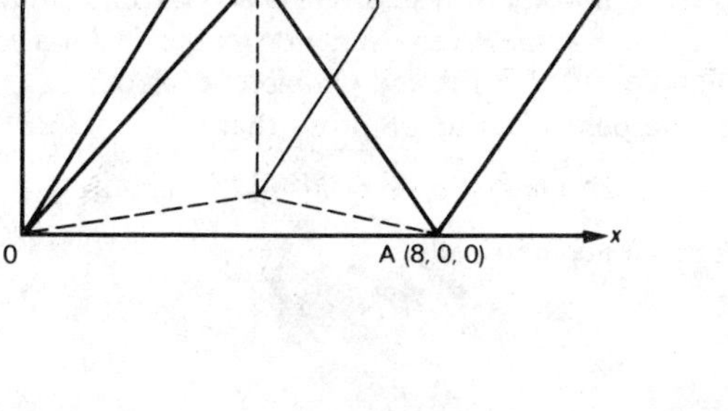

The diagram is of a roof with coordinates referred to the corner O, units are metres. Find

(a) the area of the sloping faces ODA and ODEC
(b) the angle between the faces ODA and ADEB
(c) the angle between the edges OD and DB
(d) the angle between the edges OD and CA

6 Find the volume of the parallelepiped contained by

(i) $\boldsymbol{a}, \boldsymbol{b}, \boldsymbol{c}$, with $\boldsymbol{a} = \begin{pmatrix} 1 \\ 1 \\ 1 \end{pmatrix}, \boldsymbol{b} = \begin{pmatrix} 1 \\ 2 \\ 1 \end{pmatrix}, \boldsymbol{c} = \begin{pmatrix} 1 \\ 3 \\ -1 \end{pmatrix}$

(ii) $\boldsymbol{a}, \boldsymbol{b}, \boldsymbol{d}$ with $\boldsymbol{a} = \begin{pmatrix} 1 \\ 1 \\ 1 \end{pmatrix}, \boldsymbol{b} = \begin{pmatrix} 1 \\ 2 \\ 1 \end{pmatrix}, \boldsymbol{d} = \begin{pmatrix} 0 \\ -4 \\ 6 \end{pmatrix}$

(iii) $\boldsymbol{a}, \boldsymbol{c}, \boldsymbol{d}$ (as in parts **(i)** and **(ii)**)
(iv) $\boldsymbol{b}, \boldsymbol{c}, \boldsymbol{d}$ (as in parts **(i)** and **(ii)**)

Miscellaneous examination questions 16

1 A, B, C, D have coordinates (0, 1, 3), (4, 5, −5), (−3, 0, −1) and (7, 5, 4) respectively. Show that the point P which divides AB in the ratio 1 : 3 also divides CD in the ratio 2 : 3. Find the lengths AP, PC and CA and show that the acute angle between the lines AB and CD is $\cos^{-1}(\frac{1}{6})$ (C.)

2 The position vectors of points A, B, C are $\boldsymbol{a} = 4\boldsymbol{i} - 9\boldsymbol{j} - \boldsymbol{k}$, $\boldsymbol{b} = \boldsymbol{i} + 3\boldsymbol{j} + 5\boldsymbol{k}$ and $\boldsymbol{c} = p\boldsymbol{i} - \boldsymbol{j} + 3\boldsymbol{k}$

(a) Find the unit vector parallel to the vector $\boldsymbol{AB}$.
(b) Find the value of p such that A, B, C are collinear.
(c) If $p = -2$, find the position vector of D so that ABCD is a parallelogram. (W.)

3 In a triangle ABC the perpendicular from B to the side AC meets the perpendicular from C to the side AB at H. The position vectors of A, B, and C relative to H are $\boldsymbol{a}$, $\boldsymbol{b}$ and $\boldsymbol{c}$ respectively. Express $\boldsymbol{CA}$ in terms of $\boldsymbol{a}$ and $\boldsymbol{c}$ and deduce that $\boldsymbol{a} \cdot \boldsymbol{b} = \boldsymbol{b} \cdot \boldsymbol{c}$. Prove that AH is perpendicular to BC. (J.M.B.)

4 The points A, B, C, D (which are not necessarily coplanar) have position vectors $\boldsymbol{a}, \boldsymbol{b}, \boldsymbol{c}, \boldsymbol{d}$ respectively, with respect to an origin O and the mid points of AB, BC, CD and DA are P, Q, R and S respectively. Write down the position vectors of P and Q with respect to O and prove that PR and QS bisect each other.

Given that PR is perpendicular to QS prove that

$$|\boldsymbol{a}|^2 + |\boldsymbol{c}|^2 - 2\boldsymbol{a} \cdot \boldsymbol{c} = |\boldsymbol{b}|^2 + |\boldsymbol{d}|^2 - 2\boldsymbol{b} \cdot \boldsymbol{d}$$

and interpret this result geometrically. (J.M.B.)

5 The position vectors of the points A, B, C with respect to the origin O are respectively $2\boldsymbol{j}+2\boldsymbol{k}$, $2\boldsymbol{i}+\boldsymbol{j}$, $2\boldsymbol{i}+5\boldsymbol{j}-4\boldsymbol{k}$. Calculate the angle ABC and the area of the triangle ABC. Obtain vector equations of the planes ABC and OAB and find the acute angle between the planes. Find also the volume of the tetrahedron OABC. (L.)

6 If $\boldsymbol{u} = a\boldsymbol{i}+b\boldsymbol{j}+c\boldsymbol{k}$ where $\boldsymbol{i}, \boldsymbol{j}, \boldsymbol{k}$ are mutually perpendicular unit vectors, show that $a = \boldsymbol{u}\cdot\boldsymbol{i}$, $b = \boldsymbol{u}\cdot\boldsymbol{j}$ and $c = \boldsymbol{u}\cdot\boldsymbol{k}$.

$$\text{If } \boldsymbol{u} = \frac{1}{\sqrt{3}}(\boldsymbol{i}+\boldsymbol{j}+\boldsymbol{k}) \qquad \boldsymbol{v} = \sqrt{\tfrac{2}{3}}(\boldsymbol{i}-\tfrac{1}{2}\boldsymbol{j}-\tfrac{1}{2}\boldsymbol{k}) \qquad \text{and} \qquad \boldsymbol{w} = \frac{1}{\sqrt{2}}(\boldsymbol{j}-\boldsymbol{k})$$

show that $\boldsymbol{u}$, $\boldsymbol{v}$ and $\boldsymbol{w}$ are mutually perpendicular unit vectors and express $\boldsymbol{i}$ in the form $p\boldsymbol{u}+q\boldsymbol{v}+r\boldsymbol{w}$. (J.M.B.)

7 (a) The three points A, B and C are given by position vectors $\boldsymbol{a}, \boldsymbol{b}, \boldsymbol{c}$ relative to an origin O. D is the mid point of BC. Find the vector $\boldsymbol{OA}+\tfrac{2}{3}\boldsymbol{AD}$ in terms of $\boldsymbol{a}, \boldsymbol{b}, \boldsymbol{c}$, and deduce that the medians of a triangle are concurrent.

(b) Given two vectors $\boldsymbol{p}^{\mathrm{T}} = (3 \quad -12 \quad 4)$ and $\boldsymbol{q}^{\mathrm{T}} = (1 \quad 0 \quad -1)$, find (i) the angle between them and (ii) a vector at right angles to both of them. (M.E.I.)

8 Two points P and Q have position vectors, with respect to an origin O given by $2\boldsymbol{i}-3\boldsymbol{j}+\boldsymbol{k}$ and $3\boldsymbol{i}-\boldsymbol{j}+2\boldsymbol{k}$ respectively. Calculate angle POQ. (A.E.B.)

9 Show that the equation of a plane can be expressed in the form $\boldsymbol{r}\cdot\boldsymbol{n} = p$. Find the equation of the plane through the origin parallel to the lines

$$\boldsymbol{r} = 3\boldsymbol{i}+3\boldsymbol{j}-\boldsymbol{k}+s(\boldsymbol{i}-\boldsymbol{j}-2\boldsymbol{k}) \qquad \text{and} \qquad \boldsymbol{r} = 4\boldsymbol{i}-5\boldsymbol{j}-8\boldsymbol{k}+t(3\boldsymbol{i}+7\boldsymbol{j}-6\boldsymbol{k})$$

Show that one of the lines lies in the plane, and find the distance of the other line from the plane.

Find the shortest distance between the straight lines with vector equations $\boldsymbol{r} = -3\boldsymbol{i}+5s(\boldsymbol{j}+\boldsymbol{k})$, $\boldsymbol{r} = 3\boldsymbol{i}-2\boldsymbol{j}+\boldsymbol{k}+t(-\boldsymbol{i}+2\boldsymbol{j}-\boldsymbol{k})$. (L.)

10 Find the unit vectors which are perpendicular to both of the vectors $\boldsymbol{j}+4\boldsymbol{k}$ and $3\boldsymbol{i}+2\boldsymbol{j}+4\boldsymbol{k}$. Find also the angles between these unit vectors and the vector $\tfrac{1}{2}(\boldsymbol{i}-\boldsymbol{j}-\boldsymbol{k})$. (J.M.B.)

11(a) If $\boldsymbol{a} = \boldsymbol{i}-2\boldsymbol{j}$, $\boldsymbol{b} = 2\boldsymbol{i}+5\boldsymbol{j}-4\boldsymbol{k}$ find unit vectors in the directions of the internal and external angle bisectors of the angle between $\boldsymbol{a}$ and $\boldsymbol{b}$.

(b) If $\boldsymbol{OP} = 2\boldsymbol{i}-3\boldsymbol{j}+\boldsymbol{k}$, $\boldsymbol{OQ} = 3\boldsymbol{i}+2\boldsymbol{j}-3\boldsymbol{k}$ find $\boldsymbol{OP}\times\boldsymbol{OQ}$. Hence or otherwise, find the area of the triangle OPQ and show that the area of the orthogonal projection of the triangle OPQ on the plane $y = 0$ is $4\tfrac{1}{2}$ units of area. (L.)

12 If the position vectors of points P and Q with respect to O as origin are $\boldsymbol{p}$ and $\boldsymbol{q}$ respectively, show that the area of the triangle OPQ is $\tfrac{1}{2}|\boldsymbol{p}\times\boldsymbol{q}|$.

The position vectors of the vertices A, B, C of a tetrahedron OABC with respect to O as origin are

$$\boldsymbol{OA} = 2\boldsymbol{i}-\boldsymbol{j}, \qquad \boldsymbol{OB} = \boldsymbol{j}+\boldsymbol{k}, \qquad \boldsymbol{OC} = \boldsymbol{i}+3\boldsymbol{j}-\boldsymbol{k}$$

Find the angle between (**a**) the edges AB, AC (**b**) the faces OAB, OAC. Prove that BC is perpendicular to the plane OAB and hence prove that the volume of OABC is $\frac{3}{2}$. (L.)

13 The position vectors of points A, B, C, D are respectively $\boldsymbol{i}-3\boldsymbol{k}$, $-2\boldsymbol{i}+2\boldsymbol{j}+\boldsymbol{k}$, $-\boldsymbol{j}+4\boldsymbol{k}$ and $3\boldsymbol{i}-3\boldsymbol{j}$. Find in vector form the equations of the lines AC and BD and prove that these lines meet in a point P.

Prove that ABCD is a rectangle and find the vector equation of the line through P perpendicular to the plane ABCD. (L.)

14(a) Find the values of the scalar α if the two vectors $\boldsymbol{p}^{\mathrm{T}} = (2 \quad -3 \quad 5)$ and $\boldsymbol{q}^{\mathrm{T}} = (3 \quad \alpha \quad -3)$ are inclined to each other at an angle of (i) $\frac{1}{2}\pi$, (ii) $\frac{2}{3}\pi$.

(**b**) The points A, B, C, D have position vectors $\boldsymbol{a}$, $\boldsymbol{b}$, $\boldsymbol{c}$ and $\boldsymbol{d}$ respectively with respect to a fixed origin and

$$(\boldsymbol{d}-\boldsymbol{a})\cdot(\boldsymbol{b}-\boldsymbol{c}) = 0 = (\boldsymbol{d}-\boldsymbol{b})\cdot(\boldsymbol{c}-\boldsymbol{a})$$

Show that

$$(\boldsymbol{d}-\boldsymbol{c})\cdot(\boldsymbol{a}-\boldsymbol{b}) = 0$$

Interpret this result geometrically when the points A, B, C and D are coplanar. (M.E.I.)

15 Explain how the vector equations $\boldsymbol{r} = \boldsymbol{a}+t\boldsymbol{b}$ and $\boldsymbol{r}\cdot\boldsymbol{n} = p$ represent a straight line and a plane respectively, interpreting the symbols geometrically and using sketches if you wish.

Prove that, provided $\boldsymbol{b}\cdot\boldsymbol{n} \neq 0$, the line and the plane intersect in a point whose position vector is

$$\boldsymbol{a}+\left(\frac{p-\boldsymbol{a}\cdot\boldsymbol{n}}{\boldsymbol{b}\cdot\boldsymbol{n}}\right)\boldsymbol{b}$$

(J.M.B.)

16 O, A, B and C are the vertices of a tetrahedron. The position vectors of A, B and C with respect to O are $\boldsymbol{a}$, $\boldsymbol{b}$, and $\boldsymbol{c}$ respectively. X, Y, Z are the mid points of OA, OB and OC, and X′, Y′ and Z′ are the mid points of BC, CA and AB respectively. G is the mid point of XX′. Find OG in terms of $\boldsymbol{a}$, $\boldsymbol{b}$ and $\boldsymbol{c}$, and deduce that XX′, YY′ and ZZ′ are concurrent at G.

Prove by vector methods that the lines joining O, A, B and C to the centroids of the opposite faces are also concurrent at G. (J.M.B.)

17 The vectors $\boldsymbol{p} = 3\boldsymbol{i}+4\boldsymbol{k}$ and $\boldsymbol{q} = 12\boldsymbol{i}+5\boldsymbol{j}$ are expressed in terms of unit vectors $\boldsymbol{i}$, $\boldsymbol{j}$ and $\boldsymbol{k}$ in the directions of the axes Ox, Oy, Oz, respectively. Find

(**a**) the vector $2\boldsymbol{p}-3\boldsymbol{q}$

(**b**) unit vectors in the directions of $\boldsymbol{p}$ and $\boldsymbol{q}$

(**c**) the cosine of the angle between the vectors $\boldsymbol{p}$ and $\boldsymbol{q}$

(**d**) the cosine of the angle between the vector $\boldsymbol{p}$ and the z axis

Calculate the value of α such that $(\boldsymbol{p}+\alpha\boldsymbol{q})\cdot\boldsymbol{q} = 0$ and write down the equation of the plane through the origin normal to the vector $\boldsymbol{p}+\alpha\boldsymbol{q}$. (M.E.I.)

18(a) If $\boldsymbol{a} = 5\boldsymbol{i}-\boldsymbol{j}-3\boldsymbol{k}$, and $\boldsymbol{b} = \boldsymbol{i}+3\boldsymbol{j}-5\boldsymbol{k}$, show that the vectors $\boldsymbol{a}+\boldsymbol{b}$ and $\boldsymbol{a}-\boldsymbol{b}$ are orthogonal, and find the angle between the vectors $2\boldsymbol{a}+\boldsymbol{b}$ and $\boldsymbol{a}+2\boldsymbol{b}$.

(b) Prove, by a vector method, that the lines joining the mid points of opposite edges of a tetrahedron are concurrent and bisect each other. (M.E.I.)

Chapter 17

Solution of Linear Equations

1 Matrices and equations

1.1 Interpretation of simultaneous equations

We have met in several chapters a pair of simultaneous equations in two variables that can be expressed in the form of the matrix equation

$$\boldsymbol{Mx} = \boldsymbol{d}$$

(a) In Algebra 1, page 79, we found (x, y) the coordinates of the point of intersection of the lines

$$y = 2x + 3$$

and

$$y = 3x - 4$$

These equations could be written as

$$\left.\begin{aligned} -2x + y &= 3 \\ -3x + y &= -4 \end{aligned}\right\} \quad \text{or} \quad \begin{pmatrix} -2 & 1 \\ -3 & 1 \end{pmatrix}\begin{pmatrix} x \\ y \end{pmatrix} = \begin{pmatrix} 3 \\ -4 \end{pmatrix}$$

In Coordinate Geometry 1 also, page 145, we found the point of intersection of two lines in a plane.

(b) In Vectors 1, page 266, we found the coordinates (x, y) in terms of base vectors $\begin{pmatrix} 1 \\ -3 \end{pmatrix}$ and $\begin{pmatrix} -2 \\ 1 \end{pmatrix}$ of the point whose cartesian coordinates are (3, 1). The vector equation was

$$x\begin{pmatrix} 1 \\ -3 \end{pmatrix} + y\begin{pmatrix} -2 \\ 1 \end{pmatrix} = \begin{pmatrix} 3 \\ 1 \end{pmatrix} \quad \text{or} \quad \begin{pmatrix} 1 & -2 \\ -3 & 1 \end{pmatrix}\begin{pmatrix} x \\ y \end{pmatrix} = \begin{pmatrix} 3 \\ 1 \end{pmatrix}$$

(c) In Matrices and Transformation 1, page 330, we found the coordinates (x, y) of a point which under a transformation represented by the matrix $\begin{pmatrix} -2 & 1 \\ 1 & 1 \end{pmatrix}$ was mapped into $(-5, 1)$ so that

$$\begin{pmatrix} -2 & 1 \\ 1 & 1 \end{pmatrix}\begin{pmatrix} x \\ y \end{pmatrix} = \begin{pmatrix} -5 \\ 1 \end{pmatrix}$$

We met there also, page 330, a method of solving such matrix equations by means of the inverse matrix, for if

$$\boldsymbol{Mx} = \boldsymbol{d} \qquad \text{then} \qquad \boldsymbol{x} = \boldsymbol{M}^{-1}\boldsymbol{d}$$

We also learned how to find the inverse matrix, $\boldsymbol{M}^{-1}$, by the rule that involved the adjoint matrix.

Solution of simultaneous equations using determinants

Given the equations

$$ax + by = p \tag{1}$$

$$cx + dy = q \tag{2}$$

we can eliminate y or x by first multiplying through as shown and then adding

To find x

Multiply (1) by d	$dax + dby = dp$
Multiply (2) by $-b$	$-bcx - bdy = -bq$
Add	$(ad - bc)x = dp - bq$
	$x = \dfrac{dp - bq}{ad - bc}$

To find y

Multiply (1) by $-c$	$-cax - cby = -cp$
Multiply (2) by a	$acx + ady = aq$
Add	$(ad - bc)y = aq - cp$
	$y = \dfrac{aq - cp}{ad - bc}$

The equations can alternatively be set out in matrix form

$$\begin{pmatrix} a & b \\ c & d \end{pmatrix}\begin{pmatrix} x \\ y \end{pmatrix} = \begin{pmatrix} p \\ q \end{pmatrix}$$

To find x, premultiply both sides by $(d \quad -b)$

$$(d \quad -b)\begin{pmatrix} a & b \\ c & d \end{pmatrix}\begin{pmatrix} x \\ y \end{pmatrix} = (d \quad -b)\begin{pmatrix} p \\ q \end{pmatrix}$$

$$(ad - bc)x = dp - bq$$

$$x = \frac{dp - bq}{ad - bc} = \frac{\begin{vmatrix} p & b \\ q & d \end{vmatrix}}{\begin{vmatrix} a & b \\ c & d \end{vmatrix}}$$

Similarly to find y, we premultiply both sides by $(-c \quad a)$ and

$$y = \frac{-cp + aq}{-cb + ad} = \frac{\begin{vmatrix} a & p \\ c & q \end{vmatrix}}{\begin{vmatrix} a & b \\ c & d \end{vmatrix}}$$

Ill-conditioning

There will be a unique solution to the equations unless $\begin{vmatrix} a & b \\ c & d \end{vmatrix} = 0$. However, if the determinant is almost zero and we interpret the equations as two lines in the plane, then these lines will be nearly parallel. In this case very small changes in the coefficients (i.e. small changes in the slope or position of the lines) lead to widely differing solutions. For example, consider the pair of equations

$$2x + 7y = 9$$

$$3x + 10y = 13$$

These have an exact solution (1, 1). However, the point (4.4, 0) nearly satisfies the equations, since in this case

$$2x + 7y = 8.8$$

$$3x + 10y = 13.2$$

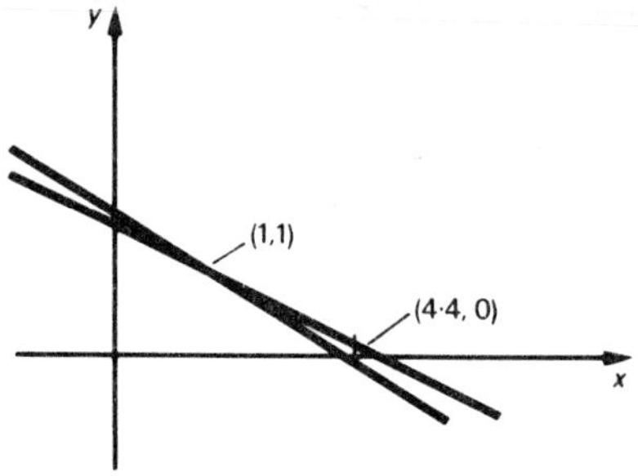

If the coefficients in the two equations had been rounded, the solution (4.4, 0) would be acceptable. The graph provides an explanation; the two lines are almost parallel.

When the equations are ill-conditioned in this way and if the coefficients are inexact, the error bounds in the solution may be too large to be acceptable and the equations become insoluble.

Extension to three variables

In Coordinate Geometry 2, page 492, we met sets of three equations in three variables, representing three planes. For example

$$2x + 3y - z = 4$$

$$x - 2y + 3z = 1$$

$$x + y + z = 1$$

These can be rewritten as the matrix equation

$$\begin{pmatrix} 2 & 3 & -1 \\ 1 & -2 & 3 \\ 1 & 1 & 1 \end{pmatrix}\begin{pmatrix} x \\ y \\ z \end{pmatrix} = \begin{pmatrix} 4 \\ 1 \\ 1 \end{pmatrix}$$

where the *rows* of the matrix represent the DRNs of the planes.

In Vectors 2, page 599, we met the position vector of a point, in terms of three base vectors, for example

$$\boldsymbol{x} = a\begin{pmatrix} 1 \\ 2 \\ 0 \end{pmatrix} + b\begin{pmatrix} 1 \\ -4 \\ 0 \end{pmatrix} + c\begin{pmatrix} 1 \\ 2 \\ 1 \end{pmatrix}$$

which can be rewritten as

$$\begin{pmatrix} x \\ y \\ z \end{pmatrix} = \begin{pmatrix} 1 & 1 & 1 \\ 2 & -4 & 2 \\ 0 & 0 & 1 \end{pmatrix}\begin{pmatrix} a \\ b \\ c \end{pmatrix}$$

where the *columns* of the matrix are the base vectors. The transformation of space is also represented by this type of matrix equation as we shall see (page 659).

As before, we can represent our set of equations as

$$\boldsymbol{Mx} = \boldsymbol{d}$$

which has the solution $\boldsymbol{x} = \boldsymbol{M}^{-1}\boldsymbol{d}$ (providing $\boldsymbol{M}^{-1}$ exists)

Our first problem in using this method of solution is to find the inverse of a 3×3 matrix.

1.2 The inverse matrix

Any 2×2 matrix, $\boldsymbol{M}$, whose determinant is non-zero, will possess an inverse, $\boldsymbol{M}^{-1}$, so that

$$\boldsymbol{MM}^{-1} = \boldsymbol{M}^{-1}\boldsymbol{M} = \boldsymbol{I} = \begin{pmatrix} 1 & 0 \\ 0 & 1 \end{pmatrix}$$

Similarly for any 3×3 matrix, $\boldsymbol{N}$

$$\boldsymbol{NN}^{-1} = \boldsymbol{N}^{-1}\boldsymbol{N} = \boldsymbol{I} = \begin{pmatrix} 1 & 0 & 0 \\ 0 & 1 & 0 \\ 0 & 0 & 1 \end{pmatrix}$$

In Chapter 9 we found that for $\boldsymbol{M} = \begin{pmatrix} a_1 & b_1 \\ a_2 & b_2 \end{pmatrix}$

$$\boldsymbol{M}^{-1} = \frac{1}{|\boldsymbol{M}|}(\text{Adjoint of } \boldsymbol{M}) = \frac{1}{(a_1b_2 - a_2b_1)}\begin{pmatrix} b_2 & -b_1 \\ -a_2 & a_1 \end{pmatrix}$$

Notice that the transpose of Adj $\boldsymbol{M}$, $(\text{Adj } \boldsymbol{M})^{\mathrm{T}} = \begin{pmatrix} b_2 & -a_2 \\ -b_1 & a_1 \end{pmatrix}$, has its first column

$\begin{pmatrix} b_2 \\ -b_1 \end{pmatrix}$ perpendicular to the second column of $\boldsymbol{M}$ and its second column $\begin{pmatrix} -a_2 \\ a_1 \end{pmatrix}$ perpendicular to the first column of $\boldsymbol{M}$. For any square matrix, of *any* order

$$\boldsymbol{M}^{-1} = \frac{1}{|\boldsymbol{M}|}\,(\text{Adjoint of } \boldsymbol{M})$$ ◀

We now investigate the problem of finding the adjoint and defining the determinant for a 3×3 matrix, $\boldsymbol{N}$. To find Adj $\boldsymbol{N}$, we first find a 'matrix of perpendiculars' whose

first column is mutually perpendicular to the second and third columns of $\boldsymbol{N}$
second column is mutually perpendicular to the third and first columns of $\boldsymbol{N}$
third column is mutually perpendicular to the first and second columns of $\boldsymbol{N}$

Suppose
$$\boldsymbol{N} = (\boldsymbol{a} \quad \boldsymbol{b} \quad \boldsymbol{c}) = \begin{pmatrix} a_1 & b_1 & c_1 \\ a_2 & b_2 & c_2 \\ a_3 & b_3 & c_3 \end{pmatrix}$$

Then the first column of the new matrix must be $\boldsymbol{b} \times \boldsymbol{c}$, since this is mutually perpendicular to $\boldsymbol{b}$ and $\boldsymbol{c}$. Similarly the second column is $\boldsymbol{c} \times \boldsymbol{a}$, and the third, $\boldsymbol{a} \times \boldsymbol{b}$. So the matrix of perpendiculars is

$$(\boldsymbol{b} \times \boldsymbol{c} \quad \boldsymbol{c} \times \boldsymbol{a} \quad \boldsymbol{a} \times \boldsymbol{b})$$

and the adjoint of $\boldsymbol{N}$ is given by the transpose of this

$$\text{Adj } \boldsymbol{N} = \begin{pmatrix} (\boldsymbol{b} \times \boldsymbol{c})^{\mathrm{T}} \\ (\boldsymbol{c} \times \boldsymbol{a})^{\mathrm{T}} \\ (\boldsymbol{a} \times \boldsymbol{b})^{\mathrm{T}} \end{pmatrix}$$ ◀

Now
$$(\text{Adj } \boldsymbol{N})\boldsymbol{N} = \begin{pmatrix} (\boldsymbol{b} \times \boldsymbol{c})^{\mathrm{T}} \\ (\boldsymbol{c} \times \boldsymbol{a})^{\mathrm{T}} \\ (\boldsymbol{a} \times \boldsymbol{b})^{\mathrm{T}} \end{pmatrix} (\mathbf{a} \quad \mathbf{b} \quad \mathbf{c})$$

$$= \begin{pmatrix} (\boldsymbol{b} \times \boldsymbol{c}) \cdot \boldsymbol{a} & (\boldsymbol{b} \times \boldsymbol{c}) \cdot \boldsymbol{b} & (\boldsymbol{b} \times \boldsymbol{c}) \cdot \boldsymbol{c} \\ (\boldsymbol{c} \times \boldsymbol{a}) \cdot \boldsymbol{a} & (\boldsymbol{c} \times \boldsymbol{a}) \cdot \boldsymbol{b} & (\boldsymbol{c} \times \boldsymbol{a}) \cdot \boldsymbol{c} \\ (\boldsymbol{a} \times \boldsymbol{b}) \cdot \boldsymbol{a} & (\boldsymbol{a} \times \boldsymbol{b}) \cdot \boldsymbol{b} & (\boldsymbol{a} \times \boldsymbol{b}) \cdot \boldsymbol{c} \end{pmatrix}$$

$$= \begin{pmatrix} \mathrm{V} & 0 & 0 \\ 0 & \mathrm{V} & 0 \\ 0 & 0 & \mathrm{V} \end{pmatrix} = \mathrm{V}\begin{pmatrix} 1 & 0 & 0 \\ 0 & 1 & 0 \\ 0 & 0 & 1 \end{pmatrix}$$

where
$$\mathrm{V} = (\boldsymbol{b} \times \boldsymbol{c}) \cdot \boldsymbol{a} = (\boldsymbol{c} \times \boldsymbol{a}) \cdot \boldsymbol{b} = (\boldsymbol{a} \times \boldsymbol{b}) \cdot \boldsymbol{c}$$

and all the other products are zero, since for example $\boldsymbol{c} \times \boldsymbol{a}$ is perpendicular to $\boldsymbol{a}$ and to $\boldsymbol{c}$ so

$$(\boldsymbol{c} \times \boldsymbol{a}) \cdot \boldsymbol{a} = (\boldsymbol{c} \times \boldsymbol{a}) \cdot \boldsymbol{c} = 0$$

We define the determinant of $\boldsymbol{N}$ to be the quantity V and discuss it in the next section. Now

$$(\text{Adj } \boldsymbol{N})\boldsymbol{N} = |\boldsymbol{N}|\boldsymbol{I}$$

so
$$\frac{1}{|\boldsymbol{N}|}(\text{Adj}\,\boldsymbol{N})\boldsymbol{N} = \boldsymbol{I}$$

and so
$$\boldsymbol{N}^{-1} = \frac{1}{|\boldsymbol{N}|}(\text{Adj}\,\boldsymbol{N})$$

Example 1

Find the inverse of the matrix

$$\boldsymbol{N} = (\boldsymbol{a} \quad \boldsymbol{b} \quad \boldsymbol{c}) = \begin{pmatrix} 1 & 0 & -4 \\ 2 & 1 & 6 \\ 1 & 1 & 3 \end{pmatrix}$$

The perpendiculars are

$$\boldsymbol{n}_1 = \boldsymbol{b} \times \boldsymbol{c} = \begin{pmatrix} 0 \\ 1 \\ 1 \end{pmatrix} \times \begin{pmatrix} -4 \\ 6 \\ 3 \end{pmatrix} = \begin{pmatrix} -3 \\ -4 \\ 4 \end{pmatrix}$$

$$\boldsymbol{n}_2 = \boldsymbol{c} \times \boldsymbol{a} = \begin{pmatrix} -4 \\ 6 \\ 3 \end{pmatrix} \times \begin{pmatrix} 1 \\ 2 \\ 1 \end{pmatrix} = \begin{pmatrix} 0 \\ 7 \\ -14 \end{pmatrix}$$

$$\boldsymbol{n}_3 = \boldsymbol{a} \times \boldsymbol{b} = \begin{pmatrix} 1 \\ 2 \\ 1 \end{pmatrix} \times \begin{pmatrix} 0 \\ 1 \\ 1 \end{pmatrix} = \begin{pmatrix} 1 \\ -1 \\ 1 \end{pmatrix}$$

The 'matrix of perpendiculars' is

$$\begin{pmatrix} -3 & 0 & 1 \\ -4 & 7 & -1 \\ 4 & -14 & 1 \end{pmatrix}$$

and Adj $\boldsymbol{N}$ is the transpose of this

$$\begin{pmatrix} -3 & -4 & 4 \\ 0 & 7 & -14 \\ 1 & -1 & 1 \end{pmatrix}$$

Since $\boldsymbol{n}_1$ is perpendicular to $\boldsymbol{b}$ and to $\boldsymbol{c}$

$$\boldsymbol{n}_1 \cdot \boldsymbol{b} = \boldsymbol{n}_1 \cdot \boldsymbol{c} = 0$$

It is useful to check that this *is* so

$$\boldsymbol{n}_1 \cdot \boldsymbol{b} = \begin{pmatrix} -3 \\ -4 \\ 4 \end{pmatrix} \cdot \begin{pmatrix} 0 \\ 1 \\ 1 \end{pmatrix} = 0 \qquad \boldsymbol{n}_1 \cdot \boldsymbol{c} = \begin{pmatrix} -3 \\ -4 \\ 4 \end{pmatrix} \cdot \begin{pmatrix} -4 \\ 6 \\ 3 \end{pmatrix} = 0$$

Similarly

$$\boldsymbol{n}_2 \cdot \boldsymbol{c} = \begin{pmatrix} 0 \\ 7 \\ -14 \end{pmatrix} \cdot \begin{pmatrix} -4 \\ 6 \\ 3 \end{pmatrix} = 0 \qquad \boldsymbol{n}_2 \cdot \boldsymbol{a} = \begin{pmatrix} 0 \\ 7 \\ -14 \end{pmatrix} \cdot \begin{pmatrix} 1 \\ 2 \\ 1 \end{pmatrix} = 0$$

$$\boldsymbol{n}_3 \cdot \boldsymbol{a} = \begin{pmatrix} 1 \\ -1 \\ 1 \end{pmatrix} \cdot \begin{pmatrix} 1 \\ 2 \\ 1 \end{pmatrix} = 0 \quad \text{and} \quad \boldsymbol{n}_3 \cdot \boldsymbol{b} = \begin{pmatrix} 1 \\ -1 \\ 1 \end{pmatrix} \cdot \begin{pmatrix} 0 \\ 1 \\ 1 \end{pmatrix} = 0$$

Now

$$(\text{Adj}\, \boldsymbol{N})\boldsymbol{N} = \begin{pmatrix} -3 & -4 & 4 \\ 0 & 7 & -14 \\ 1 & -1 & 1 \end{pmatrix} \begin{pmatrix} 1 & 0 & -4 \\ 2 & 1 & 6 \\ 1 & 1 & 3 \end{pmatrix}$$

$$= \begin{pmatrix} -7 & 0 & 0 \\ 0 & -7 & 0 \\ 0 & 0 & -7 \end{pmatrix} = -7 \begin{pmatrix} 1 & 0 & 0 \\ 0 & 1 & 0 \\ 0 & 0 & 1 \end{pmatrix}$$

Hence the determinant of $\boldsymbol{N}$, $|\boldsymbol{N}| = -7$ and

$$\boldsymbol{N}^{-1} = \frac{1}{|\boldsymbol{N}|} \text{Adj}\, \boldsymbol{N} = \frac{1}{-7} \begin{pmatrix} -3 & -4 & 4 \\ 0 & 7 & -14 \\ 1 & -1 & 1 \end{pmatrix}$$

$$= \begin{pmatrix} \frac{3}{7} & \frac{4}{7} & -\frac{4}{7} \\ 0 & -1 & 2 \\ -\frac{1}{7} & \frac{1}{7} & -\frac{1}{7} \end{pmatrix}$$

It can happen that the product of a matrix and its adjoint is the zero matrix, so that the determinant is zero. This means that the matrix is singular and has no inverse, and there is no unique solution to the matrix equation. There may indeed be *no* solution, or there may be an infinite set of solutions. We dealt with these cases in Chapter 13.

Exercise 1.2

Use the adjoint method to find the inverse of each of the following matrices (if it exists). (Keep your results for use in Exercise 2.2.)

1 $\begin{pmatrix} 1 & 0 & 2 \\ 0 & 3 & -1 \\ 2 & 2 & 0 \end{pmatrix}$ **2** $\begin{pmatrix} 4 & 0 & 2 \\ -2 & 3 & 1 \\ 3 & -4 & 2 \end{pmatrix}$ **3** $\begin{pmatrix} 3 & 0 & 0 \\ 1 & 1 & 0 \\ 2 & -2 & 1 \end{pmatrix}$

4 $\begin{pmatrix} 1 & -2 & -3 \\ 1 & 1 & -2 \\ 1 & 4 & 1 \end{pmatrix}$ **5** $\begin{pmatrix} \alpha & 1 & -1 \\ 0 & \alpha & 3 \\ 0 & 0 & \alpha \end{pmatrix}$ **6** $\begin{pmatrix} 1 & 2 & 4 \\ 1 & -1 & 1 \\ 1 & 3 & 5 \end{pmatrix}$

1.3 Determinants

A determinant is a number associated with a matrix and is defined only for square matrices.

(i) If $\boldsymbol{M} = \begin{pmatrix} a_1 & b_1 \\ a_2 & b_2 \end{pmatrix}$ then $|\boldsymbol{M}| = a_1b_2 - a_2b_1$.

(ii) If $\boldsymbol{N} = \begin{pmatrix} a_1 & b_1 & c_1 \\ a_2 & b_2 & c_2 \\ a_3 & b_3 & c_3 \end{pmatrix}$ then we define

$$|\boldsymbol{N}| \text{ as } (\boldsymbol{b} \times \boldsymbol{c}) \cdot \boldsymbol{a} = (\boldsymbol{c} \times \boldsymbol{a}) \cdot \boldsymbol{b} = (\boldsymbol{a} \times \boldsymbol{b}) \cdot \boldsymbol{c}$$ ◄

where $\boldsymbol{a} = \begin{pmatrix} a_1 \\ a_2 \\ a_3 \end{pmatrix}$, $\boldsymbol{b} = \begin{pmatrix} b_1 \\ b_2 \\ b_3 \end{pmatrix}$ and $\boldsymbol{c} = \begin{pmatrix} c_1 \\ c_2 \\ c_3 \end{pmatrix}$

Hence
$$|\boldsymbol{N}| = \begin{pmatrix} \begin{vmatrix} b_2 & c_2 \\ b_3 & c_3 \end{vmatrix} \\ \begin{vmatrix} b_3 & c_3 \\ b_1 & c_1 \end{vmatrix} \\ \begin{vmatrix} b_1 & c_1 \\ b_2 & c_2 \end{vmatrix} \end{pmatrix} \cdot \begin{pmatrix} a_1 \\ a_2 \\ a_3 \end{pmatrix}$$

$$= a_1\begin{vmatrix} b_2 & c_2 \\ b_3 & c_3 \end{vmatrix} + a_2\begin{vmatrix} b_3 & c_3 \\ b_1 & c_1 \end{vmatrix} + a_3\begin{vmatrix} b_1 & c_1 \\ b_2 & c_2 \end{vmatrix}$$

$$|\boldsymbol{N}| = a_1(b_2c_3 - b_3c_2) + a_2(b_3c_1 - b_1c_3) + a_3(b_1c_2 - b_2c_1)$$ ◄

In the same way that solving two equations in two variables by elimination leads to the introduction of the determinant of a 2×2 matrix (see page 633) so when solving three equations in three variables by elimination we should come across the quantity above which we define as the determinant of a 3×3 matrix.

If the determinant ($|\boldsymbol{M}|$ or $|\boldsymbol{N}|$) is not zero and we are solving equations there will be a unique solution. If however the determinant *is* zero then we do not have a unique solution. With two equations this corresponds to parallel lines or identical lines, whilst with three equations the situation is more complicated (see page 492).

Geometrically for a 2×2 matrix $\begin{pmatrix} a_1 & b_1 \\ a_2 & b_2 \end{pmatrix}$, $\begin{vmatrix} a_1 & b_1 \\ a_2 & b_2 \end{vmatrix}$ is equal to the *area* of the parallelogram contained by the vectors $\boldsymbol{a}$ and $\boldsymbol{b}$ where $\boldsymbol{a} = \begin{pmatrix} a_1 \\ a_2 \end{pmatrix}$ and $\boldsymbol{b} = \begin{pmatrix} b_1 \\ b_2 \end{pmatrix}$. For a 3×3 matrix the determinant gives the *volume* of the parallelepiped contained by the three vectors $\boldsymbol{a}$, $\boldsymbol{b}$ and $\boldsymbol{c}$ (see page 625). Ill-conditioning occurs with three equations in three variables when the line of intersection of two of the planes represented is almost parallel to the third plane.

Exercise 1.3

Calculate the following determinants.

1 $\begin{vmatrix} 1 & 2 & 3 \\ 4 & 5 & 6 \\ 7 & 8 & 9 \end{vmatrix}$ **2(a)** $\begin{vmatrix} 4 & 0 & 2 \\ -2 & 3 & -1 \\ 3 & -4 & 2 \end{vmatrix}$ **(b)** $\begin{vmatrix} 4 & 2 & 0 \\ -2 & -1 & 3 \\ 3 & 2 & -4 \end{vmatrix}$

3 $\begin{vmatrix} 3 & -1 & 2 \\ 1 & 2 & 3 \\ -2 & 1 & 2 \end{vmatrix}$ **4(a)** $\begin{vmatrix} 5 & 2 & 2 \\ 3 & -3 & 7 \\ 4 & 2 & 0 \end{vmatrix}$ **(b)** $\begin{vmatrix} 5 & 3 & 4 \\ 2 & -3 & 2 \\ 2 & 7 & 0 \end{vmatrix}$

5 $\begin{vmatrix} 1 & 1 & 1 \\ 1 & 2 & 3 \\ 1 & 1 & -1 \end{vmatrix}$ **6** $\begin{vmatrix} 1 & 2 & 4 \\ 1 & -1 & 1 \\ 1 & 3 & 5 \end{vmatrix}$ **7** $\begin{vmatrix} 3 & 1 & 9 \\ -2 & 1 & 4 \\ -1 & 1 & 1 \end{vmatrix}$

8 $\begin{vmatrix} -\lambda & 1 & 2 \\ 1 & -\lambda & 3 \\ 2 & 3 & -\lambda \end{vmatrix}$ **9** $\begin{vmatrix} -\lambda & 3 & 1 \\ 0 & 1-\lambda & 0 \\ 2 & 1 & 3-\lambda \end{vmatrix}$ **10** $\begin{vmatrix} 1-\lambda & 2 & 1 \\ -3 & 2-\lambda & 1 \\ 0 & 3 & 2-\lambda \end{vmatrix}$

2 Solution of three equations in three variables

2.1 Method 1, using the inverse matrix

We know that providing $\boldsymbol{M}^{-1}$ exists, if $\boldsymbol{Mx} = \boldsymbol{d}$ then $\boldsymbol{x} = \boldsymbol{M}^{-1}\boldsymbol{d}$.

Example 1

Use the inverse matrix method to solve the equations

$$\begin{aligned} -3x+11y+7z &= 1 \\ -x+4y+3z &= 1 \\ 2x-7y-5z &= -1 \end{aligned}$$

Arranging the equations as a matrix equation, $\boldsymbol{Mx} = \boldsymbol{d}$

$$\begin{pmatrix} -3 & 11 & 7 \\ -1 & 4 & 3 \\ 2 & -7 & -5 \end{pmatrix}\begin{pmatrix} x \\ y \\ z \end{pmatrix} = \begin{pmatrix} 1 \\ 1 \\ -1 \end{pmatrix}$$

Now $$\text{Adj}\,\boldsymbol{M} = \begin{pmatrix} 1 & 1 & -1 \\ 6 & 1 & 1 \\ 5 & 2 & -1 \end{pmatrix}^{\mathrm{T}} = \begin{pmatrix} 1 & 6 & 5 \\ 1 & 1 & 2 \\ -1 & 1 & -1 \end{pmatrix}$$

and
$$\text{Det}\,\boldsymbol{M} = \begin{vmatrix} -3 & 11 & 7 \\ -1 & 4 & 3 \\ 2 & -7 & -5 \end{vmatrix} = \begin{pmatrix} -3 \\ -1 \\ 2 \end{pmatrix} \cdot \begin{pmatrix} 1 \\ 6 \\ 5 \end{pmatrix} = 1$$

so
$$\boldsymbol{M}^{-1} = \begin{pmatrix} 1 & 6 & 5 \\ 1 & 1 & 2 \\ -1 & 1 & -1 \end{pmatrix}$$

and
$$\begin{pmatrix} x \\ y \\ z \end{pmatrix} = \begin{pmatrix} 1 & 6 & 5 \\ 1 & 1 & 2 \\ -1 & 1 & -1 \end{pmatrix} \begin{pmatrix} 1 \\ 1 \\ -1 \end{pmatrix} = \begin{pmatrix} 2 \\ 0 \\ 1 \end{pmatrix}$$

Hence $x = 2 \qquad y = 0 \qquad z = 1$

The solution should be checked by substitution in the original equations.

2.2 Method 2, the determinant method

Suppose the three equations to be solved are

$$a_1x + b_1y + c_1z = d_1$$
$$a_2x + b_2y + c_2z = d_2$$
$$a_3x + b_3y + c_3z = d_3$$

These can be rewritten in the form

$$\boldsymbol{a}x + \boldsymbol{b}y + \boldsymbol{c}z = \boldsymbol{d}$$

Multiplying through (i.e. taking the *dot* product) by $(\boldsymbol{b} \times \boldsymbol{c})$ we have

$$(\boldsymbol{b} \times \boldsymbol{c}) \cdot \boldsymbol{a}x + (\boldsymbol{b} \times \boldsymbol{c}) \cdot \boldsymbol{b}y + (\boldsymbol{b} \times \boldsymbol{c}) \cdot \boldsymbol{c}z = (\boldsymbol{b} \times \boldsymbol{c}) \cdot \boldsymbol{d}$$

But since $(\boldsymbol{b} \times \boldsymbol{c})$ is perpendicular to $\boldsymbol{b}$ and to $\boldsymbol{c}$,

$$(\boldsymbol{b} \times \boldsymbol{c}) \cdot \boldsymbol{b} = (\boldsymbol{b} \times \boldsymbol{c}) \cdot \boldsymbol{c} = 0$$

Hence
$$(\boldsymbol{b} \times \boldsymbol{c}) \cdot \boldsymbol{a}x = (\boldsymbol{b} \times \boldsymbol{c}) \cdot \boldsymbol{d}$$

and
$$x = \frac{(\boldsymbol{b} \times \boldsymbol{c}) \cdot \boldsymbol{d}}{(\boldsymbol{b} \times \boldsymbol{c}) \cdot \boldsymbol{a}} = \frac{|\boldsymbol{d} \quad \boldsymbol{b} \quad \boldsymbol{c}|}{|\boldsymbol{a} \quad \boldsymbol{b} \quad \boldsymbol{c}|}$$

Similarly, multiplying through by $(\boldsymbol{c} \times \boldsymbol{a})$,

$$y = \frac{(\boldsymbol{c} \times \boldsymbol{a}) \cdot \boldsymbol{d}}{(\boldsymbol{c} \times \boldsymbol{a}) \cdot \boldsymbol{b}} = \frac{|\boldsymbol{a} \quad \boldsymbol{d} \quad \boldsymbol{c}|}{|\boldsymbol{a} \quad \boldsymbol{b} \quad \boldsymbol{c}|}$$

and by $(\boldsymbol{a} \times \boldsymbol{b})$,
$$z = \frac{(\boldsymbol{a} \times \boldsymbol{b}) \cdot \boldsymbol{d}}{(\boldsymbol{a} \times \boldsymbol{b}) \cdot \boldsymbol{c}} = \frac{|\boldsymbol{a} \quad \boldsymbol{b} \quad \boldsymbol{d}|}{|\boldsymbol{a} \quad \boldsymbol{b} \quad \boldsymbol{c}|}$$

The solution exists, provided $|\boldsymbol{a} \quad \boldsymbol{b} \quad \boldsymbol{c}| \neq 0$. Notice that in the numerator determinant, $\boldsymbol{d}$ has replaced $\boldsymbol{a}$ in the expression for x, $\boldsymbol{d}$ has replaced $\boldsymbol{b}$ in the expression for y, and $\boldsymbol{c}$ in the expression for z.

Example 2

Use the determinant method to solve the same three equations as in Example 1

$$-3x+11y+7z = 1$$
$$-x+4y+3z = 1$$
$$2x-7y-5z = -1$$

As we have seen

$$\begin{vmatrix} -3 & 11 & 7 \\ -1 & 4 & 3 \\ 2 & -7 & -5 \end{vmatrix} = \begin{pmatrix} -3 \\ -1 \\ 2 \end{pmatrix} \cdot \begin{pmatrix} 1 \\ 6 \\ 5 \end{pmatrix} = 1$$

Now, replacing the first column by $\begin{pmatrix} 1 \\ 1 \\ -1 \end{pmatrix}$

$$x = \begin{vmatrix} 1 & 11 & 7 \\ 1 & 4 & 3 \\ -1 & -7 & -5 \end{vmatrix} = \begin{pmatrix} 1 \\ 1 \\ -1 \end{pmatrix} \cdot \begin{pmatrix} 1 \\ 6 \\ 5 \end{pmatrix} = 2$$

Replacing the second column

$$y = \begin{vmatrix} -3 & 1 & 7 \\ -1 & 1 & 3 \\ 2 & -1 & -5 \end{vmatrix} = \begin{pmatrix} -3 \\ -1 \\ 2 \end{pmatrix} \cdot \begin{pmatrix} -2 \\ -2 \\ -4 \end{pmatrix} = 0$$

Replacing the third column

$$z = \begin{vmatrix} -3 & 11 & 1 \\ -1 & 4 & 1 \\ 2 & -7 & -1 \end{vmatrix} = \begin{pmatrix} -3 \\ -1 \\ 2 \end{pmatrix} \cdot \begin{pmatrix} 3 \\ 4 \\ 7 \end{pmatrix} = 1$$

So $x = 2, \quad y = 0, \quad z = 1$

Exercise 2.2

In questions **1** to **6** use the inverse matrices you obtained in Exercise 1.2 to solve the following simultaneous equations. Check your solution in each case, by substitution.

1
$$x+2z = -1$$
$$3y-z = 9$$
$$2x+2y = 4$$

2
$$4x+2z = 6$$
$$-2x+3y+z = -6$$
$$3x-4y+2z = 12$$

3
$$3x = 15$$
$$x+y = 3$$
$$2x-2y+z = 17$$

4
$$x-2y-3z = 8$$
$$x+y-2z = 3$$
$$x+4y+z = -6$$

5 $2x+y-z=-7$

$2y+3z=9$

$2z=6$

6 $x+2y+4z=4$

$x-y+z=-4$

$x+3y+5z=8$

In questions 7 and 8, solve by matrix inversion the equations

7 $\boldsymbol{Ax}=\boldsymbol{b}$ with $\boldsymbol{A}=\begin{pmatrix}0 & 1 & 0\\ 0 & 0 & 1\\ -1 & 2 & 1\end{pmatrix}$ and $\boldsymbol{b}=\begin{pmatrix}2\\ -1\\ 2\end{pmatrix}$

8 $\boldsymbol{Cx}=\boldsymbol{d}$ with $\boldsymbol{C}=\begin{pmatrix}1 & -1 & 0\\ 5 & -4 & 1\\ 2 & 2 & 1\end{pmatrix}$ and $\boldsymbol{d}=\begin{pmatrix}-4\\ -12\\ 11\end{pmatrix}$

In questions 9 and 10, use the determinant method to solve the equations

9 $2x-3y+2z=2$

$x+4y-z=-4$

$5x+2y+z=-2$

10 $3x-2y+z=1$

$-4x+y+2z=-8$

$x+3y-5z=13$

2.3 Method 3, Choleski's method

It is easy to find the inverse of a 2×2 matrix but more complicated to find that of a 3×3 matrix and the process becomes progressively longer the larger the matrix. Usually, however, we are only interested in the inverse to enable us to solve equations and there is an alternative method for solving equations which involves far fewer calculations. This method is now illustrated for three equations in three unknowns. It may seem cumbersome, but it is most useful for solving equations with a large number of variables. Instead of finding the inverse of the matrix, the idea is to 'factorize' it, i.e. to find two matrices of a particular form that when multiplied together give the original matrix.

The procedure is as follows. Suppose

$$\boldsymbol{Mx}=\boldsymbol{d}$$

We find $\boldsymbol{L}$ and $\boldsymbol{U}$ where $\boldsymbol{LU}=\boldsymbol{M}$, where $\boldsymbol{L}$ is a lower diagonal matrix with zeros *above* the leading diagonal and $\boldsymbol{U}$ is an upper diagonal matrix with zeros *below* the leading diagonal. Matrices like $\boldsymbol{L}$ and $\boldsymbol{U}$ are said to be in *echelon* form. Now

$$\boldsymbol{LUx}=\boldsymbol{d}$$

Suppose $\qquad \boldsymbol{Ux}=\boldsymbol{s}$

then $\qquad \boldsymbol{Ls}=\boldsymbol{d}$

Having found $\boldsymbol{L}$ and $\boldsymbol{U}$ we solve these last two equations in reverse order

$\boldsymbol{Ls}=\boldsymbol{d} \qquad$ to find $\boldsymbol{s}$

and $\qquad \boldsymbol{Ux}=\boldsymbol{s} \qquad$ to find $\boldsymbol{x}$

Example 3

Use Choleski's method to solve the equations

$$\begin{aligned}-3x+11y+7z &= 1\\ -x+4y+3z &= 1\\ 2x-7y-5z &= -1\end{aligned}$$

We start by considering how to write the matrix $\boldsymbol{M}$ as the product of two matrices in echelon form. Suppose

$$\boldsymbol{M}=\begin{pmatrix}-3 & 11 & 7\\ -1 & 4 & 3\\ 2 & -7 & -5\end{pmatrix}=\begin{pmatrix}\cdot & 0 & 0\\ \cdot & \cdot & 0\\ \cdot & \cdot & \cdot\end{pmatrix}\begin{pmatrix}\cdot & \cdot & \cdot\\ 0 & \cdot & \cdot\\ 0 & 0 & \cdot\end{pmatrix}=\boldsymbol{LU}$$

Now when we multiply $\boldsymbol{LU}$ together we shall have nine equations in twelve unknowns. As a result we are at liberty to choose three of the unknowns to have any value we like ($\neq 0$).

We take
$$\boldsymbol{U}=\begin{pmatrix}1 & a & b\\ 0 & 1 & c\\ 0 & 0 & 1\end{pmatrix}$$

This enables us to make the first column in $\boldsymbol{L}$ the same as the first column in $\boldsymbol{M}$ therefore

$$\boldsymbol{L}=\begin{pmatrix}-3 & 0 & 0\\ -1 & p & 0\\ 2 & q & r\end{pmatrix}$$

Now
$$\boldsymbol{LU}=\boldsymbol{M}$$

$$\begin{pmatrix}-3 & 0 & 0\\ -1 & p & 0\\ 2 & q & r\end{pmatrix}\begin{pmatrix}1 & a & b\\ 0 & 1 & c\\ 0 & 0 & 1\end{pmatrix}=\begin{pmatrix}-3 & 11 & 7\\ -1 & 4 & 3\\ 2 & -7 & -5\end{pmatrix}$$

So multiplying out

$$\begin{aligned}-3a &= 11, & -3b &= 7\\ -a+p &= 4, & -b+pc &= 3\\ 2a+q &= -7, & 2b+qc+r &= -5\end{aligned}$$

These equations can be solved successively to give

$$a=-\tfrac{11}{3}\qquad b=-\tfrac{7}{3}\qquad p=\tfrac{1}{3}\qquad c=2\qquad q=\tfrac{1}{3}\qquad r=-1$$

So
$$\boldsymbol{U}=\begin{pmatrix}1 & -\frac{11}{3} & -\frac{7}{3}\\ 0 & 1 & 2\\ 0 & 0 & 1\end{pmatrix}\quad\text{and}\quad \boldsymbol{L}=\begin{pmatrix}3 & 0 & 0\\ -1 & \frac{1}{3} & 0\\ 2 & \frac{1}{3} & -1\end{pmatrix}$$

Now
$$\boldsymbol{Ls}=\boldsymbol{d}$$

so $\begin{pmatrix} 3 & 0 & 0 \\ -1 & \frac{1}{2} & 0 \\ 2 & \frac{1}{3} & -1 \end{pmatrix} \begin{pmatrix} s \\ t \\ u \end{pmatrix} = \begin{pmatrix} 1 \\ 1 \\ -1 \end{pmatrix}$ $\quad \begin{aligned} 3s &= 1 \\ -s+\tfrac{1}{2}t &= 1 \\ 2s+\tfrac{1}{3}t-u &= -1 \end{aligned}$

Hence $\quad s = \frac{1}{3}, \quad t = 2, \quad u = 1$

Also $\quad \boldsymbol{Ux} = \boldsymbol{s}$

so $\begin{pmatrix} 1 & -\frac{11}{3} & -\frac{7}{3} \\ 0 & 1 & 2 \\ 0 & 0 & 1 \end{pmatrix} \begin{pmatrix} x \\ y \\ z \end{pmatrix} = \begin{pmatrix} \frac{1}{3} \\ 2 \\ 1 \end{pmatrix}$ $\quad \begin{aligned} x-\tfrac{11}{3}y-\tfrac{7}{3}z &= \tfrac{1}{3} \\ y+2z &= 2 \\ z &= 1 \end{aligned}$

and finally $\quad z = 1 \quad y = 0 \quad x = 2$

2.4 Method 4, the elimination method

Although the problem of solving three equations in general terms of three variables by elimination is complicated by the algebra involved, it is often quite straightforward to solve three equations with numerical coefficients by this method.

Example 4

Use elimination to solve the equations

$$-3x+11y+7z = 1 \qquad (1)$$

$$-x+4y+3z = 1 \qquad (2)$$

$$2x-7y-5z = -1 \qquad (3)$$

Multiply (2) by −3 $\quad 3x-12y-9z = -3 \qquad (4)$

Add (1) and (4) $\quad -y-2z = -2 \qquad (5)$

Multiply (2) by 2 $\quad -2x+8y+6z = 2 \qquad (6)$

Add (3) and (6) $\quad y+z = 1 \qquad (7)$

Add (5) and (7) $\quad -z = -1$

$$z = 1$$

Back substitution leads to

$x = 2 \quad y = 0 \quad z = 1$ (as before)

The solution should always be checked (mentally) in the equations.

This method of solution is the basis of the method of pivotal condensation, which we meet in the next section, where the process of elimination is tackled in a more systematic way.

Summary

We have investigated the solution of three equations in three unknowns from several different points of view. You may well ask why this has been necessary. We have used

(1) The inverse matrix, because of the idea of transformation of space. The method could be extended to the solution of a large number of equations in a large number of unknowns if it were possible to find the inverse matrix. In general this is a tedious process, but the method of solution is simple, i.e. if $\boldsymbol{Ax} = \boldsymbol{b}$, then $\boldsymbol{x} = \boldsymbol{A}^{-1}\boldsymbol{b}$ ($|\mathbf{A}| \neq 0$).

(2) Determinants, since they provide the quickest method of finding the type of solution, i.e. if $|\boldsymbol{A}| = 0$, then we must look closely at the equations as the solution may not be unique. Again, the method may be extended, but is very tedious.

(3) Choleski's method, because it provides the simplest way of handling a large number of equations in a large number of unknowns and may be used on a computer.

(4) Elimination, since this method provides the basis for a way of solving the equations when the coefficients are not integral. This method is encountered later under the name of 'pivotal condensation'.

The good mathematician, given a freedom of choice, will always choose the quickest, most accurate and suitable method of solution for his particular problem. Do not use a sledge hammer to crack a nut!

Exercise 2.4

In each question check your solution by substitution.

Use the inverse matrix method to solve

1
$$\begin{aligned} 2x - y + z &= 3 \\ x + 2y + z &= 12 \\ 4x - 3y + z &= 1 \end{aligned}$$

2
$$\begin{aligned} x - 3y + z &= 10 \\ 2x - 7y - 5z &= -2 \\ x + y - 2z &= 5 \end{aligned}$$

Use elimination and substitution to solve

3
$$\begin{aligned} x + y &= 2 \\ y + z &= -2 \\ z + x &= 12 \end{aligned}$$

4
$$\begin{aligned} x + y + z &= 6 \\ 2y + z &= 9 \\ z - 2y &= 1 \end{aligned}$$

Use the determinant method to solve

5
$$\begin{aligned} 9x - 10y + z &= 1 \\ 3x + y - z &= -1 \\ 7x - y + z &= 1 \end{aligned}$$

6
$$\begin{aligned} x + 2y - 3z &= 0 \\ 3x + 3y - z &= 5 \\ x - 2y + 2z &= 1 \end{aligned}$$

Use Choleski's method to solve

7
$$\begin{aligned} x + y + z &= 4 \\ x + 2y + 3z &= 9 \\ 3x + y + 4z &= 12 \end{aligned}$$

8
$$\begin{aligned} -3x + 2y + z &= 8 \\ 9x - 5y - 2z &= -21 \\ -5x + 3y + z &= 17 \end{aligned}$$

Use any method to solve

9 $7x-y-z = 64$

$2x+5y-z = 59$

$x-3y-2z = 115$

10 $x-3y+z = 2$

$x+2y-z = -1$

$2x+y+2z = 6$

3 Numerical methods of solution

3.1 Pivotal condensation

As with the solution of equations in one variable, there are direct and indirect methods of solving simultaneous linear equations in more than one variable. The methods we have discussed so far are direct methods which are quite satisfactory when the solutions are integers or simple fractions. Choleski's method is a quick and easily programmable method for solving systems of equations in many variables whose coefficients are exact. We now introduce a direct method of elimination known as pivotal condensation which is also programmable and is suitable for solving equations whose coefficients are not exact.

The notation we shall use has x_1, x_2 and x_3 as the variables, the coefficients having double subscripts and the equations are written as

$$a_{11}x_1+a_{12}x_2+a_{13}x_3 = b_1$$

$$a_{21}x_1+a_{22}x_2+a_{23}x_3 = b_2$$

$$a_{31}x_1+a_{32}x_2+a_{33}x_3 = b_3$$

Having found approximate solutions for x_1, x_2 and x_3, these values are substituted back into the equations to find the *residuals*, R_1, R_2 and R_3, where

$$R_1 = a_{11}x_1+a_{12}x_2+a_{13}x_3-b_1$$

$$R_2 = a_{21}x_1+a_{22}x_2+a_{23}x_3-b_2$$

$$R_3 = a_{31}x_1+a_{32}x_2+a_{33}x_3-b_3$$

The sizes of the residuals are indicative of the accuracy of the solutions. The method of pivotal condensation minimizes the error due to rounding off during the calculation. However if the equations are ill-conditioned the solution obtained may not be satisfactory, the values of the residual errors being beyond the tolerance level.

To illustrate the idea, we begin by solving a system of three equations with whole number coefficients; a system which does not give rise to any round off errors.

Example 1

$$x_1+2x_2+x_3 = 8 \quad (1)$$

$$2x_1-2x_2+3x_3 = 7 \quad (2)$$

$$3x_1+12x_2-2x_3 = 21 \quad (3)$$

The solution is in three stages—first, *elimination*. Add to (2) a multiple of (1) such that the coefficient of x_1 vanishes. Clearly the multiplier required in this case is $\dfrac{-2}{1} = -2 \quad \left(-\dfrac{a_{21}}{a_{11}} \text{ in general}\right)$.

(2) − 2(1) $\quad (2-2)x_1 + (-2-4)x_2 + (3-2)x_3 = 7-16$

or

$$-6x_2 + x_3 = -9 \qquad (2')$$

Similarly, add to (3) a multiple of (1), the multiplier being $\dfrac{-a_{31}}{a_{11}} = \dfrac{-3}{1} = -3$.

(3) − 3(1) $\quad (3-3)x_1 + (12-6)x_2 + (-2-3)x_3 = 21-24$

$$6x_2 - 5x_3 = -3 \qquad (3')$$

We now discard equation (1) and eliminate x_2 from (2′) and (3′). Add to (3′) a multiple of (2′) such that the coefficient of x_2 vanishes and then discard (2′). The multiplier is $\dfrac{-6}{-6} = 1$.

(3′) + (2′) $\quad (6-6)x_2 + (-5+1)x_3 = -3-9$

$$-4x_3 = -12 \qquad (3'')$$

We now collect together the last equation and the two discarded equations ((2′) and (1)) and proceed to the second stage of the solution, known as *back substitution*.

$$-4x_3 = -12 \qquad (3'')$$

$$-6x_2 + x_3 = -9 \qquad (2')$$

$$x_1 + 2x_2 + x_3 = 8 \qquad (1)$$

From (3″) $\quad x_3 = 3$

Substituting $x_3 = 3$ in (2′) $\quad x_2 = 2$

Substituting $\left.\begin{matrix} x_3 = 3 \\ x_2 = 2 \end{matrix}\right\}$ in (1) $\quad x_1 = 1$

We now proceed to the third stage which involves *calculating the residuals*. We insert the solution into the left hand side of each of the original equations and compare the results with the right hand side constants. The differences between the results and the constants are the residuals.

In this example, where only exact numbers are involved, all the residuals are zero.

When working through a set of equations, there is no need to record the x_i since we operate only on a_{ij} and b_i. We set out the solution as follows:

Elimination

Row	*Operation on row*	*Multiplier* m	*Coefficients* a_1	a_2	a_3	*Constant* b	*Sum* Σ
(1)		*	1	2	1	8	12
(2)		−2/1	2	−2	3	7	10
(3)		−3/1	3	12	−2	21	34
(2′)	(2)−2×(1)	*		−6	1	−9	10−2(12) = −14
(3′)	(3)−3×(1)	1		6	−5	−3	34−3(12) = −2
(3″)	(3′)+1×(2′)	*			−4	−12	−2+1(−14) = −16

	x_1	x_2	x_3
Back substitution	1	2	3
Calculation of residuals	0	0	0

The third column contains the multiplier, m, at each stage. The equations that are used to find the multiplier have an asterisk in this column to show that they are used in the back substitution. The last column, labelled Σ, represents the sum of the numbers in the middle four columns and is used as a check. The figure in this column is subject to precisely the same operations as the figures in the four preceding columns and should always equal their sum.

This method is satisfactory so long as all the coefficients are exact at every stage in the working. In practice, this is seldom true and they have to be rounded off at all stages. This makes the calculation more complicated as is illustrated by the next example.

Example 2

Solve the following abbreviated system of equations, working to 5S.

a_1	a_2	a_3	b
0.0034	0.7417	0.6015	0.5529
0.8275	0.0124	0.0856	0.2188
0.5622	0.4188	0.9201	0.0123

First attempt

The multiplier for the second row is $-0.8275/0.0034 = -243.38$. We proceed to calculate the 4th row (2nd row—$243.38 \times$ 1st row)

$$a'_{22} = 0.0124-(0.7417)(243.38) = 0.0124-180.51 = -180.50$$

$$a'_{23} = 0.0856-(0.6015)(243.38) = 0.0856-146.31 = -146.31$$

$$b'_2 = 0.2188-(0.5529)(243.38) = 0.2188-134.56 = -134.34$$

(The primes indicate that the original coefficients have been modified.) Looking at these results, we see that the original numbers in the 2nd row have been swamped by the contribution from the first row. Since the multiplier is so large, 2D has been lost from each of the 2nd row coefficients, and this will affect the accuracy of the final result since these errors will be propagated throughout the later working. The multiplier for the third row, $-0.5622/0.0034 = -165.35$, is almost as large, and will give rise to further round-off errors.

The cause of the trouble, then, is that the multipliers are too large, and this in itself is caused by the fact that a_{11} (0.0034) is very small compared with a_{21} and a_{31}. Clearly, the smaller we can make the multipliers, the smaller will be the round-off errors in the multiplication. We therefore change the procedure and calculate the multipliers at each stage not from the first available equation, but from the equation with the largest leading coefficient. This coefficient is called the *pivot* and the equation to which it belongs is known as the *pivotal equation*. In this example, the pivot will be a_{21} (0.8275), and the multipliers for the first and third rows will be $-a_{11}/a_{21} = -0.00411$ and $-a_{31}/a_{21} = -0.67940$. This procedure ensures that all the multipliers will be less than 1.

Second attempt

We now solve the equations by pivotal condensation:

Elimination

		m	a_1	a_2
(1)		−0.00411	0.0034	0.7417
(2)		*	0.8275	0.0124
(3)		−0.67940	0.5622	0.4188
(1′)	(1)−0.00411×(2)	*		0.74165
(3′)	(3)−0.6794×(2)	−0.55332		0.41037
(3″)	(3′)−0.55332×(1′)	*		

		a_3	b	Σ
(1)		0.6015	0.5529	1.8995
(2)		0.0856	0.2188	1.1443
(3)		0.9201	0.0213	1.9224
(1′)	(1)−0.00411×(2)	0.60115	0.55200	1.8948
(3′)	(3)−0.6794×(2)	0.86194	−0.12735	1.1450
(3″)	(3′)−0.55332×(1′)	0.52931	−0.43278	0.09657

Back substitution

$$x_3 = -\frac{0.43278}{0.52931} = -0.81763$$

$$x_2 = \frac{0.55200 - 0.60115 \times (-0.81763)}{0.74165} = 1.4070$$

$$x_1 = \frac{0.2188 - 0.0856 \times (-0.81763) - 0.0124 \times 1.4070}{0.8275} = 0.32790$$

Calculation of residuals

On substituting the solutions in the original equations the residuals (defined on page 647) are found to be

$$R_1 = -0.000\,018$$

$$R_2 = -0.000\,005$$

$$R_3 = -0.000\,004$$

which indicates a highly satisfactory degree of accuracy in the solutions.

Discrepancies in the last figure of the $\sum$ column are to be expected, and are due to accumulated round-off error. In the sixth row, $0.529\,31 - 0.432\,78 = 0.096\,53$, makes a discrepancy of 4 in the last figure. For this reason, the working should always be carried out to one more significant figure than is needed.

The error analysis for pivotal condensation is difficult—the accuracy of the solution depending on the relative size of the coefficients.

Exercise 3.1

1 Illustrate the method of pivotal condensation for solving a set of simultaneous linear equations by solving the system of equations

$$6x_1 + 2x_2 + x_3 = 1$$

$$2x_1 + 5x_2 + x_3 = 1$$

$$3x_1 + 2x_2 + 5x_3 = 2$$

Give your solutions to three places of decimals. Calculate the residual errors. (M.E.I.)

2 Illustrate the method of pivotal condensation by solving the system of equations

$$4x_1 + x_2 + x_3 = 1$$

$$x_1 + 3x_2 + x_3 = 1$$

$$2x_1 + x_2 + 3x_3 = 2$$

Give your solution to three places of decimals. Show what checking procedure can be applied to your results.

Calculate the residuals and state whether your results imply anything about the accuracy of your solution. (M.E.I.)

3.2 Indirect methods of solution

In this type of method we take any suitable value as a first solution and use an iterative process to improve on this initial value. We shall discuss the method due to Gauss and Seidel.

The Gauss–Seidel iterative method

The equations are first rearranged so that the coefficients in the main diagonal of the matrix are dominant, that is greater than or equal to the other coefficients, if this is possible. For example

$$\left.\begin{aligned} 2x_1+4x_2-\ x_3 &= 7 \\ x_1-2x_2+5x_3 &= 12 \\ 5x_1-3x_2+\ x_3 &= 2 \end{aligned}\right\} \text{ are arranged } \begin{aligned} 5x_1-3x_2+\ x_3 &= 2 \\ 2x_1+4x_2-\ x_3 &= 7 \\ x_1-2x_2+5x_3 &= 12 \end{aligned}$$

The equations are then rewritten in the form

$$x_1 = \frac{(3x_2-x_3+2)}{5}$$

$$x_2 = \frac{(-2x_1+x_3+7)}{4}$$

$$x_3 = \frac{(-x_1+2x_2+12)}{5}$$

The x_i are then given starting values (usually 1 in computer programs), and are recalculated iteratively as follows:

$$x_1^{(0)} = x_2^{(0)} = x_3^{(0)} = 1$$

First cycle

$$x_1^{(1)} = [3(1)-1+2]/5 = 0.8$$
$$x_2^{(1)} = [-2(0.8)+1+7]/4 = 1.6$$
$$x_3^{(1)} = [-0.8+2(1.6)+12]/5 = 2.88$$

Second cycle

$$x_1^{(2)} = [3(1.6)-2.88+2]/5 = 0.784$$
$$x_2^{(2)} = [-2(0.784)+2.88+7]/4 = 2.078$$
$$x_3^{(2)} = [-0.784+2(2.078)+12]/5 = 3.231$$

The result of the first 5 cycles are tabulated below

i (cycle)	0	1	2	3	4	5
$x_1^{(i)}$	1	0.8	0.784	1.005	1.029	0.996
$x_2^{(i)}$	1	1.6	2.078	2.055	1.991	2.000 (3D)
$x_3^{(i)}$	1	2.88	3.231	3.021	2.990	3.001

It can be seen that the solution is converging to (1, 2, 3). The iteration is continued until all the x_i satisfy the criterion,

$$|x_i^{(n)} - x_i^{(n-1)}| < \text{Tol}$$

The Gauss–Seidel method will give the solution to the equations provided that they can be arranged with a dominant leading diagonal. To be precise, the diagonal elements must be at least as large as the sum of all the other elements in their row, and, in at least one case, larger.

The method is well suited to use on a computer and is particularly effective in systems of equations where the matrix of the coefficients is *sparse*—i.e. contains many zero elements.

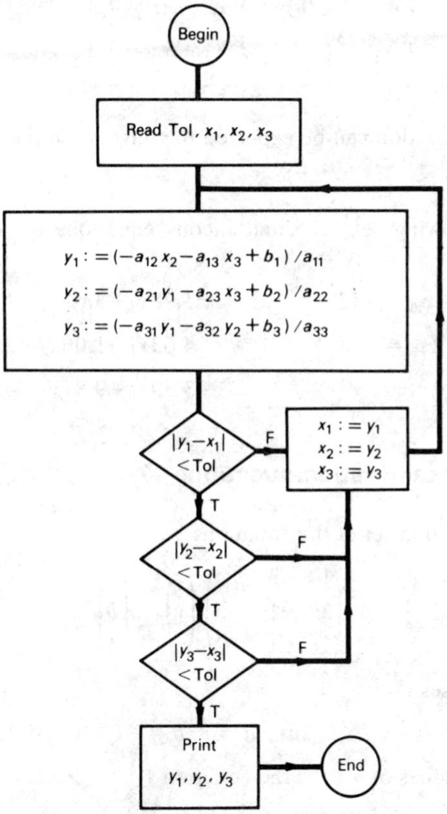

In a direct method, such as pivotal condensation, these zero elements soon take on non-zero values as the elimination proceeds. In this method, however, the coefficients are never changed and hence the calculation is much reduced. The method is also useful for large systems of equations since only the coefficients of one row need be held in the computer's main store at any one time.

Exercise 3.2

1 Taking the values $x = y = z = 1$ as the initial estimate, carry out two cycles of the Gauss–Seidel iteration for the system

$$\begin{pmatrix} 5 & 1 & 1 \\ 1 & 5 & 1 \\ 1 & 1 & 5 \end{pmatrix} \begin{pmatrix} x \\ y \\ z \end{pmatrix} = \begin{pmatrix} 6.6 \\ 5.0 \\ 1.0 \end{pmatrix}$$

2 Draw up a flow chart for the solution of a system of three linear equations by the Gauss–Seidel iterative method. Taking the initial approximation $x = y = z = 1$, carry out one cycle of the iteration of each of the systems

(a)
$$\begin{aligned} 4x+2y+z &= 7.4 \\ x+2y+z &= 4.3 \\ x+y+5z &= 7.2 \end{aligned}$$

(b)
$$\begin{aligned} x+2y+z &= 4.3 \\ x+y+5z &= 7.2 \\ 4x+2y+z &= 7.4 \end{aligned}$$

Explain why the iteration can be expected to converge in one case, but not in the other. (L.)

3 Solve the following sets of simultaneous equations by an iterative method working to 4S.

(a)
$$\begin{aligned} 2x_1+6x_2-x_3 &= -12 \\ 5x_1-x_2+2x_3 &= 29 \\ -3x_1-4x_2+x_3 &= 5 \end{aligned}$$

(b)
$$\begin{aligned} 1.78x_1+3.01x_2-4.88x_3 &= -7.70 \\ 4.63x_1-1.06x_2-2.27x_3 &= -6.36 \\ -3.39x_1+9.81x_2-4.78x_3 &= 3.95 \end{aligned}$$

Miscellaneous examination questions 17

1(a) Find the solution set of the equations

$$\begin{pmatrix} 1 & 3 & a \\ 2 & -1 & -5 \\ 1 & 1 & 2 \end{pmatrix} \begin{pmatrix} x \\ y \\ z \end{pmatrix} = \begin{pmatrix} 4 \\ b \\ 1 \end{pmatrix}$$

in the following cases

(i) $a = 9, b = -1$ (ii) $a = 8, b = -1$ (iii) $a = 8, b = -2\frac{1}{2}$

(b) For what values of a does the equation

(i) $\begin{pmatrix} a & -5 & 2 \\ 3 & -1 & 1 \\ 1 & 2 & 1 \end{pmatrix} \begin{pmatrix} x \\ y \\ z \end{pmatrix} = \begin{pmatrix} 4 \\ 7 \\ 8 \end{pmatrix}$ not have a unique solution?

(ii) $\begin{pmatrix} a & -10 & 4 \\ 3 & -1 & 1 \\ 1 & 2 & 1 \end{pmatrix} \begin{pmatrix} x \\ y \\ z \end{pmatrix} = \begin{pmatrix} 4 \\ 7 \\ 9 \end{pmatrix}$ not have a unique solution? (S.M.P.)

2(a) By solving the set of equations

$$x_1 = a$$
$$-x_1 + x_2 = b$$
$$3x_1 + 2x_2 + x_3 = c$$

or otherwise, find the inverse of the matrix

$$\boldsymbol{A} = \begin{pmatrix} 1 & 0 & 0 \\ -1 & 1 & 0 \\ 3 & 2 & 1 \end{pmatrix}$$

Given $$\boldsymbol{B} = \begin{pmatrix} 1 & 4 & -2 \\ 0 & 1 & 3 \\ 0 & 0 & 1 \end{pmatrix}$$

find $\boldsymbol{B}^{-1}$ and also, by any method, the inverse of $\boldsymbol{AB}$. State a set of equations which this inverse $(\boldsymbol{AB})^{-1}$ would help you to solve.

(b) Find the solution set of the simultaneous equations

$$2x + 3y + z = 0, \qquad 5x + 7y + z = 0$$

and interpret your solution geometrically.

Hence or otherwise solve

$$2x + 3y + z = 6, \qquad 5x + 7y + z = 13$$

giving your solution in parametric form. (M.E.I.)

3 If

$$\boldsymbol{M} = \begin{pmatrix} 1 & -1 & k \\ 4 & 7 & 3 \\ 3 & 19 & 1 \end{pmatrix}$$

find det $\boldsymbol{M}$ in terms of k.

(a) If $k = 2$ solve $\boldsymbol{Mx} = \boldsymbol{0}$ and $\boldsymbol{Mx} = \begin{pmatrix} 3 \\ 8 \\ 16 \end{pmatrix}$.

(b) If $k = 1$, solve $\boldsymbol{Mx} = \boldsymbol{0}$ and interpret the result geometrically. (M.E.I.)

4 (a) Given that

$$\boldsymbol{M}\begin{pmatrix} x \\ y \\ z \end{pmatrix} = \begin{pmatrix} 7 \\ 3 \\ 1 \end{pmatrix} \quad \text{where} \quad \boldsymbol{M} = \begin{pmatrix} 1 & 1 & 2 \\ 1 & -1 & 0 \\ 2 & 0 & -1 \end{pmatrix}$$

find x, y and z.

(b) Find the inverse of the matrix

$$\boldsymbol{M} = \begin{pmatrix} 1 & -1 & 1 \\ 3 & -9 & 5 \\ 1 & -3 & 3 \end{pmatrix}$$

Rewrite the set of equations

$$\begin{aligned} x - y + z &= 3 \\ 3x - 9y + 5z &= 6 \\ x - 3y + 3z &= 13 \end{aligned}$$

in a form using the matrix $\boldsymbol{M}$ and hence solve the equations. (M.E.I.)

5 (a) Solve

$$\begin{pmatrix} 1 & 1 & 1 \\ 1 & 2 & 3 \\ -2 & -3 & a \end{pmatrix}\begin{pmatrix} x \\ y \\ z \end{pmatrix} = \begin{pmatrix} 6 \\ 14 \\ b \end{pmatrix} \qquad \text{when } a = 4,\ b = 4$$

(b) Find the value of a for which no unique solution exists. When a has this value, find the value of b for which there is an infinite number of solutions. (L.)

6 Using any method you like, and in any order

(a) Solve the equations

$$\begin{aligned} x + 2y + 3z &= 6 \\ 2x + 3y + z &= -1 \\ 3x + y + 2z &= 7 \end{aligned}$$

(b) Find the inverse of the matrix

$$\begin{pmatrix} 1 & 2 & 3 \\ 2 & 3 & 1 \\ 3 & 1 & 2 \end{pmatrix}$$

(c) Find the value of k for which the equations

$$\begin{aligned} x + 2y + 3z &= 6 \\ 2x + 3y + z &= -1 \\ 3x + y + kz &= -47 \end{aligned}$$

are not independent. For this value of k, give the general solutions and interpret the equations geometrically. (C.)

7 Using pivotal condensation, solve the equations

$$\begin{aligned} 6x + 5y + 4z &= 2 \\ 5x - 3y + 3z &= 5 \\ 4x + 7y + 6z &= 2 \end{aligned}$$

The coefficients are exact, and the work is to be set out in tabular form with headed columns and a sum check. The solution is required in the form of rational numbers. (C.)

8 Use the method of pivotal condensation with a sum check, or any other suitable method, to find the values of x_1, x_2, x_3 from the following simultaneous equations.

Tabulate the details of your working, and give your results to 3S.

$$9.37x_1+3.04x_2-2.44x_3 = 9.23$$
$$3.04x_1+6.18x_2+1.22x_3 = 8.20$$
$$-2.44x_1+1.22x_2+8.44x_3 = 3.93$$

Find the residual when your results are substituted in the second equation. Comment on the value of this residual as a guide to the accuracy of your results. (M.E.I.)

9 Solve for w, x, y, z

$$4.00w-0.75x+1.00y-2.22z = 2.40$$
$$-2.00w+3.00x-0.98y-1.41z = 1.15$$
$$1.00w-0.75x+2.00y+0.98z = 2.39$$
$$1.14w-2.63x-1.50y+1.00z = -3.67$$

(A.E.B.)

10 Carry out two cycles of the Gauss–Seidel iteration for the following system of equations

$$\begin{aligned} 2x_1-x_2 &= 1\\ -x_1+2x_2-x_3 &= 1\\ -x_2+2x_3-x_4 &= 1\\ -x_3+2x_4-x_5 &= 1\\ -x_4+2x_5-x_6 &= 1\\ -x_5+2x_6 &= 1 \end{aligned}$$

(This is an example of a sparse system.) (M.E.I.)

11 Use an iterative method to solve

(a)
$$\begin{aligned} 11.8\,x_1+9.15x_2+2.15x_3 &= 6.88\\ 4.26x_1+15.36x_2-2.89x_3 &= -8.61\\ 6.30x_1-5.88x_2+3.85x_3 &= 12.9 \end{aligned}$$

(b)
$$\begin{aligned} 3.82x_1+7.11x_2+4.19x_3 &= 34.6\\ 5.22x_1+1.75x_2-2.13x_3 &= 30.5\\ 4.76x_1-0.87x_2+6.41x_3 &= 2.40 \end{aligned}$$

Chapter 18

Matrices and Transformations 2

1 Transformations in 3D

1.1 Transformations of points, lines and the unit cube

We now develop and extend the ideas of transformations in two and three dimensions.

Extension from 2D to 3D

(a) The transformation matrix $\boldsymbol{M} = \begin{pmatrix} a_1 & b_1 \\ a_2 & b_2 \end{pmatrix}$, of base vectors $\boldsymbol{a}$ and $\boldsymbol{b}$ becomes $\boldsymbol{N} = \begin{pmatrix} a_1 & b_1 & c_1 \\ a_2 & b_2 & c_2 \\ a_3 & b_3 & c_3 \end{pmatrix}$ of base vectors $\boldsymbol{a}$, $\boldsymbol{b}$ and $\boldsymbol{c}$. The inverse transformation matrix $\boldsymbol{M}^{-1}$ exists provided that $|\boldsymbol{M}| \neq 0$. Similarly, $\boldsymbol{N}^{-1}$ exists provided that $|\boldsymbol{N}| \neq 0$.

(b) The transformation of a point. (x, y) becomes (x, y, z).

$$\text{In 2D} \quad x' = a_1x + b_1y \qquad \text{in 3D} \quad x' = a_1x + b_1y + c_1z$$

$$y' = a_2x + b_2y \qquad y' = a_2x + b_2y + c_2z$$

$$z' = a_3x + b_3y + c_3z$$

As in a transformation using a 2×2 matrix, the origin is invariant so in a transformation involving a 3×3 matrix, O is also invariant.

(c) The transformation of a unit square becomes the transformation of a unit cube.

In 2D $\quad \begin{pmatrix} 1 \\ 0 \end{pmatrix} \to \begin{pmatrix} a_1 \\ a_2 \end{pmatrix}, \quad \begin{pmatrix} 0 \\ 1 \end{pmatrix} \to \begin{pmatrix} b_1 \\ b_2 \end{pmatrix}; \qquad |\boldsymbol{M}|$ = the area of the transformed square

In 3D $\quad \begin{pmatrix} 1 \\ 0 \\ 0 \end{pmatrix} \to \begin{pmatrix} a_1 \\ a_2 \\ a_3 \end{pmatrix}, \quad \begin{pmatrix} 0 \\ 1 \\ 0 \end{pmatrix} \to \begin{pmatrix} b_1 \\ b_2 \\ b_3 \end{pmatrix}, \quad \begin{pmatrix} 0 \\ 0 \\ 1 \end{pmatrix} \to \begin{pmatrix} c_1 \\ c_2 \\ c_3 \end{pmatrix}; \qquad |\boldsymbol{N}|$ = the volume of the transformed cube.

(d) The transformation matrix in 2D has up to two real eigenvalues, which are roots of the characteristic equation. In 3D there will be up to three real eigenvalues, which are the roots of the characteristic equation, a cubic equation this time.

(e) Transformations involving singular matrices have to be investigated.

Transformation of a point

If $$\begin{pmatrix} x' \\ y' \\ z' \end{pmatrix} = \begin{pmatrix} a_1 & b_1 & c_1 \\ a_2 & b_2 & c_2 \\ a_3 & b_3 & c_3 \end{pmatrix} \begin{pmatrix} x \\ y \\ z \end{pmatrix}$$ then $$\begin{aligned} x' &= a_1x + b_1y + c_1z \\ y' &= a_2x + b_2y + c_2z \\ z' &= a_3x + b_3y + c_3z \end{aligned}$$

or $$\begin{pmatrix} x' \\ y' \\ z' \end{pmatrix} = x\begin{pmatrix} a_1 \\ a_2 \\ a_3 \end{pmatrix} + y\begin{pmatrix} b_1 \\ b_2 \\ b_3 \end{pmatrix} + z\begin{pmatrix} c_1 \\ c_2 \\ c_3 \end{pmatrix}$$

Example 1

Suppose $\boldsymbol{N} = \begin{pmatrix} 1 & 0 & 0 \\ 0 & 2 & 0 \\ 0 & 0 & 3 \end{pmatrix}$ and we consider the transformation of the points P(8, 0, 0), Q(6, 0, 3) and R(2, 0, 3). Then

$$\mathrm{P}' = 8\begin{pmatrix} 1 \\ 0 \\ 0 \end{pmatrix} + 0\begin{pmatrix} 0 \\ 2 \\ 0 \end{pmatrix} + 0\begin{pmatrix} 0 \\ 0 \\ 3 \end{pmatrix} = \begin{pmatrix} 8 \\ 0 \\ 0 \end{pmatrix}$$

$$\mathrm{Q}' = 6\begin{pmatrix} 1 \\ 0 \\ 0 \end{pmatrix} + 0\begin{pmatrix} 0 \\ 2 \\ 0 \end{pmatrix} + 3\begin{pmatrix} 0 \\ 0 \\ 3 \end{pmatrix} = \begin{pmatrix} 6 \\ 0 \\ 9 \end{pmatrix}$$

Similarly $$\mathrm{R}' = \begin{pmatrix} 2 \\ 0 \\ 9 \end{pmatrix}$$

More concisely $$\begin{pmatrix} 1 & 0 & 0 \\ 0 & 2 & 0 \\ 0 & 0 & 3 \end{pmatrix} \overset{\begin{matrix} \mathrm{P} & \mathrm{Q} & \mathrm{R} \end{matrix}}{\begin{pmatrix} 8 & 6 & 2 \\ 0 & 0 & 0 \\ 0 & 3 & 3 \end{pmatrix}} = \overset{\begin{matrix} \mathrm{P}' & \mathrm{Q}' & \mathrm{R}' \end{matrix}}{\begin{pmatrix} 8 & 6 & 2 \\ 0 & 0 & 0 \\ 0 & 9 & 9 \end{pmatrix}}$$

Example 2

After a transformation using the matrix $\boldsymbol{M} = \begin{pmatrix} 2 & 0 & 0 \\ 1 & 1 & 0 \\ 2 & 1 & 3 \end{pmatrix}$ a point has coordinates (6, 5, 11). Find the original point.

In this example we use direct substitution since the method is easy to use when the equations are in this form.

$$\begin{pmatrix}2 & 0 & 0\\1 & 1 & 0\\2 & 1 & 3\end{pmatrix}\begin{pmatrix}x\\y\\z\end{pmatrix}=\begin{pmatrix}6\\5\\11\end{pmatrix}\Rightarrow\left.\begin{aligned}2x&=6\\x+y&=5\\2x+y+3z&=11\end{aligned}\right\}\Rightarrow\begin{aligned}x&=3\\y&=2\\z&=1\end{aligned}$$

However, in most cases we should find the inverse matrix and then solve the equation $\boldsymbol{x}=\boldsymbol{M}^{-1}\boldsymbol{x}'$. Therefore, if

$$\boldsymbol{M}=\begin{pmatrix}2 & 0 & 0\\1 & 1 & 0\\2 & 1 & 3\end{pmatrix}\qquad\text{then}\qquad\boldsymbol{M}^{-1}=\begin{pmatrix}\frac{3}{6} & 0 & 0\\-\frac{3}{6} & \frac{6}{6} & 0\\-\frac{1}{6} & -\frac{2}{6} & \frac{2}{6}\end{pmatrix}$$

Hence $$\begin{pmatrix}x\\y\\z\end{pmatrix}=\frac{1}{6}\begin{pmatrix}3 & 0 & 0\\-3 & 6 & 0\\-1 & -2 & 2\end{pmatrix}\begin{pmatrix}6\\5\\11\end{pmatrix}=\frac{1}{6}\begin{pmatrix}18\\12\\6\end{pmatrix}=\begin{pmatrix}3\\2\\1\end{pmatrix}$$

Transformation of a line

Example 3

Transform the line $\dfrac{x-1}{2}=\dfrac{y+3}{-1}=\dfrac{z}{4}$ using the matrix $\begin{pmatrix}1 & 0 & 1\\3 & -1 & -1\\0 & 2 & 0\end{pmatrix}$.

Taking the parametric equations of the line we have

$$\begin{pmatrix}x'\\y'\\z'\end{pmatrix}=\begin{pmatrix}1 & 0 & 1\\3 & -1 & -1\\0 & 2 & 0\end{pmatrix}\begin{pmatrix}2t+1\\-t-3\\4t\end{pmatrix}=\begin{pmatrix}6t+1\\3t+6\\-2t-6\end{pmatrix}$$

Thus, the equation of the transformed line is

$$\frac{x-1}{6}=\frac{y-6}{3}=\frac{z+6}{-2}$$

Transformation of the unit cube

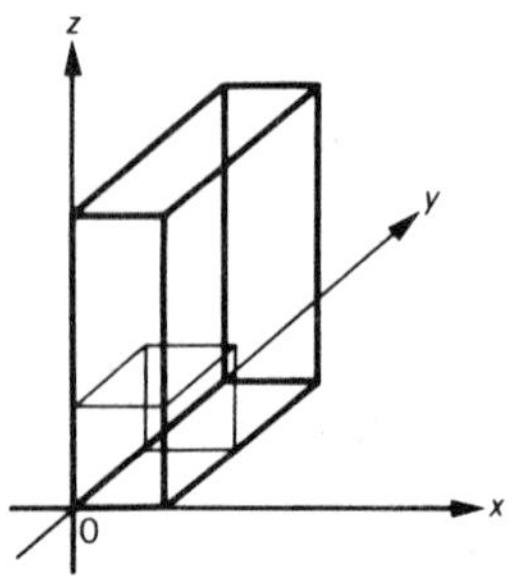

The diagram illustrates the transformation of the unit cube under the matrix

$$\boldsymbol{P} = \begin{pmatrix} 1 & 0 & 0 \\ 0 & 2 & 0 \\ 0 & 0 & 3 \end{pmatrix} \qquad \text{Note that } |\boldsymbol{P}| = 6$$

$$\boldsymbol{P}^{-1} = \begin{pmatrix} 1 & 0 & 0 \\ 0 & \frac{1}{2} & 0 \\ 0 & 0 & \frac{1}{3} \end{pmatrix}, \qquad |\boldsymbol{P}^{-1}| = \tfrac{1}{6}$$

We now give the matrices for some of the standard transformations of space.

Reflection in a plane

(a) $\begin{pmatrix} 0 & 1 & 0 \\ 1 & 0 & 0 \\ 0 & 0 & 1 \end{pmatrix}$ $\boldsymbol{a}, \boldsymbol{b}$ interchanged, reflection in the $y = x$ plane.

(b) $\begin{pmatrix} 0 & 0 & 1 \\ 0 & 1 & 0 \\ 1 & 0 & 0 \end{pmatrix}$ $\boldsymbol{a}, \boldsymbol{c}$ interchanged, reflection in the $x = z$ plane.

Rotation about an axis

$\begin{pmatrix} -1 & 0 & 0 \\ 0 & -1 & 0 \\ 0 & 0 & 1 \end{pmatrix}$ half turn about the z axis.

Stretch along an axis

$\begin{pmatrix} k & 0 & 0 \\ 0 & l & 0 \\ 0 & 0 & m \end{pmatrix}$ multiplies x by k, y by l, z by m.

Shear with an invariant plane

$\begin{pmatrix} 1 & 0 & 0 \\ 0 & 1 & 0 \\ 0 & k & 1 \end{pmatrix}$ and $\begin{pmatrix} 1 & k & 0 \\ 0 & 1 & 0 \\ 0 & 0 & 1 \end{pmatrix}$ both represent a shear with the invariant plane $y = 0$.

Translation of a plane

It is not possible to represent a *translation* using a 2×2 matrix only. However in 2D a translation can be represented by

$$\boldsymbol{M} = \begin{pmatrix} 1 & 0 & a \\ 0 & 1 & b \end{pmatrix} \qquad \text{where} \qquad \begin{pmatrix} x' \\ y' \end{pmatrix} = \begin{pmatrix} 1 & 0 & a \\ 0 & 1 & b \end{pmatrix} \begin{pmatrix} x \\ y \\ 1 \end{pmatrix} = \begin{pmatrix} x + a \\ y + b \end{pmatrix}$$

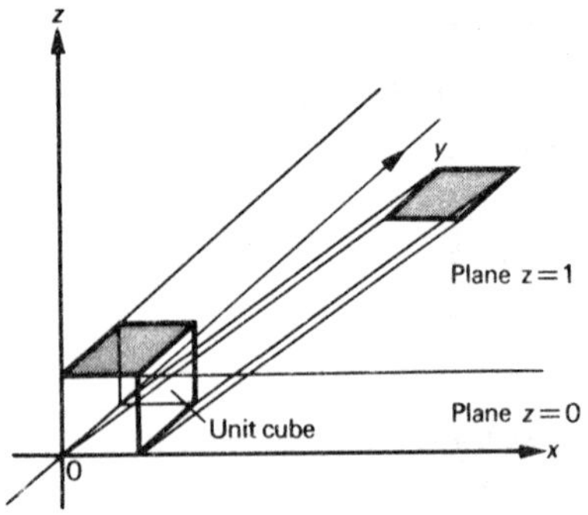

In 3D $\begin{pmatrix} x \\ y \\ 1 \end{pmatrix}$ corresponds to a point in the plane $z = 1$. Suppose $\begin{pmatrix} a \\ b \end{pmatrix} = \begin{pmatrix} 2 \\ 3 \end{pmatrix}$, for example, then every point in the $z = 1$ plane will have undergone the translation $\begin{pmatrix} 2 \\ 3 \end{pmatrix}$. Thus, in 3D the matrix

$$\begin{pmatrix} 1 & 0 & 2 \\ 0 & 1 & 3 \\ 0 & 0 & 1 \end{pmatrix}$$

represents a shear, with $z = 0$ the invariant plane, and the plane $z = 1$ undergoing the translation $\begin{pmatrix} 2 \\ 3 \end{pmatrix}$.

Note that the inverse matrix is

$$\begin{pmatrix} 1 & 0 & -2 \\ 0 & 1 & -3 \\ 0 & 0 & 1 \end{pmatrix}$$

Rotation of a plane

A rotation through α of the x, y plane is represented by $\boldsymbol{R}_\alpha = \begin{pmatrix} \cos\alpha & -\sin\alpha & 0 \\ \sin\alpha & \cos\alpha & 0 \\ 0 & 0 & 1 \end{pmatrix}$ in 3D. Similarly a rotation β of the y, z plane will be given by $\boldsymbol{R}_\beta = \begin{pmatrix} 1 & 0 & 0 \\ 0 & \cos\beta & -\sin\beta \\ 0 & \sin\beta & \cos\beta \end{pmatrix}$ and so on.

Combining transformations in a plane

As an illustration of the ideas we investigate the matrix representing a reflection in the line $y = (\tan\alpha)x + c$. We consider the problem in several steps.

First we apply a translation, $\boldsymbol{T}_{(0,-c)}$, which has the effect of moving the line of reflection to a parallel line through the origin.

$$\boldsymbol{T}_{(0,-c)} = \begin{pmatrix} 1 & 0 & 0 \\ 0 & 1 & -c \\ 0 & 0 & 1 \end{pmatrix}$$

The mirror line is then rotated through $-\alpha$ to lie along the x axis.

$$\boldsymbol{R}_{-\alpha} = \begin{pmatrix} \cos\alpha & \sin\alpha & 0 \\ -\sin\alpha & \cos\alpha & 0 \\ 0 & 0 & 1 \end{pmatrix}$$

We then consider the reflection in the x axis

$$\boldsymbol{X} = \begin{pmatrix} 1 & 0 & 0 \\ 0 & -1 & 0 \\ 0 & 0 & 1 \end{pmatrix}$$

and then apply the inverse transformations $\boldsymbol{R}_{\alpha}$ and finally $\boldsymbol{T}_{(0,c)}$. The matrix for the transformation is given by the product of the matrices

$$\underset{\boldsymbol{T}_{(0,c)}}{\begin{pmatrix} 1 & 0 & 0 \\ 0 & 1 & c \\ 0 & 0 & 1 \end{pmatrix}} \underset{\boldsymbol{R}_{\alpha}}{\begin{pmatrix} \cos\alpha & -\sin\alpha & 0 \\ \sin\alpha & \cos\alpha & 0 \\ 0 & 0 & 1 \end{pmatrix}} \underset{\boldsymbol{X}}{\begin{pmatrix} 1 & 0 & 0 \\ 0 & -1 & 0 \\ 0 & 0 & 1 \end{pmatrix}} \underset{\boldsymbol{R}_{-\alpha}}{\begin{pmatrix} \cos\alpha & \sin\alpha & 0 \\ -\sin\alpha & \cos\alpha & 0 \\ 0 & 0 & 1 \end{pmatrix}} \underset{\boldsymbol{T}_{(0,-c)}}{\begin{pmatrix} 1 & 0 & 0 \\ 0 & 1 & -c \\ 0 & 0 & 1 \end{pmatrix}}$$

Exercise 1.1

1 Show that the line joining A(1, 2, 3) to B(4, 7, −3) and the line joining C(3, 1, 0) to D(−1, −10, 9) intersect at E(7, 12, −9).

The space is now transformed by the matrix $\begin{pmatrix} 3 & 2 & 0 \\ 0 & 1 & -1 \\ 1 & 0 & -2 \end{pmatrix}$. Find

(a) A′, B′, C′ and D′ the transforms of A, B, C and D.
(b) the point of intersection of A′B′ and C′D′
(c) E′. Comment.

2 Consider A(1, 0, 0), B(0, 1, 0), C(0, 0, 1), D(2, 0, 0), E(0, 3, 0), F(0, 0, 4).
(a) Find the coordinates of the point of intersection
(i) P of AB and DE (ii) Q of AC and DF (iii) R of BC and EF.
Show that P, Q and R are collinear.

The space is now transformed by the matrix $\begin{pmatrix} 0 & 1 & 4 \\ 2 & 3 & 0 \\ 0 & 0 & 1 \end{pmatrix}$

(b) Find the coordinates A′, B′, C′, D′, E′, F′, P′, Q′, R′ and show that P′, Q′ and R′ are collinear.

3 The line with parametric equations

$$x = 2t+1$$

$$y = t-3$$

$$z = -t$$

is transformed by the matrix $\begin{pmatrix} 1 & 0 & 1 \\ 0 & 2 & 1 \\ 1 & 0 & 0 \end{pmatrix}$

(a) Find an equation of the transformed line.

(b) Find the coordinates P and P′ where the original line and the transformed line cut the $z = 0$ plane.

4 Write down the matrices representing the following transformations

(a) A reflection in the $y = z$ plane.

(b) A rotation anticlockwise.

(i) 90° about the z axis (ii) 180° about the y axis (iii) 180° about the x axis

(c) Stretches

(i) $x \times 2$, $y \times \frac{1}{3}$, $z \times -2$ (ii) $x \times 1$, $y \times -\frac{1}{5}$, $z \times 3$

(d) A shear

(i) with the invariant plane $x = 0$ (ii) with the invariant plane $z = 0$.

5 Write down the 3×3 matrices which represent the following transformations

(a) A translation of the $z = 1$ plane of $\begin{pmatrix} -1 \\ 2 \end{pmatrix}$.

(b) A half turn of the $z = 1$ plane about the point $(1, 2)$.

(c) A reflection with the mirror plane containing the z axis and the line $x = y$.

(d) A one-way stretch, with the invariant plane containing the x axis and the y axis, and with a scale factor of 3 in the direction of the z axis.

(e) A shear, with the invariant plane containing the y and z axes, and $(1, 0, 0) \to (1, 1, 0)$.

1.2 Eigenvectors and eigenvalues of a 3×3 matrix

Remember that for a 2×2 matrix we used

$$\begin{pmatrix} a_1 & b_1 \\ a_2 & b_2 \end{pmatrix}\begin{pmatrix} x \\ y \end{pmatrix} = k\begin{pmatrix} x \\ y \end{pmatrix} = \begin{pmatrix} kx \\ ky \end{pmatrix}$$

This led to the characteristic equation

$$k^2 - (a_1 + b_2)k + a_1b_2 - a_2b_1 = 0$$

The solution of this gives us the eigenvalues and from these we found corresponding eigenvectors. For a 3×3 matrix, likewise we have

$$\begin{pmatrix} a_1 & b_1 & c_1 \\ a_2 & b_2 & c_2 \\ a_3 & b_3 & c_3 \end{pmatrix}\begin{pmatrix} x \\ y \\ z \end{pmatrix} = k\begin{pmatrix} x \\ y \\ z \end{pmatrix} = \begin{pmatrix} kx \\ ky \\ kz \end{pmatrix}$$

Example

Find the eigenvalues and corresponding eigenvectors of the matrix

$$\boldsymbol{P} = \begin{pmatrix} 3 & 2 & 2 \\ 1 & 4 & 1 \\ -2 & -4 & -1 \end{pmatrix}$$

Now $$\begin{pmatrix} 3 & 2 & 2 \\ 1 & 4 & 1 \\ -2 & -4 & -1 \end{pmatrix}\begin{pmatrix} x \\ y \\ z \end{pmatrix} = k\begin{pmatrix} x \\ y \\ z \end{pmatrix}$$

or $$\begin{pmatrix} 3 & 2 & 2 \\ 1 & 4 & 1 \\ -2 & -4 & -1 \end{pmatrix}\begin{pmatrix} x \\ y \\ z \end{pmatrix} = \begin{pmatrix} k & 0 & 0 \\ 0 & k & 0 \\ 0 & 0 & k \end{pmatrix}\begin{pmatrix} x \\ y \\ z \end{pmatrix}$$

Hence $$\begin{pmatrix} 3-k & 2 & 2 \\ 1 & 4-k & 1 \\ -2 & -4 & -1-k \end{pmatrix}\begin{pmatrix} x \\ y \\ z \end{pmatrix} = \begin{pmatrix} 0 \\ 0 \\ 0 \end{pmatrix}$$

If there are to be solutions other than $x = y = z = 0$

then $$\begin{vmatrix} 3-k & 2 & 2 \\ 1 & 4-k & 1 \\ -2 & -4 & -1-k \end{vmatrix} = 0$$

If we expand this we have

$$(3-k)[(4-k)(-1-k)-(1)(-4)]-2[-1-k-(-2)]+2[-4+2(4-k)] = 0$$

which simplifies to give

$$k^3-6k^2+11k-6 = 0$$

$$(k-1)(k-2)(k-3) = 0$$

$$k = 1, 2, 3$$

When $k = 1$

$$\left.\begin{aligned} 3x+2y+2z &= x \\ x+4y+z &= y \\ -2x-4y-z &= z \end{aligned}\right\} \Rightarrow y = 0 \text{ and we can take } z = 1 \text{ and } x = -1$$

Remember that the eigenvectors are not unique!

When $k = 2$

$$\left.\begin{aligned} 3x+2y+2z &= 2x \\ x+4y+z &= 2y \\ -2x-4y-z &= 2z \end{aligned}\right\} \Rightarrow z = 0 \text{ and we can take } y = 1 \text{ and } x = -2$$

When $k = 3$

$$\left.\begin{aligned} 3x+2y+2z &= 3x \\ x+4y+z &= 3y \\ -2x-4y-z &= 3z \end{aligned}\right\} \Rightarrow x = 0 \text{ and we can take } z = 1 \text{ and } y = -1$$

Hence the eigenvalues are $k = 1$ or $k = 2$ or $k = 3$ with corresponding eigenvectors being multiples of $\begin{pmatrix}-1\\0\\1\end{pmatrix}$, $\begin{pmatrix}-2\\1\\0\end{pmatrix}$ and $\begin{pmatrix}0\\-1\\1\end{pmatrix}$.

Exercise 1.2

1 The matrix $\boldsymbol{M} = \begin{pmatrix}7 & 2 & 0\\2 & 6 & -2\\0 & -2 & 5\end{pmatrix}$ is used to transform space. Find the new position vector of $\boldsymbol{a} = \begin{pmatrix}1\\-2\\-2\end{pmatrix}$ corresponding to a point A.

A second point B is such that OB′ = 6OB. Find the position vector $\boldsymbol{b}$ of B.

A third point C is such that OC′ = kOC. Find the value of the scalar k and give a set of possible coordinates for C.

2 Show that if

$$\boldsymbol{M} = \begin{pmatrix}0 & \sqrt{2} & 0\\\sqrt{2} & 0 & \sqrt{2}\\0 & \sqrt{2} & 0\end{pmatrix}$$

then

$$|\boldsymbol{M} - \lambda \boldsymbol{I}| = -\lambda^3 + 4\lambda$$

For what values of λ is the determinant zero? What is the meaning of an eigenvalue being zero? Determine eigenvectors corresponding to the eigenvalues of $\boldsymbol{M}$.

3 The characteristic equation of a 3×3 matrix is given by $|\boldsymbol{M} - k\boldsymbol{I}| = 0$. Show that if

$$\boldsymbol{M} = \begin{pmatrix}2 & 2 & -3\\2 & 2 & 3\\-3 & 3 & 3\end{pmatrix}$$

then the characteristic equation is

$$k^3 - 7k^2 - 6k + 72 = 0$$

Solve this equation given that $k = -3$ is one solution. Hence find the eigenvalues and corresponding eigenvectors of $\boldsymbol{M}$.

4 Given that $\boldsymbol{p} = \begin{pmatrix}1\\-2\\-2\end{pmatrix}$ and $\boldsymbol{q} = \begin{pmatrix}-2\\-2\\1\end{pmatrix}$ are eigenvectors of the transformation given by

$$\boldsymbol{M} = \begin{pmatrix}-1 & -2 & 0\\-2 & 0 & 2\\0 & 2 & 1\end{pmatrix}\cdot$$

find the three eigenvalues and a third eigenvector.

5 A transformation matrix has eigenvalues $k = 3, -3, 9$ with corresponding eigenvectors $\begin{pmatrix}1\\-2\\-2\end{pmatrix}, \begin{pmatrix}-2\\1\\-2\end{pmatrix}, \begin{pmatrix}-2\\-2\\1\end{pmatrix}$. Find the matrix of the transformation.

1.3 Transformations involving a singular matrix

We found that when we used a 2×2 singular matrix for a transformation the plane was mapped on to a line through the origin (see page 334). Similarly with a 3×3 singular matrix we find that, in general, space is mapped on to a plane through the origin.

Example 1

Consider the transformation of space using $\boldsymbol{M} = \begin{pmatrix}1 & -2 & 1\\2 & -1 & 0\\3 & 0 & -1\end{pmatrix}$ where $|\boldsymbol{M}| = 0$.

(a) Which vector maps on to the origin?
(b) Which plane is the space mapped on to?

(a) Suppose the vector is $\begin{pmatrix}x\\y\\z\end{pmatrix}$ then

$$\begin{pmatrix}1 & -2 & 1\\2 & -1 & 0\\3 & 0 & -1\end{pmatrix}\begin{pmatrix}x\\y\\z\end{pmatrix} = \begin{pmatrix}0\\0\\0\end{pmatrix} \qquad \left.\begin{aligned}x-2y+z &= 0\\2x-y &= 0\\3x-z &= 0\end{aligned}\right\} \Rightarrow \begin{aligned}x &= k\\y &= 2k\\z &= 3k\end{aligned}$$

Hence the required vector is

$$k\begin{pmatrix}1\\2\\3\end{pmatrix}$$

(b) Now we know that the image plane passes through A(1, 2, 3), B(−2, −1, 0), C(1, 0, −1) (these correspond to the base vectors of the transformation). Hence the plane has normals perpendicular to AB and BC, i.e.

$$\text{DRN} = \begin{pmatrix}3\\3\\3\end{pmatrix} \times \begin{pmatrix}-3\\-1\\1\end{pmatrix} = \begin{pmatrix}6\\-12\\6\end{pmatrix} \quad \text{or} \quad \begin{pmatrix}1\\-2\\1\end{pmatrix}$$

Hence the plane is $x-2y+z = 0$ since it must pass through the origin.

Example 2

Find the matrix that will map space orthogonally on to the plane with equation $2x-y-z = 0$, i.e. DRN $2:-1:-1$.

We shall find the mapping lines corresponding to (1, 0, 0), (0, 1, 0) and (0, 0, 1). Now the line through (1, 0, 0) parallel to the normal to the plane is

$$\frac{x-1}{2} = \frac{y}{-1} = \frac{z}{-1} \qquad \text{or} \qquad \begin{aligned} x &= 2k+1 \\ y &= -k \\ z &= -k \end{aligned}$$

This meets the plane $2x-y-z=0$ where $2(2k+1)+k+k=0$ i.e. $k=-\frac{1}{3}$

and hence for (1, 0, 0) the image point is $(\frac{1}{3}, \frac{1}{3}, \frac{1}{3})$

similarly for (0, 1, 0) the image point is $(\frac{2}{6}, \frac{5}{6}, -\frac{1}{6})$

and for (0, 0, 1) the image point is $(\frac{2}{6}, -\frac{1}{6}, \frac{5}{6})$

Hence the matrix for the transformation is

$$\begin{pmatrix} \frac{2}{6} & \frac{2}{6} & \frac{2}{6} \\ \frac{2}{6} & \frac{5}{6} & -\frac{1}{6} \\ \frac{2}{6} & -\frac{1}{6} & \frac{5}{6} \end{pmatrix}$$

We should now check that the determinant of the matrix is zero.

Exercise 1.3

1 Show that the determinant of each of the following matrices is zero and in each case find a non-zero vector which maps on to the origin.

(a) $\begin{pmatrix} 0 & 1 & -1 \\ -1 & 0 & 1 \\ 1 & -1 & 0 \end{pmatrix}$ **(b)** $\begin{pmatrix} 1 & 2 & 3 \\ -2 & -1 & 0 \\ 1 & 0 & -1 \end{pmatrix}$ **(c)** $\begin{pmatrix} 1 & 4 & 7 \\ 2 & 5 & 8 \\ 3 & 6 & 9 \end{pmatrix}$

2 Each of the following matrices has determinant zero.

(a) $\begin{pmatrix} 1 & 0 & 0 \\ 0 & 0 & 0 \\ 0 & 0 & 0 \end{pmatrix}$ **(b)** $\begin{pmatrix} 1 & 1 & 1 \\ 1 & 1 & 1 \\ 1 & 1 & 1 \end{pmatrix}$ **(c)** $\begin{pmatrix} 1 & 1 & 1 \\ 2 & 2 & 2 \\ 3 & 3 & 3 \end{pmatrix}$

(d) $\begin{pmatrix} 1 & 2 & 3 \\ 2 & 4 & 6 \\ 3 & 6 & 9 \end{pmatrix}$

In each case find two different vectors which are mapped onto the origin and find the equation of the plane which contains them.

3 Find the equation of the plane on to which space is mapped by

(a) $\begin{pmatrix} 1 & -3 & 5 \\ -2 & 6 & -10 \\ 4 & -11 & 16 \end{pmatrix}$ **(b)** $\begin{pmatrix} 1 & 3 & 7 \\ 4 & 2 & 5 \\ 5 & 5 & 12 \end{pmatrix}$

& See p 72

4 Find the matrix which maps space orthogonally on to the plane $x+2y-z=0$.

5 The transformation of space using $\boldsymbol{M}=\begin{pmatrix}1 & -2 & 1\\ 2 & -1 & 0\\ 3 & 0 & -1\end{pmatrix}$ maps $\begin{pmatrix}1\\2\\3\end{pmatrix}$ onto $\begin{pmatrix}0\\0\\0\end{pmatrix}$, and maps space on to the plane $x-2y+z=0$ (see Example 1 above). Show that the three lines parallel to $\begin{pmatrix}1\\2\\3\end{pmatrix}$ and through A$(-2, 1, -1)$, B$(2, 0, -1)$ and C$(3, -1, 0)$ each map onto a particular point of the plane. Deduce that the set of *all* lines parallel to $\begin{pmatrix}1\\2\\3\end{pmatrix}$ map on to this point.

2 The powers of a matrix

2.1 Equivalent matrices

We have seen that under most transformations of a plane or of space there are certain lines, the eigenvectors, which remain invariant in direction but are 'stretched' by a scale factor which is the eigenvalue. Clearly, if the same transformation is repeated, these lines still remain invariant. We now study *repeated* transformations of the plane using 2×2 matrices, but the ideas all extend to 3×3 (and higher order) matrices.

Since the point P, (p_1, p_2), is at the tip of the position vector $\boldsymbol{p}=\begin{pmatrix}p_1\\p_2\end{pmatrix}$, we can always calculate the transform of the point P, (p_1, p_2) by transforming the vector $\boldsymbol{p}$.

Consider the transformation of the plane represented by the matrix $\boldsymbol{A}=\begin{pmatrix}4 & -1\\ 2 & 1\end{pmatrix}$.

In the cartesian plane the point

$$\text{P}, \begin{pmatrix}2\\3\end{pmatrix} \to \text{P}', \begin{pmatrix}5\\7\end{pmatrix}$$

since

$$\begin{pmatrix}4 & -1\\ 2 & 1\end{pmatrix}\begin{pmatrix}2\\3\end{pmatrix}=\begin{pmatrix}5\\7\end{pmatrix}$$

Now the eigenvectors of the matrix $\begin{pmatrix}4 & -1\\ 2 & 1\end{pmatrix}$ are $\begin{pmatrix}1\\1\end{pmatrix}$ and $\begin{pmatrix}1\\2\end{pmatrix}$ (check this). We have drawn, on the next page, superimposed on the cartesian grid, a grid with the eigenvectors as base vectors.

The new axes x' and y' are drawn through $\begin{pmatrix}1\\1\end{pmatrix}$ and $\begin{pmatrix}1\\2\end{pmatrix}$ respectively, and marked off in these units, and the parallel lines are drawn in. Now the coordinates of P with respect to these axes are $\begin{pmatrix}1\\1\end{pmatrix}$ and those of P′ are $\begin{pmatrix}3\\2\end{pmatrix}$ so

$$\text{P}, \begin{pmatrix}1\\1\end{pmatrix} \to \text{P}', \begin{pmatrix}3\\2\end{pmatrix}$$

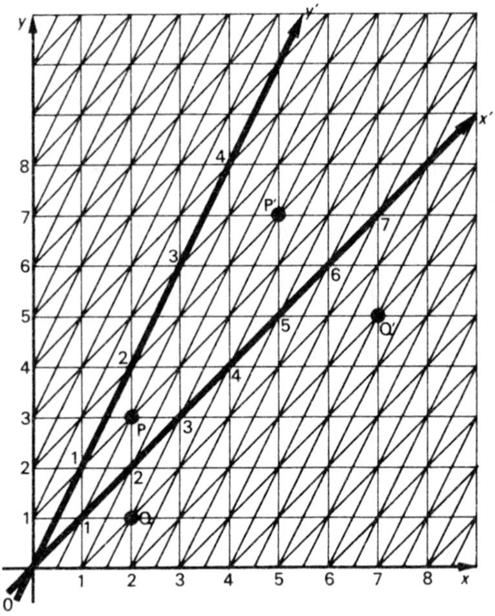

The transformation can be represented by the matrix $\boldsymbol{D} = \begin{pmatrix} 3 & 0 \\ 0 & 2 \end{pmatrix}$ since

$$\begin{matrix} & \text{P} & \text{P}' \\ \begin{pmatrix} 3 & 0 \\ 0 & 2 \end{pmatrix} & \begin{pmatrix} 1 \\ 1 \end{pmatrix} = & \begin{pmatrix} 3 \\ 2 \end{pmatrix} \end{matrix}$$

Similarly, on the cartesian grid Q, $\begin{pmatrix} 2 \\ 1 \end{pmatrix} \to$ Q′, $\begin{pmatrix} 7 \\ 5 \end{pmatrix}$

What are the coordinates of these points on the eigenvector grid? Check that the same matrix, $\begin{pmatrix} 3 & 0 \\ 0 & 2 \end{pmatrix}$, represents the transformation of Q→Q′ on that grid. If you check with any point you will find that this still works. Now $\boldsymbol{A} = \begin{pmatrix} 4 & -1 \\ 2 & 1 \end{pmatrix}$ represents a general transformation and quite a complicated one, combining a stretch and a shear, but $\boldsymbol{D} = \begin{pmatrix} 3 & 0 \\ 0 & 2 \end{pmatrix}$ represents a simple two-way stretch. In a similar way, any transformation represented by a matrix $\boldsymbol{A}$, is *equivalent* to a two-way stretch represented by $\boldsymbol{D}$, when the plane is defined by the eigenvectors of $\boldsymbol{A}$.

NOTE. (There are some difficulties here and the eigenvector grid cannot always be drawn, for instance, when the eigenvalues are equal or complex (see page 678).) In our example it is easy to see on the portion drawn of the eigenvector grid what the coordinates of certain points are on that grid. But in general, suppose P has cartesian coordinates $\begin{pmatrix} p \\ q \end{pmatrix}$ and the same point P has coordinates $\begin{pmatrix} x \\ y \end{pmatrix}$ with respect to the base vectors $\begin{pmatrix}1\\1\end{pmatrix}$ and $\begin{pmatrix}1\\2\end{pmatrix}$. Then

$$x\begin{pmatrix}1\\1\end{pmatrix}+y\begin{pmatrix}1\\2\end{pmatrix}=\begin{pmatrix}p\\q\end{pmatrix}$$

or $\begin{pmatrix}1 & 1\\1 & 2\end{pmatrix}\begin{pmatrix}x\\y\end{pmatrix}=\begin{pmatrix}p\\q\end{pmatrix}$ or $\boldsymbol{U}\begin{pmatrix}x\\y\end{pmatrix}=\begin{pmatrix}p\\q\end{pmatrix}$ where $\boldsymbol{U}=\begin{pmatrix}1 & 1\\1 & 2\end{pmatrix}$

This means

$$\begin{pmatrix}x\\y\end{pmatrix}=\boldsymbol{U}^{-1}\begin{pmatrix}p\\q\end{pmatrix}$$

Now if $\begin{pmatrix}p'\\q'\end{pmatrix}$ and $\begin{pmatrix}x'\\y'\end{pmatrix}$ are the coordinates of P′ on the cartesian and eigenvector grids respectively, then

$$\boldsymbol{U}\begin{pmatrix}x'\\y'\end{pmatrix}=\begin{pmatrix}p'\\q'\end{pmatrix}$$

But

$$\begin{pmatrix}p'\\q'\end{pmatrix}=\begin{pmatrix}4 & -1\\2 & 1\end{pmatrix}\begin{pmatrix}p\\q\end{pmatrix}=\boldsymbol{A}\begin{pmatrix}p\\q\end{pmatrix}$$

and

$$\begin{pmatrix}x'\\y'\end{pmatrix}=\begin{pmatrix}3 & 0\\0 & 2\end{pmatrix}\begin{pmatrix}x\\y\end{pmatrix}=\boldsymbol{D}\begin{pmatrix}x\\y\end{pmatrix}$$

so by successive substitution

$$\begin{pmatrix}p'\\q'\end{pmatrix}=\boldsymbol{U}\begin{pmatrix}x'\\y'\end{pmatrix}=\boldsymbol{UD}\begin{pmatrix}x\\y\end{pmatrix}=\boldsymbol{UDU}^{-1}\begin{pmatrix}p\\q\end{pmatrix}$$

and comparing this with

$$\begin{pmatrix}p'\\q'\end{pmatrix}=\boldsymbol{A}\begin{pmatrix}p\\q\end{pmatrix} \qquad \text{we see that} \qquad \boldsymbol{A}=\boldsymbol{UDU}^{-1}$$

The diagram helps to make this clear.

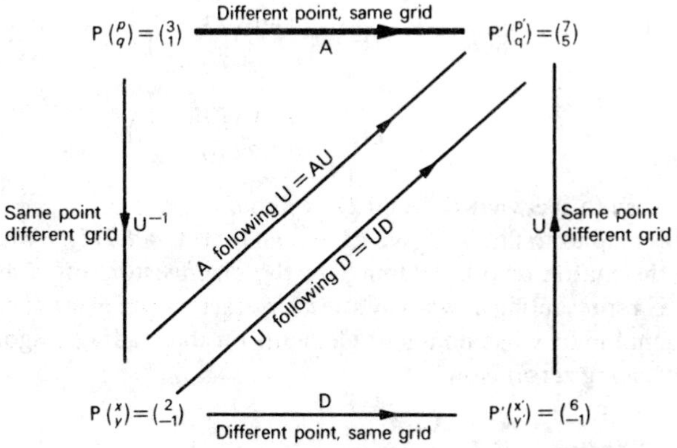

The route from P, $\begin{pmatrix}p\\q\end{pmatrix}$ to P′, $\begin{pmatrix}p'\\q'\end{pmatrix}$ can be *either* via $\boldsymbol{A}$ *or* via $\boldsymbol{U}^{-1}$ followed by $\boldsymbol{D}$ followed by $\boldsymbol{U}$

i.e. $$\boldsymbol{A} = \boldsymbol{U}\boldsymbol{D}\boldsymbol{U}^{-1}$$ ◄

The diagonals also represent equivalent processes from P, $\begin{pmatrix} x \\ y \end{pmatrix}$ to P′, $\begin{pmatrix} p' \\ q' \end{pmatrix}$

i.e. $$\boldsymbol{A}\boldsymbol{U} = \boldsymbol{U}\boldsymbol{D}$$ ◄

2.2 The powers of a matrix

We now consider *repeated* transformations. Suppose

$$\begin{pmatrix} x \\ y \end{pmatrix} \to \begin{pmatrix} x' \\ y' \end{pmatrix} \qquad \text{where} \qquad \begin{pmatrix} x' \\ y' \end{pmatrix} = \boldsymbol{M}\begin{pmatrix} x \\ y \end{pmatrix}$$

If we repeat this transformation

$$\begin{pmatrix} x' \\ y' \end{pmatrix} \to \begin{pmatrix} x'' \\ y'' \end{pmatrix} \qquad \text{where} \qquad \begin{pmatrix} x'' \\ y'' \end{pmatrix} = \boldsymbol{M}\begin{pmatrix} x' \\ y' \end{pmatrix} = \boldsymbol{M}^2\begin{pmatrix} x \\ y \end{pmatrix}$$

repeating again

$$\begin{pmatrix} x'' \\ y'' \end{pmatrix} \to \begin{pmatrix} x''' \\ y''' \end{pmatrix} = \boldsymbol{M}^3\begin{pmatrix} x \\ y \end{pmatrix}$$

The powers of a matrix are of great importance but some are much easier to calculate than others! If

$$\boldsymbol{A} = \begin{pmatrix} 4 & -1 \\ 2 & 1 \end{pmatrix} \qquad \text{then} \qquad \boldsymbol{A}^2 = \begin{pmatrix} 4 & -1 \\ 2 & 1 \end{pmatrix}\begin{pmatrix} 4 & -1 \\ 2 & 1 \end{pmatrix} = \begin{pmatrix} 14 & -5 \\ 10 & -1 \end{pmatrix}$$

and $$\boldsymbol{A}^3 = \begin{pmatrix} 4 & -1 \\ 2 & 1 \end{pmatrix}\begin{pmatrix} 14 & -5 \\ 10 & -1 \end{pmatrix} = \begin{pmatrix} 46 & -19 \\ 38 & -11 \end{pmatrix}$$

$\boldsymbol{A}^{10}$ would be very tedious to calculate and $\boldsymbol{A}^n$ impossible. But if

$$\boldsymbol{D} = \begin{pmatrix} 3 & 0 \\ 0 & 2 \end{pmatrix} \qquad \text{then} \qquad \boldsymbol{D}^2 = \begin{pmatrix} 3 & 0 \\ 0 & 2 \end{pmatrix}\begin{pmatrix} 3 & 0 \\ 0 & 2 \end{pmatrix} = \begin{pmatrix} 3^2 & 0 \\ 0 & 2^2 \end{pmatrix}$$

and $$\boldsymbol{D}^3 = \begin{pmatrix} 3 & 0 \\ 0 & 2 \end{pmatrix}\begin{pmatrix} 3^2 & 0 \\ 0 & 2^2 \end{pmatrix} = \begin{pmatrix} 3^3 & 0 \\ 0 & 2^3 \end{pmatrix}$$

and it is quite easy to see what $\boldsymbol{D}^{10}$ and $\boldsymbol{D}^n$ will be.

How will this help us to find $\boldsymbol{A}^n$? We have seen that $\boldsymbol{A} = \boldsymbol{U}\boldsymbol{D}\boldsymbol{U}^{-1}$ where $\boldsymbol{A}$ is any matrix, $\boldsymbol{U}$ is the matrix whose columns are the eigenvectors of $\boldsymbol{A}$ and $\boldsymbol{D}$ is the diagonal matrix representing a two-way stretch by factors which are the eigenvalues of $\boldsymbol{A}$. (A diagonal matrix has non-zero elements on the leading diagonal only, all other elements being zero.) Now

$$\begin{aligned} \boldsymbol{A}^2 &= \boldsymbol{A} \cdot \boldsymbol{A} \\ &= (\boldsymbol{U}\boldsymbol{D}\boldsymbol{U}^{-1})(\boldsymbol{U}\boldsymbol{D}\boldsymbol{U}^{-1}) \\ &= \boldsymbol{U}\boldsymbol{D}^2\boldsymbol{U}^{-1} \qquad \text{since} \qquad \boldsymbol{U}^{-1}\boldsymbol{U} = \boldsymbol{I} \end{aligned}$$

Similarly $$\boldsymbol{A}^3 = \boldsymbol{U}\boldsymbol{D}^3\boldsymbol{U}^{-1}$$

and so on. For example

$$A^{15} = UD^{15}U^{-1} \qquad A^{67} = UD^{67}U^{-1}$$

and finally $$A^n = UD^nU^{-1}$$

or $$A^nU = UD^n$$

◄

Worked example

To illustrate the above process, let us find powers of $A = \begin{pmatrix} 2 & 1 \\ 1 & 2 \end{pmatrix}$.

We know that if $A = \begin{pmatrix} 2 & 1 \\ 1 & 2 \end{pmatrix}$, then $U = \begin{pmatrix} 2 & -1 \\ 1 & 1 \end{pmatrix}$, so $AU = \begin{pmatrix} 3 & -1 \\ 3 & 1 \end{pmatrix}$

$$A^2 = \begin{pmatrix} 2 & 1 \\ 1 & 2 \end{pmatrix}\begin{pmatrix} 2 & 1 \\ 1 & 2 \end{pmatrix} = \begin{pmatrix} 5 & 4 \\ 4 & 5 \end{pmatrix} \qquad A^2U = \begin{pmatrix} 9 & -1 \\ 9 & 1 \end{pmatrix}$$

$$A^3 = \begin{pmatrix} 2 & 1 \\ 1 & 2 \end{pmatrix}^3 = \begin{pmatrix} 14 & 13 \\ 13 & 14 \end{pmatrix} \qquad A^3U = \begin{pmatrix} 27 & -1 \\ 27 & 1 \end{pmatrix}$$

$$A^4 = \begin{pmatrix} 2 & 1 \\ 1 & 2 \end{pmatrix}^4 = \begin{pmatrix} 41 & 40 \\ 40 & 41 \end{pmatrix} \qquad A^4U = \begin{pmatrix} 81 & -1 \\ 81 & 1 \end{pmatrix}$$

Notice the effect of A and its powers on the eigenvectors.

$$A\begin{pmatrix} 1 \\ 1 \end{pmatrix} = \begin{pmatrix} 3 \\ 3 \end{pmatrix} \qquad A^2\begin{pmatrix} 1 \\ 1 \end{pmatrix} = \begin{pmatrix} 9 \\ 9 \end{pmatrix} \qquad A^3\begin{pmatrix} 1 \\ 1 \end{pmatrix} = \begin{pmatrix} 27 \\ 27 \end{pmatrix}$$

... eigenvalue 3

$$A\begin{pmatrix} -1 \\ 1 \end{pmatrix} = \begin{pmatrix} -1 \\ 1 \end{pmatrix} \qquad A^2\begin{pmatrix} -1 \\ 1 \end{pmatrix} = \begin{pmatrix} -1 \\ 1 \end{pmatrix} \qquad A^3\begin{pmatrix} -1 \\ 1 \end{pmatrix} = \begin{pmatrix} -1 \\ 1 \end{pmatrix}$$

... eigenvalue 1

Now we know that $D = \begin{pmatrix} 3 & 0 \\ 0 & 1 \end{pmatrix}$ and we can see that

$$UD = \begin{pmatrix} 1 & -1 \\ 1 & 1 \end{pmatrix}\begin{pmatrix} 3 & 0 \\ 0 & 1 \end{pmatrix} = \begin{pmatrix} 3 & -1 \\ 3 & 1 \end{pmatrix} = AU$$

Similarly $$UD^2 = A^2U$$

$$UD^3 = A^3U$$

and $$UD^n = A^nU \quad \text{where} \quad n \in \mathbb{Z}^+$$

In this case
$$A^n = UD^nU^{-1}$$
$$= \begin{pmatrix} 1 & -1 \\ 1 & 1 \end{pmatrix}\begin{pmatrix} 3^n & 0 \\ 0 & 1^n \end{pmatrix}\begin{pmatrix} \frac{1}{2} & \frac{1}{2} \\ -\frac{1}{2} & \frac{1}{2} \end{pmatrix}$$

$$A^n = \begin{pmatrix} \dfrac{3^n+1}{2} & \dfrac{3^n-1}{2} \\ \dfrac{3^n-1}{2} & \dfrac{3^n+1}{2} \end{pmatrix}$$

Exercise 2.2

1 Write down the characteristic equations of the following matrices and hence find their eigenvalues and corresponding eigenvectors. Also, write the matrices in their equivalent forms, $\boldsymbol{A} = \boldsymbol{UDU}^{-1}$.

(a) $\begin{pmatrix} 4 & 1 \\ 2 & 3 \end{pmatrix}$ **(b)** $\begin{pmatrix} 4 & -3 \\ 2 & -3 \end{pmatrix}$ **(c)** $\begin{pmatrix} -3 & 2 \\ 5 & 0 \end{pmatrix}$ **(d)** $\begin{pmatrix} -5 & -2 \\ 4 & 4 \end{pmatrix}$

(e) $\begin{pmatrix} -4 & 1 \\ 2 & -3 \end{pmatrix}$ **(f)** $\begin{pmatrix} 5 & 2 \\ -7 & -4 \end{pmatrix}$ **(g)** $\begin{pmatrix} 3 & 1 \\ 2 & 4 \end{pmatrix}$

2(a) If $\boldsymbol{A} = \begin{pmatrix} 4 & 1 \\ 2 & 3 \end{pmatrix}$, calculate $\boldsymbol{A}^3$, $\boldsymbol{A}^4$ and give a formula for $\boldsymbol{A}^n$.

(b) If $\boldsymbol{B} = \begin{pmatrix} 4 & -1 \\ 2 & 1 \end{pmatrix}$, find $\boldsymbol{B}^5$ and $\boldsymbol{B}^n$.

3 A transformation is a reflection in the line $y = -\frac{1}{2}x$

(a) Write down the eigenvectors of the transformation matrix and the corresponding eigenvalues.

(b) (i) Write down the matrix for the reflection in the form $\boldsymbol{UDU}^{-1}$

(ii) Find the matrix $\boldsymbol{A} = \boldsymbol{UDU}^{-1}$ for the transformation.

(iii) Comment on $\boldsymbol{A}^2, \boldsymbol{A}^3, \ldots \boldsymbol{A}^n, \boldsymbol{A}^{n+1}$.

(c) Draw an accurate diagram on graph paper and illustrate the transformation of the figure PQRS where P is (5, 0), Q is (0, 5), R is (−4, −3), and S is (3, −4).

2.3 Repeated transformations of the plane

The characteristic equation of the matrix $\boldsymbol{M} = \begin{pmatrix} a & b \\ c & d \end{pmatrix}$ is

$$k^2 - (\text{trace } \boldsymbol{M})k + (\text{determinant } \boldsymbol{M}) = 0$$

where the trace, $tr = a + d$ and the determinant, $\Delta = ad - bc$. The roots of the equation are the eigenvalues of the matrix and may be real ($tr^2 \geqslant 4\Delta$) or complex ($tr^2 < 4\Delta$).

Six cases arise, five of which are summarized on page 319.

(1) The roots are unequal, and of the same sign, e.g. $\boldsymbol{A} = \begin{pmatrix} 2 & 1 \\ 1 & 2 \end{pmatrix}$ and $\boldsymbol{H} = \begin{pmatrix} 4 & -1 \\ 2 & 1 \end{pmatrix}$.

(2) The roots are unequal and of opposite sign, e.g. $\boldsymbol{B} = \begin{pmatrix} 2 & 2 \\ 2 & -1 \end{pmatrix}$.

(3) The roots are equal and of opposite sign, e.g. $\boldsymbol{C} = \begin{pmatrix} 1 & 3 \\ 1 & -1 \end{pmatrix}$.

(4) The roots are equal and of the same sign (one eigenvector only), e.g. $\boldsymbol{F} = \begin{pmatrix} 4 & -1 \\ 1 & 2 \end{pmatrix}$.

(5) One root is zero (the matrix is singular), e.g. $\boldsymbol{Z} = \begin{pmatrix} 3 & -6 \\ -1 & 2 \end{pmatrix}$.

(6) The roots are complex (no real eigenvectors), e.g. $\boldsymbol{W} = \begin{pmatrix} 3 & -1 \\ 2 & 2 \end{pmatrix}$.

We now consider repeated transformation of the plane using each of these six matrices. Each transformation is equivalent to a two-way stretch relative to the *eigenvector* grid. We therefore show in the diagrams the eigenvector axes x' and y' and find the effect of repeated transformation of vectors in each of the four regions formed by these axes. (The diagrams are not drawn to scale.) All vectors not lying on the axes will change their directions. Make sure that you understand what is happening to the vectors by taking a typical point in each region and by repeated multiplication find its image under one, two, three, . . . transformations. Then study the changes relative to the eigenvector axes. (See Exercise 2.3.)

Transformation under $\boldsymbol{A} = \begin{pmatrix} 2 & 1 \\ 1 & 2 \end{pmatrix}$ and powers of $\boldsymbol{A}$

The eigenvectors are $\begin{pmatrix} 1 \\ 1 \end{pmatrix}$ with eigenvalue $k = 3$ and $\begin{pmatrix} -1 \\ 1 \end{pmatrix}$ with eigenvalue $k = 1$.

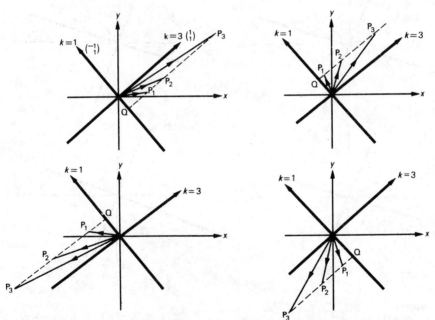

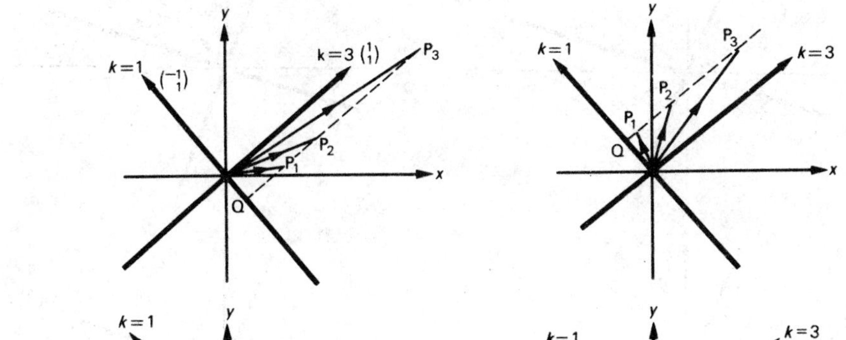

In each case, the vector $\boldsymbol{OP}_1$ is transformed to $\boldsymbol{OP}_2$ under $\boldsymbol{A}$, then $\boldsymbol{OP}_2$ is transformed to $\boldsymbol{OP}_3$ and so on.

NOTE

(1) Each vector remains in its own region.

(2) The points $P_1, P_2, P_3 \ldots$ lie on a line parallel to the eigenvector with eigenvalue 3. (The eigenvector that corresponds to the *larger* numerical eigenvalue is called the *principal* eigenvector.)

(3) $P_2Q = 3P_1Q$, $P_3Q = 3P_2Q = 3^2P_1Q$ and so on.

(4) The distance from the principal eigenvector remains the same. (This is because the 'other' eigenvalue is 1.)

(5) The angle between OP_1, OP_2, $OP_3 \dots$ and the principal eigenvector reduces as we continue.

The matrix we have been considering is easy to deal with since

(a) the eigenvectors are perpendicular

(b) the determinant is positive

(c) one of the eigenvalues is 1.

Transformation under $B = \begin{pmatrix} 2 & 2 \\ 2 & -1 \end{pmatrix}$ and powers of B

The eigenvectors are $\begin{pmatrix} 2 \\ 1 \end{pmatrix}$ with $k = 3$ and $\begin{pmatrix} -1 \\ 2 \end{pmatrix}$ with $k = -2$.

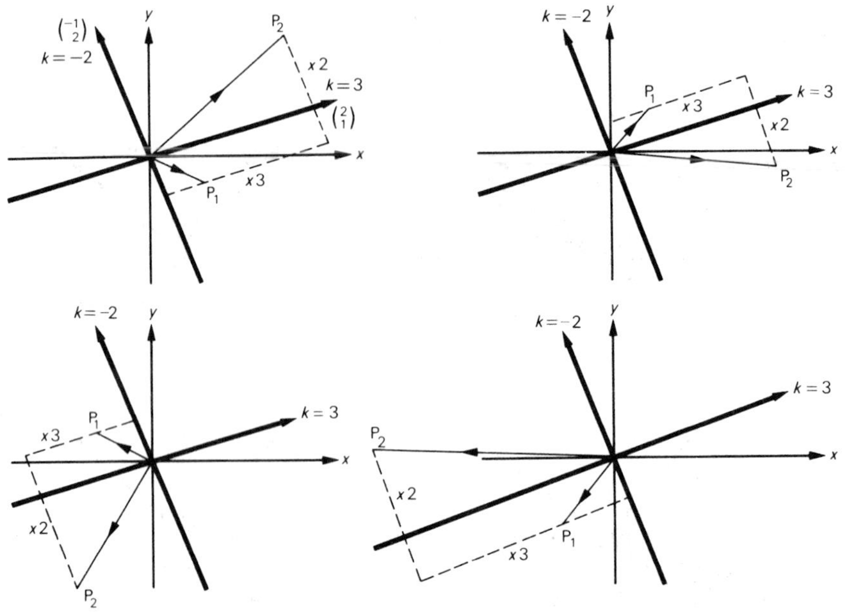

NOTE

(1) Under each transformation the vector crosses over the principal eigenvector. This is the effect of the negative eigenvalue.

(2) The point P_1 etc. moves parallel to the principal eigenvector with its distance from the other multiplied by 3 and then parallel to the other eigenvector with its distance multiplied by -2 (i.e. reflect and double).

(3) Again the eigenvectors are perpendicular. This is the case with all symmetric matrices ($\boldsymbol{M}^{\mathrm{T}} = \boldsymbol{M}$).

Transformation under $C = \begin{pmatrix} 1 & 3 \\ 1 & -1 \end{pmatrix}$ and powers of C

The eigenvectors are $\begin{pmatrix} 3 \\ 1 \end{pmatrix}$ with $k = 2$ and $\begin{pmatrix} -1 \\ 2 \end{pmatrix}$ with $k = -2$ (that is, the eigenvalues are equal and opposite).

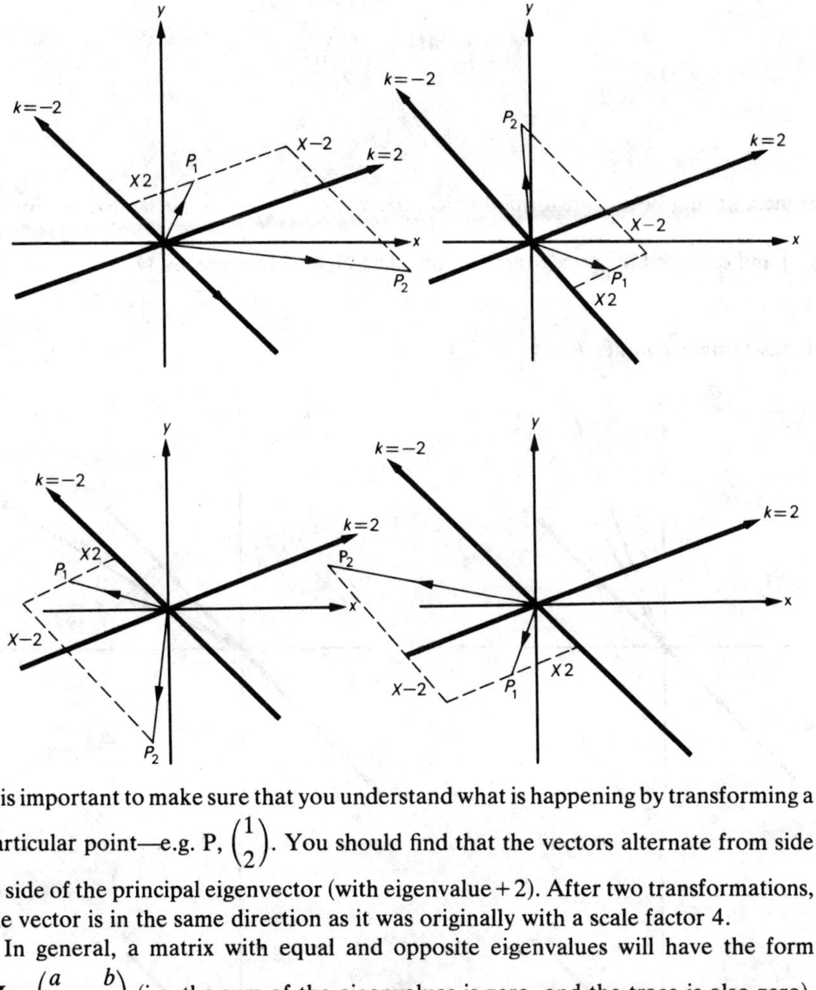

It is important to make sure that you understand what is happening by transforming a particular point—e.g. P, $\begin{pmatrix} 1 \\ 2 \end{pmatrix}$. You should find that the vectors alternate from side to side of the principal eigenvector (with eigenvalue + 2). After two transformations, the vector is in the same direction as it was originally with a scale factor 4.

In general, a matrix with equal and opposite eigenvalues will have the form $\boldsymbol{M} = \begin{pmatrix} a & b \\ c & -a \end{pmatrix}$ (i.e. the sum of the eigenvalues is zero, and the trace is also zero).

$$|\boldsymbol{M}| = -(a^2 + bc)$$

If we consider transforming $\begin{pmatrix} x \\ y \end{pmatrix}$ we have

$$\begin{pmatrix} x' \\ y' \end{pmatrix} = \begin{pmatrix} a & b \\ c & -a \end{pmatrix} \begin{pmatrix} x \\ y \end{pmatrix}$$

A second transformation gives

$$\begin{pmatrix} x'' \\ y'' \end{pmatrix} = \begin{pmatrix} a & b \\ c & -a \end{pmatrix}\begin{pmatrix} a & b \\ c & -a \end{pmatrix}\begin{pmatrix} x \\ y \end{pmatrix}$$

$$= \begin{pmatrix} a^2+bc & ab-ab \\ ac-ac & bc+a^2 \end{pmatrix}\begin{pmatrix} x \\ y \end{pmatrix}$$

$$= \begin{pmatrix} -|\boldsymbol{M}| & 0 \\ 0 & -|\boldsymbol{M}| \end{pmatrix}\begin{pmatrix} x \\ y \end{pmatrix}$$

$$\begin{pmatrix} x'' \\ y'' \end{pmatrix} = -|\boldsymbol{M}|\begin{pmatrix} x \\ y \end{pmatrix}$$

Hence, having been transformed twice, the vector $\begin{pmatrix} x'' \\ y'' \end{pmatrix}$ is in the same direction as $\begin{pmatrix} x \\ y \end{pmatrix}$ and enlarged by a scale factor $-|\boldsymbol{M}|$. The eigenvalues are $\pm\sqrt{\boldsymbol{M}}$.

Transformation under $\boldsymbol{F} = \begin{pmatrix} 4 & -1 \\ 1 & 2 \end{pmatrix}$

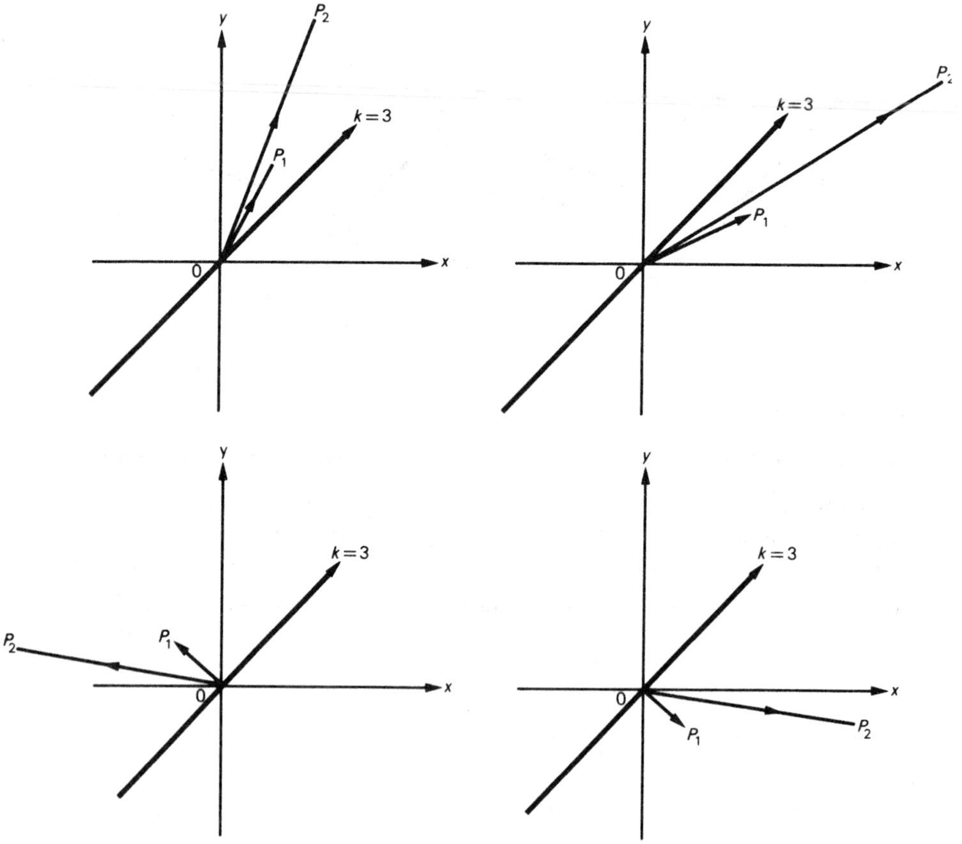

Here there is only one eigenvector with $k = 3$ since the characteristic equation $k^2 - 6k + 9 = 0$ has a repeated root. Any vector is transformed towards the eigenvector, those 'below' coming towards the 'positive' eigenvector anticlockwise, those above going towards the 'negative' eigenvector anticlockwise as shown.

Transformation under $Z = \begin{pmatrix} 3 & -6 \\ -1 & 2 \end{pmatrix}$

The matrix is singular, with eigenvectors $\begin{pmatrix} 3 \\ -1 \end{pmatrix}$ with $k = 5$ and $\begin{pmatrix} 2 \\ 1 \end{pmatrix}$ with $k = 0$. At the first transformation the whole plane is transformed onto the line $x + 3y = 0$, but each point is 5 times its distance from the other eigenvector $\begin{pmatrix} 2 \\ 1 \end{pmatrix}$.

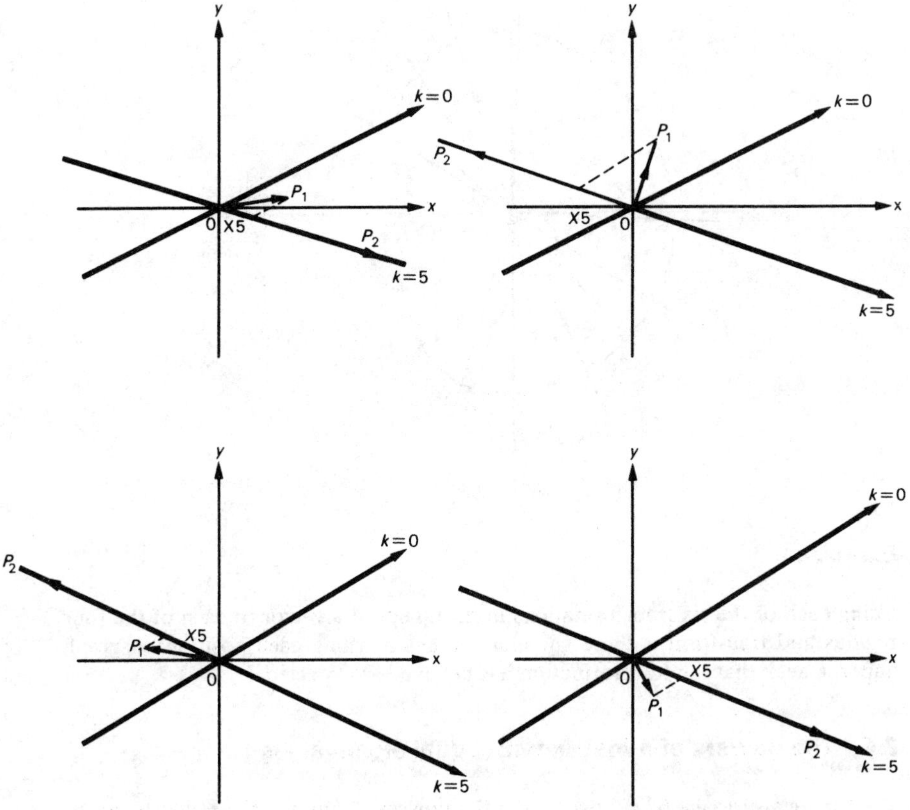

Transformation under $W = \begin{pmatrix} 3 & -1 \\ 2 & 2 \end{pmatrix}$

This matrix has the characteristic equation $k^2 + 5k + 8 = 0$, which has no real solutions (since $B^2 < 4AC$) and hence no real eigenvalues and no real eigenvectors.

It is, of course, still possible to transform the plane, but the eigenvector grid does not exist.

Investigate the transformation of the vectors $\begin{pmatrix}1\\0\end{pmatrix}, \begin{pmatrix}1\\1\end{pmatrix}, \begin{pmatrix}0\\1\end{pmatrix}, \begin{pmatrix}-1\\1\end{pmatrix} \begin{pmatrix}-1\\0\end{pmatrix}, \begin{pmatrix}-1\\-1\end{pmatrix}, \begin{pmatrix}0\\-1\end{pmatrix}, \begin{pmatrix}1\\-1\end{pmatrix}$. You will find in each case that the vector is transformed into another in an anticlockwise fashion. Whereas in the other cases repeated transformations cause all the vectors to line up eventually in the direction of the principal eigenvector, here we go round and round! Consider repeated transformations applied to $\begin{pmatrix}1\\0\end{pmatrix}$. An approximate sketch shows what happens (the directions only are shown).

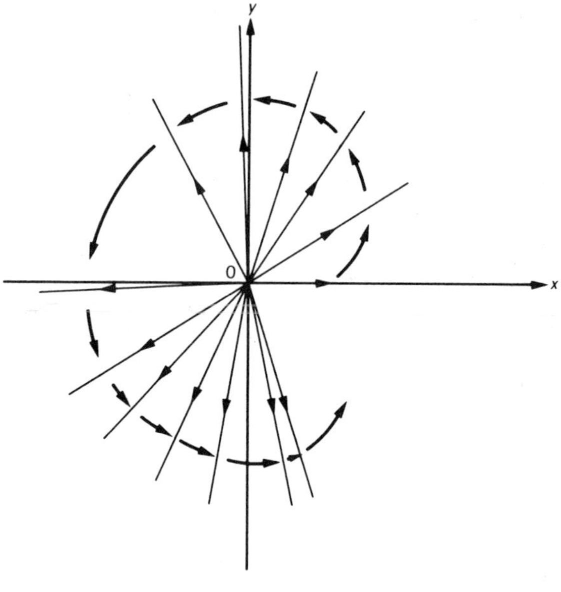

Exercise 2.3

Using each of the six transformations in turn, choose a vector in each of the four regions and transform it three successive times marking each position on graph paper. Check that the transformation has behaved as expected.

2.4 The powers of a matrix with equal eigenvalues

We have learnt (page 672) how to find the powers of any matrix $\boldsymbol{A}$ which can be expressed in the equivalent form $\boldsymbol{UDU}^{-1}$. Clearly the method breaks down if $\boldsymbol{U}$ is a singular matrix so that $\boldsymbol{U}^{-1}$ does not exist. This is the case when a matrix has equal eigenvalues and hence only one eigenvector, for example $\boldsymbol{F} = \begin{pmatrix}4 & -1\\1 & 2\end{pmatrix}$, the corresponding matrix $\boldsymbol{U}$ being $\begin{pmatrix}1 & 1\\1 & 1\end{pmatrix}$ and the eigenvalues both being 3. Now $|\boldsymbol{U}| = 0$ so

U^{-1} does not exist. The equation giving the eigenvalues was $k^2-6k+9=0$. Now

$$\boldsymbol{F}=\begin{pmatrix}4 & -1\\ 1 & 2\end{pmatrix}$$

$$\boldsymbol{F}^2=\begin{pmatrix}4 & -1\\ 1 & 2\end{pmatrix}\begin{pmatrix}4 & -1\\ 1 & 2\end{pmatrix}=\begin{pmatrix}15 & -6\\ 6 & 3\end{pmatrix}$$

Consider $\boldsymbol{F}^2-6\boldsymbol{F}+9\boldsymbol{I}\left(\text{where } \boldsymbol{I}=\begin{pmatrix}1 & 0\\ 0 & 1\end{pmatrix}\right)$

$$\begin{pmatrix}15 & -6\\ 6 & 3\end{pmatrix}-\begin{pmatrix}24 & -6\\ 6 & 12\end{pmatrix}+\begin{pmatrix}9 & 0\\ 0 & 9\end{pmatrix}=\begin{pmatrix}0 & 0\\ 0 & 0\end{pmatrix}$$

i.e.

$$\boldsymbol{F}^2-6\boldsymbol{F}+9\boldsymbol{I}=\boldsymbol{O}$$

This is a special case of the *Cayley–Hamilton theorem*—that any square matrix 'satisfies' the same equation as the equation giving the eigenvalues. Hence

$$\begin{aligned}\boldsymbol{F}^2&=6\boldsymbol{F}-9\boldsymbol{I}\\ \boldsymbol{F}^3&=6\boldsymbol{F}^2-9\boldsymbol{F}=6(6\boldsymbol{F}-9\boldsymbol{I})-9\boldsymbol{F}\\ &=27\boldsymbol{F}-54\boldsymbol{I}\\ \boldsymbol{F}^4&=27\boldsymbol{F}^2-54\boldsymbol{F}\\ &=27(6\boldsymbol{F}-9\boldsymbol{I})-54\boldsymbol{F}\\ &=(162-54)\boldsymbol{F}-243\boldsymbol{I}\\ &=108\boldsymbol{F}-243\boldsymbol{I}\end{aligned}$$

We then have a series of results $\boldsymbol{F}^2=6\boldsymbol{F}-9\boldsymbol{I}$, $\boldsymbol{F}^3=27\boldsymbol{F}-54\boldsymbol{I}$, $\boldsymbol{F}^4=108\boldsymbol{F}-243\boldsymbol{I}$ and so on. Is it possible to find a formula giving the powers of $\boldsymbol{F}$? Perhaps! The numbers in the formula confuse the issue. Let us start again, in general. If the equation has equal roots, $k_1=k_2=l$ say, then we must have had

$$k^2-2lk+l^2=0$$

Our matrix, $\boldsymbol{F}$ in this case, satisfies this equation so,

$$\boldsymbol{F}^2-2l\boldsymbol{F}+l^2\boldsymbol{I}=\boldsymbol{O}$$

(We insert $\boldsymbol{I}$ in the last term to complete the matrix equation)

$$\boldsymbol{F}^3-2l\boldsymbol{F}^2+l^2\boldsymbol{F}=\boldsymbol{O}$$

and

$$\boldsymbol{F}^4-2l\boldsymbol{F}^3+l^2\boldsymbol{F}^2=\boldsymbol{O} \qquad \text{etc.}$$

Substituting from the first equation into the second, and so on, we have

$$\begin{aligned}\boldsymbol{F}^2&=2l\boldsymbol{F}-l^2\boldsymbol{I}\\ \boldsymbol{F}^3&=3l^2\boldsymbol{F}-2l^3\boldsymbol{I}\\ \boldsymbol{F}^4&=4l^3\boldsymbol{F}-3l^4\boldsymbol{I}\end{aligned}$$

You can now guess the formula

$$\boldsymbol{F}^n = nl^{n-1}\boldsymbol{F} - (n-1)l^n\boldsymbol{I}$$

In our case $l = 3$, hence

$$\boldsymbol{F}^n = n3^{n-1}\boldsymbol{F} - (n-1)3^n\boldsymbol{I}$$

Check that this formula is correct for $n = 3$ and $n = 4$.

The Cayley–Hamilton theorem—general case

Suppose $\boldsymbol{M} = \begin{pmatrix} a & b \\ c & d \end{pmatrix}$, with eigenvalues given by the roots of

$$k^2 - (a+d)k + ad - bc = 0$$

Now $$\boldsymbol{M}^2 = \begin{pmatrix} a & b \\ c & d \end{pmatrix}\begin{pmatrix} a & b \\ c & d \end{pmatrix} = \begin{pmatrix} a^2+bc & ab+bd \\ ac+dc & bc+d^2 \end{pmatrix}$$

and $$\boldsymbol{M}^2 - (a+d)\boldsymbol{M} + (ad-bc)\boldsymbol{I} = \begin{pmatrix} a^2+bc & ab+bd \\ ac+dc & bc+d^2 \end{pmatrix} - \begin{pmatrix} a^2+da & ab+bd \\ ac+cd & ad+d^2 \end{pmatrix}$$

$$+\begin{pmatrix} ad-bc & 0 \\ 0 & ad-bc \end{pmatrix}$$

$$= \begin{pmatrix} 0 & 0 \\ 0 & 0 \end{pmatrix}$$

i.e. $$\boldsymbol{M}^2 - (a+d)\boldsymbol{M} + (ad-bc)\boldsymbol{I} = \boldsymbol{0}$$ ◀

Hence the 2×2 matrix $\boldsymbol{M}$, satisfies its own characteristic equation. This can be generalized as the Cayley–Hamilton theorem:

Any square matrix satisfies its own characteristic equation ◀

Remember that for a 3×3 matrix, this equation will be a cubic, for a 4×4, a quartic, and so on.

2.5 Powers of matrices and induction

Sometimes the *principle of mathematical induction* may be used to prove formulae involving powers of matrices.

Example

Prove that

$$\begin{pmatrix} 1 & 0 & 0 \\ 0 & 0 & -1 \\ 0 & -1 & 0 \end{pmatrix}^{2n+1} = \begin{pmatrix} 1 & 0 & 0 \\ 0 & 0 & -1 \\ 0 & -1 & 0 \end{pmatrix}$$

when n is a positive integer.

First check that the equation is true for $n = 1$

$$\text{L.H.S.}\quad \begin{pmatrix}1&0&0\\0&0&-1\\0&-1&0\end{pmatrix}^3 = \begin{pmatrix}1&0&0\\0&0&-1\\0&-1&0\end{pmatrix}\begin{pmatrix}1&0&0\\0&0&-1\\0&-1&0\end{pmatrix}\begin{pmatrix}1&0&0\\0&0&-1\\0&-1&0\end{pmatrix}$$

$$= \begin{pmatrix}1&0&0\\0&0&-1\\0&-1&0\end{pmatrix}\begin{pmatrix}1&0&0\\0&1&0\\0&0&1\end{pmatrix}$$

$$= \begin{pmatrix}1&0&0\\0&0&-1\\0&-1&0\end{pmatrix}$$

$$= \text{R.H.S.}$$

Hence it is true for $n = 1$.

Now assume that the equation is true for $n = k$, so that

$$\begin{pmatrix}1&0&0\\0&0&-1\\0&-1&0\end{pmatrix}^{2k+1} = \begin{pmatrix}1&0&0\\0&0&-1\\0&-1&0\end{pmatrix}$$

But

$$\begin{pmatrix}1&0&0\\0&0&-1\\0&-1&0\end{pmatrix}^{2(k+1)+1} = \begin{pmatrix}1&0&0\\0&0&-1\\0&-1&0\end{pmatrix}^{2k+1}\begin{pmatrix}1&0&0\\0&0&-1\\0&-1&0\end{pmatrix}^2$$

$$= \begin{pmatrix}1&0&0\\0&0&-1\\0&-1&0\end{pmatrix}\begin{pmatrix}1&0&0\\0&0&-1\\0&-1&0\end{pmatrix}^2$$

$$= \begin{pmatrix}1&0&0\\0&0&-1\\0&-1&0\end{pmatrix}\begin{pmatrix}1&0&0\\0&1&0\\0&0&1\end{pmatrix}$$

$$= \begin{pmatrix}1&0&0\\0&0&-1\\0&-1&0\end{pmatrix}$$

Hence, if the equation is true for $n = k$, then it is also true for $n = k+1$ and so by the principle of mathematical induction it is true for all positive integers $n \geqslant 1$.

Exercise 2.5

1 Suppose $\boldsymbol{A} = \begin{pmatrix}4&1\\2&3\end{pmatrix}$, find the corresponding diagonal matrix $\boldsymbol{D}$. Find the characteristic equation for $\boldsymbol{A}$ and show that it is also satisfied by $\boldsymbol{D}$. Can you suggest a way of finding $\boldsymbol{A}^n$ using this fact? First show that $\boldsymbol{A}^n = p\boldsymbol{A} + q\boldsymbol{I}$, where p and q are numbers to be found, is also satisfied by $\boldsymbol{D}$. Use this method to find $\boldsymbol{C}^4$ where $\boldsymbol{C} = \begin{pmatrix} 4 & -3 \\ 1 & 0 \end{pmatrix}$ and also $\boldsymbol{C}^n$.

2 Find the four matrices $\boldsymbol{M}$ of the form $\begin{pmatrix} a & b \\ b & a \end{pmatrix}$ such that $\boldsymbol{M}^2 = \boldsymbol{M} + \boldsymbol{I}$ where $\boldsymbol{I}$ is the unit matrix of order 2.

3 If $\boldsymbol{A} = \begin{pmatrix} -2 & -9 \\ 1 & 4 \end{pmatrix}$ prove by induction that

$$\boldsymbol{A}^n = \begin{pmatrix} 1-3n & -9n \\ n & 1+3n \end{pmatrix}$$

where n is a positive integer. Write down the matrix which is

$$\operatorname*{Limit}_{n\to\infty} \frac{1}{n}\boldsymbol{A}^n$$

4 Show that for a non-singular 2×2 matrix $\boldsymbol{A}$

$$(\boldsymbol{I} + \boldsymbol{A})^n = a\boldsymbol{I} + b\boldsymbol{A} \qquad \text{where } a, b \text{ are constants}$$

5 Find the eigenvalues of $\boldsymbol{A} = \begin{pmatrix} 1-p & q \\ p & 1-q \end{pmatrix}$.

Miscellaneous examination questions 18

1 (a) Use the method of mathematical induction to show that if

$$\boldsymbol{A} = \begin{pmatrix} a & b \\ 0 & 1 \end{pmatrix} \qquad a \neq 1$$

then

$$\boldsymbol{A}^n = \begin{pmatrix} c & d \\ 0 & 1 \end{pmatrix}$$

where $c = a^n$ and $d = \dfrac{b(a^n - 1)}{a - 1}$. State conditions on a and/or b which are sufficient to ensure that $\boldsymbol{A}^n$ approaches a finite limit as n increases. Write down the value of this limit.

(b) Find a non-singular matrix $\boldsymbol{B}$ of the form $\begin{pmatrix} 1 & 1 \\ 2 & \alpha \end{pmatrix}$ such that $\boldsymbol{B}^{-1}\boldsymbol{A}\boldsymbol{B}$ is a diagonal matrix, where

$$\boldsymbol{A} = \begin{pmatrix} -1 & 2 \\ 4 & 1 \end{pmatrix}$$

Calculate the diagonal matrix. Hence, or otherwise, calculate $\boldsymbol{A}^n$. (M.E.I.)

2 (a) Prove that the 2×2 matrix $\boldsymbol{A}$ commutes with all matrices of the form $p\boldsymbol{A} + q\boldsymbol{I}$ where p and q are real constants and $\boldsymbol{I}$ is the 2×2 unit matrix.

(b) If

$$\boldsymbol{A} = \begin{pmatrix} 3 & -1 \\ 1 & 1 \end{pmatrix}$$

prove that $\boldsymbol{A}^2 - 4\boldsymbol{A} + 4\boldsymbol{I} = \boldsymbol{0}$, where $\boldsymbol{0}$ denotes the 2×2 zero matrix.

(c) Show that the matrix $\boldsymbol{A}$ in **(b)** satisfies

$$\boldsymbol{A}^n = 2^{n-1}\begin{pmatrix} 2+n & -n \\ n & 2-n \end{pmatrix}$$

for $n = 0, \pm 1, \pm 2, \ldots$, where $\boldsymbol{A}^0$ denotes $\boldsymbol{I}$ and $\boldsymbol{A}^{-k} = (\boldsymbol{A}^k)^{-1}$. (M.E.I.)

3 If $\boldsymbol{M} = \begin{pmatrix} -1 & 0 \\ 0 & 1 \end{pmatrix}$ and $\boldsymbol{I} = \begin{pmatrix} 1 & 0 \\ 0 & 1 \end{pmatrix}$, prove that $\boldsymbol{M}^{2n} = \boldsymbol{I}$ for every positive integer n.

Write down, with elements expressed in terms of n, a 2×2 matrix $\boldsymbol{N}$, not equal to $\boldsymbol{I}$, such that $\boldsymbol{N}^{2n+1} = \boldsymbol{I}$. (L.)

4 Find all sets of values of x, y, z, t such that the matrix $\boldsymbol{A} = \begin{pmatrix} x & y \\ z & t \end{pmatrix}$ satisfies the relation $\boldsymbol{A}^2 - 4\boldsymbol{A} + 4\boldsymbol{I} = \boldsymbol{0}$ where $\boldsymbol{I}$ and $\boldsymbol{0}$ are respectively the unit and zero matrices of type 2×2. (C.)

5 The matrix $\boldsymbol{M} = \begin{pmatrix} a & b \\ c & d \end{pmatrix}$ has the property that there are non-zero vectors $\begin{pmatrix} x \\ y \end{pmatrix}$ and scalars k such that $\boldsymbol{M}\begin{pmatrix} x \\ y \end{pmatrix} = k\begin{pmatrix} x \\ y \end{pmatrix}$. Prove that the values of k are the roots of the equation

$$k^2 - (a+d)k + ad - bc = 0$$

and find in terms of k the corresponding ratios $x : y$. Find the values of k when $\boldsymbol{M} = \begin{pmatrix} -3 & 4 \\ 1 & -3 \end{pmatrix}$. If these values are k_1 and k_2, and if $\boldsymbol{V} = \begin{pmatrix} 4 & 4 \\ k_1+3 & k_2+3 \end{pmatrix}$ and $\boldsymbol{K} = \begin{pmatrix} k_1 & 0 \\ 0 & k_2 \end{pmatrix}$, verify that $\boldsymbol{MV} = \boldsymbol{VK}$. Prove by induction that $\boldsymbol{M}^n = \boldsymbol{VK}^n\boldsymbol{V}^{-1}$ for all positive integers. (L.)

6 If $\boldsymbol{M}$ denotes the matrix $\begin{pmatrix} 1 & 0 \\ 1 & 2 \end{pmatrix}$ and $\boldsymbol{I}$ denotes the unit 2×2 matrix, prove that $\boldsymbol{M}^2 = 3\boldsymbol{M} - 2\boldsymbol{I}$. Prove further that, if n is any positive integer,

$$\boldsymbol{M}^n = (2^n - 1)\boldsymbol{M} - 2(2^{n-1} - 1)\boldsymbol{I}$$

(M.E.I.)

7 (a) Write down the equation of the line joining the origin O to the point (3, 1, 2) in cartesian and parametric form.

(b) If this line is transformed by using the matrix $\boldsymbol{M}$,

where

$$\boldsymbol{M} = \begin{pmatrix} 1 & 0 & -1 \\ 0 & -1 & 1 \\ 1 & -2 & 0 \end{pmatrix}$$

find its new equation.

(c) If P′ is the new position of P, what is the angle between OP and OP′ (leave your answer in surd form).

(d) Find the equation of the plane through O, P and P′ (M.E.I.)

8 A transformation is defined by

$$\begin{pmatrix} x' \\ y' \\ z' \end{pmatrix} = \begin{pmatrix} -2 & 1 & 4 \\ 1 & 0 & -2 \\ 3 & 4 & -6 \end{pmatrix} \begin{pmatrix} x \\ y \\ z \end{pmatrix}$$

Show that the set of planes perpendicular to the y axis maps onto a set of parallel lines. What is the direction of these lines? Which of these planes is mapped onto a line through the origin? (S.M.P.)

9 Show that under the matrix transformation

$$\boldsymbol{M} = \begin{pmatrix} 1 & 2 & 3 \\ 2 & 0 & -2 \\ 3 & -2 & -7 \end{pmatrix}$$

the whole space is mapped onto the plane $x-2y+z=0$.

Find the image under the transformation of

(a) the line $x=-y=-\frac{1}{2}z$

(b) the plane $x-y-z=0$

(c) the plane $x-z=0$. (J.M.B.)

10 A matrix $\boldsymbol{M}$ is said to be transposed into the matrix $\boldsymbol{M}^{\mathrm{T}}$ if the first row of $\boldsymbol{M}$ becomes the first column of $\boldsymbol{M}^{\mathrm{T}}$, the second row of $\boldsymbol{M}$ becomes the second column of $\boldsymbol{M}^{\mathrm{T}}$, and so on. Write down the transposes of the matrices

$$\boldsymbol{M} = \begin{pmatrix} x \\ y \\ z \end{pmatrix} \quad \text{and} \quad \boldsymbol{T} = \begin{pmatrix} 0 & b & 0 \\ 0 & 0 & c \\ a & 0 & 0 \end{pmatrix}$$

Calculate the matrix products $\boldsymbol{M}^{\mathrm{T}}\boldsymbol{M}$ and $\boldsymbol{TM}$; show also that $(\boldsymbol{TM})^{\mathrm{T}} = \boldsymbol{M}^{\mathrm{T}}\boldsymbol{T}^{\mathrm{T}}$. If the elements of $\boldsymbol{M}$ are the cartesian coordinates of a point P, what information is provided by the elements of $\boldsymbol{M}^{\mathrm{T}}\boldsymbol{M}$?

If the matrix $\boldsymbol{T}$ describes a transformation of the points P of three dimensional space, interpret geometrically the equation $(\boldsymbol{TM})^{\mathrm{T}}(\boldsymbol{TM}) = \boldsymbol{M}^{\mathrm{T}}\boldsymbol{M}$, and find all appropriate values of a, b and c. (S.M.P.)

11 A transformation matrix $\boldsymbol{M}$ is given by

$$\boldsymbol{M} = \begin{pmatrix} 1 & 0 & 4 \\ 0 & 5 & 4 \\ 4 & 4 & 3 \end{pmatrix}$$

If O is the origin and A the point (1, 2, 2), what are the coordinates of the image of A under the transformation $\boldsymbol{M}$? If A′ is the image of A, what is the ratio of the lengths OA′ and OA?

A second point B has its image B′ under $\boldsymbol{M}$ such that $\boldsymbol{OB'} = 3\boldsymbol{OB}$. Find a set of possible coordinates for B.

A third point C distinct from A and B is related to its image C′ under $\boldsymbol{M}$ by $\boldsymbol{OC'} = k\boldsymbol{OC}$, where k is a scalar. Find the value of k and a set of possible coordinates of C. (M.E.I.)

12 The matrix
$$\boldsymbol{A} = \begin{pmatrix} p & 2p & 2p \\ 2p & -2p & p \\ 2p & p & -2p \end{pmatrix}$$
where p is a real number, is such that det $\boldsymbol{A} = 1$. Unit vectors in the directions of the rectangular axes Ox, Oy, Oz are denoted by $\boldsymbol{i}, \boldsymbol{j}, \boldsymbol{k}$ respectively.

(a) Evaluate p.

(b) Show that $\boldsymbol{Ai}$, $\boldsymbol{Aj}$ and $\boldsymbol{Ak}$ are orthogonal (i.e. mutually perpendicular) unit vectors.

(c) By solving $\boldsymbol{Av} = \boldsymbol{v}$ where $\boldsymbol{v} = \begin{pmatrix} x \\ y \\ z \end{pmatrix}$ show that there is a unique line of points which are invariant under the transformation performed by $\boldsymbol{A}$.

(d) Evaluate $\boldsymbol{A}^2$.

(e) Deduce the nature of the transformation giving your reasons. (M.E.I.)

13 Verify that if
$$\boldsymbol{A} = \begin{pmatrix} 3 & 4 & 5 \\ 1 & -4 & -1 \\ 1 & 0 & 1 \end{pmatrix}$$
then det $\boldsymbol{A} = 0$ and explain the significance of this result in relation to the solution of the equation $\boldsymbol{Ax} = \boldsymbol{y}$ where $\boldsymbol{x}$ and $\boldsymbol{y}$ denote the column vectors with components $(x_1 \quad x_2 \quad x_3)$ and $(y_1 \quad y_2 \quad y_3)$ respectively. If this equation represents a set of three planes, give the geometrical interpretation in the cases where $\boldsymbol{y}$ has components **(a)** $(7 \quad -3 \quad 1)$ **(b)** $(7 \quad -3 \quad -3)$.

By expressing the line of intersection of the planes
$$3x_1 + 4x_2 + 5x_3 = 7 \qquad \text{and} \qquad x_1 - 4x_2 - x_3 = -3$$
in the form
$$\frac{x_1 - \alpha}{l} = \frac{x_2 - \beta}{m} = \frac{x_3 - \gamma}{n}$$
or otherwise, find the coordinates of a point on this line in parametric form. Find the distance of this point from the third plane $x_1 + x_3 = y_3$ in each of the cases **(a)** and **(b)** and show that these verify the interpretation you have given. (M.E.I.)

14 The mapping f where $f\colon \begin{pmatrix} x \\ y \\ z \end{pmatrix} \to \begin{pmatrix} 1 & 1 & 1 \\ 1 & 2 & 3 \end{pmatrix} \begin{pmatrix} x \\ y \\ z \end{pmatrix}$ maps the set of triples of real numbers to the set of pairs of real numbers.

(a) Find the set of triples which map onto $\begin{pmatrix} 0 \\ 0 \end{pmatrix}$ under f.

(b) By trial, or otherwise, find one solution to the simultaneous equations

$$x + y + z = 31$$

$$x + 2y + 3z = 41$$

and find all *positive integral* solutions of these last two equations. (A.E.B.)

15 The transformation $\boldsymbol{T}: \boldsymbol{r} \to \boldsymbol{r}'$ of a three-dimensional space is given by $\boldsymbol{r}' = \boldsymbol{M}\boldsymbol{r}$ where

$$\boldsymbol{r} = \begin{pmatrix} x \\ y \\ z \end{pmatrix} \qquad \boldsymbol{r}' = \begin{pmatrix} x' \\ y' \\ z' \end{pmatrix} \qquad \text{and} \qquad \boldsymbol{M} = \begin{pmatrix} 1 & 2 & 3 \\ 2 & 0 & -2 \\ 3 & -2 & -7 \end{pmatrix}$$

Show that $\boldsymbol{T}$ maps the whole space onto the plane π whose equation is $x - 2y + z = 0$. (J.M.B.)

16(a) Find constants p and q such that $\boldsymbol{A}^2 + p\boldsymbol{A} + q\boldsymbol{I} = \boldsymbol{0}$ where

$$\boldsymbol{A} = \begin{pmatrix} -5 & 6 \\ -3 & 4 \end{pmatrix} \qquad \boldsymbol{I} = \begin{pmatrix} 1 & 0 \\ 0 & 1 \end{pmatrix} \qquad \boldsymbol{0} = \begin{pmatrix} 0 & 0 \\ 0 & 0 \end{pmatrix}$$

Express $\boldsymbol{A}^4$ in the form $a\boldsymbol{A} + b\boldsymbol{I}$, where a and b are constants.

(b) Find the matrix $\boldsymbol{L}$ such that $\boldsymbol{LU} = \boldsymbol{A}$ where

$$\boldsymbol{U} = \begin{pmatrix} 1 & 0 & 1 \\ 0 & 2 & 0 \\ 0 & 0 & 1 \end{pmatrix} \qquad \boldsymbol{A} = \begin{pmatrix} 5 & 0 & 5 \\ 10 & 2 & 10 \\ 0 & -2 & 1 \end{pmatrix}$$

Calculate the inverses of the matrices $\boldsymbol{L}$ and $\boldsymbol{U}$ and use them to find the inverse of $\boldsymbol{A}$. (L.)

17 Find the square and the inverse of the matrix $\boldsymbol{A}$ given by

$$\boldsymbol{A} = \begin{pmatrix} 1 & 0 & a \\ 0 & 1 & b \\ 0 & 0 & 1 \end{pmatrix}$$

where a and b are real constants.

The relation between the coordinates of the points $P(x_1, y_1)$ and $Q(x_2, y_2)$ is given by the equation

$$\begin{pmatrix} x_2 \\ y_2 \\ 1 \end{pmatrix} = \boldsymbol{A} \begin{pmatrix} x_1 \\ y_1 \\ 1 \end{pmatrix}$$

Show in a diagram the position of Q relative to P, and express the gradient of PQ in terms of a and b. Obtain the matrix equation giving the relation between the coordinates of P and those of M, the midpoint of PQ. (L.)

18 Show that if the matrix $\boldsymbol{A}$ and the vector $\boldsymbol{x}$ are given by

$$\boldsymbol{A} = \begin{pmatrix} 1 & -1 & 4 \\ 2 & 4 & -2 \\ -1 & -1 & 6 \end{pmatrix} \quad \text{and} \quad \boldsymbol{x} = \begin{pmatrix} 1 \\ 0 \\ 1 \end{pmatrix}$$

then the vector $\boldsymbol{Ax}$ is a multiple of $\boldsymbol{x}$.

Obtain the characteristic equation of the matrix $\boldsymbol{A}$, and hence find its latent roots (or eigenvalues). Find also the latent vector (or eigenvector) corresponding to each latent root. (L.)

19 In a Fibonacci sequence each number is the sum of the two preceding numbers. One example of such a sequence has as its first 8 numbers the numbers 1, 1, 2, 3, 5, 8, 13, 21.

(a) Write down the next four numbers of this sequence.

(b) Successive pairs of numbers in the sequence are written as column vectors, e.g. $\boldsymbol{V}_1 = \begin{pmatrix} 1 \\ 1 \end{pmatrix}$, $\boldsymbol{V}_2 = \begin{pmatrix} 2 \\ 3 \end{pmatrix}$, $\boldsymbol{V}_3 = \begin{pmatrix} 5 \\ 8 \end{pmatrix}$. Write down $\boldsymbol{V}_4$ and $\boldsymbol{V}_5$.

(c) Given that $\boldsymbol{T}$ is the matrix $\begin{pmatrix} a & b \\ c & d \end{pmatrix}$ such that $\boldsymbol{TV}_1 = \boldsymbol{V}_2$ and $\boldsymbol{TV}_2 = \boldsymbol{V}_3$, find the values of a, b, c, d. Verify that $\boldsymbol{TV}_3 = \boldsymbol{V}_4$ and prove that $\boldsymbol{T}^3\boldsymbol{V}_1 = \boldsymbol{V}_4$.

(d) We denote $\boldsymbol{V}_3$ as $\begin{pmatrix} x_3 \\ y_3 \end{pmatrix}$, $\boldsymbol{V}_4$ as $\begin{pmatrix} x_4 \\ y_4 \end{pmatrix}$ and so on. Prove that as we continue, successive values of y/x become more nearly equal (i) to each other and (ii) to $\frac{1}{2}(1+\sqrt{5})$.

Show that this is true to 3 decimal places for $\dfrac{y_3}{x_3}$, $\dfrac{y_4}{x_4}$ and $\dfrac{y_5}{x_5}$. (M.E.I. (amended))

Chapter 19

Coordinate Geometry—Conics

Introduction

In this chapter we shall look at conics from several different points of view. First of all we consider them as shapes obtained as sections (or slices) of a 'double cone'. We investigate their geometric properties, their *cartesian* equations and parameters. Secondly, we consider the conics as the path of a particle moving under the 'inverse square law' and investigate their equations in *polar* form. Finally, we introduce the idea of linear transformations as an aid to discovering the types of conic that are represented by a general second degree equation of the form

$$ax^2+2hxy+by^2+2gx+2fy+c = 0$$

1 Conics as loci

1.1 The conic as a slice of a 'double cone'

Conics is the name given to the study of the shapes we obtain by taking different slices through a 'double-cone' as shown here.

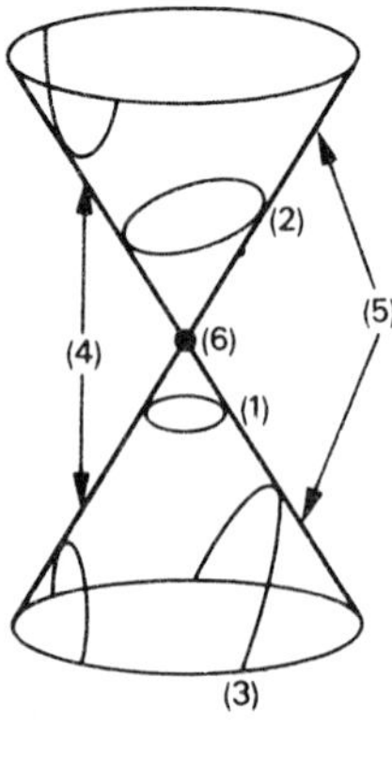

The approximate shape of the conics is shown below together with their equations.

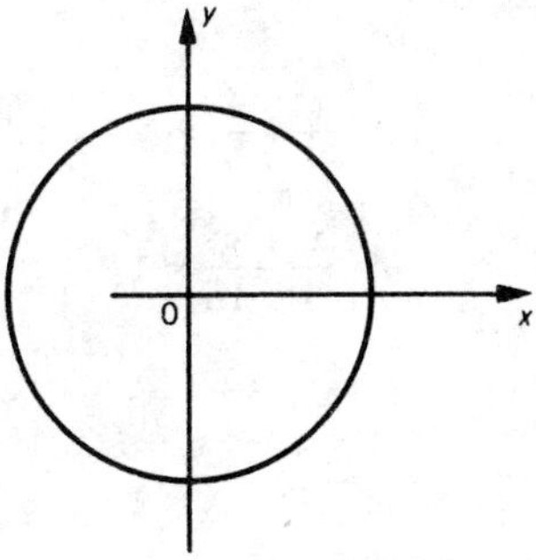

(1) The circle $x^2 + y^2 = a^2$

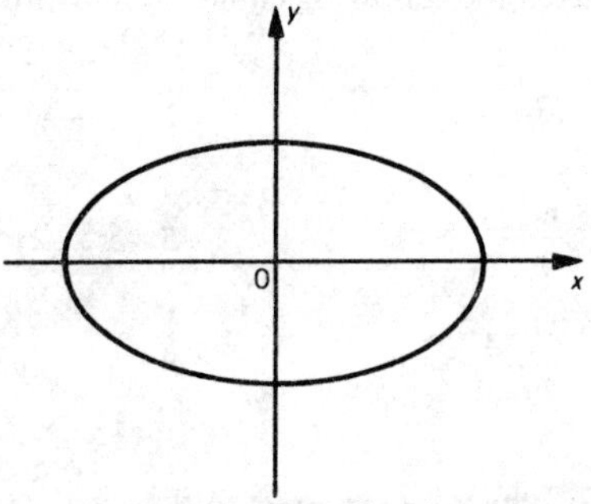

(2) The ellipse $\dfrac{x^2}{a^2} + \dfrac{y^2}{b^2} = 1$

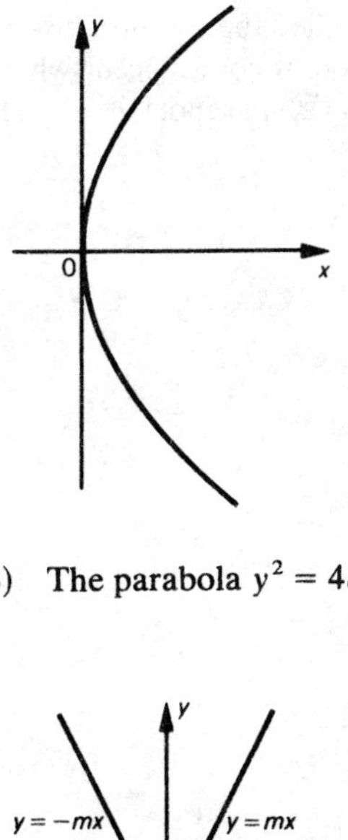

(3) The parabola $y^2 = 4ax$

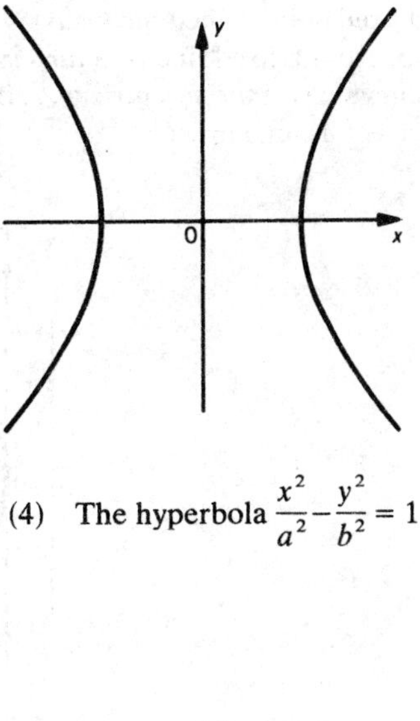

(4) The hyperbola $\dfrac{x^2}{a^2} - \dfrac{y^2}{b^2} = 1$

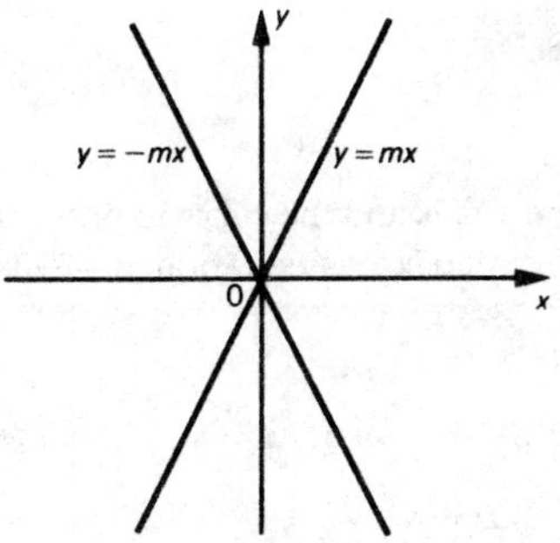

(5) The pair of lines $y = \pm mx$

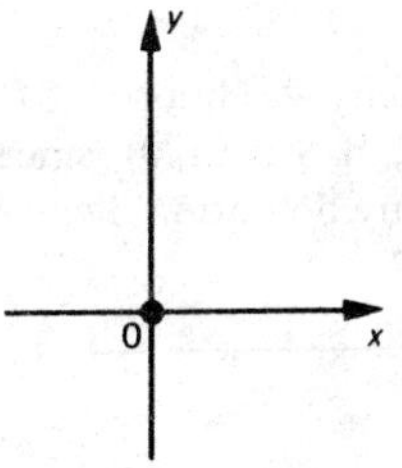

(6) The origin $x^2 + y^2 = 0$

Exercise 1.1

Sketch the following conics by substituting values for x

1 $y^2 = 4x$ **2** $x^2+y^2 = 16$ **3** $\frac{x^2}{4}+\frac{y^2}{9} = 1$

4 $\frac{x^2}{9}+\frac{y^2}{4} = 1$ **5** $x^2+2y^2 = 0$ **6** $\frac{x^2}{1}-\frac{y^2}{16} = 1$

7 $\frac{x^2}{2}-\frac{y^2}{1} = 1$ **8** $x^2-2y^2 = 0$

1.2 The parabola

Definition

A conic is the locus of a point in a plane which satisfies the condition that its distance from a fixed point (called the *focus*) is a constant (called the *eccentricity—e*) times its distance from a fixed line (the *directrix*). The different conics occur when we have different values of the eccentricity, e. If $e = 1$, we have a parabola, $e > 1$, a hyperbola and for $e < 1$, an ellipse.

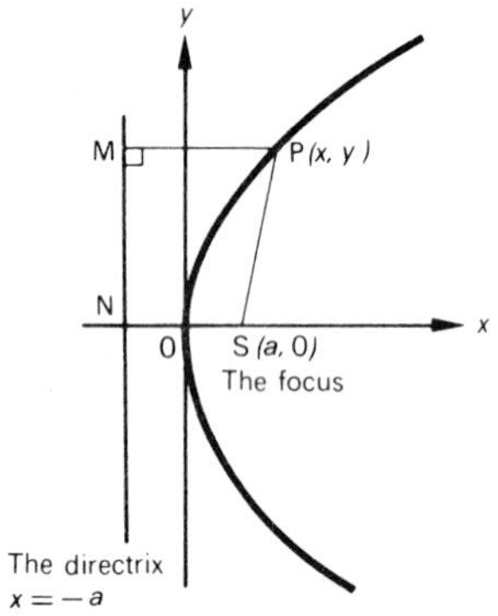

For simplicity we choose the focus S to lie on the x axis and the curve to pass through the origin. If S is $(a, 0)$, since SO = ON, the directrix has equation $x = -a$. Now SP = PM by definition, hence

$$SP^2 = PM^2$$

$$(x-a)^2+y^2 = (x+a)^2$$

$$x^2-2ax+a^2+y^2 = x^2+2ax+a^2$$

$$\mathbf{y^2 = 4ax}$$ ◀

Parameters

Usually, for calculations, for working with the parabola, and for investigating properties we use the parametric equations

$$x = at^2 \qquad \text{and} \qquad y = 2at$$ ◀

where the curve can be plotted by substituting values for t. (We met these parameters before in Chapter 4.)

The chord joining P(at^2, $2at$) to Q(aT^2, $2aT$)

Consider R(x, y), on the chord, then

$$\frac{x - at^2}{aT^2 - at^2} = \frac{y - 2at}{2aT - 2at}$$

$$\frac{(x - at^2)}{a(T - t)(T + t)} = \frac{y - 2at}{2a(T - t)}$$

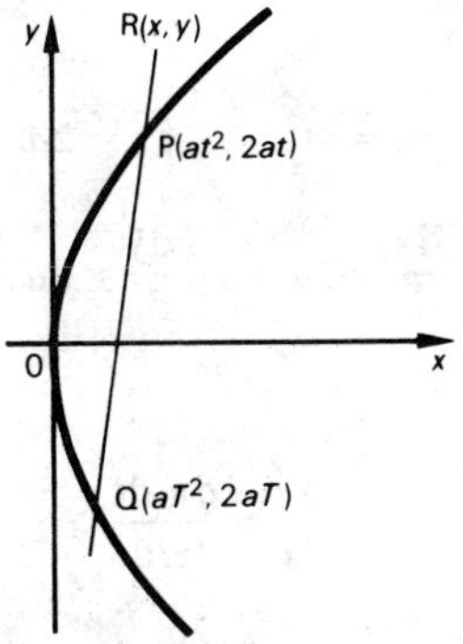

$$2x - 2at^2 = (T + t)y - (T + t)2at$$

$$= (T + t)y - 2aTt - 2at^2$$

Hence $$(T + t)y = 2x + 2aTt$$

The tangent at P

As Q moves closer to P, the chord QP approaches the tangent at P.

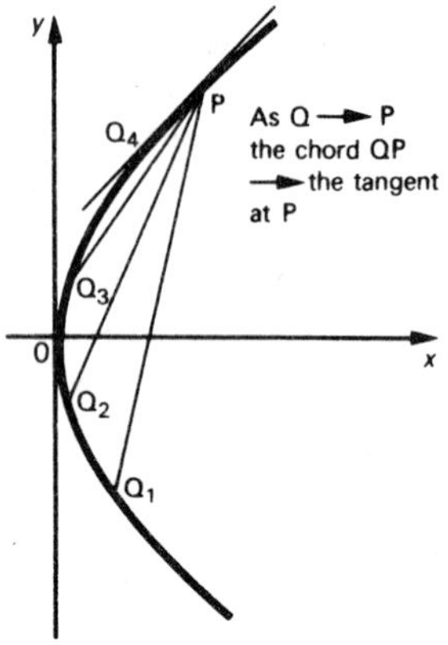

We reason that if P and Q are the same point, then the chord becomes the tangent at P. If $T = t$ we have

$$2ty = 2x + 2at^2$$

$$ty = x + at^2$$

Alternatively since

$$x = at^2 \qquad y = 2at$$

$$\frac{dx}{dt} = 2at \qquad \frac{dy}{dt} = 2a$$

Now

$$\frac{dy}{dx} = \frac{dy/dt}{dx/dt} = \frac{2a}{2at} = \frac{1}{t}$$

The equation of the line through $P(at^2, 2at)$ with slope $1/t$ or DR $t:1$ is

$$\frac{x - at^2}{t} = \frac{y - 2at}{1}$$

$$x - at^2 = ty - 2at^2$$

or

$$ty = x + at^2 \qquad \text{as before}$$

The normal at P

The normal is the line at right angles to the tangent. Since the DR of the tangent is $t:1$, the DRN is $1:-t$. Hence

$$\frac{x-at^2}{1} = \frac{y-2at}{-t}$$

$$-tx+at^3 = y-2at$$

$$y = -tx+2at+at^3$$

The midpoint of PQ

P is $(at^2, 2at)$ and Q is $(aT^2, 2aT)$. Hence the midpoint is given by (X, Y) where

$$X = \frac{at^2+aT^2}{2} \qquad Y = \frac{2at+2aT}{2}$$

Special techniques

(a) A chord through the focus

Suppose that the chord PQ passes through S(a, 0), the focus.

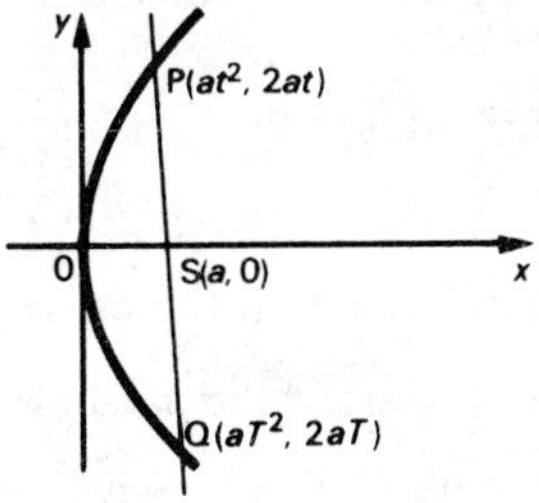

Then since the coordinates $(a, 0)$ satisfy the equation for PQ

$$(T+t)0 = 2a+2aTt$$

i.e.
$$Tt = -1$$

(b) The intersection of tangents

The tangents at P and Q meet where

$$ty = x+at^2$$

and
$$Ty = x+aT^2$$

We solve the equations simultaneously to give, by subtraction

$$ty - Ty = at^2 - aT^2$$

$$(t-T)y = a(t-T)(t+T)$$

$$y = a(t+T)$$

hence $$x = atT$$

Now, if PQ passes through S

then $$tT = -1$$

hence $$x = -a$$

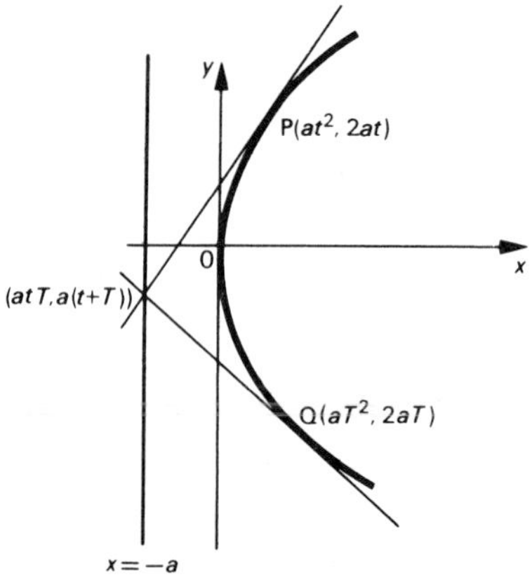

In other words, if PQ is a chord through the focus then the tangents at P and Q meet on the directrix.

(c) The intersection of a normal with the curve

In general, the normal at P will intersect the parabola again. The normal at P is

$$y = -tx + 2at + at^3$$

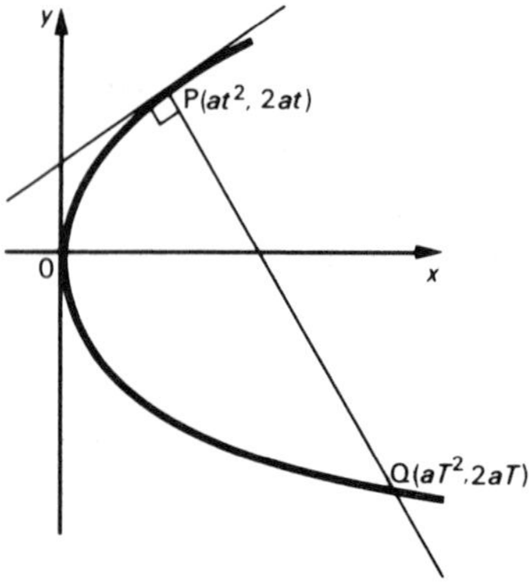

Suppose this meets the parabola again at Q(aT^2, $2aT$). Then the coordinates of Q will satisfy the equation of the normal:

$$2aT = -taT^2 + 2at + at^3$$

$$tT^2 - t^3 = 2t - 2T$$

$$t(T^2 - t^2) = 2(t - T)$$

$$t(T-t)(T+t) = 2(t-T)$$

$$t(T+t) = -2$$

$$T + t = -\frac{2}{t}$$

$$T = -\frac{2}{t} - t$$

Hence Q is $\left(a\left(-\frac{2}{t}-t\right)^2, 2a\left(-\frac{2}{t}-t\right)\right)$.

Reflective property

The parabola has a most useful property which is incorporated in the design of a variety of items. Electric fires have parabolic reflectors, torches too have parabolic reflectors. Earth communication stations have gigantic parabolic 'dishes' and so do many radar aerials. The property (as for the fire) is that if the bar is located at the *focus*, then the rays of heat are reflected *parallel* to the axis.

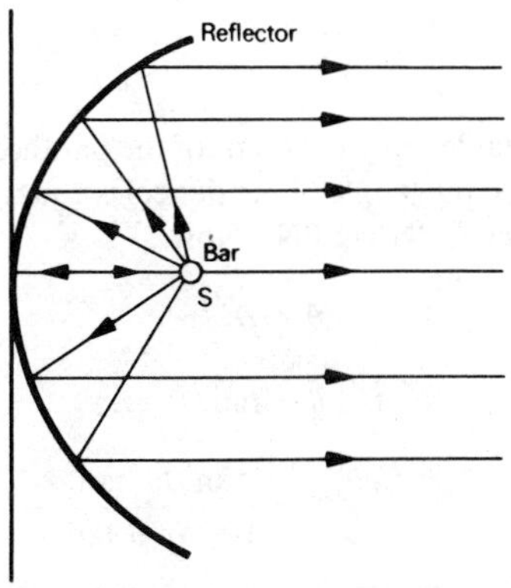

With the radio receivers, the reflector acts in the opposite sense. Radio waves from a long way away are almost parallel and are therefore reflected to pass *through the focus* where they are 'collected' and fed into the equipment.

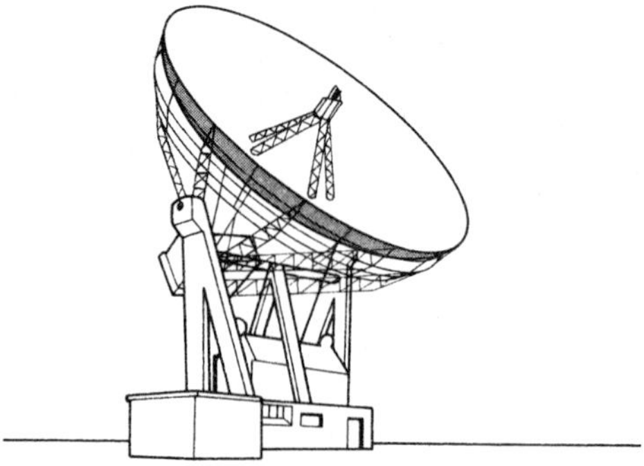

A sketch of the Goonhilly Satellite Communications Station, Cornwall

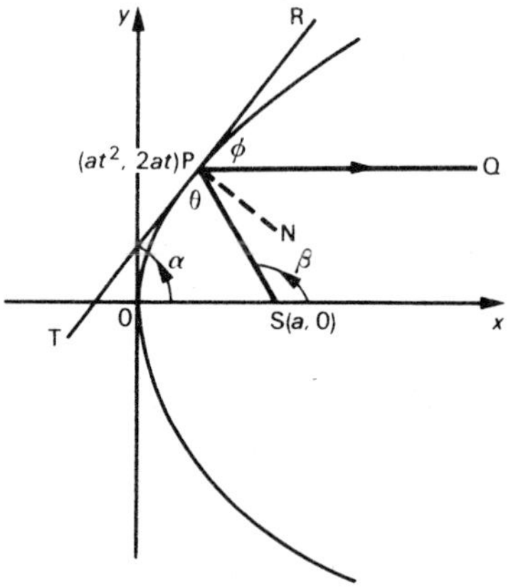

We consider a ray of heat leaving the focus of the parabola (the bar of the fire, say). It is reflected at P and since the 'angle of incidence' is equal to the 'angle of reflection' we know that $\theta = \phi$ (since $Q\hat{P}N = S\hat{P}N$). Now

$$\theta = \beta - \alpha$$

so

$$\tan\theta = \tan(\beta - \alpha)$$

$$= \frac{\tan\beta - \tan\alpha}{1 + \tan\beta\tan\alpha}$$

Now

$$\tan\beta = \frac{2at}{at^2 - a} \qquad \text{and} \qquad \tan\alpha = \frac{1}{t}$$

(the 'slope' of the tangent $ty = x + at^2$)

Hence

$$\tan\theta = \frac{\dfrac{2at}{a(t^2-1)} - \dfrac{1}{t}}{1 + \dfrac{2at}{a(t^2-1)} \times \dfrac{1}{t}}$$

$$= \frac{\dfrac{2t^2 - t^2 + 1}{(t^2-1)t}}{\dfrac{t^2 - 1 + 2}{(t^2-1)}}$$

$$= \frac{\dfrac{t^2+1}{(t^2-1)t}}{\dfrac{t^2+1}{t^2-1}}$$

$$= \frac{1}{t} = \tan\phi$$

But $\tan\alpha = \dfrac{1}{t}$ so $\alpha = \phi$ and PQ is parallel to the axis of the parabola.

General technique

A common problem in conics is to find the locus whose parametric equations (referred to two values of the parameter t, t_1 and t_2) are for example,

$$x = \frac{a(t_1^2 + t_2^2)}{2}, \qquad y = a(t_1 + t_2)$$

given that $t_1 t_2 = -1$. Here we use the identity

$$(t_1 + t_2)^2 \equiv t_1^2 + t_2^2 + 2t_1 t_2$$

Now

$$t_1 + t_2 = \frac{y}{a} \qquad t_1^2 + t_2^2 = \frac{2x}{a}$$

so

$$\left(\frac{y}{a}\right)^2 = \frac{2x}{a} - 2$$

$$\frac{y^2}{a^2} = \frac{2x - 2a}{a}$$

$$y^2 = 2a(x - a)$$

Exercise 1.2

1 The tangents at P(at^2, $2at$) and Q($aT^2, 2aT$) meet at R($-4a, 3a$). Find the coordinates of P and Q. Prove that the perpendicular from R to the chord does not intersect the parabola.

2 The tangents at P and Q to the parabola $y^2 = 4ax$ meet at R. Find the equation of the locus of R in each of the following cases

(a) when the sum of the ordinates of P and Q is $4a$.

(b) when the sum of the squares of the ordinates of P and Q is $4a^2$.

3 C is the midpoint of a variable chord PQ of the parabola. The tangents at P and Q meet at R.

(a) Prove that RC is parallel to the axis of the parabola

(b) If PQ subtends a right angle at the vertex prove that the locus of C is

$$2ax = y^2 + 8a^2$$

4 Prove that the equation of the tangent at $(at^2, 2at)$ on $y^2 = 4ax$ is $x - ty + at^2 = 0$. A and B are any two points on the parabola $y^2 = 4ax$ and the tangents at A and B meet at P. The line PM is parallel to the axis of the parabola and meets the line AB at M. Prove that M is the midpoint of AB.

If the parameters of the points A and B are t and $2t$ respectively, and the tangents meet at P, find the coordinates of P and show that it always lies on the parabola $y^2 = \dfrac{9ax}{2}$.

5 Prove that the equation of the chord joining the points $(at^2, 2at)$ and $(aT^2, 2aT)$ on the parabola $y^2 = 4ax$ is

$$2x - (t+T)y + 2aTt = 0$$

and deduce the equation of the tangent at the point whose parameter is t.

The parameters of the three points A, B and C on the parabola are t_1, t_2 and t_3. The tangents at A and B meet the tangent at C at Q and P respectively; the tangents at A and B meet at R. Prove that if P is the midpoint of QC then

$$2t_2 = t_1 + t_3$$

Prove also that RP is parallel to AC.

6 Prove that the equation of the normal at $(at^2, 2at)$ on $y^2 = 4ax$ is

$$y + tx = 2at + at^3$$

The chord PQ of the parabola subtends a right angle at the vertex, P and Q being $(at^2, 2at)$ and $(aT^2, 2aT)$. Prove that $tT + 4 = 0$ and the locus of the point of intersection of the normals at P and Q is $y^2 = 16a(x - 6a)$.

7 Show that the equation of the normal to the parabola $y^2 = 4ax$ at the point $(at^2, 2at)$ is

$$y + tx = 2at + at^3$$

If this normal meets the parabola again at the point $(aT^2, 2aT)$ show that $t^2 + tT + 2 = 0$ and deduce that T^2 cannot be less than 8.

The line $3y = 2x + 4a$ meets the parabola at the points P and Q. Show that the normals at P and Q meet on the parabola.

8 Find the equation of the tangent at $P(at^2, 2at)$ to the parabola $y^2 = 4ax$.
The tangent and the normal to the parabola at P meet the x axis at T and G respectively and M is the foot of the perpendicular from P to the line $x = -a$. S is the point $(a, 0)$. Show that ST = PM = SP and deduce that PT bisects the angle SPM. Show also that PG bisects the angle between PS and MP produced.

1.3 The ellipse

Definition

Given a fixed point S (the focus) and a fixed line (the directrix), then P lies on an ellipse if

$$SP = e PM$$

where PM is the perpendicular distance from P to the directrix and $e < 1$.
We first choose our axes.

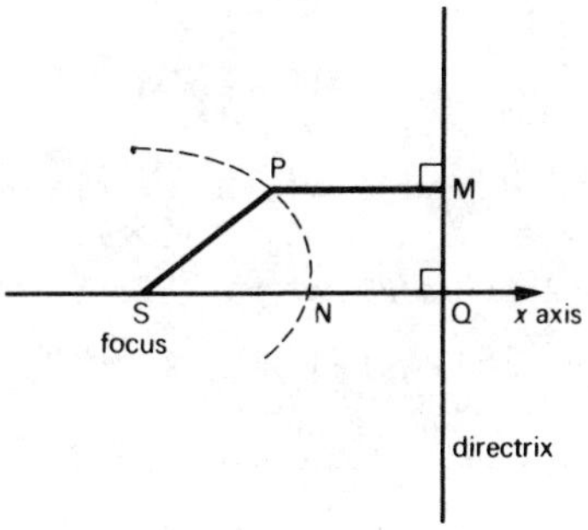

For our x axis we choose the line through S and perpendicular to the directrix. The curve will cut this axis at a point N, where SN = eNQ. We see that, since $e < 1$, the curve will also cut the axis at another point N′, where SN′ = eN′Q.

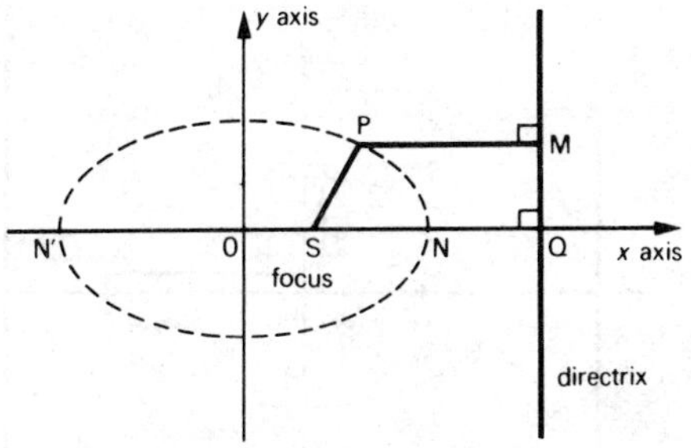

We now choose our y axis perpendicular to the x axis and bisecting NN′.
Suppose ON = ON′ = a, OQ = q and OS = s, then

$$SN = eNQ \Rightarrow a - s = e(q-a)$$

and
$$SN' = eN'Q \Rightarrow a + s = e(q+a)$$

Hence $q = \frac{a}{e}$ and $s = ae$ so the equation of the directrix is $x = \frac{a}{e}$ and S is the point $(ae, 0)$.

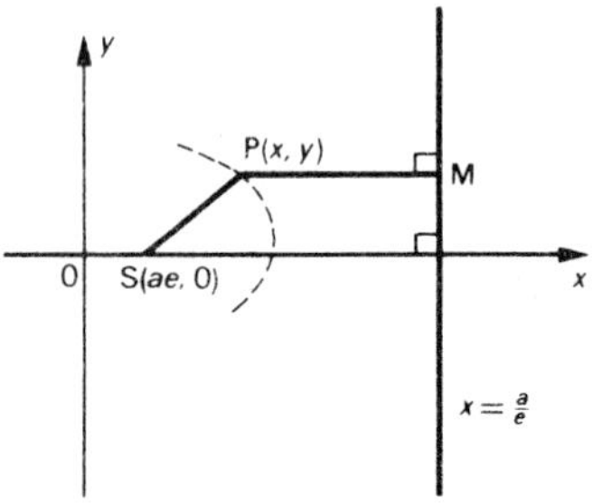

Now for a general point P(x, y) on the ellipse

$$SP = ePM \qquad e < 1$$

$$SP^2 = e^2PM^2$$

$$(x-ae)^2 + y^2 = e^2\left(\frac{a}{e} - x\right)^2$$

$$x^2 - 2aex + a^2e^2 + y^2 = a^2 - 2aex + e^2x^2$$

$$x^2(1-e^2) + y^2 = a^2(1-e^2)$$

$$\frac{x^2}{a^2} + \frac{y^2}{a^2(1-e^2)} = 1$$

and if we substitute $b^2 = a^2(1-e^2)$ we have the standard equation of the ellipse

$$\boldsymbol{\frac{x^2}{a^2} + \frac{y^2}{b^2} = 1}$$ ◀

This equation is symmetrical in x and y and the curve cuts the axes when $x = \pm a$, and when $y = \pm b$. Hence the ellipse has a focus not only at S(ae, 0) but also at S′($-ae$, 0) and a directrix not only $x = \frac{a}{e}$ but also $x = -\frac{a}{e}$.

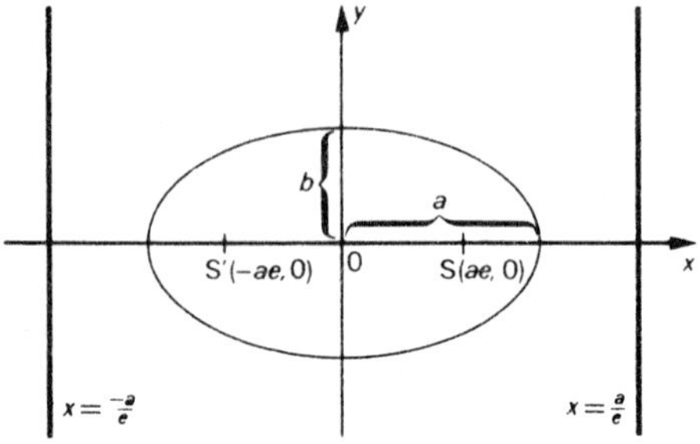

Note that since SP = ePM and S′P = ePM′,

$$\begin{aligned} SP + S'P' &= e(PM + PM') \\ &= e \cdot \frac{2a}{e} \\ &= 2a \end{aligned}$$

You may well have used this idea to sketch an ellipse using drawing pins at S and S′, joined by a piece of string. By keeping the string taut with a pencil at P it is possible to trace an ellipse.

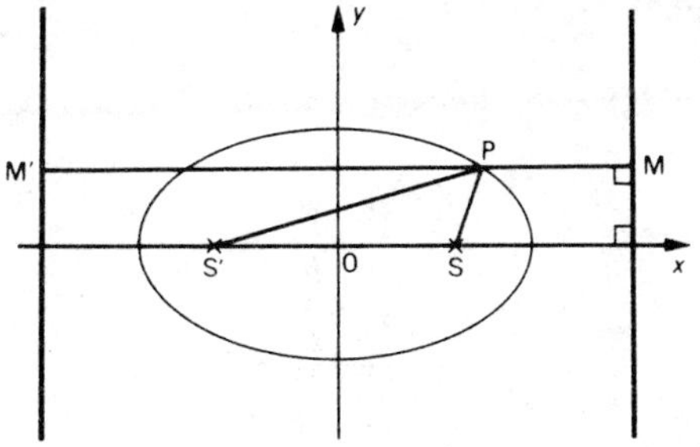

Parameters

As with the parabola, we usually work with the ellipse in parametric form. This is

$$\boldsymbol{x = a\cos\theta} \qquad \textbf{and} \qquad \boldsymbol{y = b\sin\theta}$$ ◀

The work is very similar to that of the parabola, but since the parametric equations involve trigonometrical functions, the solutions are more complicated and require a good knowledge of the trigonometrical formulae.

The chord joining P(a cos θ, b sin θ) to Q(a cos ϕ, b sin ϕ)

Consider R(x, y) on the line, then

$$\frac{x - a\cos\theta}{a\cos\phi - a\cos\theta} = \frac{y - b\sin\theta}{b\sin\phi - b\sin\theta}$$

$$y - b\sin\theta = \frac{b(\sin\phi - \sin\theta)}{a(\cos\phi - \cos\theta)}(x - a\cos\theta)$$

$$y - b\sin\theta = \frac{-b2\sin\dfrac{\phi-\theta}{2}\cos\dfrac{\phi+\theta}{2}}{a2\sin\dfrac{\phi-\theta}{2}\sin\dfrac{\phi+\theta}{2}}(x - a\cos\theta)$$

$$y - b\sin\theta = -\frac{b}{a}\cot\frac{\phi+\theta}{2}(x - a\cos\theta)$$

The tangent at P

If $\theta = \phi$ we have the equation of the tangent at P as

$$y - b \sin \theta = \frac{-b}{a} \cot \theta (x - a \cos \theta)$$

$$= \frac{-b}{a} \frac{\cos \theta}{\sin \theta}(x - a \cos \theta)$$

$$ay \sin \theta - ab \sin^2 \theta = -bx \cos \theta + ab \cos^2 \theta$$

which can be written

$$\frac{x \cos \theta}{a} + \frac{y \sin \theta}{b} = 1$$

Alternatively since

$$\frac{x^2}{a^2} + \frac{y^2}{b^2} = 1$$

$$\frac{2x}{a^2} + \frac{2y}{b^2} \cdot \frac{dy}{dx} = 0$$

$$\Rightarrow \frac{dy}{dx} = -\frac{b^2 x}{a^2 y}$$

Hence the slope of the tangent at P($a \cos \theta$, $b \sin \theta$) is given by

$$\frac{dy}{dx} = \frac{-b^2 a \cos \theta}{a^2 b \sin \theta} = -\frac{b}{a} \cot \theta$$

The equation of the tangent is

$$y - b \sin \theta = -\frac{b}{a} \frac{\cos \theta}{\sin \theta}(x - a \cos \theta)$$

and this leads to

$$\frac{x \cos \theta}{a} + \frac{y \sin \theta}{b} = 1 \qquad \text{as before}$$

The normal at P

This can be quickly found since the slope of the normal is

$$\frac{-1}{\text{slope of the tangent}}$$

$$\Rightarrow y - b \sin \theta = \frac{a \sin \theta}{b \cos \theta}(x - a \cos \theta)$$

$$(b \cos \theta)y - (a \sin \theta)x = (b^2 - a^2) \sin \theta \cos \theta$$

Exercise 1.3

1 P and Q are two points on the ellipse $x = a \cos \theta$, $y = b \sin \theta$ such that $\theta = \alpha$ for P and $\theta = \alpha + \pi/2$ for Q.

Prove that the equation of the chord PQ is

$$b(\sin \alpha - \cos \alpha)x - a(\sin \alpha + \cos \alpha)y + ab = 0$$

If PQ passes through the focus $(ae, 0)$ of the ellipse, prove that $e\sqrt{2} \geqslant 1$.

2 The points P and Q on the ellipse

$$\frac{x^2}{a^2} + \frac{y^2}{b^2} = 1$$

have coordinates $(a \cos \theta, b \sin \theta)$ and $(-a \sin \theta, b \cos \theta)$ respectively. Show that if O is the origin,

(a) $OP^2 + OQ^2 = a^2 + b^2$
(b) The area of triangle OPQ is $\frac{1}{2}ab$.
(c) The midpoint of PQ always lies on the curve whose equation is

$$\frac{2x^2}{a^2} + \frac{2y^2}{b^2} = 1$$

3 Show that if the line $y = mx + c$ is a tangent to the ellipse

$$\frac{x^2}{a^2} + \frac{y^2}{b^2} = 1 \qquad \text{then} \qquad c^2 = a^2m^2 + b^2$$

Find the gradients of the tangents to this ellipse through the point $(\sqrt{(a^2 + b^2)}, 0)$. Hence or otherwise, determine the coordinates of the vertices of a square whose sides touch the ellipse.

4 The foci of an ellipse are $S(ae, 0)$ and $H(-ae, 0)$ where $b^2 = a^2(1 - e^2)$. T and K are the feet of the perpendiculars from S and H respectively to any tangent. Prove that

(a) $ST \times HK = b^2$
(b) T lies on the circle $x^2 + y^2 = a^2$

5 Find the equations of the tangents from $(-4, 3)$ to the ellipse

$$\frac{x^2}{25} + \frac{y^2}{16} = 1$$

and prove that the tangent of the angle between them is $\frac{9}{8}$.

1.4 The hyperbola

Definition

Given a fixed point S (the focus) and a fixed line (the directrix), then P lies on a hyperbola if

$$SP = e\,PM$$

where PM is the perpendicular distance from P to the directrix and $e > 1$.

As for the ellipse, we find that there are two foci $S(ae, 0)$ and $S'(-ae, 0)$ and two directrices $x = \frac{a}{e}$ and $x = -\frac{a}{e}$.

The hyperbola is shown below.

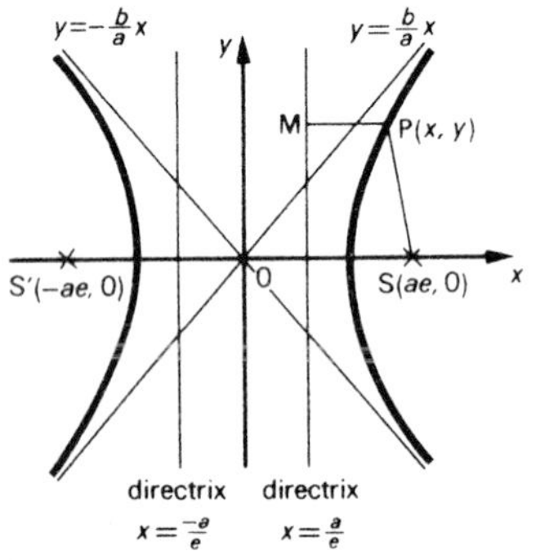

From the definition of the hyperbola

$$SP = e\,PM \qquad e > 1$$

$$(SP)^2 = e^2(PM)^2$$

$$(x-ae)^2 + y^2 = e^2\left(x - \frac{a}{e}\right)^2$$

$$x^2 - 2aex + a^2e^2 + y^2 = e^2\left(x^2 - \frac{2ax}{e} + \frac{a^2}{e^2}\right)$$

$$x^2 - 2aex + a^2e^2 + y^2 = e^2x^2 - 2aex + a^2$$

$$y^2 + (1-e^2)x^2 = a^2(1-e^2)$$

$$\frac{y^2}{a^2(1-e^2)} + \frac{x^2}{a^2} = 1$$

Put $b^2 = a^2(e^2 - 1)$ and we have

$$\boldsymbol{\frac{x^2}{a^2} - \frac{y^2}{b^2} = 1}$$ ◀

Asymptotes

The hyperbola has asymptotes $y = \pm\frac{b}{a}x$. These give us a guide for sketching the curve.

Parameters

As usual we use parameters. Again they involve trigonometrical functions and this time

$$x = a \sec \theta \qquad y = b \tan \theta$$ ◀

(There is another possibility for the parameters using the hyperbolic functions $x = a \cosh \theta$ and $y = b \sinh \theta$, which you may meet later, but here we use the first pair, $x = a \sec \theta \quad y = b \tan \theta$.)

Exercise 1.4

1 Find the equation of the chord joining P($a \sec \theta, b \tan \theta$) to Q($a \sec \phi, b \tan \phi$).

2 Find the equation of the tangent at P
(a) by considering P and Q to be identical (i.e. $\theta = \phi$ in your answer to question 1.)
(b) by finding $\frac{dy}{dx}$ and hence the tangent at P.

3 Find the equation of the normal at P.

4 Show that for the hyperbola shown opposite, S′P − SP = $2a$.

5 By solving $y = mx + c$ with $\frac{x^2}{a^2} - \frac{y^2}{b^2} = 1$ and considering the case for equal roots find the condition for the line to be a tangent to the hyperbola.
Also consider the case when the line $y = mx + c$ becomes the asymptote to the hyperbola when the equation found above has
(a) infinite roots **(b)** equal and opposite roots.

6 Prove that the equation of the tangent at the point P(x_1, y_1) on the hyperbola $\frac{x^2}{a^2} - \frac{y^2}{b^2} = 1$ is

$$\frac{xx_1}{a^2} - \frac{yy_1}{b^2} = 1$$

and that the equations of the asymptotes are $y = \pm\frac{b}{a}x$. The tangent at P meets the asymptotes at Q and R. Prove that P is the midpoint of QR.

7 A given line $lx + my = 1$ meets the hyperbola $\frac{x^2}{a^2} - \frac{y^2}{b^2} = 1$ at A and B and its

asymptotes at C and D. Prove that AB and CD have the same midpoint M. Prove that M lies on the line

$$\frac{mx}{a^2}+\frac{ly}{b^2}=0$$

8 The normal at P(a sec θ, b tan θ) on the standard hyperbola meets the axes at X and Y; the midpoint of XY is Z. Prove that if O is the centre of the hyperbola

(a) OZ is not less than $\dfrac{a^2+b^2}{2a}$.

(b) if $a = b$, then Z coincides with P.

9 Obtain the equation of the tangent at the point P(x_1, y_1) of the hyperbola $\dfrac{x^2}{a^2}-\dfrac{y^2}{b^2}=1$. Prove that, if the tangent at P meets the asymptotes at A and B, then P is the midpoint of AB.

Prove also that OA × OB $= a^2+b^2$, where O is the centre of the hyperbola.

10 The normal at P to a standard hyperbola meets the x axis at Q. Prove that SQ = eSP and S′Q = eS′P, S and S′ being the foci. Deduce that the tangent and normal at P are bisectors of the angle S′PS.

1.5 The rectangular hyperbola

Definition

Consider the equation $\dfrac{x^2}{a^2}-\dfrac{y^2}{b^2}=1$ in the case when $e^2=2$, i.e. $b^2=a^2$, and the equation becomes $x^2-y^2=a^2$. This is the equation of the *rectangular* hyperbola which with specially chosen axes has a simpler equation and can readily be adapted for use with parameters. It is called rectangular because the asymptotes are at right angles to each other ($y = \pm x$).

Consider a rotation of the axes through 45° anticlockwise. The matrix for this is

$$\begin{pmatrix} \frac{1}{\sqrt{2}} & -\frac{1}{\sqrt{2}} \\ \frac{1}{\sqrt{2}} & \frac{1}{\sqrt{2}} \end{pmatrix}$$

Our new coordinates will be given by

$$\begin{pmatrix} \frac{1}{\sqrt{2}} & -\frac{1}{\sqrt{2}} \\ \frac{1}{\sqrt{2}} & \frac{1}{\sqrt{2}} \end{pmatrix}\begin{pmatrix} x \\ y \end{pmatrix}=\begin{pmatrix} x' \\ y' \end{pmatrix}$$

so

$$\begin{pmatrix} x \\ y \end{pmatrix}=\begin{pmatrix} \frac{1}{\sqrt{2}} & \frac{1}{\sqrt{2}} \\ -\frac{1}{\sqrt{2}} & \frac{1}{\sqrt{2}} \end{pmatrix}\begin{pmatrix} x' \\ y' \end{pmatrix}$$

since the inverse of $\begin{pmatrix} \frac{1}{\sqrt{2}} & -\frac{1}{\sqrt{2}} \\ \frac{1}{\sqrt{2}} & \frac{1}{\sqrt{2}} \end{pmatrix}$ is $\begin{pmatrix} \frac{1}{\sqrt{2}} & \frac{1}{\sqrt{2}} \\ -\frac{1}{\sqrt{2}} & \frac{1}{\sqrt{2}} \end{pmatrix}$

i.e.
$$x = \frac{1}{\sqrt{2}}x' + \frac{1}{\sqrt{2}}y'$$
$$y = -\frac{1}{\sqrt{2}}x' + \frac{1}{\sqrt{2}}y'$$

Substituting in $x^2 - y^2 = a^2$

$$\left(\frac{1}{\sqrt{2}}x' + \frac{1}{\sqrt{2}}y'\right)^2 - \left(-\frac{1}{\sqrt{2}}x' + \frac{1}{\sqrt{2}}y'\right)^2 = a^2$$

$$\frac{1}{2}(x')^2 + x'y' + \frac{1}{2}(y')^2 - \frac{1}{2}(x')^2 + x'y' - \frac{1}{2}(y')^2 = a^2$$

$$2x'y' = a^2$$

$$x'y' = \frac{a^2}{2} = c^2 \text{ say}$$

Using these axes and renaming them x, y, we have the simplified equation

$$\boldsymbol{xy = c^2}$$ ◀

Parameters

The parameters are

$$\boldsymbol{x = ct \qquad y = \frac{c}{t}}$$ ◀

The chord joining P$\left(ct, \frac{c}{t}\right)$ to Q$\left(cT, \frac{c}{T}\right)$

We know that

$$\frac{x - ct}{cT - ct} = \frac{y - \frac{c}{t}}{\frac{c}{T} - \frac{c}{t}}$$

so
$$\frac{x - ct}{c(T - t)} = \frac{y - \frac{c}{t}}{\frac{c(t - T)}{Tt}}$$

$$x - ct = -Tty + cT$$
$$Tty = -x + c(T + t)$$

The tangent at $\mathbf{P}\left(ct, \frac{c}{t}\right)$

As Q is taken closer and closer to P, the chord approximates to the tangent. When $t = T$ we have the equation of the tangent at P as

$$t^2y = -x + 2ct$$

or alternatively, since $xy = c^2 \qquad y = \frac{c^2}{x}$

$$\frac{dy}{dx} = -\frac{c^2}{x^2}$$

Thus at $P\left(ct, \frac{c}{t}\right)$ $\qquad \frac{dy}{dx} = \frac{-c^2}{c^2t^2} = \frac{-1}{t^2}$

Hence DR of the tangent are $t^2 : -1$ and

$$\frac{x - ct}{t^2} = \frac{y - \frac{c}{t}}{-1}$$

$$-x + ct = t^2y - ct$$

so $\qquad t^2y = -x + 2ct \qquad$ as before

The normal at $\mathbf{P}\left(ct, \frac{c}{t}\right)$

DRN are $1 : t^2$

$$\frac{x - ct}{1} = \frac{y - \frac{c}{t}}{t^2}$$

$$t^2x - ct^3 = y - \frac{c}{t}$$

$$t^3x - ct^4 = ty - c$$

Hence $\qquad ty = t^3x - c(t^4 - 1)$

Asymptotes

We now have the axes, $y = 0$ and $x = 0$, as the asymptotes of the curve.

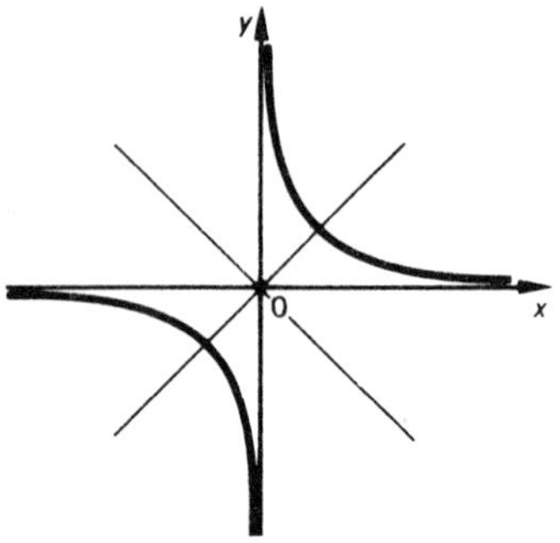

Exercise 1.5

1 Prove that the equation of the tangent PT at the point $P\left(ct, \frac{c}{t}\right)$ on the rectangular hyperbola $xy = c^2$ is $x + t^2y = 2ct$.

The perpendicular to PT from the origin O meets PT at Q and the normal at P meets the hyperbola again at R. Prove

(a) that as P varies, the locus of Q is $(x^2+y^2)^2 = 4c^2xy$.

(b) that $c^2\text{PR} = \text{OP}^3$.

2 Find the equations of the tangent and normal at $P\left(ct, \frac{c}{t}\right)$ on $xy = c^2$. The normal at P meets the hyperbola again at R, $\left(cT, \frac{c}{T}\right)$ prove that $t^3T = -1$. The tangent at P meets the y axis at Q. Find the area of the triangle PQR in terms of t and prove that the area is a minimum when $t = \pm 1$.

3 Prove that the equation of the chord joining $P\left(ct, \frac{c}{t}\right)$ and $Q\left(cT, \frac{c}{T}\right)$ on $xy = c^2$ is $x + tTy = c(t+T)$.

M is the midpoint of PQ and PQ meets the x axis at N. Prove that OM = MN where O is the origin.

The line through N parallel to OM meets the hyperbola at R and S whose parameters are t_1 and t_2; C is the midpoint of RS. Prove that

(a) CM is parallel to the y axis

(b) $t_1t_2 = -tT$.

4 Find the coordinates of the points of intersection A and B of the rectangular hyperbola $xy = c^2$ with the curve whose equation is

$$c^2y = x(2x^2 - c^2)$$

Find the points at which the normals to this curve at A and B intersect the hyperbola again, and show that a length $\frac{4}{5}c\sqrt{26}$ is cut off each of these lines by the hyperbola.

5 The normal at the point P of the rectangular hyperbola $xy = c^2$ meets the hyperbola again at Q and the tangents at P and Q meet at T. Prove that T lies on

$$(x^2 - y^2)^2 + 4c^2xy = 0$$

6 The parabola $y^2 = 4ax$ cuts $xy = c^2$ at one real point P. c and a are such that the tangent at P to the parabola is perpendicular to the tangent at P to the hyperbola. Obtain a relation connecting c and a.

The line joining P to S$(a, 0)$—the focus of the parabola—meets the axis Oy at T and the other branch of the hyperbola again at Q. Prove that S and T are points of trisection of PQ.

2 Conics as orbits

Perhaps the most important feature of the conics is that they are the paths taken by particles moving under the *inverse square law*. Planets, satellites, meteorites, electrons and projectiles all travel in one of these paths.

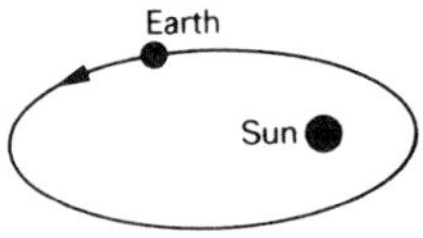

The earth moves in an ellipse with the sun as 'focus'

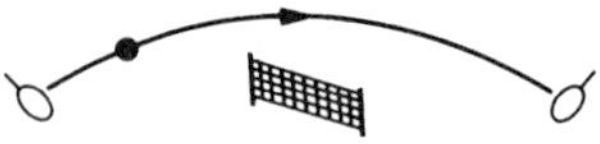

A projectile travels in a parabola

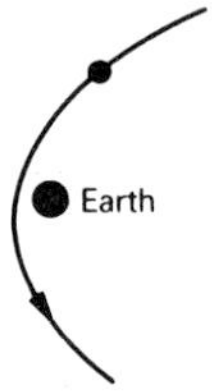

A meteorite zooms past on one arm of a hyperbola

Basically the reason for these paths is that there is a *force of attraction* between two bodies which is $\dfrac{\gamma M_1 M_2}{r^2}$, where γ is the gravitational constant, M_1 and M_2 are the masses of the bodies and r is the distance between their centres of mass. This is the force of *gravity*. It is not easy to show that under this force the path is one of these conics. To do this we have to make up differential equations involving the forces (and hence the accelerations) along and perpendicular to the line joining the centres of mass. These can be solved and lead to the equation of the path. We shall investigate this problem later on after finding the polar equation of a conic.

2.1 The polar equation of a conic

The general polar equation

We choose the focus S to be the origin, with SN perpendicular to the directrix.

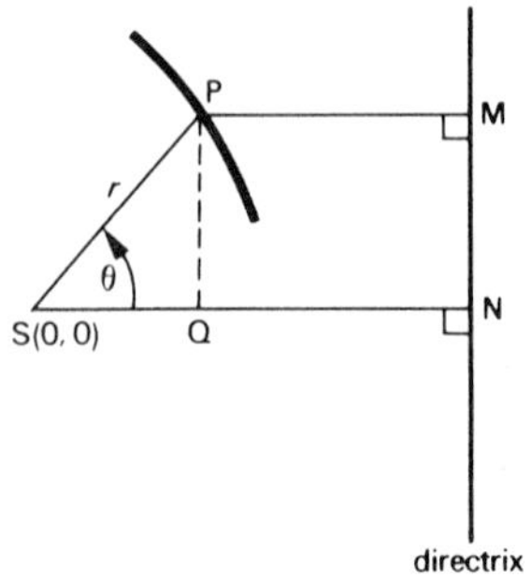

Then $$SP = e\,PM$$

so $$r = e(SN - SQ)$$
$$= e\,SN - er\cos\theta$$
$$r(1 + e\cos\theta) = e\,SN$$
$$= l \text{ (a constant)}$$

Hence $$\boldsymbol{\frac{l}{r} = 1 + e\cos\theta}$$ ◀

Notice that when $\theta = \frac{\pi}{2}$, $l = r$.

The parabola ($e = 1$)

In this case the polar equation is

$$\frac{l}{r} = 1 + \cos\theta$$

Suppose for simplicity, $l = 1$. Then

$$\frac{1}{r} = 1 + \cos\theta$$

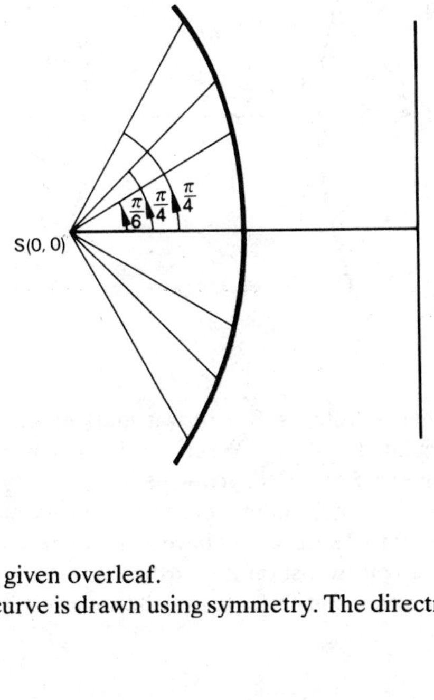

The table of values is given overleaf.
The lower half of the curve is drawn using symmetry. The directrix is drawn as shown

Table of values

θ	$\cos\theta$	$1+\cos\theta$	r
0	1.00	2.00	0.5
$\frac{\pi}{6}$	0.87	1.87	0.54
$\frac{\pi}{4}$	0.71	1.71	0.59
$\frac{\pi}{3}$	0.50	1.50	0.67

The hyperbola ($e > 1$)

This time the polar equation is

$$\frac{1}{r} = 1 + e\cos\theta$$

If we take $l = 1$ and $e = 2$, then

$$\frac{1}{r} = 1 + 2\cos\theta$$

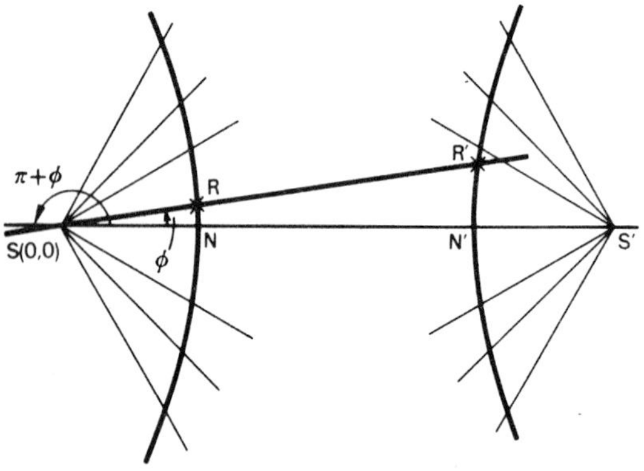

The curve was sketched as follows. S(0, 0) was marked and a line SNN′S′ drawn. Values for r were calculated as shown. When $\theta = 0$, we have SN marked, and $\theta = \pi$ gives us SN′. By symmetry SN = S′N′, giving us S′. Also from the symmetry of the hyperbola we can then mark in the other points shown. If we had made up a complete table of values for $\theta = 0$ to 2π we would have found that points on the nearer arm (like R) are given by $\theta = \phi$, whilst on the further arm (like R′) r is negative when $\theta = \pi + \phi$. It is much quicker and easier to sketch the curve using ideas of symmetry.

Table of values

θ	$\cos\theta$	$2\cos\theta$	$1+2\cos\theta$	r
0	1	2	3	0.33
$\frac{\pi}{6}$	0.87	1.74	2.74	0.36
$\frac{\pi}{4}$	0.71	1.42	2.42	0.41
$\frac{\pi}{3}$	0.50	1.00	2.00	0.50
π	−1	−2	−1	−1

The ellipse ($e < 1$)

In the polar equation

$$\frac{l}{r} = 1 + e\cos\theta$$

suppose that $l = 1$, $e = \frac{1}{2}$, then

$$\frac{1}{r} = 1 + \frac{1}{2}\cos\theta$$

The table of values is given below, from $\theta = 0$ to π. Again, the quickest method of sketching is to use symmetry. Mark S(0, 0) and draw in the line N'SN. N is given when $\theta = 0$, N' when $\theta = \pi$. Then SN = S'N'.

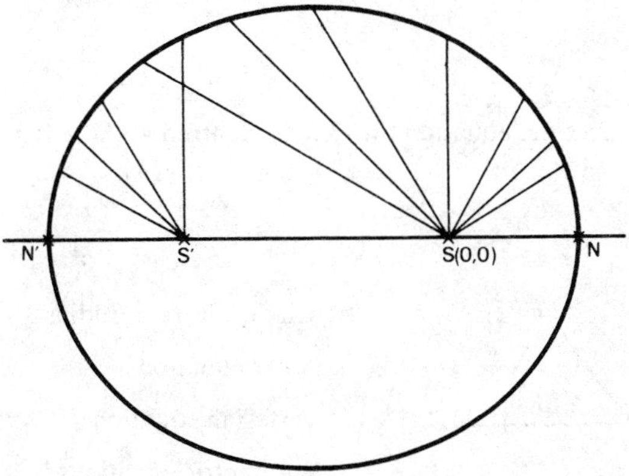

We could use the values given by $\theta = 0$ to $\theta = \pi/2$ at each focus in turn, which together with $\theta = 2\pi/3$ would give us ample points to mark. The bottom of the ellipse is a reflection of the top.

Tables of values

θ	$\cos\theta$	$\frac{1}{2}\cos\theta$	$1+\frac{1}{2}\cos\theta$	r
0	1.00	0.50	1.50	0.67
$\frac{\pi}{6}$	0.87	0.43	1.43	0.70
$\frac{\pi}{4}$	0.71	0.35	1.35	0.74
$\frac{\pi}{3}$	0.50	0.25	1.25	0.80
$\frac{\pi}{2}$	0.00	0.00	1.00	1.00
$\frac{2\pi}{3}$	−0.50	−0.25	0.75	1.33
$\frac{3\pi}{4}$	−0.71	−0.35	0.65	1.53
$\frac{5\pi}{6}$	−0.87	−0.43	0.57	1.75
π	−1.00	−0.50	0.50	2.00

2.2 Polar and cartesian equations

In this brief section we illustrate the different forms of equation for a given curve (not necessarily a conic).

A circle

$e = 0$ and $\frac{l}{r} = 1$ gives the equation for a circle, centred at the origin, and of radius l.

Example 1

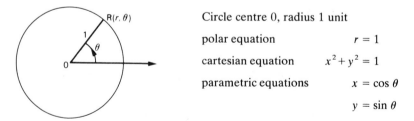

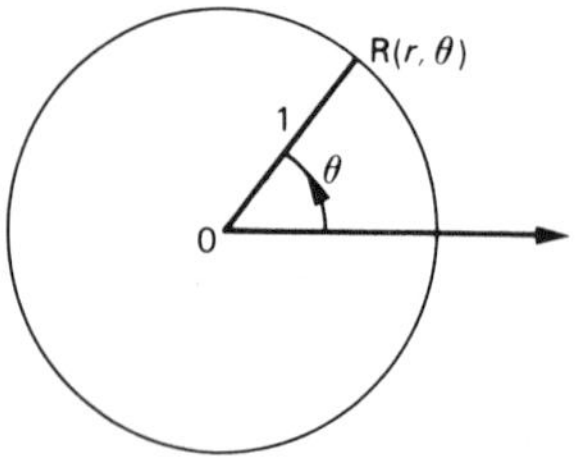

Circle centre 0, radius 1 unit

polar equation $r = 1$

cartesian equation $x^2 + y^2 = 1$

parametric equations $x = \cos\theta$

$y = \sin\theta$

The polar equation of a circle with any other centre is found by simple consideration of the geometry of the figure.

Example 2

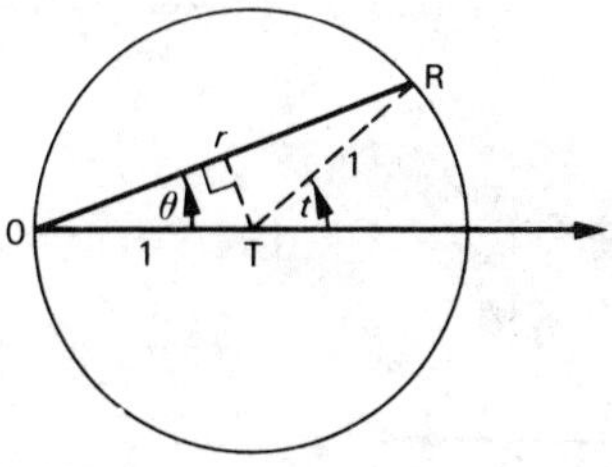

Circle centre (1, 0), radius 1 unit

polars $r = 2\cos\theta$

cartesians $(x-1)^2+y^2 = 1$

parameters (introduce the angle t)

$$x = 1+\cos t$$

$$y = \sin t$$

Example 3

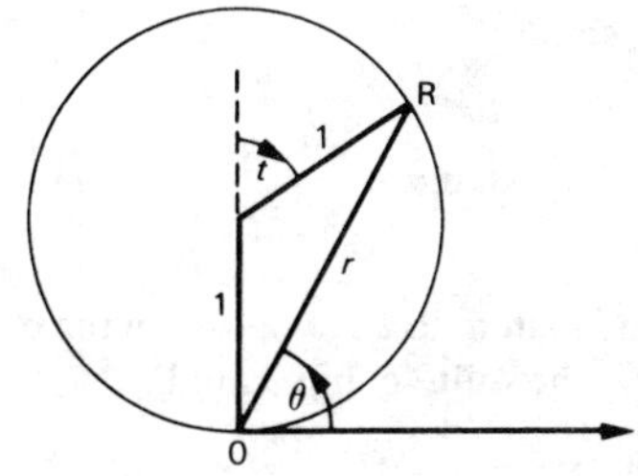

Circle centre $\left(1, \frac{\pi}{2}\right)$ radius 1 unit

polars $r = 2\cos\left(\frac{\pi}{2}-\theta\right)$

i.e. $r = 2\sin\theta$

cartesians $x^2+(y-1)^2 = 1$

parameters (introduce the angle t)

$$x = \sin t$$

$$y = 1+\cos t$$

Example 4

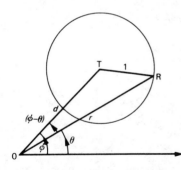

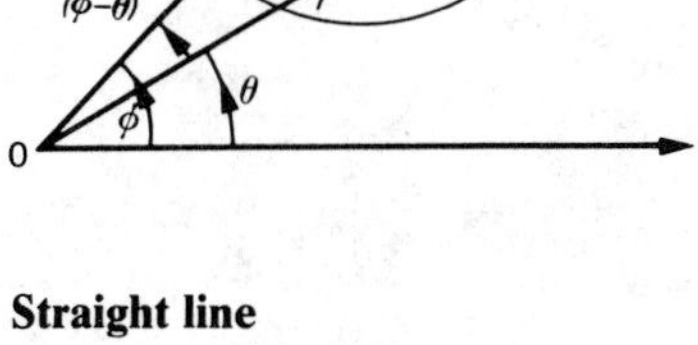

Circle centre (d, ϕ), radius 1 unit.
From the cosine rule in ΔORT

polars $r^2+d^2-2rd\cos(\phi-\theta) = 1$

cartesians $(x-d\cos\phi)^2+(y-d\sin\phi)^2 = 1$

Straight line

$$\frac{l}{r} = 1+e\cos\theta \Rightarrow \cos\theta = \frac{l-r}{re}$$

If e is infinitely large, then $\cos\theta = 0$, $\theta = \pm\frac{\pi}{2}$ and we have the straight line through the origin and perpendicular to the base line.

Conversion to and from cartesian and polar equations

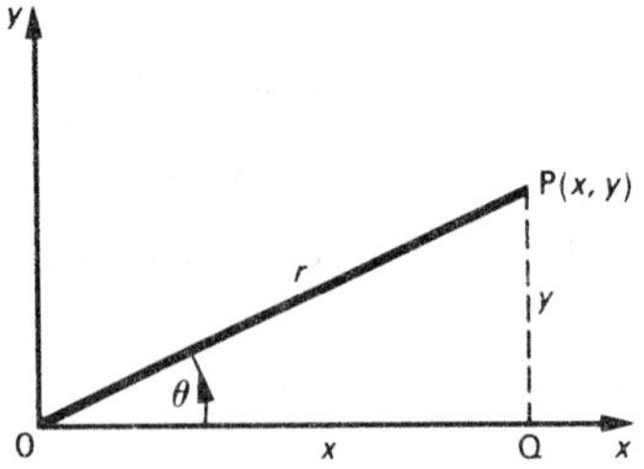

We can see that $\quad OQ = x = r\cos\theta$

$$QP = y = r\sin\theta$$

Also $\quad r^2 = x^2+y^2 \quad$ and $\quad \tan\theta = \dfrac{y}{x}$

It is possible to change from an equation in one system to an equation in the other by substitution. However, the new equations may be quite complicated.

Example 5

Change the equation $r = 1+\cos\theta$ into cartesian coordinates. (This is a cardioid.)
Now $r^2 = x^2+y^2$, $r\cos\theta = x$. Hence

$$r^2 = r+r\cos\theta$$

$$x^2+y^2 = \sqrt{(x^2+y^2)}+x$$

$$x^2+y^2-x = \sqrt{(x^2+y^2)}$$

$$(x^2+y^2-x)^2 = x^2+y^2$$

Exercise 2.2

Rewrite the following equations in polar form

1 $y = 2x$ **2** $x^2+y^2 = 25$ **3** $xy = 1$

4 $y^2 = 4x$ **5** $y = 2x-1$ **6** $\dfrac{x^2}{4}-\dfrac{y^2}{9} = 1$

7 $(x-2)^2+(y-3)^2 = 2$ **8** $\dfrac{x^2}{1}+\dfrac{y^2}{16} = 1$

Rewrite the following equations in cartesian form

9 $r = \frac{1}{2}\cos\theta$ **10** $r = 1 + \frac{1}{2}\cos\theta$ **11** $\frac{1}{r} = 1 + \frac{1}{2}\cos\theta$

12 $r = \cos 2\theta$ **13** $r = \frac{1}{2} + \cos\theta$ **14** $\frac{1}{r} = \frac{1}{2} + \cos\theta$

15 $r = \cos 3\theta$

2.3 Orbits

In the following sections we derive formulae for the velocity and acceleration of a mass P by considering it to lie in the Argand diagram. We can do this because of the 1–1 correspondence between complex numbers $x + jy$ shown in the Argand diagram and the points (x, y) in the plane.

Position

The position of a mass P is given in complex numbers on the Argand diagram as

$$z = r\,e^{j\theta} \qquad \text{or} \qquad z = r(\cos\theta + j\sin\theta)$$

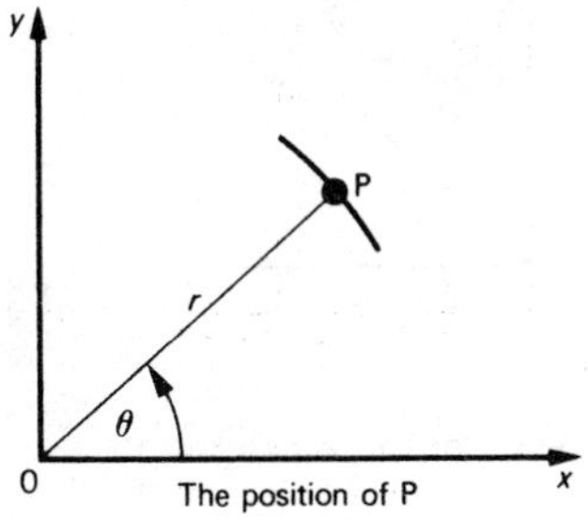

The position of P

Velocity

To find the velocity of P we differentiate this equation with respect to time

$$\dot{z} = rje^{j\theta}\dot{\theta} + \dot{r}e^{j\theta}$$
$$= jr\dot{\theta}e^{j\theta} + \dot{r}e^{j\theta}$$

NOTE. Here e is the exponential, *not* the eccentricity of the conic.

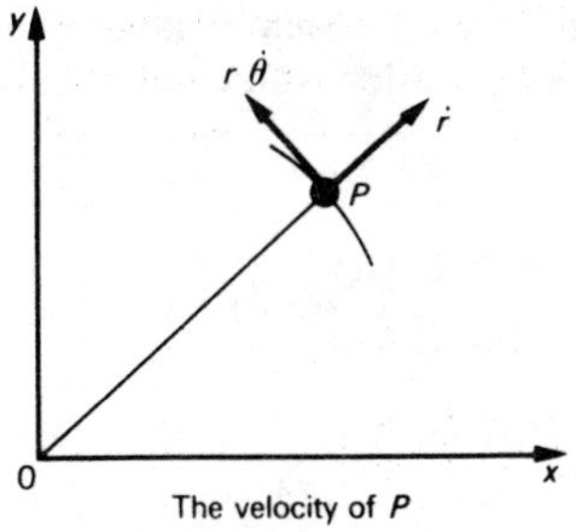

The velocity of *P*

The components of velocity are thus $\dot{r}$ in the direction OP and $r\dot{\theta}$ at right angles to this along the tangent (since multiplication by j represents a rotation through 90° anticlockwise).

Acceleration

To find the acceleration we now differentiate again. It looks difficult, but if we arrange the first term of $\dot{z}$ as $\mathrm{j}\dot{\theta} \cdot r\,\mathrm{e}^{\mathrm{j}\theta}$ it is possible to differentiate it since we already know the differential of $r\,\mathrm{e}^{\mathrm{j}\theta}$. Using the idea of differentiation of a product we have

$$\ddot{z} = \mathrm{j}\dot{\theta}(\mathrm{j}r\dot{\theta}\mathrm{e}^{\mathrm{j}\theta} + \dot{r}\mathrm{e}^{\mathrm{j}\theta}) + r\mathrm{e}^{\mathrm{j}\theta}\mathrm{j}\ddot{\theta} + \dot{r}\mathrm{e}^{\mathrm{j}\theta}\mathrm{j}\dot{\theta} + \mathrm{e}^{\mathrm{j}\theta}\ddot{r}$$

$$= (\ddot{r} - r\dot{\theta}^2)\mathrm{e}^{\mathrm{j}\theta} + \mathrm{j}(2\dot{r}\dot{\theta} + r\ddot{\theta})\mathrm{e}^{\mathrm{j}\theta}$$

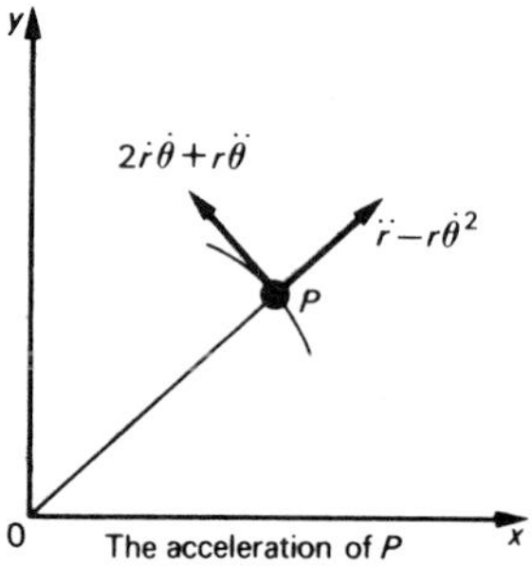

The acceleration of P

Again we have the components of the acceleration

$$\ddot{r} - r\dot{\theta}^2 \quad \text{along OP}$$

$$2\dot{r}\dot{\theta} + r\ddot{\theta} \quad \text{along the tangent}$$

Central force

In most cases the mass P is acted on by some force towards O. This is certainly true when the orbit is a conic. (Two masses attract each other with a force along the line joining their centres.) Hence we can assume that there is no force along the tangent (since force is mass times acceleration—Newton's 1st law of Motion). Thus

$$2\dot{r}\dot{\theta} + r\ddot{\theta} = 0$$

or

$$\frac{1}{r}\frac{\mathrm{d}}{\mathrm{d}t}(r^2\dot{\theta}) = 0 \qquad \text{(Check that this is true)}$$

so $r^2\dot{\theta}$ is constant and equal to h, say,

$$r^2\dot{\theta} = h$$

Conical orbit

Consider a mass following the path of a conic with eccentricity e, then

$$r(1+e\cos\theta) = l$$

Differentiating with respect to t

$$\dot{r}(1+e\cos\theta) - re\sin\theta\dot{\theta} = 0$$

Multiplying through by r and substituting

$$\dot{r}l - r^2e\sin\theta\dot{\theta} = 0$$

$$\dot{r}l - eh\sin\theta = 0 \qquad \text{since} \qquad \dot{\theta} = \frac{h}{r^2}$$

Differentiating again with respect to t

$$\ddot{r}l - eh\cos\theta\dot{\theta} = 0$$

$$\ddot{r}l - eh\cos\theta\frac{h}{r^2} = 0$$

Now radially the acceleration is

$$\ddot{r} - r\dot{\theta}^2 = \frac{eh^2}{lr^2}\cos\theta - \frac{rh^2}{r^4}$$

$$= \frac{h^2}{r^2}\left[\frac{\frac{l}{r}-1}{l} - \frac{1}{r}\right] \qquad \text{since} \qquad e\cos\theta = \frac{l}{r}-1$$

$$= \frac{h^2}{r^2}\left[\frac{l-r-l}{lr}\right]$$

$$= -\frac{h^2}{lr^2}$$

This shows that whilst the mass follows a conical orbit, it does so under a force towards the centre proportional to $1/r^2$. Most masses or particles obey this *inverse square law.*

3 Matrices and conics

3.1 Transformations of the parabola and circle

We now consider briefly the effects of matrix transformations on a conic. As an example we transform the parabola $y^2 = 4x$ and the circle $x^2+y^2 = 25$ using the four matrices

$$\mathbf{D} = \begin{pmatrix}2 & 0\\0 & 1\end{pmatrix} \qquad \mathbf{S} = \begin{pmatrix}1 & 1\\0 & 1\end{pmatrix} \qquad \mathbf{A} = \begin{pmatrix}2 & 1\\1 & 2\end{pmatrix} \qquad \text{and} \qquad \mathbf{C} = \begin{pmatrix}1 & 3\\1 & -1\end{pmatrix}$$

The transformation can easily be carried out by finding points on the curve and transforming them, e.g. (1, 2) lies on $y^2 = 4x$. This is transformed under **A** to $\begin{pmatrix} 2 & 0 \\ 0 & 1 \end{pmatrix}\begin{pmatrix} 1 \\ 2 \end{pmatrix} = \begin{pmatrix} 2 \\ 2 \end{pmatrix}$ and so on.

Finding the 'new' equation for $y^2 = 4x$

Consider the transformation of $y^2 = 4x$ under **D** and then **A**.
*Using **D*** the new value of (x, y) is given by

$$\begin{pmatrix} x' \\ y' \end{pmatrix} = \begin{pmatrix} 2 & 0 \\ 0 & 1 \end{pmatrix}\begin{pmatrix} x \\ y \end{pmatrix}$$

$$\Rightarrow \begin{pmatrix} x \\ y \end{pmatrix} = \begin{pmatrix} \frac{1}{2} & 0 \\ 0 & 1 \end{pmatrix}\begin{pmatrix} x' \\ y' \end{pmatrix} = \begin{pmatrix} \frac{1}{2}x' \\ y' \end{pmatrix}$$

Hence in the equation $y^2 = 4x$, we substitute $x = \frac{1}{2}x'$ and $y = y'$ and obtain

$$(y')^2 = 4 \cdot \tfrac{1}{2}x' = 2x'$$

It is customary to drop the prime (′) and write the equation $y^2 = 2x$ as a general relationship.

*Using **A*** the new value of (x, y) is given by

$$\begin{pmatrix} x' \\ y' \end{pmatrix} = \begin{pmatrix} 2 & 1 \\ 1 & 2 \end{pmatrix}\begin{pmatrix} x \\ y \end{pmatrix}$$

$$\Rightarrow \begin{pmatrix} x \\ y \end{pmatrix} = \frac{1}{3}\begin{pmatrix} 2 & -1 \\ -1 & 2 \end{pmatrix}\begin{pmatrix} x' \\ y' \end{pmatrix} = \begin{pmatrix} \frac{1}{3}(2x' - y') \\ \frac{1}{3}(-x' + 2y') \end{pmatrix}$$

Hence in $y^2 = 4x$ we have

$$[\tfrac{1}{3}(-x' + 2y')]^2 = 4[\tfrac{1}{3}(2x' - y')].$$

Dropping the prime

$$\tfrac{1}{9}(x^2 - 4xy + 4y^2) = \tfrac{4}{3}(2x - y)$$

$$x^2 - 4xy + 4y^2 = 24x - 12y$$

$$x^2 - 4xy + 4y^2 - 24x + 12y = 0$$

Transformation of the parabola $y^2 = 4x$

We now give sketches of the parabola $y^2 = 4x$ after it has been transformed using the matrices **D**, **S**, **A** and **C**. Derive the new equations for the parabola under **S** and **C**, and sketch the curves yourself.

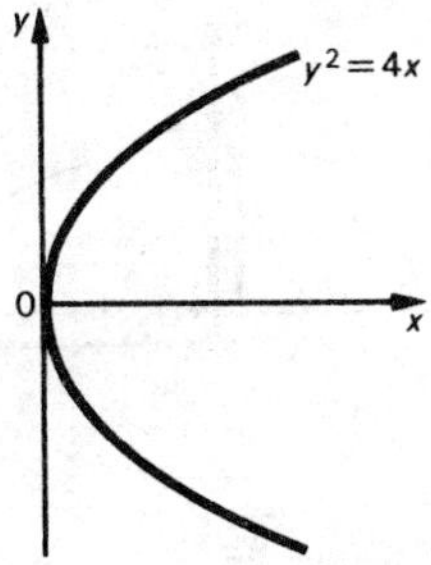

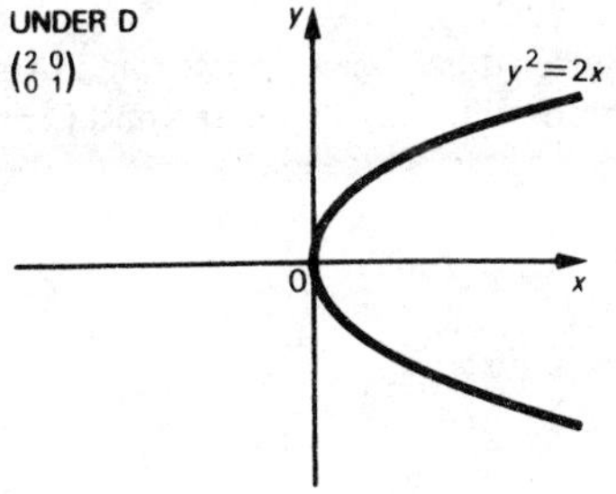

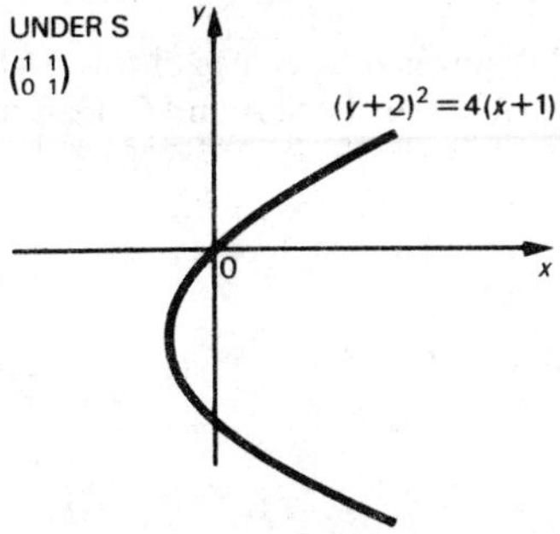

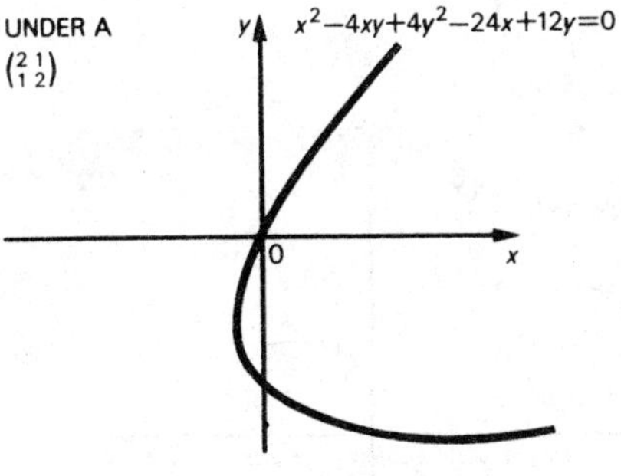

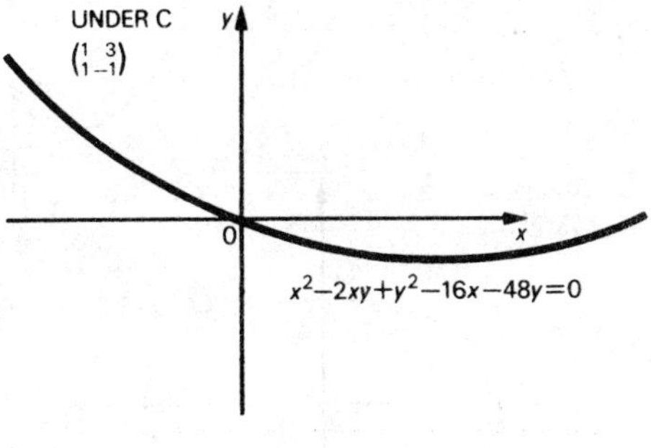

Transformation of the circle

First, consider the transformation of the circle $x^2+y^2=1$ using the matrix $\begin{pmatrix} a & 0 \\ 0 & b \end{pmatrix}$.

$$\begin{pmatrix} x' \\ y' \end{pmatrix} = \begin{pmatrix} a & 0 \\ 0 & b \end{pmatrix}\begin{pmatrix} x \\ y \end{pmatrix}$$

$$\begin{pmatrix} x \\ y \end{pmatrix} = \begin{pmatrix} \frac{1}{a} & 0 \\ 0 & \frac{1}{b} \end{pmatrix}\begin{pmatrix} x' \\ y' \end{pmatrix}$$

The new equation is that of the ellipse

$$\frac{(x')^2}{a^2}+\frac{(y')^2}{b^2}=1$$

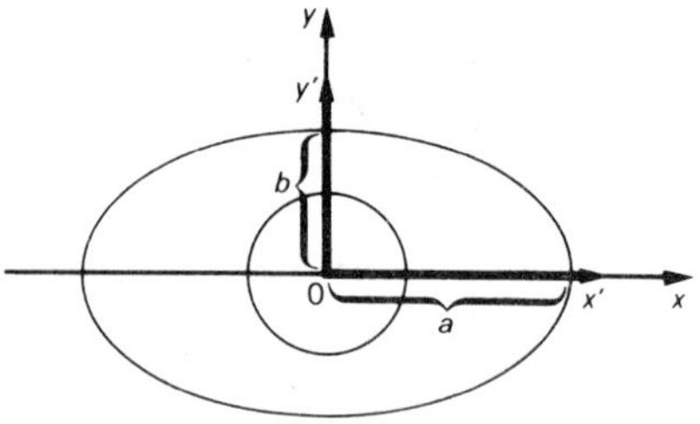

Transformation of the circle $x^2+y^2 = 25$

We now give sketches of the circle $x^2+y^2 = 25$ after it has been transformed using the matrices **D**, **S**, **A** and **C**. Derive the new equations of the circle under **S** and **C**, and sketch the curves yourself.

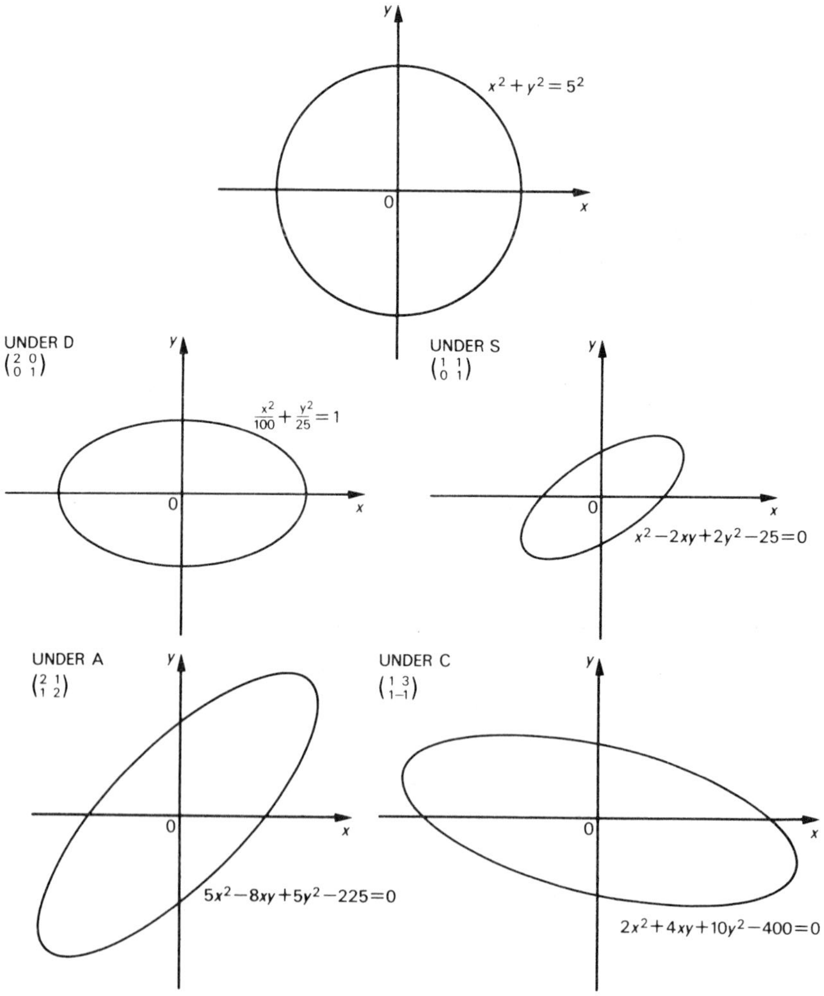

3.2 Non-central conics

So far all the conics studied have their centres at the origin and their equations refer to the usual x and y axes. We now investigate what happens if the centre of the conic is translated from O.

Translation of the axes

Circle

Consider a circle, centre (α, β) and radius r.

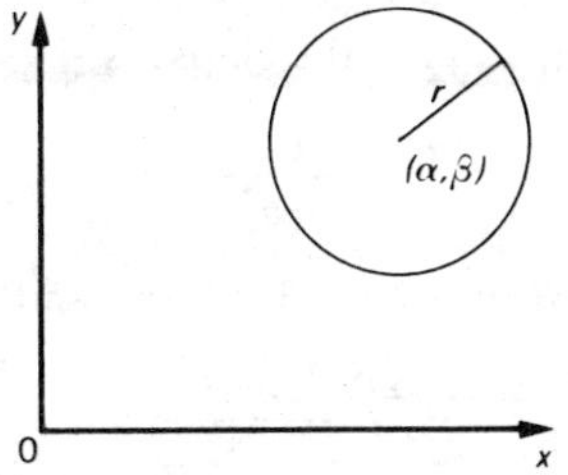

Introduce new axes, x' and y', through the centre of the circle. With respect to these, the equation of the circle is $(x')^2+(y')^2 = r^2$. But $x' = x-\alpha$ and $y' = y-\beta$.

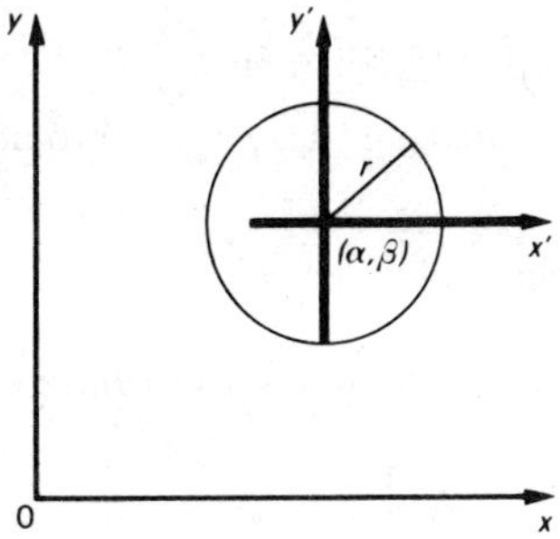

Hence, referred to the x and y axes, the equation is

$$(x-\alpha)^2+(y-\beta)^2 = r^2$$

Ellipse

Consider an ellipse, centre (α, β) and semi-axes a and b.

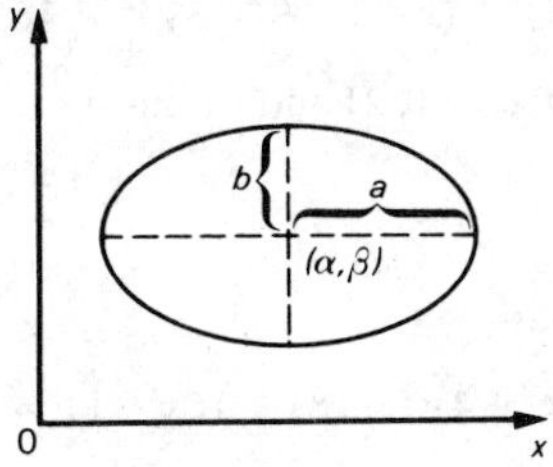

Introduce new axes, x' and y', through the centre of the ellipse as shown.

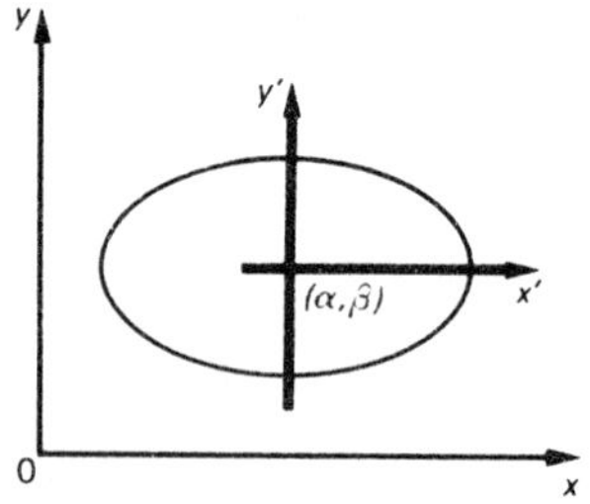

With respect to these the equation of the ellipse is

$$\frac{(x')^2}{a^2}+\frac{(y')^2}{b^2}=1$$

But $x'=x-\alpha$ and $y'=y-\beta$ so, referred to the x and y axes, the equation is

$$\frac{(x-\alpha)^2}{a^2}+\frac{(y-\beta)^2}{b^2}=1$$

Parabola

Similarly the equation of a parabola with centre (α, β) will be

$$(y-\beta)^2=4a(x-\alpha)$$

NOTE. In all these examples the conic has *not* been rotated in any way.

Finding the centre of a conic

Before sketching a conic we have to discover its centre from its equation.

Example 1

Given a circle with equation

$$x^2+y^2+2x-4y-11=0$$

find its centre and radius.

We can rewrite the equation as

$$(x+1)^2+(y-2)^2=16$$

This represents a circle, centre $(-1, 2)$ and radius 4.

Example 2

Given an ellipse with equation

$$9x^2+4y^2-18x+16y-11=0$$

find its centre.

Rearranging

$$9x^2-18x+4y^2+16y = 11$$

$$9(x^2-2x)+4(y^2+4y) = 11$$

$$9(x^2-2x+1)+4(y^2+4y+4) = 11+9+16$$

(completing the square)

$$9(x-1)^2+4(y+2)^2 = 36$$

$$\frac{(x-1)^2}{4}+\frac{(y+2)^2}{9} = 1$$

This is an ellipse, centre (1, −2) with semi-axes $a = 2$, $b = 3$.

Exercise 3.2

Convert the following equations into a recognizable form and sketch the curves.

1 $x^2+y^2+2x-6y+1 = 0$

2 $2x^2+3y^2-8x-24y+50 = 0$

3 $y^2-6y-16x-23 = 0$

4 $x^2-9y^2+2x+18y-17 = 0$

5 $3x^2-4y^2+18x+8y+11 = 0$

3.3 The general conic

$$\boldsymbol{ax^2+2hxy+by^2+2gx+2fy+c = 0}$$ ◀

The problem

Given a second degree equation such as

$$5x^2+6xy+5y^2+12x+4y+6 = 0$$

(i) What type of conic is it?—a circle, parabola, ellipse or hyperbola?
(ii) What are the axes of the conic?
(iii) What is the centre of the conic? . . . and so on.

The solution

Naturally, with such a complicated equation, the solution will not be straightforward. Here we only give a brief insight into the method of solution, which is not complete. Later on, you may meet the ideas again formally (at university). Here are several points to note.

1 The most important part of the equation is the part involving $ax^2+2hxy+by^2$ (the parts involving x, y and any numbers relate to any translation of the centre).

This part is called the *quadratic form* of the equation and may be written

$$(x \quad y)\begin{pmatrix} a & h \\ h & b \end{pmatrix}\begin{pmatrix} x \\ y \end{pmatrix} = \boldsymbol{Q}(x, y)$$

Multiply out to check. From this it is possible to tell what type of conic it is:

(i) $h = 0$, $a = b$, a circle;
(ii) $h^2 = ab$, a parabola;
(iii) $h^2 < ab$, an ellipse;
(iv) $h^2 > ab$, an hyperbola.

2 Since $\begin{pmatrix} a & h \\ h & b \end{pmatrix}$ is a *symmetric* matrix (i.e. it has the same numbers above and below the leading diagonal $\begin{pmatrix} a & \cdot \\ \cdot & b \end{pmatrix}$) we know that:

(i) the eigenvectors are perpendicular;

(ii) the eigenvectors of $\begin{pmatrix} a & h \\ h & b \end{pmatrix}$ give the *directions* of the axes of the conic;

(iii) from the eigenvalues of $\begin{pmatrix} a & h \\ h & b \end{pmatrix}$ it is possible to find the length of the *intercepts* on the axes of the conic.

A simplified version of the solution to the problem involves finding the eigenvalues and eigenvectors of $\begin{pmatrix} a & h \\ h & b \end{pmatrix}$, applying a rotation of the axes to get them parallel to the axes of the conic and then transferring the origin to the centre of the conic. At each step the equation of the conic alters as its equation is referred to the new axes. Finally, the equation becomes one of the recognizable forms for the equation of a parabola, hyperbola or ellipse.

Diagrammatically

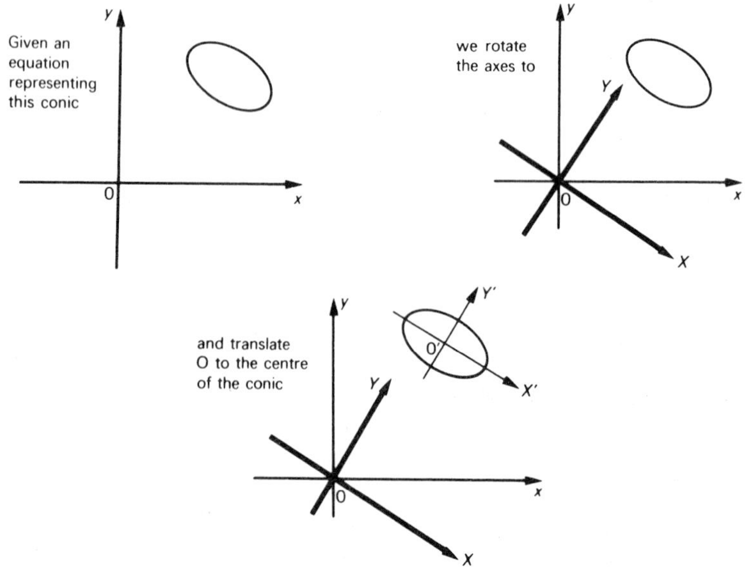

Here the equation will be in the recognizable form of the ellipse

$$\frac{(x')^2}{a^2}+\frac{(y')^2}{b^2}=1$$

3 Sometimes the equation $ax^2+2hxy+by^2+2gx+2fy+c=0$ does not represent a conic. Instead, the equation might represent a pair of lines or it might represent a point. We say that these are *degenerate conics*. For example, the equation

$$(x+2y-1)(x-3y+2)=0$$

represents the pair of lines

$$x+2y-1=0 \qquad \text{and} \qquad x-3y+2=0$$

The equation of this pair when multiplied together is

$$x^2-xy-6y^2+x+7y-2=0$$

which we should know as the equation of a conic. How do we know that the conic degenerates? The condition for this, which we state without proof, is

$$\begin{vmatrix} a & h & g \\ h & b & f \\ g & f & c \end{vmatrix} = 0$$

Check that this is true for the equation above.

Exercise 3.3

1 Transform the rectangular hyperbola $xy = 12$ using the four matrices ***D***, ***S***, ***A*** and ***C*** (see page 721). Give the new equation each time and sketch the curve.

2 Write the equations
 (a) $x^2-4xy+4y^2-24x+12y=0$
 (b) $x^2-2xy+y^2-16x-48y=0$
using quadratic form. From the quadratic form show that in each case the conic is a parabola.
 Find the eigenvectors of $\begin{pmatrix} a & h \\ h & b \end{pmatrix}$ in each case and show that they give the axes of the parabolas.

3 Write the equations
 (a) $x^2-2xy+2y^2-25=0$
 (b) $2x^2+4xy+10y^2-400=0$
using quadratic form. From the quadratic form show that in each case, the conic is an ellipse.
 Find the eigenvectors and eigenvalues of $\begin{pmatrix} a & h \\ h & b \end{pmatrix}$ in each case and show that the eigenvectors give the axes of the ellipses. What relationship have the eigenvalues to the conic?

4 Prove that the eigenvectors of $\begin{pmatrix} a & h \\ h & b \end{pmatrix}$ are perpendicular.

5 Sketch the curves with equations

(a) $3x^2-2xy+3y^2=12$ **(b)** $2x^2+4xy-y^2=10$
(c) $x^2+y^2-4x+6y=49$ **(d)** $5x^2+6xy+5y^2=20$

6 Show that the following equations represent degenerate conics and hence sketch them.

(a) $x^2+2xy-3y^2-2x+10y-8=0$ **(b)** $x^2-4xy+4y^2-6x+12y+9=0$
(c) $x^2+3xy+2x-6y-8=0$ **(d)** $2x^2+5xy-3y^2-5x+6y-3=0$

Miscellaneous examination questions 19

1 Obtain the equation of the normal at the point $P(at^2, 2at)$ on the parabola $y^2=4ax$ and prove that it intersects the parabola again at the point Q whose parameter is $-\left(t+\dfrac{2}{t}\right)$. Find the coordinates of the midpoint of PQ in terms of t. Call these coordinates x, y and eliminate t between the equations to obtain the equation of the locus as

$$y^4+2a(2a-x)y^2+8a^4=0$$

(O. & C.)

2 P is the point $(at^2, 2at)$ on the parabola $y^2=4ax$ and OQ is the chord passing through the origin O and parallel to the tangent at P. Find the coordinates of the point of intersection, R, of the tangents at P and Q. Give a reason to show that the locus of R is another parabola.

If S is the midpoint of OQ, prove that PSR is a right-angled triangle and that the area of PQR is $\frac{1}{2}a^2t^3$. (O. & C.)

3 Prove that if the chord PQ (where P is $(at^2, 2at)$, Q is $(aT^2, 2aT)$) passes through the focus, then

$$PQ = a\left(t+\frac{1}{t}\right)^2$$

The tangents of the parabola from the point (h, k) meet the tangent at the vertex O at B and C. Prove that the product of OB and OC is independent of k. (O. & C.)

4 Prove that the line $y=mx+\dfrac{a}{m}$ is a tangent to the parabola $y^2=4ax$ for all values of m.

Two tangents to the parabola $y^2=4ax$ meet at an angle of 60°. Prove that the locus of their point of intersection is the curve

$$y^2-4ax=3(x+a).^2$$

(O. & C.)

5 A chord PQ of the parabola $y^2=4ax$ passes through the focus. Prove that the point of intersection T of the tangents at P and Q lies on the directrix.

If the circle on PQ as diameter meets the parabola again at two real points, prove that the distance of T from the axis of the parabola is greater than $2a\sqrt{3}$. (O. & C.)

6 Prove that the equation of the normal at the point $P(at^2, 2at)$ on the parabola $y^2 = 4ax$ is $tx + y = 2at + at^3$ and that it meets the parabola again at $Q(aT^2, 2aT)$ where $T = -t - \frac{2}{t}$.

The tangents at P and Q meet at R. Prove that if P is a variable point on the parabola, the locus of R is

$$y^2(x+2a)+4a^3 = 0$$

(O. & C.)

7 The chord joining $P\left(ct_1, \frac{c}{t_1}\right)$ to $Q\left(ct_2, \frac{c}{t_2}\right)$ on the hyperbola $xy = c^2$ meets the x axis at A. C is the midpoint of PQ and O is the origin. Prove that OC = AC. (L.)

8 The perpendicular from the origin to the tangent at a point P on the hyperbola $xy = c^2$ meets the curve at Q and R. The chords PQ and PR meet the x axis at U and V. Prove that the midpoint of UV is the foot of the perpendicular from P to the x axis. (L.)

9 Show that the gradient of the chord joining the points $Q\left(cq, \frac{c}{q}\right)$ and $R\left(cr, \frac{c}{r}\right)$ on the hyperbola $xy = c^2$ is $-\frac{1}{qr}$. If $P\left(ct, \frac{c}{t}\right)$ is a fixed point on the curve and QR subtends a right angle at P, show that

(a) Q and R are on different branches of the hyperbola
(b) the direction of QR is fixed
(c) the midpoint of QR lies on a fixed straight line through the origin. (L.)

10 The line $y = mx$ meets the hyperbola $xy = c^2$ (where $x > 0$) at the points R and S. Prove that the tangents to the hyperbola at R and S are parallel. Find the distance between the parallel tangents and show that as m varies, the maximum distance between them is $2c\sqrt{2}$.

The tangents and normals at R and S form a rectangle. Find the area of the rectangle and show that, when $m = 3$, the area is $6.4c^2$. (L.)

11 Find the equation of the normal to the curve $xy = c^2$ at the point $\left(ct, \frac{c}{t}\right)$. The normal at a point P on this curve meets the coordinate axes at Q and R. Find the locus of the midpoint of QR. (L.)

12 Find the equation of the normal to the hyperbola $xy = c^2$ at the point P, whose coordinates are $\left(ct, \frac{c}{t}\right)$. Find the coordinates of the point P′ in which the normal at P cuts the hyperbola again and write down the coordinates of the point P″ in which the normal at P′ cuts the hyperbola again. Find the equation of the locus of the midpoint of PP′. (L.)

13 Prove that the equation of the normal at $P(a \cos \phi, b \sin \phi)$ on the standard ellipse is

$$\frac{ax}{\cos \phi} - \frac{by}{\sin \phi} = a^2 - b^2$$

The tangent and normal at P cut the x axis at K and L respectively, O is the centre of the ellipse, H and S are the foci, and e is the eccentricity. Prove that

(a) $\mathrm{OK}\times\mathrm{OL} = a^2e^2$ **(b)** HL:LS = HK:SK (O. & C.)

14 Verify that the line given by the equation

$$\frac{x}{a}\cos\frac{\phi+\psi}{2}+\frac{y}{b}\sin\frac{\phi+\psi}{2}=\cos\frac{\phi-\psi}{2}$$

passes through the points with parametric angles ϕ and ψ on the standard ellipse.

Points P, Q on the ellipse have eccentric angles ϕ, ψ respectively. The line through Q parallel to the tangent at P meets the ellipse again at R, find the parametric angle of R.

Prove that if PR is also parallel to the tangent at Q then PQ is parallel to the tangent at R and express the parametric angles of Q and R in terms of ϕ. (O. & C.)

15 Prove that the tangent at the point (x_1, y_1) on the standard ellipse is

$$\frac{xx_1}{a^2}+\frac{yy_1}{b^2}=1$$

and that for any value of m

$$y = mx \pm \surd(a^2m^2+b^2)$$

are tangents to the ellipse.

A tangent whose gradient m is positive, meets the positive x axis at A and the negative y axis at B. Prove that the area of the triangle OAB is

$$\frac{1}{2m}(a^2m^2+b^2)$$

where O is the centre of the ellipse.

Prove also that when the area of the triangle OAB is a minimum, the coordinates of the point of contact are $(\tfrac{1}{2}a\surd 2, -\tfrac{1}{2}b\surd 2)$. (O. & C.)

16 The centre of the hyperbola $\dfrac{x^2}{a^2}-\dfrac{y^2}{b^2}=1$ is O, and the point $(a, 0)$ is A. Let P be any point on the hyperbola, N the foot of the perpendicular from P to OA, and T the point of contact of one of the tangents from N to the circle with centre O that passes through A. If the choice of tangent is suitably made, and if the angle AOT is ϕ prove that the coordinates of P are $(a \sec\phi, b\tan\phi)$.

(a) State briefly what happens as ϕ passes through the value $\pi/2$.

(b) If N is a focus of the hyperbola, prove that OT is an asymptote and show that if the tangent at A meets the asymptote at B then AB = NT. (L.)

17 Find the equation of that chord of the hyperbola

$$S \equiv \frac{x^2}{a^2}-\frac{y^2}{b^2}-1=0$$

whose midpoint is (α, β).

Prove that the chord so obtained is the same for all hyperbolas having the same asymptotes as S.

Deduce or prove otherwise that if a straight line cuts a hyperbola at P and Q and its asymptotes are at A and B, then AP = QB. (L.)

18 Prove that the equation of the normal to the hyperbola $\frac{x^2}{a^2}-\frac{y^2}{b^2}=1$ at the point $(a \sec \phi, b \tan \phi)$ is

$$ax \sin \phi + by = (a^2+b^2) \tan \phi$$

Prove that if Q is the foot of the perpendicular from the origin O to the normal at P, the area of the triangle OPQ is

$$\frac{ab(a^2+b^2) \sin \phi}{2(a^2 \sin^2 \phi + b^2)}$$

(O. & C.)

19 Sketch the curve whose parametric equations are

$$x = \frac{t}{1+t} \qquad y = \frac{t}{1-t}$$

(a) State the equations of the asymptotes of this curve.
(b) Find the equations of the lines about which the curve is symmetrical.

(M.E.I.)

20 Find the equation of the tangent to the curve $x^2y = c^3$ at the point P with coordinates $\left(ct, \frac{c}{t^2}\right)$. Find the coordinates of the points A and B in which the tangent meets the x axis and the y axis respectively. Show that P can be reached from A by the displacements $-\frac{1}{2}ct$ parallel to the x axis and $\frac{c}{t^2}$ parallel to the y axis. Show also that the point Q, which is reached from B by the same displacements, is on AB produced and also on the curve.

Find the equation of the curve if it is referred to parallel axes with $(-c, c)$ as origin. (O. & C.)

21 The coordinates of a point A on the curve

$$27ay^2 = 4(x-2a)^3$$

are given parametrically as $x = 2a+3ap^2$, $y = -2ap^3$. The tangent at this point meets the curve again at B and AB is produced to meet the parabola $y^2 = 4ax$ at the point P. Find the coordinates of P in terms of p and verify that the tangent AP is also normal to the parabola at P. (M.E.I.)

22 Find the equations of the tangent to the curve $xy = 1$ at the point $\left(t, \frac{1}{t}\right)$ and the equation of the normal to the curve $27y^2 = 4x^3$ at the point $(3u^2, 2u^3)$.

Show that just one tangent to the first curve is also a normal to the second.

(M.E.I.)

23 Prove that the equation of the parabola $y^2 = 4ax$ when referred to parallel axes through the focus $F(a, 0)$ is $y^2 = 4a(x+a)$. Hence show that the polar equation of the parabola when the origin of the polar coordinates is the focus and the initial line is the axis of the parabola is $2a = r(1-\cos\theta)$.

A line through F, making an angle α with the initial line, cuts the parabola at A and B. Prove that

$$\frac{1}{FA}+\frac{1}{FB}=\frac{1}{a}$$

and find an expression for

$$\frac{1}{FA^2}+\frac{1}{FB^2}$$

in terms of a and α. (O. & C.)

24 A straight line cuts the initial line $\theta = 0$ at the point A, and the perpendicular from the origin O to the line meets it at N. The length ON is p and the angle AON is α. A general point P on the line has polar coordinates (r, θ); prove that $p = r\cos(\theta-\alpha)$.

Find the polar coordinates of the point of intersection of the lines whose polar equations are

$$r\sin\left(\theta-\frac{\pi}{6}\right)=\sqrt{3}$$

$$r\cos\left(\theta-\frac{\pi}{6}\right)=3$$

Show that this point lies on the curve whose parametric equations are $x = a\tan^2\phi$ and $y = 2a\tan\phi$ if $a = \dfrac{3\sqrt{3}}{4}$. Sketch the lines on a diagram. (O. & C.)

25 Two loci are defined by the polar equations

(a) $r = 3\cos\theta - 4\sin\theta$

(b) $\dfrac{9}{r} = 3\cos\theta - 4\sin\theta$

Find their cartesian equations, identify their loci and draw their graphs in one diagram. Prove that any straight line through the pole cuts the two loci at equal or supplementary angles. (O. & C.)

Answers

CHAPTER 1 SERIES 1

Exercise 1.1 (page 2)

1 5, 6, r
2 9, 11, $2r-1$
3 32, 64, 2^{r-1}
4 25, 36, r^2
5 19, 23, $4r-1$
6 34, 47, r^2+2r-1
7 567, 1701, $7\times 3^{r-1}$

Exercise 1.2a (page 3)

1 $1^3+2^3+3^3+4^3$
2 $3+5+7+9+11+13$
3 $10+11+12+13+14+15$
4 $10+11+12+13+14+15$
5 $3^2+3^4+3^6+3^8+3^{10}$
6 $\frac{2}{7}+\frac{5}{12}+\frac{8}{17}+\frac{11}{22}+\frac{14}{27}$
7 $\sum_1^7 r^2$
8 $\sum_1^{15} 2r$
9 $\sum_1^{77} \frac{1}{r}$
10 $\sum_1^{10} r^3$
11 $\sum_1^{19} \frac{r(r+2)}{(r+1)(r+3)}$
12 $\sum_1^{12} (2r-1)(2r+3)$
13 $\sum_1^{20} (4r-1)^2$
14 $\sum_1^{21} [a+5(r-1)]$
15 $\sum_1^{51} [a+d(r-1)]$
16 $\sum_1^{21} 2\times 3^{r-1}$
17 $\sum_1^{21} a\times 3^{r-1}$
18 $\sum_1^{21} a\times k^{r-1}$

Exercise 1.2b (page 3)

1 (a) $x_1+x_2+x_3+x_4+x_5+x_6$
(b) 6 (c) 6 (d) 36 (e) 18 (f) n
2 (a) 3 (b) 9 (c) 5
3 (a) 225 (b) 77
4 Sum then square; square then sum
5 (a) 21 (b) 63 (c) 63
6 (a) Yes (b) No
7 (a) 125 (b) 125
8 Yes
9 (a) $-1, +1, -1, +1$
(b) $-x+x-x+x$
(c) $-x, 0, -x$
10 (a) $1-4+9-16+25$
(b) $-3+5-7+9-11$
(c) $-4-5-6-7-8$
11 88

Exercise 1.3 (page 6)

1 2, 8, 26, 80, 242
2 5, 5.5, 5.55, 5.555, 5.5555
3 $0, \frac{1}{3}, \frac{3}{8}, \frac{8}{21}, \frac{21}{55}$
4 1, 3, 7, 17, 41
5 0, 1, 3, 8, 21
6 $u_k=u_{k-1}+2;\ u_1=1$
7 $u_k=3u_{k-1};\ u_1=4$
8 $u_k=3u_{k-1}+2;\ u_1=1$
9 $u_k=u_{k-1}+k-1;\ u_1=1$
10 $u_k=u_{k-1}+u_{k-2};\ u_0=0,\ u_1=1$

Exercise 1.5 (page 9)

1 10, 11, 22 . . .
2 $2^n=\sum_{r=0}^{r=n}\binom{n}{r}$
3 $10r-r$
4 1, 2, 4, 8, 16, 31, 57
5 2, 4, 8, 16, 8

Exercise 3.1 (page 14)

1 (a), (b), (d)
2 (a) 3, 21, $3(n+1)$
(b) $-2, -4, 8-2n$
(d) $-1, -\frac{11}{3}, \frac{7}{3}-n$
3 (a) 11
(b) $-1, -5$
(c) $\frac{3}{5}, \frac{5}{5}, \frac{7}{5}$

4 (**a**) 92 (**b**) -55
(**c**) 156 (**d**) 67.5
5 (**a**) 1275 (**b**) 650 (**c**) 625
6 (**a**) 50 (**b**) -8 (**c**) 19.5

Exercise 3.2 (page 17)

1 $\frac{1}{3}n(n+1)(n+2)$
2 $\dfrac{n}{2(n+2)}$
3 $\dfrac{7}{24}-\dfrac{2n+7}{2(n+3)(n+4)}$

Exercise 3.3b (page 21)

1 $\frac{1}{2}n(n+1)(2n+1)$
2 (**a**) 155
(**b**) $\frac{1}{6}n(n+1)(4n+11)$
3 $\frac{1}{3}n(4n^2+6n-1)$
4 $\frac{1}{6}n(n+1)(2n+31)$
5 $\frac{1}{12}n(n+1)(3n^2+11n+4)$
6 (**a**) 490
(**b**) $\frac{1}{12}n(n+1)(n+2)(3n+13)$

Exercise 3.4 (page 23)

1 (a), (b), (c), (d)
2 (**a**) 2, $64x$, $2^n x$
(**b**) 2, $\frac{32}{3}$, $\frac{1}{3}\times 2^{n-1}$
(**c**) $-\frac{3}{4}$, $-\frac{243}{1024}$, $(-\frac{3}{4})^{n-1}$
(**d**) $\frac{2}{3}$, $\frac{32}{9}$, $\frac{1}{27}(\frac{2}{3})^{n-1}$
3 (**a**) ± 10
(**b**) $3x^2$, $9x^3$
(**c**) $a^2/8$
4 (**a**) 8 (**b**) $2n-1$ (**c**) 9
5 (**a**) -63, 129, -255
(**b**) $\dfrac{a^7-3^7}{3^6(a-3)}$ (**c**) 11.5
6 £9232

Exercise 4.4 (page 28)

1 Diverges
2 $\frac{3}{2}$
3 $\frac{3}{4}$
4 $S_{2n}=0$, $S_{2n-1}=2$
5 1
6 $S_{3n}=0$, $S_{3n-1}=6$, $S_{3n-2}=2$
7 $\frac{1}{6}\pi^2$
8 $\frac{1}{4}\pi$
9 1
10 1
11 perimeter $\to\infty$ as $n\to\infty$
12 S_∞ does not exist

Exercise 5.2 (page 32)

1 $A+3^kB$
2 $(-3)^kA+B$
3 $6^kA+(-2)^kB$
4 $2^{k-1}-1$
5 $\frac{1}{14}(2(-5)^k+5(2)^k)$
6 $(k-1)2^{k-1}$
7 3^{k-1}
8 $A+kB+k^2C$

Exercise 5.3 (page 35)

1 $3n-1$
2 $1-3n+2n^2$
3 $1+4n-2n^2$
4 $-1+n-3n^2+2n^3$
5 $\frac{1}{24}(24-18n+23n^2-6n^3+n^4)$

Miscellaneous examination questions 1

1 (**a**) 2460 (**b**) 8.01
2 (**a**) $\frac{3}{4}$ (**b**) 6
3 (**a**) 7 (**b**) 630, 63.0
4 (**a**) 2, 12, $10n-8$ (**b**) £1770
5 £23 900, £198
6 £6940, 25 years
7 $\dfrac{n(n+1)}{2}$; $\dfrac{n(n+1)}{2}$; n; 24
8 $\dfrac{n(n+1)}{2}$; n^2; m^2+2mn
9 2
10 $a=27$, $r=\frac{1}{3}$; $a=54$, $r=-\frac{1}{3}$
11 $\dfrac{(x+x^2)(1-x^{3m})}{1-x^3}$
12 $\frac{5}{11}$, $\frac{5}{31}$
13 (**a**) (i) 1110 (ii) 17.3
15 $\dfrac{3}{4}-\dfrac{1}{2}\left(\dfrac{1}{n+1}+\dfrac{1}{n+2}\right)$
19 $\dfrac{(2n+1)(2n+3)}{2(n+1)(n+2)}-\dfrac{3}{4}$
20 $A=\frac{1}{2}$, $B=-\frac{1}{2}$
21 $2n^2(n+1)^2$; $n^2(2n^2-1)$
25 $\dfrac{n}{2}(6n^2-3n-1)$
28 (**a**) 5, 3, 1
29 (**a**) $A=4$, $B=-18$, $C=12$; $n^2(n^2-1)$
(**b**) $\dfrac{(3n+2)(n-1)}{4n(n+1)}$

30 $\dfrac{n(n+3)}{4(n+1)(n+2)}$

31 9

CHAPTER 2 ALGEBRA 1

Exercise 2.2 (page 49)

1 $-2, -3$
2 $1, -4$
3 $1, 6$
4 $-1, 6$
5 $1, \frac{3}{2}$
6 $-\frac{2}{3}, \frac{3}{4}$
7 $\frac{3}{8}, -1$
8 $\frac{2}{3}$ (twice)

Exercise 2.3a (page 51)

1 $(3 \pm \sqrt{41})/4$
2 $(1 \pm \sqrt{5})/4$
3 $-\frac{4}{3}, 2$
4 $-1 \pm \sqrt{3}$
5 $(5 \pm \sqrt{73})/4$
6 $-\frac{1}{3}, 1$
7 $(2 \pm \sqrt{19})/3$
8 $(5 \pm \sqrt{17})/2$
9 $(7 \pm \sqrt{17})/4$
10 $-\frac{1}{3}, \frac{5}{2}$

Exercise 2.3b (page 52)

1 $-2 \pm \sqrt{5}\text{j}$
2 $\frac{1}{4}(3 \pm \sqrt{39}\text{j})$
3 $\frac{1}{6}(1 \pm \sqrt{35}\text{j})$
4 $\frac{1}{3}(1 \pm \sqrt{23}\text{j})$
5 $\pm 3\text{j}$
6 $\pm \sqrt{3}\text{j}$
7 $\frac{1}{4}(-1 \pm \sqrt{23}\text{j})$
8 $\frac{1}{10}(1 \pm \sqrt{79}\text{j})$
9 $\frac{1}{4}(1 \pm \sqrt{39}\text{j})$
10 $-3 \pm \sqrt{13}\text{j}$

Exercise 2.4 (page 53)

1 $1, 1\frac{1}{3}$
2 $\frac{1}{6}(7 \pm \sqrt{11}\text{j})$
3 $2, \frac{2}{3}$
4 $1, 1\frac{2}{3}$
5 $2.15, -4.65$
6 $2.19, -0.69$
7 $1.15, -12.15$
8 $-1 \pm 1\sqrt{2}\text{j}$
9 $2.32, -4.32$
10 3 (twice)
11 $7.12, -1.12$
12 $2, \frac{1}{2}$

Exercise 2.5 (page 60)

1 $18x^2 + 9x - 5 = 0$
2 $\alpha^2 + \beta^2 = \frac{15}{4}$; $\alpha^3 + \beta^3 = \frac{11}{4}$
3 $g = 2\frac{1}{3}$, $f = -2$
4 **(a)** $\alpha^3 + \beta^3 = 18$ **(b)** $\alpha^6 + \beta^6 = 322$
5 **(a)** $\frac{13}{4}$ **(b)** $\frac{17}{4}$
(c) $-\dfrac{3\sqrt{17}}{4}$ **(d)** $-\dfrac{45}{8}$ **(e)** $\dfrac{25}{4}$
6 $\frac{9}{8}$
7 **(a)** $x^2 - 7x + 3 = 0$
(b) $9x^2 - 43x + 1 = 0$
(c) $x^2 - 7x + 3 = 0$
(d) $27x^2 - 280x + 1 = 0$
(e) $3x^2 - 14x + 4 = 0$
(f) $3x^2 + 14x - 33 = 0$
8 **(a)** $prx^2 + q(2r + p)x + (2r + p)^2 = 0$
(b) $prx^2 - (8pr - q^2)x + 16pr - 3q^2 = 0$
9 $bx^2 - a(b+1)x + (b+1)^2 = 0$
10 **(a)** $x^2 + 5px + 25q = 0$
(b) $qx^2 + px + 1 = 0$
(c) $x^2 + (p+4)x + 2p + q + 4 = 0$
(d) $qx^2 + (p - 2q)x + q - p + 1 = 0$
(e) $4qx^2 - 2px + 1 = 0$

Exercise 3.1 (page 63)

1 $-2.49, 0.66, 1.83$
2 2
3 1.78

Exercise 3.2 (page 66)

1 **(a)** 9 **(b)** 0
(c) 0 **(d)** -1
(e) 23 **(f)** 21
2 **(a)** $-2, 3$ **(b)** $3, 4$
(c) $1, 2, 3$ **(d)** $\pm 1, -3$
(e) $2, 3, -4$ **(f)** $0, 2, -4$
3 **(a)** $2, 1 \pm \text{j}$ **(b)** $-1, \dfrac{-3 \pm \sqrt{13}}{2}$
(c) $2, \dfrac{3 \pm \sqrt{17}}{4}$ **(d)** $-3, -5, 2$
(e) $\pm 2, 3$ **(f)** $2, -1 \pm \sqrt{3}\text{j}$
4 **(a)** $(3x + 8)(4x - 7)$
(b) $(x - 1)(x^2 + x + 1)$
(c) $(x - 2)(x^2 + x + 1)$
5 $-\frac{3}{2}, 5$
6 $k = -4$

7 $a = 5, b = 3$; $x - 1$
8 2
9 $(x + a)(3x + 2a)(2x - a)$

Exercise 4.2a (page 68)

1 (**a**) 4 (**b**) $\frac{1}{8}$ (**c**) 9 (**d**) $\frac{1}{64}$
2 $y^2/2x^3$
3 (**a**) 2^5 (**b**) 2^{-3} (**c**) 2^8
(**d**) 2^{x-7} (**e**) 2^{4t+1}
4 $8, \frac{1}{3}, 1, 9$
5 12

Exercise 4.2b (page 69)

2 (**a**) 7.590 (**b**) 1.148
3 1.07, 0.928
4 (**b**) 0.8271
5 4.53
6 0.07918; $\bar{1}.86967$
7 $x = 39.8$; $y = x^3/10$
8 6.28
9 3.21
10 (**b**) 6.21

Exercise 4.3 (page 70)

1 1.6829
2 6.2881
3 -0.6197
4 -5.2249
5 19.57
6 208.9
7 294.3
8 4424

Exercise 5.3 (page 76)

1 $P = 24.4$
2 $A = 21$
3 (**a**) $A = 96$
(**b**) $K = 1.6, n = 3$; $x = 10, y = 345.6$
4 $A = \frac{3}{4}\sqrt{C}$
5 $A = 2, B = \frac{4}{3}$

Exercise 6.3 (page 79)

1 1 or 1.585
2 -1 or 0
3 26
4 (**a**) 6.2 (**b**) 1.40
5 3 or 35

Exercise 6.4 (page 81)

1 $(-\frac{1}{2}, \frac{5}{4})$; $(1, -1)$
2 $(8, 2)$; $(-7, -3)$
3 $(2, 3)$; $(4, -1)$
4 $(1, 3)$; $(\frac{5}{2}, -\frac{3}{2})$
5 $(5, -2)$; $(-2, 5)$
6 $(\frac{7}{2}, 2, -\frac{3}{2})$
7 $(1, -2, 3)$
8 $(12, 8, 6)$ or $(-12, -8, -6)$

Miscellaneous examination questions 2

1 $9x^2 + (6p - 4)x + p^2 = 0$
2 (**a**) $-4, -12$ (**b**) $-2, \frac{2}{5}$ (**c**) -3
4 $x^2 + k^3x + k^4 = 0$; $k < -2$ or $k > 2$
6 (**a**) $5, -3$ (**b**) $(x - 3)(x + 2)(2x + 1)$
7 -33
8 (**a**) $(x^2 + x + 1)(x^2 - x + 1)$ (**b**) $-7, -2$, $(x + 1)$
9 (**a**) $(x - 1)(x - 2)$ (**b**) 17, 16, 24
10 (**a**) $x^2 + 4xy + 3y^2$ (**b**) 0, 9; $(x - 1)(x + 3)(2x + 1)$
11 (**a**) $4\frac{8}{9}$ (**b**) 0; $(3x + 2)(2x - 1)(x + 3)$
12 0.393
13 2
14 (**a**) $8, \frac{1}{4}, 1$ (**b**) $x^3 + x^{3/2} - 5 + 3x^{-3/2}$
(**c**) $(4, 8)$
15 25.1, 0.0251
16 $2\frac{1}{2}$ or 4
17 4
18 (**a**) $(\frac{84}{25}, -25)$ (**b**) $(2, 1)$, $(-\frac{3}{2}, -\frac{5}{2})$
19 (**a**) $\pm 8, \pm\frac{1}{27}$ (**b**) $(-1, 2)$; $(-\frac{1}{2}, \frac{7}{4})$
20 (**a**) $0, -2$ (**b**) $(\pm 3, \mp 2)$; $(\pm 4, \mp\frac{3}{2})$
21 $(4, 1)$; $(-11, -4)$; $(5, 2)$; $(-\frac{44}{5}, -\frac{13}{5})$
22 (**a**) 3 (**b**) $(1, -\frac{1}{2})$; $(-1, 2)$
23 (**a**) $(4, -3, 6)$; $(-16, 12, -24)$
(**b**) $1, 3, 2 \pm \sqrt{5}$
24 $(1, -1)$; $(2, 1)$
25 $(1, -1)$; $(-\frac{49}{26}, \frac{12}{13})$

CHAPTER 3 TRIGONOMETRY 1

NOTE. In Exercises 1.1, 1.2, 1.3a, 3.2a and 3.3 answers are given to some ODD numbers only.

Exercise 1.1 (page 88)

1 (**a**) sin 55° (**c**) −sin 15° (**e**) −sin 80° (**g**) −sin 40° (**i**) sin 40°
2 (**a**) −cos 76° (**c**) −cos 1° (**e**) cos 60° (**g**) cos 90° = 0 (**i**) −cos 10°

Exercise 1.2 (page 89)

1 (**a**) −tan 89° (**c**) tan 70° (**e**) tan 82° (**g**) −tan 50° (**i**) −tan 1°

Exercise 1.3a (page 91)

1 $-\cos 30°$
3 $\tan 60°$
5 $\sec 45°$
7 $-\cos 40°$
9 $-\tan 60°$
11 $-\sec 80°$
13 $\cos 20°$
15 $-\tan 50°$
17 $-\sec 68°$

Exercise 1.3b (page 91)

1 63.26°, 116.74°
2 63.98°, 296.02°
3 143.57°, 323.57°
4 25.22°, 154.78°
5 164.60°, 195.40°
6 65.68°, 245.68°

Exercise 1.4 (page 95)

(Answers to nearest degree)

1 97°, 173°, 277°, 353°
2 45°, 75°, 165°, 195°, 285°, 315°
3 38°, 158°, 278°
4 No solution
5 87°
6 96°
7 180°
8 23°, 180°
9 106°, 314°
10 0°, 90°, 180°, 360°

Exercise 1.5 (page 96)

1 $1^c = 57.3°$
2 $2\pi, \frac{\pi}{2}, \frac{\pi}{6}, \frac{\pi}{4}, \frac{3\pi}{4}, \frac{\pi}{3}$
3 270°, $22\frac{1}{2}°$, 240°, 720°, 540°, 330°
4 $2\pi, 2\pi, \pi, 2\pi, 2\pi, \pi$
6 **(a)** 1.3090 **(b)** 1.3963 **(c)** 2.0944 **(d)** 4.1888 **(e)** 1.1019 **(f)** 5.4454 **(g)** 3.3161 **(h)** 6.8068 **(i)** 0.6434 **(j)** 3.7996
7 $\frac{1}{2}\theta r^2$
9 **(a)** 0.4755, 2.6661 **(b)** 2.3284, 3.9550 **(c)** 0.3589, 3.5005 **(d)** 1.8650, 2.8472, 5.007, 5.989 **(e)** No solution **(f)** No solution
10 $0, \pi, 2\pi$

Exercise 2.1a (page 105)

1 $\pm\frac{3}{5}, \pm\frac{3}{4}, \pm\frac{5}{3}$, 36.87° or 323.13°
2 $\pm\frac{12}{13}, \pm\frac{5}{12}, \pm\frac{13}{12}$
3 $\pm\frac{1}{10}\sqrt{2}, \pm\frac{7}{10}\sqrt{2}, \pm 5\sqrt{2}$
4 $\pm\frac{4}{5}, \mp\frac{4}{3}$
5 $\pm\frac{5}{13}, \mp\frac{12}{5}$

Exercise 2.1b (page 105)

1 $\operatorname{cosec}\theta$
2 $\sec\theta$
3 $\cos\theta$
4 $-\sin\theta$
5 $-\cos\theta$
6 $-\cot\theta$
7 $\sec\theta$
8 $-\tan\theta$
9 $-\cos\theta$
10 $\sin\theta$

Exercise 2.2 (page 106)

1 $2\frac{3}{4}$
2 $3\sqrt{3}$
3 1
4 $\frac{1}{2}(3-2\sqrt{3})$
5 $\frac{1}{2}(4-\sqrt{2})$
6 0
7 $\frac{1}{2}(4+3\sqrt{3})$
8 $-\sqrt{2}$
9 $\frac{1}{2}(3\sqrt{2}-10)$
10 $\frac{1}{3}(18+5\sqrt{3})$

Exercise 2.4 (page 112)

1 $C = 51°$, $b = 4.52$ cm, $c = 9.81$ cm, Area $= 21.1\ \text{cm}^2$
2 $A = 63.9°$, $C = 68.1°$, $c = 59.9$ m, area $= 1292\ \text{m}^2$ or $A = 116.1°$. $C = 15.9°$, $c = 17.7$ m, area $= 381\ \text{m}^2$
3 $c = 20$ cm, $A = 22.5°$, $B = 27.4°$, Area $= 46\ \text{cm}^2$
4 $A = 29.0°$, $B = 46.5°$, $C = 104.5°$, Area $= 2.91\ \text{m}^2$
5 120°, $6.495\ \text{m}^2$
6 5.26 cm, 39.7°
7 9.42 cm, 8.28 cm, $38.9\ \text{cm}^2$
8 **(a)** 60° **(b)** 13 cm
9 5.40 cm, 48.53°, 2.31 cm
10 111.6 m
11 9.77 knots, 210°
12 64.7 m

Exercise 3.2a (page 116)

1 $\cos\alpha\cos\beta - \sin\alpha\sin\beta$
3 $\cos A\cos 2B + \sin A\sin 2B$
5 $\cos 2x\cos y + \sin 2x\sin y$
7 $2\sin A\cos A$
9 $\dfrac{\tan y - \tan 2x}{1+\tan y\tan 2x}$
11 $\dfrac{1-\tan A\tan B}{\tan A + \tan B}$
13 $\dfrac{3\tan A - \tan^3 A}{1-3\tan^2 A}$
15 $1-\sin^2 A$ or $\frac{1}{2}(\cos 2A + 1)$
17 $\cos(x-y)$
19 $-\cos(C+D)$
21 $\cos(60°+\phi)$
23 $\sin(2\theta - 30°)$
25 1

27 $\cos 3\theta$

29 $\sin 60° = \frac{\sqrt{3}}{2}$

Exercise 3.2b (page 116)

1 $2 \sin D \cos C$
2 $2 \cos C \cos D$
3 $2 \sin \theta \cos \phi$
4 $-2 \sin \theta \sin \phi$

Exercise 3.3 (page 118)

1 $2 \sin \theta \cos \theta$
3 $\frac{2 \tan 3\theta}{1-\tan^2 3\theta}$
5 $2 \cos^2 B$
7 $-\cos 2\theta$
9 $\frac{1}{2} \sin \phi/2$
11 $1-\sin 2\theta$
13 $\frac{1-\tan^2 \phi}{1+\tan^2 \phi}$
15 $2 \sin^2 A/2$
17 $\tan 45°$
19 $\cos 30°$

Exercise 4.1 (page 121)

1 (**a**) (i) $r \sin \theta = 4$; $y = 4$
(ii) $r \sin (360° - \theta) = 4$; $y = -4$
(**b**) (i) $r \cos \theta = 3$; $x = 3$
(ii) $r \cos (180° - \theta) = 3$; $x = -3$
(**c**) (i) $\theta = 135°$; $y = -x$
(ii) $\theta = 225°$; $y = x$
2 (**a**) $r \sin (\theta + \alpha) = 2 \sin \alpha$; $\tan \alpha = 2$; $y = -2x + 4$ (**b**) $r \sin (360° - \theta + \alpha) = 2 \sin \alpha$; $\tan \alpha = 2$; $y = 2x + 4$
(**c**) $r \sin (180° - \theta + \alpha) = 2 \sin \alpha$; $\tan \alpha = \frac{1}{2}$; $y = \frac{1}{2}x + 1$ (**d**) $r \sin (\theta - 180° + \alpha) = 2 \sin \alpha$; $\tan \alpha = -\frac{1}{2}$; $y = -\frac{1}{2}x - 1$
3 (**a**) $r \sin (\theta - 45°) = 2 \sin 45°$; $y = x + 2\sqrt{2}$ (**b**) $r \sin (\theta - 135°) = 2 \sin 135°$; $y = -x + 2\sqrt{2}$
4 (**a**) $r \sin (\theta - 30°) = 4$; $y = x \tan 30° - 4 \sec 30°$ (**b**) $r \sin (\theta - 60°) = 4$; $y = x \tan 60° - 4 \sec 60°$ (**c**) $r \sin (\theta - 120°) = 4$; $y = x \tan 120° - 4 \sec 120°$

Exercise 4.2 (page 122)

1 (**a**) $(2, 60°)$ (**b**) $r \sin (\theta - 30°) = \frac{3}{2}$
2 $(a, 60°)$; $(a, 300°)$; $r \cos \theta = \frac{a}{2}$

Miscellaneous examination questions 3

1 (**a**) $\frac{11}{10}$ (**b**) $\frac{3}{4}, \frac{1}{8}$
2 (**a**) 75.2°, 11.93°, 92.87° (**b**) ±90°, ±120°
3 (**a**) 3.61, 56.3°
4 (**a**) (i) 66.4°, 293.6° (ii) 25.8°, 334.2°
5 20 units
6 (**a**) $\frac{\pi}{3}$ (**b**) $\frac{5\pi}{6}$, 5.2 m, 2.0 m^2
7 65 cm; $\frac{56}{65}, \frac{33}{65}, \frac{56}{33}$; 56 cm; 62 cm; 12.2 cm
8 10 cm, 1 cm/sec, $\frac{1}{3}$ rad., 1 cm
9 (**b**) $AB = 5.52$ cm, $BC = 5.34$ cm
13 342 km, 057°
14 902 m, 640 m, 565 m

CHAPTER 4
COORDINATE GEOMETRY 1

Exercise 1.2 (page 129)

1 $\sqrt{13}, \sqrt{65}, \sqrt{146}, \sqrt{41}$
2 (**a**) $x^2+y^2=25$ (**b**) $x^2+y^2=49$
(**c**) $x^2+y^2-2x-4y-31=0$
(**d**) $x^2+y^2+4x-6y-3=0$
(**e**) $x^2+y^2+6x+8y+16=0$
3 (**a**) (6, 2), 7 (**b**) (3, −1), 4
(**c**) $(12\frac{1}{2}, 0)$, $2\frac{1}{2}$
4 $\sqrt{40}, \sqrt{10}, \sqrt{8}, \sqrt{58}, \sqrt{50}$
6 $(12\frac{1}{2}, 0)$, $2\frac{1}{2}$

Exercise 1.5 (page136)

1 $8x^2-24x+9y^2-144=0$
2 $15x^2+74x+16y^2+39=0$

Exercise 1.6a (page 138)

1 $8x^2-y^2-8=0$
2 $15x^2-12x-y^2=0$

Exercise 1.6b (page 139)

2 $4y = x^2-6x+13$ (parabola)
3 (**a**) $2x+y=9$ (straight line)
(**b**) $x^2+2x+y^2-2y=23$ (circle)
5 (**a**) $3x^2-4x+3y^2+2y-5=0$ (circle)
(**b**) $3x^2+16x+3y^2-8y+20=0$ (circle)
(**c**) $4x-2y+5=0$ (straight line)
6 (**a**) $\frac{x^2}{4}+\frac{y^2}{3}=1$ (ellipse)
(**b**) $y=0$, $x \leqslant -1$ (part of x axis)

(c) $x^2 - \frac{y^2}{3} = \frac{1}{4}$ (hyperbola)
(d) $x = 0$ (y axis)

7 **(a)** $4x + y^2 + 4 = 0$ (parabola)
(b) $3x^2 - 4x - y^2 - 4 = 0$ (hyperbola)
(c) $3x^2 + 16x + 4y^2 + 16 = 0$ (ellipse)

Exercise 2.1 (page 142)

NOTE. Equations in ratio and in parametric form are not unique.

1 **(a)** $\frac{x}{-2} = \frac{y}{1}$; $x = -2k$, $y = k$
(b) $\frac{x+3}{-1} = \frac{y+2}{5}$; $x = -k-3$, $y = 5k-2$

2 **(a)** $\frac{x}{3} = \frac{y}{-1}$; $x = 3k$, $y = -k$
(b) $\frac{x}{2} = \frac{y}{3}$; $x = 2k$, $y = 3k$
(c) $\frac{x+5}{5} = \frac{y-1}{-1}$; $x = 5k-5$, $y = -k+1$
(d) $\frac{x-2}{5} = \frac{y-3}{-1}$; $x = 5k+2$, $y = -k+3$
(e) $\frac{x+5}{7} = \frac{y-1}{2}$; $x = 7k-5$, $y = 2k+1$
(f) $\frac{x+2}{3} = \frac{y-1}{0}$; $x = 3k-2$, $y = 1$
(g) $\frac{x+3}{0} = \frac{y-5}{-5}$; $x = -3$, $y = -5k+5$

3 **(f)** 0; 1 **(g)** 1; 2 **(h)** −2; −1
(i) −6; 0 **(j)** 3; −3 **(k)** −2; $\frac{3}{2}$

Exercise 2.2 (page 146)

1 Coincident lines
2 (2, −3)
3 $(2\frac{1}{2}, -1\frac{1}{2})$
4 (2, 1), (3, 5), (6, 3)
6 $\frac{x-4}{1} = \frac{y-1}{3}$; (6, 7)

Exercise 2.3 (page 152)

1 $1\frac{1}{5}$
2 $9/\sqrt{13}$
3 **(a)** $14/\sqrt{5}$ **(b)** $11/\sqrt{5}$
4 (5, 5) or $(-\frac{31}{5}, \frac{17}{5})$
5 $\frac{x-3}{-1} = \frac{y-4}{2}$; $\frac{x-3}{2} = \frac{y-4}{1}$; $15\frac{3}{5}$
6 $8\frac{2}{3}$ units
7 6 units
8 $(x-5)^2 + (y-2)^2 = 25$
9 $x^2 - x + y^2 + y - 8 = 0$, circle

Exercise 2.4 (page 155)

1 **(a)** $-\frac{7}{\sqrt{65}}$ **(b)** $\frac{11}{\sqrt{410}}$ **(c)** −1 **(d)** 0
2 127°, $26\frac{1}{2}°$, $26\frac{1}{2}°$
3 57.34°, $19\frac{1}{2}$ units
4 5 units
5 $\frac{x}{2} = \frac{y}{5}$; $\frac{x-2}{2} = \frac{y-5}{-3}$
$\theta = \cos^{-1} \frac{11}{\sqrt{377}} = 55.49°$

Exercise 3.1 (page 158)

1 $x = 3t^2$, $y = 6t$
2 $x = 4 \cos \phi$, $y = 3 \sin \phi$
3 $x = a \operatorname{cosec} \phi$, $y = b \cot \phi$
4 $x = t^2$, $y = t^3$
5 $x = t^2 + 1$, $y = t^3 + t$
6 $x = \frac{3}{t^2-1}$, $y = \frac{3t}{t^2-1}$
7 $x = \frac{1}{t-5}$, $y = \frac{t}{t-5}$
8 $x = \frac{1-t}{t}$, $y = 1-t$
9 $x = t-4$, $y = t^2 - 4t$
10 $x = \frac{9}{t(3-t)}$, $y = \frac{9}{3-t}$

Exercise 3.3 (page 161)

1 $16y = 3x^2 + 6x + 35$
2 $9x^3 = 8y^2$
3 $x^3 + y^3 = 2xy$
4 $y = 4x^2 - 8$
5 $y = -x$
6 $x^{2/3} + y^{2/3} = a^{2/3}$
7 $(x^2 + y^2)^3 = a^2 x^2 y$
8 $x^2(y^2 + 2y) = y^2 + 4y + 4$
9 $y^2 + 2x^4 - 2xy^2 + 2y + 1 = 0$

Miscellaneous examination questions 4

1 $(\frac{6}{5}, -\frac{2}{5})$; $(x-3)^2 + (y-2)^2 = 9$
2 $(x-24)^2 + (y-7)^2 = 25$;
$x^2 + y^2 = 24x + 7y$

3 $\frac{x-3}{4}=\frac{y-2}{3}$; $\frac{x-3}{5}=\frac{y-2}{3}$; $\frac{x-15}{3}=\frac{y-11}{-4}$; $\frac{x-3}{1}=\frac{y-2}{-1}$ or $x+y=5$

4 $H(-\frac{3}{2}, \frac{1}{2})$; $C(5, 1)$

5 $(-1, 1)$; $(-5, -2)$

6 6, (7, 5), $5\sqrt{2}$, $(x-7)^2+(y-5)^2=50$

7 $A(-1, 2)$; $B(0, -6)$; $C(3, 0)$; $\lambda=2$, $\mu=1$; $y=-2x$

8 $M(4, 2)$; $C(2, 1)$; $D(1, 8)$; 30

9 $A(1, 4)$; $\frac{1}{3}$; 3; $y=-x$, $(-\frac{11}{4}, \frac{11}{4})$; $y=x$, $(\frac{11}{2}, \frac{11}{2})$

10 $B(4, 9)$; $D(-4, -3)$

11 Area $=2+\frac{\pi}{2}$ units^2; 1st quadrant

12 $y=3x-27$; $R(0, -27)$; $Q(18, -3)$

13 $A(4\frac{1}{2}, 0)$; $2x+4y=9$; $Q(2, \frac{5}{4})$

14 $B(1, -4)$; $P(\frac{9}{4}, 6)$

15 $4y+x=3$; $B(-1, 1)$

16 $x+2y=3$; $-1\frac{1}{2}$; $\frac{5}{4}\sqrt{5}$

17 $36y+x=26$; $36y+x=\pm 24$; $u^2y+x=4u$; $t=5, -1$

18 $9y-4x=3$; $t=-\frac{1}{3}$ or $-\frac{5}{3}$

19 $x-y=3\frac{1}{4}$; $x+y=1\frac{3}{4}$, $-\frac{1}{2}$; $x+y=\frac{3}{4}$

20 $y=\frac{3}{2}ux-\frac{1}{2}u^3$; $(u^2/4, -u^3/8)$; $x=\frac{5u^2}{8}$, $y=\frac{7u^3}{16}$

22 $x=a(\theta-\sin\theta)$, $y=a(1-\cos\theta)$

CHAPTER 5 SERIES 2

Exercise 1.2 (page 174)

1 $1-14x+84x^2-280x^3$; $-128x^7$

2 $1+10x+40x^2+80x^3$; $32x^5$

3 $1-3x+\frac{15}{4}x^2-\frac{5}{2}x^3$; $\frac{1}{64}x^6$

4 $6561+17\,496x+20\,412x^2+13\,608x^3$; x^8

5 $64-576x+2160x^2-4320x^3$; $729x^6$

6 $x^{10}+20x^9y+180x^8y^2+960x^7y^3$; $1024y^{10}$

7 $243y^5+810y^4x+1080y^3x^2+720y^2x^3$; $32x^5$

8 $2^7(x^7-14x^6y+84x^5y^2-280x^4y^3$; $-128y^7)$

9 $x^{14}+7x^{12}y^2+21x^{10}y^4+35x^8y^6$; y^{14}

10 $8-12x+18x^2-13x^3$; x^6

11 $\binom{n}{r}2^r$

12 $\binom{n}{r}(-3)^r$

13 $\binom{n}{r}2^{-r}$

14 $\binom{n}{r/2}$

15 $\binom{n}{r}2^r(-3y)^{n-r}$

16 512 192

17 (**a**) 1080 (**b**) 160

18 2, 8

19 (**a**) $1-10x+45x^2-120x^3$ (**b**) 96 059 601

Exercise 1.5 (page 180)

1 (**a**) $1-3x+6x^2-10x^3$, $|x|<1$
(**b**) $1-\frac{3}{2}x-\frac{3}{8}x^2-\frac{5}{16}x^3$, $|x|<\frac{1}{2}$
(**c**) $1-\frac{1}{2}x^2+\frac{3}{8}x^4-\frac{5}{16}x^6$, $|x|<1$
(**d**) $1+2x+3x^2+4x^3$, $|x|<1$
(**e**) $1-\frac{3}{2}x+\frac{27}{8}x^2-\frac{135}{16}x^3$, $|x|<\frac{1}{3}$
(**f**) $1+10x+75x^2+500x^3$, $|x|<\frac{1}{5}$
(**g**) $1-\frac{4}{3}x-\frac{4}{9}x^2-\frac{32}{81}x^3$, $|x|<\frac{1}{2}$
(**h**) $1+\frac{4}{5}x^2+\frac{18}{25}x^4+\frac{84}{125}x^6$, $|x|<1$
(**i**) $3\left(1+\frac{x^2}{18}-\frac{x^4}{648}+\frac{x^6}{11\,664}\right)$, $|x|<3$
(**j**) $x+\frac{1}{2}x^3+\frac{3}{8}x^5+\frac{5}{16}x^7$, $|x|<1$
(**k**) $1+x+\frac{(1-n)}{2!}x^2+\frac{(1-n)(1-2n)}{3!}x^3$, $|x|<\frac{1}{n}$

2 (**a**) $405x^4$ (**b**) $-\frac{1}{2}x^3$
(**c**) $-1001\times3^6x^{10}2^{-8}$
(**d**) $\frac{n(n+1)(n+2)(n+3)(n+4)(n+5)5^6x^6}{6!}$

3 (**a**) $x^{-3}-3x^{-4}+6x^{-5}-10x^{-6}$, $|x|>1$
(**b**) $(-2)^{3/4}(x^{3/4}-\frac{3}{8}x^{-1/4}-\frac{3}{128}x^{-5/4}-\frac{5}{1024}x^{-9/4})$, $x<-\frac{1}{2}$
(**c**) $x^{-1}-\frac{1}{2}x^{-3}+\frac{3}{8}x^{-5}-\frac{5}{16}x^{-7}$, $|x|>1$
(**d**) $x^{-2}+2x^{-3}+3x^{-4}+4x^{-5}$, $|x|>1$
(**e**) $3^{-1/2}(x^{-1/2}-\frac{1}{6}x^{-3/2}+\frac{1}{24}x^{-5/2}-\frac{5}{432}x^{-7/2})$, $x>\frac{1}{3}$
(**f**) $\frac{1}{25}(x^{-2}+\frac{2}{5}x^{-3}+\frac{3}{25}x^{-4}-\frac{4}{125}x^{-5})$, $|x|>\frac{1}{5}$
(**g**) $(-2)^{2/3}(x^{2/3}-\frac{1}{3}x^{-1/3}-\frac{1}{36}x^{-4/3}-\frac{1}{162}x^{-7/3})$, $|x|>\frac{1}{2}$
(**h**) $x^{-8/5}(1+\frac{4}{5}x^{-2}+\frac{18}{25}x^{-4}+\frac{84}{125}x^{-6})$, $|x|>1$
(**i**) $x+\frac{9}{2}x^{-1}-\frac{81}{8}x^{-3}+\frac{243}{16}x^{-5}$, $|x|>3$
(**j**) impossible
(**k**) $(nx)^{1/n}\left(1+\frac{1}{n^2}x^{-1}+\frac{(1-n)}{2n^4}x^{-2}+\frac{(1-n)(1-2n)}{6n^6}x^{-3}\right)$, $x>\frac{1}{n}$

Exercise 1.6 (page 182)

1 (**a**) 184% (−0.25 for 0.2963)
(**b**) 4.5% (2.1481 for 2.25)

2 (**a**) 1.019 80 (**b**) 9.611 80
(**c**) 2.645 75

3 (**a**) $-x^2/3 - x^3/9$
(**b**) $1 + x + x^2/2 + x^3/2$
(**c**) $1 - \frac{2}{3}x + \frac{5}{9}x^2 - \frac{68}{81}x^3$
(**d**) $1 - \frac{5}{2}x^2 + \frac{5}{3}x^3$
(**e**) $-\frac{13}{36}x - \frac{49}{2592}x^2 - \frac{2827}{279936}x^3$
(**f**) $1 - 8x + 52x^2 - 320x^3$

Exercise 2.1 (page 184)

1 −1, −2	**2** 1, 1, 4
3 1, 4, 3	**4** 2, 6, 5, 1
5 $\frac{2}{3}, \frac{1}{3}$	**6** 3, −4
7 −6, 4	**8** $-\frac{5}{4}, \frac{8}{5}, -\frac{7}{20}$
9 $1, -\frac{1}{3}, \frac{1}{3}$	

Exercise 2.2 (page 186)

1 $\frac{3}{4}(x+3)^{-1} + \frac{5}{4}(x-1)^{-1}$
2 $-7(x+3)^{-2} + (x+3)^{-1}$
3 $\frac{17}{9}(x+4)^{-1} + \frac{1}{9}(x-5)^{-1}$
4 $-\frac{2}{3}(x-2)^{-2} + \frac{11}{9}(x-2)^{-1} - \frac{11}{9}(x+1)^{-1}$
5 $\frac{9}{7}(x-1)^{-1} + \frac{1}{7}(1-9x)(x^2+2x+4)^{-1}$
6 $\frac{1}{3}(x+1)^{-1} + \frac{5}{3}(x-2)^{-1}$
7 $-\frac{3}{2}(x+1)^{-1} + \frac{5}{2}(x+3)^{-1}$
8 $-\frac{1}{2}(x+1)^{-3} - \frac{1}{4}(x+1)^{-2} - \frac{1}{8}(x+1)^{-1} + \frac{1}{8}(x-1)^{-1}$
9 7 or −9
10 3, 1, 2; Max. 3

Exercise 2.3 (page 189)

1 $\frac{1}{3}(x-1)^{-1} - \frac{1}{3}(x+2)^{-1} + (x+2)^{-2}$; $a = -\frac{1}{4}$, $b = -\frac{1}{2}$, $c = -\frac{3}{16}$, $|x| < 1$
2 $-(x+1)^{-1} - (x-2)^{-1} + 2(x-2)^{-2}$
3 $2(x+1)^{-1} + x^{-1} + (x-2)^{-1}$
4 $\frac{1}{3}(1+x)^{-1} + \frac{2}{3}(1-2x)^{-1}$; $\frac{1}{3}\{2^{n+1} + (-1)^n\}$; $|x| < \frac{1}{2}$
5 A = 8, B = −1, C = −1; $\frac{9}{2}x^3 - \frac{23}{4}x^4$
6 $a = 3$, $b = \frac{15}{8}$

Miscellaneous examination questions 5

1 A = 4, B = −2, C = −1
2 $1 + \frac{1}{2}x - \frac{1}{8}x^2$
3 $\dfrac{1}{x+1} + \dfrac{2}{x-1} + \dfrac{2}{(x-1)^2}$
4 $1 + x + \frac{3}{2}x^2 + \frac{5}{2}x^3 + \frac{35}{8}x^4$; $\dfrac{1 \times 3 \times 5 \times \cdots (2r-1)}{r!}$; 2·236
5 $(x+1)^{-1} - (x+2)^{-1} + 2(x+2)^{-2}$; $1 - \frac{5}{4}x + \frac{5}{4}x^2 - \frac{19}{16}x^3$, $|x| < 1$
6 $\frac{4}{9}(2x+1)^{-1} - \frac{2}{9}(x+2)^{-1} - \frac{1}{3}(x+2)^{-2}$; $\frac{1}{4} - \frac{3}{4}x + \frac{27}{16}x^2 - \frac{7}{2}x^3$; $\dfrac{(-1)^2}{9}\left[2^{n+2} - \dfrac{3n+7}{2^{n+2}}\right]$; $-\frac{1}{8}$
9 $\dfrac{2}{2x+1} + \dfrac{1-x}{1+x^2}$
10 $a = 1$, $b = \frac{1}{8}$, $c = \frac{63}{128}$

CHAPTER 6 ALGEBRA 2

Exercise 1.2 (page 196)

1 $x > -10$
2 $x < -\frac{3}{5}$
3 $x \geqslant 2\frac{1}{3}$
4 $x > \frac{1}{3}$
5 $x > 6$
6 $x < 6$
7 $x \leqslant -3\frac{2}{3}$

Exercise 1.3 (page 203)

1 $-1 < x < -\frac{1}{2}$
2 $x < \frac{2}{3}$ or $x > 1$
3 $-2 < x < -\frac{1}{3}$
4 $x < \frac{1}{7}$ or $x > \frac{1}{2}$
5 $-1 < x < \frac{2}{3}$
6 $-\frac{17}{20} < x < -\frac{3}{4}$
7 $x < -\frac{1}{2}$ or $x \geqslant 0$
8 $-3 < x < -\frac{5}{3}$ or $x > 1$
9 $-4 < x < -2$ or $x > -1$
10 $x < -\frac{16}{11}$ or $-\frac{2}{3} < x < \frac{3}{2}$
11 $x < -3$ or $x > 4$

Exercise 2.1 (page 205)

1 $x \leqslant -2$ or $x \geqslant 2$
2 $-2 < x < -1$
3 $x < -\frac{3}{2}$ or $x > \frac{1}{3}$
4 $x \leqslant 1$ or $x \geqslant \frac{3}{2}$
5 $x < 3$ or $x > 3$ (i.e. $x \neq 3$)

Exercise 2.2 (page 208)

1 $x < -1$, $3 < x < 5$
3 (**a**) $-1 - \sqrt{5} < x < -1$ or $1 < x < -1 + \sqrt{5}$ (**b**) $x < -2$ or $x > 1$
4 $x > -1$; No

Exercise 2.4 (page 212)

1 Min. $-\frac{25}{4}$	**2** Min. $-\frac{17}{4}$
3 Min. $\frac{31}{8}$	**4** Min. 2

5 Min. 2 **6** Max. 4
7 Max. $\frac{17}{8}$ **8** Max. 3
9 Max. $-\frac{23}{12}$ **10** Max. 0

Exercise 2.5 (page 214)

1 $-3 \leqslant y \leqslant \frac{3}{11}$

3 $1 - \dfrac{2}{3}\sqrt{3} \leqslant \dfrac{x^2 - 4x + 3}{x^2 + 3} \leqslant 1 + \dfrac{2}{3}\sqrt{3}$

Exercise 3.1 (page 216)

8 $x < -4$ or $x > 0$
9 minimum value is 2
10 $\frac{1}{2}(5 - \sqrt{13}) < x < \frac{1}{2}(5 + \sqrt{13})$

Miscellaneous examination questions 6

1 $2 < x < 2\frac{1}{2}$
3 $1 < x < 3$
4 $x < 1$, $x > \frac{4}{3}$
7 (**a**) $x \leq -\frac{5}{3}$, $x > \frac{1}{3}$ (**b**) $2 < x < 4$
(**c**) $-2 + \sqrt{5} \leqslant x \leqslant \frac{1}{3}$ (**d**) $x < (9 - \sqrt{21})/6$ or $x > (9 + \sqrt{21})/6$
9 (**a**) 1 (**b**) $-\sqrt{2}$
11 $p = 3$, $q = 1$
13 $x < -1$, $2 < x < 3$, $x \neq 1$
14 $x < -3$ or $-2 < x < -1$
15 $x < -2$ or $1 < x < 3$
17 $-\frac{1}{2} \leqslant \dfrac{2x + 1}{x^2 + 2} \leqslant 1$
18 $a = 2$, $b = 1$
19 $-2 < x < \frac{2}{3}$, $x < -6$
20 -1.58 or 0.38
21 (**a**) $x < -\frac{3}{7}$, $x > 1$ (**b**) $|x| > 1$

CHAPTER 7 TRIGONOMETRY 2

Exercise 1.2a (page 231)

1 $\frac{1}{4}(\sqrt{6} - \sqrt{2})$
2 $2 + \sqrt{3}$
3 $\frac{1}{4}(\sqrt{6} + \sqrt{2})$
4 $\frac{1}{4}(\sqrt{6} + \sqrt{2})$
5 $-(2 + \sqrt{3})$
6 $\frac{1}{4}(\sqrt{2} - \sqrt{6})$
7 $\frac{1}{2}\sqrt{[\frac{1}{2}(4 - \sqrt{6} - \sqrt{2})]}$
8 $\frac{1}{2}\sqrt{(2 + \sqrt{2})}$
9 $\dfrac{1 + \sqrt{6} - \sqrt{3}}{1 + \sqrt{3} - \sqrt{2}}$
10 $\frac{1}{2}(2 + \sqrt{2})$
11 (**a**) $\pm\frac{24}{25}$ (**b**) $\pm\frac{24}{7}$ (**c**) $-\frac{7}{25}$
(**d**) $\pm\frac{1}{10}(3 + 4\sqrt{3})$
12 (**a**) $\pm\frac{120}{169}$ (**b**) $\frac{7\sqrt{2}}{26}$ or $-\frac{17\sqrt{2}}{26}$ (**c**) $-\frac{119}{169}$

Exercise 1.2b (page 232)

1 $12.5°$
2 $90°$
3 $63.4°$
4 $0°$

Exercise 1.3a (page 235)

1 $2 \sin 40° \cos 20°$
3 $-2 \sin 40° \sin 20°$
13 $2 \cos \frac{5}{2}x \cos \frac{1}{2}x$
15 $2 \cos \frac{3}{2}A \cos (A + 2B)$
21 $2 \cos \left(\dfrac{\pi}{4} + x\right) \sin \left(\dfrac{\pi}{4} - 2x\right)$

Exercise 1.3b (page 236)

1 $\sin 50° + \sin 10°$
7 $\cos 10° - \cos 90° = \cos 10°$
13 $\frac{1}{2}(\cos 10° - \cos 60°)$
21 $\frac{1}{2} \sin (4A + 2B)$
23 $\frac{1}{2}(\cos \theta + \cos \phi)$

Exercise 2.1 (page 241)

1 (i) $\theta = 180n + (-1)^n\alpha$
(ii) $\theta = 360n \pm \alpha$ (iii) $\theta = 180n \pm \alpha$
2 (**a**) (i) $2\pi n \pm \frac{1}{3}\pi$ (ii) $360n \pm 60$
(**b**) (i) $\pi n + (-1)^n\frac{1}{3}\pi$ (ii) $180n + (-1)^n 60$
(**c**) (i) $\pi n + \frac{1}{4}\pi$ (ii) $180n + 45$
(**d**) (i) $2\pi n \pm 0.927$ (ii) $360n \pm 53.1$
(**e**) (i) $\pi n + (-1)^n\frac{1}{4}\pi$ (ii) $180n + (-1)^n 45$
(**f**) (i) $\pi n + 1.107$ (ii) $180n + 63.4$
(**g**) (i) $2\pi n \pm 2.301$ (ii) $360n \pm 131.8$
(**h**) (i) $\pi n + (-1)^n 4.069$
(ii) $180n + (-1)^n 233.1$
(**i**) (i) $\pi n + 2.471$ (ii) $180n + 141.6$
(**j**) (i) $2\pi n \pm 2.214$ (ii) $360n \pm 126.9$
(**k**) (i) $\pi n + (-1)^n 3.497$
(ii) $180n + (-1)^n 200.4$
(**l**) (i) $\pi n + 3.019$ (ii) $\pi n + 173.0$

Exercise 2.2 (page 245)

1 (**a**) 202.1°, 337.9° (**b**) 120°, 240°
(**c**) 230.1°, 355.1°
2 (**a**) 310.9° (**b**) 41.8°, 138.2°
(**c**) 90.0°, 290.0°
3 (**a**) 136.8°, 222.9° (**b**) 120°, 240°
(**c**) 165°, 345°
4 (**a**) 215.6° (**b**) 26.6°, 45°, 206.6°, 225° (**c**) 64.[illegible]°, 222.6°
5 (**a**) 26.3^c, 125.7° (**b**) $\frac{1}{9}\pi$, $\frac{1}{2}\pi$, $\frac{5}{9}\pi$, $\frac{7}{9}\pi$, $\frac{11}{9}\pi$, $\frac{13}{9}\pi$, $\frac{3}{2}\pi$

6 (**a**) $\frac{2}{3}\pi$, $\frac{4}{3}\pi$ (**b**) 8.2°, 90°
7 (**a**) $\frac{1}{8}\pi$, $\frac{5}{8}\pi$, $\frac{9}{8}\pi$, $\frac{7}{4}\pi$, $\frac{13}{8}\pi$ (**b**) 72.4°, 220.2°
8 (**a**) 51.3°, 128.7° (**b**) 69°12′, 327°40′

Exercise 3.1 (page 252)

1 35.7 cm
2 (**a**) 2.87 cm, 5.74 cm (**b**) 14.9°
3 (**a**) 125 s (**b**) 11.4°
4 34.5 cm, 103.4 cm, 20°
5 354 m, 11.6°

Miscellaneous examination questions 7

5 (**a**) 0°, 90°, 120°, 180° (**b**) 22.6°, 90°
6 (**a**) $r=\sqrt{10}$, $\alpha=18.4°$, $\theta=360n+53.2°$ or $360n-90°$
(**b**) (i) $\frac{1}{2}\pi n$ (ii) $\frac{1}{8}\pi(2n+1)$ or $\frac{1}{9}\pi(6n\pm1)$
(iii) $\frac{1}{4}\pi(4n+1+(-1)^n)$
7 (**a**) $360n+22.6°\pm32.2°$ (**b**) 18°, 90°, 162°, 234°, 270°, 306°
8 (**a**) 0, $\frac{1}{6}\pi$, $\frac{5}{6}\pi$, $\frac{3}{2}\pi$, 2π (**b**) 18°, 30°, 90°, 150°, 162°
9 (**a**) (i) 66.4°, 70.5°, 293.6°, 339.5° (ii) 0°, 60°, 90°, 270°, 300°, 360°
(**b**) $R=\sqrt{29}$, $\alpha=21.8°$ (i) $\sqrt{29}$, 338.2°, $-\sqrt{29}$, 158.2° (ii) 46.4°, 270°
10 (**a**) (i) 0°, 60°, 180°, 300° (ii) 63.4°, 108.4°, 243.4°, 288.4° (**b**) $R=2$, $\alpha=60°$ (ii) 2, 300° (iii) 120°
11 (**a**) $n\pi$ or $2\pi n\pm\frac{1}{6}\pi$ (**b**) $R=5$, $\alpha=36.9°$ (i) 73.7°, 180° (ii) 1, $\frac{1}{11}$
12 151°
14 32 m
15 44.9 m
16 γ, where $\tan^2\gamma=\tan^2\alpha+\tan^2\beta$
1.22 m
17 (**a**) 68° (**b**) 43° (**c**) 94°; 0.64 a^3
18 $\sin \text{EDC}=\dfrac{\cos\alpha\sin\beta}{\sqrt{(1-\sin^2\alpha\sin^2\beta)}}$;

$\arcsin\sqrt{\left(\dfrac{1-\sin^2\alpha\sin^2\beta}{2(1+\cos\beta)}\right)}$

CHAPTER 8 VECTORS 1

Exercise 1.2 (page 265)

1 2, −1
2 1, 3
3 −3, 1
4 −1, −2
5 1, −1; 3, 0 etc.
6 no solution

Exercise 1.3 (page 268)

1 (**a**) 3:1:2 (**b**) −3:4:1
2 (**a**) 7:5:−4 (**b**) 4:17:−7
3 2:−3:1; 0
4 (**d**) $-\frac{2}{3}$, 1 (**e**) −2, 5

Exercise 1.4a (page 270)

1 (**a**) $\boldsymbol{a}+\frac{1}{2}\boldsymbol{b}$, $\frac{1}{2}\boldsymbol{a}+\boldsymbol{b}$, $\frac{1}{2}\boldsymbol{b}$, $\frac{1}{2}\boldsymbol{a}$, $\frac{1}{2}(\boldsymbol{a}+\boldsymbol{b})$
(**b**) $-\frac{1}{2}(\boldsymbol{a}+\boldsymbol{b})$, $\frac{1}{2}\boldsymbol{a}$, $-(\boldsymbol{a}+\frac{1}{2}\boldsymbol{b})$, $-\boldsymbol{a}+\boldsymbol{b}$, $-\frac{1}{2}\boldsymbol{a}+\boldsymbol{b}$

Exercise 1.4b (page 271)

1 (**b**) $s=-1$, $t=1$; Q(4, 0)
(**c**) $\boldsymbol{x}=\begin{pmatrix}4\\0\end{pmatrix}+s\begin{pmatrix}3\\1\end{pmatrix}$
2 A parallelogram
MP: $\boldsymbol{x}=\begin{pmatrix}-3\\4\end{pmatrix}+t\begin{pmatrix}2\\4\end{pmatrix}$
QL: $\boldsymbol{x}=\begin{pmatrix}1\\-2\end{pmatrix}+t\begin{pmatrix}2\\4\end{pmatrix}$
MQ: $\boldsymbol{x}=\begin{pmatrix}-3\\4\end{pmatrix}+t\begin{pmatrix}4\\-6\end{pmatrix}$
PL: $\boldsymbol{x}=\begin{pmatrix}-1\\8\end{pmatrix}+t\begin{pmatrix}4\\-6\end{pmatrix}$
ML: $\boldsymbol{x}=\begin{pmatrix}-3\\4\end{pmatrix}+t\begin{pmatrix}6\\-2\end{pmatrix}$
PQ: $\boldsymbol{x}=\begin{pmatrix}-1\\8\end{pmatrix}+t\begin{pmatrix}2\\-10\end{pmatrix}$

Exercise 1.5 (page 275)

1 (**a**) $6\boldsymbol{i}+7\boldsymbol{j}$ (**b**) $5\boldsymbol{i}+13\boldsymbol{j}$
(**c**) $-2\boldsymbol{i}-19\boldsymbol{j}$ (**d**) $-8\boldsymbol{i}+3\boldsymbol{j}$
2 $\boldsymbol{p}=\begin{pmatrix}4\\5\end{pmatrix}$, $\boldsymbol{q}=\begin{pmatrix}-4\\-3\end{pmatrix}$
3 (**a**) −1:2:−1 (**b**) 1:−2:1
4 1:2
5 3/2, 7/2

Exercise 2.1 (page 278)

1 (i) (**a**) $\sqrt{10}+\sqrt{40}+\sqrt{50}=16.6$
(**b**) 32.1 (ii) (**a**) $\sqrt{13}+\sqrt{52}+\sqrt{117}=21.6$
(**b**) 43.3
2 (**a**) (i) $\begin{pmatrix}-3/5\\-4/5\end{pmatrix}$, $\begin{pmatrix}5/13\\12/13\end{pmatrix}$, $\begin{pmatrix}1/\sqrt{50}\\-7/\sqrt{50}\end{pmatrix}$
(ii) $\begin{pmatrix}3\\1\end{pmatrix}$ (iii) $\begin{pmatrix}4\\-3\end{pmatrix}$ (**b**) (i) $18+5\sqrt{2}$
(ii) 3 (iii) $\sqrt{10}$ (iv) 5
3 $\sqrt{50}$, $\sqrt{50}$; a rectangle

Exercise 2.2 (page 282)

1 (**a**) 102.8° (**b**) $\sqrt{5}$, $\sqrt{53}$
2 (**a**) 45°, 39.1°
3 90°, 63.4°, 26.6°
4 (**a**) $3\sqrt{3}$, 13, $\sqrt{109}$ (**b**) 45°, 16.7°, 118.3° (**c**) 19.5
5 1.6
6 (**a**) 1.8 (**b**) 3.2

Exercise 2.3 (page 284)

3 Area = 2

Exercise 3.1 (page 287)

1 (**a**) $\begin{pmatrix}4\\8\end{pmatrix}$

(**b**) PR: $\boldsymbol{x} = \boldsymbol{p} + t(-\boldsymbol{p} + \boldsymbol{r}) = \begin{pmatrix}-4\\2\end{pmatrix} + t\begin{pmatrix}8\\6\end{pmatrix}$

QS: $\boldsymbol{x} = \boldsymbol{q} + t(-\boldsymbol{q} + \boldsymbol{s}) = \begin{pmatrix}2\\4\end{pmatrix} + t\begin{pmatrix}-4\\2\end{pmatrix}$

(**c**) $\begin{pmatrix}0\\5\end{pmatrix}$ (**d**) $\begin{pmatrix}2\\7\frac{1}{3}\end{pmatrix}$

2 (**b**) $\begin{pmatrix}0\\4\frac{1}{2}\end{pmatrix}$, $\frac{1}{4}(\boldsymbol{a} + \boldsymbol{b} + \boldsymbol{c} + \boldsymbol{d})$ (**c**) LN: $\boldsymbol{x} = \begin{pmatrix}-3\\5\end{pmatrix} + t\begin{pmatrix}6\\-1\end{pmatrix}$ PM: $\boldsymbol{x} = \begin{pmatrix}-1\\3\end{pmatrix} + t\begin{pmatrix}2\\3\end{pmatrix}$

3 (*a*) $\frac{1}{\sqrt{10}}\begin{pmatrix}3\\-1\end{pmatrix}$, $\frac{1}{\sqrt{10}}\begin{pmatrix}1\\3\end{pmatrix}$ (**b**) 5:2

(**c**) $\boldsymbol{x} = t\begin{pmatrix}3\\-1\end{pmatrix}$

Exercise 3.2 (page 291)

2 (**a**) $-\boldsymbol{p}+\boldsymbol{q}$, $2\boldsymbol{p}+\boldsymbol{q}$, $-2\boldsymbol{p}+2\boldsymbol{q}$, $3\boldsymbol{p}$, $-\boldsymbol{p}+\boldsymbol{q}$, $-4\boldsymbol{p}+\boldsymbol{q}$ (**b**) $\frac{1}{2}(\boldsymbol{p}+\boldsymbol{q})$, $\frac{1}{2}(3\boldsymbol{p}+2\boldsymbol{q})$, $\frac{1}{2}(2\boldsymbol{p}+3\boldsymbol{q})$, $\boldsymbol{q}$ (**c**) $\frac{1}{3}(4\boldsymbol{p}+2\boldsymbol{q})$, $\boldsymbol{p}+\boldsymbol{q}$, $\frac{1}{3}(2\boldsymbol{p}+4\boldsymbol{q})$
3 (**a**) $\boldsymbol{d} = \boldsymbol{a} + \boldsymbol{c} - \boldsymbol{b}$
7 $\boldsymbol{d} = \boldsymbol{a} - 2\boldsymbol{b} + 2\boldsymbol{c}$, $\boldsymbol{e} = 2\boldsymbol{a} - 3\boldsymbol{b} + 2\boldsymbol{c}$, $\boldsymbol{f} = 2\boldsymbol{a} - 2\boldsymbol{b} + \boldsymbol{c}$

Miscellaneous examination questions 8

3 $\boldsymbol{h} = \begin{pmatrix}-4\\-3\end{pmatrix}$

7 $\boldsymbol{p} = \frac{1}{5}(2\boldsymbol{a} + 3\boldsymbol{b})$; $x = \frac{3}{2}$
8 (i) $\frac{1}{63}\sqrt{21}(15\boldsymbol{a} - \boldsymbol{b})$ (ii) $\frac{1}{9}(15\boldsymbol{a} - \boldsymbol{b})$
9 (**a**) 115° (**b**) $\sqrt{35}$, $\sqrt{15}$ (**c**) 72°
10 $l = 3$, $m = 2$
11 $\lambda = \frac{4}{5}$, $\mu = \frac{2}{5}$
12 (**b**) 2 m, 5.29 m
13 53, 477, 0; 79.5 units^2

CHAPTER 9 MATRICES AND TRANSFORMATIONS 1

Exercise 1.3 (page 314)

1 (**a**) $\dfrac{x-1}{-1} = \dfrac{y-3}{2}$ (**b**) $\dfrac{x+2}{3} = \dfrac{y}{1}$

(i) 81.7° (ii) the same

2 $\dfrac{x+10}{-5} = \dfrac{y-2}{2}$; $\dfrac{x}{2} = \dfrac{y}{1}$; $\dfrac{x}{5} = \dfrac{y}{2}$

3 $(-6, -24)$
4 $(-1, 8)$
5 (**a**) (4, 3), (−3, 14) (**b**) $(2, \frac{3}{2})$, $(-\frac{3}{2}, 7)$ 63.4°, 38.7°

6 $\dfrac{x}{2} = \dfrac{y}{-1}$, (−7, −21), (−140, −420)

(**a**) $\dfrac{x+7}{2} = \dfrac{y}{-1}$ (**b**) $\dfrac{x+140}{2} = \dfrac{y}{-1}$

Exercise 1.4b (page 319)

1 $-1, \begin{pmatrix}1\\1\end{pmatrix}$; $1, \begin{pmatrix}3\\1\end{pmatrix}$

2 $2, \begin{pmatrix}1\\1\end{pmatrix}$; $3, \begin{pmatrix}1\\0\end{pmatrix}$

3 $1, \begin{pmatrix}2\\5\end{pmatrix}$; $2, \begin{pmatrix}1\\3\end{pmatrix}$

4 $-1, \begin{pmatrix}2\\1\end{pmatrix}$; $4, \begin{pmatrix}1\\3\end{pmatrix}$

5 $1, \begin{pmatrix}2\\1\end{pmatrix}$; $4, \begin{pmatrix}1\\2\end{pmatrix}$

6 $\frac{1}{3}, \begin{pmatrix}1\\0\end{pmatrix}$; $\frac{1}{2}, \begin{pmatrix}1\\1\end{pmatrix}$

7 $-1, \begin{pmatrix}1\\2\end{pmatrix}$; $4, \begin{pmatrix}2\\-1\end{pmatrix}$

Exercise 2.2 (page 330)

1 (**a**) $\frac{1}{13}\begin{pmatrix}5 & -3\\1 & 2\end{pmatrix}$ (**b**) $\frac{1}{10}\begin{pmatrix}2 & 4\\-1 & 3\end{pmatrix}$

(**c**) $\frac{1}{5}\begin{pmatrix}-2 & 3\\1 & 1\end{pmatrix}$ (**d**) no inverse

2 (**a**) (3, 1) (**b**) (−1, −2) (**c**) (1, −4) (**d**) no solution

3 $\dfrac{x-\frac{5}{2}}{2} = \dfrac{y-\frac{7}{2}}{5}$

4 $\dfrac{x}{3} = \dfrac{y}{2}$, $\dfrac{x}{2} = \dfrac{y}{3}$

5 $x = y$, $\dfrac{x}{11} = \dfrac{y}{3}$

Exercise 2.4 (page 335)

1 $y=0,\ y=x$

2 $\frac{1}{10}\begin{pmatrix} 9 & -3 \\ -3 & 1 \end{pmatrix}$

3 $y=-2x,\ y=\frac{3}{2}x$

Exercise 3.5 (page 350)

1 **(a)** $\frac{1}{2}\begin{pmatrix} 1 & -\sqrt{3} \\ \sqrt{3} & 1 \end{pmatrix}$ **(b)** $\frac{1}{2}\begin{pmatrix} 1 & \sqrt{3} \\ -\sqrt{3} & 1 \end{pmatrix}$

2 **(a)** $\begin{pmatrix} 1 & 0 \\ -\frac{1}{2} & 1 \end{pmatrix}$ **(b)** $\begin{pmatrix} 2 & -1 \\ 1 & 0 \end{pmatrix}$

(c) $\begin{pmatrix} 2 & -\frac{1}{2} \\ 2 & 0 \end{pmatrix}$ **(d)** $\frac{1}{5}\begin{pmatrix} -3 & 4 \\ 4 & 3 \end{pmatrix}$

(e) $\frac{1}{\sqrt{5}}\begin{pmatrix} -2 & -1 \\ 1 & -2 \end{pmatrix}$ **(f)** $\frac{1}{\sqrt{5}}\begin{pmatrix} 1 & -2 \\ 2 & 1 \end{pmatrix}$

3 **(a)** $\begin{pmatrix} 0 & 1 \\ 1 & 0 \end{pmatrix}$ **(b)** $\begin{pmatrix} 0 & -1 \\ -1 & 0 \end{pmatrix}$

(c) $\begin{pmatrix} 0 & 3 \\ 2 & 0 \end{pmatrix}$ **(d)** $\begin{pmatrix} 0 & 2 \\ 3 & 0 \end{pmatrix}$

(e) $\begin{pmatrix} 1 & -1 \\ 1 & 1 \end{pmatrix}$ **(f)** $\begin{pmatrix} 1 & -1 \\ 1 & 1 \end{pmatrix}$

(g) $\begin{pmatrix} 0 & -1 \\ 1 & 1 \end{pmatrix}$ **(h)** $\begin{pmatrix} 1 & -1 \\ 1 & 0 \end{pmatrix}$

4 **(a)** $\begin{pmatrix} \sqrt{2} & 6/\sqrt{5} \\ \sqrt{2} & -3/\sqrt{5} \end{pmatrix}$ **(b)** $\begin{pmatrix} 0 & -1 \\ 1 & 1 \end{pmatrix}$

5 **(a)** $\begin{pmatrix} 0 & -2 \\ 3 & 0 \end{pmatrix}$ **(b)** $\begin{pmatrix} 0 & -3 \\ 2 & 0 \end{pmatrix}$

Miscellaneous examination questions 9

1 $\boldsymbol{Q}=\begin{pmatrix} 0 & 1 \\ 1 & 0 \end{pmatrix},\ \theta=n\pi$

2 $k=1,\ -5;\ \ y/x=\pm 1$

3 $\theta=-30°$ or $60°$

4 $x-y=0,\ m=\frac{1}{2}(-1\pm\sqrt{5})$

5 $y=\frac{1}{2}(2\pm\sqrt{6})x$

6 **(a)** $\boldsymbol{X}=\begin{pmatrix} 0 & 1 \\ 1 & 0 \end{pmatrix}$ **(b)** yes, in each case

7 $\boldsymbol{M}^2=\begin{pmatrix} 1 & 0 \\ 0 & 1 \end{pmatrix},\ k=\pm 1$

9 $y=\frac{1}{2}x,\ m=\pm 2$

10 **(a)** $x+y=0$ **(b)** $3x-y=0$ **(c)** $(0, \frac{3}{4})$, $(\frac{3}{2}, 0)$, $4x-6y=-15$

11 $x+3y=1,\ 2p+q=0$

12 $\begin{pmatrix} t \\ -2t \end{pmatrix},\ \lambda=10,\ \begin{pmatrix} 2 \\ 2 \end{pmatrix},\ 10^5\begin{pmatrix} -2 \\ 4 \end{pmatrix}$

13 $\boldsymbol{A}=\begin{pmatrix} 0 & 1 \\ -\frac{1}{2} & 1\frac{1}{2} \end{pmatrix}$

14 $\frac{1}{3}\pi,\ \begin{pmatrix} -\frac{1}{2} & -\frac{\sqrt{3}}{2} \\ \frac{\sqrt{3}}{2} & -\frac{1}{2} \end{pmatrix},\ \begin{pmatrix} -1 & 0 \\ 0 & -1 \end{pmatrix}$

$\boldsymbol{D}=\begin{pmatrix} 0 & -1 \\ -1 & 0 \end{pmatrix}$

15 $\det \boldsymbol{M}=1,\ \operatorname{tr} \boldsymbol{M}=-2.5$

16 $\boldsymbol{BA}=\begin{pmatrix} 0 & -1 \\ 1 & 0 \end{pmatrix},\ \boldsymbol{D}=\begin{pmatrix} 1 & 0 \\ 0 & -1 \end{pmatrix},\ n=4$

17 **(a)** $\boldsymbol{P}=\begin{pmatrix} 0 & -1 \\ 1 & 0 \end{pmatrix},\ \boldsymbol{Q}=\begin{pmatrix} 0 & 1 \\ 1 & 0 \end{pmatrix},$

$\boldsymbol{R}=\begin{pmatrix} -1 & 0 \\ 0 & -1 \end{pmatrix}$

(b) $x=0,\ \pm 2$; $(0, 0)$, $(8, 4)$, $(10, 5)$, $(2, 1)$

18 $\lambda=2, 5;\ y=-\frac{1}{2}x,\ y=x;\ \boldsymbol{D}=\begin{pmatrix} 2 & 0 \\ 0 & 5 \end{pmatrix}$

CHAPTER 10 FLOW CHARTS AND ALGORITHMS

Exercise 2.1 (page 364)

1 2, 1; complex; 4, 0
2 6, 11, 20
3 4, 21
4 $N=4,\ S=16;\ N=6,\ S=36$

Exercise 2.2 (page 367)

1

Term	–	2	5	8	11	14	17
Sum	0	2	7	15	26	40	57
i		1	2	3	4	5	6	7

Arithmetic series

2

Term	–	3	6	12	24	48	96
Sum	0	3	9	21	45	93	189
i	1	2	3	4	5	6	7

Geometric series

3

i	1	2	3	4	5	6
Sum	0	1	1.5	$1.8\dot{3}$	$2.08\dot{3}$	$2.28\dot{3}$
Term	1	$\frac{1}{2}$	$\frac{1}{3}$	$\frac{1}{4}$	$\frac{1}{5}$	$\frac{1}{6}$

4

Sum	0	2	7	18	41	88	183
Term	2	5	11	23	47	95	191

5

Term		–	3	6	10	15	21	28
Sum		0	3	9	19	34	55	83
Term 1	0	1	3	6	10	15	
Term 2	1	3	6	10	15	21	

Miscellaneous examination questions 10

1 (1, 1) (2, 4) (3, 9) (4, 16);

$x_n=n^2=\sum_{r=1}^{n}(2r-1)$

2 (**a**)

a	144	144	108	72	36
b	180	36	36	36	36

(**b**)

a	29	8	8	8	3	3	1	1
b	21	21	13	5	5	2	2	1

HCF by Euclid's method

3 $f = 1.618$

4 $e := \sqrt{d}$ should read $e := \sqrt{-d}$

(***a***) (2, 0.5) (2, −0.5) (***b***) 3.98, 0.0201

5 (**a**) 24.25 (**b**) 4.86 (**c**) $3.1\dot{3}$

$S = 1 + (1 + x) + \frac{1}{2}(2 + 3x) + \frac{1}{6}(6 + 11x) + \frac{1}{12}(12 + 25x)$

6 $S = \frac{1}{3}n(n+1)(n+2)$

7

r	0	1	2	3
a	1	2	5	10
p	1	2	4	8
b	1	3	3	1
d	3	2	1	0

CHAPTER 11 COMPLEX NUMBERS

Exercise 1.1 (page 380)

1 6 − 9j
2 9 − j
3 34 − 13j
4 −3 + 2j
5 −5 + 12j
6 25
7 19 + 4j
8 41
9 43 − 32j
10 18 − 26j

Exercise 1.2 (page 381)

1 $\frac{1}{41}(-7 + 22j)$
2 $\frac{1}{41}(5 - 4j)$
3 $\frac{1}{5}(3 + j)$
4 $\frac{1}{13}(-7 + 9j)$
5 $\frac{5}{481}(16 + 15j)$
6 $\frac{1}{4}(1 - 3j)$

Exercise 1.3 (page 384)

1 $-2 \pm \sqrt{5}j$
2 $1 \pm 2j$
3 $\frac{1}{2}(-3 \pm \sqrt{5})$
4 $-1, \frac{1}{6}(3 \pm \sqrt{15}j)$
5 $\pm\sqrt{\frac{5}{2}}j$
6 $\frac{1}{5}(-1 \pm \sqrt{14}j)$
7 −1, 2, 3
8 1, 2 (twice)
9 $-3, \frac{1}{2}(1 \pm \sqrt{7}j)$

Exercise 2.2 (page 393)

1 (**a**) $r = 5$, $\theta = 0.9$ (**b**) $r = 2.24$, $\theta = -2.68^c$ (**c**) $r = 25$, $\theta = -1.29^c$ (**d**) $r = 1$, $\theta = 0^c$ (**e**) $r = 1$, $\theta = \pi^c$ (**f**) $r = 5$, $\theta = \pi^c$ (**g**) $r = 3$, $\theta = \frac{1}{2}\pi^c$ (**h**) $r = 2$, $\theta = -0.52^c$ (**i**) $r = 2.65$, $\theta = 0.71^c$ (**j**) $r = 2.45$, $\theta = -2.53^c$ (**k**) $r = 0.56$, $\theta = -0.46^c$ (**l**) $r = 0.70$, $\theta = 2.85^c$

2 (**a**) $2\sqrt{3} + 2j$ (**b**) $\frac{1}{2}(\sqrt{6} + \sqrt{2}j)$ (**c**) $1 - \sqrt{3}j$ (**d**) $\frac{1}{2}(\sqrt{3} + j)$

3 (**a**) 4.47 (**b**) 8.06 (**c**) 5 (**d**) 12.04 (**e**) 36.06 (**f**) 0.56

Exercise 2.3 (page 396)

2 (**a**) $r = 23.1$, $\theta = 0.087^c$ (**b**) $r = 1$, $\theta = -1.18^c$ (**c**) $r = 3.60$, $\theta = 0.98^c$ (**d**) $r = 6.5$, $\theta = -1.18^c$ (**e**) $r = 2.30$, $\theta = 2.17^c$ (**f**) $r = 1$, $\theta = 0.93^c$

3 (**a**) $r = 15$, $\theta = \frac{11}{12}\pi$ (**b**) $r = 0.6$, $\theta = \frac{5}{12}\pi$ (**c**) $r = 1.7$, $\theta = -\frac{5}{12}\pi$ (**d**) $r = 9$, $\theta = \frac{1}{3}\pi$ (**e**) $r = 15$, $\theta = \frac{1}{2}\pi$ (**f**) $r = 2.9$, $\theta = -\frac{5}{6}\pi$

4 (**a**) $10(\cos 7\theta + j\sin 7\theta)$ (**b**) $1(\cos 2\theta + j\sin 2\theta)$ (***c***) $1(\cos\frac{1}{2}\pi + j\sin\frac{1}{2}\pi) = j$ (**d**) $1(\cos 0 + j\sin 0) = 1$

5 (**a**) $4(\cos\theta + j\sin\theta)$
(**b**) $1(\cos 3\phi + j\sin 3\phi)$
(**c**) $1(\cos 3\theta - j\sin 3\theta)$
(**d**) $1(\cos 2\theta - j\sin 2\theta)$

Exercise 2.4 (page 398)

1 (**a**) 2j (**b**) −8 (**c**) −41 − 38j

2 (**a**) $3(\cos 0.84 + j\sin 0.84)$
(**b**) $9(\cos 1.68 + j\sin 1.68)$
(**c**) $\sqrt{3}(\cos 0.42 + j\sin 0.42)$

3 (**a**) $\sqrt[4]{13}(\cos\frac{1}{2}\theta + j\sin\frac{1}{2}\theta)$, $\theta = \tan^{-1}\frac{3}{-2}$

$$= 1.90(\cos 1.08 + j\sin 1.08)$$
$$= 0.896 + 1.676j$$

(**b**) $\sqrt[4]{2}(\cos\frac{1}{2}\phi - j\sin\frac{1}{2}\phi)$, $\phi = \tan^{-1}\frac{-1}{1}$

$$= 1.19(\cos\tfrac{1}{8}\pi - j\sin\tfrac{1}{8}\pi)$$
$$= 1.10 - 0.456j$$

(**c**) $\cos\frac{1}{4}\pi + j\sin\frac{1}{4}\pi$

$$= \frac{1}{\sqrt{2}}(1 + j)$$

4 $z_1 = \frac{1}{13}(55 + 24j)$, $z_2 = \frac{1}{13}(10 - 24j)$
5 $z = \frac{1}{2}(4 \pm \sqrt{15} + j)$
6 $x^2 - 2jx + 2$, rem. $-j$
7 $(x + 2j)(x - 2j)$

8 (**a**) $1[\cos(-\alpha)+\text{j}\sin(-\alpha)]$
(**b**) $\cos\frac{1}{2}\beta(\cos\frac{1}{2}\beta+\text{j}\sin\frac{1}{2}\beta)$
(**c**) $4\cos^2\frac{1}{2}\gamma(\cos\gamma+\text{j}\sin\gamma)$
(**d**) $-\frac{1}{4}\operatorname{cosec}^2\frac{1}{2}\delta(\cos\delta+\text{j}\sin\delta)$

Exercise 2.5 (page 405)

1 (**a**) $(x-3)^2+(y+2)^2=5^2$ (**b**) $y=\frac{1}{5}x$
(**c**) $3x^2-10x+3y^2-28y+39=0$
(**d**) $\left(\frac{x}{4}\right)^2+\left(\frac{y}{2\sqrt{3}}\right)^2=1$

3 (**a**) $y=-x-1$ $(x<1)$ (**b**) $y=\sqrt{3}x+2$ $(x>0)$ (**c**) $(x+\frac{1}{2})^2+(y-1)^2=\frac{\sqrt{5}}{2}$ $(y<2x+2)$
(**d**) $y=2x+2$ $(x<-1, x>0)$

Exercise 2.6 (page 406)

1 (**a**) (i) $x^2+y^2=16$ (ii) $y=\sqrt{3}x$ $(x>0)$
(**b**) (i) $(x-3)^2+(y+2)^2=16$
(ii) $y=\sqrt{3}x-3\sqrt{3}-2$ $(x>3)$
(**c**) (i) $x^2+y^2=16$ (ii) $y=-\frac{1}{\sqrt{3}}$ $(x<0)$
(**d**) (i) $x^2+y^2=16$ (ii) $y=-\sqrt{3}x$ $(x>0)$
(**e**) (i) $x^2+y^2=256$ (ii) $y=-\sqrt{3}x$ $(x<0)$
(**f**) (i) $x^2+y^2=4$ $(x\geqslant 0)$ (ii) $y=\frac{1}{\sqrt{3}}x$ $(x>0)$
(**g**) (i) $\left(x+\frac{2}{15}\right)^2+y^2=\left(\frac{8}{15}\right)^2$
(ii) $(x-\frac{1}{2})^2+\left(y-\frac{1}{2\sqrt{3}}\right)^2=\left(\frac{1}{\sqrt{3}}\right)^2$
(minor arc from (1, 0) to (0, 0))
(**h**) (i) $x^2+\left(y+\frac{2}{15}\right)^2=\left(\frac{8}{15}\right)^2$
(ii) $\left(x+\frac{1}{2\sqrt{3}}\right)^2+(y-\frac{1}{2})^2=\left(\frac{1}{\sqrt{3}}\right)^2$
(minor arc from (0, 1) to (0, 0))
(**i**) (i) $\left(x+\frac{2}{15}\right)^2+y^2=(\frac{8}{15})^2$
(ii) $\left(x-\frac{1}{2}\right)^2+\left(y+\frac{\sqrt{3}}{2}\right)^2=1$ (minor arc from (1, 0) to (0, 0))

2 (**a**) (i) unchanged, $x^2+y^2=1$
(ii) unchanged (**b**) (i) translation $\begin{pmatrix}3\\-2\end{pmatrix}$,
$(x-3)^2+(y+2)^2=1$ (ii) translation $\begin{pmatrix}3\\-2\end{pmatrix}$
(**c**) (i) unchanged, $x^2+y^2=1$ (ii) line is rotated through 90° clockwise (**d**) (i) unchanged, $x^2+y^2=1$ (ii) line is reflected in the real axis (**e**) (i) unchanged, but described twice (ii) line is reflected in the imaginary axis (**f**) (i) cut in half, $x^2+y^2=1$ $(x\geqslant 0)$
(**g**) (i) $x=\frac{1}{2}$ (**h**) (i) $y=\frac{1}{2}$ (**i**) (i) $x=\frac{1}{2}$

Exercise 3.1 (page 408)

1 $\cos 4\theta+\text{j}\sin 4\theta$
2 $\cos 5\theta-\text{j}\sin 5\theta$
3 $\cos 3\theta-\text{j}\sin 3\theta$
4 $\cos 2\theta+\text{j}\sin 2\theta$
5 $\cos 4\theta-\text{j}\sin 4\theta$
6 $\cos 9\theta-\text{j}\sin 9\theta$
7 $\cos 24\theta-\text{j}\sin 24\theta$
8 $\cos 11\theta+\text{j}\sin 11\theta$

Exercise 3.2 (page 410)

1 $\frac{1}{4}(3\sin\theta-\sin 3\theta)$
2 $\frac{1}{8}(\cos 4\theta+4\cos 2\theta+3)$
3 $\frac{1}{16}(\sin 5\theta-5\sin 3\theta+10\sin\theta)$
4 $\frac{1}{16}(\cos 5\theta+5\cos 3\theta+10\cos\theta)$
5 $\frac{1}{32}(10-15\cos 2\theta+6\cos 4\theta-\cos 6\theta)$
6 $3\sin\theta-4\sin^3\theta$
7 $8\cos^4\theta-8\cos^2\theta+1$
8 $16\sin^5\theta-20\sin^3\theta+5\sin\theta$
9 $32\cos^6\theta-48\cos^4\theta+18\cos^2\theta-1$
10 $\cos\theta\sin\theta(6-32\sin^2\theta+32\sin^4\theta)$

Exercise 3.3 (page 413)

1 -3, $3(\cos\frac{1}{3}\pi+\text{j}\sin\frac{1}{3}\pi)$, $3(\cos\frac{5}{3}\pi+\text{j}\sin\frac{5}{3}\pi)$
2 $r=1$, $\theta=\frac{3}{8}\pi(4k+1)$, $k=0, 1, 2, 3$
3 $r={}^5\sqrt{5}$, $\theta=\frac{1}{5}(2k\pi+53°)$, $k=0, 1, 2, 3, 4$
4 $0, \pm\sqrt{3}$
6 $r=2^{0.3}$, $\theta=\frac{3}{20}\pi(8k+1)$, $k=0, 1, 2, 3, 4$
7 $r=[\frac{1}{2}(\sqrt{5}-1)]^{\frac{1}{4}}$, $\theta=\frac{1}{2}k\pi$ or $r=[\frac{1}{2}(\sqrt{5}+1)]^{\frac{1}{4}}$, $\theta=\frac{1}{4}\pi(2k+1)$, $k=0, 1, 2, 3$
8 $r=2^{\frac{1}{3}}$, $\theta=\frac{1}{9}\pi(6k+1)$, $k=0, 1, 2$
9 $x=r(\cos\phi+\text{j}\sin\phi)$ where $r=1$, $\phi=\theta+\frac{2k\pi}{n}$, $k=0, 1, 2, \ldots (n-1)$
10 $-\frac{1}{2}\left(1+\text{j}\cot\frac{k\pi}{n}\right)$, $k=1, 2, 3\ldots(n-1)$

Exercise 3.4 (page 416)

1 (**a**) $e(\cos\pi+\text{j}\sin\pi)=-e$ (**b**) $2\cos 1^c$
(**c**) e^{2a} (**d**) $\exp(r\cos\theta+\sin\cos\phi)\times[\cos(r\sin\theta+s\sin\phi)+\text{j}\sin(r\sin\theta+s\sin\phi)]$
2 (**a**) $X^2+Y^2=e^{2c}$ (**b**) $Y/X=\tan k$
3 $X=u^2-v^2$, $Y=2uv$
5 $u=x\left(1+\frac{1}{x^2+y^2}\right)$, $v=y\left(1-\frac{1}{x^2+y^2}\right)$; $u=2\cos\theta$, $v=0$

Miscellaneous examination questions 11

1 (**a**) $0.7+0.9\text{j}$ (**b**) $\frac{1}{16}(\sin 5\theta - 5\sin 3\theta + 10\sin\theta)$, $n\pi \pm \frac{1}{6}\pi$, $n\pi$

2 (**a**) $p = 1-\text{j}$, $q = \frac{1}{\sqrt{2}}(1+\sqrt{3}\text{j})$; $\sqrt{2}$, $-\frac{1}{4}\pi$; $\sqrt{2}$, $\frac{1}{3}\pi$; $\frac{1}{24}\pi$
(**b**) $-\frac{1}{32}(\cos 6\theta + 2\cos 4\theta - \cos 2\theta - 2)$

3 ± 1, $2+3\text{j}$

4 (**a**) $z_1 = 5+4\text{j}$, $z_2 = 2-3\text{j}$
(**b**) $2|\cos\frac{1}{2}\theta|$, $\frac{1}{2}\theta$; $\sqrt{3}$, $\frac{1}{6}\pi$; 27, π

5 (**a**) $x^2+2x+4=0$ (**b**) $z=1$

6 $r=4$, $\theta = \frac{1}{3}\pi$, π, $-\frac{1}{3}\pi$, $1.27+3.73\text{j}$, $4.73+0.27\text{j}$

7 (**b**) 6.5, $-\tan^{-1}\frac{5}{12}$

8 $z=-1+2\text{j}$; $(x-1)^2+(y-\frac{1}{2})^2 = \frac{5}{4}$

9 $-a$, $\sqrt{(a^2-b)}$;
$x^2-2a^2x+2a^2(a^2-b)+b^2=0$

10 (**a**) $2\sqrt{2}$, $\pm\frac{3}{4}\pi$; $\frac{1}{2}\text{j}$

12 (**b**) $\theta = \frac{1}{2}\pi$, $r = \frac{\text{OB}}{\text{OC}}$, $\theta = \angle\text{BOC}$

13 $\pm\text{j}$, $2\pm 3\text{j}$

14 $x' = x-y$, $y' = x+y$ (**a**) $x'+y'=4$
(**b**) $x'^2+y'^2 = 2r^2$ (**c**) $y' = x'\tan(\frac{1}{4}\pi+\theta)$

15 (**a**) $-7+24\text{j}$, $y^2 = 324-36x$
(**b**) $x = \frac{u}{u^2+9}$, $y = \frac{-3}{u^2+9}$

16 (**a**) (i) $2\sqrt{10}$ (ii) 10 (iii) $2\sqrt{10}$
(**b**) $\frac{1}{5}(-2+6\text{j})$

17 (**a**) $-2+5\text{j}$, $-1+30\text{j}$, $1\frac{1}{2}+\frac{1}{2}\text{j}$

18 (**a**) $3+\text{j}$, 2j, $2-2\text{j}$
(**b**) $-1+18\cos^2\theta - 48\cos^4\theta + 32\cos^6\theta$
$48\cos^4\theta + 32\cos^6\theta$

19 $\frac{1}{4}(-1\pm\sqrt{15}\text{j})$; $\frac{1}{2}(-1\pm\sqrt{3}\text{j})$

20 9, 6θ

CHAPTER 12 ALGEBRAIC STRUCTURE

Exercise 1.2a (page 426)

1 (**a**) (i) 3 (ii) 0 (iii) 1
(**b**)

×	1	3	7	9
1	1	3	7	9
3	3	9	1	7
7	7	1	9	3
9	9	7	3	1

Cyclic in order 1, 3, 9, 7
(i) $e=1$ (ii) 1 and 9 self inverse, 3 and 7 inverse of each other

2

×	2	4	6	8
2	4	8	2	6
4	8	6	4	2
6	2	4	6	8
8	6	2	8	4

Cyclic in order 6, 8, 4, 2
(i) $e=6$

3 Cyclic, $e=1$

4 Cyclic, $e = \begin{pmatrix} 1 & 0 \\ 0 & 1 \end{pmatrix}$

5 Klein, $e = \begin{pmatrix} 1 & 0 \\ 0 & 1 \end{pmatrix}$

Exercise 1.2b (page 427)

1

*	I	X	Y	Z
I	I	X	Y	Z
X	X	I	Z	Y
Y	Y	Z	I	X
Z	Z	Y	X	I

Klein

2

*	I	R	R^2	R^3
I	I	R	R^2	R^3
R	R	R^2	R^3	I
R^2	R^2	R^3	I	R
R^3	R^3	I	R	R^2

Cyclic

3 Klein

4 Cyclic

Exercise 2.1a (page 429)

1 $e=10$, 8 and 10 self inverse, 14 and 2, 16 and 4 inverses of each other

2 $e=12$, 10 and 12 self inverse; 2, 6; 4, 14; 8, 18; 16, 20

3 $e=8$, 6 and 8 self; 2, 4; 10, 12

4 $e=6$, 6 and 9 self; 3, 12

Exercise 2.1b (page 429)

1 (**a**) *Not* associative, e.g. R(ST) ≠ (RS)T
(**b**) Associative, closed, identity = I, I, R, S, T self inverse, P and Q inverses of each other

2 Others are R, U, RU, R^2U, R^2; $R^3 = U^3$ = identity

Exercise 3.1 (page 439)

1 Ring

2 Ring

3 Field
4 Field
5 Ring
6 Neither; system is not closed under +
7 Field
8 Neither; not closed under ×
9 Field
10 Neither; there is no set B, such that $A \cup B = \phi$

Exercise 3.2 (page 441)

2 (a) 2, 5 (b) 2 (c) 1, 3 (d) no solution (e) no solution (f) 1
3 (a) commutative (b) (i) 5, 7 (ii) $3 * (4 * 4) = 7$ (c) 2 (d) −2
4 (a) (i) 5 (ii) 13 (iii) 13 (b) Associative (c) 0 (d) 0 is self inverse
5 (a) e.g. 1, 2, 4 (b) 0 (c) all self inverse (d) (i) no solution (ii) 3, 9 (iii) 2, 8, 14
6 (a) (i) 9 (ii) 4 (iii) $-9\frac{1}{2}$ (b) No identity (c) $a = c$
7 (a) 8 (b) 12 (c) 6 (d) 12 (e) 2, 12

Miscellaneous examination questions 12

1 (a) (1, 0) (b) $\left(\frac{1}{a}, \frac{-b}{a}\right)$
2 (a) c (b) no solution (c) a, d (d) a
3 (b) a
5 $e = (1, 0)$
7 No, yes
9 {1, 2, 4, 8}, {1, 4, 7, 13}, {1, 4, 11, 14}
11 (a) (i) Yes (ii) yes (iii) 0. m odd, $q^2 = 2pr$ (b) no, yes, no
13 (a) Yes (b) yes (c) yes, 1 (d) no inverses. Yes, yes, no, no inverses
14 −1 under ⊕, 0 under ⊗; $-2-m$ under ⊕, $\dfrac{m}{m-1}$ $(m \neq 1)$ under ⊗
15 No; $P = (0, 0)$, $Q = (a_1 - a_2, a_2 - a_1)$
16 (1, 0); $\left(\dfrac{a_1}{a_1^2+a_2^2}, \dfrac{-a_2}{a_1^2+a_2^2}\right)$; $(a_2, -a_1)$
17 (a) Yes (b) yes (c) no (d) no
18 (a) Yes, yes (b) 0, (for $a \neq 1$, i.e. for S) (c) $\dfrac{a}{a-1}$ (for $a \neq 1$, i.e. for S) $x = \frac{5}{4}$

CHAPTER 13 COORDINATE GEOMETRY—3D

Exercise 1.1 (page 454)

1 (±1, 0, 0), (0, ±1, 0), (0, 0, ±1)
2 (a) O(0, 0, 0), A(8, 0, 0), B(8, 0, 5), C(0, 0, 5), D(8, 6, 0), E(8, 6, 5), F(0, 6, 5), G(0, 6, 0)
3 (a) V(0, 0, 3), A($\sqrt{2}$, 0, 0), B(0, $\sqrt{2}$, 0), C($-\sqrt{2}$, 0, 0), D(0, $-\sqrt{2}$, 0) (b) AB: $x + y = \sqrt{2}$, $z = 0$. VA: $\dfrac{x-\sqrt{2}}{\sqrt{2}} = \dfrac{z}{3}$, $y = 0$
4 (a) B(2, 4, 6), C(5, 10, 15) (b) Q(1, 4, 7), R(1, 7, 13)
5 (a) −2 : −3 : 3 (b) −5 : −2 : −2
6 (a) $\sqrt{62}$ (b) $5\sqrt{2}$
7 (a) $\dfrac{x+1}{4} = \dfrac{y-2}{-3} = \dfrac{z}{1}$, $\dfrac{x-3}{4} = \dfrac{y+1}{-3} = \dfrac{z}{1}$ (b) $\dfrac{x}{1} = \dfrac{y-2}{0} = \dfrac{z-3}{1}$, $\dfrac{x+2}{1} = \dfrac{y-2}{0} = \dfrac{z-1}{1}$
8 (a) $x = 2 - 3\lambda$, $y = 1 + \lambda$, $z = 3 - 5\lambda$; $x = -1 - 3\mu$, $y = 2 + \mu$, $z = -2 - 5\mu$ (b) $x = -\lambda$, $y = -1 - 2\lambda$, $z = 2$; $x = -1 - \mu$, $y = -3 - 2\mu$, $z = 2$
9 (a) (1, −3, −1), (3, 1, −2), (−1, −7, 0) ⋯ (b) (0, −1, 5), (−3, −1, 7), (3, −1, 3) ⋯ (c) (−1, 4, 1), (2, 6, 0), (−4, 2, 2) ⋯ (d) (2, 2, 0), (2, −1, 1), (2, 5, −1) ⋯

Exercise 1.2 (page 462)

1 All different
2 $\dfrac{x+1}{-1} = \dfrac{y-2}{2} = \dfrac{z-3}{3}$; (−2, 4, 6), (0, 0, 0), (−3, 6, 9)
3 (1, 3, 2)
5 $\dfrac{x}{1} = \dfrac{y}{3} = \dfrac{z}{4}$

Exercise 1.3 (page 468)

1 4 : −5 : −6
2 5 : 19 : 3
3 $\dfrac{x}{1} = \dfrac{y}{-3} = \dfrac{z}{-1}$
4 $x = 2$, $y = 1$ *or* $\dfrac{x-2}{0} = \dfrac{y-1}{0} = \dfrac{z}{1}$
5 $\dfrac{x}{1} = \dfrac{y}{-1} = \dfrac{z}{0}$

Exercise 1.4 (page 472)

1 $\frac{1}{11}\sqrt{506}$
2 (**a**) $\frac{1}{6}\sqrt{30}$ (**b**) $2\sqrt{3}$
3 (**a**) $\frac{1}{3}\sqrt{1222}$ (**b**) $\frac{1}{3}\sqrt{66}$
4 (**a**) $\frac{1}{10}\sqrt{10}$ (**b**) $2\sqrt{3}$

Exercise 2.1a (page 474)

1 $x=0, x=8, y=0, y=6, z=0, z=5$
2 $(0, 2, -3)$
3 (**a**) $(1, 2, k)$; $x-1=y-2=0$
(**b**) $(k, -3, 0)$; $y+3=z=0$
(**c**) $(k, -k, 3)$; $\dfrac{x}{1}=\dfrac{y}{-1}=\dfrac{z-3}{0}$
(**d**) $(6, -6, k)$; $x-6=y+6=0$
(**e**) $(1, 1+k, -k)$; $\dfrac{x-1}{0}=\dfrac{y-1}{1}=\dfrac{z}{-1}$
(**f**) $(k, 1, 2-k)$; $\dfrac{x}{1}=\dfrac{y-1}{0}=\dfrac{z-2}{-1}$
4 The planes form a prism.

Exercise 2.1b (page 478)

1 $x+3y-z=0$; $(-3, 1, 0)$, $(0, 1, 3)$, $(1, 0, 1)\cdots$
2 $(6, 0, 0)$, $(0, -4, 0)$, $(0, 0, -12)$, $\frac{6}{7}\sqrt{14}$
3 (**a**) $\frac{1}{3}\sqrt{30}$ (**b**) $\frac{2}{3}\sqrt{30}$

Exercise 2.2 (page 481)

1 $2x-y-5z=0$
2 $x+3y+z=0$
3 $2x+y=0$
4 $4x+2y-z=0$
5 $x+3y+4z=11$
6 $2x-3y+z=-1$
7 $x+5y+2z=-3$
8 $9x+y+3z=-12$
9 $x-2y+z=9$
10 $2x-y+3z=11$

Exercise 2.3 (page 488)

1 (**a**) $x+y+z=6\sqrt{3}$ (**b**) $108\sqrt{3}$ cubic units (**c**) $x+y+z=10\sqrt{3}$ (**d**) $394\sqrt{3}$ cubic units
2 $2y+z=2\pm5\sqrt{5}$
3 $20/\sqrt{83}$
4 $2/\sqrt{5}$
6 $2/\sqrt{14}$
7 (**a**) $x+2y-z=-3$ (**b**) $x+2y-z=8$ $11/\sqrt{6}$

Exercise 2.4a (page 492)

2 $(-\frac{2}{3}, \frac{1}{3}, \frac{4}{3})$
3 $\dfrac{x+3}{2}=\dfrac{y}{1}=\dfrac{z-5}{-1}$, $(7, 5, 0)$
4 $\dfrac{x}{1}=\dfrac{y-3}{0}=\dfrac{z-1}{0}$
5 $\dfrac{x-1}{14}=\dfrac{y}{-27}=\dfrac{z-1}{-11}$, -3

Exercise 2.4b (page 494)

1 3 coincident planes
2 3 parallel planes
3 1 line, $(k, 7k-10, 4k-7)$
4 3 parallel lines, $(7, k, k-10)$, $(4, k, k-7)$, $(6, k, k-8)$
5 1 point $(2, 0, 1)$
6 2 coincident, 1 parallel plane
7 2 coincident, 1 intersecting plane $(k, 2k-7, 3k-10)$
8 2 parallel, 1 intersecting plane

Exercise 2.5 (page 503)

1 (**a**) $1/\sqrt{3}$, $1/\sqrt{3}$, $1/\sqrt{3}$ (**b**) $2/\sqrt{14}$, $1/\sqrt{14}$, $-3/\sqrt{14}$ (**c**) $-1/\sqrt{11}$, $-3/\sqrt{11}$, $1/\sqrt{11}$
2 35.3°, 90°, 54.7°
3 $4/\sqrt{70}$
5 79.5°
6 $1/\sqrt{15}$
7 18.9°
8 $x-2y-3z=-2$
9 $x-2y-3z=8\sqrt{14}$
10 (**a**) $5/\sqrt{14}$ (**b**) 36.7°, 57.7°, 105.5°

Miscellaneous examination questions 13

1 $P(3, 1, 2)$, $Q(-1, 2, 1)$; $PQ=3\sqrt{2}$
2 (**b**) $PQ=RS=\frac{1}{2}\sqrt{[(a_1-c_1)^2+(a_2-c_2)^2+(a_3-c_3)^2]}$ (**c**) DR of PQ = DR of RS $= a_1-c_1 : a_2-c_2 : a_3-c_3$ (**d**) parallelogram
3 $P(1, -1, 2)$; 46 units^3
4 $B(2, 2\sqrt{3}, 0)$, $C(2, \frac{2}{3}\sqrt{3}, \frac{4}{3}\sqrt{6})$; $0, -\frac{1}{3}\sqrt{3}, \frac{1}{3}\sqrt{6}$; $\dfrac{x-2}{0}=\dfrac{y-2\sqrt{3}}{-1}=\dfrac{z}{\sqrt{2}}$; $y\sqrt{2}-z=2\sqrt{6}$
5 (**a**) (i) $\frac{1}{3}\sqrt{6}a$ (ii) $\frac{1}{2}\sqrt{2}a$
(**b**) $x+y+2z=2$, $5x+5y+2z=10$
6 $3x-y+z=2$; $(k, -\frac{1}{3}k-\frac{15}{23}, \frac{1}{3}k+\frac{15}{23})$

7 (**a**) $x-y-2z=0$

(**b**) $\dfrac{x-1}{-2}=\dfrac{y-3}{-1}=\dfrac{z-2}{1}$ (**c**) 30°

8 (**a**) 9, 15 units^3 (**c**) $5/\sqrt{30}$, $2/\sqrt{30}$, $-1/\sqrt{30}$; $(\frac{5}{3}, \frac{2}{3}, -\frac{1}{3})$

9 $x-y-2z=15$; $\frac{2}{3}$, $-\frac{1}{3}$, $-\frac{2}{3}$;

$\dfrac{x-1}{2}=\dfrac{y-1}{-1}=\dfrac{z-1}{-2}$

10 (**a**) $2x+2y+z=11$; (2, 3, 1)

11 (**a**) (1, 2, 3) (**b**) $2x-3z=-1$; $\frac{1}{4}$

12 $2x+3y+4z=0$; (13/29, 34/29, −32/29)

13 (**b**) (i) 2 : 1 : −1 (ii) $2x+y-z=2$ (iii) $(\frac{2}{3}, \frac{1}{3}, -\frac{1}{3})$

14 (1, 2, 3); $x-3y+z=-2$; $x-3y+z=-13$, $x-3y+z=9$

15 (**a**) (i) (1, 3, 1) (ii) $4/\sqrt{21}$ (**b**) (−2, 1, 2), (16/7, 13/7, −4/7)

16 $2x-y+z=5$; (3, 2, 1); $x-2z=1$

17 $\dfrac{x}{3}=\dfrac{y}{2}=\dfrac{z}{-4}$; $3/\sqrt{29}$

18 $5\sqrt{\frac{2}{33}}$

19 $\dfrac{x+1}{9}=\dfrac{y-4}{-38}=\dfrac{z-2}{19}$; $x-y-z=-4$; $6/\sqrt{5}$

20 (**a**) (−24, −18, 0) (**b**) $\dfrac{x}{4}=\dfrac{y}{3}=\dfrac{z-12}{3}$ (**c**) $4/\sqrt{29}, 3/\sqrt{29}, 2/\sqrt{29}$ (**d**) $26\frac{1}{2}°$, $33\frac{1}{2}°$

21 $-2x=-2y=5z+9-\sqrt{2}$

22 $\dfrac{x}{-12}=\dfrac{y-5}{5}=\dfrac{z}{0}$; rock layer NOT a plane

CHAPTER 14 ERRORS

Exercise 1.2 (page 511)

1 (**a**) 0.1285 (**b**) 0.0013 (**c**) 0.8088 (**d**) 12.5000

2 (**a**) 0.003 535 (**b**) 37 520 (**c**) 0.8889 (**d**) 0.000 808 1

3 (**a**) $1.225 \leqslant x \leqslant 1.235$ (**b**) $5735 \leqslant x \leqslant 5745$ (**c**) $14.045 \leqslant x \leqslant 14.055$ (**d**) $18.9 \leqslant x \leqslant 19.7$ (**e**) $27.455 \leqslant x \leqslant 27.629$ (**f**) $0.004\,38 \leqslant x \leqslant 0.004\,86$

4 (**a**) 671.1 ± 0.1 (**b**) 791.9 ± 0.1 (**c**) −791.9 ± 0.1 (**d**) 541 367 ± 84 (**e**) 2.801 41 ± 0.000 43 (**f**) 0.356 963 ± 0.000 055

5 (**a**) 3675.96 ± 0.98 (**b**) 10.24 ± 0.98 (**c**) 5.1159 ± 0.0015 (**d**) −3.5391 ± 0.0015

Exercise 1.4 (page 515)

1 The answers given are the maximum absolute error and the maximum relative error, as a percentage.
(**a**) 0.05, 2% (**b**) 0.005, 0.2% (**c**) 0.0005, 0.02% (**d**) 0.000 05, 0.4% (**e**) 5, 0.04% (**f**) 0.005, 10% (**g**) 0.0025, 5% (**h**) 1.75×10^{-7}, 10% (**i**) 60, $2\frac{1}{2}$%

2 Relative error is given as a percentage. p, 0.0041%; q, 0.011% (**a**) 0.0060% (**b**) & (**c**) 0.013% (**d**) 0.016% (**e**) 0.015% (**f**) 0.015%

3 (**a**) 3675.96 ± 0.027% (**b**) 10.24 ± 9.6% (**c**) 5.1159 ± 0.029% (**d**) −3.5391 ± 0.042%

Exercise 1.5 (page 519)

1 $\dfrac{\delta a+\delta b+\delta c}{a+b-c} \times 100\%$

(**a**) 1 ± 1.5% (**b**) 10 ± 0.06% (**c**) 0.002 ± 0.3%

2 $\left(\dfrac{\delta a}{a}+\dfrac{\delta b}{b}+\dfrac{\delta c}{c}\right) \times 100\%$

(**a**) 1.058 ± 2% (**b**) 1.1165 ± 0.48% (**c**) 0.001 385 6 ± 0.49%

3 (**a**) $\pm(\delta a+\delta b)$ (**b**) $\pm bc\left(\dfrac{\delta b}{b}+\dfrac{\delta c}{c}\right)$

(**c**) $\pm\left(\delta a+bc\left[\dfrac{\delta b}{b}+\dfrac{\delta c}{c}\right]\right)$

(**d**) $\pm(a-b)c\left(\dfrac{\delta a+\delta b}{a-b}+\dfrac{\delta c}{c}\right)$

(**e**) $\pm\dfrac{a+b}{c}\left(\dfrac{\delta a+\delta b}{a+b}+\dfrac{\delta c}{c}\right)$

(**f**) $\pm\left(\dfrac{a}{b}\left[\dfrac{\delta a}{a}+\dfrac{\delta b}{b}\right]+\dfrac{c}{d}\left[\dfrac{\delta c}{c}+\dfrac{\delta d}{d}\right]\right)$

(**g**) $\pm\left(\delta a+\dfrac{b}{c}\left[\dfrac{\delta b}{b}+\dfrac{\delta c}{c}\right]\right)$

4 (**a**) 8.2 ± 1.2% (**b**) 3.144 ± 2.5% (**c**) 8.94 ± 1.4% (**d**) 4.45 ± 3.3% (**e**) 6.26 ± 1.6% (**f**) 3.94 ± 2.2% (**g**) 3.97 ± 2.4%

Exercise 2.1 (page 523)

1 (**a**) $3a^2\delta a$ (i) $50.7 \pm 4.1\%$ (ii) $5.065 \pm 0.41\%$ (iii) $5.07 \times 10^{-5} \pm 4.1\%$
(**b**) $6a\delta a$ (i) $41.1 \pm 2.7\%$
(ii) $4.107 \times 10^5 \pm 0.27\%$
(iii) $4.11 \times 10^{-3} \pm 2.7\%$
(**c**) $\frac{1}{2}a^{-\frac{1}{2}}\delta a$ (i) $1.924 \pm 0.68\%$
(ii) $19.235 \pm 0.068\%$ (iii) $0.1924 \pm 0.68\%$
(**d**) $10a^{-3}\delta a$ (i) $0.3652 \pm 2.7\%$
(ii) $3.6523 \pm 0.27\%$ (iii) $3650 \pm 2.7\%$
2 913 ± 12
3 150.65 ± 0.31
4 14.06 ± 0.87
5 $6044 \pm 80\ \text{cm}^3$
6 $976.1 \pm 8.3\ \text{cm s}^{-2}$

Exercise 2.2 (page 525)

1 (**a**) $3 \cos x\, \delta x$, $\cot x\, \delta x$
(**b**) $\frac{2}{x}\delta x$, $\frac{1}{x \ln x}\delta x$
(**c**) $8 \sin x \cos x\, \delta x$, $2 \tan x\, \delta x$
(**d**) $2e^x\, \delta x\, \delta x$ (**e**) $2e^x(x+1)\, \delta x$, $\left(1+\frac{1}{x}\right)\delta x$
(**f**) $\frac{5}{x}\log e\, \delta x$, $\frac{\log e}{x \log x}\delta x$ (**g**) $(x^2 \sec^2 x + 2x \tan x)\, \delta x$, $\left(2 \operatorname{cosec} 2x + \frac{2}{x}\right)\delta x$
(**h**) $2 \ln 10 \times 10^{2x}\, \delta x$, $2 \ln 10\, \delta x$ (**i**) $4e^{4x}\, \delta x$, $4\, \delta x$
2 (**a**) 2.9659 ± 0.0022, (0.076%)
(**b**) 0.7013 ± 0.0070, (1.0%) (**c**) 0.0904 ± 0.0059, (6.6%) (**d**) 8.274 ± 0.041, (0.5%)
(**e**) 11.75 ± 0.10, (0.85%) (**f**) 0.7614 ± 0.0076, (1.0%) (**g**) 13.29 ± 0.54, (4.1%)
(**h**) 692 ± 16, (2.3%) (**i**) 293.0 ± 5.9, (2.0%)

Exercise 2.3 (page 528)

1 (**a**) 16 ± 7.5 (**b**) 17.674 ± 0.077
(**c**) -10.9668 ± 0.0015
2 15.522 ± 0.024
3 -198, -210.86, -223.79, -236.72, -249.56, -262.25
4 (**a**) 9 (**b**) 6, $\frac{1}{2}(n^2+3n)$, $2n$
5 $\pm\left(2a - \frac{4}{a^2}\right)\delta a$, $7.85 \pm 1.4\%$
6 (**a**) $\left(2x + \frac{2}{x^3}\right)\delta x$, -1.154 ± 0.030
(**b**) $\left(-\frac{8}{x^2} + 18 + 2x\right)\delta x$, 36.784 ± 0.028
(**c**) $\frac{x(6-x)}{(3-x)^2}\delta x$, 0.2579 ± 0.0040

Exercise 2.4 (page 533)

1 (**a**) $\frac{b}{a}\left(\frac{\delta a}{a} + \frac{\delta b}{b}\right)$, 1.511 ± 0.017
(**b**) $\frac{a}{a+b}\left(\frac{\delta a}{a} + \frac{\delta b}{b}\right)$, 0.662 ± 0.022
(**c**) $\left(\frac{\delta a}{a^2} + \frac{\delta b}{b^2} + \frac{\delta c}{c^2}\right)\left(\frac{1}{a} + \frac{1}{b} + \frac{1}{c}\right)^{-2}$, 0.671 ± 0.021
2 (**a**) $ab \cos \theta\left(\frac{\delta a}{a} + \frac{\delta b}{b} + \tan \theta\, \delta\theta\right)$
(**b**) $e^a \sin \theta(\delta a + \cot \theta\, \delta\theta)$ (**c**) $2a\, \delta a + \frac{1}{b}\delta b$
(**d**) $e^{-a}(1-a)\, \delta a + \tan \theta\, \delta b + b \sec^2 \theta\, \delta\theta$
(**e**) $(3a^2 - b)\, \delta a + a\, \delta b$ (**f**) $\left(1 - \frac{b}{a^2}\right)\delta a + \frac{1}{a}\delta b$
(**g**) $\sin \theta\, \delta a + \cos \theta\, \delta b + (a \cos \theta - b \sin \theta)\, \delta\theta$
(**h**) $\frac{e^{ab}}{(a+b)^2}[(a+b)(b\, \delta a + a\delta b) - (\delta a + \delta b)]$
3 (**a**) -0.2175 ± 0.0098
(**b**) 0.151 ± 0.010 (**c**) -0.0994 ± 0.0049
(**d**) -0.497 ± 0.024 (**e**) -1.145 ± 0.056
(**f**) 0.8249 ± 0.0057
4 -4.9123 ± 0.0040

Exercise 2.5 (page 537)

1 (**a**) 0.02 (**b**) 0.014 196 2, 41%
(**c**) 0.014 20, 0.03%
2 1S, $f(x) = \frac{2}{\sqrt{(x^2+1)} + \sqrt{(x^2-1)}}$, 0.0500, 0.0476, 0.0455, 0.0435, 0.0417, 0.0400
3 (**a**) -98.0, 0.0102 (**b**) 1600, 0.000 938
(**c**) -7.00×10^{20}, 7.14×10^{-21}
4 0.0, $f(x) = \frac{\sin x}{1 + \cos x}$, 0.0150
5 0.0055, 0.005 46
6 10, 1 S (at most), 7.72

Exercise 3.1 (page 545)

1 $f(8) = 51$
2 (**a**) $\Delta^2 f = 2$ (**b**) $\Delta^3 f = 6$ (**c**) $\Delta^4 f = 24$
3 $\Delta^3 f = 0.006$
4 $f(0.9) = 1.349$, $f(1.0) = 2.000$
5 $f(1.1) = -1.099$, $f(1.2 = -1.192$, $f(1.3) = -1.273$, $f(1.4) = -1.336$
6 $f(1.6) = -5.44$
7 $f(1.2) = 0.528$
8 $(\Delta+1)^2 y_n = y_{n+2}$, $(\Delta+1)^r y_n = y_{n+r}$
9 $y_{n+4} - 4y_{n+3} + 6y_{n+2} - 4y_{n+1} + y_n$
10 No, not a polynomial function

Exercise 3.2 (page 548)

1 $\frac{1}{2}(3x^3-9x^2+4x+2)$
2 $f(2)=-1, f(3)=5$
3 87.25, 2.12, 0, 0.54, $g(5)=130.25$, $g(6)=164.77$, $g(7)=215.49$, $g(8)=285.65$
4 $f(2)=-1, f(x)=x^3-3x^2+2x-1$

Miscellaneous examination questions 14

1 $x=0$ or $30°\pm1°$
2 2.5%
3 $\dfrac{1}{\sqrt{(x^2+2)}+\sqrt{(x^2+1)}}=0.020\,80$
4 3.0%
5 $a=2\pi Ss\sin x(1+\sin x)$
$V=3429\text{ mm}^3$, $A=1672\text{ mm}^2$
$v=245\text{ mm}^3$, $a=80\text{ mm}^2$
6 $\delta=\frac{1}{2}(b\gamma+c\beta)\sin A$
$a=36.50\pm0.45$, $\Delta=436\pm14$
7 Max. relative error $=d$
8 2.592 ± 0.016, 5.905 ± 0.049, -3.313 ± 0.065
9 174 m to 238 m; α, β not too small, $|\alpha-\beta|$ as large as possible
11 13.1%, 13.7%
12 (**a**) -0.05 (**b**) x^3-3x^2-2x+5
13 $\frac{1}{2}(b+c)+\dfrac{h}{r+h}(d+a)$
14 Max. error = 10E; $g(1.3)=1.67$ NOT 1.76
15 (**a**) $x=6$, $y=72$ (**b**) 0.347

CHAPTER 15 APPROXIMATIONS

Exercise 1.1 (page 553)

1 0.095 31
2 1.648 72
3 (**a**) $u_i=u_{i-1}\times2x\times(i-1)/i$, $u_1=-2x$, $-0.510\,826$ (**b**) $u_i=-u_{i-1}\times3x/i$, $u_1=1$, $0.548\,812$ (**c**) $u_i=-u_{i-1}\times x^2/2i(2i-1)$, $u_1=1$, $0.980\,067$
4 $1-\frac{1}{2}x^2-\frac{1}{8}x^4-\frac{1}{16}x^6$, 3.316 62

Exercise 1.2 (page 559)

1 (**a**) $-1.014\,51$ (**b**) $-0.992\,46$ (**c**) $-1.175\,25$ (**d**) 5.924 93 (**e**) 4.956 34 (**f**) 5.005 12
2 (**a**) 1.88 (**b**) 1.86 (**c**) 1.856
3 0.49, 0.24, 0.7
4 1.493

Exercise 2.2 (page 565)

1 (**a**) 1.5082 (**b**) 0.9943 (**c**) 5.9590 (**d**) 4.3750
2 (**a**) 1.5087 (**b**) 1.0000 (**c**) 5.8409 (**d**) 4.5000
3 (**a**) 0.116 (**b**) 0.116
4 (**a**) 3.069 (**b**) 3.143
5 0.6956, 0.6956
6 0.5236, 3.1416

Exercise 2.3 (page 574)

5 (**a**) 0.5 (**b**) 0.536

Exercise 3.1 (page 576)

1 0.357
2 1.618
3 0.877
4 1.756
5 0.431
6 1.618
7 1.217
8 5.627

Exercise 3.2 (page 581)

1 (**a**) 1.32 (**b**) -0.47, 1.39 (**c**) 0.62, 1.5
2 (**a**) -0.83, 1.9 (**b**) 0.5 (**c**) $0.\dot{2}$

Exercise 3.3 (page 585)

1 $f_1'(1.3)=5.07$, $f_2'(1.3)=-5.46$, $f_3'(1.3)=0.19$
2 e.g. $x=(2x^2+7)^{\frac{1}{4}}$
3 e.g. $x=2(x\,e^{-x})^{\frac{1}{2}}$
4 0.436
5 $x=(2x+5)^{\frac{1}{3}}$, 2.095

Exercise 3.4 (page 590)

1 1.100
2 0.6823
3 -1.77
4 1.564, 0.138
5 $x_{n+1}=\frac{1}{10}(15x_n-x_n^3)$
6 0.9702
7 1.146
8 1.022

Exercise 3.5 (page 592)

1 40, 0.04
2 500, 0.1
3 282, -0.02
4 -100, 0.111

Miscellaneous examination questions 15

1 (**a**) 16.699 (**b**) 16.678 (**a**) is nearer (16.775)
2 0.7854, 3.142, 0.7440, 5.28%
3 37.33
4 0.7052, 0.7016, $h < 0.16$
5 $F(2) = 10.605$, $F(4) = 26.349$, $F(6) = 42.594$
6 1.776
7 0.0375
8 2.8437 ± 0.0042
9 Error bound: $\frac{2}{3n} + 2\varepsilon$; 167
10 $f(x) = 2.5x^3 - 0.5x + 0.6344$; $f_4 = 6.7944$
11 (**a**) 1.553 (**b**) 0.569; $0.48k$, $0.12k$
12 5.4803
13 $g(x) = (2 + 2/x)^{\frac{1}{2}}$, 1.77
14 0.146, 6.854
15 1.93
16 $n = 2$, $x_1 = 2.20$, $x_2 = 2.19$
17 1.022
18 5.357, 3.961, 2.996, 2.280, 1.702
19 1.030
20 x_1: −5 −4.7 −4.6809
x_2: −0.3 −0.319 −0.3205

CHAPTER 16 VECTORS 2

Exercise 1.1 (page 603)

1 (**a**) $x = \begin{pmatrix} 3 \\ 1 \\ -1 \end{pmatrix} + t\begin{pmatrix} 1 \\ 2 \\ 3 \end{pmatrix}$;
$\begin{pmatrix} 2 \\ -1 \\ -4 \end{pmatrix}, \begin{pmatrix} 4 \\ 3 \\ 2 \end{pmatrix}, \begin{pmatrix} 5 \\ 5 \\ 5 \end{pmatrix}$

(**b**) $x = \begin{pmatrix} 0 \\ 3 \\ 1 \end{pmatrix} + t\begin{pmatrix} 0 \\ -2 \\ -4 \end{pmatrix}$; $\begin{pmatrix} 0 \\ 5 \\ 5 \end{pmatrix}, \begin{pmatrix} 0 \\ 1 \\ -3 \end{pmatrix}, \begin{pmatrix} 0 \\ -1 \\ -7 \end{pmatrix}$

(**c**) $x = \begin{pmatrix} 1 \\ 2 \\ -1 \end{pmatrix} + t\begin{pmatrix} 2 \\ -1 \\ 0 \end{pmatrix}$; $\begin{pmatrix} -1 \\ 3 \\ -1 \end{pmatrix}, \begin{pmatrix} 3 \\ 1 \\ -1 \end{pmatrix}, \begin{pmatrix} 5 \\ 0 \\ -1 \end{pmatrix}$

3 (**a**) $\frac{1}{3}\begin{pmatrix} 14 \\ -7 \\ 16 \end{pmatrix}$ (**b**) $\begin{pmatrix} 1 + \sqrt{6} \\ -\frac{1}{2}\sqrt{6} \\ 3 - \frac{1}{2}\sqrt{6} \end{pmatrix}$

4 (**a**) $x = i + 5j - 3k + t(2i - 8j + 2k)$;
$\hat{l} = \frac{1}{3\sqrt{2}}(i - 4j + k)$
(**b**) $x = 4j - k + t(3i - 3j - 4k)$;
$\hat{m} = \frac{1}{\sqrt{34}}(3i - 3j - 4k)$

5 (**a**) $x = 3i - 5j + 6k + t(-3i + 2j - k)$
(**b**) $x = 2i - j + 2k + t(2i - j - k)$
(**c**) $x = 2i - j + 5k + t(10i + 3j - 15k)$
(**d**) $x = 3i + 10j - 9k + t(i - j + k)$;
(5, 8, −7) (**e**) $x = 3i - 4j - k + t(i + 2j)$

Exercise 1.2 (page 608)

1 (**a**) P(3, 2, 1); Q(1, 10, 3)
(**b**) R(4, −2, 0), $\lambda = 0$, $\mu = 2$
(**c**) L no, M yes, N no
2 (**a**) $p^T = (9 \; 3 \; 0)$ (**b**) $q^T = (-8 \; -3 \; 2)$
(**c**) $|q| = \sqrt{77}$ (**d**) L yes, M yes, N no
3 (**a**) P(−5, −4, 9); Q(−4, −4, 7)
(**b**) L no, M yes

4 $x = \begin{pmatrix} -1 \\ 1 \\ -2 \end{pmatrix} + \lambda\begin{pmatrix} 2 \\ 1 \\ -3 \end{pmatrix} + \mu\begin{pmatrix} 3 \\ -4 \\ 3 \end{pmatrix}$

5 (**a**) $x = \lambda\begin{pmatrix} 1 \\ 3 \\ 1 \end{pmatrix} + \mu\begin{pmatrix} -1 \\ 4 \\ -1 \end{pmatrix}$

(**b**) $x = \begin{pmatrix} 4 \\ -1 \\ 2 \end{pmatrix} + \lambda\begin{pmatrix} 1 \\ 3 \\ 1 \end{pmatrix} + \mu\begin{pmatrix} -1 \\ 4 \\ -1 \end{pmatrix}$

6 $x = \begin{pmatrix} 3 \\ -2 \\ 0 \end{pmatrix} + \lambda\begin{pmatrix} -1 \\ 2 \\ 3 \end{pmatrix} + \mu\begin{pmatrix} -2 \\ 1 \\ 1 \end{pmatrix}$

7 $x \cdot \begin{pmatrix} 1 \\ 1 \\ -3 \end{pmatrix} = 8$; $8/\sqrt{11}$

8 $m = \frac{5}{13}(1 + \sqrt{14})$
9 (**a**) $x \cdot (2i + 3j - k) = 10$
(**b**) $x \cdot (2i + 3j - k) = -5$

Exercise 1.3 (page 612)

1 (3, 0)
2 (13/3, 17/3, 14/3)
3 skew
6 (8, 24, 8)
7 (4, 4, 0)
8 (4, 2, −1)
9 (8/3, −1/3, 14/3)

Exercise 1.4 (page 615)

1 $x = \frac{2}{7}\begin{pmatrix}17\\-1\\0\end{pmatrix} + t\begin{pmatrix}2\\-3\\-7\end{pmatrix}$

2 $x \cdot \begin{pmatrix}-5\\3\\1\end{pmatrix} = 7$

3 $x \cdot \begin{pmatrix}5\\6\\-7\end{pmatrix} = 12$

4 $x = (1-\lambda)a + \lambda a' + \mu b$

6 $x = 37i + 38j + 27k$

7 $x = \begin{pmatrix}-2\\3\\-4\end{pmatrix} + \lambda\begin{pmatrix}3\\-2\\-5\end{pmatrix} + \mu\begin{pmatrix}2\\2\\-3\end{pmatrix}$

Exercise 2.1 (page 619)

1 1, $-8/3$

2 $\sqrt{\dfrac{185}{21}} = 2.97$

3 $x \cdot \begin{pmatrix}1\\1\\-1\end{pmatrix} = 2$, $x \cdot \begin{pmatrix}1\\1\\-1\end{pmatrix} = -1$; $\sqrt{3}$

4 $x = \begin{pmatrix}4\\6\\-2\end{pmatrix} + t\begin{pmatrix}3\\1\\-4\end{pmatrix}$

5 $x = \begin{pmatrix}-1\\-2\\3\end{pmatrix} + t\begin{pmatrix}13\\18\\-12\end{pmatrix}$

6 $\sqrt{21}$

7 $1/\sqrt{6}$

8 $5/\sqrt{3}$

9 $\sqrt{(6/7)}$, $\sqrt{3}$

Exercise 2.2 (page 621)

1 29.2°

2 60°

3 48°

4 75.7°

5 $\begin{pmatrix}1\\0\end{pmatrix}, \begin{pmatrix}\frac{3}{5}\\-\frac{4}{5}\end{pmatrix}$

6 $x \cdot \begin{pmatrix}1\\-1\\\pm\sqrt{\frac{2}{3}}\end{pmatrix} = 0$

7 $x \cdot \begin{pmatrix}1\\0\\\frac{3}{\sqrt{2}}-1\end{pmatrix} = 0$

Exercise 2.3 (page 626)

1 $\frac{1}{2}\sqrt{537} = 11.6$

2 $\frac{1}{2}\sqrt{474} = 10.9$

3 **(a)** 3 **(b)** 63.4°

4 **(a)** $\frac{1}{3}\sqrt{2}$ **(b)** $\frac{1}{2}\sqrt{2}$

5 **(a)** $4\sqrt{17}$, $20\sqrt{2}$ **(b)** 80.1° **(c)** 96.6° **(d)** 63.1°

6 (i) 2 (ii) 6 (iii) 4 (iv) 2

Miscellaneous examination questions 16

1 $\sqrt{6}$, $2\sqrt{6}$, $\sqrt{26}$

2 **(a)** $1/\sqrt{21}(-i+4j+2k)$ **(b)** 2 **(c)** $i - 13j - 3k$

5 $\cos^{-1}\sqrt{2}/6 = 76.4°$, $2\sqrt{17}$, $x \cdot \begin{pmatrix}3\\2\\2\end{pmatrix} = 8$, $x \cdot \begin{pmatrix}1\\-2\\2\end{pmatrix} = 0$, $\cos^{-1} 1/\sqrt{17} = 76°$, $5.\dot{3}$

7 **(a)** $\frac{1}{3}(a+b+c)$
(b) (i) $\cos^{-1} 1/13\sqrt{2} = 86.9°$
(ii) $k\begin{pmatrix}12\\12\\7\end{pmatrix}$

8 $\cos^{-1} 11/14 = 38.2°$

9 $r \cdot (2i+k) = 0$, $\sqrt{5}$, $3\sqrt{2}$

10 $\pm\frac{1}{13}(4\mathbf{i} - 12\mathbf{j} + 3\mathbf{k})$, $\cos^{-1} 1\sqrt{3} = 54.7°$, $\cos^{-1}(-1/\sqrt{3}) = 125.3°$

11 **(a)** $1/\sqrt{42}(5i - j - 4k)$, $\pm 1/\sqrt{138}(i - 11j + 4k)$
(b) $7i + 9j + 13k$, $\frac{1}{2}\sqrt{299}$

12 **(a)** $\cos^{-1} 1/\sqrt{2} = 45°$
(b) $\cos^{-1} 1/\sqrt{6} = 65.9°$

13 $x = i - 3k + s(i + j - 7k)$
$x = -2i + 2j + k + t(-5i + 5j + k)$
$x = \frac{1}{2}(i - j + k) + p(18i + 17j + 5k)$

14 **(a)** (i) -3 (ii) $54 \pm 12\sqrt{19}$
(b) Altitudes of a triangle are concurrent

17 **(a)** $-30i - 15j + 8k$
(b) $\frac{3}{5}i + \frac{4}{5}k$, $\frac{12}{13}i + \frac{5}{13}j$
(c) 36/65 **(d)** 4/5
$\alpha = -36/169$,
$x \cdot \begin{pmatrix}75\\-180\\676\end{pmatrix} = 0$

18 **(a)** $\cos^{-1} 225/243 = 22.2°$

CHAPTER 17 SOLUTION OF LINEAR EQUATIONS

Exercise 1.2 (page 638)

1 $\frac{1}{10}\begin{pmatrix} -2 & -4 & 6 \\ 2 & 4 & -1 \\ 6 & 2 & -3 \end{pmatrix}$

2 $\frac{1}{38}\begin{pmatrix} 10 & -8 & -6 \\ 7 & 2 & -8 \\ -1 & 16 & 12 \end{pmatrix}$

3 $\frac{1}{3}\begin{pmatrix} 1 & 0 & 0 \\ -1 & 3 & 0 \\ -4 & 6 & 3 \end{pmatrix}$

4 $\frac{1}{6}\begin{pmatrix} 9 & -10 & 7 \\ -3 & 4 & -1 \\ 3 & -6 & 3 \end{pmatrix}$

5 $\begin{pmatrix} 1/\alpha & -1/\alpha^2 & (3+\alpha)/\alpha^3 \\ 0 & 1/\alpha & -3/\alpha^2 \\ 0 & 0 & 1/\alpha \end{pmatrix}$

6 No inverse

Exercise 1.3 (page 640)

1 0
2 (**a**) 6 (**b**) −6
3 21
4 (**a**) 22 (**b**) 22
5 −2
6 0
7 0
8 $-\lambda^3+14\lambda+12$
9 $-\lambda^3+4\lambda^2-\lambda-2$
10 $-\lambda^3+5\lambda^2-14\lambda+4$

Exercise 2.2 (page 642)

1 (−1, 3, 0)
2 (18/19, −33/19, 21/19)
3 (5, −2, 3)
4 (0, −1, −2)
5 (−2, 0, 3)
6 no unique solution
7 (1, 2, −1)
8 (−1/3, 11/3, 13/3)
9 (1, −2, −3)
10 (2, 2, −1)

Exercise 2.4 (page 646)

1 (3, 4, 1)
2 (10, 1, 3)
3 (8, −6, 4)
4 (−1, 2, 5)
5 (0, 0, 1)
6 (1, 1, 1)
7 (1, 1, 2)
8 (4, 17, −14)
9 (1, 0, −57)
10 (9/14, 4/14, 31/14)

Exercise 3.1 (page 651)

1 (0.080, 0.106, 0.310)
R: (0.002) (0) (0.002)
2 (0.077, 0.115, 0.577)
R: (0) (−0.001) (0)

Exercise 3.2 (page 654)

1 (0.92, 0.616, −0.1072), (1.218, 0.7778, −0.1992) [solution is (1.2, 0.8, −0.2)]
2 (**a**) (1.1, 1.1, 1.0) (**b**) (1.3, 0.9, 0.4)
Residual elements NOT dominant in (**b**)
3 (**a**) (3.000, −2.000, 6.000)
(**b**) (0.6834, 2.186, 3.175)

Miscellaneous examination questions 17

1 (**a**) (i) (1, −2, 1) (ii) No solution
(iii) $(k-\frac{1}{2}, \frac{3}{2}-3k, k)$ (**b**) (i) 8 (ii) 16

2 (**a**) $\boldsymbol{A}^{-1}=\begin{pmatrix} 1 & 0 & 0 \\ 1 & 1 & 0 \\ -5 & -2 & 1 \end{pmatrix}$

$\boldsymbol{B}^{-1}=\begin{pmatrix} 1 & -4 & 14 \\ 0 & 1 & -3 \\ 0 & 0 & 1 \end{pmatrix}$

$(\boldsymbol{AB})^{-1}=\begin{pmatrix} -73 & -32 & 14 \\ 16 & 7 & -3 \\ -5 & -2 & 1 \end{pmatrix}$

(**b**) $x:y:z=4:-3:1$, $(1+4t, 1-3t, 1+t)$

3 Det $\boldsymbol{M}=55(k-1)$ (**a**) (0, 0, 0); (−2, 1, 3) (**b**) $(-10t, t, 11t)$

4 (**a**) (2, −1, 3) (**b**) $\frac{1}{4}\begin{pmatrix} 6 & 0 & -2 \\ 2 & -1 & 1 \\ 0 & -1 & 3 \end{pmatrix}$, (−2, 3.25, 8.25)

5 (**a**) (1, 2, 3) (**b**) $a=-4$, $b=-20$

6 (**a**) (1, −2, 3) (**b**) $\frac{1}{18}\begin{pmatrix} -5 & 1 & 7 \\ 1 & 7 & -5 \\ 7 & -5 & 1 \end{pmatrix}$

(**c**) $k=16$

7 $(\frac{1}{4}, -\frac{1}{2}, \frac{3}{4})$

8 (0.897, 0.764, 0.614), R: 0.0025

9 (1.6635, 2.3241, 0.5575, 1.3822)
10 (1.25, 2, 2.437, 2.687, 2.578, 1.789)
11 (**a**) (0.8000, −0.5589, 1.188)
(**b**) (3.714, 4.130, −1.823)

CHAPTER 18 MATRICES AND TRANSFORMATIONS 2

Exercise 1.1 (page 663)

1 (**a**) (7, −1, −5), (26, 10, 10), (11, 1, 3), (−23, −19, −19) (**b**) (45, 21, 45)
(**c**) (45, 21, 45)
2 (**a**) (4, −3, 0), (3, 0, −2), (0, 9, −8)
(**b**) (0, 2, 0), (1, 3, 0), (4, 0, 1), (0, 4, 0), (3, 9, 0), (16, 0, 4), (−3, −1, 0), (−8, 6, −2), (−23, 27, −8)
3 (**a**) $x = t+1$, $y = t-6$, $z = 2t+1$
(**b**) (1, −3, 0), $(\frac{1}{2}, -6\frac{1}{2}, 0)$

4 (**a**) $\begin{pmatrix} 1 & 0 & 0 \\ 0 & 0 & 1 \\ 0 & 1 & 0 \end{pmatrix}$ (**b**) (i) $\begin{pmatrix} 0 & -1 & 0 \\ 1 & 0 & 0 \\ 0 & 0 & 1 \end{pmatrix}$

(ii) $\begin{pmatrix} -1 & 0 & 0 \\ 0 & 1 & 0 \\ 0 & 0 & -1 \end{pmatrix}$ (iii) $\begin{pmatrix} 1 & 0 & 0 \\ 0 & -1 & 0 \\ 0 & 0 & -1 \end{pmatrix}$

(**c**) (i) $\begin{pmatrix} 2 & 0 & 0 \\ 0 & \frac{1}{3} & 0 \\ 0 & 0 & -2 \end{pmatrix}$ (ii) $\begin{pmatrix} 1 & 0 & 0 \\ 0 & -\frac{1}{5} & 0 \\ 0 & 0 & 3 \end{pmatrix}$

(**d**) (i) $\begin{pmatrix} 1 & 0 & 0 \\ k & 1 & 0 \\ 0 & 0 & 1 \end{pmatrix}$ or $\begin{pmatrix} 1 & 0 & 0 \\ 0 & 1 & 0 \\ k & 0 & 1 \end{pmatrix}$

(ii) $\begin{pmatrix} 1 & 0 & k \\ 0 & 1 & 0 \\ 0 & 0 & 1 \end{pmatrix}$ or $\begin{pmatrix} 1 & 0 & 0 \\ 0 & 1 & k \\ 0 & 0 & 1 \end{pmatrix}$

5 (**a**) $\begin{pmatrix} 1 & 0 & -1 \\ 0 & 1 & 2 \\ 0 & 0 & 1 \end{pmatrix}$ (**b**) $\begin{pmatrix} -1 & 0 & 2 \\ 0 & -1 & 4 \\ 0 & 0 & 1 \end{pmatrix}$

(**c**) $\begin{pmatrix} 0 & 1 & 0 \\ 1 & 0 & 0 \\ 0 & 0 & 1 \end{pmatrix}$ (**d**) $\begin{pmatrix} 1 & 0 & 0 \\ 0 & 1 & 0 \\ 0 & 0 & 3 \end{pmatrix}$

(**e**) $\begin{pmatrix} 1 & 0 & 0 \\ 1 & 1 & 0 \\ 0 & 0 & 1 \end{pmatrix}$

Exercise 1.2 (page 666)

1 $\begin{pmatrix} 3 \\ -6 \\ -6 \end{pmatrix}$, $\begin{pmatrix} 2 \\ -1 \\ 2 \end{pmatrix}$, $k = 3, 6, 9$; (2, 2, −1)

2 $\lambda = 0, -2, 2$; $\begin{pmatrix} 0 \\ 0 \\ 0 \end{pmatrix}$, $\begin{pmatrix} 1 \\ -\sqrt{2} \\ 1 \end{pmatrix}$, $\begin{pmatrix} 1 \\ \sqrt{2} \\ 1 \end{pmatrix}$

3 $k = -3, 4, 6$; $\begin{pmatrix} 1 \\ -1 \\ 1 \end{pmatrix}$, $\begin{pmatrix} 1 \\ 1 \\ 0 \end{pmatrix}$, $\begin{pmatrix} 1 \\ -1 \\ -2 \end{pmatrix}$

4 $k = 0, -3, 3$; $\begin{pmatrix} 2 \\ -1 \\ 2 \end{pmatrix}$

5 $\begin{pmatrix} 3 & 4 & -4 \\ 4 & 5 & 0 \\ -4 & 0 & 1 \end{pmatrix}$

Exercise 1.3 (page 668)

1 (**a**) $\begin{pmatrix} 1 \\ 1 \\ 1 \end{pmatrix}$ (**b**) $\begin{pmatrix} 1 \\ -2 \\ 1 \end{pmatrix}$ (**c**) $\begin{pmatrix} 1 \\ -2 \\ 1 \end{pmatrix}$

2 (**a**) $\begin{pmatrix} 0 \\ 1 \\ 1 \end{pmatrix}$, $\begin{pmatrix} 0 \\ 1 \\ 2 \end{pmatrix}$; $x = 0$ (**b**) $\begin{pmatrix} 2 \\ -1 \\ -1 \end{pmatrix}$, $\begin{pmatrix} -1 \\ 2 \\ 1 \end{pmatrix}$; $x+y+z=0$ (**c**) $\begin{pmatrix} 2 \\ -1 \\ -1 \end{pmatrix}$, $\begin{pmatrix} -1 \\ 2 \\ 1 \end{pmatrix}$; $x+y+z=0$

(**d**) $\begin{pmatrix} 5 \\ -1 \\ -1 \end{pmatrix}$, $\begin{pmatrix} -1 \\ 2 \\ -1 \end{pmatrix}$; $x+2y+3z=0$

3 (**a**) $2x+y=0$ (**b**) $x+y-z=0$

4 $\dfrac{1}{6}\begin{pmatrix} 5 & -2 & 1 \\ -2 & 2 & 2 \\ 1 & 2 & 5 \end{pmatrix}$

Exercise 2.2 (page 674)

1 (**a**) 2, $\begin{pmatrix} -1 \\ 2 \end{pmatrix}$; 5, $\begin{pmatrix} 1 \\ 1 \end{pmatrix}$ (**b**) −2, $\begin{pmatrix} 1 \\ 2 \end{pmatrix}$; 3, $\begin{pmatrix} 3 \\ 1 \end{pmatrix}$ (**c**) −5, $\begin{pmatrix} -1 \\ 1 \end{pmatrix}$; 2, $\begin{pmatrix} 2 \\ 5 \end{pmatrix}$ (**d**) −4, $\begin{pmatrix} -2 \\ 1 \end{pmatrix}$; 3, $\begin{pmatrix} -1 \\ 4 \end{pmatrix}$ (**e**) −5, $\begin{pmatrix} -1 \\ 1 \end{pmatrix}$; −2, $\begin{pmatrix} 1 \\ 2 \end{pmatrix}$ (**f**) −2, $\begin{pmatrix} -2 \\ 7 \end{pmatrix}$; 3, $\begin{pmatrix} -1 \\ 1 \end{pmatrix}$ (**g**) 2, $\begin{pmatrix} -1 \\ 1 \end{pmatrix}$; 5, $\begin{pmatrix} 1 \\ 2 \end{pmatrix}$

2 **(a)** $\begin{pmatrix}86 & 39\\78 & 47\end{pmatrix}, \begin{pmatrix}422 & 203\\406 & 219\end{pmatrix},$
$\frac{1}{3}\begin{pmatrix}2\times5^n+2^n & 5^n-2^n\\2\times5^n-2^{n+1} & 5^n+2^{n+1}\end{pmatrix}$
(b) $\begin{pmatrix}454 & -211\\422 & -179\end{pmatrix},$
$\begin{pmatrix}2\times3^n-2^n & -3^n+2^n\\2\times3^n-2^{n+1} & -3^n+2^{n+1}\end{pmatrix}$

3 **(a)** $1, \begin{pmatrix}-2\\1\end{pmatrix}; -1, \begin{pmatrix}1\\2\end{pmatrix}$ **(b)** $\frac{1}{5}\begin{pmatrix}3 & -4\\-4 & 3\end{pmatrix}$

Exercise 2.5 (page 683)

1 $D=\begin{pmatrix}5 & 0\\0 & 2\end{pmatrix}, C^4=\begin{pmatrix}121 & -120\\40 & -39\end{pmatrix},$
$C^n=\frac{1}{2}\begin{pmatrix}3^{n+1}-1 & -3^{n+1}+3\\3^n-1 & -3^n+3\end{pmatrix}$

2 $\frac{1}{2}\begin{pmatrix}1 & \pm\sqrt{5}\\\pm\sqrt{5} & 1\end{pmatrix}, \frac{1}{2}\begin{pmatrix}1\pm\sqrt{5} & 0\\0 & 1\pm\sqrt{5}\end{pmatrix}$

3 $\begin{pmatrix}-3 & -9\\1 & 3\end{pmatrix}$

5 $1, 1-p-q$

Miscellaneous examination questions 18

1 **(a)** $|a|<1, A^n=\begin{pmatrix}0 & \dfrac{b}{1-a}\\0 & 1\end{pmatrix}$
(b) $\alpha=-1, \begin{pmatrix}3 & 0\\0 & 3\end{pmatrix},$
$A^n=3^{n-1}\begin{pmatrix}1+2(-1)^n & 1-(-1)^n\\2-2(-1)^n & 2+(-1)^n\end{pmatrix}$

3 $\begin{pmatrix}\cos\left(\dfrac{2\pi}{2n+1}\right) & -\sin\left(\dfrac{2\pi}{2n+1}\right)\\\sin\left(\dfrac{2\pi}{2n+1}\right) & \cos\left(\dfrac{2\pi}{2n+1}\right)\end{pmatrix}$

4 $t=4-x, yz=-(x-2)^2$
5 $k=-5, -1$
7 **(a)** $x/3=y/1=z/2;\ x=3t, y=t, z=2t$ **(b)** $x=y=z$ **(c)** $\cos\theta=\sqrt{(6/7)}$ **(d)** $-x-y+z=0$
8 DR $-2:1:3, y=0$
9 **(a)** $\dfrac{x}{-7}=\dfrac{y}{6}=\dfrac{z}{19}$ **(b)** $x-2y+z=0$
(c) $\dfrac{x}{1}=\dfrac{y}{0}=\dfrac{z}{-1}$

10 $(x^2+y^2+z^2), \begin{pmatrix}by\\cz\\ax\end{pmatrix}, a=b=c=\pm1$

11 $(9, 18, 18);\ 9:1;\ (2\lambda, -2\lambda, \lambda);\ k=3;\ (2\lambda, \lambda, -2\lambda)$
12 **(a)** $\frac{1}{3}$ **(d)** **I**
13 $x=1+t, y=1+\frac{1}{2}t, z=-t$ **(a)** 0 **(b)** $-2\sqrt{2}$

14 **(a)** $\begin{pmatrix}\lambda\\-2\lambda\\\lambda\end{pmatrix}$ **(b)** $\begin{pmatrix}21+\lambda\\10-2\lambda\\\lambda\end{pmatrix},$
$\lambda=1, 2, 3, 4$

16 **(a)** $p=1, q=-2; -5A+6I$
(b) $L=\begin{pmatrix}5 & 0 & 0\\10 & 1 & 0\\0 & -1 & 1\end{pmatrix}, L^{-1}=\begin{pmatrix}\frac{1}{5} & 0 & 0\\-2 & 1 & 0\\-2 & 1 & 1\end{pmatrix},$
$U^{-1}=\begin{pmatrix}1 & 0 & -1\\0 & \frac{1}{2} & 0\\0 & 0 & 1\end{pmatrix}, A^{-1}=\begin{pmatrix}\frac{11}{5} & -1 & -1\\-1 & \frac{1}{2} & 0\\-2 & 1 & 1\end{pmatrix}$

17 $A^2=\begin{pmatrix}1 & 0 & 2a\\0 & 1 & 2b\\0 & 0 & 1\end{pmatrix}, A^{-1}=\begin{pmatrix}1 & 0 & -a\\0 & 1 & -b\\0 & 0 & 1\end{pmatrix},$
gradient $=b/a$

18 $5, \begin{pmatrix}1\\0\\1\end{pmatrix}; 4, \begin{pmatrix}1\\1\\1\end{pmatrix}; 2, \begin{pmatrix}1\\-1\\0\end{pmatrix}$

19 **(a)** 34, 55, 89, 144 **(b)** $\begin{pmatrix}13\\21\end{pmatrix}, \begin{pmatrix}34\\55\end{pmatrix}$
(c) $\begin{pmatrix}1 & 1\\1 & 2\end{pmatrix}$

CHAPTER 19 COORDINATE GEOMETRY—CONICS

Exercise 1.2 (page 699)

1 $(16a, 8a), (a, -2a)$
2 **(a)** $y=2a$ **(b)** $y^2-2ax=a^2$
4 $P(2at^2, 3at)$

Exercise 1.3 (page 705)

3 $\pm1;\ (\pm\sqrt{(a^2+b^2)}, 0)$ and $(0, \pm\sqrt{(a^2+b^2)})$
5 $x-3y+13=0, 7x-3y+37=0$

Exercise 1.4 (page 707)

1 $y - b\tan\theta = \dfrac{b\cos\frac{1}{2}(\phi-\theta)}{a\sin\frac{1}{2}(\phi+\theta)}(x - a\sec\theta)$

2 $y - b\tan\theta = \dfrac{b}{a}\operatorname{cosec}\theta\,(x - a\sec\theta)$ or $\dfrac{x\sec\theta}{a} - \dfrac{y\tan\theta}{b} = 1$

3 $ax\sin\theta\cos\theta + by\cos\theta = (a^2+b^2)\cos\theta$

5 $c^2 = a^2m^2 - b^2$

Exercise 1.5 (page 711)

2 $\Delta\,\mathrm{PQR} = \dfrac{c^2(t^4+1)^2}{2t^4}$

4 $(\pm c, \pm c), (\pm 5c, \pm\frac{1}{5}c)$

6 $c^2 = 4\sqrt{2}a^2$

Exercise 2.2 (page 718)

1 $\tan\theta = 2$
2 $r = 5$
3 $r^2\sin 2\theta = 2$
4 $r = 4\cos\theta\operatorname{cosec}^2\theta$
5 $r(\sin\theta - 2\cos\theta) + 1 = 0$
6 $r^2(13\cos^2\theta - 4) = 36$
7 $r^2 - 4r\cos\theta - 6r\sin\theta + 11 = 0$
8 $r^2(15\cos^2\theta + 1) = 16$
9 $x^2 + y^2 - \frac{1}{2}x = 0$
10 $(x^2 + y^2 - \frac{1}{2}x)^2 = x^2 + y^2$
11 $3x^2 + 4y^2 + 4x - 4 = 0$
12 $(x^2 + y^2)^3 = (x^2 - y^2)^2$
13 $4(x^2 + y^2 - x)^2 = x^2 + y^2$
14 $y^2 = 3x^2 - 8x + 4$
15 $(x^2 + y^2)^2 = x^2 - 3y^2$

Exercise 3.2 (page 727)

1 $(x+1)^2 + (y-3)^2 = 9$

2 $\dfrac{(x-2)^2}{3} + \dfrac{(y-4)^2}{2} = 1$

3 $(y-3)^2 = 16(x+2)$

4 $\dfrac{(x+1)^2}{9} - \dfrac{(y-1)^2}{1} = 1$

5 $\dfrac{(x+3)^2}{4} - \dfrac{(y-1)^2}{3} = 1$

Exercise 3.3 (page 729)

1 Under $\boldsymbol{D}$ $xy = 24$, under $\boldsymbol{S}$ $y^2 - xy + 12 = 0$, under $\boldsymbol{A}$ $2x^2 - 5xy + 2y^2 + 108 = 0$, under $\boldsymbol{C}$ $x^2 + 2xy - 3y^2 - 192 = 0$

2 **(a)** $(x \quad y)\begin{pmatrix} 1 & -2 \\ -2 & 4 \end{pmatrix}\begin{pmatrix} x \\ y \end{pmatrix} = 24x - 12y$;
Axes: $y = \frac{1}{2}x$, $y = -2x$

(b) $(x \quad y)\begin{pmatrix} 1 & -1 \\ -1 & 1 \end{pmatrix}\begin{pmatrix} x \\ y \end{pmatrix} = 16x + 48y$;
Axes: $y = x$, $y = -x$

3 **(a)** $(x \quad y)\begin{pmatrix} 1 & -1 \\ -1 & 2 \end{pmatrix}\begin{pmatrix} x \\ y \end{pmatrix} = 25$;
Axes: $y = \frac{1}{2}(-1 \pm \sqrt{5})x$

(b) $(x \quad y)\begin{pmatrix} 2 & 2 \\ 2 & 10 \end{pmatrix}\begin{pmatrix} x \\ y \end{pmatrix} = 400$;
Axes: $y = (2 \pm \sqrt{5})x$

Miscellaneous examination questions 19

1 $\left(at^2 + 2a + \dfrac{2a}{t^2}, \dfrac{2a}{t}\right)$

2 $\mathrm{R}(2at^2, 3at)$

10 $4c\sqrt{\dfrac{m}{m^2+1}}$, $\left|8c^2\left(\dfrac{m^2-1}{m^2+1}\right)\right|$

11 $yt - c = t^3(x - ct)$, $4x^3y^3 + c^2(x^2 - y^2)^2 = 0$

12 $\mathrm{P}'\left(-\dfrac{c}{t^2}, -ct^3\right)$, $\mathrm{P}''\left(ct^9, \dfrac{c}{t^9}\right)$, $4x^3y^3 + c^2(x^2 - y^2)^2 = 0$

14 $2\phi - \psi$; $\phi + \frac{2}{3}\pi$, $\phi - \frac{2}{3}\pi$

17 $\alpha^2\beta y = b^2\alpha x + \alpha^2\beta^2 - b^2\alpha^2$

19 **(a)** $x = \frac{1}{2}$(when $t = 1$), $y = -\frac{1}{2}$ (when $t = -1$) **(b)** $y = -x$, $y = x - 1$

20 $t^3y + 2x = 3ct$, $\mathrm{A}(\frac{3}{2}ct, 0)$, $\mathrm{B}\left(0, \dfrac{3c}{t^2}\right)$, $y(x-c)^2 + cx(x - 2c) = 0$

21 $\mathrm{P}(ap^2, 2ap)$

22 $t^2y + x = 2t$, $uy + x = 3u^2 + 2u^4$

23 $\dfrac{1}{\mathrm{FA}^2} + \dfrac{1}{\mathrm{FB}^2} = \dfrac{1 + \cos^2\alpha}{2a^2}$

24 $(2\sqrt{3}, \pi/3)$

25 **(a)** $x^2 + y^2 - 3x + 4y = 0$
(b) $3x - 4y = 9$

Index

M

N

O

P

Q

R

S